ROBERT SOUTHEY

From the painting by John Opie

more worthily conferred. For I am not such an ass as not to know that you are my better in poetry, though I have had, probably but for a time, the tide of popularity in my favour' (Lockhart's *Life of Scott*, chap. xxvi). Now, no doubt in this letter Scott was anxious to say pleasant things in a pleasant manner. But he was no humbug. He would never have gone out of his way to coin a false and empty compliment, and he could not have written as he did, unless he had felt a sincere admiration for Southey's poetical powers. Byron, again, whose principles were as opposed to those of Southey in poetry as they were in politics, morality, and religion, was yet constrained to admit the Laureate's claims to admiration as a poet. 'Of his poetry,' he wrote in his journal for November 22, 1813, 'there are various opinions : there is, perhaps, too much of it for the present generation ; —posterity will probably select. He has *passages* equal to anything' (Moore's *Life of Byron*, chap. xviii). And at a later date he spoke of *Roderick* as 'the first poem of the time'. To this testimony we may add the witness of another political adversary of Southey, in the person of Macaulay. The young champion of the *Edinburgh Review* was not the man to deal tenderly with the leading writer of the opposing party. He must have felt towards Southey something of that desire to 'dust the varlet's jacket for him in the next number of the Blue and Yellow', which, a year later, animated his notorious attack upon John Wilson Croker. And in his review of Southey's *Colloquies on the Progress and Prospects of Society* he criticizes his opponent's writings both in prose and verse with unsparing severity. Yet in the midst of his censure he makes the following remarkable admission : 'His poems, taken in the mass, stand far higher than his prose works. His official Odes, indeed, among which the *Vision of Judgement* must be classed, are, for the most part, worse than Pye's and as bad as Cibber's ; nor do we think him generally happy in short pieces. But his longer poems, though full of faults, are nevertheless very extraordinary productions. We doubt greatly whether they will be read fifty years hence ; but that, if they are read, they will be admired, we have no doubt whatever.' And, to come down to more recent times, we may cite in conclusion the favourable judgements pronounced upon Southey as a poet by men so eminent and so different from one another, as Cardinal Newman and Thomas Carlyle. The influence exercised upon the former by *Thalaba* is well known. '*Thalaba*', he wrote in 1850, 'has ever been to my feelings the most sublime of English poems—(I don't know Spenser)—I mean morally sublime. The versification of *Thalaba* is most melodious too—many persons will not perceive they are reading blank verse.' (Quoted in *Lord Acton and his Circle*, ed. Abbot Gasquet, O.S.B., p. xix.) Carlyle, though far from being unqualified in

---

OXFORD EDITION

POEMS OF
ROBERT SOUTHEY

CONTAINING

THALABA, THE CURSE OF KEHAMA
RODERICK, MADOC, A TALE OF PARAGUAY
AND SELECTED MINOR POEMS

EDITED BY

MAURICE H. FITZGERALD, M.A.

HENRY FROWDE
OXFORD UNIVERSITY PRESS
LONDON, NEW YORK, TORONTO, MELBOURNE
1909

EDITOR'S PREFACE

'FEW people,' it has been said, 'have written so much and so well as Southey, and have been so little read.' The remark refers to his work as a whole—in prose as well as in verse—but it is singularly applicable to his poetry. As a poet Southey is now scarcely known, save as the author of the lines beginning: 'My days among the Dead are past,' and of a few ballads such as *The Battle of Blenheim* and *The Inchcape Rock*, which are learnt by children in the nursery. The general estimation in which he is held may be illustrated by the *obiter dictum* in a recent review, that 'it is impossible to take Southey as a poet seriously'; and he is usually condemned as unreadable without a trial. But it is surely impossible to accept so summary a verdict—a verdict, be it remarked, which is in direct contradiction to that pronounced upon Southey's poetry by the most competent judges of his own day. No one, indeed, would pretend that Southey was one of the greatest of English poets. His position in our poetical hierarchy is far more modest. But a man may attain to an honourable place on the roll of Parnassus, although he fall considerably short of the highest rank, and in his lifetime Southey had no cause to fear the judgement of his peers. The praise bestowed upon his poetry by S. T. Coleridge, and by W. S. Landor, might perhaps be discounted on the ground that each of these two critics was influenced by close personal friendship for its author. But we may cite the opinions of other men free from any suspicion of such bias and equally well qualified to speak. In 1813 Sir Walter Scott declined the laureateship which had been offered him, (though without the Regent's knowledge or approval), by Lord Liverpool ; and in declining he suggested to Croker that the post should be offered to Southey. On September 4 of that year he writes to Southey to explain what he has done, and to make it clear, as he expresses it, that he has not himself refused the laurel 'from any foolish prejudice against the situation: otherwise, how durst I mention it to you, my elder brother in the muse ?—but from a sort of internal hope that they would give it to you, upon whom it would be so much his praise, tells us in his *Reminiscences* how his early prejudice against Southey, derived from the *Edinburgh Review*, was overcome by the reading of his chief poems. ' It must have been a year or two later,' he says, ' when his *Thalaba, Curse of Kehama, Joan of Arc*, &c., came into my hands, or some one of them came, which awakened new effort for the others. I recollect the much kindlier and more respectful feeling these awoke in me, which has continued ever since. I much recognize the piety, the gentle deep affection, the reverence for God and man, which reigned in these pieces : full of soft pity, like the wailings of a mother, and yet with a clang of chivalrous valour finely audible too.' (T. Carlyle's *Reminiscences*, vol. ii, Appendix, p. 311 [1881].)

Each of us ought doubtless to form his own opinions on literary questions, as on others, without a slavish deference to authority, however great. But the criticisms quoted above from men so well qualified to judge may at least give us pause before we decide to condemn Southey to oblivion as no better than a laborious poetaster.

Meanwhile there can be little doubt that it is more difficult for us than it was for his contemporaries adequately to appreciate such a writer as Southey. We are under the influence of greater and very different minds. We shall not find in Southey the creative imagination, the philosophic insight, of Browning or of Tennyson. We shall miss in him the dramatic power of the one, and the mastery of diction, the *curiosa felicitas*, of the other. Southey plumbs no depths of thought. He soars to no heights of lyric rapture. The sensuous element is almost wholly absent from his writings. It is not his to stir the deepest feelings of our nature ; and many of his poems may justly be charged with a lack of human interest. Again, his imagination is not always completely master of the materials with which it works. He can construct rather than create. His exuberant fancy leads him at times unconsciously to cross the borderland which separates what is strange and striking from what is merely strange and grotesque. His diction is wanting in those ' inevitable ' touches which mark the work of all really great poets. His style is apt to be diffuse ; and he has a tendency to preach too obviously. But, when full allowance has been made for all defects, there remains in Southey's poetry much that is wholly admirable. He may utter no very profound message to the world ; he may not see very far into the mystery of human life. But he has seen enough to inspire him to high and unfaltering action. The spirit of Christian Stoicism which animated his whole life breathes through all his writings. In them Southey has given noble expression to the power of the human will, based on religious faith, to resist evil and to rise superior to all untoward circumstance. His poetry, as all else that he wrote, reveals a firm trust in the ultimate triumph of good, a cheerful courage to endure suffering, a passion to resist all tyranny and oppression, an unshakable resolve to cleave to all that is fair and pure and true. Such a spirit is far removed from certain tendencies of modern thought. But, while it is content to leave much unexplained, it will seem to many to have laid hold upon the larger portion of the truth.

But other qualifications go to make a poet besides nobility of thought and aim ; and in such qualifications Southey is not wanting. He commands a flexible and ample diction, a style which can rise and fall in accordance with its subject. His imagination is rich and powerful, if at times somewhat undisciplined. Many of his characters are finely conceived and clearly presented to the reader's mind. This is more especially true of *Roderick*. Indeed, there are few scenes in English poetry of a more intense dramatic feeling than that in which Florinda confesses to the guilty king, changed beyond recognition in his hermit's garb, the story of their common fall. Add to this that Southey is a master of spirited narrative ; that his hoards of curious learning furnish him with a wealth of exotic and picturesque ornament and illustration ; that he possesses great metrical dexterity, and a vein of real, if somewhat simple, humour ; and it will easily be understood that he commands a great variety of range. Nor, in trying to form a just estimate of Southey's poetry, must we forget to take into consideration his historical importance as a factor in the development of our literature. This is perhaps generally underrated. Southey did far more than is usually recognized in breaking the fetters which had been riveted upon our poetry by the genius and authority of Pope. Cowper, Crabbe, and, still more, Burns, had already begun to teach men to admire what is simple and natural instead of worshipping exclusively a glittering and artificial perfection of form ; but Southey was almost the first to strike out an entirely new line. *Joan of Arc* is not a good poem, but it heralded the dawn of the romantic school. *Thalaba* was published four years before *The Lay of the Last Minstrel*. At that time Southey's verse was far more widely read than that of Wordsworth or Coleridge, and he did much to make smooth the way for greater poets than himself. His English Eclogues, again, and his Monodramas—crude and uninspired as in themselves they are—furnished the rough models for some of the most striking work of Browning and of Tennyson. And in some of his Ballads his humorous treatment of mediaeval fables and his mastery of rhyme and metre are a distinct anticipation of the *Ingoldsby Legends*. It would be most misleading to judge of Southey's historical importance as a poet by looking solely at his reputation to-day.

One further caution must be added. All poets—even the greatest—have written a quantity of verse that is comparatively worthless. Southey himself frankly admitted that many of his shorter pieces were fit for little but the flames. But he could at least plead in excuse that he had written them under pressure of sheer necessity, in order to earn money wherewith to maintain his own family and others dependent upon his generosity. For several years he wrote verses for the *Morning Post* at a guinea a week ; and these and other like pieces of task-work could not be expected to reach a very high level of merit. The necessity for doing such task-work to some extent spoilt Southey as a poet. But those who have learnt to know and to love him can hardly wish that it had been otherwise. For the noble self-denial, the ceaseless industry, the unfailing cheerfulness with which he bore this burden, are among the most attractive features in his character. If Southey missed greatness as a poet, he attained it as a man : and to know him as a man is to gain immensely in appreciation of his poetry, for his character is stamped upon everything that he wrote. In this connexion let us listen to the witness of Sir Henry Taylor, himself a poet and a man of a keen critical faculty. He had been the intimate friend of Southey's later years and had known him as he was ; and this is how he writes of him :—

' If he expected for himself a larger measure of attention from posterity than may now seem likely to be accorded him, it should be remembered that, though as long as his mind lasted he " lived laborious days " for the sake of his family and of others whom, in the generosity of his heart, he helped to support, yet all the labours of all the days did not enable him to do more than make preparations for the three great works which it was the object and ambition of his life to accomplish.

' Of what he did accomplish a portion will not soon be forgotten. There were greater poets in his generation, and there were men of a deeper and more far-reaching philosophic faculty ; but take him for all in all—his ardent and genial piety, his moral strength, the magnitude and variety of his powers, the field which he covered in literature, and the beauty of his life—it may be said of him, justly and with no straining of the truth, that of all his contemporaries he was the greatest MAN.' (*The English Poets*, ed. T. H. Ward, iv, p. 164.)

It does not fall within the scope of this series to give critical estimates of the authors whose works are published in it. But it seemed worth while to say so much in order to justify the inclusion of Southey among the ' Oxford Poets '. The nature of the present volume may now be briefly explained.

In 1837–8 Southey published his collected Poetical Works in ten volumes. That edition included a few pieces not previously printed, and all those poems already published which Southey thought, for any reason, worthy of preservation. It was originally intended to reprint in the present volume all the poems published in 1837–8 together with the following additions :—

1. '*Oliver Newman : a New-England Tale* (unfinished) : With Other Poetical Remains.' A volume under this title was published in 1845, after Southey's death, by Herbert Hill, his cousin and son-in-law ; and the poems contained in it were subsequently included in a one-volume reprint of the collected edition of 1837–8.

2. *Robin Hood*, Part I ; *The Three Spaniards* ; and *March* ; all of which appeared in 1847 in a small volume published by Mrs. Southey, entitled ' *Robin Hood* : . . . A Fragment. By the late Robert Southey and Caroline Southey. With Other Fragments and Poems by R.S. and C.S.'

3. The *Inscription for a Coffee-Pot* and the *Lines to Charles Lamb* (see pp. 378 and 402).

It was discovered, however, that such an edition would demand a volume of no less than 1,100 pages. It therefore became clear that some system of selection must be adopted. The loss involved in this change of plan was the less important since, as has been noticed above, Southey was impelled by the stern necessity of winning his daily bread to write for the newspapers great quantities of verse admittedly of very little merit. Such productions of uninspired drudgery may safely be disregarded in forming an estimate of a poet's true worth. Again, while in the case of a Shakespeare or a Milton there may be some justification for gathering together every line of verse that the author ever wrote, the same argument does not apply to the works of lesser men. The office of a literary Resurrection Man has little to recommend it. And a poet may fairly claim that the reputation due to the best that he has given us should not be buried beneath a mass of writings which he would himself wish forgotten. Further, it should be remembered in the present instance that Southey himself set the example of making a selection from his own poems : for there were many of his early pieces which he deliberately did not republish in 1837–8.

The necessity of selection once admitted, it was clear that the only rational principle on which that selection could be based was the literary merit of each particular poem. Upon that principle I have tried to act in preparing the present volume. I have, indeed, retained a few pieces which have no great claim to survival except as they serve to illustrate Southey's own personality or the development of his art. And no poem here printed appears in a mutilated form. But I believe that I have omitted nothing of

permanent value as literature. Indeed, I doubt whether Southey himself
would have fought very strenuously for the retention of any of the poems
excluded, apart from the *Vision of Judgement*. In that particular instance,
it must be admitted, we should probably have failed to convince him :
and we should have been reduced to retort upon him his own reply to certain
critics of the *Vision,* that ' de gustibus non est disputandum '. A word,
however, should perhaps be said as to the omission of *Joan of Arc.* On
grounds of historical interest I wish it had been possible to retain the poem
by which Southey first made his name. But considerations of space
demanded its sacrifice, and no serious plea could be advanced in support of
its literary excellence. Even the historical interest of *Joan of Arc,* as it
appeared in 1837, is comparatively small. The poem was practically
re-written no less than three times after its first publication, and in its
final form it presents but a pale reflexion of the sentimental ardours which
mark the original version of 1796. Of Southey's longer poems, as it is
the earliest, so it is from a literary standpoint the least worthy of preservation. And it may therefore be the more readily omitted from an edition
intended for lovers of poetry in general rather than for the professional
student. Two pieces only will be found in the present volume which have
not previously appeared in any collected edition of Southey's Poems—
the *Lines to Charles Lamb* and the *Inscription for a Coffee-Pot.* The
reasons for reprinting these verses are given in the Notes.

For the convenience of any students of our literature who may wish
to gain an acquaintance with the whole extent of Southey's verse I have
added in the Appendix the chief sources in which poems not reprinted in
this volume may be found. But, as stated above, none of those pieces
can be regarded as making any serious contribution towards Southey's
poetical reputation.

The poems have been arranged in the present edition upon the following
plan. In the first 378 pages will be found grouped together *Thalaba, The
Curse of Kehama,* and *Roderick,* the three finest of Southey's long poems, and
also a small selection of the best of his minor pieces. It is hoped that this
arrangement may be a help to the reader, who will find most of Southey's
best work brought together in a convenient form, instead of having to hunt
it out for himself from the entire mass of the poetry. It was inevitable
that such a selection should produce a certain effect of incongruity ; and
this is more especially the case, since one or two lighter pieces have been
included in it, rather as being characteristic of the writer than as making
any claim to poetical merit. But the end may in this case justify the means ;
and the very variety of style and subject serves to illustrate the extent

of Southey's range. After the Selected Minor Poems the arrangement
is that adopted by Southey in 1837-8—with the addition, as mentioned
above, of the *Lines to Charles Lamb*.

The editor of Southey's poems finds himself free from one great difficulty
common to editors : he is called upon to decide no question of variant
readings. The text of the poems as revised by Southey himself in 1837-8
is clearly final. In reprinting that text I have made no change, apart from
the correction of one or two plain misprints, and of certain obvious inad-
vertencies in punctuation. I have not thought it worth while to alter
a few archaisms of spelling. Such forms as 'chuse', 'controul', or 'gulph',
can confuse no one ; and, as Southey preferred to use these forms, there
seems no good reason why we should revise them for him.

It may here be noted in passing that, while Southey spared no pains in
correcting his earlier poems, when once he had mastered his craft, he wrote
little which he afterwards saw cause to alter. Thus *Joan of Arc*
was practically rewritten at least three times ; the second edition of *Thalaba*
is an immense improvement on the first, and is in its turn far inferior in
symmetry and polish to the final version of the poem as it appeared in
1838 ; and many of the early minor pieces were recast after their first
publication in almost every line. On the other hand, the variations between
the first and later editions of *Madoc* are comparatively few and unimportant,
and the latest text of *The Curse of Kehama* and of *Roderick* differs scarcely
at all from that originally published. In such cases as *Joan of Arc* and
Thalaba it is not without interest to trace the alterations introduced by
Southey into successive editions of the poems ; but to have cumbered the
present volume with an Apparatus Criticus would have been only to annoy
the general reader in order to gratify the literary pedant. I have, however,
reprinted Southey's Prefaces to the first nine volumes of the ten-volume
edition of 1837-8, both on account of the light which they throw upon
the composition of many of the poems and for their great personal
interest. But the Preface to the tenth volume has been omitted, as
it is wholly concerned with a discussion of criticisms directed against
the *Vision of Judgement*—a poem which is not included in the present
edition.

Southey usually printed at the beginning of his shorter pieces full quotations from the sources whence the subjects of the different poems had
been drawn. In a few instances I have preserved these quotations *in
extenso*, but for the most part, in order to save space, I have contented
myself with giving the reference. I have been able in many cases to give
the date and place of the first publication of particular poems, but I have

not attempted to do so in all. Probably it would not be possible to attain completeness in this respect ; nor would any important object be served by doing so. But I have endeavoured to trace the first publication of all the more notable of the shorter pieces ; and I regret that in one or two such instances my search has not met with success. For all those notes which are enclosed in square brackets at the beginning of particular poems I am responsible. The date appended at the foot of any poem is that of its original composition, as printed by Southey in 1837-8.

Southey published with his poems an immense mass of illustrative notes, consisting for the most part of extracts from different authors collected in the course of his wide and varied reading. These notes are full of curious information, but are not always particularly relevant to the poems to which they are attached. From considerations of space they have been almost entirely omitted in the present edition. Some of them, however, will be found quoted—in whole or in part—in the Notes at the end of this volume ; the substance of a few others is given in an abridged paraphrase. The letter (S.) after any Note shows that either its actual words or its substance may be found in Southey's note on the passage in question ; and in the case of actual quotation the words quoted are marked by inverted commas.

For those Notes which are not followed by the letter (S.) I am responsible. As has been explained above, no textual questions can arise in connexion with Southey's poetry. I have therefore confined myself to inserting a few Notes in order to explain various allusions, to give information as to the composition and publication of certain poems, or to add a touch of personal or critical interest connected with them. In so doing I can hardly hope to escape the charge of having on occasion either inserted or omitted too much. But I trust that, in spite of mistakes, my object has been in great measure attained.

The Chronological Table of Southey's life on pp. xxi–xxviii may perhaps be found useful. In preparing it I have been much indebted to a similar Table in Mr. T. Hutchinson's edition of Wordsworth in the present series.

Of the imperfections of this edition of Southey's Poems I am very sensible. They may be explained in part by the fact that I have been obliged to prepare it at a distance from libraries and in the occasional intervals of other and very different work. Under these circumstances I am the more grateful to those friends without whose help my task could hardly have been completed. In particular my thanks are due to the Reverend Canon Rawnsley for kindly allowing me to see his Southey MSS. ; to Miss Geraldine Fitz-Gerald for the work that she has done on my behalf at the British Museum,

and also for her help in reading through some of the proofs ; and to
Mr. E. H. Coleridge for his great kindness in answering my requests for
information on various points and in making many useful suggestions.
But above all I desire to express my gratitude to Professor Dowden.   In
preparing this edition I have received from him most generous help in
counsel and encouragement.   But I owe him a debt of far longer standing ;
for it was he who, by his delightful volume in the ' English Men of Letters '
series, first taught me to know and to love Robert Southey.

M. H. F. G.

CONTENTS

CONTENTS

LIST OF AUTHORITIES

THIS list of books given below makes no pretence to being a complete bibliography. It is intended to refer the reader to (a) the principal authorities for Southey's life : and (b) a few books and essays which are of special interest from their bearing upon Southey's character and writings.

(a) AUTHORITIES

1. *The Life and Correspondence of Robert Southey.* Edited by his son, the Rev. C. C. Southey, 6 vols., 1849–50.

2. *Selections from the Letters of Robert Southey.* Edited by J. W. Warter, 4 vols., 1856.

3. *The Correspondence of Robert Southey with Caroline Bowles.* Edited by E. Dowden, 1881.

4. *Letters from the Lake Poets*—Samuel Taylor Coleridge, William Wordsworth, Robert Southey—to Daniel Stuart, editor of *The Morning Post* and *The Courier,* 1800–38. Printed for private circulation, 1889.

5. *The Letters of Samuel Taylor Coleridge.* Edited by E. H. Coleridge, 2 vols., 1895.

6. *Reminiscences of S. T. Coleridge and R. Southey.* By Joseph Cottle, 1847. [A recast of Cottle's *Early Recollections* (1837) with additions.]

7. *The Life and Writings of William Taylor of Norwich.* By J. W. Robberds, 2 vols., 1843.

8. *The Life of W. S. Landor.* By John Forster, 2 vols., 1869 (reprinted in vol. i of Landor's *Works and Life,* 1876).

9. *The Works of Charles and Mary Lamb.* Edited by E. V. Lucas, 1903–5, vols. vi and vii, (containing C. Lamb's Correspondence).

(b) MISCELLANEOUS

1. *Southey.* By E. Dowden (' English Men of Letters ' series), 1879.

2. *The Literary Associations of the English Lakes.* By the Rev. Canon H. D. Rawnsley, vol. i, 1894.

3. De Quincey's *Recollections of the Lake Poets,* and *Autobiography.*

4. Hazlitt's *Spirit of the Age.*

5. *The Diary, Reminiscences, and Correspondence of H. Crabb Robinson.* Edited by T. Sadler, 3 vols., 1869.

6. T. Carlyle's *Reminiscences,* vol. ii, Appendix, pp. 309–29, 1881.

7. *Robert Southey :* an essay by Sir Henry Taylor in *The English Poets* (ed. T. H. Ward), vol. iv, pp. 155–64, 1880.

8. *Poems by Robert Southey.* Edited, with an Introduction, by E. Dowden (' Golden Treasury ' series), 1895.

9. *Selections from the Poems of Robert Southey.* Edited with a biographical and critical Introduction, by Sidney R. Thompson (' Canterbury Poets '), 1888.

BIOGRAPHICAL TABLE

CONTAINING THE CHIEF EVENTS OF SOUTHEY'S LIFE AND SOME
IMPORTANT DATES IN THE LIVES OF CONTEMPORARY WRITERS

S. = Robert Southey, the Poet.
Thomas, &c. S. = Thomas, &c. Southey.
S. T. C. = Samuel Taylor Coleridge.

A.D.	ÆT.	
1735	—	About this year Thomas Southey, son of a yeoman farmer of Wellington in Somerset, settles on a farm at Holford, a village in the Quantock Hills.
1754	—	[George Crabbe born.]
1762	—	[William Lisle Bowles born.]
1763	—	[Samuel Rogers born.]
1764	—	[*The Traveller* (O. Goldsmith).]
1765	—	[Percy's *Reliques*.]
1770	—	[William Wordsworth born. James Hogg born. Chatterton died. *The Deserted Village* (Goldsmith).]
1771	—	[Gray died. Scott born. *The Minstrel* (Beattie).]
1772	—	Robert Southey, a linen-draper at Bristol, (born 1745, second son of Thomas S.), married Margaret Hill. To them were born nine children, five of whom died young. The surviving children were Robert, Thomas, Henry Herbert, and Edward. [S. T. Coleridge born.]
1774	—	ROBERT SOUTHEY born at Bristol, August 12, his parents' second and eldest surviving child.
1775	1	[Charles Lamb born. W. Savage Landor born.]
1776	2	During 1776–80 S. spends most of his time with his mother's half-sister, Miss Tyler, at Bath.
1777	3	Thomas S. born. [H. Hallam born. Thomas Campbell born.]
1778	4	[W. Hazlitt born.]
1779	5	[Thomas Moore born.]
1780	6	S. sent as a day-boy to a school kept by a Mr. Foot at Bristol.
1781	7	S. removed to a school at Corston, nine miles from Bristol. [*The Library* (Crabbe).]
1782	8	(Or Jan. 1783) S. placed as a day-boarder at a school at Bristol kept by a Mr. Williams, spending his holidays in general with Miss Tyler. From 1778 onwards Miss Tyler regularly takes him to the theatre. He reads Shakespeare and Beaumont and Fletcher before he is eight years old. He also reads *The Faerie Queene* about this time. [Cowper's first volume of *Poems*.]
1783	9	Henry Herbert Southey born (d. 1865). S. begins to write verses, Epics on the Trojan Brutus, Egbert, &c. [*The Village* (Crabbe).]
1784	10	[Dr. Johnson died. Leigh Hunt born.]
1785	11	[De Quincey born. Thomas Love Peacock born. Henry Kirke White born. *The Task* (Cowper).]

A.D.	ÆT.	
1786	12	At the end of this year or early in 1787 S. sent as a day-boy to a Mr. Lewis, a clergyman in Bristol, who took pupils. [*Poems* (Robert Burns, Kilmarnock ed.). Caroline Bowles born.]
1788	14	S. goes to school at Westminster, where his chief friends are C. W. W. Wynn, subsequently Secretary at War and Chancellor of the Duchy of Lancaster, and G. C. Bedford. [Byron born.]
1789	15	[*Sonnets* (W. L. Bowles). *The Loves of the Plants* (Darwin).]
1790	16	[Burke's *Reflections on the French Revolution.*]
1791	17	[John Wesley died.]
1792	18	S. expelled from Westminster for writing an article in a school newspaper, *The Flagellant*, ascribing the invention of flogging to the devil. He returns to Miss Tyler at Bristol. His father fails in business, and dies just after S., having been refused admission at Christ Church on account of the expulsion from Westminster, has matriculated at Balliol College. [Shelley born. Keble born. *Pleasures of Memory* (Rogers).]
1793	19	S. goes into residence at Balliol (Jan.), his expenses (as at Westminster) being paid by his uncle, the Rev. Herbert Hill, Chaplain to the British Factory at Lisbon. Reads and is much influenced by Epictetus. Friendship with Edmund Seward. S. writes first draft of *Joan of Arc* in Long Vacation. Shocked by the fate of the Girondins, and especially by the execution of Brissot (Oct. 31). Begins to think of retiring to America, there to live an Arcadian life in the forest. [*Evening Walk* and *Descriptive Sketches* (Wordsworth). *Tam o'Shanter*, &c. (Burns). Felicia Hemans born.]
1794	20	S. decides that he cannot conscientiously take Orders, as his uncle, Mr. Hill, had wished. His religious opinions at this time Unitarian. Meets S. T. Coleridge for the first time at Oxford (June). Together with four or five friends they form a scheme for a communistic settlement in America—Pantisocracy. S. writes Acts II and III of *The Fall of Robespierre*, S. T. C. supplying Act I. *Wat Tyler* written. *Madoc* begun. Miss Tyler breaks off all relations with S. on hearing of Pantisocracy and of his engagement to Edith Fricker (Oct.). S. proposes that for financial reasons Pantisocracy should first be tried in Wales instead of in America. *Poems by Robert Lovell and Robert Southey* published (autumn: dated on title-page, 1795).
1795	21	S. introduced to C. Lamb by S. T. C. (Jan.). S. and S. T. C. lecture at Bristol. Death of Edmund Seward (June). S. definitely declines Mr. Hill's proposal that he should take Orders, and decides to read for the bar. Abandons Pantisocracy, thereby causing a breach with S. T. C. Marries Edith Fricker, Nov. 14, and immediately after the wedding starts with Mr. Hill for Lisbon, leaving Mrs. S. in the care of Cottle's sisters. The marriage for the time kept secret. S. T. C. marries Sarah Fricker (Oct. 4). [Keats born. T. Carlyle born.]
1796	22	*Joan of Arc* published by Joseph Cottle. S. returns from Lisbon in May and settles with his wife at Bristol. Partial reconciliation with S. T. C. Death of S.'s brother-in-law, Lovell. S. writing *Letters from Spain and Portugal* and contributing also to *The Monthly Magazine*. Reads William Taylor's translations from German writers. [Burns died. Hartley Coleridge born. *Poems*, 1st ed., S. T. C.]

A.D.	ÆT.	
1797	23	*Letters from Spain and Portugal* and *Poems* published. S. in London and at Burton (near Christchurch in Hampshire) studying law. Becomes acquainted with J. Rickman, afterwards one of his closest friends. C. Lamb visits S. at Burton. S. receives an annuity of £160 from C. W. W. Wynn.
1798	24	S. writes verses for *The Morning Post* at a guinea a week, which he continues to do up to 1803. Visits Norwich, where he makes acquaintance with William Taylor and Dr. Sayers. Settles at Westbury, two miles from Bristol (June). In constant intercourse with Humphry Davy. Editing first vol. of *The Annual Anthology*. Second ed. of *Joan of Arc*. S. in indifferent health at end of this year. [*Lyrical Ballads* (Coleridge and Wordsworth). *Gebir* (W. S. Landor).]
1799	25	Westbury; London; Burton. *Madoc* finished (July 11). *Thalaba* begun (July 12). More complete reconciliation with S. T. C. (Aug.). S. and his wife visit the Coleridges at Nether Stowey. Walking tour with S. T. C. in Devonshire. First volume of *The Annual Anthology* and second volume of *Poems* published. S. reads and greatly admires *Gebir*. His health still unsatisfactory. [T. Hood born. *Pleasures of Hope* (Campbell).]
1800	26	S. collaborates with J. Cottle in preparing an edition of Chatterton's *Works* for the benefit of the latter's sister. Leaves England for Portugal with Mrs. S. for the benefit of his health (April). *Thalaba* finished (July). S. begins to collect materials for a *History of Portugal*. S. T. C. settles at Greta Hall, Keswick (Aug.). Second volume of *The Annual Anthology* published. [Cowper died. Macaulay born. Henry Taylor born.]
1801	27	*Thalaba* published. *Curse of Kehama* begun (May). S. returns to England (June). Completely abandons all idea of adopting the law as a profession. Begins to review again, a task-work from which he is unable to free himself for the rest of his active life. Stays with S. T. C. at Keswick (Sept.). Accepts post of private secretary to Mr. Corry, Chancellor of the Exchequer for Ireland. [*Lyrical Ballads*, 2nd ed. (pub. Jan.). *Poems* ('Thos. Little'). *Tales of Wonder* (M. G. Lewis).]
1802	28	Death of S.'s mother (Jan.). S. resigns his post as secretary. At Bristol (May). Birth of his first child, Margaret (Sept.). S. translating *Amadis of Gaul*, writing portions of a *History of Portugal*, reviewing, and continuing *Curse of Kehama*. Chatterton's *Works* (ed. Southey and Cottle) published by subscription. Peace of Amiens. This of critical importance in the development of S.'s political opinions. 'It restored in me the English feeling which had been deadened; it placed me in sympathy with my country, bringing me thus into that natural and healthy state of mind upon which time, and knowledge, and reflection were sure to produce their proper and salutary effect.' (*Warter*, iii, 320.) [Erasmus Darwin died.]
1803	29	Bristol. *Amadis of Gaul* published. Death of Margaret S. (Aug.). S. and his wife go to stay with S. T. C. at Keswick (Sept.).
1804	30	Keswick. S. T. C. starts for Malta (April 2). Edith May S. born (May 1). S. finally correcting *Madoc* for the press. *Letters from England by Don Manuel Espriella* begun.

A.D.	ÆT.	
1805	31	*Madoc* and *Metrical Tales and Other Poems* published. S. visits Scotland, and stays with Sir W. Scott at Ashestiel (Oct.). Plans to go to Lisbon for two years in the following spring. [*Lay of the Last Minstrel* (Scott). *The Prelude* finished (Wordsworth).]
1806	32	*Curse of Kehama* resumed. S. visits William Taylor at Norwich (April). Hopes to be given the Secretaryship of the Legation at Lisbon. S. T. C. returns to England (Aug.). *Chronicle of the Cid* and *Palmerin of England* begun. Herbert S. born (Oct. 11). S. undertakes to edit Henry Kirke White's *Remains* gratuitously for the White family. [*Simonidea* (Landor). *Odes and Epistles* (T. Moore). Elizabeth Barrett born.]
1807	33	Wynn obtains for S. a pension from Government of £144 net per annum, and S. therefore resigns the annuity of £160 paid him by Wynn since 1797. S. declines Scott's suggestion that he should contribute to the *Edinburgh Review*, on the ground of his complete disagreement with its principles. Decides to settle permanently at Greta Hall. *Palmerin of England, Letters from England by Don Manuel Espriella, Remains of Henry Kirke White*, and *Specimens of the later English Poets* (edited in conjunction with G. C. Bedford) published. *Madoc*, 2nd ed. S. begins to write the *History of Brazil* as the first part of his projected *History of Portugal*. Plans an edition of the *Morte d'Arthur*. [*Poems in Two Volumes* (Wordsworth). *The Parish Register* (Crabbe). *Hours of Idleness* (Byron).]
1808	34	Emma S. born (Feb.). S. meets W. S. Landor for the first time at Bristol. Landor urges him to continue his mythological poems, and offers to pay for the printing. Stung by this generous offer, S. resumes *The Curse of Kehama*, though without thought of accepting Landor's proposal. Prophesies that Spain will eventually prove Buonaparte's destruction. Plans a poem on Pelayo. S. T. C. domesticated with Wordsworth at Allan Bank, Grasmere (Sept.). *The Quarterly Review* planned. S. writes an article on the Baptist Mission in India for the first number, published Feb. 1809. *Chronicle of the Cid* published. [*Marmion* (Scott).]
1809	35	Bertha S. born (March 27), Emma S. died (May). S. T. C. publishes first number of *The Friend* at Penrith (June 1). S. takes a lease of Greta Hall for twenty-one years. Continues *History of Brazil*. Corresponds with Ebenezer Elliott, who asks him to criticize his poems. Undertakes to write the historical part of Ballantyne's new *Edinburgh Annual Register* at a salary of £400 a year. Finishes *Curse of Kehama*. Plans a poem on Robin Hood. *Roderick* begun (Dec. 2). *Thalaba*, 2nd ed. [Tract on the Convention of Cintra (Wordsworth). *English Bards and Scotch Reviewers* (Byron). *Gertrude of Wyoming* (Campbell). A. Tennyson, Charles Darwin, and W. E. Gladstone born.]
1810	36	*Curse of Kehama* and first vol. of *History of Brazil* published. Katharine S. born. S. T. C. spends four or five months at Greta Hall before leaving in October for London with Basil Montagu. Breach between S. T. C. and Wordsworth. [*The Borough* (Crabbe). *The Lady of the Lake* (Scott).]

A.D.	ÆT.	
1811	37	S. plans *Oliver Newman* and *The Book of the Church.* At work on *Life of Nelson,* an expansion of an article in the fifth number of the *Quarterly Review.* Visits Landor at Llanthony (July ?). Shelley at Keswick, winter of 1811–12. S. writes an article in the *Quarterly* (Oct.) on the Bell and Lancaster system of Education, advocating the establishment in every parish of a national school. This article subsequently enlarged and published separately. *Curse of Kehama,* 2nd ed. [Thackeray born. *Don Roderick* (Scott).]
1812	38	S. T. C. at Greta Hall, Feb. 23 – March 26,—his last visit to the Lake Country. Isabel S. born (Nov.). Dr. Bell at Keswick. *Omniana* published. [Charles Dickens and Robert Browning born. *Tales in Verse* (Crabbe). *Count Julian* (Landor). *Childe Harolde,* Cantos i and ii (Byron). *Rejected Addresses* (J. and H. Smith).]
1813	39	S. ceases to write for the *Edinburgh Annual Register* owing to irregularity of payment. Visits Streatham and London (Sept.). Meets Lord Byron at Holland House. Appointed Poet Laureate (partly on Scott's recommendation) on Scott declining the office (Oct.). *Life of Nelson* published. *The Doctor* begun. *Ode Written during Negotiations with Buonaparte.* [*Rokeby ; The Bridal of Triermain* (Scott). *Remorse* (S. T. C.) performed at Drury Lane (Jan.).]
1814	40	S. endeavours, through Cottle, to induce S. T. C. to return to Greta Hall (April). Failing even to get an answer from S. T. C. to his letters, he gets up a subscription among friends and relations to pay Hartley C.'s college expenses (autumn). Begins correspondence with Bernard Barton. *Roderick* published. S. appointed Member of the Royal Academy of Madrid. *A Tale of Paraguay* begun. [*The Excursion* (Wordsworth). *The Feast of the Poets* (Leigh Hunt).]
1815	41	*Oliver Newman* begun. *Minor Poems* (rearranged, &c.) published 3 vols. *Roderick,* 2nd ed. Tour in Holland and Belgium with Mrs. and Edith S. and Edward Nash, the artist (Sept.–Oct.). [First collective ed. of Wordsworth's poems published. *The White Doe of Rylstone* (Wordsworth). *The Lord of the Isles* (Scott).]
1816	42	Death of Herbert S. (April 17),—a blow from which S. never recovers. *The Poet's Pilgrimage* and *The Lay of the Laureate* published. An endeavour made by the Ministry to induce S. to conduct a political journal in London in opposition to revolutionary principles. This proposal S. declines. At this time S. advocates as palliatives of social distress the establishment of savings banks and a national system of education, the colonization of waste lands in the British Isles, and the encouragement of emigration. [*Alastor* (Shelley). *Christabel* (S. T. C.). *The Story of Rimini* (Leigh Hunt). *Childe Harold,* Canto iii (Byron).]
1817	43	*Wat Tyler* surreptitiously published (spring). S., in consequence, attacked by William Smith, member for Norwich, in House of Commons as ' a renegado ' (March 14). Replies in a letter to *The Courier* (reprinted in his *Essays*), and is defended in that paper by S. T. C. Declines a proposal that he should write chief leading article in *The Times,* (and, apparently, act in some measure as editor), at a salary of £2,000 a year, together with a share in the profits. Tour through

A.D.	ÆT.	
		Switzerland to Italian Lakes and back through Black Forest, Cologne, and Brussels (May–Aug.). *Life of Wesley* begun. *Morte d'Arthur* and *History of Brazil*, vol. ii, published. [*Sibylline Leaves ; Biographia Literaria* (S. T. C.). *Poems* (Keats). *Lalla Rookh* (Moore). *Harold the Dauntless* (Scott). The *Whistlecraft* Poem (J. H. Frere).]
1818	44	S. refuses the offer of the post of Librarian to the Advocates' Library, Edinburgh. Caroline Bowles writes to him (April 25) to ask his opinion of a MS. poem, thus beginning a correspondence continued without interruption until their marriage in 1839. [*Childe Harold*, Canto iv (Byron). *Revolt of Islam* (Shelley). *Poems* (C. Lamb, in his collected Works). *Foliage* (Leigh Hunt). *Endymion* (Keats).]
1819	45	Cuthbert S. born (Feb.). Tour in Scotland with Rickman and Telford (autumn). *History of Brazil*, vol. iii, published. S. learns from Wynn of the existence of the Dedication of *Don Juan*. [*Peter Bell* and *The Waggoner* (Wordsworth). *Don Juan*, Canto i, &c. (Byron). *Tales of the Hall* (Crabbe). *Dramatic Scenes* (Procter). *Poems, Rosalind and Helen, The Euganean Hills, Hymn to Intellectual Beauty, The Cenci* (Shelley). J. Ruskin, A. H. Clough, and Charles Kingsley born.]
1820	46	*Colloquies on the Prospects of Society* and *Book of the Church* begun. In Wales and London (April, May, and June). Meets Caroline Bowles for the first time at Chelsea. D.C.L., Oxford Univ. (June 14). *Life of Wesley* published. [*The River Duddon ; A Series of Sonnets* (Wordsworth). *Lamia, Isabella, Hyperion*, &c. (Keats). *Prometheus Bound* (Shelley). *Ellen Fitzarthur* (Caroline Bowles).]
1821	47	*Vision of Judgement* published. Its Preface involves S. in a public controversy with Byron. Hearing that his friend John May has lost his fortune, S. makes over to him his entire savings, amounting to £625. *Expedition of Orsua* published. [Keats died. *Adonais* (Shelley). *Cain*, &c. (Byron).]
1822	48	*History of the Peninsular War*, vol. i, published. [*Ecclesiastical Sketches* (Wordsworth). *Hellas* (Shelley). *The Widow's Tale* (Caroline Bowles). Shelley drowned.]
1823	49	Caroline Bowles at Greta Hall (Sept.). S. writes to her (Nov. 4) to suggest that they should collaborate in a poem on *Robin Hood*. Visits London (Nov.). Renews his friendship with C. Lamb, which had been momentarily interrupted through the latter misunderstanding a reference by S. in the *Quarterly* to the *Essays of Elia*. [*The Loves of the Angels* (T. Moore). *Essays of Elia* (Lamb).]
1824	50	*Robin Hood* begun. *The Book of the Church* and *History of the Peninsular War*, vol. ii, published. [Byron died. *Imaginary Conversations*, vols. i and ii (Landor).]
1825	51	*Vindiciae Ecclesiae Anglicanae* begun,—an answer to C. Butler's reply to *The Book of the Church*. S. now, as always, strongly opposed to Catholic Emancipation. Tour in Belgium and Holland with Henry Taylor and two other friends (June and July). S. is laid up with an injured foot at Leyden, and stays there for a fortnight with the poet Bilderdijk, whose wife had translated *Roderick* into Dutch verse. *A Tale of Paraguay* published.

A.D.	ÆT.	
1826	52	S. visits Caroline Bowles at Buckland, near Lymington. Tours in Holland (June) with H. Taylor and Rickman. During his absence is returned to Parliament for the borough of Downton, through the influence of Lord Radnor ; but refuses to accept the honour. Death of Isabel S. (July 16). From this last blow Mrs. S. never really recovers. *Vindiciae Ecclesiae Anglicanae* published.
		[*Solitary Hours* (Caroline Bowles).]
1827	53	S. undertakes to edit the poems of John Jones, a servant in a Yorkshire family, for Jones's benefit, and to prefix a sketch of the lives of un-educated poets. Mrs. S. plainly failing in health.
		[*Poems* (T. Hood). *The Christian Year* (Keble). *Poems by Two Brothers* (A. and C. Tennyson).]
1828	54	In London in order to undergo an operation (May). His portrait painted by Sir T. Lawrence for Sir R. Peel. Visits Caroline Bowles at Buckland. Death of his uncle, Mr. Hill (Sept.). Is paid £150 by Murray for a paper in the *Quarterly* on the Roman Catholic Question and Ireland, strongly opposing Catholic Emancipation.
		[*History of Peninsular War*, vol. i (Sir W. Napier).]
1829	55	*Lives of Uneducated Poets—Prefixed to Verses by John Jones* published. *All for Love* and *The Legend of a Cock and a Hen* (1 vol.), and *Colloquies on the Progress and Prospects of Society* published. Mrs. Coleridge and Sara C. leave Greta Hall on the marriage of the latter to H. N. Coleridge, Mrs. C. subsequently taking up her residence with her daughter and son-in-law. S. continues to advocate the establishment of Co-operative Societies.
		[*Chapters on Churchyards* (Caroline Bowles). *Imaginary Conversations*, second series (Landor).]
1830	56	S. engaged in writing *Life of Bunyan* and *Naval History of England*. *Life of Bunyan* published, prefixed to an edition of *Pilgrim's Progress*.
		[Hazlitt died. *Poems, Chiefly Lyrical* (A. Tennyson).]
1831	57	S. visits Caroline Bowles at Buckland (Jan.). Visits Dr. Bell at Cheltenham (June). *Select Works of British Poets from Chaucer to Jonson* published. S. continues (as, like Wordsworth, he had done from the first) strongly to oppose Parliamentary Reform.
		[*Corn Law Rhymes* (Ebenezer Elliott).]
1832	58	*Essays, Moral and Political* published (Jan. or ? Dec. 1831). *History of the Peninsular War*, vol. iii, published. Death of Dr. Bell, who leaves S. £1000, with a request that he should write his Life. S. refuses offer of a Professorship of History at Durham University. Landor visits S. at Keswick (June).
		[Sir W. Scott died. Crabbe died. Bentham died. Dr. Arnold buys Fox How.]
1833	59	Correspondence with Lord Ashley on Factory Legislation. S. begins to work at Dr. Bell's *Life and Correspondence*. *Naval History of England*, vols. i and ii, published.
		[*Pauline* (R. Browning). *Poems* (Hartley Coleridge).]
1834	60	*The Doctor, &c.*, vols. i and ii, published. Edith May S. marries the Rev. J. W. Warter (Jan.). *Naval History*, vol. iii, published. *Life of Cowper* begun. Mrs. S. loses her reason (Sept.) and is removed to the asylum at York.
		[S. T. C. died (July 25). C. Lamb died (Dec. 27). *Philip van Artevelde* (H. Taylor).]

A.D.	ÆT.	
1835	61	S. declines the offer of a baronetcy from Sir R. Peel, who then obtains for him an additional pension of £300 a year. Mrs. S., though without regaining her reason, so far recovers as to be allowed to return to Keswick (March). Publication of *Life and Works of Cowper* (15 vols., 1835–37) begun. [*Yarrow Revisited and other Poems* (Wordsworth). Mrs. Hemans died. James Hogg died. *Paracelsus* (R. Browning).]
1836	62	Tour in West of England with Cuthbert S. (Oct.–Feb. 1837). Meets Landor at Clifton and stays at Bremhill with W. L. Bowles. [*Pericles and Aspasia* (Landor). *The Birthday* (Caroline Bowles). William Taylor of Norwich died.]
1837	63	S. corresponds with Charlotte Brontë in answer to a request for his criticism of her poems. ' Mr. Southey's letter was kind and admirable, a little stringent, but it did me good ' (C. Brontë). Publication of collected edition of S.'s poems in 10 vols. begun. Cuthbert S. matriculates at Oxford. Mrs. S. died (Nov. 16). [*Strafford* (R. Browning). *The French Revolution* (T. Carlyle).]
1838	64	Tour in Normandy, Brittany, and Touraine with Cuthbert S., H. C. Robinson, and three other friends (Aug., Sept.). S. now first begins to show signs of failing powers. At Buckland with Caroline Bowles (Oct.–Dec.).
1839	65	Bertha S. marries her cousin Herbert Hill. S. marries Caroline Bowles (June 5). Soon afterwards his mind fails rapidly, until its powers are completely lost. In this condition he lives at Keswick until his death.
1843	69	Robert Southey died (March 21). Buried in Crosthwaite Churchyard.

PREFACES

TO THE COLLECTED EDITION OF TEN VOLUMES,
PUBLISHED IN 1837, 1838.

PREFACE TO THE FIRST VOLUME

AT the age of sixty-three I have undertaken to collect and edite my Poetical Works, with the last corrections that I can expect to bestow upon them. They have obtained a reputation equal to my wishes; and I have this ground for hoping it may not be deemed hereafter more than commensurate with their deserts, that it has been gained without ever accommodating myself to the taste or fashion of the times. Thus to collect and revise them is a duty which I owe to that part of the Public by whom they have been auspiciously received, and to those who will take a lively concern in my good name when I shall have departed.

The arrangement was the first thing to be considered. In this the order wherein the respective poems were written has been observed, so far as was compatible with a convenient classification. Such order is useful to those who read critically, and desire to trace the progress of an author's mind in his writings; and by affixing dates to the minor pieces, under whatever head they are disposed, the object is sufficiently attained.

Next came the question of correction. There was no difficulty with those poems which were composed after the author had acquired his art (so far as he has acquired it), and after his opinions were matured. It was only necessary to bear in mind the risk there must ever be of injuring a poem by verbal alterations made long after it was written; inas-much as it must be impossible to recall the precise train of thought in which any passage was conceived, and the considerations upon which not the single verse alone, but the whole sentence, or paragraph, had been constructed: but with regard to more important changes, there could be no danger of introducing any discrepance in style. With juvenile pieces the case is different. From these the faults of diction have been weeded wherever it could be done without more trouble than the composition originally cost, and than the piece itself was worth. But inherent faults of conception and structure are incurable; and it would have been mere waste of time to recompose what it was impossible otherwise to amend.

If these poems had been now for the first time to be made public, there are some among them which, instead of being committed to the press, would have been consigned to the flames; not for any disgrace which could be reflected upon me by the crude compositions of my youth, nor for any harm which they could possibly do the reader, but merely that they might not cumber the collection. But '*nescit vox missa reverti*'. Pirated editions would hold out as a recommendation, that they contained what I had chosen to suppress, and thus it becomes prudent, and therefore proper, that such pieces should be retained.

It has ever been a rule with me when I have imitated a passage, or borrowed an expression, to acknowledge the specific obligation. Upon the present occasion it behoves me to state the more general and therefore more important obligations which I am conscious of owing either to my predecessors, or my contemporaries.

My first attempts in verse were much too early to be imitative, but I was fortunate enough to find my way, when very young, into the right path. I read the *Jerusalem Delivered* and the *Orlando Furioso* again and again, in Hoole's translations : it was for the sake of their stories that I perused and re-perused these poems with ever new delight ; and by bringing them thus within my reach in boyhood, the translator rendered me a service which, when I look back upon my intellectual life, I cannot estimate too highly. I owe him much also for his notes, not only for the information concerning other Italian romances which they imparted, but also for introducing me to Spenser ;—how early, an incident which I well remember may show. Going with a relation into Bull's circulating library at Bath (an excellent one for those days), and asking whether they had the *Faery Queen*, the person who managed the shop said ' yes, they had it, but it was in obsolete language, and the young gentleman would not understand it '. But I, who had learned all I then knew of the history of England from Shakespear, and who had moreover read Beaumont and Fletcher, found no difficulty in Spenser's English, and felt in the beauty of his versification a charm in poetry of which I had never been fully sensible before. From that time I took Spenser for my master. I drank also betimes of Chaucer's well. The taste which had been acquired in that school was confirmed by Percy's *Reliques* and Warton's *History of English Poetry* ; and a little later by Homer and the Bible. It was not likely to be corrupted afterwards.

My school-boy verses savoured of Gray, Mason, and my predecessor Warton ; and in the best of my juvenile pieces it may be seen how much the writer's mind had been imbued by Akenside. I am conscious also of having derived much benefit at one time from Cowper, and more from Bowles ; for which, and for the delight which his poems gave me at an age when we are most susceptible of such delight, my good friend at Bremhill, to whom I was then and long afterwards personally unknown, will allow me to make this grateful and cordial acknowledgment.

My obligation to Dr. Sayers is of a different kind. Every one who has an ear for metre and a heart for poetry, must have felt how perfectly the metre of Collins's *Ode to Evening* is in accordance with the imagery and the feeling. None of the experiments which were made of other unrhymed stanzas proved successful. They were either in strongly marked and well-known measures which unavoidably led the reader to expect rhyme, and consequently baulked him when he looked for it ; or they were in stanzas as cumbrous as they were ill constructed. Dr. Sayers went upon a different principle, and succeeded admirably. I read his *Dramatic Sketches of Northern Mythology* when they were first published, and convinced myself when I had acquired some skill in versification, that the kind of verse in which his choruses were composed was not less applicable to narration than to lyrical poetry. Soon after I had begun the Arabian romance, for which this measure seemed the most appropriate vehicle, *Gebir* fell into my hands, and my verse was greatly improved by it, both in vividness and strength. Several years elapsed before I knew that Walter Landor was the author, and more before I had the good fortune to meet the person to whom I felt myself thus beholden. The days which I have passed with him in the Vale of Ewias, at Como, and lastly in the neighbourhood of Bristol, are some of those which have left with me ' a joy for memory '.

I have thus acknowledged all the specific obligations to my elders or contemporaries in the art, of which I am distinctly conscious. The advantages arising from intimate intercourse with those who were engaged in similar pursuits cannot be in like manner specified, because in their nature they are imperceptible ; but of such advantages no man has ever possessed more or greater, than at different times it has been my lot to enjoy. Personal attachment first, and family circumstances afterwards, connected me long and closely with Mr. Coleridge; and three-and-thirty years have ratified a friendship with Mr Wordsworth, which we believe will not terminate with this life, and which it is a pleasure for us to know will be continued and cherished as an heirloom by those who are dearest to us both.

When I add what has been the greatest of all advantages, that I have passed more than half my life in retirement, conversing with books rather than men, constantly and unweariably engaged in literary pursuits, communing with my own heart, and taking that course which upon mature consideration seemed best to myself, I have said every thing necessary to account for the characteristics of my poetry, whatever they may be.

It was in a mood resembling in no slight degree that wherewith a person in sound health, both of body and mind, makes his will and sets his worldly affairs in order, that I entered upon the serious task of arranging and revising the whole of my poetical works. What, indeed, was it but to bring in review before me the dreams and aspirations of my youth, and the feelings whereto I had given that free utterance which by the usages of this world is permitted to us in poetry, and in poetry alone ? Of the smaller pieces in this collection there is scarcely one concerning which I cannot vividly call to mind when and where it was composed. I have perfect recollection of the spots where many, not of the scenes only, but of the images which I have described from nature, were observed and noted. And how would it be possible for me to forget the interest taken in these poems, especially the longer and more ambitious works, by those persons nearest and dearest to me then, who witnessed their growth and completion ? Well may it be called a serious task thus to resuscitate the past ! But serious though it be, it is not painful to one who knows that the end of his journey cannot be far distant, and, by the blessing of God, looks on to its termination with sure and certain hope.

Keswick, May 10, 1837.

PREFACE TO THE SECOND VOLUME,

BEING THE FIRST OF TWO VOLUMES ENTITLED ' JUVENILE AND MINOR POEMS ', BEGINNING WITH ' THE TRIUMPH OF WOMAN ', AND ENDING WITH ' HYMN TO THE PENATES '

THE earliest pieces in these Juvenile and Minor Poems were written before the writer had left school ; between the date of these and of the latest there is an interval of six-and-forty years : as much difference, therefore, may be perceived in them, as in the different stages of life from boyhood to old age.

Some of the earliest appeared in a little volume published at Bath in the autumn of 1794, with this title :—
' *Poems, containing the Retrospect, &c.* by Robert Lovell and Robert Southey, 1795 ; ' and with this motto—

' Minuentur atrae
Carmine curae.'   *Horace.*

At the end of that volume, *Joan of Arc* was announced as to be published by subscription.

Others were published at Bristol, 1797, in a single volume, with this motto from Akenside :—

' Goddess of the Lyre,—
              with thee comes
Majestic Truth ; and where Truth deigns to
come
Her sister Liberty will not be far.'

A second volume followed at Bristol in 1799, after the second edition of *Joan of Arc*, and commencing with the *Vision of the Maid of Orleans*. The motto to this was from the Epilogue to Spenser's *Shepherds' Calendar* :—

' The better, please ; the worse, displease :
      I ask no more.'

In the third edition of *Joan of Arc*, the *Vision* was printed separately, at the end ; and its place was supplied in the second edition of the Poems by miscellaneous pieces.

A separate volume, entitled *Metrical Tales and other Poems*, was published in 1805, with this advertisement :—' These Poems were published some years ago in the *Annual Anthology*. (Bristol, 1799, 1800.) They have now been revised and printed in this collected form, because they have pleased those readers whom the Author was most desirous of pleasing. Let them be considered as the desultory productions of a man sedulously employed upon better things.'

These various pieces were re-arranged in three volumes, under the title of *Minor Poems*, in 1815, with this motto,

      ' Nos haec novimus esse nihil ; '

and they were published a second time in the same form, 1823.

The Ballads and Metrical Tales contained in those volumes, belong to a different part of this collection ; their other contents are comprised here ; and the present volume consists, with very few exceptions, of pieces written in youth or early manhood. One of these written in my twentieth year, not having been published at the time, would never have been made public by my own act and deed ; but as *Wat Tyler* obtained considerable notoriety upon its surreptitious publication, it seemed proper that a production which will be specially noticed whenever the author shall be delivered over to the biographers, should be included here. They who may desire to know more than is stated in the advertisement now prefixed to it, are referred to a Letter addressed to William Smith, Esq. M.P., 1817, reprinted in the second volume of my *Essays Moral and Political*, 1832.

The second volume of this part of the Collection contains one juvenile piece, and many which were written in early manhood. The remainder were composed in middle or later life, and comprise (with one exception, that will more conveniently be arranged elsewhere,) all the odes which as Poet Laureat I have written upon national occasions. Of these the *Carmen Triumphale*, and the *Carmina Aulica*, were separately published in quarto in 1814, and reprinted together in a little volume in 1821.

The Juvenile and Minor Poems in this Collection bear an inconsiderable proportion to those of substantive length : for a small part only of my youthful effusions were spared from those autos-da-fé in which from time to time piles upon piles have been consumed. In middle life works of greater extent, or of a different kind, left me little leisure for occasional poetry ; the impulse ceased, and latterly the inclination was so seldom felt, that it required an effort to call it forth.

Sir William Davenant, in the Preface to *Gondibert*, ' took occasion to accuse and condemn all those hasty digestions of thought which were published in his youth ; a sentence, said he, not pronounced out of melancholy rigour, but from a cheerful obedience to the just authority of experience. For that grave mistress of the world, experience, (in whose profitable school those before the Flood stayed long, but we, like wanton children, come thither late, yet too soon are called out of it, and fetched home by death,) hath taught me that the engenderings of unripe age become abortive and deformed; and that 'tis a high presumption to entertain a nation (who are a poet's standing guest, and require monarchical respect,) with hasty provisions; as if a poet might imitate the familiar despatch of faulconers, mount his Pegasus, unhood his Muse, and, with a few flights, boast he hath provided a feast for a prince. Such posting upon Pegasus I have long since foreborne.' Yet this eminently thoughtful poet was so far from seeking to suppress the crude compositions which he thus condemned, that he often expressed a great desire to see all his pieces collected in one volume; and, conformably to his wish, they were so collected, after his decease, by his widow and his friend Herringman the bookseller.

Agreeing with Davenant in condemning the greater part of my juvenile pieces, it is only as crudities that I condemn them; for in all that I have written, whether in prose or verse, there has never been a line which for any compunctious reason, living or dying, I could wish to blot.

Davenant had not changed his opinion of his own youthful productions so as to overlook in his age the defects which he had once clearly perceived; but he knew that pieces which it would indeed have been presumptuous to reproduce on the score of their merit, might yet be deemed worthy of preservation on other grounds; that to his family and friends, and to those who might take any interest in English poetry hereafter, they would possess peculiar value, as characteristic memorials of one who had held no inconsiderable place in the literature of his own times; feeling, too, that he was not likely to be forgotten by posterity, he thought that after the specimen which he had produced in his *Gondibert* of a great and elaborate poem, his early attempts would be regarded with curiosity by such of his successors as should, like him, study poetry as an art,—for as an art it must be studied by those who would excel in it, though excellence in it is not attainable by art alone.

The cases are very few in which any thing more can be inferred from juvenile poetry, than that the aspirant possesses imitative talent, and the power of versifying, for which, as for music, there must be a certain natural aptitude. It is not merely because ' they have lacked culture and the inspiring aid of books ',[1] that so many poets who have been ' sown by Nature', have 'wanted the accomplishment of verse', and brought forth no fruit after their kind. Men of the highest culture, of whose poetical temperament no doubt can be entertained, and who had 'taken to the height the measure of themselves', have yet failed in their endeavour to become poets, for want of that accomplishment. It is frequently possessed without any other qualification, or any capacity for improvement; but then the innate and incurable defect that renders it abortive, is at once apparent.

The state of literature in this kingdom during the last fifty years has produced the same effect upon poetry that academies produce upon painting; in both arts every possible assistance is afforded to imitative talents, and in both they are carried as far as the talent of imitation can reach. But there is one respect in which poetry differs widely from the sister arts. Its fairest promise frequently proves deceitful, whereas both in painting and music the early indications of genius are unequivocal. The children who were called musical prodigies, have become great musicians; and great painters, as far as their history is known, have displayed in childhood that accuracy of eye, and dexterity of hand, and shaping faculty, which are the prime requisites for their calling. But it is often found that young poets of whom great expectations were formed, have made no progress, and have even fallen short of their first performances. It may be said that this is because men apply themselves to music and to painting as their professions, but that no one makes poetry the business of his

[1] Wordsworth.

life. This, however, is not the only reason : the indications, as has already been observed, are far less certain ; and the circumstances of society are far less favourable for the moral and intellectual culture which is required for all the higher branches of poetry, ... all indeed that deserves the name.

My advice as to publishing, has often been asked by young poets, who suppose that experience has qualified me to give it, and who have not yet learnt how seldom advice is taken, and how little therefore it is worth. As a general rule, it may be said that one who is not deceived in the estimate which he has

Keswick, Sept. 30, 1837.

formed of his own powers, can neither write too much in his youth, nor publish too little. It cannot, however, be needful to caution the present race of poetical adventurers against hurrying with their productions to the press, for there are obstacles enough in the way of publication. Looking back upon my own career, and acknowledging my imprudence in this respect, I have nevertheless no cause to wish that I had pursued a different course. In this, as in other circumstances of my life, I have reason to be thankful to that merciful Providence which shaped the ends that I had roughly hewn for myself.

PREFACE TO THE THIRD VOLUME,

BEING THE SECOND OF 'JUVENILE AND MINOR POEMS

In a former Preface my obligations to Akenside were acknowledged, with especial reference to the *Hymn to the Penates* ; the earliest of my Inscriptions also originated in the pleasure with which I perused those of this favourite author. Others of a later date bear a nearer resemblance to the general character of Chiabrera's epitaphs. Those which relate to the Peninsular War are part of a series which I once hoped to have completed. The epitaph for Bishop Butler was originally composed in the lapidary style, to suit the monument in Bristol Cathedral : it has been remodelled here, that I might express myself more at length, and in a style more accordant with my own judgement.

One thing remains to be explained, and I shall then have said all that it becomes me to say concerning these Minor Poems.

It was stated in some of the newspapers that Walter Scott and myself became competitors for the Poet-Laureateship upon the death of Mr. Pye ; that we met accidentally at the Prince Regent's levee, each in pursuit of his pretensions, and that some words which

were not over-courteous on either side passed between us on the occasion ;— to such impudent fabrications will those persons resort who make it their business to pander for public curiosity. The circumstances relating to that appointment have been made known in Mr. Lockhart's *Life* of Sir Walter. His conduct was, as it always was, characteristically generous, and in the highest degree friendly. Indeed, it was neither in his nature nor in mine to place ourselves in competition with any one, or ever to regard a contemporary as a rival. The world was wide enough for us all.

Upon his declining the office, and using his influence, without my knowledge, to obtain it for me, his biographer says,[1] 'Mr. Southey was invited to accept the vacant laurel ; and to the honour of the Prince Regent, when he signified that his acceptance must depend on the office being thenceforth so modified as to demand none of the old formal odes, leaving it to the Poet-Laureate to choose his own time for celebrating any great public event that

[1] Vol. iii, p. 88.

might occur, his Royal Highness had the good sense and good taste at once to acquiesce in the propriety of this alteration. The office was thus relieved from the burden of ridicule which had, in spite of so many illustrious names, adhered to it.' The alteration, however, was not brought about exactly in this manner.

I was on the way to London when the correspondence upon this subject between Sir Walter Scott and Mr. Croker took place. A letter from Scott followed me thither, and on my arrival in town I was informed of what had been done. No wish for the Laureateship had passed across my mind, nor had I ever dreamt that it would be proposed to me. My first impulse was to decline it; not from any fear of ridicule, still less of obloquy, but because I had ceased for several years to write occasional verses: the inclination had departed; and though willing as a bee to work from morn till night in collecting honey, I had a great dislike to spinning like a spider. Other considerations overcame this reluctance, and made it my duty to accept the appointment. I then expressed a wish to Mr. Croker that it might be placed upon a footing which would exact from the holder nothing like a schoolboy's task, but leave him at liberty to write when, and in what manner, he thought best, and thus render the office as honourable as it was originally designed to be. Upon this, Mr. Croker, whose friendliness to me upon every occasion I gladly take this opportunity of acknowledging, observed that it was not for us to make terms with the Prince Regent. 'Go you', said he, 'and write your Ode for the New Year. You can never have a better subject than the present state of the war affords you.' He added that some fit time might be found for representing the matter to the Prince in its proper light.

My appointment had no sooner been made known, than I received a note with Sir William Parsons's compliments, requesting that I would let him have the Ode as soon as possible, Mr. Pye having always provided him with it six weeks before the New Year's Day. I was not wanting in punctuality; nevertheless, it was a great trouble to Sir William that the office should have been conferred upon a poet who did not walk in the ways of his predecessor, and do according to all things that he had done; for Mr Pye had written his odes always in regular stanzas and in rhyme. Poor Sir William, though he had not fallen upon evil tongues and evil times, thought he had fallen upon evil ears when he was to set verses like mine to music.

But the labour which the Chief Musician bestowed upon the verses of the Chief Poet was so much labour lost. The performance of the Annual Odes had been suspended from the time of the King's illness, in 1810. Under the circumstances of his malady, any festal celebration of the birth-day would have been a violation of natural feeling and public propriety. On those occasions it was certain that nothing would be expected from me during the life of George III. But the New Year's performance might perhaps be called for, and for that, therefore, I always prepared. Upon the accession of George IV, I made ready an Ode for St. George's Day, which Mr. Shield, who was much better satisfied with his yokefellow than Sir William had been, thought happily suited for his purpose. It was indeed well suited for us both. All my other Odes related to the circumstances of the passing times, and could have been appropriately performed only when they were composed; but this was a standing subject, and, till this should be called for, it was needless to provide any thing else. The annual performance had, however, by this time fallen completely into disuse; and thus terminated a custom which may truly be said to have been more honoured in the breach than in the observance.

Keswick, Dec. 12, 1837.

PREFACE TO THE FOURTH VOLUME,

CONTAINING 'THALABA THE DESTROYER'

It was said, in the original Preface to *Joan of Arc*, that the Author would not be in England to witness its reception, but that he would attend to liberal criticism, and hope to profit by it in the composition of a poem upon the discovery of America by the Welsh prince Madoc.

That subject I had fixed upon when a schoolboy, and had often conversed upon the probabilities of the story with the schoolfellow to whom, sixteen years afterwards, I had the satisfaction of inscribing the poem. It was commenced at Bath in the autumn of 1794; but, upon putting *Joan of Arc* to the press, its progress was necessarily suspended, and it was not resumed till the second edition of that work had been completed. Then it became my chief occupation during twelve months that I resided in the village of Westbury, near Bristol. This was one of the happiest portions of my life. I never before or since produced so much poetry in the same space of time. The smaller pieces were communicated by letter to Charles Lamb, and had the advantage of his animadversions. I was then also in habits of the most frequent and intimate intercourse with Davy,—then in the flower and freshness of his youth. We were within an easy walk of each other, over some of the most beautiful ground in that beautiful part of England. When I went to the Pneumatic Institution, he had to tell me of some new experiment or discovery, and of the views which it opened for him; and when he came to Westbury there was a fresh portion of *Madoc* for his hearing. Davy encouraged me with his hearty approbation during its progress; and the bag of nitrous oxyde with which he generally regaled me upon my visits to him, was not required for raising my spirits to the degree of settled fair, and keeping them at that elevation.

In November, 1836, I walked to that village with my son, wishing to show him a house endeared to me by so many recollections; but not a vestige of it remained, and local alterations rendered it impossible even to ascertain its site,—which is now included within the grounds of a Nunnery! The bosom friends with whom I associated there have all departed before me; and of the domestic circle in which my happiness was then centered, I am the sole survivor.

When we removed from Westbury at Midsummer, 1799, I had reached the penultimate book of *Madoc*. That poem was finished on the 12th of July following, at Kingsdown, Bristol, in the house of an old lady, whose portrait hangs, with that of my own mother, in the room wherein I am now writing. The son who lived with her was one of my dearest friends, and one of the best men I ever knew or heard of. In those days I was an early riser: the time so gained was usually employed in carrying on the poem which I had in hand; and when Charles Danvers came down to breakfast on the morning after *Madoc* was completed, I had the first hundred lines of *Thalaba* to show him, fresh from the mint.

But this poem was neither crudely conceived nor hastily undertaken. I had fixed upon the ground, four years before, for a Mahommedan tale; and in the course of that time the plan had been formed and the materials collected. It was pursued with unabating ardour at Exeter, in the village of Burton, near Christ Church, and afterwards at Kingsdown, till the ensuing spring, when Dr. Beddoes advised me to go to the south of Europe, on account of my health. For Lisbon, therefore, we set off; and, hastening to Falmouth, found the packet, in which we wished to sail, detained in harbour by westerly winds. ' Six days we watched the weathercock, and sighed for north-easters. I walked on the beach, caught soldier-crabs, admired the sea-anemonies in their ever-varying shapes of beauty, read *Gebir*, and wrote half a book of *Thalaba*.' This sentence is from a letter written on our arrival at Lisbon ; and it is here inserted because the sea anemonies (which I have never had any other opportunity of observing) were introduced in *Thalaba* soon afterwards ; and because, as already stated, I am sensible of having derived great improvement from the frequent perusal of *Gebir* at that time.

Change of circumstances and of climate effected an immediate cure of what proved to be not an organic disease. A week after our landing at Lisbon I resumed my favourite work, and I completed it at Cintra, a year and six days after the day of its commencement.

A fair transcript was sent to England. Mr. Rickman, with whom I had fallen in at Christ Church in 1797, and whose friendship from that time I have ever accounted among the singular advantages and happinesses of my life, negociated for its publication with Messrs. Longman and Rees. It was printed at Bristol by Biggs and Cottle, and the task of correcting the press was undertaken for me by Davy and our common friend Danvers, under whose roof it had been begun.

The copy which was made from the original draught, regularly as the poem proceeded, is still in my possession. The first corrections were made as they occurred in the process of transcribing, at which time the verses were tried upon

Keswick, Nov. 8, 1837.

my own ear, and had the advantage of being seen in a fair and remarkably legible handwriting. In this transcript the dates of time and place were noted, and things which would otherwise have been forgotten have thus been brought to my recollection. Herein also the alterations were inserted which the poem underwent before it was printed. They were very numerous. Much was pruned off, and more was ingrafted. I was not satisfied with the first part of the concluding book ; it was therefore crossed out, and something substituted altogether different in design ; but this substitution was so far from being fortunate, that it neither pleased my friends in England nor myself. I then made a third attempt, which succeeded to my own satisfaction and to theirs.

I was in Portugal when *Thalaba* was published. Its reception was very different from that with which *Joan of Arc* had been welcomed : in proportion as the poem deserved better it was treated worse. Upon this occasion my name was first coupled with Mr. Wordsworth's. We were then, and for some time afterwards, all but strangers to each other ; and certainly there were no two poets in whose productions the difference not being that between good and bad, less resemblance could be found. But I happened to be residing at Keswick when Mr. Wordsworth and I began to be acquainted ; Mr. Coleridge also had resided there ; and this was reason enough for classing us together as a school of poets. Accordingly, for more than twenty years from that time, every tyro in criticism who could smatter and sneer, tried his ' prentice hand ' upon the Lake Poets ; and every young sportsman who carried a popgun in the field of satire, considered them as fair game.

PREFACE TO THE FIFTH VOLUME,

CONTAINING 'MADOC'

WHEN *Madoc* was brought to a close in the summer of 1799, Mr. Coleridge advised me to publish it at once, and to defer making any material alterations, if any should suggest themselves, till a second edition. But four years had passed over my head since *Joan of Arc* was sent to the press, and I was not disposed to commit a second imprudence. If the reputation obtained by that poem had confirmed the confidence which I felt in myself, it had also the effect of making me perceive my own deficiencies, and endeavour with all diligence to supply them. I pleased myself with the hope that it would one day be likened to Tasso's *Rinaldo*, and that as the *Jerusalem* had fulfilled the promise of better things whereof that poem was the pledge, so might *Madoc* be regarded in relation to the juvenile work which had preceded it. Thinking that this would probably be the greatest poem I should ever produce, my intention was to bestow upon it all possible care, as indeed I had determined never again to undertake any subject without due preparation. With this view it was my wish, before *Madoc* could be considered as completed, to see more of Wales than I had yet seen. This I had some opportunity of doing in the autumn of 1801, with my old friends and schoolfellows Charles Wynn and Peter Elmsley. And so much was I bent upon making myself better acquainted with Welsh scenery, manners, and traditions, than could be done by books alone, that if I had succeeded in obtaining a house in the Vale of Neath, for which I was in treaty the year following, it would never have been my fortune to be classed among the Lake Poets.

Little had been done in revising the poem till the first year of my abode at Keswick: there, in the latter end of 1803, it was resumed, and twelve months were diligently employed in reconstructing it. The alterations were more material than those which had been made in *Joan of Arc*, and much more extensive. In its original form the poem consisted of fifteen books, containing about six thousand lines. It was now divided into two parts, and enlarged in the proportion of a full third. Shorter divisions than the usual one of books, or cantos, were found more convenient; the six books therefore, which the first part comprised, were distributed in seventeen sections, and the other nine in twenty-seven. These changes in the form of the work were neither capriciously made, nor for the sake of novelty. The story consisted of two parts, almost as distinct as the *Iliad* and *Odyssey*; and the subdivisions were in like manner indicated by the subject. The alterations in the conduct of the piece occasioned its increase of length.

When Matthew Lewis published the *Castle Spectre*, he gave as his reason for introducing negro guards in a drama which was laid in feudal times, that he thought their appearance would produce a good effect; and if the effect would have been better by making them blue instead of black, blue, said he, they should have been. He was not more bent upon pleasing the public by stage effect, (which no dramatist ever studied more successfully,) than I was upon following my own sense of propriety, and thereby obtaining the approbation of that fit audience, which, being contented that it should be few, I was sure to find. Mr. Sotheby, whose *Saul* was published about the same time as *Madoc*, said to me a year or two afterwards, ' You and I, Sir, find that blank verse will not do in these days ; we must stand upon another tack.' Mr. Sotheby considered the decision of the Pie-Poudre Court as final. But my suit was in that Court of Record which sooner or later pronounces unerringly upon the merits of the case.

Madoc was immediately reprinted in America in numbers, making two octavo volumes. About nine years afterwards there appeared a paper in the *Quarterly Review,* which gave great offence to the Americans, If I am not mistaken in my recollections, it was the first in that journal which had any such tendency. An American author, whose name I heard, but had no wish to remember, supposed it to have been written by me; and upon this gratuitous supposition, (in which, moreover, he happened to be totally mistaken,) he attacked me in a pamphlet, which he had the courtesy to send me, and which I have preserved among my Curiosities of Literature. It is noticed in this place, because, among other vituperative accusations, the pamphleteer denounced the author of *Madoc* as having ' meditated a most serious injury against the reputation of the New World, by attributing its discovery and colonization to a little vagabond Welsh Prince'. This, he said, ' being a most insidious attempt against the honour of America and the reputation of Columbus.' [1]

This poem was the means of making me personally acquainted with Miss Seward. Her encomiastic opinion of it was communicated to me through Charles Lloyd, in a way which required some courteous acknowledgement; this led to an interchange of letters, and an invitation to Lichfield, where, accordingly, I paid her a visit, when next on my way to London, in 1807. She resided in the Bishop's palace. I was ushered up the broad brown stair-case

[1] The title of this notable pamphlet is, ' The United States and England; being a Reply to the Criticism on Inchiquin's Letters, contained in the *Quarterly Review* for January 1814. New York : published by A. H. Inskeep ; and Bradford and Inskeep, Philadelphia. Van Winkle and Wiley, Printers, 1815.'

by her cousin, the Reverend Henry White, then one of the minor canons of that cathedral, a remarkable person, who introduced me into the presence with jubilant but appalling solemnity. Miss Seward was seated at her desk. She had just finished some verses to be ' inscribed on the blank leaves of the poem *Madoc* ', and the first greeting was no sooner past, than she requested that I would permit her to read them to me. It was a mercy that she did not ask me to read them aloud. But she read admirably herself. The situation, however, in which I found myself, was so ridiculous, and I was so apprehensive of catching the eye of one person in the room, who was equally afraid of meeting mine, that I never felt it more difficult to control my emotions, than while listening, or seeming to listen, to my own praise and glory. But, bending my head as if in a posture of attentiveness, and screening my face with my hand, and occasionally using some force to compress the risible muscles, I got through the scene without any misbehaviour, and expressed my thanks, if not in terms of such glowing admiration as she was accustomed to receive from others, and had bestowed upon my unworthy self, yet as well as I could. I passed two days under her roof, and corresponded with her from that time till her death.

Miss Seward had been crippled by having repeatedly injured one of her knee-pans. Time had taken away her bloom and her beauty, but her fine countenance retained its animation, and her eyes could not have been brighter nor more expressive in her youth. Sir Walter Scott says of them, ' they were auburn, of the precise shade and hue of her hair. In reciting, or in speaking with animation, they appeared to become darker, and as it were to flash fire. I should have hesitated,' he adds, ' to state the impression which this peculiarity made upon me at the time, had not my observation been confirmed by that of the first actress on this or any other stage, with whom I lately happened to converse on our deceased friend's expressive powers of countenance.' [1] Sir Walter has not observed that this peculiarity was hereditary. Describing, in one of her earlier letters, a scene with her mother, she says, 'I grew so saucy to her, that she looked grave, and took her pinch of snuff, first at one nostril, and then at the other, with swift and angry energy, and her eyes began to grow dark and to flash. 'Tis an odd peculiarity : but the balls of my mother's eyes change from brown into black, when she feels either indignation or bodily pain.' [2]

Miss Seward was not so much overrated at one time, as she has since been unduly depreciated. She was so considerable a person when her reputation was at its height, that Washington said no circumstance in his life had been so mortifying to him as that of having been made the subject of her invective in her Monody on Major André. After peace had been concluded between Great Britain and the United States, he commissioned an American officer, who was about to sail for England, to call upon her at Lichfield, and explain to her, that instead of having caused André's death, he had endeavoured to save him ; and she was requested to peruse the papers in proof of this, which he sent for her perusal. ' They filled me with contrition ', says Miss Seward, ' for the rash injustice of my censure.' [3]

An officer of her name served as lieutenant in the garrison at Gibraltar during the siege. To his great surprise, . . . for he had no introduction which could lead him to expect the honour of

such notice, . . . he received an invitation to dine with General Elliot. The General asked him if he were related to the author of the Monody on Major André. The Lieutenant replied that he had the honour of being very distantly related to her, but he had not the happiness of her acquaintance. ' It is sufficient, Mr. Seward,' said the General, ' that you bear her name, and a fair reputation, to entitle you to the notice of every soldier who has it in his power to serve and oblige a military brother. You will always find a cover for you at my table, and a sincere welcome ; and whenever it may be in my power to serve you essentially, I shall not want the inclination.' [4]

These anecdotes show the estimation in which she was, not undeservedly, held. Her epistolary style was distorted and disfigured by her admiration of Johnson ; and in her poetry she set, rather than followed, the brocade fashion of Dr. Darwin. Still there are unquestionable proofs of extraordinary talents and great ability both in her letters and her poems. She was an exemplary daughter, a most affectionate and faithful friend. Sir Walter has estimated, with characteristic skill, her powers of criticism, and her strong prepossessions upon literary points. And believing that the more she was known, the more she would have been esteemed and admired, I bear a willing testimony to her accomplishments and her genius, to her generous disposition, her frankness, and her sincerity and warmth of heart.

Keswick, Feb. 19, 1838.

[1] Biographical Preface to the *Poetical Works of Anna Seward*, p. xxiii.
[2] *Literary Correspondence.* Ib., p. cxxi.
[3] *Letters of Anna Seward*, vol. v, p. 143.

[4] *Letters of Anna Seward*, vol. i, p. 298.

PREFACE TO THE SIXTH VOLUME,

BEING THE FIRST OF 'BALLADS AND METRICAL TALES'

MOST of the pieces in this volume were written in early life, a few are comparatively of recent date, and there are some of them which lay unfinished for nearly thirty years.

Upon reading, on their first appearance, certain of these Ballads, and of the lighter pieces now comprised in the third volume of this collective edition, Mr. Edgeworth said to me, ' Take my word for it, Sir, the bent of your genius is for comedy.' I was as little displeased with the intended compliment as one of the most distinguished poets of this age was with Mr. Sheridan, who, upon returning a play which he had offered for acceptance at Drury Lane, told him it was a comical tragedy.

My late friend, Mr. William Taylor of Norwich, whom none who knew him intimately can ever call to mind without affection and regret, has this passage in his *Life of Dr. Sayers* :—' Not long after this (the year 1800), Mr. Robert Southey visited Norwich, was introduced to Dr. Sayers, and partook those feelings of complacent admiration which his presence was adapted to inspire.— Dr. Sayers pointed out to us in conversation, as adapted for the theme of a ballad, a story related by Olaus Magnus of a witch, whose coffin was confined by three chains, sprinkled with holy water; but who was, nevertheless, carried off by demons. Already, I believe, Dr. Sayers had made a ballad on the subject, so did I, and so did Mr. Southey ; but after seeing the *Old Woman of Berkeley*, we agreed in awarding to it the preference. Still, the very different manner in which each had employed the same basis of narration might render welcome the opportunity of comparison ; but I have not found among the papers of Dr. Sayers a copy of his poem.'

There is a mistake here as to the date. This, my first visit to Norwich, was in the spring of 1798 ; and I had so much to interest me there in the society of my kind host and friend, Mr. William Taylor, that the mention at Dr. Sayers's table of the story in Olaus Magnus made no impression on me at the time, and was presently forgotten. Indeed, if I had known that either he or his friend had written or intended to write a ballad upon the subject, that knowledge, however much the story might have pleased me, would have withheld me from all thought of versifying it. In the autumn of the same year, I passed some days at Hereford with Mr. William Bowyer Thomas, one of the friends with whom, in 1796, I had visited the Arrabida Convent near Setubal. By his means I obtained permission to make use of the books in the Cathedral Library, and accordingly I was locked up for several mornings in that part of the Cathedral where the books were kept in chains. So little were these books used at that time, that in placing them upon the shelves, no regard had been had to the length of the chains ; and when the volume which I wished to consult was fastened to one of the upper shelves by a short chain, the only means by which it was possible to make use of it was, by piling upon the reading desk as many volumes with longer chains as would reach up to the length of its tether ; then, by standing on a chair, I was able to effect my purpose. There, and thus, I first read the story of the Old Woman of Berkeley, in Matthew of Westminster, and transcribed it into a pocket-book. I had no recollection of what had passed at Dr. Sayers's ; but the circumstantial details in the monkish Chronicle impressed me so strongly, that I began to versify them that very evening. It was the last day of our pleasant visit at Hereford; and on the following morning the remainder of the Ballad was pencilled in a post-chaise on our way to Abberley.

Mr. Wathen, a singular and obliging person, who afterwards made a voyage to the East Indies, and published an account of what he saw there, traced for me a facsimile of a wooden cut in the *Nuremberg Chronicle* (which was among the prisoners in the Cathedral). It represents the Old Woman's forcible abduction from her intended place of burial. This was put into the hands of a Bristol artist; and the engraving in wood which he made from it was prefixed to the Ballad when first published, in the second volume of my poems, 1799. The Devil alludes to it in his Walk, when he complains of a certain poet as having ' put him in ugly ballads with libellous pictures for sale '.

The passage from Matthew of Westminster was prefixed to the Ballad when first published, and it has continued to be so in every subsequent edition of my minor poems from that time to the present : for whenever I have founded either a poem, or part of one, upon any legend, or portion of history, I have either extracted the passage to which I was indebted, if its length allowed, or have referred to it. Mr. Payne Collier, however, after the Ballad, with its parentage affixed, had been twenty years before the public, discovered that I had copied the story from Heywood's *Nine Books of various History concerning Women*, and that I had not thought proper to acknowledge the obligation. The discovery is thus stated in that

gentleman's *Poetical Decameron* (vol. i, p. 323). Speaking of the book, one of his Interlocutors says, ' It is not of such rarity or singularity as to deserve particular notice now ; only if you refer to p. 443, you will find the story on which Mr. Southey founded his mock-ballad of the *Old Woman of Berkeley*. You will see, too, that the mode in which it is told is extremely similar.

' MORTON. Had Mr. Southey seen Heywood's book ?

' BOURNE. It is not improbable ; or some quotation from it, the resemblance is so exact : you may judge from the few following sentences.'

Part of Heywood's narration is then given ; upon which one of the speakers observes, ' The resemblance is exact, and it is not unlikely that Heywood and Southey copied from the same original.

' BOURNE. Perhaps so : Heywood quotes Guillerimus, *in Special. Histor.* lib. xxvi. c. 26. He afterwards relates, as Southey, that the Devil placed the Old Woman of Berkeley before him on a black horse, and that her screams were heard four miles off.'

It cannot, however, be disputed, that Mr. Payne Collier has made one discovery relating to this subject ; for he has discovered that the *Old Woman of Berkeley* is a mock-ballad. Certainly this was never suspected by the Author, or any of his friends. It obtained a very different character in Russia, where having been translated and published, it was prohibited for this singular reason, that children were said to be frightened by it. This I was told by a Russian traveller who called upon me at Keswick.

Keswick, March 8, 1838.

ADVERTISEMENT TO THE SEVENTH VOLUME,

OR SECOND OF 'BALLADS AND METRICAL TALES'

THE two volumes of this collection which consist of Ballads and Metrical Tales contain the Author's earliest and latest productions of that kind: those which were written with most facility and most glee, and those upon which most time and pains were bestowed, according to the subject and the mode of treating it.

The *Tale of Paraguay* was published separately in 1825, having been so long in hand that the Dedication was written many years before the Poem was completed.

All for Love, and *The Legend of a Cock and a Hen*, were published together in a little volume in 1829.

PREFACE TO THE EIGHTH VOLUME,

CONTAINING 'THE CURSE OF KEHAMA'

SEVERAL years ago, in the Introduction of my 'Letters to Mr. Charles Butler, vindicating the Book of the Church', I had occasion to state that, while a school-boy at Westminster, I had formed an intention of exhibiting the most remarkable forms of Mythology which have at any time obtained among mankind, by making each the ground-work of a narrative poem. The performance, as might be expected, fell far short of the design, and yet it proved something more than a dream of juvenile ambition.

I began with the Mahommedan religion, as being that with which I was then best acquainted myself, and of which every one who had read the *Arabian Nights' Entertainments* possessed all the knowledge necessary for readily understanding and entering into the intent and spirit of the poem. Mr. Wilberforce thought that I had conveyed in it a very false impression of that religion, and that the moral sublimity which he admired in it was owing to this flattering misrepresentation. But *Thalaba the Destroyer* was professedly an Arabian Tale. The design required that I should bring into view the best features of that system of belief and worship which had been developed under the Covenant with Ishmael, placing in the most favourable light the morality of the Koran, and what the least corrupted of the Mahommedans retain of the patriarchal faith. It would have been altogether incongruous to have touched upon the abominations engrafted upon it; first by the false Prophet himself, who appears to have been far more remarkable for audacious profligacy than for any intellectual endowments, and afterwards by the spirit of Oriental despotism which accompanied Mahommedanism wherever it was established.

Heathen Mythologies have generally been represented by Christian poets as the work of the Devil and his Angels; and the machinery derived from them was thus rendered credible, according to what was during many ages a received opinion. The plan upon which I proceeded in *Madoc* was to produce the effect of machinery as far as was consistent with the character of the poem, by representing the most remarkable religion of the New World such as it was, a system of atrocious priestcraft. It was not here as in *Thalaba* the foundation of the poem, but, as usual in what are called epic poems, only incidentally connected with it.

When I took up, for my next subject, that mythology which Sir William Jones had been the first to introduce into English poetry, I soon perceived that the best mode of treating it would be to construct a story altogether mythological. In what form to compose it was then to be determined. No such question had arisen concerning any of my former poems. I should never for a moment have thought of any other measure than blank verse for *Joan of Arc*, and for *Madoc*, and afterwards for *Roderick*. The reason why the irregular rhymeless lyrics of Dr. Sayers were preferred for *Thalaba* was, that the freedom and variety of such verse were suited to the story. Indeed, of all the laudatory criticisms with which I have been favoured during a long literary life, none ever gratified me more than that of Henry Kirke White upon this occasion, when he observed, that if any other known measure had been adopted, the poem would have been deprived of half its beauty, and all its propriety. And when he added, that the author never seemed to inquire how other men would treat a subject, or what might be the fashion of the times, but took that course which his own sense of fitness pointed out, I could not have desired more appropriate commendation.

The same sense of fitness which made me choose for an Arabian tale the simplest and easiest form of verse, induced me to take a different course in an Indian poem. It appeared to me, that here neither the tone of morals, nor the strain of poetry, could be pitched too high; that nothing but moral sublimity could compensate for the extravagance of the fictions, and that all the skill I might possess in the art of poetry was required to counterbalance the disadvantage of a mythology with which few readers were likely to be well acquainted, and which would appear monstrous if its deformities were not kept out of sight. I endeavoured, therefore, to combine the utmost rich-

ness of versification with the greatest freedom. The spirit of the poem was Indian, but there was nothing Oriental in the style. I had learnt the language of poetry from our own great masters and the great poets of antiquity.

No poem could have been more deliberately planned, nor more carefully composed. It was commenced at Lisbon on the first of May, 1801, and recommenced in the summer of the same year at Kingsdown, in the same house (endeared to me by many once delightful but now mournful recollections) in which *Madoc* had been finished, and *Thalaba* begun. A little was added during the winter of that year in London. It was resumed at Kingsdown in the summer of 1802, and then laid aside till 1806, during which interval *Madoc* was reconstructed and published. Resuming it then once more, all that had been written was recast at Keswick : there I proceeded with it leisurely, and finished it on the 25th of November, 1809. It is the only one of my long poems of which detached parts were written to be afterwards inserted in their proper places. Were I to name the persons to whom it was communicated during its progress, it would be admitted now that I might well be encouraged by their approbation ; and indeed, when it was published, I must have been very unreasonable if I had not been satisfied with its reception.

It was not till the present edition of these Poems was in the press, that, eight-and-twenty years after *Kehama* had been published, I first saw the article upon it in the *Monthly Review*, parts of which cannot be more appropriately preserved any where than here ; it shows the determination with which the Reviewer entered upon his task, and the importance which he attached to it.

'Throughout our literary career we cannot recollect a more favourable opportunity than the present for a full discharge of our critical duty. We are indeed bound now to make a firm stand for the purity of our poetic taste against this last and most desperate assault, conducted as it is by a writer of considerable reputation, and unquestionably of considerable abilities. If this poem were to be tolerated, all things after it may demand impunity, and it will be in vain to contend hereafter for any one established rule of poetry as to design and subject, as to character and incident, as to language and versification. We may return at once to the rude hymn in honour of Bacchus, and indite strains adapted to the recitation of rustics in the season of vintage :—

" Quae canerent agerentque peruncti faecibus ora."

It shall be our plan to establish these points, we hope, beyond reasonable controversy, by a complete analysis of the twenty-four sections (as they may truly be called) of the portentous work, and by ample quotations interspersed with remarks, in which we shall endeavour to withhold no praise that can fairly be claimed, and no censure that is obviously deserved.'

The reviewer fulfilled his promises, however much he failed in his object. He was not more liberal of censure than of praise, and he was not sparing of quotations. The analysis was sufficiently complete for the purposes of criticism, except that the critic did not always give himself the trouble to understand what he was determined to ridicule. 'It is necessary for us,' he said, 'according to our purpose of deterring future writers from the choice of such a story, or from such a management of that story, to detail the gross follies of the work in question ; and tedious as the operation may be, we trust that in the judgement of all those lovers of literature who duly value the preservation of sound principles of composition among us, the end will excuse the means.' The means were ridicule and reprobation, and the end at

which he aimed was thus stated in the Reviewer's peroration.

'We know not that Mr. Southey's most devoted admirers can complain of our having omitted a single incident essential to the display of his character or the developement of his plot. To other readers we should apologize for our prolixity, were we not desirous, as we hinted before, of giving a death-blow to the gross extravagancies of the author's school of poetry, if we cannot hope to reform so great an offender as himself. In general, all that nature and all that art has lavished on him is rendered useless by his obstinate adherence to his own system of fancied originality, in which every thing that is good is old, and every thing that is new is good for nothing. Convinced as we are that many of the author's faults proceed from mere idleness, deserving even less indulgence than the erroneous principles of his poetical system, we shall conclude by a general exhortation to all critics to condemn, and to all writers to avoid the example of combined carelessness and perversity which is here afforded by Mr. Southey ; and we shall mark this last and worst eccentricity of his Muse with the following character: —Here is the composition of a poet not more distinguished by his genius and knowledge, than by his contempt for public opinion, and the utter depravity of his taste,—a depravity which is incorrigible, and, we are sorry to add, most unblushingly rejoicing in its own hopelessness of amendment.'

The *Monthly Review* has, I believe, been for some years defunct. I never knew to whom I was beholden for the good service rendered me in that Journal, when such assistance was of most value ; nor by whom I was subsequently, during several years, favoured in the same Journal with such flagrant civilities as those of which the reader has here seen a sample.

Keswick, May 19, 1838.

PREFACE TO THE NINTH VOLUME,

CONTAINING 'RODERICK, THE LAST OF THE GOTHS'.

THIS poem was commenced at Keswick, Dec. 2, 1809, and finished there July 14, 1814.

A French translation, by M. B. de S., in three volumes 12mo., was published in 1820, and another by M. le Chevalier * * *, in one volume 8vo, 1821. Both are in prose.

When the latest of these versions was nearly ready for publication, the publisher, who was also the printer, insisted upon having a life of the author prefixed. The French public, he said, knew nothing of M. Southey, and in order to make the book sell, it must be managed to interest them for the writer. The Chevalier represented as a conclusive reason for not attempting any thing of the kind, that he was not acquainted with M. Southey's private history. 'Would you believe it?' says a friend of the translator's, from whose letter I transcribe what follows; 'this was his answer verbatim: *N'importe, écrivez toujours ; brodez, brodez-la un peu ; que ce soit vrai ou non ce ne fait rien ; qui prendra la peine de s'informer?'* Accordingly a *Notice sur M. Southey* was composed, not exactly in conformity with the publisher's notions of biography, but from such materials as could be collected from magazines and other equally unauthentic sources.

In one of these versions a notable mistake occurs, occasioned by the French pronunciation of an English word. The whole passage indeed, in both versions, may be regarded as curiously exemplifying the difference between French and English poetry.

'The lamps and tapers now grew pale,
And through the eastern windows slanting fell
The roseate ray of morn. Within those walls

Returning day restored no cheerful sounds
Or joyous motions of awakening life ;
But in the stream of light the speckled motes,
As if in mimicry of insect play,
Floated with mazy movement. Sloping down
Over the altar pass'd the pillar'd beam,
And rested on the sinful woman's grave
As if it enter'd there, a light from Heaven.
So be it! cried Pelayo, even so!
As in a momentary interval,
When thought expelling thought, had left his mind
Open and passive to the influxes
Of outward sense, his vacant eye was there, . .
So be it, Heavenly Father, even so!
Thus may thy vivifying goodness shed
Forgiveness there ; for let not thou the groans
Of dying penitence, nor my bitter prayers
Before thy mercy-seat, be heard in vain !
And thou, poor soul, who from the dolorous house
Of weeping and of pain, dost look to me
To shorten and assuage thy penal term,
Pardon me that these hours in other thoughts
And other duties than this garb, this night
Enjoin, should thus have pass'd ! Our mother-land
Exacted of my heart the sacrifice ;
And many a vigil must thy son perform
Henceforth in woods and mountain fastnesses,
And tented fields, outwatching for her sake
The starry host, and ready for the work
Of day, before the sun begins his course.'[1]

[1] See *Roderick*, VIII, lines 101-33.

Il se livrait à toutes ces reflexions quand la lumière des lampes et des cierges commença à pâlir, et que les premières teintes de l'aurore se montrèrent à travers les hautes croisées tournées vers l'orient. Le retour du jour ne ramena point dans ces murs des sons joyeux ni les mouvemens de la vie qui se réveille ; les seuls papillons de nuit, agitant leurs ailes pesantes, bourdonnaient encore sous les voûtes ténébreuses. Bientôt le premier rayon du soleil, glissant obliquement par-dessus l'autel, vint s'arrêter sur la tombe de la femme pécheresse, et la lumière du ciel sembla y pénétrer. ' Que ce présage s'accomplisse,' s'écria Pelage, qui, absorbé dans ses méditations, fixait en ce moment ses yeux sur le tombeau de sa mère ; ' Dieu de miséricorde, qu'il en soit ainsi ! Puisse ta bonté vivifiante y verser de même le pardon ! Que les sanglots de la pénitence expirante, et que mes prières amères ne montent point en vain devant le trône éternel. Et toi, pauvre âme, qui de ton séjour douloureux de souffrances et de larmes espères en moi pour abréger et adoucir ton supplice temporaire, pardonne-moi d'avoir, sous ces habits et dans cette nuit, détourné mes pensées sur d'autres devoirs. Notre patrie commune a exigé de moi ce sacrifice, et ton fils doit dorénavant accomplir plus d'une veille dans la profondeur des forêts, sur la cime des monts, dans les plaines couvertes de tentes, observant, pour l'amour de l'Espagne, la marche des astres de la nuit, et préparant l'ouvrage de sa journée avant que le soleil ne commence sa course.'—T. i, pp. 175–177.

In the other translation the *motes* are not converted into moths,—but the image is omitted.

Consumées dans des soins pareils les rapides heures s'écouloient, les lampes et les torches commençoient à pâlir, et l'oblique rayon du matin doroit déjà les vitraux élevés qui regardoient vers l'Orient : le retour du jour ne ramenoit point, dans cette sombre enceinte, les sons joyeux, ni le tableau mouvant de la vie qui se réveille ; mais, tombant d'en haut, le céleste rayon, passant au-dessus de l'autel, vint frapper le tombeau de la femme pécheresse.

' *Ainsi soit-il,' s'écria Pelage, ' ainsi soit-il, ô divin Créateur ! Puisse ta vivifiante bonté verser ainsi le pardon en ce lieu ! Que les gémissemens d'une mort pénitente, que mes amères prières ne soient pas arrivées en vain devant le trône de miséricorde ! Et toi, qui, de ton séjour de souffrances et de larmes, regardes vers ton fils, pour abréger et soulager tes peines, pardonne, si d'autres devoirs ont rempli les heures que cette nuit et cet habit m'enjoignoient de te consacrer ! Notre patrie exigeoit ce sacrifice ; d'autres vigiles m'attendent dans les bois et les défilés de nos montagnes ; et bientôt sous la tente, il me faudra veiller, le soir, avant que le ciel ne se couvre d'étoiles, être prêt pour le travail du jour, avant que le soleil ne commence sa course.'*—pp. 92, 93.

A very good translation in Dutch verse was published in two volumes, 8vo, 1823–4, with this title :—' Rodrigo de Goth, Koning van Spanje. Naar het Engelsch van Southey gevolgd, door Vrouwe Katharina Wilhelmina Bilderdijk. Te 's Gravenhage.' It was sent to me with the following epistle from her husband Mr. Willem Bilderdijk.

' Roberto Southey, viro spectatissimo, Gulielmus Bilderdijk, S. P. D.

' Etsi ea nunc temporis passim invaluerit opinio, poetarum genus quam maxima gloriae cupiditate flagrare, mihi tamen contraria semper insedit persuasio, qui divinae Poëseos altitudinem veramque laudem non nisi ab iis cognosci putavi quorum prae caeteris e meliori luto finxerit praecordia Titan, neque aut verè aut justè judicari vatem nisi ab iis qui eodem afflatu moveantur. Sexagesimus autem jam agitur annus ex quo et ipse meos inter aequales poëta salutor, eumque locum quem ineunte adolescentia occupare contigit, in hunc usque diem tenuisse videor, popularis aurae nunquam captator, quin immo perpetuus contemptor ; parcus ipse laudator, censor gravis et nonnunquam molestus. Tuum vero nomen, Vir celeberrime ac spectatissime, jam antea veneratus, perlecto tuo de Roderico rege poëmate, non potui non summis extollere laudibus, quo doctissimo simul ac venustissimo opere, si minus *divinam Aeneida*, saltem immortalem Tassonis Epopeiam *tentasse*, quin et certo respectu ita superasse videris, ut majorum perpaucos, aequalium neminem, cum vera fide ac pietate in Deum, tum ingenio omnique poëtica dote tibi comparandum existimem. Ne mireris itaque, carminis tui gravitate ac dulcedine captam, meoque judicio fultam non illaudatam in nostratibus Musam tuum illud nobile poema foeminea manu sed insueto labore attrectasse, Belgicoque sermone reddidisse. Hanc certe, per quadrantem seculi et quod excurrit felicissimo connubio mihi junctam, meamque in Divina arte alumnam ac sociam, nimium in eo sibi sumpsisse nemo facile arbitrabitur cui vel minimum Poëseos nostrae sensum usurpare contigerit ; nec ego hos ejus conatus quos illustri tuo nomini dicandos putavit, tibi mea manu offerre dubitabam. Haec itaque utriusque nostrum in te observantiae specimina accipe, Vir illustrissime, ac si quod communium studiorum, si quod verae pietatis est vinculum, nos tibi ex animo habe addictissimos. Vale.

' Dabam Lugduni in Batavis. Ipsis idib. Februar. CIƆIƆCCCXXIV.'

I went to Leyden, in 1825, for the purpose of seeing the writer of this epistle and the lady who had translated my poem, and addressed it to me in some very affecting stanzas. It so happened, that on my arrival in that city, I was laid up under a surgeon's care ; they took me into their house, and made the days of my confinement as pleasurable as they were memorable. I have never been acquainted with a man of higher intellectual power, nor of greater learning, nor of more various and extensive knowledge than Bilderdijk, confessedly the most distinguished man of letters in his own country. His wife was worthy of him. I paid them another visit the following year. They are now both gone to their rest, and I shall not look upon their like again.

Soon after the publication of *Roderick*, I received the following curious letter from the Ettrick Shepherd, (who had passed a few days with me in the preceding autumn,) giving me an account of his endeavours to procure a favourable notice of the poem in the *Edinburgh Review*.

' Edinburgh, Dec. 15, 1814.

' MY DEAR SIR,

' I was very happy at seeing the postmark of Keswick, and quite proud of the pleasure you make me believe my *Wake* has given to the beauteous and happy group at Greta Hall. Indeed few things could give me more pleasure, for I left my heart a sojourner among them. I have had a higher opinion of matrimony since that period than ever I had before, and I desire that you will positively give my kindest respects to each of them individually.

' The *Pilgrim of the Sun* is published, as you will see by the Papers, and if I may believe some communications that I have got, the public opinion of it is high ; but these communications to an author are not to be depended on.

' I have read *Roderick* over and over again, and am the more and more convinced that it is the noblest epic poem of the age. I have had some correspondence and a good deal of conversation with Mr. Jeffrey about it, though he does not agree with me in every particular. He says it is too long, and wants *elasticity*, and will not, he fears, be generally read, though much may be said in its favour. I had even teazed him to let me review it for him, on account, as I said, that he could not appreciate its merits. I copy one sentence out of the letter he sent in answer to mine :—

' " For Southey I have, as well as you, great respect, and when he will let me, great admiration ; but he is a most provoking fellow, and at least as conceited as his neighbour Wordsworth. I cannot just trust you with his *Roderick* ; but I shall be extremely happy to talk over that and other kindred subjects with you, for I am every way disposed to give Southey a lavish allowance of praise, and few things would give me greater pleasure than to find he had afforded me a fair opportunity. But I must do my duty according to my own apprehensions of it."

'I supped with him last night, but there was so many people that I got but little conversation with him, but what we had was solely about you and Wordsworth. I suppose you have heard what a crushing review he has given the latter. I still found him persisting in his first asseveration, that it was heavy; but what was my pleasure to find that he had only got to the seventeenth division. I assured him he had the marrow of the thing to come at as yet, and in that I was joined by Mr. Alison. There was at the same time a Lady M—— joined us at the instant; short as her remark was, it seemed to make more impression on Jeffrey than all our arguments:—"Oh, I do love Southey!" that was all.

Keswick, June 15, 1838.

'I have no room to tell you more. But I beg that you will not do any thing, nor publish any thing that will nettle Jeffrey for the present, knowing as you do how omnipotent he is with the fashionable world, and seemingly so well disposed toward you.

'I am ever your's most truly,
'JAMES HOGG.

'I wish the Notes may be safe enough. I never looked at them. I wish these large quartos were all in hell burning.'

The reader will be as much amused as I was with poor Hogg's earnest desire that I would not say any thing which might tend to frustrate his friendly intentions.

But what success the Shepherd met
Is to the world a secret yet.

There can be no reason, however, for withholding what was said in my reply of the *crushing* review which had been given to Mr. Wordsworth's poem :— '*He* crush the *Excursion* !! Tell him he might as easily crush Skiddaw !'

THALABA THE DESTROYER

Ποιημάτων ἀκρατὴς ἡ ἐλευθερία, καὶ νόμος εἷς, τὸ δόξαν τῷ ποιητῇ.
LUCIAN, *Quomodo Hist. Scribenda.*

PREFACE TO THE FIRST EDITION

IN the continuation of the *Arabian Tales*, the Domdaniel is mentioned; a seminary for evil magicians, under the roots of the sea. From this seed the present romance has grown. Let me not be supposed to prefer the rhythm in which it is written, abstractedly considered, to the regular blank verse; the noblest measure, in my judgement, of which our admirable language is capable. For the following Poem I have preferred it, because it suits the varied subject: it is the *Arabesque* ornament of an Arabian tale.

The dramatic sketches of Dr. Sayers, a volume which no lover of poetry will recollect without pleasure, induced me, when a young versifier, to practise in this rhythm. I felt that while it gave the poet a wider range of expression, it satisfied the ear of the reader. It were easy to make a parade of learning, by enumerating the various feet which it admits: it is only needful to observe that no two lines are employed in *sequence* which can be read into one. Two six-syllable lines, it will perhaps be answered, compose an Alexandrine: the truth is, that the Alexandrine, when harmonious, is composed of two six-syllable lines.

One advantage this metre assuredly possesses,—the dullest reader cannot distort it into discord: he may read it prosaically, but its flow and fall will still be perceptible. Verse is not enough favoured by the English reader: perhaps this is owing to the obtrusiveness, the regular Jew's harp *twing-twang*, of what has been foolishly called heroic measure. I do not wish the *improvisatorè* tune;—but something that denotes the sense of harmony, something like the accent of feeling,—like the tone which every poet necessarily gives to poetry.

Cintra, October, 1800.

THALABA THE DESTROYER

THE FIRST BOOK

. . Worse and worse, young Orphane, be thy payne,
If thou due vengeance doe forbeare,
Till guiltie blood her guerdon do obtayne.
Faery Queen, B. ii. Can. I.

1

How beautiful is night !
A dewy freshness fills the silent air ;
No mist obscures, nor cloud, nor speck, nor stain,
Breaks the serene of heaven ;
In full-orb'd glory yonder Moon divine
Rolls through the dark blue depths.

Beneath her steady ray
The desert-circle spreads,
Like the round ocean, girdled with the sky.
How beautiful is night !   10

2

Who at this untimely hour
Wanders o'er the desert sands ?
No station is in view,
Nor palm-grove, islanded amid the waste.
The mother and her child,   [boy,
The widow'd mother and the fatherless
They at this untimely hour
Wander o'er the desert sands.

3

Alas! the setting sun
Saw Zeinab in her bliss,   20
Hodeirah's wife beloved.
Alas! the wife beloved,
The fruitful mother late,
Whom when the daughters of Arabia
named,
They wish'd their lot like hers,
She wanders o'er the desert sands
A wretched widow now;
The fruitful mother of so fair a race,
With only one preserved,
She wanders o'er the wilderness. 30

4

No tear relieved the burthen of her heart;
Stunn'd with the heavy woe, she felt
like one   [blood.
Half-waken'd from a midnight dream of
But sometimes when the boy
Would wet her hand with tears,
And, looking up to her fix'd countenance,
Sob out the name of Mother! then
she groan'd.   [eyes
At length collecting, Zeinab turn'd her
To heaven, and praised the Lord;
' He gave, he takes away !'   40
The pious sufferer cried,
' The Lord our God is good !'

5

' Good is He !' quoth the boy:
' Why are my brethren and my sisters
slain ?
Why is my father kill'd ?
Did ever we neglect our prayers,
Or ever lift a hand unclean to Heaven ?
Did ever stranger from our tent
Unwelcomed turn away ?
Mother, He is not good !'   50

6

Then Zeinab beat her breast in agony,
' O God, forgive the child !
He knows not what he says;

Thou know'st I did not teach him
thoughts like these;
O Prophet, pardon him !'

7

She had not wept till that assuaging
prayer. . .   [then,
The fountains of her grief were open'd
And tears relieved her heart.
She raised her swimming eyes to Heaven,
' Allah, thy will be done !   60
Beneath the dispensations of that will
I groan, but murmur not.
A day will come, when all things that
are dark
Will be made clear; . . then shall I know,
O Lord !
Why in thy mercy thou hast stricken me;
Then see and understand what now
My heart believes and feels.'

8

Young Thalaba in silence heard reproof;
His brow in manly frowns was knit,
With manly thoughts his heart was full.
' Tell me who slew my father ?' cried
the boy.   71
Zeinab replied and said,   [foe.
' I knew not that there lived thy father's
The blessings of the poor for him
Went daily up to Heaven;
In distant lands the traveller told his
praise; . .
I did not think there lived
Hodeirah's enemy.'

9

' But I will hunt him through the world!'
Young Thalaba exclaim'd.   80
' Already I can bend my father's bow;
Soon will my arm have strength
To drive the arrow-feathers to his heart.'

10

Zeinab replied, ' O Thalaba, my child,
Thou lookest on to distant days,
And we are in the desert, far from men !

11

Not till that moment her afflicted heart
Had leisure for the thought.
She cast her eyes around,
Alas ! no tents were there   90
Beside the bending sands,
No palm-tree rose to spot the wilderness ;
The dark blue sky closed round,
And rested like a dome
Upon the circling waste.
She cast her eyes around,
Famine and Thirst were there ;
And then the wretched Mother bow'd
her head,
And wept upon her child.

12

A sudden cry of wonder   100
From Thalaba aroused her ;
She raised her head, and saw
Where high in air a stately palace rose.
Amid a grove embower'd
Stood the prodigious pile ;
Trees of such ancient majesty
Tower'd not on Yemen's happy hills,
Nor crown'd the lofty brow of Lebanon :
Fabric so vast, so lavishly enrich'd,
For Idol, or for Tyrant, never yet   110
Raised the slave race of man,
In Rome, nor in the elder Babylon,
Nor old Persepolis,
Nor where the family of Greece
Hymn'd Eleutherian Jove.

13

Here studding azure tablatures
And ray'd with feeble light,
Star-like the ruby and the diamond
shone :
Here on the golden towers
The yellow moon-beam lay,   120
Here with white splendour floods the
silver wall.
Less wondrous pile and less magnificent
Sennamar built at Hirah, though his art
Seal'd with one stone the ample edifice,

And made its colours, like the serpent's
skin,   [Lord,
Play with a changeful beauty : him, its
Jealous lest after effort might surpass
The then unequall'd palace, from its
height
Dash'd on the pavement down.

14

They enter'd, and through aromatic
paths   130
Wondering they went along.
At length, upon a mossy bank,
Beneath a tall mimosa's shade,
Which o'er him bent its living canopy,
They saw a man reclined.
Young he appear'd, for on his cheek
there shone
The morning glow of health,
And the brown beard curl'd close around
his chin.
He slept, but at the sound
Of coming feet awaking, fix'd his eyes
In wonder, on the wanderer and her
child.   141
' Forgive us,' Zeinab cried,
' Distress hath made us bold.
Relieve the widow and the fatherless !
Blessed are they who succour the
distrest ;
For them hath God appointed Paradise.'

15

He heard, and he look'd up to heaven,
And tears ran down his cheeks :
' It is a human voice !
I thank thee, O my God ! . .   150
How many an age hath pass'd
Since the sweet sounds have visited my
ear !
I thank thee, O my God,
It is a human voice ! '

16

To Zeinab turning then, he said,
' O mortal, who art thou,

Whose gifted eyes have pierced
The shadow of concealment that hath
                            wrapt
These bowers, so many an age,
     From eye of mortal man ?   160
For countless years have pass'd,
     And never foot of man
The bowers of Irem trod, . .
Save only I, a miserable wretch
From Heaven and Earth shut out ! '

17

Fearless, and scarce surprised,
     For grief in Zeinab's soul
All other feebler feelings overpower'd,
     She answer'd, ' Yesterday
     I was a wife beloved,   170
The fruitful mother of a numerous race.
     I am a widow now,
Of all my offspring this alone is left.
     Praise to the Lord our God,
     He gave, He takes away ! '

18

Then said the stranger, ' Not by Heaven
            unseen,   [reach'd
Nor in unguided wanderings, hast thou
     This secret place, be sure !
Nor for light purpose is the veil,
That from the Universe has long shut
                            out   180
     These ancient bowers, withdrawn.
Hear thou my words, O mortal, in thine
                            heart
     Treasure what I shall tell ;
     And when amid the world
     Thou shalt emerge again,
     Repeat the warning tale. [make
Why have the fathers suffer'd, but to
     The children wisely safe ?

19

' The Paradise of Irem this,   189
And this that wonder of the world,
The Palace built by Shedad in his pride.
     Alas ! in the days of my youth,
     The hum of mankind

Was heard in yon wilderness waste ;
     O'er all the winding sands
     The tents of Ad were pitch'd ;
     Happy Al-Ahkâf then,
For many and brave were her sons,
Her daughters were many and fair.

20

     ' My name was Aswad then . .   200
     Alas ! alas ! how strange
     The sound so long unheard !
     Of noble race I came,
One of the wealthy of the earth my sire.
An hundred horses in my father's stall,
     Stood ready for his will ;
     Numerous his robes of silk ;
The number of his camels was not known.
     These were my heritage,
     O God ! thy gifts were these ;   210
But better had it been for Aswad's soul
     Had he ask'd alms on earth
And begg'd the crumbs which from his
                            table fell,
     So he had known thy Word.

21

' Boy, who hast reach'd my solitude,
Fear the Lord in the days of thy youth !
     My knee was never taught
     To bend before my God ;
     My voice was never taught
     To shape one holy prayer.   220
We worshipp'd Idols, wood and stone,
The work of our own foolish hands,
     We worshipp'd in our foolishness.
     Vainly the Prophet's voice
     Its frequent warning raised,
" REPENT AND BE FORGIVEN ! " . .
We mock'd the messenger of God,
We mock'd the Lord, long-suffering,
                            slow to wrath.

22

' A mighty work the pride of Shedad
                            plann'd,
     Here in the wilderness to form   230
     A Garden more surpassing fair

Than that before whose gate
The lightning of the Cherub's fiery sword
Waves wide to bar access,
Since Adam, the transgressor, thence
    was driven.
Here, too, would Shedad build
A kingly pile sublime,
The palace of his pride.
For this exhausted mines
Supplied their golden store;   241
For this the central caverns gave their
    gems;
For this the woodman's axe
Open'd the cedar forest to the sun:
The silkworm of the East
Spun her sepulchral egg;
    The hunter Afri   [rage;
Provok'd the danger of the Elephant's
The Ethiop, keen of scent,
    Detects the ebony,   249
That deep-inearth'd, and hating light,
A leafless tree and barren of all fruit,
With darkness feeds its boughs of raven
    grain.   [pile;
Such were the treasures lavish'd in yon
Ages have pass'd away,
And never mortal eye
Gazed on their vanity.

23

' The Garden, . . copious springs
Blest that delightful spot,
And every flower was planted there
That makes the gale of evening sweet.
He spake, and bade the full-grown forest
    rise,   261
His own creation; should the King
Wait for slow Nature's work?
All trees that bend with luscious fruit,
Or wave with feathery boughs,
Or point their spiring heads to heaven,
Or spreading wide their shadowy
    arms,   [noon, . .
Invite the traveller to repose at
Hither, uprooted with their native soil,

The labour and the pain of multitudes, . .
Mature in beauty, bore them. 271
Here, frequent in the walks
The marble statue stood
Of heroes and of chiefs.
The trees and flowers remain,
By Nature's care perpetuate and self-
    sown.   [trace
The marble statues long have lost all
Of heroes and of chiefs;
Huge shapeless stones they lie,
O'ergrown with many a flower. 280

24

' The work of pride went on;
Often the Prophet's voice
Denounced impending woe:
We mock'd at the words of the Seer,
We mock'd at the wrath of the Lord.
A long-continued drought first troubled
    us;
Three years no cloud had form'd,
Three years no rain had fallen;
The wholesome herb was dry,
The corn matured not for the food of
    man,   290
The wells and fountains fail'd.
O hard of heart, in whom the punishment
Awoke no sense of guilt!
Headstrong to ruin, obstinately blind,
We to our Idols still applied for aid;
Sakia we invoked for rain,
We called on Razeka for food;
They did not hear our prayers, they
    could not hear!
No cloud appear'd in Heaven,
No nightly dews came down. 300

25

' Then to the Place of Concourse mes-
    sengers   [came,
Were sent, to Mecca, where the nations
Round the Red Hillock kneeling, to
    implore
God in his favour'd place.

We sent to call on God ; [earth
Ah fools ! unthinking that from all the
The soul ascends to him.
We sent to call on God ;
Ah fools ! to think the Lord
Would hear their prayers abroad, 310
Who made no prayers at home !

26

' Meantime the work of pride went on,
And still before our Idols, wood and
          stone,
We bow'd the impious knee.
" Turn, men of Ad, and call upon the
          Lord,"
The Prophet Houd exclaim'd ;
" Turn men of Ad, and look to Heaven,
And fly the wrath to come."—
We mock'd the Prophet's words ; . .
" Now dost thou dream, old man, 320
Or art thou drunk with wine ?
Future woe and wrath to come,
Still thy prudent voice forebodes ;
When it comes will we believe,
Till it comes will we go on
In the way our fathers went.
Now are thy words from God ?
Or dost thou dream, old man,
Or art thou drunk with wine ? "

27

' So spake the stubborn race, 330
The unbelieving ones.
I too, of stubborn unbelieving heart,
Heard him, and heeded not.
It chanced, my father went the way of
          man,
He perish'd in his sins.
The funeral rites were duly paid,
We bound a Camel to his grave,
And left it there to die,
So if the resurrection came
Together they might rise. 340
I pass'd my father's grave,
I heard the Camel moan.
She was his favourite beast,

One who had carried me in infancy,
The first that by myself I learn'd to
          mount.   [her eyes
Her limbs were lean with famine, and
Ghastly and sunk and dim.
She knew me as I pass'd,
She stared me in the face ;
My heart was touch'd, . . had it been
          human else ?   350
I thought that none was near, and cut
          her bonds,
And drove her forth to liberty and life.
The Prophet Houd had seen ;
He lifted up his voice,
" Blessed art thou, young man,
Blessed art thou, O Aswad, for the deed !
In the Day of Visitation,
In the fearful hour of Judgement,
God will remember thee ! "

28

' The Day of Visitation was at hand, 360
The fearful hour of Judgement hastened
          on.
Lo ! Shedad's mighty pile complete,
The Palace of his pride.
Would ye behold its wonders, enter in !
I have no heart to visit it.
Time hath not harm'd the eternal monu-
          ment ;
Time is not here, nor days, nor months,
          nor years,
An everlasting NOW of solitude ! .

29

' Ye must have heard their fame ;
Or likely ye have seen   370
The mighty Pyramids, . . [lived
For sure those aweful piles have over-
The feeble generations of mankind.
What though unmoved they bore the
          deluge weight,
Survivors of the ruined world ?
What though their founder fill'd with
          miracles   [vaults ?
And wealth miraculous their spacious

Compared with yonder fabric, and they
                        shrink
The baby wonders of a woman's work.

30

' Here emerald columns o'er the marble
                        courts   380
Shed their green rays, as when amid a
                        shower   [corn.
The sun shines loveliest on the vernal
Here Shedad bade the sapphire floor be
                        laid,
As though with feet divine
        To tread on azure light,   [ment.
Like the blue pavement of the firma-
Here self-suspended hangs in air,
As its pure substance loathed material
                        touch,
        The living carbuncle ;
        Sun of the lofty dome,   390
Darkness hath no dominion o'er its
                        beams ;
Intense it glows, an ever-flowing spring
Of radiance, like the day-flood in its
                        source.

31

' Impious ! the Trees of vegetable gold
Such as in Eden's groves
        Yet innocent it grew ;
Impious ! he made his boast, though
                        Heaven had hid
        So deep the baneful ore,   [him,
That they should branch and bud for
That art should force their blossoms
                        and their fruit,   400
        And re-create for him whate'er
        Was lost in Paradise.
Therefore at Shedad's voice
Here tower'd the palm, a silver trunk,
The fine gold net-work growing out
        Loose from its rugged boughs.
Tall as the cedar of the mountain, here
Rose the gold branches, hung with
                        emerald leaves,

Blossom'd with pearls, and rich with
                        ruby fruit.

32

' O Ad ! my country ! evil was the day
        That thy unhappy sons   411
Crouch'd at this Nimrod's throne,
And placed him on the pedestal of power,
And laid their liberties beneath his feet,
Robbing their children of the heritage
        Their fathers handed down.
What was to him the squander'd wealth?
What was to him the burthen of the land,
        The lavish'd misery ?
        He did but speak his will,   420
And, like the blasting Siroc of the sands,
        The ruin of the royal voice
        Found its way every-where.
I marvel not that he, whose power
No earthly law, no human feeling curb'd,
        Mock'd at the living God !

33

' And now the King's command went
                        forth   [young,
Among the people, bidding old and
Husband and wife, the master and the
                        slave,
All the collected multitudes of Ad,   430
Here to repair, and hold high festival,
That he might see his people, they behold
        Their King's magnificence and power.
        The day of festival arrived ;
Hither they came, the old man and the
                        boy,
        Husband and wife, the master and
                        the slave,
Hither they came.   From yonder high
                        tower top,
The loftiest of the Palace, Shedad look'd
        Down on his tribe : their tents on
                        yonder sands
        Rose like the countless billows of
                        the sea ;   440
Their tread and voices like the ocean
                        roar,

One deep confusion of tumultuous
　　　　sounds.
They saw their King's magnificence,
　　　　beheld　　　　[domes
His palace sparkling like the Angel
Of Paradise, his Garden like the bowers
Of early Eden, and they shouted out,
　" Great is the King! a God upon
　　　　the earth!"

34

� Intoxicate with joy and pride,
He heard their blasphemies;
And in his wantonness of heart he bade
The Prophet Houd be brought; 451
　And o'er the marble courts,
　And o'er the gorgeous rooms
Glittering with gems and gold,
He led the Man of God.
" Is not this a stately pile?"
Cried the monarch in his joy.
　" Hath ever eye beheld,
　Hath ever thought conceived,
　Place more magnificent?　460
Houd, they say that Heaven imparteth
Words of wisdom to thy lips;
　　Look at the riches round,
　　And value them aright,
　If so thy wisdom can."

35

' The Prophet heard his vaunt,
And, with an aweful smile, he answer'd
　　　　him,
" O Shedad! only in the hour of death
We learn to value things like these
　　　　aright."

36

� " Hast thou a fault to find　470
In all thine eyes have seen?"
With unadmonished pride, the King ex-
　　　　claim'd.
　" Yea!" said the Man of God;
" The walls are weak, the building ill
　　　　secure.

Azrael can enter in!
The Sarsar can pierce through,
　The Icy Wind of Death."

37

' I was beside the Monarch when he
　　　　spake;
　Gentle the Prophet spake,
　But in his eye there dwelt　480
A sorrow that disturb'd me while I gazed.
　The countenance of Shedad fell,
And anger sat upon his paler lips.
He to the high tower-top the Prophet led,
　And pointed to the multitude,
　And as again they shouted out,
" Great is the King! a God upon the
　　　　Earth!"
With dark and threatful smile to Houd
　　he turn'd,
" Say they aright, O Prophet? is the
　　　　King
Great upon earth, a God among man-
　　　　kind?"　490
　The Prophet answer'd not;
　Over that infinite multitude
　He roll'd his ominous eyes,
And tears which could not be supprest
　　　　gush'd forth.

38

' Sudden an uproar rose,
　A cry of joy below;
" The messenger is come!
Kaïl from Mecca comes,
He brings the boon obtain'd!"

39

' Forth as we went we saw where over-
　　　　head　　　　500
　There hung a deep black cloud,
　To which the multitude
　With joyful eyes look'd up,
　And blest the coming rain.
The Messenger addrest the King
And told his tale of joy.

40

' " To Mecca I repair'd,
By the Red Hillock knelt,
And call'd on God for rain.
My prayer ascended, and was heard ;
Three clouds appear'd in heaven, 511
One white, and like the flying cloud of
noon, [beams,
One red, as it had drunk the evening
One black and heavy with its load of rain.
A voice went forth from Heaven,
' Choose, Kaïl, of the three ! '
I thank'd the gracious Power,
And chose the black cloud, heavy with
its wealth."
" Right ! right ! " a thousand tongues
exclaim'd,
And all was merriment and joy. 520

41

' Then stood the Prophet up, and cried
aloud,
" Woe, woe to Irem ! woe to Ad !
DEATH is gone up into her palaces !
Woe ! woe ! a day of guilt and punish-
ment ;
A day of desolation ! "—As he spake,
His large eye roll'd in horror, and so deep
His tone, it seem'd some Spirit from
within
Breathed through his moveless lips the
unearthly voice.

42

' All looks were turn'd to him. " O Ad ! "
he cried,
" Dear native land, by all remembrances
Of childhood, by all joys of manhood
dear ; 531
O Vale of many Waters ; morn and
night [grave
My age must groan for you, and to the
Go down in sorrow. Thou wilt give thy
fruits, [will ripen,
But who shall gather them ? thy grapes

But who shall tread the wine-press ? Fly
the wrath, [alive !
Ye who would live and save your souls
For strong is his right hand that
bends the Bow,
The Arrows that he shoots are sharp,
And err not from their aim ! " 540

43

' With that a faithful few
Prest through the throng to join him.
Then arose
Mockery and mirth ; " Go, bald head ! "
and they mix'd [once
Curses with laughter. He set forth, yet
Look'd back : . . his eye fell on me, and
he call'd [fied ; . .
" Aswad ! " . . it startled me . . it terri-
" Aswad ! " again he call'd, . . and
I almost [soon !
Had follow'd him. . . O moment fled too
O moment irrecoverably lost !
The shouts of mockery made a coward
of me ; 550
He went, and I remain'd, in fear of MAN !

44

' He went, and darker grew
The deepening cloud above.
At length it open'd, and . . O God !
O God !
There were no waters there !
There fell no kindly rain !
The Sarsar from its womb went forth,
The Icy Wind of Death.

45

' They fell around me ; thousands fell
around,
The King and all his people fell ; 560
All ! all ! they perish'd all !
I . . only I . . was left.
There came a Voice to me and said,
" In the Day of Visitation,
In the fearful hour of Judgement,
God hath remember'd thee."

46

ᶠ When from an agony of prayer I rose,
And from the scene of death
Attempted to go forth,
The way was open, I could see 570
No barrier to my steps.
But round these bowers the Arm of God
Had drawn a mighty chain,
A barrier that no human force might
break.
Twice I essay'd to pass ;
With that a Voice was heard,
" O Aswad, be content, and bless the
Lord !
One charitable deed hath saved
Thy soul from utter death.
O Aswad, sinful man ! 580
When by long penitence
Thou feel'st thy soul prepared
Breathe up the wish to die,
And Azrael comes in answer to thy
prayer."

47

ᶠ A miserable man
From Earth and Heaven shut out,
I heard the dreadful Voice.
I look'd around my prison-place,
The bodies of the dead were there,
Where'er I look'd they lay, 590
They moulder'd, moulder'd here, . .
Their very bones have crumbled into
dust,
So many years have pass'd !
So many weary ages have gone by !
And still I linger here, [sins,
Still groaning with the burthen of my
Not yet have dared to breathe
The prayer to be released.

48

' Oh ! who can tell the unspeakable'
misery
Of solitude like this ! 600
No sound hath ever reach'd my ear
Save of the passing wind,

The fountain's everlasting flow,
The forest in the gale,
The pattering of the shower,
Sounds dead and mournful all.
No bird hath ever closed her wing
Upon these solitary bowers,
No insect sweetly buzz'd amid these
groves,
From all things that have life, 610
Save only me, conceal'd.
This Tree alone, that o'er my head
Hangs down its hospitable boughs,
And bends its whispering leaves
As though to welcome me,
Seems to partake of life ;
I love it as my friend, my only friend !

49

' I know not for what ages I have dragg'd
This miserable life ;
How often I have seen 620
These ancient trees renew'd ;
What countless generations of mankind
Have risen and fallen asleep,
And I remain the same !
My garment hath not waxen old,
And the sole of my shoe is not worn.

50

' Sinner that I have been,
I dare not offer up a prayer to die.
O merciful Lord God ! . .
But when it is thy will, 630
But when I have atoned
For mine iniquities,
And sufferings have made pure
My soul with sin defiled,
Release me in thine own good time ; . .
I will not cease to praise thee, O my
God ! '

51

Silence ensued awhile ;
Then Zeinab answer'd him ;
' Blessed art thou, O Aswad ! for the
Lord,
Who saved thy soul from Hell, 640

Will call thee to him in his own good
 time.
And would that when my soul
Breathed up the wish to die,
Azrael might visit me!
Then would I follow where my babes
 are gone,
And join Hodeirah now!

52

She ceased; and the rushing of wings
Was heard in the stillness of night,
And Azrael, the Death-Angel, stood
 before them.
 His countenance was dark,   650
 Solemn, but not severe,
It awed, but struck no terror to the heart.
'Zeinab, thy wish is heard!
Aswad, thine hour is come!'
They fell upon the ground and blest the
 voice;
 And Azrael from his sword
Let fall the drops of bitterness and death.

53

'Me too! me too!' young Thalaba
 exclaim'd,
As wild with grief he kiss'd
His Mother's livid hand,   660
His Mother's livid lips;
'O Angel! take me too!'

54

'Son of Hodeirah!' the Death-Angel
 said,
'It is not yet the hour.
Son of Hodeirah, thou art chosen forth
To do the will of Heaven;
To avenge thy father's death,
The murder of thy race;
To work the mightiest enterprize
That mortal man hath wrought.   670
Live! and REMEMBER DESTINY
HATH MARK'D THEE FROM MANKIND!'

55

He ceased, and he was gone.
Young Thalaba look'd round, . .
The Palace and the groves were seen no
 more,
He stood amid the Wilderness, alone.

THE SECOND BOOK

Sint licet expertes vitae sensusque, capessunt
Jussa tamen superum venti.
    Mambruni Constantinus.

1

 NOT in the desert,
 Son of Hodeirah,
 Thou art abandon'd!
The co-existent fire, [for thee,
Which in the Dens of Darkness burnt
Burns yet, and yet shall burn.

2

In the Domdaniel caverns,
Under the Roots of the Ocean,
Met the Masters of the Spell.
 Before them in the vault,   10
Blazing unfuel'd from its floor of rock,
 Ten magic flames arose.
'Burn, mystic fires;' Abdaldar cried;
'Burn while Hodeirah's dreaded race
 exist.
This is the appointed hour, [night.'
The hour that shall secure these dens of

3

'Dim they burn!' exclaim'd Lobaba;
'Dim they burn, and now they waver!
Okba lifts the arm of death:
They waver, . . they go out!'   20

4

'Curse on his hasty hand!'
Khawla exclaim'd in wrath,
The woman-fiend exclaim'd, [fail'd!
'Curse on his hasty hand, the fool hath
Eight only are gone out.'

5

A Teraph stood against the cavern-side,
A new-born infant's head,
Which Khawla at its hour of birth had
        seized,
And from the shoulders wrung.
It stood upon a plate of gold,   30
An unclean Spirit's name inscrib'd
        beneath.
The cheeks were deathy dark,
Dark the dead skin upon the hairless
        skull;
The lips were bluey pale;
Only the eyes had life,
They gleam'd with demon light.

6

'Tell me!' quoth Khawla, 'is the Fire
        gone out
That threats the Masters of the Spell?'
The dead lips moved and spake,
'The Fire still burns that threats   40
The Masters of the Spell.'

7

'Curse on thee, Okba!' Khawla cried,
As to the den the Sorcerer came;
He bore the dagger in his hand,
Red from the murder of Hodeirah's race.
'Behold those unextinguish'd flames!
The Fire still burns that threats
The Masters of the Spell!
Okba, wert thou weak of heart?
Okba, wert thou blind of eye?   50
Thy fate and ours were on the lot,
And we believ'd the lying Stars,
That said thy hand might seize the
        auspicious hour!
Thou hast let slip the reins of Destiny, ..
Curse thee, curse thee, Okba!'

8

The Murderer, answering, said,
'O versed in all enchanted lore,
Thou better knowest Okba's soul!
Eight blows I struck, eight home-driven
        blows,
Needed no second stroke   60
From this envenom'd blade.
Ye frown at me as if the will had fail'd;
As if ye did not know
My double danger from Hodeirah's race,
        The deeper hate I feel,   [arm!
The stronger motive that inspir'd my
Ye frown as if my hasty fault,
        My ill-directed blow,
        Had spared the enemy;
And not the Stars that would not give,
        And not your feeble spells   71
That could not force, the sign
        Which of the whole was he.
Did ye not bid me strike them all?
Said ye not root and branch should be
        destroy'd?
I heard Hodeirah's dying groan,
I heard his Children's shriek of death,
And sought to consummate the work;
        But o'er the two remaining lives
        A cloud unpierceable had risen,   80
A cloud that mock'd my searching eyes.
I would have probed it with the
        dagger-point,
        The dagger was repell'd;
        A Voice came forth and said,
"Son of Perdition, cease! Thou canst
        not change
What in the Book of Destiny is written."'

9

Khawla to the Teraph turn'd,
'Tell me where the Prophet's hand
Hides our destined enemy?'
        The dead lips spake again,   90
'I view the seas, I view the land,
I search the Ocean and the Earth!
Not on Ocean is the Boy,
Not on Earth his steps are seen.'

10

'A mightier power than we,' Lobaba cried
        'Protects our destined foe.
Look! look! one Fire burns dim!
        It quivers! it goes out!'

11

It quiver'd, it was quench'd.
One Flame alone was left,   100
A pale blue Flame that trembled on the
        floor,   [edge
A hovering light, upon whose shrinking
The darkness seem'd to press.
Stronger it grew, and spread
        Its lucid swell around,
Extending now where all the ten had
        stood
        With lustre more than all.

12

At that portentous sight
The Children of Evil trembled,
And terror smote their souls.   110
Over the den the Fire
        Its fearful splendour cast,
The broad base rolling up in wavy
                streams,   [spreads
Bright as the summer lightning when it
Its glory o'er the midnight heaven.
The Teraph's eyes were dimm'd,
        Which like two twinkling stars
        Shone in the darkness late.
The Sorcerers on each other gazed,
And every face, all pale with fear, 120
And ghastly, in that light was seen
Like a dead man's by the sepulchral
        lamp.

13

Even Khawla, fiercest of the enchanter
        brood,
        Not without effort drew
        Her fear-suspended breath.
        Anon a deeper rage
        Inflamed her reddening eye.
' Mighty is thy power, Mahommed ! '
Loud in blasphemy she cried ;
' But Eblis would not stoop to Man,
When Man, fair-statured as the stately
        palm   131
        From his Creator's hand
        Was undefiled and pure.

Thou art mighty, O Son of Abdallah !
        But who is he of woman born
That shall vie with the might of Eblis ?
That shall rival the Prince of the
        Morning ? '

14

She said, and raised her skinny hand
        As in defiance to high Heaven,
And stretch'd her long lean finger forth,
And spake aloud the words of power.
        The Spirits heard her call,   140
        And lo ! before her stands
        Her Demon Minister.
' Spirit ! ' the Enchantress cried,
' Where lives the Boy, coeval with whose
        life
        Yon magic Fire must burn ? '

15

DEMON

Mistress of the mighty Spell,
        Not on Ocean, not on Earth,
        Only eyes that view   150
        Allah's glory-throne,
        See his hiding-place.   [learn.
From some believing Spirit, ask and

16

' Bring the dead Hodeirah here,'
Khawla cried, ' and he shall tell ! '
The Demon heard her bidding, and was
        gone.
A moment pass'd, and at her feet
        Hodeirah's corpse was laid ;
His hand still held the sword he grasp'd
        in death,
The blood not yet had clotted on his
        wound.   160

17

The Sorceress look'd, and with a smile
        That kindled to more fiendishness
        Her hideous features, cried,
' Where art thou, Hodeirah, now ?
        Is thy soul in Zemzem-well ?
        Is it in the Eden groves ?

Waits it for the judgement-blast
　　In the trump of Israfil ?
Is it, plumed with silver wings,
Underneath the throne of God ?　170
Even though beneath His throne,
　　Hodeirah, thou shalt hear
　　Thou shalt obey my voice !'

18

She said, and mutter'd charms which
　　Hell in fear,
And Heaven in horror heard.
Soon the stiff eye-balls roll'd,
The muscles with convulsive motion
　　shook,　　[her soul
The white lips quiver'd. Khawla saw,
　　Exulted, and she cried,
' Prophet ! behold my power !　180
　　Not even death secures
Thy slaves from Khawla's spell !
Where, Hodeirah, is thy child ?'

19

Hodeirah groan'd and closed his eyes,
As if in the night and the blindness of
　　death
　　He would have hid himself.

20

' Speak to my question !' she exclaim'd,
' Or in that mangled body thou shalt live
　　Ages of torture ! Answer me !
　　Where can we find the boy ?'　190

21

' God ! God !' Hodeirah cried,
　　' Release me from this life,
　　From this intolerable agony !'

22

' Speak !' cried the Sorceress, and she
　　snatch'd
　　A Viper from the floor
And with the living reptile lash'd his
　　neck.
Wreath'd round him with the blow,
The reptile tighter drew her folds,
　　And raised her wrathful head,
　　And fix'd into his face　200

Her deadly teeth and shed
　　Poison in every wound. [prayer,
In vain ! for Allah heard Hodeirah's
　　And Khawla on a corpse
　　Had wreak'd her baffled rage.
The fated Fire moved on, [flames.
And round the Body wrapt its funeral
The flesh and bones in that portentous
　　pile
Consumed ; the Sword alone,
　　Circled with fire, was left.　210

23

Where is the Boy for whose hand it is
　　destined ?　　[wield
Where the Destroyer who one day shall
The Sword that is circled with fire ?
Race accursed, try your charms !
　　Masters of the mighty Spell,
Mutter o'er your words of power !
Ye can shatter the dwellings of man ;
Ye can open the womb of the rock ;
Ye can shake the foundations of earth,
　　But not the Word of God :　220
But not one letter can ye change
　　Of what his Will hath written.

24

Who shall seek through Araby
　　Hodeirah's dreaded son ?
They mingle the Arrows of Chance,
　　The lot of Abdaldar is drawn.
Thirteen moons must wax and wane
Ere the Sorcerer quit his quest.
　　He must visit every tribe
That roam the desert wilderness, 230
Or dwell beside perennial streams ;
Nor leave a solitary tent unsearch'd,
Till he hath found the Boy, . .
The dreaded Boy, whose blood alone
　　Can quench that fated Fire.

25

A crystal ring Abdaldar wore ;
　　The powerful gem condensed
Primeval dews, that upon Caucasus
　　Felt the first winter's frost.

Ripening there it lay beneath   240
Rock above rock, and mountain ice up-
                        piled   [assumed,
On mountain, till the incumbent mass
So huge its bulk, the Ocean's azure hue.

26

With this he sought the inner den
Where burnt the Eternal Fire.
Like waters gushing from some chan-
                        nell'd rock   [a chasm
Full through a narrow opening, from
The Eternal Fire stream'd up.
            No eye beheld the spring
            Of that up-flowing Flame,   250
Which blazed self-nurtured, and for ever,
                        there.
It was no mortal element ; the Abyss
Supplied it, from the fountains at the
                        first   [and glows
Prepared. In the heart of earth it lives
Her vital heat, till, at the day decreed,
The voice of God shall let its billows loose,
To deluge o'er with no abating flood
            Our consummated World ;
Which must from that day in infinity
            Through endless ages roll,   260
            A penal orb of Fire.

27

Unturban'd and unsandal'd there,
Abdaldar stood before the Flame,
And held the Ring beside, and spake
The language that the Elements obey.
The obedient Flame detach'd a portion
                        forth,   [densed,
Which, in the crystal entering, was con-
Gem of the gem, its living Eye of fire.
When the hand that wears the spell
            Shall touch the destined Boy,   270
Then shall that Eye be quench'd,
            And the freed Element
Fly to its sacred and remember'd Spring.

28

Now go thy way, Abdaldar !
Servant of Eblis,

            Over Arabia
            Seek the Destroyer !
Over the sands of the scorching Tehama,
Over the waterless mountains of Naÿd ;
In Arud pursue him, and Yemen the
                        happy,   280
And Hejaz, the country beloved by
                        believers,
            Over Arabia,
            Servant of Eblis,
            Seek the Destroyer !

29

From tribe to tribe, from town to town,
From tent to tent, Abdaldar pass'd.
Him every morn the all-beholding Eye
Saw from his couch, unhallow'd by a
                        prayer,
            Rise to the scent of blood ;
            And every night lie down,   290
That rankling hope within him, that by
                        day   [sleep,
Goaded his steps, still stinging him in
And startling him with vain accomplish-
                        ment
From visions still the same.
Many a time his wary hand
To many a youth applied the Ring ;
And still the imprison'd Fire
Within its crystal socket lay comprest,
Impatient to be free.

30

At length to the cords of a tent,   300
That were stretch'd by an Island of
                        Palms,
In the desolate sea of the sands,
            The seemly traveller came.
            Under a shapely palm,
Herself as shapely, there a Damsel stood ;
            She held her ready robe,
            And look'd towards a Boy,
            Who from the tree above,
With one hand clinging to its trunk,
Cast with the other down the cluster'd
                        dates.   31

31

The Magician approach'd the Tree,
He lean'd on his staff, like a way-faring
    man,   [his brow.
And the sweat of his travel was seen on
He ask'd for food, and lo!
The Damsel proffers him her lap of dates;
And the Stripling descends, and runs
    to the tent,
And brings him forth water, the draught
    of delight.

32

Anon the Master of the tent,
    The Father of the family,
Came forth, a man in years, of aspect
    mild.   320
To the stranger approaching he gave
    The friendly saluting of peace,
    And bade the skin be spread.
Before the tent they spread the skin,
    Under a Tamarind's shade,
That, bending forward, stretch'd
    Its boughs of beauty far.

33

They brought the Traveller rice,
With no false colours tinged to tempt
    the eye,
But white as the new-fallen snow, 330
When never yet the sullying Sun
    Hath seen its purity,
Nor the warm zephyr touch'd and
    tainted it.
The dates of the grove before their guest
They laid, and the luscious fig,
    And water from the well.

34

The Damsel from the Tamarind tree
    Had pluck'd its acid fruit,
    And steep'd it in water long;
And whoso drank of the cooling draught,
    He would not wish for wine. 341
This to their guest the Damsel brought,
And a modest pleasure kindled her
    cheek,

When raising from the cup his moisten'd
    lips,   [drank again.
The stranger smiled, and praised, and

35

Whither is gone the Boy?
He had pierced the Melon's pulp,
    And closed with wax the wound,
    And he had duly gone at morn
    And watch'd its ripening rind, 350
And now all joyfully he brings
    The treasure now matured;
His dark eyes sparkling with a boy's
    delight,
As out he pours its liquid lusciousness,
    And proffers to the guest.

36

Abdaldar ate, and he was satisfied:
    And now his tongue discoursed
    Of regions far remote,   [long.
As one whose busy feet had travell'd
    The father of the family, 360
With a calm eye and quiet smile,
    Sate pleased to hearken him.
The Damsel who removed the meal,
    She loiter'd on the way,
    And listen'd with full hands
    A moment motionless.

37

All eagerly the Boy
    Watches the Traveller's lips;
    And still the wily man
With seemly kindness, to the eager Boy
    Directs his winning tale. 371
    Ah, cursed one! if this be he,
If thou hast found the object of thy
    search,
    Thy hate, thy bloody aim, ..
Into what deep damnation wilt thou
    plunge
    Thy miserable soul! ..

38

Look! how his eye delighted watches
    thine! ..
    Look! how his open lips

Gape at the winning tale ! . .
And nearer now he comes, 380
To lose no word of that delightful talk.
Then, as in familiar mood,
Upon the stripling's arm
The Sorcerer laid his hand,
And the Fire of the Crystal fled.

39

While the sudden shoot of joy
Made pale Abdaldar's cheek,
The Master's voice was heard ;
' It is the hour of prayer, . .
My children, let us purify ourselves,
And praise the Lord our God ! ' 391
The Boy the water brought ;
After the law they purified themselves,
And bent their faces to the earth in
prayer.

40

All, save Abdaldar ; over Thalaba
He stands, and lifts the dagger to destroy.
Before his lifted arm received
Its impulse to descend,
The Blast of the Desert came.
Prostrate in prayer, the pious family
Felt not the Simoom pass. 401
They rose, and lo ! the Sorcerer lying
dead,
Holding the dagger in his blasted hand.

THE THIRD BOOK

Time will produce events of which thou
canst have no idea ; and he to whom thou
gavest no commission, will bring thee unexpected news.—*MOALLAKAT, Poem of Tarafat*

1

THALABA

ONEIZA, look ! the dead man has a ring, . .
Should it be buried with him ?

ONEIZA

Oh yes . . yes !   [needs
A wicked man ! whate'er is his must
Be wicked too !

THALABA

But see, . . the sparkling stone ?
How it hath caught the glory of the Sun,
And shoots it back again in lines of light !

ONEIZA

Why do you take it from him, Thalaba ?
And look at it so close ? . . it may have
charms 10
To blind, or poison ; . . throw it in the
grave !
I would not touch it !

THALABA

And around its rim
Strange letters . .

ONEIZA

Bury it . . oh ! bury it !

THALABA

It is not written as the Koran is :
Some other tongue perchance ; . . the
accursed man
Said he had been a traveller.

MOATH (*coming from the tent*)
Thalaba,
What hast thou there ? 20

THALABA

A ring the dead man wore ;
Perhaps, my father, you can read its
meaning.

MOATH

No, Boy ; . . the letters are not such as
ours.
Heap the sand over it ! a wicked man
Wears nothing holy.

THALABA

Nay ! not bury it !
It may be that some traveller, who shall
enter
Our tent, may read it : or if we approach
Cities where strangers dwell and learned
men,
They may interpret. 30

MOATH

It were better hid
Under the desert sands. This wretched man,   [purpose
Whom God hath smitten in the very
And impulse of his unpermitted crime,
Belike was some magician, and these lines
Are of the language that the Demons use.

ONEIZA

Bury it ! bury it . . dear Thalaba !

MOATH

Such cursed men there are upon the earth,   [powers,
In league and treaty with the Evil
The covenanted enemies of God 40
And of all good ; dear purchase have they made   [sway,
Of rule and riches, and their life-long
Masters, yet slaves of Hell. Beneath the roots
Of Ocean, the Domdaniel caverns lie,
Their impious meeting ; there they learn the words
Unutterable by man who holds his hope   [and let
Of heaven ; there brood the pestilence,
The earthquake loose.

THALABA

And he who would have kill'd me
Was one of these ?   50

MOATH

I know not ; . . but it may be
That on the Table of Destiny, thy name
Is written their Destroyer, and for this
Thy life by yonder miserable man
So sought, so saved by interfering Heaven.

THALABA

His ring has some strange power then ?

MOATH

Every gem,   [science,
So sages say, hath virtue ; but the
Of difficult attainment ; some grow pale,

Conscious of poison, or with sudden change   60
Of darkness, warn the wearer ; some preserve
From spells, or blunt the hostile weapon's edge ;
Some open rocks and mountains, and lay bare   [sight
Their buried treasures ; others make the
Strong to perceive the presence of those Beings   [empty air
Through whose pure essence as through
The unaided eye would pass ;
And in yon stone I deem
Some such mysterious quality resides.

THALABA

My father, I will wear it.   70

MOATH

Thalaba !

THALABA

In God's name, and the Prophet's ! be its power   [evil,
Good, let it serve the righteous ; if for
God, and my trust in Him, shall hallow it.

2

So Thalaba drew on
The written ring of gold.
Then in the hollow grave
They laid Abdaldar's corpse,
And levell'd over him the desert dust.

3

The Sun arose, ascending from beneath
The horizon's circling line.   81
As Thalaba to his ablutions went,
Lo ! the grave open, and the corpse exposed !
It was not that the winds of night
Had swept away the sands which cover'd it ;
For heavy with the undried dew
The desert dust lay dark and close around ;   [still,
And the night air had been so calm and
It had not from the grove
Shaken a ripe date down.   90

4

Amazed to hear the tale,
Forth from the tent came Moath and his
            child.   [corpse
Awhile he stood contemplating the
    Silent and thoughtfully;
Then turning, spake to Thalaba, and
            said,   [the abode
'I have heard that there are places by
    Of holy men, so holily possess'd,
That should a corpse be laid irreverently
    Within their precincts, the insulted
            ground,
    Impatient of pollution, heaves and
            shakes   100
        The abomination out.
Have then in elder times the happy feet
Of Patriarch, or of Prophet bless'd
            the place,
Ishmael, or Houd, or Saleah, or than all,
Mahommed, holier name? Or is the man
So foul with magic and all blasphemy,
That Earth, like Heaven, rejects him?
            It is best   [tent.
Forsake the station. Let us strike our
    The place is tainted .. and behold
The Vulture hovers yonder, and his
            scream   110
Chides us that still we scare him from
            the prey.
    So let the accursed one,
    Torn by that beak obscene,
    Find fitting sepulchre.'

5

Then from the pollution of death
With water they made themselves pure;
    And Thalaba drew up
    The fastening of the cords;
    And Moath furl'd the tent;   119
And from the grove of palms Oneiza led
The Camels, ready to receive their load.

6

    The dews had ceased to steam
    Toward the climbing Sun,

When from the Isle of Palms they went
            their way;
And when the Sun had reach'd his
            southern height,
    As back they turn'd their eyes,
    The distant Palms arose
Like to the top-sails of some fleet far-off
    Distinctly seen, where else
The Ocean bounds had blended with the
            sky;   130
    And when the eve came on,
The sight returning reach'd the grove no
            more.
    They planted the pole of their tent,
    And they laid them down to repose.

7

    At midnight Thalaba started up,
For he felt that the ring on his finger
            was moved;
    He call'd on Allah aloud,
And he call'd on the Prophet's name.
    Moath arose in alarm;
'What ails thee, Thalaba?' he cried, 140
    'Is the robber of night at hand?'
'Dost thou not see,' the youth ex-
            claim'd,
        'A Spirit in the tent?'
    Moath look'd round and said,
    'The moon-beam shines in the tent,
    I see thee stand in the light,
And thy shadow is black on the ground.'

8

    Thalaba answer'd not.
'Spirit!' he cried, 'what brings thee
            here?
In the name of the Prophet, speak, 150
    In the name of Allah, obey!'

9

He ceased, and there was silence in the
            tent.
'Dost thou not hear?' quoth Thalaba;
    The listening man replied,
    'I hear the wind, that flaps
    The curtain of the tent.'

c 3

10

'The Ring! the Ring!' the youth ex-
claim'd.
'For that the Spirit of Evil comes;
By that I see, by that I hear.
In the name of God, I ask thee,   160
Who was he that slew my Father?'

DEMON

Master of the powerful Ring!
Okba, the dread Magician, did the deed.

THALABA

Where does the Murderer dwell?

DEMON

In the Domdaniel caverns,
Under the Roots of the Ocean.

THALABA

Why were my Father and my brethren
slain?

DEMON

We knew from the race of Hodeirah
The destined Destroyer would come.

THALABA

Bring me my father's sword!   170

DEMON

A Fire surrounds the fatal sword;
No Spirit or Magician's hand
Can pierce that fated Flame.

THALABA

Bring me his bow and his arrows!

11

Distinctly Moath heard the youth, and
She   [watch'd
Who, through the Veil of Separation,
The while in listening terror, and
suspense
All too intent for prayer.
They heard the voice of Thalaba;
But when the Spirit spake, the motion-
less air   180
Felt not the subtile sounds,
Too fine for mortal sense.

12

On a sudden the rattle of arrows was
heard,
And a quiver was laid at the feet of
the youth,
And in his hand they saw Hodeirah's
bow.
He eyed the bow, he twang'd the string,
And his heart bounded to the joyous
tone.
Anon he raised his voice and cried,
'Go thy way, and never more,
Evil spirit, haunt our tent!   190
By the virtue of the Ring,
By Mahommed's holier might,
By the holiest name of God,
Thee, and all the Powers of Hell,
I adjure and I command
Never more to trouble us!'

13

Nor ever from that hour
Did rebel Spirit on the tent intrude,
Such virtue had the Spell.

14

Thus peacefully the vernal years   200
Of Thalaba pass'd on,
Till now, without an effort, he could bend
Hodeirah's stubborn bow.
Black were his eyes and bright,
The sunny hue of health
Glow'd on his tawny cheek,
His lip was darken'd by maturing life;
Strong were his shapely limbs, his
stature tall;
Peerless among Arabian youths was he.

15

Compassion for the child   210
Had first old Moath's kindly heart pos-
sess'd,
An orphan, wailing in the wilderness;
But when he heard his tale, his wondrous
tale,   [truth,
Told by the Boy, with such eye-speaking

Now with sudden burst of anger,
Now in the agony of tears,
And now with flashes of prophetic joy,
What had been pity became reverence
then,
And, like a sacred trust from Heaven,
The Old Man cherish'd him.   220
Now, with a father's love,
Child of his choice, he loved the Boy,
And, like a father, to the Boy was dear.
Oneiza call'd him brother; and the youth
More fondly than a brother loved
the maid ;
The loveliest of Arabian maidens she.
How happily the years
Of Thalaba went by !

16

It was the wisdom and the will of
Heaven,
That in a lonely tent had cast   230
The lot of Thalaba ;
There might his soul develope best
Its strengthening energies ;
There might he from the world
Keep his heart pure and uncontaminate,
Till at the written hour he should be
found
Fit servant of the Lord, without a spot.

17

Years of his youth, how rapidly ye fled
In that beloved solitude !
Is the morn fair, and doth the freshening
breeze   240
Flow with cool current o'er his cheek ?
Lo ! underneath the broad-leaved
sycamore
With lids half-closed he lies,
Dreaming of days to come.
His dog beside him, in mute blandish-
ment,
Now licks his listless hand ;
Now lifts an anxious and expectant eye,
Courting the wonted caress.

18

Or comes the Father of the Rains
From his caves in the uttermost West,
Comes he in darkness and storms ? 251
When the blast is loud ;
When the waters fill
The traveller's tread in the sands ;
When the pouring shower
Streams adown the roof ;
When the door-curtain hangs in heavier
folds :
When the out-strain'd tent flags loosely :
Within there is the embers' cheerful
glow,
The sound of the familiar voice, 260
The song that lightens toil, . .
Domestic Peace and Comfort are within.
Under the common shelter, on dry sand,
The quiet Camels ruminate their food ;
The lengthening cord from Moath falls,
As patiently the Old Man
Entwines the strong palm-fibres ; by
the hearth
The Damsel shakes the coffee-grains,
That with warm fragrance fill the tent ;
And while, with dexterous fingers,
Thalaba   270
Shapes the green basket, haply at his feet
Her favourite kidling gnaws the twig,
Forgiven plunderer, for Oneiza's sake.

19

Or when the winter torrent rolls
Down the deep-channel'd rain-course,
foamingly,
Dark with its mountain spoils,
With bare feet pressing the wet sand,
There wanders Thalaba,
The rushing flow, the flowing roar,
Filling his yielded faculties,   280
A vague, a dizzy, a tumultuous joy.

20

Or lingers it a vernal brook
Gleaming o'er yellow sands ?
Beneath the lofty bank reclined,

With idle eye he views its little waves,
Quietly listening to the quiet flow ;
While in the breathings of the stirring
gale,
The tall canes bend above,
Floating like streamers on the wind
Their lank uplifted leaves.   290

21

Nor rich, nor poor, was Moath ; God
hath given   [content.
Enough, and blest him with a mind
No hoarded gold disquieted his dreams :
But ever round his station he beheld
Camels that knew his voice,
And home-birds, grouping at Oneiza's
call,
And goats that, morn and eve,
Came with full udders to the Damsel's
hand.
Dear child ! the tent beneath whose
shade they dwelt
It was her work ; and she had twined 300
His girdle's many hues ;
And he had seen his robe
Grow in Oneiza's loom.
How often, with a memory-mingled joy
Which made her Mother live before his
sight,   [the woof !
He watch'd her nimble fingers thread
Or at the hand-mill, when she knelt and
toil'd,
Toss'd the thin cake on spreading palm,
Or fix'd it on the glowing oven's side
With bare wet arm, and safe dexterity.

22

'Tis the cool evening hour :   311
The Tamarind from the dew
Sheathes its young fruit, yet green.
Before their tent the mat is spread ;
The Old Man's solemn voice
Intones the holy Book.
What if beneath no lamp-illumined
dome,   [truth,
Its marble walls bedeck'd with flourish'd

Azure and gold adornment ? sinks the
word
With deeper influence from the Imam's
voice,   320
Where in the day of congregation,
crowds
Perform the duty-task ?
Their Father is their Priest,
The Stars of Heaven their point of
prayer,
And the blue Firmament
The glorious Temple, where they feel
The present Deity.

23

Yet through the purple glow of eve
Shines dimly the white moon.
The slacken'd bow, the quiver, the long
lance,   330
Rest on the pillar of the Tent.
Knitting light palm-leaves for her bro-
ther's brow,
The dark-eyed damsel sits ;
The old Man tranquilly
Up his curl'd pipe inhales
The tranquillizing herb.
So listen they the reed of Thalaba,
While his skill'd fingers modulate
The low, sweet, soothing, melancholy
tones.

24

Or if he strung the pearls of Poesy, 340
Singing with agitated face
And eloquent arms, and sobs that reach
the heart,
A tale of love and woe ;
Then, if the brightening Moon that lit
his face,
In darkness favour'd hers,   [say,
Oh ! even with such a look, as fables
The Mother Ostrich fixes on her egg,
Till that intense affection
Kindle its light of life,
Even in such deep and breathless ten-
derness   350

Oneiza's soul is centred on the youth,
So motionless, with such an ardent
gaze, . .
Save when from her full eyes
She wipes away the swelling tears
That dim his image there.

25

She call'd him Brother; was it sister-
love
For which the silver rings
Round her smooth ankles and her tawny
arms, [eye
Shone daily brighten'd? for a brother's
Were her long fingers tinged, 360
As when she trimm'd the lamp,
And through the veins and delicate skin
The light shone rosy? that the darken'd
lids
Gave yet a softer lustre to her eye?
That with such pride she trick'd
Her glossy tresses, and on holy-day
Wreathed the red flower-crown round
Their waves of glossy jet?
How happily the days
Of Thalaba went by! 370
Years of his youth how rapidly ye fled!

26

Yet was the heart of Thalaba
Impatient of repose;
Restless he ponder'd still
The task for him decreed,
The mighty and mysterious work an-
nounced.
Day by day, with youthful ardour,
He the call of Heaven awaits;
And oft in visions, o'er the murderer's
head,
He lifts the avenging arm! 380
And oft, in dreams, he sees
The Sword that is circled with fire.

27

One morn, as was their wont, in sportive
mood, [bow;
The youth and damsel bent Hodeirah's

For with no feeble hand, nor erring aim,
Oneiza could let loose the obedient shaft.
With head back-bending, Thalaba
Shot up the aimless arrow high in air,
Whose line in vain the aching sight
pursued,
Lost in the depth of Heaven. 390
' When will the hour arrive,' exclaim'd
the youth,
' That I shall aim these fated shafts
To vengeance long delay'd?
Have I not strength, my father, for the
deed?
Or can the will of Providence
Be mutable like man?
Shall I never be call'd to the task?'

28

' Impatient boy!' quoth Moath, with
a smile:
' Impatient Thalaba!' Oneiza cried,
And she too smiled; but in her smile 400
A mild reproachful melancholy mix'd.

29

Then Moath pointed where a cloud
Of locusts, from the desolated fields
Of Syria wing'd their way.
' Lo! how created things
Obey the written doom!'

30

Onward they came, a dark continuous
cloud
Of congregated myriads numberless,
The rushing of whose wings was as the
sound
Of some broad river, headlong in its
course 410
Plunged from a mountain summit; or
the roar
Of a wild ocean in the autumnal storm,
Shattering its billows on a shore of rocks,
Onward they came, the winds impell'd
them on,
Their work was done, their path of
ruin past,
Their graves were ready in the wilderness.

31

'Behold the mighty army!' Moath
              cried,
  'Blindly they move, impell'd
      By the blind Element.
And yonder birds our welcome visitants,
See! where they soar above the em-
              bodied host,   421
  Pursue their way, and hang upon the
              rear,
  And thin the spreading flanks,
Rejoicing o'er their banquet! Deemest
              thou   [mosque
The scent of water on some Syrian
  Placed with priest-mummery and fan-
              tastic rites   [here
Which fool the multitude, hath led them
  From far Khorassan?   Allah who
              appoints
Yon swarms to be a punishment of man,
These also hath he doom'd to meet their
              way: 430
      Both passive instruments
      Of his all-acting will,
Sole mover He, and only spring of all.'

32

While thus he spake, Oneiza's eye looks
              up
    Where one toward her flew,
Satiate, for so it seem'd, with sport and
              food.
    The Bird flew over her,
    And as he pass'd above,
From his relaxing grasp a Locust fell; . .
  It fell upon the Maiden's robe,   440
And feebly there it stood, recovering
              slow.

33

    The admiring girl survey'd
    His out-spread sails of green;
  His gauzy underwings, [furl'd,
One closely to the grass-green body
One ruffled in the fall, and half unclosed.
  She view'd his jet-orb'd eyes,

    His glossy gorget bright,
    Green glittering in the sun;
    His plumy pliant horns,   450
  That, nearer as she gazed,
Bent tremblingly before her breath.
  She mark'd his yellow-circled front
    With lines mysterious vein'd;
And 'know'st thou what is here in-
              scribed,
    My father?' said the Maid.
'Look, Thalaba! perchance these lines
  Are in the letters of the Ring,
Nature's own language written here.'

34

The youth bent down, and suddenly
    He started, and his heart   461
  Sprung, and his cheek grew red,
For these mysterious lines were legible,. .
WHEN THE SUN SHALL BE DARKENED AT
              NOON,
    SON OF HODEIRAH, DEPART.
And Moath look'd, and read the lines
              aloud;
  The Locust shook his wings and fled,
    And they were silent all.

35

Who then rejoiced but Thalaba?
Who then was troubled but the Arabian
              Maid?   470
    And Moath sad of heart,
Though with a grief supprest, beheld
              the youth
    Sharpen his arrows now,
    And now new-plume their shafts,
  Now, to beguile impatient hope,
    Feel every sharpen'd point.

36

'Why is that anxious look,' Oneiza ask'd,
    'Still upward cast at noon?
  Is Thalaba aweary of our tent?'
'I would be gone,' the youth replied, 480
      'That I might do my task,
  And full of glory to the tent return,
    Whence I should part no more.'

37

But on the noontide sun,
As anxious and as oft, Oneiza's eye
Was upward glanced in fear.
And now, as Thalaba replied, her cheek
Lost its fresh and lively hue ;
For in the Sun's bright edge
She saw, or thought she saw, a little
speck.   490
The sage Astronomer
Who, with the love of science full,
Trembled that day at every passing
cloud, . .   [small.
He had not seen it, 'twas a speck so

38

Alas ! Oneiza sees the spot increase !
And lo ! the ready youth
Over his shoulder the full quiver slings,
And grasps the slacken'd bow.
It spreads, and spreads, and now
Hath shadow'd half the sun,   500
Whose crescent-pointed horns
Now momently decrease.

39

The day grows dark, the birds retire to
rest :
Forth from her shadowy haunt
Flies the large-headed screamer of the
night.
Far off the affrighted African,
Deeming his God deceased,
Falls on his knees in prayer,
And trembles as he sees
The fierce hyena's eyes   510
Glare in the darkness of that dreadful
noon.

40

Then Thalaba exclaim'd, ' Farewell,
My father ! my Oneiza !' the Old Man
Felt his throat swell with grief.
' Where wilt thou go, my child ?' he
cried,
' Wilt thou not wait a sign

To point thy destined way ?'
' God will conduct me !' said the faith-
ful youth.
He said, and from the tent,
In the depth of the darkness departed.
They heard his parting steps,   521
The quiver rattling as he pass'd away.

THE FOURTH BOOK

——Fas est quoque brutae
Telluri, docilem monitis coelestibus esse.
Mambruni Constantinus.

1

Whose is yon dawning form,
That in the darkness meets
The delegated youth ?
Dim as the shadow of a fire at noon,
Or pale reflection on the evening brook
Of glow-worm on the bank,
Kindled to guide her winged paramour.

2

A moment, and the brightening image
shaped   [she cried,
His Mother's form and features.   ' Go,'
' To Babylon, and from the Angels learn
What talisman thy task requires.'   11

3

The Spirit hung toward him when she
ceased,
As though with actual lips she would
have given
A mother's kiss. His arms outstretch'd,
His body bending on,
His mouth unclosed and trembling into
speech,   [wind
He prest to meet the blessing, . . but the
Play'd on his cheek : he look'd, and
he beheld   [he cried,
The darkness close. ' Again ! again !'
' Let me again behold thee !' from the
darkness   20
His Mother's voice went forth ;
' Thou shalt behold me in the hour of
death.'

4

Day dawns, the twilight gleam dilates,
  The Sun comes forth, and like a god
  Rides through rejoicing heaven.
Old Moath and his daughter, from their
          tent,
  Beheld the adventurous youth,
  Dark-moving o'er the sands,
A lessening image, trembling through
          their tears.
      Visions of high emprize   30
      Beguiled his lonely road ;
And if sometimes to Moath's tent
  The involuntary mind recurr'd,
Fancy, impatient of all painful thoughts,
Pictured the bliss should welcome his
          return.
    In dreams like these he went,
      And still of every dream
      Oneiza form'd a part,
And hope and memory made a mingled
          joy.

5

  In the eve he arrived at a Well ;   40
  An Acacia bent over its side,
Under whose long light-hanging boughs
  He chose his night's abode.
There, due ablutions made, and prayers
          perform'd,
    The youth his mantle spread,
      And silently produced
      His solitary meal.
The silence and the solitude recall'd
Dear recollections ; and with folded
          arms,
Thinking of other days, he sate, till
          thought   50
Had left him, and the Acacia's moving
          shade
      Upon the sunny sand,
      Had caught his idle eye ;
      And his awaken'd ear
  Heard the grey Lizard's chirp,
  The only sound of life.

6

  As thus in vacant quietness he sate,
A Traveller on a Camel reached the Well,
  And courteous greeting gave.
    The mutual salutation past,   60
He by the cistern too his garment spread
And friendly converse cheer'd the social
          meal.

7

    The Stranger was an ancient man,
      Yet one whose green old age
Bore the fair characters of temperate
          youth :
So much of manhood's strength his
          limbs retain'd,   [bore.
It seem'd he needed not the staff he
His beard was long, and grey, and crisp ;
      Lively his eyes and quick,
      And reaching over them   70
  The large broad eye-brow curl'd.
His speech was copious, and his winning
          words   [tive youth
Enrich'd with knowledge, that the atten-
Sate listening with a thirsty joy.

8

      So in the course of talk,
      The adventurer youth enquired
      Whither his course was bent ?
The Old Man answered, ' To Bagdad I
          go.'
At that so welcome sound, a flash of joy
      Kindled the eye of Thalaba ;   80
      ' And I too,' he replied,
    ' Am journeying thitherward ;
Let me become companion of thy way ! '
    Courteous the Old Man smiled,
      And willing in assent.

9

OLD MAN

Son, thou art young for travel.

THALABA

Until now
I never pass'd the desert boundary.

OLD MAN

It is a noble city that we seek.
Thou wilt behold magnificent palaces,
And lofty minarets, and high-domed
          Mosques,   90
And rich Bazars, whither from all the
          world   [ket there
Industrious merchants meet, and mar-
The World's collected wealth.

THALABA

Stands not Bagdad
Near to the site of ancient Babylon
And Nimrod's impious temple ?

OLD MAN

From the walls
'Tis but a long day's distance.

THALABA

And the ruins ?

OLD MAN

A mighty mass remains ; enough to
          tell us   100
How great our fathers were, how little
          we.
Men are not what they were ; their
          crimes and follies
Have dwarf'd them down from the old
          hero race
To such poor things as we !

THALABA

At Babylon
I have heard the Angels expiate their
          guilt,
Haruth and Maruth.

OLD MAN

'Tis a history
Handed from ages down ; a nurse's
          tale . .   109
Which children open-eyed and mouth'd
          devour ;   [relates,
And thus as garrulous ignorance
We learn it and believe. . . But all things
          feel   [and grass
The power of Time and Change ; thistles

Usurp the desolate palace, and the
          weeds   [Truth.
Of falsehood root in the aged pile of
How have you heard the tale ?

THALABA

Thus . . on a time
The Angels at the wickedness of man
Express'd indignant wonder ; that in
          vain
Tokens and signs were given, and
          Prophets sent, . .   120
Strange obstinacy this ! a stubbornness
Of sin, they said, that should for ever
          bar   [heard
The gates of mercy on them.   Allah
Their unforgiving pride, and bade that
          two
Of these untempted Spirits should
          descend,
Judges on Earth.   Haruth and Maruth
          went,   [heard
The chosen Sentencers ; they fairly
The appeals of men to their tribunal
          brought,
And rightfully decided.   At the length
A Woman came before them ; beautiful
Zohara was, as yonder Evening Star, 131
In the mild lustre of whose lovely light
Even now her beauty shines. They gazed
          on her   [sin.
With fleshly eyes, they tempted her to
The wily woman listen'd, and required
A previous price, the knowledge of the
          name   [name,
Of God. She learnt the wonder-working
And gave it utterance, and its virtue
          bore her
Up to the glorious Presence, and she told
Before the aweful Judgement-Seat her
          tale.   140

OLD MAN

I know the rest.   The accused Spirits
          were call'd ;
Unable of defence, and penitent,

They own'd their crime, and heard the
        doom deserved.
Then they besought the Lord, that
        not for ever
His wrath might be upon them ; and
        implored
That penal ages might at length restore
        them   [Babylon,
Clean from offence ; since then by
In the cavern of their punishment, they
        dwell.
        Runs the conclusion so ?

OLD MAN
Even so
Things view'd at distance through the
        mist of fear,
By their distortion terrify and shock
        The abused sight.   170

THALABA
        So I am taught.   150

OLD MAN
The common tale ! And likely thou hast
        heard
How that the bold and bad, with
        impious rites
Intrude upon their penitence, and force,
Albeit from loathing and reluctant lips,
        The sorcery-secret ?

THALABA
        Is it not the truth ?

OLD MAN
Son, thou hast seen the Traveller in the
        sands
Move through the dizzy light of hot
        noon-day,
Huge as the giant race of elder times ;
And his Camel, than the monstrous
        Elephant,   160
        Seem of a vaster bulk.

THALABA
        A frequent sight.

OLD MAN
And hast thou never, in the twilight,
        fancied
Familiar object into some strange shape
        And form uncouth ?

THALABA
        Ay ! many a time.

THALABA
But of these Angels' fate
Thus in the uncreated book is written.

OLD MAN
Wisely from legendary fables, Heaven
        Inculcates wisdom.

THALABA
How then is the truth ?
Is not the dungeon of their punishment
        By ruin'd Babylon ?

OLD MAN
By Babylon
Haruth and Maruth may be found.

THALABA
And there   180
Magicians learn their impious sorcery ?

OLD MAN
Son, what thou say'st is true, and it is
        false.
But night approaches fast ; I have
        travell'd far,
And my old lids are heavy ; . . on our
        way   [us now
We shall have hours for converse ; . . let
Turn to our due repose. Son, peace
        be with thee !
10
So in his loosen'd cloak
The Old Man wrapt himself,
And laid his limbs at length ;
And Thalaba in silence laid him down.
Awhile he lay, and watch'd the lovely
        Moon,   191
O'er whose broad orb the boughs
A mazy fretting framed,
Or with a pale transparent green
Lighting the restless leaves,
The thin Acacia leaves that play'd above.

The murmuring wind, the moving
    leaves,
  Soothed him at length to sleep,
With mingled lullabies of sight and
    sound.

11

Not so the dark Magician by his side, 200
Lobaba, who from the Domdaniel caves
  Had sought the dreaded youth.
Silent he lay, and simulating sleep,
Till by the long and regular breath he
    knew
  The youth beside him slept.
    Carefully then he rose,
And bending over him, survey'd him
    near ;
    And secretly he cursed
    The dead Abdaldar's ring,
    Arm'd by whose amulet 210
  He slept from danger safe.

12

Wrapt in his mantle Thalaba reposed,
His loose right arm pillowing his easy
    head.
  The Moon was on the Ring,
  Whose crystal gem return'd
  A quiet, moveless light.
Vainly the Wizard vile put forth his
    hand,
And strove to reach the gem ;
Charms, strong as hell could make them,
    kept it safe.
  He call'd his servant-fiends, 220
He bade the Genii rob the sleeping youth.
    By the virtue of the Ring,
    By Mahommed's holier power,
    By the holiest name of God,
Had Thalaba disarm'd the evil race.

13

Baffled and weary, and convinced at
    length,   [him,
Anger, and fear, and rancour gnawing
The accursed Sorcerer ceased his vain
    attempts,

    Content perforce to wait
    Temptation's likelier aid. 230
Restless he lay, and brooding many a
    wile,
  And tortured with impatient hope,
And envying with the bitterness of hate
  The innocent youth, who slept so
    sweetly by.

14

The ray of morning on his eye-lids fell,
    And Thalaba awoke,
And folded his mantle around him,
  And girded his loins for the day ;
Then the due rites of holiness observed.
    His comrade too arose, 240
    And with the outward forms
Of righteousness and prayer insulted
    God.
They fill'd their water skin, they gave
    The Camel his full draught.
Then on the road, while yet the morn
    was young,
  And the air was fresh with dew,
  Forward the travellers went,
With various talk beguiling the long way.
But soon the youth, whose busy mind
Dwelt on Lobaba's wonder-stirring
    words, 250
Renew'd the unfinish'd converse of the
    night.

15

THALABA

Thou said'st that it is true, and yet is
    false,
That men accurst attain at Babylon
Forbidden knowledge from the Angel
    pair : . .
    How mean you ?

LOBABA

  All things have a double power,
Alike for good and evil. The same fire
That on the comfortable hearth at eve
Warm'd the good man, flames o'er the
    house at night ;

Should we for this forego   260
The needful element ?
Because the scorching summer Sun
Darts fever, would'st thou quench the
      orb of day ?   [form'd
Or deemest thou that Heaven in anger
Iron to till the field, because when man
Had tipt his arrows for the chase, he
      rush'd
A murderer to the war ?

THALABA

What follows hence ?

LOBABA

That nothing in itself is good or evil,
But only in its use. Think you the man
Praiseworthy, who by painful study
      learns   271
The knowledge of all simples, and their
      power,
Healing or harmful ?

THALABA

All men hold in honour
The skilful Leech. From land to land
      he goes
Safe in his privilege ; the sword of war
Spares him ; Kings welcome him with
      costly gifts ;   [pain
And he who late had from the couch of
Lifted a languid look to him for aid,
Beholds him with glad eyes, and blesses
      him   280
In his first thankful prayer.

LOBABA

Yet some there are
Who to the purposes of wickedness
Apply this knowledge, and from herbs
      distil
Poison, to mix it in the trusted draught.

THALABA

Allah shall cast them in the eternal fire
Whose fuel is the cursed ! there shall
      they
Endure the ever-burning agony,

Consuming still in flames, and still
      renew'd.

LOBABA

But is their knowledge therefore in itself
      Unlawful ?   290

THALABA

That were foolishness to think.

LOBABA

O what a glorious animal were Man,
Knew he but his own powers, and,
      knowing, gave them
Room for their growth and spread ! The
      Horse obeys
His guiding will ; the patient Camel
      bears him   [wafts
Over these wastes of sand ; the Pigeon
His bidding through the sky ; . . and
      with these triumphs
He rests contented ! . . with these
      ministers, . .
When he might awe the Elements, and
      make
      Myriads of Spirits serve him !   300

THALABA

But as how ?
By a league with Hell, a covenant that
      binds
The soul to utter death !

LOBABA

Was Solomon
Accurst of God ? Yet to his talismans
Obedient, o'er his throne the birds of
      Heaven,
Their waving wings his sun-shield, fann'd
      around him   [to place,
The motionless air of noon ; from place
As his will rein'd the viewless Element,
He rode the Wind ; the Genii rear'd
      his temple,   310
And ceaselessly in fear while his dread
      eye   [their toil,
O'erlook'd them, day and night pursued
So dreadful was his power.

THALABA

But 'twas from Heaven
His wisdom came ; God's special gift, . .
the guerdon
Of early virtue.

LOBABA

Learn thou, O young man !
God hath appointed wisdom the reward
Of study ! 'Tis a well of living waters,
Whose inexhaustible bounties all might
drink,   320
But few dig deep enough.   Son ! thou
art silent, . .
Perhaps I say too much, . . perhaps
offend thee.

THALABA

Nay, I am young, and willingly, as
becomes me,
Hear the wise words of age.

LOBABA

Is it a crime
To mount the Horse, because forsooth
thy feet   [sin,
Can serve thee for the journey ? . . Is it
Because the Hern soars upward in
the sky   [Falcon
Above the arrow's flight, to train the
Whose beak shall pierce him there ? The
powers which Allah   330
Granted to man, were granted for his
use ;   [weakness
All knowledge that befits not human
Is placed beyond its reach. . . They who
repair
To Babylon, and from the Angels learn
Mysterious wisdom, sin not in the deed.

THALABA

Know you these secrets ?

LOBABA

I ? alas ! my Son,
My age just knows enough to understand
How little all its knowledge! Later years
Sacred to study, teach me to regret 340

Youth's unforeseeing indolence, and
hours   [I know
That cannot be recall'd ! Something
The properties of herbs, and have some-
times   [relief
Brought to the afflicted comfort and
By the secrets of my art ; under His
blessing   [Gems
Without whom all had fail'd ! Also of
I have some knowledge, and the
characters   [set,
That tell beneath what aspect they were

THALABA

Belike you can interpret then the graving
Around this Ring !   350

LOBABA

My sight is feeble, Son,
And I must view it closer ; let me try !

16

The unsuspecting Youth
Held forth his finger to draw off the spell.
Even whilst he held it forth,
There settled there a Wasp,
And just above the Gem infix'd its dart ;
All purple-swoln the hot and painful flesh
Rose round the tighten'd Ring.
The baffled Sorcerer knew the hand of
Heaven,   360
And inwardly blasphemed.

17

Ere long Lobaba's heart,
Fruitful in wiles, devised new stratagem.
A mist arose at noon,
Like the loose hanging skirts
Of some low cloud that, by the breeze
impell'd,
Sweeps o'er the mountain side.
With joy the thoughtless youth
That grateful shadowing hail'd ;
For grateful was the shade,   370
While through the silver-lighted haze,
Guiding their way, appear'd the beam-
less Sun.

But soon that beacon fail'd ;
A heavier mass of cloud,
Impenetrably deep,
Hung o'er the wilderness.
'Knowest thou the track ?' quoth
Thalaba,
'Or should we pause, and wait the wind
To scatter this bewildering fog ?'
The Sorcerer answer'd him,   380
'Now let us hold right on, . . for if we
stray,   [course.'
The Sun to-morrow will direct our
So saying, he toward the desert depths
Misleads the youth deceived.

18

Earlier the night came on,
Nor moon, nor stars, were visible in
heaven ;   [his eyes,
And when at morn the youth unclosed
He knew not where to turn his face in
prayer.
'What shall we do ?' Lobaba cried,
'The lights of heaven have ceased
To guide us on our way.   391
Should we remain and wait
More favourable skies,
Soon would our food and water fail us
here :
And if we venture on,
There are the dangers of the wilderness!'

19

'Sure it were best proceed !'
The chosen youth replies ;
'So haply we may reach some tent, or
grove
Of dates, or station'd tribe.   400
But idly to remain,
Were yielding effortless, and waiting
death.'
The wily sorcerer willingly assents,
And farther in the sands,
Elate of heart, he leads the credulous
youth.

20

Still o'er the wilderness
Settled the moveless mist.
The timid Antelope, that heard their
steps,   [dim light ;
Stood doubtful where to turn in that
The Ostrich, blindly hastening, met
them full.   410
At night, again in hope,
Young Thalaba lay down ;   [ray
The morning came, and not one guiding
Through the thick mist was visible,
The same deep moveless mist that
mantled all.

21

Oh for the Vulture's scream,
Who haunts for prey the abode of
humankind !
Oh for the Plover's pleasant cry
To tell of water near !
Oh for the Camel-driver's song   420
For now the water-skin grows light,
Though of the draught, more eagerly
desired,   [thirst.
Imperious prudence took with sparing
Oft from the third night's broken sleep,
As in his dreams he heard
The sound of rushing winds,
Started the anxious youth, and look'd
abroad,   [dured.
In vain ! for still the deadly calm en-
Another day pass'd on ;
The water-skin was drain'd ;   430
But then one hope arrived,
For there was motion in the air !
The sound of the wind arose anon,
That scatter'd the thick mist,
And lo ! at length the lovely face of
Heaven !

22

Alas ! . . a wretched scene
Was open'd on their view.
They look'd around, no wells were near,
No tent, no human aid !

Flat on the Camel lay the water-skin, 440
And their dumb servant difficultly now,
Over hot sands and under the hot sun,
Dragg'd on with patient pain.

23

But oh the joy ! the blessed sight !
When in that burning waste the
   Travellers [besprent,
Saw a green meadow, fair with flowers
Azure and yellow, like the beautiful
   fields [grass
Of England, when amid the growing
The blue-bell bends, the golden king-cup
   shines, [air,
And the sweet cowslip scents the genial
  In the merry month of May ! 451
Oh joy ! the Travellers
Gaze on each other with hope-brighten'd
  eyes, [flows
For sure through that green meadow
The living stream ! And lo ! their
  famish'd beast
Sees the restoring sight !
Hope gives his feeble limbs a sudden
  strength,
  He hurries on ! . .

24

The herbs so fair to eye
Were Senna, and the Gentian's blossom
  blue, 460
And kindred plants, that with unwater'd
  root [leaves
Fed in the burning sand, whose bitter
  Even frantic Famine loathed.

25

In uncommunicating misery
Silent they stood. At length Lobaba
  said,
' Son, we must slay the Camel, or we die
For lack of water ! thy young hand
  is firm, . .
Draw forth the knife and pierce him !'
  Wretch accurst !

Who that beheld thy venerable face,
Thy features stiff with suffering, the dry
  lips, 470
The feverish eyes, could deem that
  all within
Was magic ease, and fearlessness secure,
And wiles of hellish import ? The young
  man
Paused with reluctant pity . but he saw
His comrade's red and painful coun-
  tenance,
And his own burning breath came short
  and quick,
And at his feet the gasping beast
Lies, over-worn with want.

26

Then from his girdle Thalaba took the
  knife
With stern compassion, and from side
  to side 480
Across the Camel's throat,
Drew deep the crooked blade.
Servant of man, that merciful deed
For ever ends thy suffering ; but what
  doom [death
Waits thy deliverer ? ' Little will thy
  Avail us !' thought the youth,
As in the water-skin he pour'd
The Camel's hoarded draught ;
  It gave a scant supply, 489
The poor allowance of one prudent day.

27

Son of Hodeirah, though thy steady soul
  Despair'd not, firm in faith,
Yet not the less did suffering nature feel
Its pangs and trials. Long their craving
  thirst
Struggled with fear, by fear itself in-
  flamed ;
But drop by drop, that poor,
  That last supply is drain'd.
Still the same burning sun ! no cloud in
  heaven !

The hot air quivers, and the sultry mist
Floats o'er the desert with a show 500
Of distant waters, mocking their distress.

28

The youth's parch'd lips were black,
His tongue was dry and rough,
His eye-balls red with heat.
Lobaba gazed on him with looks
That seem'd to speak of pity, and he said,
' Let me behold thy Ring ;
It may have virtue that can save us yet ! '
With that he took his hand
And view'd the writing close, 510
Then cried with sudden joy,
' It is a stone that whoso bears,
The Genii must obey !
Now raise thy voice, my Son,
And bid them in His name that here is written
Preserve us in our need.'

29

' Nay ! ' answer'd Thalaba,
' Shall I distrust the providence of God ?
Is it not He must save ?
If Allah wills it not, 520
Vain were the Genii's aid.'

30

Whilst he spake, Lobaba's eye,
Upon the distance fix'd,
Attended not his speech.
Its fearful meaning drew
The looks of Thalaba ;
Columns of sand came moving on,
Red in the burning ray,
Like obelisks of fire,
They rush'd before the driving wind. 530
Vain were all thoughts of flight !
They had not hoped escape,
Could they have back'd the Dromedary then,
Who in his rapid race   [force.
Gives to the tranquil air a drowning

31

High . . high in heaven upcurl'd
The dreadful sand-spouts moved :
Swift as the whirlwind that impell'd their way,
They came toward the travellers !
The old Magician shriek'd, 540
And lo ! the foremost bursts,
Before the whirlwind's force,
Scattering afar a burning shower of sand.
' Now by the virtue of the Ring,
· Save us ! ' Lobaba cried,
' While yet thou hast the power,
Save us ! O save us ! now ! '
The youth made no reply,
Gazing in aweful wonder on the scene.

32

' Why dost thou wait ? ' the Old Man exclaim'd, 550
' If Allah and the Prophet will not save,
Call on the powers that will ! '

33

' Ha ! do I know thee, Infidel accurst ? '
Exclaim'd the awaken'd youth.
' And thou hast led me hither, Child of Sin !
That fear might make me sell
My soul to endless death ! '

34

' Fool that thou art ! ' Lobaba cried,
' Call upon Him whose name
Thy charmed signet bears, 560
Or die the death thy foolishness deserves ! '

35

' Servant of Hell ! die thou ! ' quoth Thalaba.
And leaning on his bow
He fitted the loose string
And laid the arrow in its resting-place.
' Bow of my Father, do thy duty now ! '

He drew the arrow to its point,
   True to his eye it fled,
   And full upon the breast
    It smote the Sorcerer.   570
Astonish'd Thalaba beheld
   The blunted point recoil.

36

A proud and bitter smile
   Wrinkled Lobaba's cheek.
'Try once again thine earthly arms!'
    he cried.
  ' Rash Boy! the Power I serve
   Abandons not his votaries.
It is for Allah's wretched slaves, like
    thou,
To serve a master, who in the hour of
    need
  Forsakes them to their fate!   580
I leave thee!' . . and he shook his staff,
    and call'd
   The Chariot of his charms.

37

Swift as the viewless wind,
Self-moved, the Chariot came;
   The Sorcerer mounts the seat.
' Yet once more weigh thy danger!' he
    resumed,
  ' Ascend the car with me,
  And with the speed of thought
  We pass the desert bounds.'
The indignant youth vouchsafed not to
    reply,   590
And lo! the magic car begins its course!

38

Hark! hark! . . he shrieks . . Lobaba
    shrieks!
What, wretch, and hast thou raised
The rushing terrors of the Wilderness
  To fall on thine own head?
  Death! death! inevitable death!
  Driven by the breath of God,
A column of the Desert met his way.

THE FIFTH BOOK

Thou hast girded me with strength unto
the battle; thou hast subdued under me
those that rose up against me. — *Psalm*
xviii. 39.

1

WHEN Thalaba from adoration rose,
   The air was cool, the sky
  With welcome clouds o'ercast,
  Which soon came down in rain.
He lifted up his fever'd face to heaven,
And bared his head and stretch'd his
    hands
   To that delightful shower,
And felt the coolness permeate every
    limb,
   Freshening his powers of life.

2

A loud quick panting! Thalaba looks
    up,   10
He starts, and his instinctive hand
Grasps the knife hilt; for close beside
   A Tiger passes him.
  An indolent and languid eye
   The passing Tiger turn'd;
   His head was hanging down,
   His dry tongue lolling low,
And the short panting of his breath
Came through his hot parch'd nostrils
    painfully.
   The young Arabian knew   20
  The purport of his hurried pace,
   And following him in hope,
   Saw joyful from afar
   The Tiger stoop and drink.

3

A desert Pelican had built her nest
   In that deep solitude,
And now, return'd from distant flight,
   Fraught with the river-stream,
Her load of water had disburthen'd there.
  Her young in the refreshing bath 30
   Dipt down their callow heads,

Fill'd the swoln membrane from their
        plumeless throat
Pendant, and bills yet soft ;
And buoyant with arch'd breast,
Plied in unpractised stroke
The oars of their broad feet.
They, as the spotted prowler of the wild
Laps the cool wave, around their mother
        crowd,   [wings.
And nestle underneath her outspread
The spotted prowler of the wild   40
Lapt the cool wave, and satiate, from
        the nest,
Guiltless of blood, withdrew.

4

The mother-bird had moved not,
But cowering o'er her nestlings,
Sate confident and fearless,
And watch'd the wonted guest.
But when the human visitant approach'd,
The alarmed Pelican
Retiring from that hostile shape
Gathers her young, and menaces with
        wings,   50
And forward thrusts her threatening
        neck,
Its feathers ruffling in her wrath,
Bold with maternal fear.
Thalaba drank, and in the water-skin
Hoarded the precious element.
Not all he took, but in the large nest left
Store that sufficed for life ;
And journeying onward, blest the Carrier
        Bird,
And blest, in thankfulness,
Their common Father, provident for all.

5

With strength renew'd, and confident in
        faith,   61
The son of Hodeirah proceeds ;
Till after the long toil of many a day,
At length Bagdad appear'd,
The City of his search.
He hastening to the gate,

Roams o'er the city with insatiate eyes ;
Its thousand dwellings, o'er whose
        level roofs   [mosques,
Fair cupolas appear'd, and high-domed
And pointed minarets, and cypress
        groves   70
Every where scatter'd in unwithering
        green.

6

Thou too art fallen, Bagdad ! City of
        Peace
Thou too hast had thy day ;
And loathsome Ignorance and brute
        Servitude,
Pollute thy dwellings now,
Erst for the Mighty and the Wise re-
        nown'd.
O yet illustrious for remember'd fame,—
Thy founder the Victorious,—and the
        pomp   [defiled,
Of Haroun, for whose name by blood
Yahia's, and the blameless Barmecides',
Genius hath wrought salvation,—and
        the years   81
When Science with the good Al-Maimon
        dwelt :   [Mosques
So one day may the Crescent from thy
Be pluck'd by Wisdom, when the
        enlighten'd arm
Of Europe conquers to redeem the East !

7

Then Pomp and Pleasure dwelt within
        her walls ;   [West
The Merchants of the East and of the
        Met in her arch'd Bazars ;
All day the active poor
Shower'd a cool comfort o'er her
        thronging streets ;   90
Labour was busy in her looms ;
Through all her open gates
Long troops of laden Camels lined the
        roads,   [stream
And Tigris bore upon his tameless
Armenian harvests to her multitudes.

8

But not in sumptuous Caravansery
The adventurer idles there,
Nor satiates wonder with her pomp and
        wealth;
A long day's distance from the walls
        Stands ruined Babylon;   100
The time of action is at hand;
The hope that for so many a year
Hath been his daily thought, his nightly
        dream,
        Stings to more restlessness.
He loaths all lingering that delays the
        hour   [return'd,
When, full of glory, from his quest
He on the pillar of the Tent beloved
        Shall hang Hodeirah's sword.

9

The many-coloured domes
        Yet wore one dusky hue;   110
        The Cranes upon the Mosque
        Kept their night-clatter still;
When through the gate the early Tra-
        veller pass'd.   [plain
And when at evening o'er the swampy
        The Bittern's boom came far,
        Distinct in darkness seen
Above the low horizon's lingering light,
Rose the near ruins of old Babylon.

10

Once from her lofty walls the Charioteer
Look'd down on swarming myriads;
        once she flung   120
Her arches o'er Euphrates' conquer'd
        tide,   [she pour'd
And through her brazen portals when
Her armies forth, the distant nations
        look'd   [fear,
As men who watch the thunder-cloud in
Lest it should burst above them. She
        was fallen,
The Queen of cities, Babylon, was fallen!
        Low lay her bulwarks; the black
        Scorpion bask'd

In the palace courts; within the sanc-
        tuary
        The She-Wolf hid her whelps.
Is yonder huge and shapeless heap,
        what once   130
Hath been the aërial Gardens, height on
        height   [with wood,
Rising like Media's mountains crown'd
Work of imperial dotage? Where the
        fane   [now,
Of Belus? Where the Golden Image
Which at the sound of dulcimer and lute,
Cornet and sacbut, harp and psaltery,
        The Assyrian slaves adored?
A labyrinth of ruins, Babylon
Spreads o'er the blasted plain:
The wandering Arab never sets his tent
Within her walls; the Shepherd eyes
        afar   141
Her evil towers, and devious drives his
        flock.   [tide,
Alone unchanged, a free and bridgeless
        Euphrates rolls along,
        Eternal Nature's work.

11

Through the broken portal,
        Over weedy fragments,
        Thalaba went his way.
Cautious he trod, and felt
The dangerous ground before him with
        his bow.   150
        The Jackal started at his steps;
The Stork, alarm'd at sound of man,
From her broad nest upon the old pillar
        top,
Affrighted fled on flapping wings;
The Adder, in her haunts disturb'd,
Lanced at the intruding staff her arrowy
        tongue.

12

Twilight and moonshine dimly mingling
        gave
        An aweful light obscure,
        Evening not wholly closed,

The Moon still pale and faint :   160
An aweful light obscure,
Broken by many a mass of blackest shade;
Long column stretching dark through
        weeds and moss,
Broad length of lofty wall,
Whose windows lay in light,
And of their former shape, low arch'd
        or square,
Rude outline on the earth
Figured, with long grass fringed.

13

Reclined against a column's broken shaft,
Unknowing whitherward to bend his
        way,   170
He stood, and gazed around.
The Ruins closed him in ;
It seem'd as if no foot of man
For ages had intruded there.

14

Soon at approaching step
Startling, he turn'd and saw
A Warrior in the moon-beam drawing
        near.
Forward the Stranger came,
And with a curious eye
Perused the Arab youth.   180

15

' And who art thou,' the Stranger cried,
    ' That at an hour like this
        Wanderest in Babylon ?
A way-bewilder'd traveller, seekest thou
        The ruinous shelter here ?
    Or comest thou to hide
    The plunder of the night ?
    Or hast thou spells to make
These ruins, yawning from their rooted
        base,
    Disclose their secret wealth ? '   190

16

The youth replied, ' Nor wandering
        traveller,
    Nor robber of the night,

Nor skill'd in spells am I.
    I seek the Angels here,
Haruth and Maruth.   Stranger, in thy
        turn,
    Why wanderest thou in Babylon,
    And who art thou, the questioner ? '

17

The man was fearless, and the temper'd
        pride
Which toned the voice of Thalaba
Displeased not him, himself of haughty
        heart.   200
Heedless he answered, ' Knowest thou
    Their cave of punishment ? '

18

THALABA

Vainly I seek it.

STRANGER

Art thou firm of foot
To tread the ways of danger ?

THALABA

Point the path !

STRANGER

Young Arab ! if thou hast a heart can
        beat   [not
Evenly in danger ; if thy bowels yearn
With human fears, at scenes where
        undisgraced
The soldier tried in battle might look
        back   210
And tremble, follow me ! . . for I am
        bound
    Into that cave of horrors.

19

Thalaba

Gazed on his comrade : he was young,
        of port
Stately and strong ; belike his face
        had pleased   [in it
A woman's eye ; but the youth read
Unrestrain'd passions, the obdurate soul
Bold in all evil daring ; and it taught,

By Nature's irresistible instinct, doubt
Well-timed and wary. Of himself
            assured,
Fearless of man, and firm in faith,   220
' Lead on ! ' cried Thalaba.
    Mohareb led the way ;
And through the ruin'd streets,
    And through the farther gate,
They pass'd in silence on.

20

What sound is borne on the wind ?
    Is it the storm that shakes
The thousand oaks of the forest ?
    But Thalaba's long locks
Flow down his shoulders moveless, and
            the wind   230
In his loose mantle raises not a fold.
    Is it the river's roar
Dash'd down some rocky descent ?
    Along the level plain
Euphrates glides unheard.
What sound disturbs the night,
Loud as the summer forest in the storm,
As the river that roars among rocks ?

21

And what the heavy cloud
    That hangs upon the vale,   240
Thick as the mist o'er a well-water'd
            plain
Settling at evening, when the cooler air
    Lets its day-vapours fall ;
    Black as the sulphur-cloud,
That through Vesuvius, or from Hecla's
            mouth,   [fires ?
Rolls up, ascending from the infernal

22

From Ait's bitumen-lake
    That heavy cloud ascends ;
    That everlasting roar
From where its gushing springs   250
Boil their black billows up.
    Silent the Arabian youth,
Along the verge of that wide lake,

Follow'd Mohareb's way,
Toward a ridge of rocks that bank'd its
            side.
There from a cave, with torrent force,
    And everlasting roar,
    The black bitumen roll'd.
The moonlight lay upon the rocks ;
    Their crags were visible,   260
    The shade of jutting cliffs,
And where broad lichens whiten'd some
            smooth spot,
    And where the ivy hung
    Its flowing tresses down.
A little way within the cave
The moonlight fell, glossing the sable
            tide
That gush'd tumultuous out.
A little way it entered, then the rock
Arching its entrance, and the winding
            way,
    Darken'd the unseen depths.   270

23

No eye of mortal man,
If unenabled by enchanted spell,
Had pierced those fearful depths ;
    For mingling with the roar
Of the portentous torrent, oft were heard
    Shrieks, and wild yells that scared
The brooding Eagle from her midnight
            nest.
    The affrighted countrymen
    Call it the mouth of Hell ;
And ever when their way leads near
    They hurry with averted eyes,   281
And dropping their beads fast,
    Pronounce the Holy Name.

24

There pausing at the cavern-mouth,
    Mohareb turn'd to Thalaba :
' Now darest thou enter in ? '
    ' Behold ! ' the youth replied,
And leading in his turn the dangerous
            way,
    Set foot within the cave.

25

'Stay, Madman!' cried his comrade:
        'Wouldst thou rush   290
Headlong to certain death?
Where are thine arms to meet
The Keeper of the Passage?' A loud
                shriek,   [cave,
That shook along the windings of the
Scatter'd the youth's reply.

26

Mohareb, when the long re-echoing
                ceased,
Exclaim'd, 'Fate favour'd thee,
Young Arab! when she wrote upon thy
                brow
The meeting of to-night;
        Else surely had thy name   300
This hour been blotted from the Book
        of Life!'

27

So saying, from beneath
His cloak a bag he drew:
'Young Arab! thou art brave,' he cried,
'But thus to rush on danger unprepared,
As lions spring upon the hunter's spear,
Is blind, brute courage. Zohak keeps
        the cave:
Against that Giant of primeval days
No force can win the passage.' Thus he
                said,
And from his wallet drew a human hand,
        Shrivell'd and dry and black;   311
        And fitting as he spake
        A taper in its hold,
Pursued: 'A murderer on the stake
                had died!   [lopt
I drove the Vulture from his limbs, and
The hand that did the murder, and
                drew up
The tendon strings to close its grasp,
        And in the sun and wind
Parch'd it, nine weeks exposed.
The Taper, .. but not here the place to
                impart,   320

Nor hast thou undergone the rites,
That fit thee to partake the mystery.
Look! it burns clear, but with the air
                around,
Its dead ingredients mingle deathiness.
This when the Keeper of the Cave shall
                feel,
        Maugre the doom of Heaven,
                The salutary spell
Shall lull his penal agony to sleep,
And leave the passage free.'

28

        Thalaba answer'd not.   330
Nor was there time for answer now,
        For lo! Mohareb leads,
        And o'er the vaulted cave,
Trembles the accursed taper's feeble
                light.
        There where the narrowing chasm
                Rose loftier in the hill,
Stood Zohak, wretched man, condemn'd
                to keep
        His Cave of punishment.
His was the frequent scream
Which when far off the prowling Jackal
                heard,   340
        He howl'd in terror back:
For from his shoulders grew
Two snakes of monster size,
        Which ever at his head
        Aim'd their rapacious teeth
To satiate raving hunger with his brain.
He, in the eternal conflict, oft would
                seize   [grasp
Their swelling necks, and in his giant
Bruise them, and rend their flesh with
                bloody nails,
        And howl for agony,   350
Feeling the pangs he gave, for of himself
Co-sentient and inseparable parts,
        The snaky torturers grew.

29

        To him approaching now,
Mohareb held the wither'd arm,

The taper of enchanted power.
The unhallow'd spell in hand unholy
          held,
Then minister'd to mercy ; heavily
The wretch's eyelids closed ;
     And welcome and unfelt,   360
     Like the release of death,
A sudden sleep surprised his vital powers.

30

Yet though along the cave relax'd
     Lay Zohak's giant limbs,   [pass,
The twin-born serpents kept the narrow
     Kindled their fiery eyes,
Darted their tongues of terror, and
          roll'd out
     Their undulating length,   [ship
Like the long streamers of some gallant
     Buoy'd on the wavy air,   370
Still struggling to flow on, and still with-
          held.
     The scent of living flesh
     Inflamed their appetite.

31

Prepared for all the perils of the cave,
Mohareb came. He from his wallet drew
     Two human heads, yet warm.
O hard of heart ! whom not the visible
          power
Of retributive Justice, and the doom
     Of Zohak in his sight,
     Deterr'd from equal crime !   380
Two human heads, yet warm, he laid
Before the scaly guardians of the pass ;
They to their wonted banquet of old
          years   [free.
Turn'd eager, and the narrow pass was

32

     And now before their path
     The opening cave dilates ;
     They reach a spacious vault,
Where the black river-fountains burst
          their way.
     Now as a whirlwind's force

     Had center'd on the spring,   390
     The gushing flood roll'd up ;
     And now the deaden'd roar
Echoed beneath, collapsing as it sunk
     Within a dark abyss,
Adown whose fathomless gulphs the eye
          was lost.

33

Blue flames that hover'd o'er the springs
Flung through the cavern their uncer
          tain light ;
     Now waving on the waves they lay,
     And now their fiery curls
     Flow'd in long tresses up,   400
And now contracting, glow'd with
          whiter heat !
     Then up they shot again,
     Darting pale flashes through the
          tremulous air ;   [smoke,
The flames, the red and yellow sulphur-
     And the black darkness of the vault,
     Commingling indivisibly.

34

' Here,' quoth Mohareb, ' do the Angels
          dwell,
The Teachers of Enchantment.' Thalaba
     Then raised his voice, and cried,
' Haruth and Maruth, hear me ! Not
          with rites   410
Accursed, to disturb your penitence,
     And learn forbidden lore,
Repentant Angels, seek I your abode ;
But sent by Allah and the Prophet here,
     Obediently I come,
     Their chosen servant I.
     Tell me the Talisman '—

35

     ' And dost thou think,'
Mohareb cried, as with a smile of scorn
He glanced upon his comrade, ' dost
          thou think   420
To trick them of their secret ? For the
          dupes

Of human-kind keep this lip-righteous-
ness !
'Twill serve thee in the Mosque
And in the Market-place,
But Spirits view the heart.
Only by strong and torturing spells
enforced,
Those stubborn angels teach the charm
By which we must descend.'

36

' Descend ?' said Thalaba.
But then the wrinkling smile   430
Forsook Mohareb's cheek,
And darker feelings settled on his brow.
' Now by my soul,' quoth he, ' and I
believe,
Idiot ! that I have led
Some camel-knee'd prayer-monger
through the cave !
What brings thee hither ? Thou
should'st have a hut   [way,
By some Saint's grave beside the public
There to less-knowing fools
Retail thy Koran-scraps,   439
And in thy turn die civet-like at last
In the dung-perfume of thy sanctity ! . .
Ye whom I seek ! that, led by me,
Feet uninitiate tread
Your threshold, this atones !——
Fit sacrifice he falls ! '
And forth he flash'd his scymetar,
And raised the murderous blow.

37

There ceased his power ; his lifted arm,
Suspended by the spell,
Hung impotent to strike.   450
' Poor hypocrite ! ' cried he,
' And this then is thy faith
In Allah and the Prophet ! They had
fail'd
To save thee, but for Magic's stolen aid ;
Yea, they had left thee yonder Serpent's
meal,

But that, in prudent cowardice,
The chosen Servant of the Lord came in,
Safe follower of my path ! '

38

' Blasphemer ! dost thou boast of guid-
ing me ? '
Quoth Thalaba, with virtuous pride
inflamed,   460
' Blindly the wicked work
The righteous will of Heaven !
Sayest thou that diffident of God,
In Magic spells I trust ?
Liar ! let witness this ! '
And he drew off Abdaldar's Ring,
And cast it in the gulph.
A skinny hand came up,
And caught it as it fell,
And peals of devilish laughter shook the
Cave.   470

39

Then joy suffused Mohareb's cheek,
And Thalaba beheld
The blue blade gleam, descending to
destroy.

40

The undefended youth
Sprung forward, and he seized
Mohareb in his grasp,
And grappled with him breast to breast.
Sinewy and large of limb Mohareb was,
Broad-shoulder'd, and his joints
Knit firm, and in the strife   480
Of danger practised well.
Time had not thus matured young
Thalaba ;
But high-wrought feeling now,
The inspiration and the mood divine,
Infused a force portentous, like the
strength
Of madness through his frame.
Mohareb reels before him ; he right on,
With knee, with breast, with arm,
Presses the staggering foe ;

And now upon the brink   490
Of that tremendous spring, . .
There with fresh impulse and a rush of
        force,
He thrust him from his hold.
The upwhirling flood received
    Mohareb, then, absorb'd,
    Engulph'd him in the abyss.

41

Thalaba's breath came fast,
And panting, he breath'd out
A broken prayer of thankfulness.
    At length he spake and said,   500
' Haruth and Maruth ! are ye here ?
Or hath that evil guide misled my
        search ?
I, Thalaba, the Servant of the Lord,
Invoke you. Hear me, Angels ! so may
        Heaven
Accept and mitigate your penitence.
I go to root from earth the Sorcerer
        brood,
Tell me the needful Talisman ! '

42

Thus as he spake, recumbent on the
        rock
    Beyond the black abyss,
    Their forms grew visible.   510
A settled sorrow sate upon their brows, . .
Sorrow alone, for trace of guilt and
        shame
None now remain'd ; and gradual as
        by prayer
    The sin was purged away,
Their robe of glory, purified of stain,
Resumed the lustre of its native light.

43

In awe the youth received the answering
        voice,
' Son of Hodeirah ! thou hast proved it
        here ;
    The Talisman is Faith.'

THE SIXTH BOOK

Then did I see a pleasant Paradise,
    Full of sweet flowers and daintiest delights,
Such as on earth man could not more devise
    With pleasures choice to feed his cheerful
        sprights ;
    Not that which Merlin by his magic slights
Made for the gentle squire to entertain
His fair Belphoebe, could this garden stain.
        SPENSER, *Ruins of Time.*

1

So from the inmost cave
    Did Thalaba retrace
    The windings of the rock.
Still on the ground the giant limbs
    Of Zohak lay dispread ;
    The spell of sleep had ceased,
And his broad eyes were glaring on the
        youth :
Yet raised he not his arm to bar the way,
    Fearful to rouse the snakes
    Now lingering o'er their meal.   10

2

Oh then, emerging from that dreadful
        cave,
    How grateful did the gale of night
    Salute his freshen'd sense !
    How full of lightsome joy,
Thankful to Heaven, he hastens by the
        verge
    Of that bitumen-lake,
    Whose black and heavy fumes,
    Surge heaving after surge,   [sea.
Roll'd like the billowy and tumultuous

3

The song of many a bird at morn   20
    Aroused him from his rest.
Lo ! at his side a courser stood ;
    More animate of eye,
Of form more faultless never had he
        seen,   [strength,
More light of limbs and beautiful in
    Among the race whose blood,

D

Pure and unmingled, from the royal
steeds
Of Solomon came down.

4

The chosen Arab's eye
Glanced o'er his graceful shape, 30
His rich caparisons,
His crimson trappings gay.
But when he saw the mouth
Uncurb'd, the unbridled neck,
Then his heart leapt, and then his cheek
was flush'd ; [sent
For sure he deem'd that Heaven had
A courser, whom no erring hand might
guide.
And lo ! the eager Steed
Throws his head and paws the ground,
Impatient of delay ! 40
Then up leapt Thalaba,
And away went the self-govern'd courser.

5

Over the plain
Away went the steed ;
With the dew of the morning his fetlocks
were wet, [of noon,
The foam froth'd his limbs in the journey
Nor stay'd he till over the westerly heaven
The shadows of evening had spread.
Then on a shelter'd bank
The appointed Youth reposed, 50
And by him laid the docile courser down.
Again in the grey of the morning
Thalaba bounded up ;
Over hill, over dale,
Away goes the steed.
Again at eve he stops,
Again the Youth alights ;
His load discharg'd, his errand done,
The courser then bounded away.

6

Heavy and dark the eve ; 60
The Moon was hid on high,
A dim light tinged the mist

That crost her in the path of Heaven.
All living sounds had ceased,
Only the flow of waters near was heard,
A low and lulling melody.

7

Fasting, yet not of want
Percipient, he on that mysterious steed
Had reach'd his resting-place,
For expectation kept his nature up.
Now as the flow of waters near 71
Awoke a feverish thirst,
Led by the sound he moved
To seek the grateful wave.

8

A meteor in the hazy air
Play'd before his path ;
Before him now it roll'd
A globe of living fire ;
And now contracted to a steady light,
As when the solitary hermit prunes 80
His lamp's long undulating flame ;
And now its wavy point
Up-blazing rose, like a young cypress tree
Sway'd by the heavy wind ;
Anon to Thalaba it moved,
And wrapt him in its pale innocuous fire ;
Now, in the darkness drown'd,
Left him with eyes bedimm'd,
And now, emerging, spread the scene to
sight.

9

Led by the sound and meteor-flame,
The Arabian youth advanced. 91
Now to the nearest of the many rills
He stoops ; ascending steam
Timely repels his hand,
For from its source it sprung, a boiling
tide.
A second course with better hap he tries,
The wave intensely cold
Tempts to a copious draught.
There was a virtue in the wave :
His limbs, that stiff with toil 100

Dragg'd heavy, from the copious draught
        received
    Lightness and supple strength.
O'erjoyed, and weening the benignant
        Power,
    Who sent the reinless steed,
Had blest these healing waters to his use,
    He laid him down to sleep,
Lull'd by the soothing and incessant
        sound,
The flow of many waters, blending oft
With shriller tones and deep low mur-
        murings,
    Which from the fountain caves 110
        In mingled melody   [came.
Like faery music, heard at midnight,

10

The sounds which last he heard at night
Awoke his recollection first at morn.
A scene of wonders lay before his eyes.
    In mazy windings o'er the vale
    A thousand streamlets stray'd,
        And in their endless course
Had intersected deep the stony soil,
With labyrinthine channels islanding 120
    A thousand rocks, which seem'd
Amid the multitudinous waters there
Like clouds that freckle o'er the summer
        sky,
The blue ethereal ocean circling each,
        And insulating all.

11

    Those islets of the living rock
        Were of a thousand shapes,
And Nature with her various tints
Diversified anew their thousand forms ;
    For some were green with moss, 130
Some ruddier tinged, or grey, or silver-
        white,
    And some with yellow lichens glow'd
        like gold,   [sun.
Some sparkled sparry radiance to the
    Here gush'd the fountains up,

Alternate light and blackness, like the
        play   [arms.
Of sunbeams on a warrior's burnish'd
Yonder the river roll'd, whose ample bed,
    Their sportive lingerings o'er,
Received and bore away the confluent
        rills.

12

This was a wild and wondrous scene, 140
    Strange and beautiful, as where
    By Oton-tala, like a sea of stars,
The hundred sources of Hoangho burst.
    High mountains closed the vale,
Bare rocky mountains, to all living
        things
Inhospitable ; on whose sides no herb
Rooted, no insect fed, no bird awoke
Their echoes, save the Eagle, strong of
        wing,
    A lonely plunderer, that afar
    Sought in the vales his prey.   150

13

Thither toward those mountains Thalaba
Following, as he believed, the path
        prescribed
    By Destiny, advanced.
Up a wide vale that led into their depths,
A stony vale between receding heights
        Of stone, he wound his way.
A cheerless place ! the solitary Bee,
Whose buzzing was the only sound of
        life,
    Flew there on restless wing,   [fix.
Seeking in vain one flower, whereon to

14

    Still Thalaba holds on ;   161
The winding vale now narrows on his
        view,
        And steeper of ascent,
Rightward and leftward rise the rocks,
    And now they meet across the vale.
    Was it the toil of human hands
    Had hewn a passage in the rock,

Through whose rude portal-way
The light of heaven was seen ?
Rude and low the portal-way ;   170
Beyond, the same ascending straits
Went winding up the wilds.

15

Still a bare, silent, solitary glen,
A fearful silence, and a solitude
That made itself be felt ;
And steeper now the ascent,
A rugged path, that tired
The straining muscles, toiling slowly up.
At length again a rock
Stretch'd o'er the narrow vale ;   180
There also had a portal-way been hewn,
But gates of massy iron barr'd the pass,
Huge, solid, heavy-hinged.

16

There hung a horn beside the gate,
Ivory-tipt and brazen-mouth'd ;
He took the ivory tip,
And through the brazen-mouth he
breath'd ;
Like a long thunder-peal,
From rock to rock rebounding rung the
blast ;
The gates of iron, by no human arm   190
Unfolded, turning on their hinges slow,
Disclosed the passage of the rock.
He enter'd, and the iron gates fell to,
And with a clap like thunder closed
him in.

17

It was a narrow winding way ;
Dim lamps suspended from the vault,
Lent to the gloom an agitated light.
Winding it pierced the rock,
A long descending path
By gates of iron closed ;   200
There also hung a horn beside
Of ivory tip and brazen mouth ;
Again he took the ivory tip,
And gave the brazen mouth its voice
again.

Not now in thunder spake the horn,
But breathed a sweet and thrilling
melody :
The gates flew open, and a flood of light
Rush'd on his dazzled eyes.

18

Was it to earthly Eden, lost so long,
The fated Youth had found his won-
drous way ?   210
But earthly Eden boasts
No terraced palaces,
No rich pavilions bright with woven gold,
Like these that in the vale
Rise amid odorous groves.
The astonish'd Thalaba,
Doubting as though an unsubstantial
dream
Beguiled him, closed his eyes,
And open'd them again ;
And yet uncertified,   220
He prest them close, and as he look'd
around
Question'd the strange reality again.
He did not dream ;
They still were there,
The glittering tents,
The odorous groves,
The gorgeous palaces.

19

And lo ! a man, reverend in comely age,
Advancing greets the youth.
' Favour'd of Fortune,' thus he said,
' go taste   230
The joys of Paradise !
The reinless steed that ranges o'er the
world,
Brings hither those alone for lofty deeds
Mark'd by their horoscope ; permitted
thus
A foretaste of the full beatitude,
That in heroic acts they may go on
More ardent, eager to return and reap
Endless enjoyment here, their destined
meed.

Favour'd of Fortune thou, go taste
    The joys of Paradise !'   240

20

This said, he turn'd away, and left
    The Youth in wonder mute;
For Thalaba stood mute,
    And passively received
The mingled joy which flow'd on every
        sense.
    Where'er his eye could reach,
Fair structures, rainbow-hued, arose ;
And rich pavilions through the opening
        woods
Gleam'd from their waving curtains
        sunny gold ;
And winding through the verdant vale,
    Went streams of liquid light ;   251
    And fluted cypresses rear'd up
      Their living obelisks ;
And broad-leav'd plane-trees in long
      colonnades
O'er-arch'd delightful walks,
Where round their trunks the thousand
      tendrill'd vine
Wound up and hung the boughs with
      greener wreaths,
    And clusters not their own. [eyes
Wearied with endless beauty, did his
Return for rest ? beside him teems the
      earth   260
With tulips, like the ruddy evening
      streak'd ;
And here the lily hangs her head of snow ;
    And here amid her sable cup
Shines the red-eye spot, like one
      brightest star,
The solitary twinkler of the night ;
    And here the rose expands
      Her paradise of leaves.

21

Then on his ear what sounds
    Of harmony arose !
Far music and the distance-mellow'd
      song   270

From bowers of merriment ;
    The waterfall remote ;
The murmuring of the leafy groves ;
    The single nightingale
Perch'd in the rosier by, so richly toned,
That never from that most melodious
      bird,
Singing a love-song to his brooding mate,
Did Thracian shepherd by the grave
    Of Orpheus hear a sweeter melody,
Though there the Spirit of the Sepulchre
All his own power infuse, to swell   281
    The incense that he loves.

22

And oh ! what odours the voluptuous
      vale
    Scatters from jasmine bowers,
    From yon rose wilderness,
From cluster'd henna and from orange
      groves,
That with such perfumes fill the breeze
    As Peris to their Sister bear,
When from the summit of some lofty
      tree
She hangs encaged, the captive of the
      Dives.   290
    They from their pinions shake
    The sweetness of celestial flowers,
And, as her enemies impure
From that impervious poison far away
Fly groaning with the torment, she the
      while
    Inhales her fragrant food.

23

Such odours flow'd upon the world,
When at Mohammed's nuptials, word
    Went forth in Heaven, to roll
    The everlasting gates of Paradise 300
Back on their living hinges, that its
      gales
Might visit all below ; the general bliss
Thrill'd every bosom, and the family
Of man, for once, partook one common
      joy.

24

Full of the bliss, yet still awake
To wonder, on went Thalaba ;
On every side the song of mirth,
The music of festivity,
Invite the passing youth.
Wearied at length with hunger and with
　　　　heat,　　　　　310
He enters in a banquet room,
Where round a fountain brink,
On silken carpets sate the festive train.
Instant through all his frame
Delightful coolness spread ;
The playing fount refresh'd
　　The agitated air ;
The very light came cool'd through
　　silvering panes　　[tinged ;
Of pearly shell, like the pale moon-beam
Or where the wine-vase fill'd the
　　　　aperture,　　　　320
Rosy as rising morn, or softer gleam
Of saffron, like the sunny evening mist :
Through every hue, and streak'd by all,
　　The flowing fountain play'd.
Around the water-edge
Vessels of wine, alternate placed,
Ruby and amber, tinged its little waves.
From golden goblets there
The guests sate quaffing the delicious
　　　　juice
　　Of Shiraz' golden grape.　　330

25

But Thalaba took not the draught ;
For rightly he knew had the Prophet
　　　　forbidden
That beverage, the mother of sins.
Nor did the urgent guests
Proffer a second time the liquid fire,
When in the youth's strong eye they saw
　　No moveable resolve.
Yet not uncourteous, Thalaba
Drank the cool draught of innocence,
That fragrant from its dewy vase　　340
Came purer than it left its native bed ;

And he partook the odorous fruits,
　For all rich fruits were there ;
　Water-melons rough of rind,
　Whose pulp the thirsty lip
　Dissolved into a draught ;
Pistachios from the heavy-cluster'd trees
Of Malavert, or Haleb's fertile soil ;
And Casbin's luscious grapes of amber
　　　hue,
　That many a week endure　　350
　The summer sun intense,
　Till by its powerful heat
All watery particles exhaled, alone
The strong essential sweetness ripens
　　　there.
Here cased in ice the apricot,
　A topaz, crystal-set :
　Here, on a plate of snow,
　The sunny orange rests ;
And still the aloes and the sandal-wood,
From golden censers, o'er the banquet
　　　room　　　360
　Diffuse their dying sweets.

26

Anon a troop of females form'd the dance,
Their ankles bound with bracelet-bells,
That made the modulating harmony.
Transparent garments to the greedy eye
　　Exposed their harlot limbs,
Which moved, in every wanton gesture
　　　skill'd.

27

With earnest eyes the banqueters
　Fed on the sight impure ;
　And Thalaba, he gazed,　　370
But in his heart he bore a talisman,
　Whose blessed alchemy
　To virtuous thoughts refined
The loose suggestions of the scene impure.
Oneiza's image swam before his sight,
　His own Arabian Maid.
He rose, and from the banquet room he
　　　rush'd,
　Tears coursed his burning cheek ;

And nature for a moment woke the
thought,
And murmur'd, that, from all domestic
joys   380
Estranged, he wander'd o'er the world
A lonely being, far from all he loved.
Son of Hodeirah, not among thy crimes
That momentary murmur shall be
written !

28

From tents of revelry,
From festal bowers, to solitude he ran ;
And now he came where all the rills
Of that well-water'd garden in one tide
Roll'd their collected waves.
     A straight and stately bridge   390
Stretch'd its long arches o'er the ample
stream.   [shade
Strong in the evening and distinct its
Lay on the watery mirror, and his eye
Saw it united with its parent pile,
One huge fantastic fabric. Drawing near,
Loud from the chambers of the bridge
below,
Sounds of carousal came and song,
And unveil'd women bade the advancing
youth
Come merry-make with them !
     Unhearing, or unheeding, he   400
Pass'd o'er with hurried pace,
And sought the shade and silence of the
grove.

29

Deserts of Araby !
His soul return'd to you.
He cast himself upon the earth,
And closed his eyes and call'd
The voluntary vision up.
     A cry, as of distress,
Aroused him ; loud it came and near !
He started up, he strung his bow,   410
He pluck'd an arrow forth.
Again a shriek . . a woman's shriek !
And lo ! she rushes through the trees,

Her veil is rent, her garments torn !
     The ravisher follows close.
' Prophet, save me ! save me, God !
Help ! help me, man ! ' to Thalaba she
cried ;
     Thalaba drew the bow.
The unerring arrow did its work of death.
Then turning to the woman, he beheld
His own Oneiza, his Arabian Maid. 421

THE SEVENTH BOOK

Now all is done ; bring home the Bride again,
   Bring home the triumph of our victory !
Bring home with you the glory of her gain,
   With joyance bring her, and with jollity.
Never had man more joyful day than this,
Whom Heaven would heap with bliss.
           SPENSER, *Epithalamium.*

1

FROM fear, and from amazement, and
           from joy,   [speech,
At length the Arabian Maid recovering
Threw around Thalaba her arms, and
           cried,
' My father ! O my father ! ' .. Thalaba
In wonder lost, yet fearing to enquire,
     Bent down his cheek on hers,
And their tears met, and mingled as
           they fell.

2

ONEIZA

At night they seized me, Thalaba ! in
           my sleep ; ..
Thou wert not near, .. and yet when
           in their grasp
I woke, my shriek of terror called on
           thee.   10
My father could not save me, .. an old
           man !   [my God,
And they were strong and many : .. O
The hearts they must have had to hear
           his prayers,
     And yet to leave him childless !

THALABA

We will seek him ;
We will return to Araby.

ONEIZA

Alas !
We should not find him, Thalaba ! Our
                            tent
Is desolate ! the wind hath heap'd
                the sands   [is left
Within its door ; the lizard's track
Fresh on the untrodden dust ; prowling
                by night   20
The tiger, as he passes, hears no
                            breath
Of man, and turns to search the vacancy.
Alas ! he strays a wretched wanderer
Seeking his child ! old man, he will
                            not rest, . .
He cannot rest, . . his sleep is misery, . .
His dreams are of my wretchedness, my
                            wrongs.
O Thalaba ! this is a wicked place !
Let us be gone !

THALABA

But how to pass again
The iron doors that opening at a breath
Gave easy entrance ? armies in their
                might   31
Would fail to move those hinges for
                            return.

ONEIZA

But we can climb the mountains that
                shut in
This dreadful garden.

THALABA

Are Oneiza's limbs
Equal to that long toil ?

ONEIZA

Oh I am strong,
Dear Thalaba ! for this . . fear gives me
                            strength,
And you are with me !

3

So she took his hand,   40
And gently drew him forward, and they
                            went
Toward the mountain chain.

4

It was broad moonlight, and obscure or
                            lost
The garden beauties lay,
But the great boundary rose, distinctly
                            mark'd.
These were no little hills,
No sloping uplands lifting to the sun
Their vineyards, with fresh verdure, and
                the shade
Of ancient woods, courting the loiterer
To win the easy ascent : stone moun-
                tains these,   50
Desolate rock on rock,
The burthens of the earth,
Whose snowy summits met the morning
                            beam
When night was in the vale, whose
                feet were fix'd   [beheld
In the world's foundations. Thalaba
The heights precipitous,
Impending crags, rocks unascendible,
And summits that had tired the eagle's
                            wing ;
' There is no way ! ' he said ;
                Paler Oneiza grew,   60
And hung upon his arm a feebler weight.

5

But soon again to hope
                Revives the Arabian Maid,
As Thalaba imparts the sudden thought.
' I pass'd a river,' cried the youth,
        ' A full and copious stream.
The flowing waters cannot be restrain'd,
And where they find or force their way,
        There we perchance may follow ;
                            thitherward
                The current roll'd along.'   70

So saying, yet again in hope
Quickening their eager steps,
They turn'd them thitherward.

6

Silent and calm the river roll'd along,
And at the verge arrived
Of that fair garden, o'er a rocky bed
Toward the mountain-base,
Still full and silent, held its even way.
But farther as they went its deepening
sound
Louder and louder in the distance rose,
As if it forced its stream   81
Struggling through crags along a narrow
pass.   [course
And lo! where raving o'er a hollow
The ever-flowing flood
Foams in a thousand whirlpools! There
adown
The perforated rock
Plunge the whole waters; so precipitous,
So fathomless a fall,
That their earth-shaking roar came
deaden'd up
Like subterranean thunders.   90

7

'Allah save us!'
Oneiza cried; 'there is no path for
man
From this accursed place!'
And as she spake, her joints
Were loosen'd, and her knees sunk under
her.
'Cheer up, Oneiza!' Thalaba replied;
'Be of good heart. We cannot fly
The dangers of the place,
But we can conquer them!'

8

And the young Arab's soul   100
Arose within him; 'What is he,' he
cried,   [delight,
'Who hath prepared this garden of
And wherefore are its snares?'

9

The Arabian Maid replied,
'The Women, when I enter'd, welcomed
me
To Paradise, by Aloadin's will
Chosen, like themselves, a Houri of the
Earth.   [phemies,
They told me, credulous of his blas-
That Aloadin placed them to reward
His faithful servants with the joys of
Heaven.   110
O Thalaba, and all are ready here
To wreak his wicked will, and work all
crimes!
How then shall we escape?'

10

'Woe to him!' cried the Appointed, a
stern smile
Darkening with stronger shades his
countenance;
'Woe to him! he hath laid his toils
To take the Antelope;
The Lion is come in!'

11

She shook her head, 'A Sorcerer he,
And guarded by so many! Thalaba, ..
And thou but one!'   120

12

He raised his hand to Heaven,
'Is there not God, Oneiza?
I have a Talisman, that, whoso bears,
Him, nor the Earthly, nor the Infernal
Powers
Of Evil, can cast down.
Remember, Destiny
Hath mark'd me from mankind!
Now rest in faith, and I will guard thy
sleep!'

13

So on a violet bank   130
The Arabian Maid laid down,
Her soft cheek pillow'd upon moss and
flowers.

She lay in silent prayer,
Till prayer had tranquillized her fears,
And sleep fell on her. By her side
    Silent sate Thalaba,
    And gazed upon the Maid,
    And as he gazed, drew in
New courage and intenser faith,   139
And waited calmly for the eventful day.

14

Loud sung the Lark, the awaken'd Maid
Beheld him twinkling in the morning
                                  light,
And wish'd for wings and liberty like his.
The flush of fear inflamed her cheek,
    But Thalaba was calm of soul,
        Collected for the work.
    He ponder'd in his mind
    How from Lobaba's breast
    His blunted arrow fell.
    Aloadin too might wear   150
    Spell perchance of equal power
    To blunt the weapon's edge.

15

    Beside the river-brink
Grew a young poplar, whose unsteady
                                  leaves
Varying their verdure to the gale,
    With silver glitter caught
        His meditating eye.
Then to Oneiza turn'd the youth,
    And gave his father's bow,
And o'er her shoulders slung   160
    The quiver arrow-stored.
' Me other weapon suits,' said he ;
' Bear thou the Bow : dear Maid,
The days return upon me, when these
                          shafts,   [palm
True to thy guidance, from the lofty
Brought down its cluster, and thy
                gladden'd eye,   [praise.
Exulting, turn'd to seek the voice of
Oh ! yet again, Oneiza, we shall share
Our desert-joys!' So saying, to the bank
    He moved, and stooping low,   170

With double grasp, hand below hand,
                          he clench'd,
        And from its watery soil
        Uptore the poplar trunk.

16

Then off he shook the clotted earth,
    And broke away the head
    And boughs, and lesser roots ;
        And lifting it aloft,
Wielded with able sway the massy club.
' Now for this child of Hell ! ' quoth
                              Thalaba ;
    ' Belike he shall exchange to-day   180
        His dainty Paradise
For other dwelling, and its cups of joy
    For the unallayable bitterness
        Of Zaccoum's fruit accurst.'

17

With that the Arabian youth and maid
Toward the centre of the garden went.
It chanced that Aloadin had convoked
        The garden-habitants,
    And with the assembled throng
Oneiza mingled, and the Appointed
                              Youth.   190
Unmark'd they mingled ; or if one
With busier finger to his neighbour notes
The quiver'd Maid, ' Haply,' he says,
' Some daughter of the Homerites,
Or one who yet remembers with delight
Her native tents of Himiar.'   ' Nay ! '
                              rejoins
His comrade, ' a love-pageant ! for the
                  man   [club
Mimics with that fierce eye and knotty
Some savage lion-tamer ; she forsooth
Must play the heroine of the years
                      of old ! '   200

18

Radiant with gems upon his throne of
                  gold   [head
    Sate Aloadin ; o'er the Sorcerer's
Hover'd a Bird, and in the fragrant air

Waved his wide winnowing wings,
A living canopy.
Large as the hairy Cassowar
Was that o'ershadowing Bird ;
So huge his talons, in their grasp
The Eagle would have hung a helpless
prey.
His beak was iron, and his plumes
Glitter'd like burnish'd gold,   211
And his eyes glow'd, as though an in-
ward fire
Shone through a diamond orb.

19

The blinded multitude
Adored the Sorcerer,
And bent the knee before him,
And shouted forth his praise ;
' Mighty art thou, the bestower of joy,
The Lord of Paradise ! '   219
Then Aloadin rose and waved his hand.
And they stood mute, and moveless,
In idolizing awe.

20

' Children of Earth,' he said,
' Whom I have guided here
By easier passage than the gate of Death,
The infidel Sultan, to whose lands
My mountains stretch their roots,
Blasphemes and threatens me.
Strong are his armies, many are his
guards,
Yet may a dagger find him.   230
Children of Earth, I tempt ye not
With the vain promise of a bliss unseen,
With tales of a hereafter Heaven,
Whence never Traveller hath return'd !
Have ye not tasted of the cup of joy
That in these groves of happiness
For ever over-mantling tempts
The ever-thirsty lip ?
Who is there here that by a deed
Of danger will deserve   240
The eternal joys of actual Paradise ? '

21

' I ! ' Thalaba exclaim'd ;
And springing forward, on the Sorcerer's
head
He dash'd his knotty club.

22

Aloadin fell not, though his skull
Was shattered by the blow,
For by some talisman
His miserable life imprison'd still
Dwelt in the body.   The astonish'd
crowd
Stand motionless with fear,   250
Expecting to behold
Immediate vengeance from the wrath
of Heaven.
And lo ! the Bird . . the monster Bird,
Soars up . . then pounces down
To seize on Thalaba !
Now, Oneiza, bend the bow,
Now draw the arrow home ! . .
True fled the arrow from Oneiza's hand ;
It pierc'd the monster Bird,
It broke the Talisman, . .   260
Then darkness cover'd all, . .
Earth shook, Heaven thunder'd, and
amid the yells
Of evil Spirits perished
The Paradise of Sin.

23

At last the earth was still ;
The yelling of the Demons ceased !
Opening the wreck and ruin to their
sight,
The darkness roll'd away. Alone in life,
Amid the desolation and the dead,
Stood the Destroyer and the Arabian
Maid.   270
They look'd around, the rocks were rent,
The path was open, late by magic closed ;
Awe-struck and silent down the stony
glen
They wound their thoughtful way.

24

Amid the vale below
Tents rose, and streamers play'd,
And javelins sparkled to the sun ;
And multitudes encamp'd
Swarm'd, far as eye could travel o'er the
plain.
There in his war pavilion sate   280
In council with his Chiefs
The Sultan of the Land.
Before his presence there a Captain led
Oneiza and the Appointed Youth.

25

' Obedient to our Lord's command,' said
he,   [began
' We pass'd toward the mountains, and
The ascending strait ; when suddenly
Earth shook,
And darkness, like the midnight, fell
around,
And fire and thunder came from Heaven,
As though the Retribution-day were
come.   290
After the terror ceased, and when with
hearts   [on,
Somewhat assured, again we ventured
This youth and woman met us on the
way.
They told us, that from Aloadin's hold
They came, on whom the judgement
stroke hath fallen,
He and his sinful Paradise at once
Destroy'd by them, the agents they of
Heaven.   [repeat
Therefore I brought them hither to
The tale before thy presence ; that as
search
Shall prove it false or faithful, to their
merit   l300
Thou mayest reward them.'
' Be it done to us,'
Thalaba answer'd, ' as the truth shall
prove ! '

26

The Sultan while he spake
Fix'd on him the proud eye of sove-
reignty ;
' If thou hast play'd with us,
By Allah and by Ali, Death shall seal
The lying lips for ever ! But if the thing
Be as thou say'st, Arabian, thou shalt
stand
Next to ourself ! ' . .   310
Hark ! while he speaks, the cry,
The lengthening cry, the increasing
shout
Of joyful multitudes !
Breathless and panting to the tent
The bearer of good tidings comes,
' O Sultan, live for ever ! be thy foes
Like Aloadin all !
The wrath of God hath smitten him.'

27

Joy at the welcome tale
Shone in the Sultan's cheek ;   320
' Array the Arabian in the robe
Of honour,' he exclaim'd,
' And place a chain of gold around his
neck,
And bind around his brow the diadem,
And mount him on my steed of state,
And lead him through the camp,
And let the Heralds go before and cry,
Thus shall the Sultan reward
The man who serves him well ! '

28

Then in the purple robe   330
They vested Thalaba,
And hung around his neck the golden
chain,
And bound his forehead with the diadem,
And on the royal steed
They led him through the camp,
And Heralds went before and cried,
' Thus shall the Sultan reward
The man who serves him well ! '

29

When from the pomp of triumph
    And presence of the King,   340
Thalaba sought the tent allotted him,
Thoughtful the Arabian Maid beheld
    His animated eye,
    His cheek inflamed with pride.
' Oneiza ! ' cried the youth,
'The King hath done according to his
        word,
And made me in the land
Next to himself be named ! . .
But why that serious melancholy smile ?
Oneiza, when I heard the voice that
        gave me   350
Honour, and wealth, and fame, the
        instant thought   [hear
Arose to fill my joy, that thou would'st
The tidings, and be happy.'

ONEIZA
Thalaba,
Thou would'st not have me mirthful !
    Am I not
An orphan, . . among strangers ?

THALABA
But with me !

ONEIZA
My Father ! . .

THALABA
Nay, be comforted ! Last night
To what wert thou exposed ! in what a
        peril   [wealth,
The morning found us ! . . safety, honour,
These now are ours. This instant who
        thou wert   361
The Sultan ask'd. I told him from our
        childhood
We had been plighted ; . . was I wrong,
        Oneiza ?
And when he said with bounties he
        would heap
Our nuptials, . . wilt thou blame me if
    I blest

His will, that bade me fix the marriage
        day ! . .
    In tears, my love ? . .

ONEIZA
REMEMBER, DESTINY
HATH MARK'D THEE FROM MANKIND !

THALABA
Perhaps when Aloadin was destroy'd
The mission ceased ; and therefore
        Providence   371
With its rewards and blessings strews
        my path
Thus for the accomplished service.

ONEIZA
Thalaba !

THALABA
Or if haply not, yet whither should I go?
Is it not prudent to abide in peace
    Till I am summon'd ?

ONEIZA
Take me to the Deserts !

THALABA
But Moath is not there ; and would'st
        thou dwell   [might seek
In a stranger's tent ? thy father then
In long and fruitless wandering for his
        child.   381

ONEIZA
Take me then to Mecca !
    There let me dwell a servant of the
        Temple.   [eye
Bind thou thyself my veil, . . to human
It never shall be lifted. There, whilst
        thou   [prayers,
Shalt go upon thine enterprize, my
Dear Thalaba ! shall rise to succour thee,
And I shall live, . . if not in happiness,
    Surely in hope.

THALABA
Oh think of better things !   390
The will of Heaven is plain ! by won-
        drous ways   [voice
It led us here, and soon the common

Will tell what we have done, and how
          we dwell
Under the shadow of the Sultan's wing ;
So shall thy father hear the fame, and
          find us   [tears !
What he hath wish'd us ever . . Still in
Still that unwilling eye ! nay . . nay . .
          Oneiza . .
I dare not leave thee other than my
          own, . .
My wedded wife.   Honour and gratitude
As yet preserve the Sultan from all
          thoughts   400
That sin against thee ; but so sure as
          Heaven
Hath gifted thee above all other maids
With loveliness, so surely would those
          thoughts
Of wrong arise within the heart of Power.
If thou art mine, Oneiza, we are safe,
But else, there is no sanctuary could
          save.

ONEIZA
Thalaba !   Thalaba !

30
With song, with music, and with dance,
          The bridal pomp proceeds.
     Following the deep-veil'd Bride   410
          Fifty female slaves attend
          In costly robes that gleam
               With interwoven gold,
          And sparkle far with gems.
An hundred slaves behind them bear
Vessels of silver and vessels of gold,
And many a gorgeous garment gay,
     The presents that the Sultan gave.
     On either hand the pages go   419
With torches flaring through the gloom,
And trump and timbrel merriment
     Accompanies their way ;
And multitudes with loud acclaim
     Shout blessings on the Bride.
And now they reach the palace pile,
     The palace home of Thalaba,

And now the marriage feast is spread,
And from the finish'd banquet now
     The wedding guests are gone.

31
Who comes from the bridal chamber ? . .
     It is Azrael, the Angel of Death.   431

THE EIGHTH BOOK

Quas potius decuit nostro te inferre sepul-
          chro,
     Petronilla, tibi spargimus has lacrimas.
Spargimus has lacrimas moesti monumenta
          parentis,—
     Et tibi pro thalamo sternimus hunc tumu-
          lum.
Sperabam genitor taedas praeferre jugales,
     Et titulo patris jungere nomen avi ;
Heu ! gener est Orcus ; quique, O dulcis-
          sima ! per te
     Se sperabat avum, desinit esse pater.
                    Joach. Bellaius.

1
WOMAN
Go not among the tombs, Old Man !
     There is a madman there.

OLD MAN
Will he harm me if I go ?

WOMAN
Not he, poor miserable man !
But 'tis a wretched sight to see
     His utter wretchedness.
For all day long he lies on a grave,
     And never is he seen to weep,
     And never is he heard to groan,
     Nor ever at the hour of prayer   10
Bends his knee nor moves his lips.
I have taken him food for charity,
     And never a word he spake :
     But yet so ghastly he look'd,
That I have awaken'd at night
With the dream of his ghastly eyes.
Now, go not among the Tombs, Old Man !

OLD MAN
Wherefore has the wrath of God
     So sorely stricken him ?

WOMAN

He came a stranger to the land, 20
And did good service to the Sultan,
And well his service was rewarded.
The Sultan named him next himself,
And gave a palace for his dwelling,
And dower'd his bride with rich domains.
But on his wedding night
There came the Angel of Death.
Since that hour, a man distracted
Among the sepulchres he wanders.
The Sultan, when he heard the tale,
Said that for some untold crime 31
Judgement thus had stricken him,
And asking Heaven forgiveness
That he had shown him favour,
Abandon'd him to want.

OLD MAN

A Stranger did you say ?

WOMAN

An Arab born, like you.
But go not among the Tombs,
For the sight of his wretchedness
Might make a hard heart ache ! 40

OLD MAN

Nay, nay, I never yet have shunn'd
A countryman in distress !
And the sound of his dear native tongue
May be like the voice of a friend.

2

Then to the Sepulchre
Whereto she pointed him,
Old Moath bent his way.
By the tomb lay Thalaba,
In the light of the setting eve ;
The sun, and the wind, and the rain, 50
Had rusted his raven locks ;
His cheeks were fallen in,
His face-bones prominent ;
Reclined against the tomb he lay,
And his lean fingers play'd,
Unwitting, with the grass that grew
beside.

3

The Old Man knew him not,
But drawing near him, said,
' Countryman, peace be with thee ! '
The sound of his dear native tongue 60
Awaken'd Thalaba ;
He raised his countenance,
And saw the good Old Man,
And he arose and fell upon his neck,
And groan'd in bitterness.
Then Moath knew the youth,
And fear'd that he was childless ; and
he turned
His asking eyes, and pointed to the
tomb.
' Old Man ! ' cried Thalaba,
' Thy search is ended here ! ' 70

4

The father's cheek grew white,
And his lip quiver'd with the misery ;
Howbeit, collectedly, with painful voice
He answer'd, ' God is good ! His will
be done ! '

5

The woe in which he spake,
The resignation that inspired his speech,
They soften'd Thalaba.
' Thou hast a solace in thy grief,' he
cried,
' A comforter within !
Moath ! thou seest me here, 80
Deliver'd to the Evil Powers,
A God-abandon'd wretch.'

6

The Old Man look'd at him incredulous.
' Nightly,' the youth pursued,
' Thy daughter comes to drive me to
despair.
Moath, thou thinkest me mad ;
But when the Cryer from the Minaret
Proclaims the midnight hour,
Hast thou a heart to see her ? '

7

In the Meidan now   90
The clang of clarions and of drums
Accompanied the Sun's descent.
' Dost thou not pray, my son ? '
    Said Moath, as he saw
The white flag waving on the neigh-
    bouring Mosque :
    Then Thalaba's eye grew wild,
' Pray ! ' echoed he ; ' I must not pray ! '
And the hollow groan he gave
    Went to the Old Man's heart.
And bowing down his face to earth,
In fervent agony he call'd on God. 101

8

A night of darkness and of storms !
    Into the Chamber of the Tomb
    Thalaba led the Old Man,
    To roof him from the rain.
A night of storms ! the wind
Swept through the moonless sky,
And moan'd among the pillar'd sepul-
    chres ;
    And in the pauses of its sweep
    They heard the heavy rain   110
    Beat on the monument above.
    In silence on Oneiza's grave
Her Father and her husband sate.

9

The Cryer from the Minaret
    Proclaim'd the midnight hour.
' Now, now ! ' cried Thalaba ;
And o'er the chamber of the tomb
    There spread a lurid gleam,
Like the reflection of a sulphur fire ;
    And in that hideous light   120
Oneiza stood before them. It was She, . .
Her very lineaments, . . and such as death
Had changed them, livid cheeks, and
    lips of blue ;
    But in her eyes there dwelt
    Brightness more terrible
Than all the loathsomeness of death.
' Still art thou living, wretch ? '

In hollow tones she cried to Thalaba ;
' And must I nightly leave my grave
    To tell thee, still in vain,   130
    God hath abandon'd thee ? '

10

' This is not she ! ' the Old Man ex-
    claim'd ;
    ' A Fiend ; a manifest Fiend ! '
And to the youth he held his lance ;
    ' Strike, and deliver thyself ! '
    ' Strike HER ! ' cried Thalaba,
    And, palsied of all power,
Gazed fixedly upon the dreadful form.
' Yea, strike her ! ' cried a voice, whose
    tones
Flow'd with such sudden healing through
    his soul,   140
    As when the desert shower
    From death deliver'd him ;
But unobedient to that well-known voice,
    His eye was seeking it,
    When Moath, firm of heart,
Perform'd the bidding : through the
    vampire corpse
    He thrust his lance ; it fell,
    And howling with the wound,
    Its fiendish tenant fled.
A sapphire light fell on them,   150
And garmented with glory, in their sight
    Oneiza's Spirit stood.

11

' O Thalaba ! ' she cried,
    ' Abandon not thyself !
Would'st thou for ever lose me ? . . O
    my husband,
    Go and fulfil thy quest,
That in the Bowers of Paradise
    I may not look for thee
    In vain, nor wait thee long.'

12

To Moath then the Spirit   160
Turn'd the dark lustre of her heavenly
    eyes :

' Short is thy destined path,
O my dear Father ! to the abode of bliss.
Return to Araby,
There with the thought of death
Comfort thy lonely age,
And Azrael, the Deliverer, soon
Will visit thee in peace.'

13

They stood with earnest eyes,   169
And arms out-reaching, when again
The darkness closed around them.
The soul of Thalaba revived ;
He from the floor his quiver took,
And as he bent the bow, exclaim'd,
' Was it the over-ruling Providence
That in the hour of frenzy led my hands
Instinctively to this ?   [anew
To-morrow, and the sun shall brace
The slacken'd cord, that now sounds
loose and damp ;   179
To-morrow, and its livelier tone will sing,
In tort vibration to the arrow's flight.
I . . but I also, with recover'd health
Of heart, shall do my duty.
My Father ! here I leave thee then ! '
he cried,
' And not to meet again,
Till at the gate of Paradise
The eternal union of our joys commence.
We parted last in darkness ! ' . . and
the youth
Thought with what other hopes ;
But now his heart was calm,   190
For on his soul a heavenly hope had
dawn'd.

14

The Old Man answered nothing, but he
held
His garment, and to the door
Of the Tomb Chamber followed him.
The rain had ceased, the sky was wild,
Its black clouds broken by the storm.
And, lo ! it chanced, that in the chasm
Of Heaven between, a star,

Leaving along its path continuous light,
Shot eastward. ' See my guide ! ' quoth
Thalaba ;   200
And turning, he received
Old Moath's last embrace,   [Man.
And the last blessing of the good Old

15

Evening was drawing nigh,
When an old Dervise, sitting in the sun
At his cell door, invited for the night
The traveller ; in the sun
He spread the plain repast,
Rice and fresh grapes, and at their feet
there flowed
The brook of which they drank.   210

16

So as they sate at meal,
With song, with music, and with dance,
A wedding train went by ;
The deep-veil'd bride, the female slaves,
The torches of festivity,
And trump and timbrel merriment
Accompanied their way.
The good old Dervise gave
A blessing as they pass'd ;
But Thalaba look'd on,   220
And breathed a low deep groan, and hid
his face.   [felt
The Dervise had known sorrow, and he
Compassion ; and his words
Of pity and of piety
Open'd the young man's heart,
And he told all his tale.

17

' Repine not, O my Son ! ' the Old Man
replied,
' That Heaven hath chasten'd thee. Be-
hold this vine,
I found it a wild tree, whose wanton
strength
Had swoln into irregular twigs   230
And bold excrescences,
And spent itself in leaves and little rings,

So in the flourish of its outwardness
Wasting the sap and strength
That should have given forth fruit.
But when I pruned the plant,
Then it grew temperate in its vain ex-
pense   [see'st,
Of useless leaves, and knotted, as thou
Into these full clear clusters, to repay
The hand that wisely wounded it.
Repine not, O my Son !   241
In wisdom and in mercy Heaven inflicts
Its painful remedies.'

18

Then pausing, . . ' Whither goest thou
now ? ' he ask'd.
' I know not,' answered Thalaba ;
' My purpose is to hold
Straight on, secure of this,
That travel where I will, I cannot stray,
For Destiny will lead my course aright.'

19

' Far be it from me,' the Old Man
replied,   250
' To shake that pious confidence ;
And yet, if knowledge may be gain'd,
methinks
Thy course should be to seek it painfully.
In Kaf the Simorg hath his dwelling
place,   [seen
The all-knowing Bird of Ages, who hath
The World, with all its children, thrice
destroy'd.
Long is the path,
And difficult the way, of danger full ;
But that unerring Bird
Could to a certain end   260
Direct thy weary search.'

20

Easy assent the youth
Gave to the words of wisdom ; and
behold   [Kaf.
At dawn, the adventurer on his way to
And he hath travelled many a day,

And many a river swum over,
And many a mountain ridge hath crost,
And many a measureless plain ;
And now amid the wilds advanced,
Long is it since his eyes   270
Have seen the trace of man.

21

Cold ! cold ! 'tis a chilly clime
That the youth in his journey hath
reach'd,
And he is aweary now,
And faint for lack of food.
Cold ! cold ! there is no Sun in Heaven,
A heavy and uniform cloud
Overspreads the face of the sky,
And the snows are beginning to fall.
Dost thou wish for thy deserts, O Son of
Hodeirah ?   280
Dost thou long for the gales of Arabia ?
Cold ! cold ! his blood flows languidly,
His hands are red, his lips are blue,
His feet are sore with the frost.
Cheer thee ! cheer thee ! Thalaba !
A little yet bear up !

22

All waste ! no sign of life
But the track of the wolf and the bear !
No sound but the wild, wild wind,
And the snow crunching under his feet !
Night is come ; neither moon, nor stars,
Only the light of the snow !   292
But behold a fire in a cave of the hill,
A heart-reviving fire ;
And thither with strength renew'd
Thalaba presses on.

23

He found a Woman in the cave,
A solitary Woman,
Who by the fire was spinning,
And singing as she spun.   300
The pine boughs were cheerfully blazing,
And her face was bright with the flame ;
Her face was as a Damsel's face,

And yet her hair was grey.
She bade him welcome with a smile,
And still continued spinning,
And singing as she spun.
The thread the woman drew
Was finer than the silkworm's,
Was finer than the gossamer ;   310
The song she sung was low and sweet,
But Thalaba knew not the words.

24

He laid his bow before the hearth,
For the string was frozen stiff ;
He took the quiver from his neck,
For the arrow-plumes were iced.
Then as the cheerful fire
Revived his languid limbs,
The adventurer ask'd for food.
The Woman answer'd him,   320
And still her speech was song :
' The She Bear she dwells near to me,
And she hath cubs, one, two, and three ;
She hunts the deer, and brings him here,
And then with her I make good cheer ;
And now to the chase the She Bear is
      gone,
And she with her prey will be here anon.'

25

She ceased her spinning while she spake ;
And when she had answer'd him,
Again her fingers twirl'd the thread,
And again the Woman began,   331
In low, sweet tones to sing
The unintelligible song.

26

The thread she spun it gleam'd like gold
In the light of the odorous fire,
Yet was it so wondrously thin,
That, save when it shone in the light,
You might look for it closely in vain.
The youth sate watching it,
And she observed his wonder,   340
And then again she spake,
And still her speech was song ;

' Now twine it round thy hands I say,
Now twine it round thy hands I pray !
My thread is small, my thread is fine,
But he must be
A stronger than thee,
Who can break this thread of mine ! '

27

And up she raised her bright blue eyes,
And sweetly she smiled on him,   350
And he conceived no ill ;
And round and round his right hand,
And round and round his left,
He wound the thread so fine.
And then again the Woman spake,
And still her speech was song,
' Now thy strength, O Stranger, strain !
Now then break the slender chain.'

28

Thalaba strove, but the thread
By magic hands was spun,   360
And in his cheek the flush of shame
Arose, commixt with fear.
She beheld and laugh'd at him
And then again she sung,
' My thread is small, my thread is fine,
But he must be
A stronger than thee,
Who can break this thread of mine ! '

29

And up she raised her bright blue eyes,
And fiercely she smiled on him :   370
' I thank thee, I thank thee, Hodeirah's
      son !   [undone,
I thank thee for doing what can't be
For binding thyself in the chain I have
      spun ! '
Then from his head she wrench'd
A lock of his raven hair,
And cast it in the fire,
And cried aloud as it burnt,
' Sister ! Sister ! hear my voice !
Sister ! Sister ! come and rejoice !
The thread is spun,   380

The prize is won,
The work is done,
For I have made captive Hodeirah's
Son.'

30

Borne in her magic car
The Sister Sorceress came,
Khawla, the fiercest of the Sorcerer brood.
She gazed upon the youth,
She bade him break the slender thread,
She laugh'd aloud for scorn,
She clapt her hands for joy,   390

31

The She Bear from the chase came in,
She bore the prey in her bloody mouth,
She laid it at Maimuna's feet,
And then look'd up with wistful eyes
As if to ask her share.
'There! there!' quoth Maimuna,
And pointing to the prisoner-youth,
She spurn'd him with her foot,
And bade her make her meal.
But then their mockery fail'd them,   400
And anger and shame arose;
For the She Bear fawn'd on Thalaba,
And quietly lick'd his hand.

32

The grey-hair'd Sorceress stampt the
ground,
And call'd a Spirit up;
'Shall we bear the Enemy
To the dungeon dens below?'

SPIRIT

Woe! woe! to our Empire woe!
If ever he tread the caverns below.

MAIMUNA

Shall we leave him fetter'd here   410
With hunger and cold to die?

SPIRIT

Away from thy lonely dwelling fly!
Here I see a danger nigh,
That he should live and thou should'st
die.

MAIMUNA

Whither then must we bear the foe?

SPIRIT

To Mohareb's island go,
There shalt thou secure the foe,
There prevent thy future woe.

33

Then in the Car they threw
The fetter'd Thalaba,   420
And took their seats, and set
Their feet upon his neck;
Maimuna held the reins,
And Khawla shook the scourge,
And away! away! away!

34

They were no steeds of mortal race
That drew the magic car
With the swiftness of feet and of wings.
The snow-dust rises behind them,
The ice-rock's splinters fly,   430
And hark in the valley below
The sound of their chariot wheels. . .
And they are far over the mountains!
Away! away! away!
The Demons of the air
Shout their joy as the Sisters pass,
The Ghosts of the Wicked that wander
by night
Flit over the magic car.

35

Away! away! away!
Over the hills and the plains,   440
Over the rivers and rocks,
Over the sands of the shore;
The waves of ocean heave
Under the magic steeds;
With unwet hoofs they trample the deep,
And now they reach the Island coast,
And away to the city the Monarch's abode.
Open fly the city gates,
Open fly the iron doors,
The doors of the palace-court.   450
Then stopt the charmed car.

36

The Monarch heard the chariot wheels,
And forth he came to greet
The mistress whom he served.
He knew the captive youth,
And Thalaba beheld
Mohareb in the robes of royalty,
Whom erst his arm had thrust
Down the bitumen pit.

THE NINTH BOOK

Conscience ! . .
Poor plodding Priests and preaching Friars
may make
Their hollow pulpits and the empty aisles
Of churches ring with that round word : but
we,   .
That draw the subtile and more piercing air
In that sublimed region of a court,
Know all is good we make so, and go on
Secured by the prosperity of our crimes.
B. JONSON, *Mortimer's Fall.*

1

' Go up my Sister Maimuna,
Go up and read the stars ! '

2

Lo ! on the terrace of the topmost tower
She stands ; her darkening eyes,
Her fine face raised to Heaven ;
Her white hair flowing like the silver
streams
That streak the northern night.

3

They hear her coming tread,
They lift their asking eyes :
Her face is serious, her unwilling lips
Slow to the tale of ill.   11
' What hast thou read ? what hast thou
read ? '
Quoth Khawla in alarm.
' Danger . . death . . judgement ! '
Maimuna replied.

4

' Is that the language of the lights of
Heaven ? '
Exclaim'd the sterner Witch ;
' Creatures of Allah, they perform his
will,   [daunt
And with their lying menaces would
Our credulous folly . . . Maimuna,
I never liked this uncongenial lore ! 20
Better befits to make the Sacrifice
Of Divination ; so shall I
Be mine own Oracle.
Command the victims thou, O King !
Male and female they must be,
Thou knowest the needful rites.
Meanwhile I purify the place.'

5

The Sultan went ; the Sorceress rose,
And North, and South, and East, and
West,
She faced the points of Heaven ; 30
And ever where she turn'd
She laid her hand upon the wall ;
And up she look'd, and smote the air,
And down she stoopt, and smote the
floor.
' To Eblis and his servants
I consecrate the place ;
Let enter none but they !
Whatever hath the breath of life,
Whatever hath the sap of life,
Let it be blasted and die ! '   40

6

Now all is prepared ;
Mohareb returns,
The Circle is drawn,
The Victims have bled,
The Youth and the Maid.
She in the circle holds in either hand,
Clench'd by the hair, a head,
The heads of the Youth and the Maid.
' Go out, ye lights ! ' quoth Khawla,
And in darkness began the spell. 5c

7

With spreading arms she whirls around
Rapidly, rapidly,
Ever around and around ;
And loudly she calls the while,
'Eblis! Eblis!'
Loudly, incessantly,
Still she calls, 'Eblis! Eblis!'
Giddily, giddily, still she whirls,
Loudly, incessantly, still she calls ;
The motion is ever the same,   60
Ever around and around ;
The calling is still the same,
Still it is, 'Eblis! Eblis!'
Till her voice is a shapeless yell,
And dizzily rolls her brain,
And now she is full of the Fiend.
She stops, she rocks, she reels !
Look ! look ! she appears in the dark-
ness !
Her flamy hairs curl up
All living, like the Meteor's locks of
light !   70
Her eyes are like the sickly Moon !

8

It is her lips that move,
Her tongue that shapes the sound ;
But whose is the Voice that proceeds ? . .
'Ye may hope and ye may fear,
The danger of his stars is near.
Sultan ! if he perish, woe !
Fate hath written one death-blow
For Mohareb and the Foe !
Triumph ; triumph ! only she   80
That knit his bonds can set him free.'

9

She spake the Oracle,
And senselessly she fell.
They knelt in care beside her, . .
Her Sister and the King ;
They sprinkled her palms with water,
They wetted her nostrils with blood.

10

She wakes as from a dream,
She asks the utter'd voice ;
But when she heard, an anger and a
grief   90
Darken'd her wrinkling brow.
'Then let him live in long captivity !'
She answer'd : but Mohareb's quicken'd
eye
Perused her sullen countenance,
That lied not with the lips.
A miserable man !
What boots it that in central caves,
The Powers of Evil at his Baptism
pledged
The Sacrament of Hell ?
His death secures them now.   100
What boots it that they gave
Abdaldar's guardian ring,
When, through another's life,
The blow may reach his own ?

11

He sought the dungeon cell
Where Thalaba was laid.
'Twas the grey morning twilight, and
the voice
Of Thalaba in prayer [his ear.
With words of hallow'd import smote
The grating of the heavy hinge   110
Roused not the Arabian youth ;
Nor lifted he his earthward face,
At sound of coming feet.
Nor did Mohareb with unholy speech
Disturb the duty : silent, spirit-awed,
Envious, heart-humbled, he beheld
The peace which piety alone can give.

12

When Thalaba, the perfect rite per-
form'd, [Island-Chief :
Raised his calm eye, then spake the
'Arab ! my guidance through the
dangerous Cave   120
Thy service overpaid,

An unintended friend in enmity.
The Hand that caught thy ring
Received and bore me to the scene I
    sought.
Now know me grateful. I return
That amulet, thy only safety here.'

13

Artful he spake, with show of gratitude
    Veiling the selfish deed.
    Lock'd in his magic chain,
Thalaba on his passive powerless hand
    Received again the Spell.   131
Remembering then with what an
    ominous faith
First he drew on the ring,
The youth repeats his words of augury ;
' In God's name and the Prophet's ! be
    its power   [evil,
Good, let it serve the righteous ! if for
God and my trust in Him shall hallow it,
    Blindly the wicked work
    The righteous will of Heaven ! '
    So Thalaba received again   140
    The written ring of gold.

14

    Thoughtful awhile Mohareb stood,
    And eyed the captive youth.
Then, building skilfully sophistic speech,
Thus he began. ' Brave art thou,
    Thalaba !   [would buy
And wherefore are we foes ? . . for I
Thy friendship at a princely price, and
    make thee
    To thine own welfare wise.
Hear me ! in Nature are two hostile
    Gods,
Makers and Masters of existing things,
    Equal in power : . . nay, hear me
    patiently ! . .   151
Equal . . for look around thee ! The
    same Earth   [Camel finds
Bears fruit and poison ; where the
His fragrant food, the horned Viper
    there

Sucks in the juice of death : the
    Elements
Now serve the use of man, and now
    assert   [hear
Dominion o' er his weakness : dost thou
The sound of merriment and nuptial
    song ? [mourner's cry,
From the next house proceeds the
Lamenting o' er the dead. Say'st thou
    that Sin   160
Enter'd the world of Allah ? that the
    Fiend,
Permitted for a season, prowls for prey ?
When to thy tent the venomous
    serpent creeps,   [so,
Dost thou not crush the reptile ? Even
Be sure, had Allah crush'd his Enemy,
But that the power was wanting. From
    the first,
Eternal as themselves their warfare is ;
To the end it must endure. Evil and
    Good . .   [the strife
What are they, Thalaba, but words ? in
Of Angels, as of Men, the weak are
    guilty ;   170
Power must decide. The Spirits of the
    Dead
Quitting their mortal mansion, enter
    not,   [seat
As falsely ye are preach'd, their final
Of bliss, or bale ; nor in the sepulchre
Sleep they the long, long sleep : each
    joins the host
Of his great leader, aiding in the war
    Whose fate involves his own.
    Woe to the vanquish'd then !
Woe to the sons of man who follow'd
    him !   [eternity,
    They, with their Leader, through
    Must howl in central fires.   181
Thou, Thalaba, hast chosen ill thy part,
If choice it may be call'd, where will
    was not,
Nor searching doubt, nor judgement
    wise to weigh.

Hard is the service of the Power,
                beneath   [discipline
Whose banners thou wert born; his
Severe, yea cruel; and his wages, rich
Only in promise; who hath seen the
                pay?   [ours,
For us .. the pleasures of the world are
Riches and rule, the kingdoms of the
                Earth.   190
We met in Babylon adventurers both,
Each zealous for the hostile Power
                he served: [art,
We meet again; thou feelest what thou
Thou seest what I am, the Sultan here,
The Lord of Life and Death.
Abandon him who has abandon'd thee,
And be, as I am, great among
                mankind!'

15

The Captive did not, hasty to confute,
Break off that subtle speech;
But when the expectant silence of the
                King   200
        Look'd for his answer, then spake
                Thalaba.
'And this then is thy faith! this mon-
                strous creed!   [Stars,
This lie against the Sun, and Moon, and
And Earth, and Heaven! Blind man,
        who canst not see
How all things work the best! who
        wilt not know, [whate'er
That in the Manhood of the World,
Of folly mark'd its Infancy, of vice
Sullied its Youth, ripe Wisdom shall
                cast off,   [safe.
Stablish'd in good, and, knowing evil,
Sultan Mohareb, yes, ye have me here
In chains; but not forsaken, though
                opprest;   211
Cast down, but not destroy'd. Shall
                danger daunt,
Shall death dismay his soul, whose life
        is given

For God, and for his brethren of man-
                kind?
Alike rewarded, in that holy cause,
The Conqueror's and the Martyr's palm
                above   [my blood
Beam with one glory. Hope ye that
Can quench the dreaded flame? and
                know ye not, [and Wise,
That leagued against ye are the Just
And all Good Actions of all ages past,
Yea, your own crimes, and Truth, and
                God in Heaven?'   221

16

'Slave!' quoth Mohareb, and his lip
        Quiver'd with eager wrath,
'I have thee! thou shalt feel my power,
        And in thy dungeon loathsomeness
        Rot piece-meal, limb from limb!'
        And out the Tyrant rushes,
        And all impatient of the thoughts
        That canker'd in his heart,
        Seeks in the giddiness of boisterous
                sport   230
Short respite from the avenging power
                within.

17

        What Woman is she
        So wrinkled and old,
        That goes to the wood?
        She leans on her staff
        With a tottering step,
        She tells her bead-string slow
        Through fingers dull'd by age.
        The wanton boys bemock her;
        The babe in arms that meets her 240
        Turns round with quick affright
        And clings to his nurse's neck.

18

        Hark! hark! the hunter's cry;
        Mohareb has gone to the chase.
        The dogs, with eager yelp,
        Are struggling to be free;
        The hawks in frequent stoop

Token their haste for flight ;
And couchant on the saddle-bow,
With tranquil eyes and talons sheathed,
The ounce expects his liberty.   251

19

Propt on the staff that shakes
Beneath her trembling weight,
The Old Woman sees them pass.
Halloa ! halloa !
The game is up !
The dogs are loosed,
The deer bounds over the plain :
The dogs pursue
Far, far behind   260
Though at full stretch,
With eager speed,
Far, far behind.
But lo ! the Falcon o'er his head
Hovers with hostile wings,
And buffets him with blinding strokes !
Dizzy with the deafening strokes
In blind and interrupted course,
Poor beast, he struggles on ;
And now the dogs are nigh !   270
How his heart pants ! you see
The panting of his heart ;
And tears like human tears
Roll down, along the big veins fever-
swoln ;   [dun hide ;
And now the death-sweat darkens his
His fear, his groans, his agony, his death,
Are the sport, and the joy, and the
triumph !

20

Halloa ! another prey,
The nimble Antelope !
The ounce is freed ; one spring,   280
And his talons are sheathed in her
shoulders,
And his teeth are red in her gore.
There came a sound from the wood,
Like the howl of the winter wind at
night,
Around a lonely dwelling ;

The ounce, whose gums were warm in
his prey,
He hears the summoning sound.
In vain his master's voice,
No longer dreaded now,
Calls and recalls with threatful tone ;
Away to the forest he goes ;   291
For that Old Woman had laid [lips,
Her shrivell'd finger on her shrivell'd
And whistled with a long, long breath ;
And that long breath was the sound
Like the howl of the winter wind at
night,
Around a lonely dwelling.

21

Mohareb knew her not,
As to the chase he went,
The glance of his proud eye   300
Passing in scorn o'er age and wretched-
ness.
She stands in the depth of the wood.
And panting to her feet,
Fawning and fearful, creeps
The ounce by charms constrain'd.
Well may'st thou fear, and vainly dost
thou fawn !
Her form is changed, her visage new,
Her power, her art the same !
It is Khawla that stands in the wood.

22

She knew the place where the Mandrake
grew,   310
And round the neck of the ounce,
And round the Mandrake's head,
She tightens the ends of her cord.
Her ears are closed with wax,
And her prest finger fastens them,
Deaf as the Adder, when, with grounded
head,
And circled form, both avenues of sound
Barr'd safely, one slant eye
Watches the charmer's lips   319
Waste on the wind his baffled witchery,
The spotted ounce so beautiful,

Springs forceful from the scourge ;
With that the dying plant all agony,
Feeling its life-strings crack,
Utter'd the unimaginable groan
That none can hear and live.

23

Then from her victim servant Khawla
　　　　loosed　　　　[hand,
The precious poison.　Next with naked
She pluck'd the boughs of the man-
　　　chineel ;
And of the wormy wax she took, 330
That, from the perforated tree forced
　　　out,
Bewray'd its insect-parent's work within.

24

In a cavern of the wood she sits,
And moulds the wax to human form ;
And, as her fingers kneaded it,
By magic accents, to the mystic shape,
Imparted with the life of Thalaba,
In all its passive powers,
Mysterious sympathy.
With the mandrake and the manchineel
　　　She builds her pile accurst.　341
She lays her finger to the pile,
And blue and green the flesh
　　　Glows with emitted fire,
A fire to kindle that strange fuel meet.

25

Before the fire she placed the imaged
　　　　wax :　　　　[cried,
' There, waste away ! ' the Enchantress
' And with thee waste Hodeirah's Son ! '

26

Fool ! fool ! go thaw the everlasting ice,
　Whose polar mountains bound the
　　　human reign.　　　350
　Blindly the wicked work
　The righteous will of Heaven !
The doom'd Destroyer wears Abdaldar's
　　　ring ;
Against the danger of his horoscope

Yourselves have shielded him ;
And on the sympathizing wax,
The unadmitted flames play power-
　　　lessly,　　　[snow.
As the cold moon-beam on a plain of

27

' Curse thee ! curse thee ! ' cried the
　　　fiendly woman,
' Hast thou yet a spell of safety ? ' 360
　And in the raging flames
　She threw the imaged wax.
　It lay amid the flames,
　Like Polycarp of old,
When, by the glories of the burning
　　　stake
　O'er-vaulted, his grey hairs
　Curl'd, life-like, to the fire
That haloed round his saintly brow.

28

' Wherefore is this ! ' cried Khawla, and
　　　she stampt
　　Thrice on the cavern floor :　370
　　' Maimuna ! Maimuna ! '
　Thrice on the floor she stampt,
Then to the rocky gateway glanced
Her eager eyes, and Maimuna was there.
' Nay, Sister, nay ! ' quoth she, ' Mo-
　　　hareb's life
　Is link'd with Thalaba's !
Nay, Sister, nay ! the plighted oath !
　The common sacrament ! '

29

' Idiot ! ' said Khawla, ' one must die,
　　　or all !
Faith kept with him were treason to the
　　　rest.　　　380
Why lies the wax like marble in the fire ?
　What powerful amulet
　Protects Hodeirah's Son ? '

30

　Cold, marble-cold, the wax
　Lay on the raging pile,
Cold in that white intensity of fire.

The Bat, that with her hook'd and
leathery wings
Clung to the cave-roof, loosed her hold,
Death-sickening with the heat;
The Toad, which to the darkest nook
had crawl'd, 390
Panted fast with fever pain;
The Viper from her nest came forth,
Leading her quicken'd brood,
That, sportive with the warm delight,
roll'd out [rings,
Their thin curls, tender as the tendril
Ere the green beauty of their brittle
youth [summer sun.
Grows brown, and toughens in the
Cold, marble-cold, the wax
Lay on the raging pile,
The silver quivering of the element 400
O'er its pale surface shedding a dim gloss.

31

Amid the red and fiery smoke,
Watching the portent strange,
The blue-eyed Sorceress and her Sister
stood,
Seeming a ruined Angel by the side
Of Spirit born in hell.
Maimuna raised at length her thought-
ful eyes:
' Whence, Sister, was the wax?
The work of the worm, or the bee?
Nay then I marvel not! 410
It were as wise to bring from Ararat
The fore-world's wood to build the
magic pile,
And feed it from the balm bower,
through whose veins [out
The Martyr's blood sends such a virtue
That the fond mother from beneath its
shade [playful child.
Wreathes the horn'd viper round her
This is the eternal, universal strife!
There is a Grave-wax, .. I have seen the
Gouls [ing.' ..
Fight for the dainty at their banquet-

32

' Excellent Witch!' quoth Khawla
and she went 420
To the cave-arch of entrance, and
scowl'd up,
Mocking the blessed Sun:
' Shine thou in Heaven, but I will
shadow Earth!
Thou wilt not shorten day,
But I will hasten darkness!' Then the
Witch
Began a magic song,
One long low tone, through teeth half-
closed, [slow;
Through lips slow-moving, muttered
One long-continued breath,
Till to her eyes a darker yellowness
Was driven, and fuller-swoln the pro-
minent veins 431
On her loose throat grew black.
Then looking upward, thrice she
breathed
Into the face of Heaven;
The baneful breath infected Heaven;
A mildewing fog it spread
Darker and darker; so the evening sun
Pour'd his unentering glory on the mist,
And it was night below.

33

' Bring now the wax,' quoth Khawla,
' for thou know'st 440
The mine that yields it.' Forth went
Maimuna, [forth;
In mist and darkness went the Sorceress
And she hath reach'd the Place of Tombs,
And in their sepulchres the Dead
Feel feet unholy trampling over them.

34

Thou startest, Maimuna,
Because the breeze is in thy lifted locks!
Is Khawla's spell so weak?
Sudden came the breeze and strong;
The heavy mist wherewith the lungs
opprest 450

Were labouring late, flies now before the
        gale,
    Thin as an infant's breath,
Seen in the sunshine of an autumn frost.
Sudden it came, and soon its work
        was done,
    And suddenly it ceased ;
Cloudless and calm it left the firmament,
    And beautiful in the blue sky
    Arose the summer Moon.

35

She heard the quicken'd action of her
        blood,
    She felt the fever in her cheeks. 460
Daunted, yet desperate, in a tomb
Entering, with impious hand she traced
    Circles and squares and trines
        And magic characters,
Till, riven by her charms, the tomb
Yawn'd and disclosed its dead ;
Maimuna's eyes were open'd, and she saw
    The secrets of the Grave.

36

    There sate a Spirit in the vault, 469
In shape, in hue, in lineaments, like life ;
And by him couch'd, as if intranced,
The hundred-headed Worm that never
        dies.

37

' Nay, Sorceress ! not to-night ! ' the
        Spirit cried,   [to-night
' The flesh in which I sinn'd may rest
From suffering ; all things, even I,
        to-night,
    Even the Damn'd, repose ! '

38

    The flesh of Maimuna   [knees
Crept on her bones with terror, and her
Trembled with their trembling weight.
' Only this Sabbath ! and at dawn the
        Worm   480
Will wake, and this poor flesh must grow
        to meet

The gnawing of his hundred poison-
        mouths !   [death ! '
God ! God ! is there no mercy after

39

    Soul-struck, she rush'd away,
    She fled the Place of Tombs,
    She cast herself upon the earth,
All agony, and tumult, and despair.
And in that wild and desperate agony
Sure Maimuna had died the utter death,
    If aught of evil had been possible
        On this mysterious night ;   491
For this was that most holy night
    When all Created Things adore
The Power that made them ; Insects,
        Beasts, and Birds,
The Water-Dwellers, Herbs, and Trees,
        and Stones,
Yea, Earth and Ocean, and the infinite
        Heaven,   [know
With all its Worlds. Man only doth not
The universal Sabbath, doth not join
With Nature in her homage. Yet the
        prayer   [love,
Flows from the righteous with intenser
A holier calm succeeds, and sweeter
        dreams   501
Visit the slumbers of the penitent.

40

Therefore on Maimuna the Elements
Shed healing ; every breath she drew
        was balm.   [up
For every flower sent then in incense
Its richest odours ; and the song of birds
Now, like the music of the Seraphim,
        Enter'd her soul, and now
Made silence aweful by their sudden
        pause.
    It seem'd as if the quiet Moon   510
Pour'd quietness ; its lovely light
Was like the smile of reconciling Heaven.

41

    Is it the dew of night
    That on her glowing cheek

Shines in the moon-beam ? Oh ! she
    weeps . . she weeps !
And the Good Angel that abandoned her
At her hell-baptism, by her tears drawn
        down,
Resumes his charge. Then Maimuna
Recall'd to mind the double oracle ;
    Quick as the lightning flash   520
Its import glanced upon her, and the hope
  Of pardon and salvation rose,
    As now she understood
  The lying prophecy of truth.
She pauses not, she ponders not ;
The driven air before her fann'd the face
Of Thalaba, and he awoke and saw
  The Sorceress of the Silver Locks.

42

  One more permitted spell.
  She takes the magic thread.   530
With the wide eye of wonder, Thalaba
Watches her snowy fingers round and
      round,
  Unwind the loosening chain.
Again he hears the low sweet voice,
  The low sweet voice so musical,
    That sure it was not strange,
  If in those unintelligible tones
  Was more than human potency,
That with such deep and undefined de-
      light
    Fill'd the surrender'd soul.   540
The work is done, the song hath ceased ;
He wakes as from a dream of Paradise,
And feels his fetters gone, and with
    the burst
Of wondering adoration, praises God.

43

Her charm hath loosed the chain it bound,
  But massy walls and iron gates
    Confine Hodeirah's Son.
Heard ye not, Genii of the Air, her spell,
  That o'er her face there flits
    The sudden flush of fear ?   550
Again her louder lips repeat the charm ;

Her eye is anxious, her cheek pale,
  Her pulse plays fast and feeble.
Nay, Maimuna ! thy power hath ceased,
    And the wind scatters now
    The voice which ruled it late.

44

' Be comforted, my soul ! ' she cried,
    her eye   [forted !
Brightening with sudden joy, ' be com-
We have burst through the bonds which
    bound us down
To utter death ; our covenant with Hell
Is blotted out ! The Lord hath given
    me strength !   561
  Great is the Lord, and merciful !
Hear me, ye rebel Spirits ! in the name
Of Allah and the Prophet, hear the spell !'

45

Groans then were heard, the prison walls
    were rent,
The whirlwind wrapt them round, and
    forth they flew,
  Borne in the chariot of the Winds
    abroad.

THE TENTH BOOK

And the Angel that was sent unto me
said, Thinkest thou to comprehend the way
of the Most High ! . . Then said I, Yea, my
Lord. And he answered me, and said, I am
sent to shew thee three ways, and to set
forth three similitudes before thee ; whereof
if thou canst declare me one, I will shew
thee also the way that thou desirest to see,
and I shall shew thee from whence the
wicked heart cometh. And I said, Tell on,
my Lord. Then said he unto me, Go thy
way, weigh me the weight of the fire, or
measure me the blast of the wind, or call
me again the day that is past.—*Esdras*, ii. 4.

1

Ere there was time for wonder or for fear,
  The way was pass'd, and lo ! again
    Amid surrounding snows,
Within the cavern of the Witch they
    stand.

2

Then came the weakness of her natural
                              age
At once on Maimuna ;
The burthen of her years
Fell on her, and she knew
That her repentance in the sight of God
Had now found favour, and her hour
                    was come.   10
Her death was like the righteous: 'Turn
                    my face
To Mecca !' in her languid eyes
The joy of certain hope
Lit a last lustre, and in death
A smile was on her cheek.

3

No faithful crowded round her bier,
No tongue reported her good deeds,
For her no mourners wail'd and wept,
No Iman o'er her perfumed corpse
For her soul's health intoned the prayer;
Nor column raised by the way-side 21
    Implored the passing traveller
    To say a requiem for the dead.
Thalaba laid her in the snow,
And took his weapons from the hearth,
And then once more the youth began
    His weary way of solitude.

4

The breath of the East is in his face,
And it drives the sleet and the snow.
    The air is keen, the wind is keen, 30
His limbs are aching with the cold,
His eyes are aching with the snow,
        His very heart is cold,
His spirit chill'd within him. He looks on
        If aught of life be near ;
But all is sky, and the white wilderness,
    And here and there a solitary pine,
Its branches broken by the weight of
                    snow.
    His pains abate, his senses, dull
    With suffering, cease to suffer. 40
        Languidly, languidly,

Thalaba drags along,
A heavy weight is on his lids,
His limbs move slow for heaviness,
    And he full fain would sleep.
Not yet, not yet, O Thalaba,
    Thy hour of rest is come !
Not yet may the Destroyer sleep :
    The comfortable sleep :
    His journey is not over yet,   50
His course not yet fulfill'd ! . .
Run thou thy race, O Thalaba !
    The prize is at the goal.

5

It was a Cedar-tree
Which woke him from that deadly
                    drowsiness ;
Its broad round-spreading branches,
            when they felt   [heaven,
The snow, rose upward in a point to
And standing in their strength erect,
    Defied the baffled storm.
    He knew the lesson Nature gave, 60
    And he shook off his heaviness,
    And hope revived within him.

6

Now sunk the evening sun,
A broad and beamless orb,
    Adown the glowing sky ;
Through the red light the snow-flakes
        fell like fire.
Louder grows the biting wind,
And it drifts the dust of the snow.
The snow is clotted in his hair,
        The breath of Thalaba   70
        Is iced upon his lips.
He looks around ; the darkness,
The dizzy floating of the feathery sky
    Close in his narrow view.

7

At length, through the thick atmosphere,
                    a light
    Not distant far appears.
He, doubting other wiles of sorcery,

With mingled joy and fear, yet quicken'd
step,
Bends thitherward his way.

8

It was a little, lowly dwelling-place,
Amid a garden whose delightful air 81
Was mild and fragrant as the evening
wind
Passing in summer o'er the coffee-groves
Of Yemen, and its blessed bowers of
balm.
A fount of Fire that in the centre play'd
Roll'd all around its wondrous rivulets,
And fed the garden with the heat of life.
Every where magic! the Arabian's heart
Yearn'd after human intercourse.
A light; . . the door unclosed! . . 90
All silent . . he goes in.

9

There lay a Damsel, sleeping on a couch:
His step awoke her, and she gazed at
him
With pleased and wondering look,
Fearlessly, like a happy child,
Too innocent to fear.
With words of courtesy
The young intruder spake.
At the sound of his voice, a joy
Kindled her bright black eyes; 100
She rose and took his hand;
But at the touch the joy forsook her
cheek:
'Oh! it is cold!' she cried,
'I thought I should have felt it warm,
like mine,
But thou art like the rest!'

10

Thalaba stood mute awhile,
And wondering at her words:
'Cold? Lady!' then he said: 'I have
travell'd long
In this cold wilderness,
Till life is well-nigh spent!' 110

11

LAILA

Art thou a Man, then?

THALABA

Nay . . I did not think
Sorrow and toil could so have alter'd me,
As to seem otherwise.

LAILA

And thou canst be warm
Sometimes? life-warm as I am?

THALABA

Surely, Lady.
As others are, I am, to heat and cold
Subject like all. You see a Traveller,
Bound upon hard adventure, who
requests   120
Only to rest him here to-night, . . to-
morrow
He will pursue his way.

LAILA

Oh . . not to-morrow!
Not, like a dream of joy, depart so soon!
And whither wouldst thou go? for all
around
Is everlasting winter, ice and snow,
Deserts unpassable of endless frost.

THALABA

He who has led me here, will still sustain
me
Through cold and hunger.

12

'Hunger?' Laila cried: 130
She clapt her lily hands,
And whether from above, or from below,
It came, sight could not see, [food.
So suddenly the floor was spread with

13

LAILA

Why dost thou watch with hesitating
eyes   [come.
The banquet? 'tis for thee! I bade it

THALABA

Whence came it?

LAILA

Matters it from whence it came ?
My Father sent it : when I call, he hears.
Nay, . . thou hast fabled with me!
    and art like   140
The forms that wait upon my solitude,
Human to eye alone , . . thy hunger
    would not
    Question so idly else.

THALABA

I will not eat !
It came by magic ! fool, to think that
    aught   [here.
But fraud and danger could await me
    Let loose my cloak ! . .

LAILA

Begone then, insolent !
Why dost thou stand and gaze upon
    me thus ?
Ay ! eye the features well that threaten
    thee   150
With fraud and danger ! in the wilder-
    ness   [want,
They shall avenge me, . . in the hour of
Rise on thy view, and make thee feel
How innocent I am :
And this remember'd cowardice and
    insult,   [thy cheek,
With a more painful shame will burn
Than now heats mine in anger !

THALABA

Mark me, Lady !
Many and restless are my enemies ;
My daily paths have been beset with
    snares   160
Till I have learnt suspicion, bitter
    sufferings
Teaching the needful vice.   If I have
    wrong'd you, . .   [cence, . .
For yours should be the face of inno-
I pray you pardon me ! In the name
    of God
And of his Prophet, I partake your food.

LAILA

Lo, now ! thou wert afraid of sorcery,
    And yet hast said a charm !

THALABA

A charm ?

LAILA

And wherefore ? . .
Is it not delicate food ? . .   What mean
    thy words ?   170
I have heard many spells, and many
    names,
That rule the Genii and the Elements,
    But never these.

THALABA

How ! never heard the names
Of God and of the Prophet ?

LAILA

Never . . nay now !
Again that troubled eye ? . . thou art
    a strange man,
And wondrous fearful . . . but I must
    not twice   [pectest still,
Be charged with fraud : If thou sus-
    Depart and leave me !   180

THALABA

And you do not know
The God that made you ?

LAILA

Made me, man ! . . my Father
Made me. He made this dwelling, and
    the grove,   [morn
And yonder fountain-fire ; and every
He visits me, and takes the snow, and
    moulds   [into them
Women and men, like thee ; and breathes
Motion, and life, and sense, . . but, to
    the touch   [night closes
They are chilling cold ; and ever when
They melt away again, and leave me
    here   190
Alone and sad. Oh then how I rejoice
When it is day, and my dear Father
    comes

And cheers me with kind words and
    kinder looks!
My dear, dear Father!.. Were it not
    for him,
I am so weary of this loneliness,
That I should wish I also were of snow,
That I might melt away, and cease to be.

THALABA

And have you always had your dwelling
    here
    Amid this solitude of snow ?

LAILA

    I think so.   200
I can remember, with unsteady feet
Tottering from room to room, and
    finding pleasure
In flowers, and toys, and sweetmeats,
    things which long
Have lost their power to please ; which,
    when I see them,
Raise only now a melancholy wish,
I were the little trifler once again
Who could be pleased so lightly !

THALABA

    Then you know not
    Your Father's art ?

LAILA

    No. I besought him once   210
To give me power like his, that where he
    went   [head,
I might go with him ; but he shook his
And said, it was a power too dearly
    bought,   [tears.
And kiss'd me with the tenderness of

THALABA

And wherefore hath he hidden you thus
    far
From all the ways of humankind ?

LAILA

    'Twas fear,
Fatherly fear and love. He read the
    stars,
And saw a danger in my destiny,

And therefore placed me here amid the
    snows,   220
And laid a spell that never human eye,
If foot of man by chance should reach
    the depth
Of this wide waste, shall see one trace of
    grove,   [fire,
Garden or dwelling-place, or yonder
That thaws and mitigates the frozen sky.
And, more than this, even if the Enemy
Should come, I have a Guardian here.

THALABA

    A Guardian ?

LAILA

'Twas well, that when my sight unclosed
    upon thee,   [face,
There was no dark suspicion in thy
Else I had called his succour ! Wilt
    thou see him ?   231
But, if a woman can have terrified thee,
How wilt thou bear his unrelaxing brow,
    And lifted lightnings ?

THALABA

    Lead me to him, Lady !

14

    She took him by the hand,
    And through the porch they pass'd.
    Over the garden and the grove
    The fountain-streams of fire
    Pour'd a broad light like noon : 240
    A broad unnatural light,
Which made the rose's blush of beauty
    pale,   [blaze.
And dimm'd the rich geranium's scarlet
The various verdure of the grove
Wore here one undistinguishable grey,
    Chequer'd with blacker shade.
    Suddenly Laila stopt,
'I do not think thou art the enemy,'
    She said, ' but He will know ! .
    If thou hast meditated wrong,   250
    Stranger, depart in time ..
I would not lead thee to thy death.'

E

15

She turn'd her gentle eyes
Toward him then with anxious tender-
                                  ness.   [Thalaba,
'So let him pierce my breast,' cried
'If it hide thought to harm you!'

LAILA

'Tis a figure,
Almost I fear to look at ! . . yet come on.
'Twill ease me of a heaviness that seems
To sink my heart; and thou may'st
                        dwell here then   260
In safety; . . for thou shalt not go to-
                                  morrow,
Nor on the after, nor the after day,
Nor ever! It was only solitude
Which made my misery here, . .
And now, that I can see a human face,
And hear a human voice . . .
Oh no! thou wilt not leave me!

THALABA

Alas, I must not rest!
The star that ruled at my nativity,
Shone with a strange and blasting in-
                                  fluence.   270
O gentle Lady! I should draw upon you
A killing curse!

LAILA

But I will ask my Father
To save you from all danger; and you
                        know not   [I ask,
The wonders he can work; and when
It is not in his power to say me nay.
Perhaps thou know'st the happiness it is
To have a tender Father?

THALABA

He was one,   [tainted
Whom, like a loathsome leper, I have
With my contagious destiny. One
                        evening   280
He kiss'd me as he wont, and laid his
                        hands   [slept.
Upon my head, and blest me ere I

His dying groan awoke me, for the
                        Murderer
Had stolen upon our sleep! . . For me
                        was meant
The midnight blow of death; my Father
                        died;
The brother playmates of my infancy,
The baby at the breast, they perish'd
                        all, . .   [saved
All in that dreadful hour! . . but I was
To remember and revenge.

16

She answer'd not; for now,   290
Emerging from the o'er-arch'd avenue,
The finger of her upraised hand
Mark'd where the Guardian of the
                        garden stood.
It was a brazen Image, every limb
And swelling vein and muscle true to life:
The left knee bending on,   [hand
The other straight, firm planted, and his
Lifted on high to hurl
The lightning that it grasp'd.

17

When Thalaba approach'd,   300
The enchanted Image knew Hodeirah's
                        son,   [foe.
And hurl'd the lightning at the dreaded
But from Mohareb's hand
Had Thalaba received Abdaldar's Ring.
Blindly the wicked work
The righteous will of Heaven.
Full in his face the lightning-bolt was
                        driven;
The scatter'd fire recoil'd;
Like the flowing of a summer gale he felt
Its ineffectual force;   310
His countenance was not changed,
Nor a hair of his head was singed.

18

He started, and his glance
Turn'd angrily upon the Maid.
The sight disarm'd suspicion; . . breath-
                        less, pale,

Against a tree she stood ;
Her wan lips quivering, and her eyes
Upraised, in silent supplicating fear.

19

Anon she started with a scream of joy,
    Seeing her Father there,   320
And ran and threw her arms around his
        neck.   [come!
' Save me ! ' she cried, ' the Enemy is
Save me ! save me ! Okba ! '

20

' Okba ! ' repeats the youth ;
    For never since that hour,
When in the tent the Spirit told his name,
    Had Thalaba let slip
The memory of his Father's murderer ;
' Okba ! ' . . and in his hand
He graspt an arrow-shaft,   330
And he rush'd on to strike him.

21

' Son of Hodeirah ! ' the Old Man replied,
    ' My hour is not yet come ; '
    And putting forth his hand
    Gently he repell'd the Youth.
    ' My hour is not yet come !
But thou may'st shed this innocent
        Maiden's blood ;
That vengeance God allows thee ! '

22

    Around her Father's neck
Still Laila's hands were clasp'd ;   340
Her face was turn'd to Thalaba,
A broad light floated o'er its marble
        paleness,
As the wind waved the fountain fire,
Her large dilated eye, in horror raised,
Watch'd every look and movement of
        the youth :
    ' Not upon her,' said he,
' Not upon her, Hodeirah's blood cries
        out   [arm
For vengeance ! ' and again his lifted
    Threaten'd the Sorcerer :

Again withheld, it felt   350
A barrier that no human strength could
        burst.

23

' Thou dost not aim the blow more
        eagerly,'   [meet it !
Okba replied, ' than I would rush to
    But that were poor revenge.
        O Thalaba, thy God
    Wreaks on the innocent head
His vengeance ; . . I must suffer in my
        child ! [victim ? Allah
Why dost thou pause to strike thy
    Permits, . . commands the deed.'

24

    ' Liar ! ' quoth Thalaba.   360
    And Laila's wondering eye [face.
Look'd up, all anguish, to her father's
' By Allah and the Prophet,' he replied,
    ' I speak the words of truth.
        Misery ! misery !
That I must beg mine enemy to speed
The inevitable vengeance now so near !
I read it in her horoscope ; [race.
Her birth-star warn'd me of Hodeirah's
I laid a spell, and call'd a Spirit up ;
    He answered, one must die,   371
    Laila or Thalaba. . .
    Accursed Spirit ! even in truth
    Giving a lying hope !
Last, I ascended the seventh Heaven,
And on the Everlasting Table there,
        In characters of light,
    I read her written doom.
The years that it has gnawn me ! and
        the load
Of sin that it has laid upon my soul ! 380
Curse on this hand, that in the only hour
    The favouring Stars allow'd,
Reek'd with other blood than thine.
Still dost thou stand and gaze incredu-
        lous ?
Young man, be merciful, and keep her not
        Longer in agony.'

25

Thalaba's unbelieving frown
  Scowl'd on the Sorcerer, [heard,
When in the air the rush of wings was
And Azrael stood before them. 390
  In equal terror at the sight,
The Enchanter, the Destroyer stood,
And Laila, the victim Maid.

26

' Son of Hodeirah ! ' said the Angel of
      Death,
  ' The accursed fables not.
When from the Eternal Hand I took
  The yearly scroll of Fate,
Her name was written there ; . .
Her leaf had wither'd on the Tree of Life.
This is the hour, and from thy hands 400
  Commission'd to receive the Maid
      I come.'

27

' Hear me, O Angel ! ' Thalaba replied ;
  ' To avenge my father's death,
  To work the will of Heaven, [race,
To root from earth the accursed sorcerer
I have dared danger undismay'd,
I have lost all my soul held dear,
I am cut off from all the ties of life,
Unmurmuring. For whate'er awaits me
      still,   409
Pursuing to the end the enterprize,
Peril or pain, I bear a ready heart.
But strike this Maid ! this innocent ! . .
  Angel, I dare not do it.'

28

' Remember,' answer'd Azrael, ' all thou
      say'st   [word
Is written down for judgement ! every
In the balance of thy trial must be
      weigh'd ! '

29

  ' So be it ! ' said the Youth :
' He who can read the secrets of the
      heart,

Will judge with righteousness !
  This is no doubtful path ;   420
The voice of God within me cannot lie. . .
  I will not harm the innocent.'

30

  He said, and from above,
As though it were the Voice of Night,
  The startling answer came.
  ' Son of Hodeirah, think again !
  One must depart from hence,
      Laila, or Thalaba ;
She dies for thee, or thou for her ;
  It must be life for life !   430
Son of Hodeirah, weigh it well,
While yet the choice is thine ! '

31

  He hesitated not,
But, looking upward, spread his hands
      to Heaven,
  ' Oneiza, in thy bower of Paradise,
  Receive me, still unstain'd ! '

32

' What ! ' exclaim'd Okba, ' darest thou
      disobey,
  Abandoning all claim
  To Allah's longer aid ? '

33

The eager exultation of his speech
Earthward recall'd the thoughts of
      Thalaba.   441
' And dost thou triumph, Murderer ?
  dost thou deem
Because I perish, that the unsleeping lids
Of Justice shall be closed upon thy
      crime ?
Poor, miserable man ! that thou canst
      live
With such beast-blindness in the present
      joy,   [God
When o'er thy head the sword of
Hangs for the certain stroke ! '

34

' Servant of Allah, thou hast disobey'd ;
   God hath abandon'd thee ;   450
This hour is mine ! ' cried Okba,
And shook his daughter off,
And drew the dagger from his vest,
And aim'd the deadly blow.

35

All was accomplish'd.   Laila rush'd
                  between
   To save the saviour Youth.
She met the blow, and sunk into his
                  arms,
And Azrael, from the hands of Thalaba,
   Received her parting soul.

THE ELEVENTH BOOK

Those, Sir, that traffic in these seas,
Fraught not their bark with fears.
                  SIR ROBERT HOWARD.

1

O FOOL, to think thy human hand
Could   check   the   chariot-wheels   of
            Destiny !
To dream of weakness in the all-
            knowing Mind,
   That its decrees should change !
   To hope that the united Powers
      Of Earth, and Air, and Hell,
Might blot one letter from the Book of
            Fate,   [chain !
Might break one link of the eternal
Thou miserable, wicked, poor old man !
Fall now upon the body of thy child, 10
Beat now thy breast, and pluck the
            bleeding hairs
   From thy grey beard, and lay
Thine ineffectual hand to close her
            wound,
      And call on Hell to aid,
      And call on Heaven to send
      Its merciful thunderbolt !

2

   The young Arabian silently
      Beheld his frantic grief.
The presence of the hated youth
   To raging anguish stung   20
      The wretched Sorcerer.
' Ay ! look and triumph ! ' he exclaim'd :
   ' This is the justice of thy God !
   A righteous God is he, to let
His vengeance fall upon the innocent
                  head ! ..
   Curse thee, curse thee, Thalaba ! '

3

      All feelings of revenge
      Had left Hodeirah's son.
Pitying and silently he heard
The victim of his own iniquities ; 30
   Not with the officious hand
Of consolation, fretting the sore wound
   He could not hope to heal.

4

So as the Servant of the Prophet stood,
   With sudden motion the night-air
      Gently fann'd his cheek.
   'Twas a Green Bird, whose wings
      Had waved the quiet air.
   On the hand of Thalaba
The Green Bird perch'd, and turn'd 40
   A mild eye up, as if to win
      The Adventurer's confidence ;
Then, springing on, flew forward ;
      And now again returns
   To court him to the way ;
   And now his hand perceives
Her rosy feet press firmer, as she leaps
      Upon the wing again.

5

      Obedient to the call,
By the pale moonlight Thalaba pursued,
   O'er trackless snows, his way ;   51
Unknowing he what blessed messenger
   Had come to guide his steps, ..
That Laila's spirit went before his path.

Brought up in darkness, and the child
　　　of sin,
Yet, as the meed of spotless innocence,
Just Heaven permitted her by one good
　　　　deed　　　[death;
To work her own redemption after
So, till the Judgement day,
　　Sho might abide in bliss,　　60
Green warbler of the Bowers of Paradise.

6

The morning sun came forth,
　Wakening no eye to life
　In this wide solitude;
His radiance, with a saffron hue, like
　　heat,
Suffused the desert snow.
The Green Bird guided Thalaba;
Now oaring with slow wing her upward
　　way,
Descending now in slant descent
On out-spread pinions motionless; 70
Floating now, with rise and fall alternate,
As if the billows of the air
Heaved her with their sink and swell.
And when beneath the moon
　The icy glitter of the snow
　Dazzled his aching sight,
Then on his arm alighted the Green Bird,
　And spread before his eyes
　Her plumage of refreshing hue.

7

Evening came on; the glowing clouds
Tinged with a purple ray the mountain
　　ridge　　　　81
　That lay before the Traveller.
　Ah! whither art thou gone,
Guide and companion of the youth,
　　whose eye
Has lost thee in the depth of Heaven?
　Why hast thou left alone
The weary wanderer in the wilderness?
And now the western clouds grow pale,
And night descends upon his solitude.

8

　The Arabian youth knelt down, 90
And bow'd his forehead to the ground,
　And made his evening prayer.
When he arose the stars were bright in
　　heaven,
The sky was blue, and the cold Moon
　Shone over the cold snow.
　A speck in the air!
　Is it his guide that approaches?
For it moves with the motion of life!
Lo! she returns, and scatters from her
　　　　pinions　　[morning
Odours diviner than the gales of
　　Waft from Sabea.　　101

9

Hovering before the youth she hung,
Till from her rosy feet, that at his touch
　Uncurl'd their grasp, he took
　The fruitful bough they bore.
He took and tasted: a new life
Flow'd through his renovated frame;
His limbs, that late were sore and stiff,
　Felt all the freshness of repose;
　His dizzy brain was calm'd,　110
The heavy aching of his lids was gone;
For Laila, from the Bowers of Paradise,
　Had borne the healing fruit.

10

　So up the mountain steep,
　With untired foot he pass'd,
　The Green Bird guiding him,
　Mid crags, and ice, and rocks,
A difficult way, winding the long ascent.
How then the heart of Thalaba rejoiced,
When, bosom'd in the mountain depths,
A shelter'd Valley open'd on his view!
　It was the Simorg's vale,　122
　The dwelling of the Ancient Bird.

11

　On a green and mossy bank,
　　Beside a rivulet,
　The Bird of Ages stood.

No sound intruded on his solitude,
Only the rivulet was heard,
Whose everlasting flow,
From the birth-day of the world, had
made   130
The same unvaried murmuring.
Here dwelt the all-knowing Bird
In deep tranquillity,
His eye-lids ever closed
In full enjoyment of profound repose.

12

Reverently the youth approach'd
That old and only Bird,
And crost his arms upon his breast,
And bow'd his head and spake.
'Earliest of existing things,   140
Earliest thou, and wisest thou,
Guide me, guide me, on my way!
I am bound to seek the Caverns
Underneath the roots of Ocean,
Where the Sorcerers have their seat;
Thou the eldest, thou the wisest,
Guide me, guide me, on my way!'

13

The ancient Simorg on the youth
Unclosed his thoughtful eyes,
And answer'd to his prayer.   150
'Northward by the stream proceed;
In the Fountain of the Rock
Wash away thy worldly stains
Kneel thou there, and seek the Lord,
And fortify thy soul with prayer.
Thus prepared, ascend the Sledge;
Be bold, be wary; seek and find!
God hath appointed all.'
The Ancient Simorg then let fall his lids,
Relapsing to repose.   160

14

Northward, along the rivulet,
The adventurer went his way;
Tracing its waters upward to their
source.
Green Bird of Paradise,

Thou hast not left the youth!..
With slow associate flight,
She companies his way;
And now they reach the Fountain of the
Rock.

15

There, in the cold clear well,   169
Thalaba wash'd away his earthly stains,
And bow'd his face before the Lord,
And fortified his soul with prayer.
The while, upon the rock,
Stood the celestial Bird,   [pass,
And pondering all the perils he must
With a mild, melancholy eye,
Beheld the youth beloved.

16

And lo! beneath yon lonely pine, the
Sledge:..
There stand the harness'd Dogs,
Their wide eyes watching for the youth,
Their ears erect, and turn'd toward his
way.   181
They were lean as lean might be,
Their furrow'd ribs rose prominent,
And they were black from head to foot,
Save a white line on every breast,
Curved like the crescent moon.
Thalaba takes his seat in the sledge;
His arms are folded on his breast,
The Bird is on his knees;
There is fear in the eyes of the Dogs, 190
There is fear in their pitiful moan.
And now they turn their heads,
And seeing him seated, away!

17

The youth, with the start of their speed,
Falls back to the bar of the sledge;
His hair floats straight in the stream of
the wind
Like the weeds in the running brook.
They wind with speed their upward way,
An icy path through rocks of ice:
His eye is at the summit now,   200

And thus far all is dangerless ;
And now upon the height
The black Dogs pause and pant ;
They turn their eyes to Thalaba
As if to plead for pity ;
They moan and whine with fear.

18

Once more away ! and now
The long descent is seen,
A long, long, narrow path ;
Ice-rocks aright, and hills of snow,
Aleft the precipice.   211
Be firm, be firm, O Thalaba !
One motion now, one bend,
And on the crags below
Thy shatter'd flesh will harden in the
frost.
Why howl the Dogs so mournfully ?
And wherefore does the blood flow fast
All purple o'er their sable skin ?
His arms are folded on his breast,
Nor scourge nor goad hath he,   220
No hand appears to strike,
No sounding lash is heard ;
But piteously they moan and whine,
And track their way with blood.

19

Behold ! on yonder height
A giant Fiend aloft
Waits to thrust down the tottering
avalanche !
If Thalaba looks back, he dies ;
The motion of fear is death.
On . . on . . with swift and steady pace,
Adown that dreadful way !   231
The Youth is firm, the Dogs are fleet,
The Sledge goes rapidly ;
The thunder of the avalanche
Re-echoes far behind.
On . . on . . with swift and steady pace,
Adown that dreadful way !
The Dogs are fleet, the way is steep,
The Sledge goes rapidly ;
They reach the plain below.   240

20

A wide, blank plain, all desolate.
Nor tree, nor bush, nor herb !
On go the Dogs with rapid course,
The Sledge slides after rapidly,
And now the sun went down.
They stopt and look'd at Thalaba,
The Youth perform'd his prayer !
They knelt beside him while he pray'd,
They turn'd their heads to Mecca,
And tears ran down their cheeks. 250
Then down they laid them in the snow,
As close as they could lie,
They laid them down and slept.
And backward in the sledge,
The Adventurer laid himself ;
There peacefully slept Thalaba,
And the Green Bird of Paradise
Lay nestling in his breast.

21

The Dogs awoke him at the dawn,
They knelt and wept again ;   260
Then rapidly they journey'd on,
And still the plain was desolate,
Nor tree, nor bush, nor herb !
And ever at the hour of prayer,
They stopt, and knelt, and wept ;
And still that green and graceful Bird
Was as a friend to him by day,
And, ever when at night he slept,
Lay nestling in his breast.

22

In that most utter solitude   270
It cheer'd his heart to hear
Her soft and soothing voice.
Her voice was soft and sweet,
It rose not with the blackbird's thrill,
Nor warbled like that dearest bird that
holds
The solitary man
A loiterer in his thoughtful walk at eve ;
But if it swell'd with no exuberant joy,
It had a tone that touch'd a finer string,

A music that the soul received and
          own'd.   280
Her bill was not the beak of blood ;
There was a human meaning in her eye
     When fix'd on Thalaba,
     He wonder'd while he gazed,
     And with mysterious love
Felt his heart drawn in powerful sym-
          pathy.

23

     Oh joy ! the signs of life appear,
          The first and single Fir
That on the limits of the living world
     Strikes in the ice its roots.   290
     Another, and another now ;
And now the Larch, that flings its
          arms
Down-curving like the falling wave ;
And now the Aspin's scatter'd leaves
Grey-glittering on the moveless twig ;
     The Poplar's varying verdure now,
     And now the Birch so beautiful
          Light as a lady's plumes.
Oh joy ! the signs of life ! the Deer
Hath left his slot beside the way ; 300
     The little Ermine now is seen,
          White wanderer of the snow ;
And now from yonder pines they hear
     The clatter of the Grouse's wings ;
And now the snowy Owl pursues
The Traveller's sledge, in hope of food ;
     And hark ! the rosy-breasted bird,
          The Throstle of sweet song !
Joy ! joy ! the winter-wilds are left !
Green bushes now, and greener grass,
Red thickets here, all berry-bright, 311
     And here the lovely flowers !

24

When the last morning of their way
          was come,
     After the early prayer,
The Green Bird fix'd on Thalaba
     A sad and supplicating eye,

And speech was given her then :
' Servant of God, I leave thee now ;
     If rightly I have guided thee,
          Give me the boon I beg ! '   320

25

' O gentle Bird ! ' quoth Thalaba,
' Guide and companion of my dangerous
          way,
Friend and sole solace of my solitude,
How can I pay thee benefits like these ?
Ask what thou wilt that I can give,
     O gentle Bird, the poor return
          Will leave me debtor still ! '

26

' Son of Hodeirah ! ' she replied,
' When thou shalt see an Old Man bent
          beneath
The burthen of his earthly punishment,
          Forgive him, Thalaba !   331
Yea, send a prayer to God in his behalf !'

27

A flush o'erspread the young Destroyer's
          cheek ;
     He turn'd his eye towards the Bird
As if in half repentance ; for he thought
Of Okba ; and his Father's dying groan
Came on his memory.   The celestial
          Bird
     Saw and renew'd her speech ;
' O Thalaba, if she who in thine arms
Received the dagger-blow and died for
          thee   340
Deserve one kind remembrance, . . save,
          O save   [less death ! '
The Father that she loves from end-

28

' Laila ! and is it thou ? ' the youth
          replied,   [thee ?
' What is there that I durst refuse to
This is no time to harbour in my heart
     One evil thought ; . . here I put off
          revenge,

The last rebellious feeling. . . Be it so!
God grant to me the pardon that I need,
  As I do pardon him !. .
  But who am I, that I should save 350
    The sinful soul alive ?'

29

' Enough!' said Laila. 'When the
    hour shall come,
Remember me! my task is done.
We meet again in Paradise!'
She said, and shook her wings, and up
    she soar'd
With arrowy swiftness through the
    heights of Heaven.

30

His aching eye pursued her path,
When starting onward went the Dogs;
  More rapidly they hurried now,
    In hope of near repose. 360
It was the early morning yet,
When, by the well-head of a brook
They stopt, their journey done.
The spring was clear, the water deep;
A venturous man were he, and rash,
That should have probed its depths,
For all its loosen'd bed below,
Heaved strangely up and down,
And to and fro, from side to side,
It heaved, and waved, and toss'd, 370
And yet the depths were clear,
And yet no ripple wrinkled o'er
The face of that fair Well.

31

And on that Well, so strange and fair,
  A little boat there lay,
Without an oar, without a sail,
One only seat it had, one seat,
  As if for only Thalaba.
And at the helm a Damsel stood,
A Damsel bright and bold of eye, 380
  Yet did a maiden modesty
  Adorn her fearless brow;

Her face was sorrowful, but sure
More beautiful for sorrow.
To her the Dogs look'd wistful up,
And then their tongues were loosed :
' Have we done well, O Mistress dear !
And shall our sufferings end ?'

32

The gentle Damsel made reply; 389
' Poor servants of the God I serve,
When all this witchery is destroy'd,
  Your woes will end with mine.
A hope, alas ! how long unknown !
This new adventurer gives ;
Now God forbid, that he, like you,
  Should perish for his fears !
Poor servants of the God I serve,
  Wait ye the event in peace.'
A deep and total slumber as she spake
Seized them. Sleep on, poor sufferers !
    be at rest ! 400
Ye wake no more to anguish :. . ye
    have borne
The Chosen, the Destroyer ! . . soon his
    hand
Shall strike the efficient blow ;
And shaking off your penal forms, shall
    ye,
With songs of joy, amid the Eden groves,
  Hymn the Deliverer's praise.

33

Then did the Damsel say to Thalaba,
' The morn is young, the Sun is fair,
And pleasantly through pleasant banks
    Yon quiet stream flows on . . 410
  Wilt thou embark with me ?
Thou knowest not the water's way ;
Think, Stranger, well ! and night must
    come, . .
  Darest thou embark with me ?
Through fearful perils thou must pass, . .
Stranger, the wretched ask thine aid !
  Thou wilt embark with me !'
She smiled in tears upon the youth ; . .

What heart were his, who could gainsay
  That melancholy smile ?   420
' I will,' quoth Thalaba,
  ' I will, in Allah's name ! '

34

He sate him on the single seat,
  The little boat moved on.
Through pleasant banks the quiet stream
  Went winding pleasantly ;
By fragrant fir-groves now it pass'd,
  And now, through alder-shores,
Through green and fertile meadows now
  It silently ran by.   430
The flag-flower blossom'd on its side,
  The willow tresses waved,
The flowing current furrow'd round
  The water-lily's floating leaf,
The fly of green and gauzy wing,
  Fell sporting down its course ;
And grateful to the voyager
  The freshness that it breathed,
  And soothing to his ear
Its murmur round the prow.   440
  The little boat falls rapidly
  Adown the rapid stream.

35

But many a silent spring meantime,
  And many a rivulet and rill
Had swoln the growing stream ;
And when the southern Sun began
To wind the downward way of heaven,
  It ran a river deep and wide,
Through banks that widen'd still.
Then once again the Damsel spake : 450
' The stream is strong, the river broad,
  Wilt thou go on with me ?
The day is fair, but night must come . .
  Wilt thou go on with me ?
Far, far away, the sufferer's eye
For thee hath long been looking, . .
  Thou wilt go on with me ! '
' Sail on, sail on,' quoth Thalaba,
  ' Sail on, in Allah's name ! '

  The little boat falls rapidly   460
  Adown the river-stream.

36

A broader and yet broader stream,
  That rock'd the little boat !
The Cormorant stands upon its shoals,
  His black and dripping wings
  Half open'd to the wind.
The Sun goes down, the crescent Moon
  Is brightening in the firmament ;
  And what is yonder roar,
That sinking now, and swelling now,
  But evermore increasing,   471
  Still louder, louder, grows ?
  The little boat falls rapidly
  Adown the rapid tide ;
  The Moon is bright above,
And the great Ocean opens on their way.

37

Then did the Damsel speak again,
  ' Wilt thou go on with me ?
The Moon is bright, the sea is calm,
  I know the ocean-paths ;   480
Wilt thou go on with me ? . .
Deliverer ! yes ! thou dost not fear !
  Thou wilt go on with me ! '
' Sail on, sail on ! ' quoth Thalaba,
  ' Sail on, in Allah's name ! '

38

The Moon is bright, the sea is calm,
  The little boat rides rapidly
  Across the ocean waves ;
The line of moonlight on the deep
  Still follows as they voyage on ; 490
  The winds are motionless ;
  The gentle waters gently part
  In dimples round the prow.
He looks above, he looks around,
The boundless heaven, the boundless
    sea,
The crescent moon, the little boat,
  Nought else above, below.

39

The Moon is sunk; a dusky grey
　　Spreads o'er the Eastern sky;
The stars grow pale and paler;.. 500
　　Oh beautiful! the godlike Sun
　　　Is rising o'er the sea!
Without an oar, without a sail,
　The little boat rides rapidly;..
Is that a cloud that skirts the sea?
. There is no cloud in heaven!
And nearer now, and darker now..
　　It is.. it is.. the Land!
For yonder are the rocks that rise
　Dark in the reddening morn; 510
For loud around their hollow base
　The surges rage and foam.

40

The little boat rides rapidly,
And pitches now with shorter toss
　Upon the narrower swell;
　And now so near, they see
The shelves and shadows of the cliff,
　And the low-lurking rocks,
O'er whose black summits, hidden half,
　The shivering billows burst;.. 520
And nearer now they feel the breaker's
　　　spray.
Then said the Damsel: ' Yonder is our
　　　path
　Beneath the cavern arch.
Now is the ebb, and till the ocean
　　　flow
We cannot over-ride the rocks.
Go thou, and on the shore
Perform thy last ablutions, and with
　　　prayer
Strengthen thy heart.. I too have need
　　　to pray.'

41

She held the helm with steady hand
　Amid the stronger waves; 530
Through surge and surf she drove;
　The adventurer leapt to land.

THE TWELFTH BOOK

Why should he that loves me sorry be
For my deliverance, or at all complain
My good to hear, and toward joys to see?
I go, and long desired have to go,
I go with gladness to my wished rest.
　　　　SPENSER, *Daphnaïda.*

1

THEN Thalaba drew off Abdaldar's ring,
And cast it in the sea, and cried aloud,
' Thou art my shield, my trust, my hope,
　　　O God!
　　Behold and guard me now,
　　Thou who alone canst save.
If from my childhood up I have look'd on
　With exultation to my destiny;
If in the hour of anguish I have own'd
　The justice of the hand that chasten'd
　　　me;
　If of all selfish passions purified 10
I go to work thy will, and from the world
　　Root up the ill-doing race, [arm
Lord! let not thou the weakness of my
　Make vain the enterprize!'

2

The Sun was rising all magnificent,
Ocean and Heaven rejoicing in his beams.
　　And now had Thalaba　　[stood
Perform'd his last ablutions, and he
　　And gazed upon the little boat
　　　Riding the billows near,　20
Where, like a sea-bird breasting the
　　　broad waves,
　It rose and fell upon the surge,
Till from the glitterance of the sunny
　　　main
　　He turn'd his aching eyes;
And then upon the beach he laid him
　　　down,
　And watch'd the rising tide.
He did not pray, he was not calm for
　　　prayer;　　　　[hope,
His spirit, troubled with tumultuous

Toil'd with futurity ;   29
His brain, with busier workings, felt
The roar and raving of the restless sea,
The boundless waves that rose and
    roll'd and rock'd :
    The everlasting sound
Opprest him, and the heaving infinite :
He closed his lids for rest.

3

Meantime with fuller reach and stronger
    swell,
    Wave after wave advanced ;
Each following billow lifted the last
    foam   [hues ;
That trembled on the sand with rainbow
The living flower that, rooted to the
    rock,   40
    Late from the thinner element
Shrunk down within its purple stem to
    sleep,
    Now feels the water, and again
    Awakening, blossoms out
    All its green anther-necks.

4

Was there a Spirit in the gale
That fluttered o'er his cheek ?
For it came on him like the new-risen
    sun   [closed flower,
Which plays and dallies o'er the night-
And woos it to unfold anew to joy ; 50
For it came on him as the dews of eve
    Descend with healing and with life
    Upon the summer mead ;
Or liker the first sound of seraph song
And Angel greeting, to the soul
Whose latest sense had shudder'd at the
    groan
Of anguish, kneeling by a death-bed side.

5

He starts, and gazes round to seek
The certain presence.   ' Thalaba !'
    exclaim'd
    The Voice of the Unseen ; ..   60

' Father of my Oneiza !' he replied,
' And have thy years been number'd ?
    art thou too
Among the Angels ?' .. 'Thalaba !'
A second and a dearer voice repeats,
    ' Go in the favour of the Lord,
        My Thalaba, go on !   [bliss.
My husband, I have drest our bower of
    Go, and perform the work ;
    Let me not longer suffer hope in
        Heaven !'

6

He turn'd an eager glance toward the
    sea.   70
' Come !' quoth the Damsel, and she
    drove
    Her little boat to land.
Impatient through the rising wave,
    He rush'd to meet its way,
    His eye was bright, his cheek was
        flush'd with joy. [she ask'd.
'Hast thou had comfort in thy prayers ?'
    ' Yea,' Thalaba replied,
    ' A heavenly visitation.' ' God be
        praised !'   [vain !'
She answer'd, ' then I do not hope in
And her voice trembled, and her lip
    Quiver'd, and tears ran down.   81

7

' Stranger,' said she, ' in years long past
    Was one who vow'd himself
The Champion of the Lord, like thee,
    Against the race of Hell.
    Young was he, as thyself,
    Gentle, and yet so brave !
    A lion-hearted man.   [love
Shame on me, Stranger ! in the arms of
I held him from his calling, till the hour
Was past ; and then the Angel who
    should else   91
Have crown'd him with his glory-wreath,
Smote him in anger .. Years and years
    are gone ..
And in his place of penance he awaits

Thee, the Deliverer, .. surely thou art
                he !
It was my righteous punishment,
In the same youth unchanged,
And love unchangeable,
Sorrow for ever fresh,
And bitter penitence,   100
That gives no respite night nor day
                from grief,
To abide the written hour, when I
        should waft   [here.
The doom'd Destroyer and Deliverer
Remember thou, that thy success affects
No single fate, no ordinary woes.'

8

As thus she spake, the entrance of the
                cave
Darken'd the boat below.
Around them from their nests,
The screaming sea-birds fled,
Wondering at that strange shape, 110
Yet unalarm'd at sight of living man,
Unknowing of his sway and power mis-
                used :
The clamours of their young
Echoed in shriller cries,
Which rung in wild discordance round
                the rock.
And farther as they now advanced,
The dim reflection of the darken'd day
        Grew fainter, and the dash [yet,
Of the out-breakers deaden'd ; farther
        And yet more faint the gleam,   120
And there the waters, at their utmost
                bound,
Silently rippled on the rising rock.
They landed and advanced, and deeper
                in,
        Two adamantine doors
        Closed up the cavern pass.

9

        Reclining on the rock beside,
        Sate a grey-headed man,
        Watching an hour-glass by.

        To him the Damsel spake,
' Is it the hour appointed ? ' The Old
                Man   130
        Nor answer'd her awhile,
        Nor lifted he his downward eye,
        For now the glass ran low,
        And, like the days of age,
        With speed perceivable,
        The latter sands descend ;
        And now the last are gone.
Then he look'd up, and raised his hand,
                and smote
        The adamantine gates.

10

        The gates of adamant   140
        Unfolding at the stroke,
Open'd and gave the entrance. Then she
                turn'd
        To Thalaba and said,
        ' Go, in the name of God !
I cannot enter, .. I must wait the end
        In hope and agony.
        God and Mahommed prosper thee,
        For thy sake and for ours ! '

11

        He tarried not, .. he pass'd   149
The threshold, over which was no return.
All earthly thoughts, all human hopes
        And passions now put off,
        He cast no backward glance
        Toward the gleam of day.
        There was a light within,   [Sun,
A yellow light, as when the autumnal
        Through travelling rain and mist
        Shines on the evening hills :
Whether, from central fires effused,
        Or that the sun-beams, day by day,
        From earliest generations, there
                absorb'd,   161
Were gathering for the wrath-flame. Shade
                was none
        In those portentous vaults ;
Crag overhanging, nor columnal rock
        Cast its dark outline there ;

For with the hot and heavy atmosphere
The light incorporate, permeating all,
Spread over all its equal yellowness.
There was no motion in the lifeless air ;
He felt no stirring as he pass'd   170
Adown the long descent ;
He heard not his own footsteps on the
      rock   [no sound.
That through the thick stagnation sent
How sweet it were, he thought,
To fool the flowing wind !
With what a thirst of joy
He should breathe in the open gales of
    heaven !

12

Downward, and downward still, and
    still the way,
The lengthening way is safe.
Is there no secret wile,   180
No lurking enemy ?
His watchful eye is on the wall of rock, . .
And warily he marks the roof,
And warily surveys
The path that lies before.
Downward, and downward still, and
    still the way,
The long, long way is safe ;
Rock only, the same light,
The same dead atmosphere,
And solitude, and silence like the grave.

13

At length the long descent   191
Ends on a precipice ;
No feeble ray enter'd its dreadful gulph ;
For in the pit profound,
Black Darkness, utter Night,
Repell'd the hostile gleam,
And o'er the surface the light atmosphere
Floated, and mingled not. [wings,
Above the depth, four over-awning
Unplumed and huge and strong, 200
Bore up a little car ;
Four living pinions, headless, bodiless,

Sprung from one stem that branch'd
    below
In four down-arching limbs,
And clench'd the car-rings endlong and
    athwart
With claws of griffin grasp.

14

But not on these, the depth so terrible
The wondrous wings, fix'd Thalaba his
    eye ;
For there, upon the brink,   209
With fiery fetters fasten'd to the rock,
A man, a living man, tormented lay,
The young Othatha ; in the arms of love
He who had linger'd out the auspicious
    hour,
Forgetful of his call.
In shuddering pity, Thalaba exclaim'd,
'Servant of God, can I not succour thee?'
He groan'd, and answer'd, ' Son of Man,
I sinn'd, and am tormented ; I endure
In patience and in hope. [Hell,
The hour that shall destroy the Race of
That hour shall set me free.'   221

15

' Is it not come ?' quoth Thalaba,
' Yea ! by this omen !' . . and with
    fearless hand   [name
He grasp'd the burning fetters, ' in the
Of God !' . . and from the rock
Rooted the rivets, and adown the gulph
Dropt them. The rush of flames roar'd
    up,
For they had kindled in their fall
The deadly vapours of the pit profound,
And Thalaba bent on and look'd below.
But vainly he explored   231
The deep abyss of flame, [eye,
That sunk beyond the plunge of mortal
Now all ablaze, as if infernal fires
Illumed the world beneath.
Soon was the poison-fuel spent,
The flame grew pale and dim

And dimmer now it fades, and now is
quench'd,
And all again is dark,
Save where the yellow air   240
Enters a little in, and mingles slow.

16

Meantime, the freed Othatha claspt
his knees,
And cried, 'Deliverer!' struggling then
With joyful hope, 'and where is she,'
he cried,
'Whose promised coming for so many
a year...'
'Go!' answered Thalaba,
'She waits thee at the gates.'
'And in thy triumph,' he replied,
'There thou wilt join us?' . . The
Deliverer's eye
Glanced on the abyss, way else was
none . .   250
The depth was unascendable.
'Await not me,' he cried,
'My path hath been appointed! go . .
embark!
Return to life, . . live happy!'

OTHATHA

But thy name? . .   [it, . .
That through the nations we may blazon
That we may bless thee!

THALABA

Bless the Merciful!

17

Then Thalaba pronounced the name of
God,
And leapt into the car.   260
Down, down, it sunk, . . down, down, . .
He neither breathes nor sees;
His eyes are closed for giddiness,
His breath is sinking with the fall.
The air that yields beneath the car,
Inflates the wings above.
Down . . down . . a measureless depth! . .
down . . down,

Was then the Simorg with the Powers
of ill
Associate to destroy?
And was that lovely Mariner   270
A fiend as false as fair?
For still the car sinks down;
But ever the uprushing wind
Inflates the wings above,
And still the struggling wings
Repel the rushing wind.
Down . . down . . and now it strikes.

18

He stands and totters giddily,
All objects round awhile
Float dizzy on his sight;   280
Collected soon, he gazes for the way.
There was a distant light that led his
search;
The torch a broader blaze,
The unpruned taper flares a longer flame,
But this was strong as is the noontide sun,
So, in the glory of its rays intense,
It quiver'd with green glow.
Beyond was all unseen,
No eye could penetrate
That unendurable excess of light. 290

19

It veil'd no friendly form, thought
Thalaba:
And wisely did he deem,
For at the threshold of the rocky door,
Hugest and fiercest of his kind accurst,
Fit warden of the sorcery-gate,
A rebel Afreet lay;
He scented the approach of human food,
And hungry hope kindled his eye of
fire.   [sense,
Raising his hand to screen the dazzled
Onward held Thalaba,   300
And lifted still at times a rapid glance;
Till the due distance gain'd,
With head abased, he laid
An arrow in its rest.

With steady effort and knit forehead
        then,
    Full on the painful light
He fix'd his aching eye, and loosed
        the bow.

20

    A hideous yell ensued ;
And sure no human voice had scope or
        power
For that prodigious shriek   310
Whose pealing echoes thundered up the
        rock.
    Dim grew the dying light ;
But Thalaba leapt onward to the doors
    Now visible beyond,
And while the Afreet warden of the way
Was writhing with his death-pangs,
        over him
    Sprung and smote the stony doors,
And bade them, in the name of God,
        give way !

21

The dying Fiend beneath him, at that
        name
    Tost in worse agony,   320
And the rocks shudder'd, and the rocky
        doors
Rent at the voice asunder. Lo! within . .
    The Teraph and the Fire,
    And Khawla, and in mail complete
Mohareb for the strife.
But Thalaba, with numbing force,
Smites his raised arm, and rushes by ;
For now he sees the fire, amid whose
        flames,
On the white ashes of Hodeirah, lies
    Hodeirah's holy sword.   330

22

    He rushes to the Fire :
    Then Khawla met the youth,
And leapt upon him, and with clinging
        arms   [aim
Clasps him, and calls Mohareb now to

The effectual vengeance. O fool ! fool !
        he sees
His Father's Sword, and who shall bar
        his way ?
Who stand against the fury of that arm
    That spurns her to the ground ? . .
She rises half, she twists around his
        knees, . .
    A moment . . and he vainly strives
    To shake her from her hold ;   341
Impatient then he seized her leathery
        neck
With throttling grasp, and as she loosed
        her hold,
    Thrust her aside, and unimpeded now
Springs forward to the Sword.

23

    The co-existent Flame
Knew the Destroyer ; it encircled him,
Roll'd up his robe, and gather'd round
        his head :
Condensing to intenser splendour there,
His Crown of Glory and his Light of Life,
    Hover'd the irradiate wreath.   351

24

The instant Thalaba had laid his hand
    Upon his Father's Sword,
    The Living Image in the inner cave
Smote the Round Altar. The Domdaniel
        rock'd
Through all its thundering vaults ;
Over the Surface of the reeling Earth,
    The alarum shock was felt ;
The Sorcerer brood, all, all, where'er
        dispersed,
Perforce obey'd the summons ; all, . .
        they came   360
    Compell'd by Hell and Heaven ;
    By Hell compell'd to keep
    Their baptism-covenant,
And with the union of their strength
Oppose the common danger ; forced by
        Heaven
    To share the common doom.

25

Vain are all spells ! the Destroyer
Treads the Domdaniel floor.
They crowd with human arms and
        human force
    To crush the single foe.   370
    Vain is all human force !
He wields his Father's Sword,
The vengeance of awaken'd Deity.
But chief on Thalaba Mohareb prest ;
    The Witch in her oracular speech
Announced one fatal blow for both,
And, desperate of self-safety, yet he hoped
To serve the cause of Eblis, and uphold
    His empire, true in death.

26

Who shall withstand the Destroyer ? 380
Scatter'd before the sword of Thalaba
    The Sorcerer throng recede,
And leave him space for combat. Wretch-
        ed man, . .   [avail
What shall the helmet or the shield
Against Almighty anger ? . . Wretched
        man,   [chosen
Too late Mohareb finds that he hath
The evil part ! . . He rears his shield
To meet the Arabian's sword, . .
Under the edge of that fire-hardened
        steel,
The shield falls sever'd ; his cold arm
    Rings with the jarring blow : . . 391
        He lifts his scymetar ;
A second stroke, and lo ! the broken hilt
Hangs from his palsied hand :
And now he bleeds, and now he flies,
And fain would hide himself amid the
        troop ;
But they feel the sword of Hodeirah,
    But they also fly from the ruin,
    And hasten to the inner cave,
        And fall all fearfully   400
    Around the Giant Idol's feet,
Seeking protection from the Power they
        served.

27

It was a Living Image, by the art
Of magic hands, of flesh and bones com-
        posed,
And human blood, through veins and
        arteries
That flow'd with vital action. In the
        shape
    Of Eblis it was made ;
Its stature such, and such its strength,
    As when among the sons of God 409
Pre-eminent he raised his radiant head,
Prince of the Morning. On his brow
    A coronet of meteor flames,
        Flowing in points of light.
    Self-poised in air before him
Hung the Round Altar, rolling like the
        World
On its diurnal axis, like the World
    Chequer'd with sea and shore,
        The work of Demon art.
For where the sceptre in the Idol's
        hand
Touch'd the Round Altar, in its answer-
        ing realm,   420
Earth felt the stroke, and Ocean rose
        in storms,
And shatter'd Cities, shaken from their
        seat,
    Crush'd all their habitants.
His other arm was raised, and its spread
        palm
    Sustain'd the ocean-weight,
Whose naked waters arch'd the sanc-
        tuary ;
    Sole prop and pillar he.

28

Fallen on the ground, around his feet,
The Sorcerers lay. Mohareb's quivering
        arms
    Clung to the Idol's knees ;   430
        The Idol's face was pale,
    And calm in terror he beheld
    The approach of the Destroyer.

29

Sure of his stroke, and therefore in pursuit [foe,
Following, nor blind, nor hasty, on his
Moved the Destroyer. Okba met his way,
Of all that brotherhood
He only fearless, miserable man,
The one that had no hope.
' On me, on me,' the childless Sorcerer
cried, 440
' Let fall the weapon ! I am he who stole
Upon the midnight of thy Father's
tent ;
This is the hand that pierced Hodeirah's
heart, [blood
That felt thy brethren's and thy sisters'
Gush round the dagger-hilt. Let fall
on me
The fated sword ! the vengeance-hour
is come !
Destroyer, do thy work ! '

30

Nor wile, nor weapon, had the desperate
wretch ;
He spread his bosom to the stroke.
' Old Man, I strike thee not ! ' said
Thalaba ; 450
' The evil thou hast done to me and
mine
Brought its own bitter punishment.
For thy dear Daughter's sake I pardon
thee,
As I do hope Heaven's pardon . . For
her sake
Repent while time is yet ! . . thou hast
my prayers
To aid thee ; thou poor sinner, cast
thyself
Upon the goodness of offended God !
I speak in Laila's name ; and what if
now
Thou canst not think to join in Paradise
Her spotless Spirit, . . hath not Allah
made 460

Al-Araf, in his wisdom ? where the sight
Of Heaven may kindle in the penitent
The strong and purifying fire of hope,
Till, at the Day of Judgement, he shall
see
The Mercy-Gates unfold.'

31

The astonish'd man stood gazing as he
spake, [tears
At length his heart was soften'd, and the
Gush'd, and he sobb'd aloud.
Then suddenly was heard
The all-beholding Prophet's voice divine,
' Thou hast done well, my Servant ! 471
Ask and receive thy reward !

32

A deep and aweful joy
Seem'd to dilate the heart of Thalaba ;
With arms in reverence cross'd upon his
breast,
Upseeking eyes suffused with tears
devout,
He answered to the Voice, ' Prophet of
God,
Holy, and good, and bountiful !
One only earthly wish have I, to work
Thy will ; and thy protection grants me
that. 480
Look on this Sorcerer ! heavy are his
crimes,
But infinite is mercy ! if thy servant
Have now found favour in the sight of
God, [save
Let him be touch'd with penitence, and
His soul from utter death.'

33

' The groans of penitence,' replied the
Voice,
' Never arise unheard !
But, for thyself, prefer the prayer ;
The Treasure-house of Heaven
Is open to thy will.' 490

34

'Prophet of God!' then answered
Thalaba,
'I am alone on earth;
Thou knowest the secret wishes of my
heart!
Do with me as thou wilt! thy will is
best.'

35

There issued forth no Voice to answer
him;   [see
But, lo! Hodeirah's Spirit comes to
His vengeance, and beside him, a
pure form
Of roseate light, his Angel mother hung.

'My Child, my dear, my glorious . .
blessed . . Child,
My promise is perform'd . . fulfil thy
work!'   500

36

Thalaba knew that his death-hour was
come;
And on he leapt, and springing up,
Into the Idol's heart
Hilt deep he plunged the Sword.
The Ocean-vault fell in, and all were
crush'd.
In the same moment, at the gate
Of Paradise, Oneiza's Houri form
Welcomed her Husband to eternal bliss.

THE CURSE OF KEHAMA

ΚΑΤΑΡΑΙ, ΩΣ ΚΑΙ ΤΑ ΑΛΕΚΤΡΥΟΝΟΝΕΟΤΤΑ, ΟΙΚΟΝ ΑΕΙ ΟΨΕ ΚΕΝ
ΕΠΑΝΗΞΑΝ ΕΓΚΑΘΙΣΟΜΕΝΑΙ
’Απόφθ. ’Ανέκ. τοῦ Γυλιέλ. τοῦ Μήτ.

CURSES ARE LIKE YOUNG CHICKENS, THEY ALWAYS COME HOME TO ROOST.

TO

THE AUTHOR OF GEBIR,

WALTER SAVAGE LANDOR,

THIS POEM IS INSCRIBED,

BY

ROBERT SOUTHEY.

ΣΤΗΣΑΤΕ ΜΟΙ ΠΡΩΤΑ ΠΟΛΥΤΡΟΠΟΝ ΟΦΡΑ ΦΑΝΕΙΗ
ΠΟΙΚΙΛΟΝ ΕΙΔΟΣ ΕΧΩΝ, ΟΤΙ ΠΟΙΚΙΛΟΝ ΥΜΝΟΝ ΑΡΑΣΣΩ.   *Νόν. Διόν.*

FOR I WILL FOR NO MAN'S PLEASURE
CHANGE A SYLLABLE OR MEASURE ;
PEDANTS SHALL NOT TIE MY STRAINS
TO OUR ANTIQUE POETS' VEINS ;
BEING BORN AS FREE AS THESE,
I WILL SING AS I SHALL PLEASE.

GEORGE WITHER.

ORIGINAL PREFACE

In the religion of the Hindoos, which of all false religions is the most monstrous in its fables, and the most fatal in its effects, there is one remarkable peculiarity. Prayers, penances, and sacrifices are supposed to possess an inherent and actual value, in no degree depending upon the disposition or motive of the person who performs them. They are drafts upon Heaven, for which the Gods cannot refuse payment. The worst men, bent upon the worst designs, have in this manner obtained power which has made them formidable to the Supreme Deities themselves, and rendered an *Avatar*, or Incarnation of Veeshnoo the Preserver, necessary. This belief is the foundation of the following Poem. The story is original ; but, in all its parts, consistent with the superstition upon which it is built : and however startling the fictions may appear, they might almost be called credible when compared with the genuine tales of Hindoo mythology.

No figures can be imagined more anti-picturesque, and less poetical, than the mythological personages of the Bramins. This deformity was easily kept out of sight :—their hundred hands are but a clumsy personification of power ; their numerous heads only a gross image of divinity, ' whose countenance,' as the Bhagvat-Geeta expresses it, ' is turned on every side.' To the other obvious objection, that the religion of Hindostan is not generally known enough to supply fit machinery for an English poem, I can only answer, that, if every allusion to it throughout the work is not sufficiently self-explained to render the passage intelligible, there is a want of skill in the poet. Even those readers who should be wholly unacquainted with the writings of our learned Orientalists, will find all the preliminary knowledge that can be needful, in the brief explanation of mythological names prefixed to the Poem.

BRAMA, ... the Creator.
VEESHNOO, . . the Preserver.
SEEVA, ... the Destroyer.
These form the Trimourtee, or Trinity, as it has been called, of the Bramins. The allegory is obvious, but has been made for the Trimourtee, not the Trimourtee for the allegory ; and these Deities are regarded by the people as three distinct and personal Gods. The two latter have at this day their hostile sects of worshippers ; that of Seeva is the most numerous ; and in this Poem, Seeva is represented as Supreme among the Gods. This is the same God whose name is variously written Seeb, Sieven, and Siva, Chiven by the French, Xiven by the Portuguese, and whom European writers sometimes denominate Eswara, Iswaren, Mahadeo, Mahadeva, Rutren, —according to which of his thousand and eight names prevailed in the country where they obtained their information.

INDRA, ... God of the Elements.
The SWERGA, . . his Paradise,—one of the Hindoo heavens.
YAMEN, ... Lord of Hell, and Judge of the Dead.
PADALON, ... Hell, — under the Earth, and, like the Earth, of an octagon shape; its eight gates are guarded by as many Gods.
MARRIATALY, . . the Goddess who is chiefly worshipped by the lower casts.
POLLEAR, ... or Ganesa,—the Protector of Travellers. His statues are placed in the highways, and sometimes in a small lonely sanctuary, in the streets and in the fields.
CASYAPA, ... the Father of the Immortals.
DEVETAS, ... the Inferior Deities.
SURAS, ... Good Spirits.
ASURAS, ... Evil Spirits, or Devils.
GLENDOVEERS, . the most beautiful of the Good Spirits, the Grindouvers of Sonnerat.

THE CURSE OF KEHAMA

I. THE FUNERAL

1

MIDNIGHT, and yet no eye
Through all the Imperial City closed in
　　　　sleep !
Behold her streets a-blaze
With light that seems to kindle the red
　　　　sky,
Her myriads swarming through the
　　　　crowded ways !
Master and slave, old age and infancy,
All, all abroad to gaze ;
House-top and balcony
Clustered with women, who throw back
　　　　their veils
With unimpeded and insatiate sight
To view the funeral pomp which passes
　　　　by,　　　　11
As if the mournful rite
Were but to them a scene of joyance and
　　　　delight.

2

Vainly, ye blessed twinklers of the night,
　　　　Your feeble beams ye shed,
Quench'd in the unnatural light which
　　　　might out-stare
　　　　Even the broad eye of day ;
And thou from thy celestial way
Pourest, O Moon, an ineffectual ray !
For lo ! ten thousand torches flame and
　　　　flare　　　　20
　　　　Upon the midnight air,
　　　　Blotting the lights of heaven
　　　　With one portentous glare.
Behold the fragrant smoke in many a fold
Ascending, floats along the fiery sky,
And hangeth visible on high,
A dark and waving canopy.

3

Hark ! 'tis the funeral trumpet's breath !
　　　　'Tis the dirge of death !
At once ten thousand drums begin, 30

With one long thunder-peal the ear
        assailing ;
Ten thousand voices then join in,
And with one deep and general din
    Pour their wild wailing.
    The song of praise is drown'd
    Amid the deafening sound ;
You hear no more the trumpet's tone,
You hear no more the mourner's moan,
Though the trumpet's breath, and the
        dirge of death,
Swell with commingled force the funeral
        yell.   40
But rising over all in one acclaim
Is heard the echoed and re-echoed name,
    From all that countless rout ;
        Arvalan ! Arvalan !
        Arvalan ! Arvalan !
Ten times ten thousand voices in one
        shout
Call Arvalan ! The overpowering sound,
From house to house repeated rings
        about,
    From tower to tower rolls round.

4

The death-procession moves along ;
Their bald heads shining to the torches'
        ray,   51
    The Bramins lead the way,
    Chaunting the funeral song.
    And now at once they shout,
        Arvalan ! Arvalan !
    With quick rebound of sound,
        All in accordance cry,
        Arvalan ! Arvalan !
The universal multitude reply.
In vain ye thunder on his ear the name ;
    Would ye awake the dead ?   61
    Borne upright in his palankeen,
    There Arvalan is seen !
A glow is on his face, . . a lively red ;
    It is the crimson canopy
Which o'er his cheek a reddening shade
        hath shed ;

He moves, . . he nods his head, . .
But the motion comes from the bearers'
        tread,
    As the body, borne aloft in state,
Sways with the impulse of its own dead
        weight.   70

5

Close following his dead son, Kehama
        came,
    Nor joining in the ritual song,
    Nor calling the dear name ;
    With head deprest and funeral vest,
    And arms enfolded on his breast,
Silent and lost in thought he moves along.
King of the World, his slaves, unenvying
        now,   [they see
Behold their wretched Lord ; rejoiced
    The mighty Rajah's misery ;
That Nature in his pride hath dealt the
        blow,   80
And taught the Master of Mankind to
        know
Even he himself is man, and not exempt
        from woe.

6

O sight of grief ! the wives of Arvalan,
Young Azla, young Nealliny, are seen !
    Their widow-robes of white,
    With gold and jewels bright,
    Each like an Eastern queen.
Woe ! woe ! around their palankeen,
        As on a bridal day,   89
With symphony, and dance, and song,
Their kindred and their friends come on.
The dance of sacrifice ! the funeral song !
And next the victim slaves in long array,
Richly bedight to grace the fatal day,
    Move onward to their death ;
    The clarions' stirring breath
Lifts their thin robes in every flowing
        fold,
    And swells the woven gold,
    That on the agitated air   99
Flutters and glitters to the torch's glare.

7

A man and maid of aspect wan and wild,
Then, side by side, by bowmen guarded,
                came ;
O wretched father ! O unhappy child !
Them were all eyes of all the throng
                exploring . .
            Is this the daring man
Who raised his fatal hand at Arvalan ?
Is this the wretch condemn'd to feel
        Kehama's dreadful wrath ?
Then were all hearts of all the throng
                deploring ;
For not in that innumerable throng
Was one who loved the dead ; for who
                could know   111
        What aggravated wrong
        Provoked the desperate blow !

8

Far, far behind, beyond all reach of
                sight,
In order'd files the torches flow along,
One ever-lengthening line of gliding
                light :
        Far . . far behind,
Rolls on the undistinguishable clamour,
Of horn, and trump, and tambour ;
        Incessant as the roar   120
Of streams which down the wintry
                mountain pour,
And louder than the dread commotion
        Of breakers on a rocky shore,
When the winds rage over the waves,
        And Ocean to the Tempest raves.

9

And now toward the bank they go,
Where winding on their way below,
Deep and strong the waters flow.
Here doth the funeral pile appear
With myrrh and ambergris bestrew'd,
And built of precious sandal wood.
They cease their music and their outcry
                here,   132
        Gently they rest the bier ;

They wet the face of Arvalan,
No sign of life the sprinkled drops excite ;
They feel his breast, . . no motion there ;
        They feel his lips, . . no breath ;
For not with feeble, nor with erring hand,
The brave avenger dealt the blow of
                death.
Then with a doubling peal and deeper
                blast,   140
The tambours and the trumpets sound
                on high,
        And with a last and loudest cry,
                They call on Arvalan.

10

Woe ! woe ! for Azla takes her seat
        Upon the funeral pile !
        Calmly she took her seat,
Calmly the whole terrific pomp survey'd;
        As on her lap the while
The lifeless head of Arvalan was laid.

11

        Woe ! woe ! Nealliny,   150
        The young Nealliny !
They strip her ornaments away,
Bracelet and anklet, ring, and chain, and
                zone ;
        Around her neck they leave
        The marriage knot alone, . .
        That marriage band, which when
        Yon waning moon was young,
        Around her virgin neck
        With bridal joy was hung.
Then with white flowers, the coronal of
                death,   160
        Her jetty locks they crown.

12

        O sight of misery !
You cannot hear her cries, . . their sound
In that wild dissonance is drown'd ; . .
        But in her face you see
The supplication and the agony, . .
See in her swelling throat the desperate
                strength

That with vain effort struggles yet for
     life;   [strife,
Her arms contracted now in fruitless
     Now wildly at full length   170
Towards the crowd in vain for pity
     spread, . .
They force her on, they bind her to the
     dead.

13

Then all around retire;
Circling the pile, the ministering
     Bramins stand,
Each lifting in his hand a torch on fire.
Alone the Father of the dead advanced
     And lit the funeral pyre.

14

At once on every side
The circling torches drop,
    At once on every side   180
The fragrant oil is pour'd,
    At once on every side
The rapid flames rush up.
Then hand in hand the victim band
Roll in the dance around the funeral
     pyre;
Their garments' flying folds
Float inward to the fire;
In drunken whirl they wheel around;
One drops, . . another plunges in;
And still with overwhelming din 190
The tambours and the trumpets sound;
And clap of hand, and shouts, and cries,
From all the multitude arise;
While round and round, in giddy wheel,
Intoxicate they roll and reel,
Till one by one whirl'd in they fall,
And the devouring flames have swal-
     low'd all.

15

Then all was still; the drums and
     clarions ceased;   [awe;
The multitude were hush'd in silent
Only the roaring of the flames was
     heard.   200

II. THE CURSE

1

ALONE towards the Table of the Dead
Kehama moved; there on the altar-
     stone
    Honey and rice he spread.
There with collected voice and painful
     tone
    He call'd upon his son.
    Lo! Arvalan appears;
Only Kehama's powerful eye beheld
The thin ethereal spirit hovering nigh;
    Only the Rajah's ear
    Received his feeble breath.   10
And is this all? the mournful Spirit said,
This all that thou canst give me after
     death?
    This unavailing pomp,
These empty pageantries that mock the
     dead!

2

In bitterness the Rajah heard,
And groan'd, and smote his breast, and
     o'er his face
    Cowl'd the white mourning vest.

3

ARVALAN

Art thou not powerful, . . even like
     a God?
And must I, through my years of
     wandering,
Shivering and naked to the elements, 20
    In wretchedness await
    The hour of Yamen's wrath?
I thought thou wouldst embody me anew,
    Undying as I am, . .
Yea, re-create me! . . Father, is this all?
    This all? and thou Almighty!

4

But in that wrongful and upbraiding
     tone,
    Kehama found relief,
For rising anger half supprest his grief.

Reproach not me ! he cried,   30
Had I not spell-secured thee from disease,
Fire, sword, . . all common accidents
        of man, . .
And thou ! . . fool, fool . . to perish by
        a stake !
And by a peasant's arm ! . .
Even now, when from reluctant Heaven,
Forcing new gifts and mightier attri-
        butes,
So soon I should have quell'd the Death-
        God's power.

5

Waste not thy wrath on me, quoth
        Arvalan,
It was my hour of folly ! Fate prevail'd,
Nor boots it to reproach me that I fell.
I am in misery, Father ! Other souls
Predoom'd to Indra's Heaven, enjoy
        the dawn   42
Of bliss, . . to them the temper'd ele-
        ments
Minister joy : genial delight the sun
Sheds on their happy being, and the
        stars
Effuse on them benignant influences ;
And thus o'er earth and air they roam
        at will,
And when the number of their days is
        full,
Go fearlessly before the aweful throne.
But I, . . all naked feeling and raw life, . .
What worse than this hath Yamen's hell
        in store ?   51
If ever thou didst love me, mercy,
        Father !
Save me, for thou canst save . . the
        Elements
Know and obey thy voice.

6

KEHAMA

The Elements
Shall sin no more against thee ; whilst
        I speak

Already dost thou feel their power is
        gone.
Fear not ! I cannot call again the
        past,
Fate hath made that its own ; but Fate
        shall yield
To me the future ; and thy doom be
        fix'd   60
By mine, not Yamen's will. Meantime
        all power
Whereof thy feeble spirit can be made
Participant, I give. Is there aught else
        To mitigate thy lot ?

ARVALAN

Only the sight of vengeance. Give me
        that !
Vengeance, full, worthy, vengeance ! . .
        not the stroke
Of sudden punishment, . . no agony
That spends itself and leaves the wretch
        at rest,
        But lasting long revenge.

KEHAMA

What, boy ? is that cup sweet ? then
        take thy fill !   70

7

So as he spake, a glow of dreadful pride
Inflamed his cheek, with quick and
        angry stride
        He moved toward the pile,
And raised his hand to hush the crowd,
        and cried,
Bring forth the murderer ! At the
        Rajah's voice,
Calmly, and like a man whom fear had
        stunn'd,
Ladurlad came, obedient to the call ;
        But Kailyal started at the sound,
And gave a womanly shriek, and back
        she drew,   79
And eagerly she roll'd her eyes around,
As if to seek for aid, albeit she knew
        No aid could there be found.

8

It chanced that near her on the river
brink,
The sculptured form of Marriataly
stood ;
It was an Idol roughly hewn of wood,
Artless, and mean, and rude ;
The Goddess of the poor was she ;
None else regarded her with piety.
But when that holy Image Kailyal
view'd,   89
To that she sprung, to that she clung,
On her own Goddess, with close-clasping
arms,
For life the maiden hung.

9

They seized the maid ; with unrelenting
grasp
They bruised her tender limbs ;
She, nothing yielding, to this only hope
Clings with the strength of frenzy and
despair.
She screams not now, she breathes not
now,
She sends not up one vow,
She forms not in her soul one secret
prayer,
All thought, all feeling, and all powers
of life   100
In the one effort centering. Wrathful
they
With tug and strain would force the
maid away ; . .
Didst thou, O Marriataly, see their strife,
In pity didst thou see the suffering maid ?
Or was thine anger kindled, that rude
hands
Assail'd thy holy Image ? . . for behold
The holy image shakes !

10

Irreverently bold, they deem the maid
Relax'd her stubborn hold,
And now with force redoubled drag their
prey ;   110

And now the rooted Idol to their sway
Bends, . . yields, . . and now it falls.
But then they scream,
For lo ! they feel the crumbling bank
give way,
And all are plunged into the stream.

11

She hath escaped my will, Kehama cried,
She hath escaped, . . but thou art here,
I have thee still,
The worser criminal !
And on Ladurlad, while he spake, severe
He fix'd his dreadful frown.   120
The strong reflection of the pile
Lit his dark lineaments,
Lit the protruded brow, the gathered,
front,
The steady eye of wrath.

12

But while the fearful silence yet endured,
Ladurlad roused himself ;
Ere yet the voice of destiny
Which trembled on the Rajah's lips was
loosed,
Eager he interposed,   129
As if despair had waken'd him to hope ;
Mercy ! oh mercy ! only in defence . .
Only instinctively, . .
Only to save my child, I smote the
Prince ;
King of the world, be merciful !
Crush me, . . but torture not !

13

The Man-Almighty deign'd him no reply,
Still he stood silent ; in no human mood
Of mercy, in no hesitating thought
Of right and justice. At the length he
raised
His brow yet unrelax'd, . . his lips
unclosed,   140
And uttered from the heart,
With the whole feeling of his soul en-
forced,
The gathered vengeance came.

14

I charm thy life
From the weapons of strife,
From stone and from wood,
From fire and from flood,
From the serpent's tooth,
And the beasts of blood :
From Sickness I charm thee,   150
And Time shall not harm thee ;
But Earth which is mine,
Its fruits shall deny thee ;
And Water shall hear me,
And know thee and fly thee ;
And the Winds shall not touch thee
When they pass by thee,
And the Dews shall not wet thee,
When they fall nigh thee :
And thou shalt seek Death   160
To release thee, in vain ;
Thou shalt live in thy pain
While Kehama shall reign,
With a fire in thy heart,
And a fire in thy brain ;
And Sleep shall obey me,
And visit thee never,
And the Curse shall be on thee
For ever and ever.

15

There where the Curse had stricken him,
There stood the miserable man,   171
There stood Ladurlad, with loose-hang-
ing arms,
And eyes of idiot wandering.
Was it a dream ? alas,
He heard the river flow,
He heard the crumbling of the pile,
He heard the wind which shower'd
The thin white ashes round.
There motionless he stood,
As if he hoped it were a dream,   180
And feared to move, lest he should prove
The actual misery ;
And still at times he met Kehama's eye,
Kehama's eye that fastened on him still.

III. THE RECOVERY

1

THE Rajah turn'd toward the pile again,
Loud rose the song of death from all the
crowd ;
Their din the instruments begin,
And once again join in
With overwhelming sound.
Ladurlad starts, . . he looks around ;
What hast thou here in view,
O wretched man ! in this disastrous
scene ;
The soldier train, the Bramins who
renew
Their ministry around the funeral pyre,
The empty palankeens,   11
The dimly-fading fire.

2

Where too is she whom most his heart
held dear,
His best-beloved Kailyal, where is she,
The solace and the joy of many a year
Of widowhood ? is she then gone,
And is he left all-utterly alone,
To bear his blasting curse, and none
To succour or deplore him ?
He staggers from the dreadful spot ; the
throng   20
Give way in fear before him ;
Like one who carries pestilence about,
Shuddering they shun him, where he
moves along.
And now he wanders on
Beyond the noisy rout ;
He cannot fly and leave his Curse behind,
Yet doth he seem to find
A comfort in the change of circumstance.
Adown the shore he strays,
Unknowing where his wretched feet
shall rest,   30
But farthest from the fatal place is best.

3

By this in the orient sky appears the
          gleam
Of day.   Lo ! what is yonder in the
          stream,
Down the slow river floating slow,
In distance indistinct and dimly seen ?
The childless one with idle eye
Followed its motion thoughtlessly ;
Idly he gazed unknowing why,
And half unconscious that he watch'd
          its way.
          Belike it is a tree   40
Which some rude tempest, in its sudden
          sway,
Tore from the rock, or from the hollow
          shore
The undermining stream hath swept
          away.

4

But when anon outswelling by its side,
A woman's robe he spied,
Oh then Ladurlad started,
As one, who in his grave
Had heard an Angel's call.
Yea, Marriataly, thou hast deign'd to
          save !
          Yea, Goddess ! it is she,   50
Kailyal, still clinging senselessly
To thy dear Image, and in happy hour
Upborne amid the wave
By that preserving power.

5

Headlong in hope and in joy
Ladurlad plunged in the water ;
The Water knew Kehama's spell,
The Water shrunk before him.
Blind to the miracle,
He rushes to his daughter,   60
And treads the river-depths in transport
          wild,
And clasps and saves his child.

6

Upon the farther side a level shore
Of sand was spread : thither Ladurlad
          bore
His daughter, holding still with senseless
          hand
The saving Goddess ; there upon the sand
          He laid the livid maid,
Raised up against his knees her drooping
          head ;
Bent to her lips, . . her lips as pale as
          death, . .
          If he might feel her breath,   70
His own the while in hope and dread
          suspended ;
Chafed her cold breast, and ever and
          anon
Let his hand rest upon her heart ex-
          tended.

7

Soon did his touch perceive, or fancy
          there,
The first faint motion of returning life.
He chafes her feet and lays them bare
In the sun ; and now again upon her
          breast
Lays his hot hand ; and now her lips he
          prest,
For now the stronger throb of life he
          knew ;
          And her lips tremble too !   80
The breath comes palpably :
Her quivering lids unclose,
Feebly and feebly fall,
Relapsing as it seem'd to dead repose.

8

So in her father's arms thus languidly,
While over her with earnest gaze he
          hung,
          Silent and motionless she lay,
And painfully and slowly writhed at fits,
At fits to short convulsive starts was
          stung.   89

Till when the struggle and strong agony
Had left her, quietly she lay reposed :
Her eyes now resting on Ladurlad's face,
Relapsing now, and now again unclosed.
The look she fix'd upon his face, implies
Nor thought nor feeling ; senselessly
she lies. [eyes.
Composed like one who sleeps with open

9

Long he leant over her,
In silence and in fear.
Kailyal ! . . at length he cried in such
a tone
As a poor mother ventures who draws
near, 100
With silent footstep, to her child's sick
bed. [her head,
My Father ! cried the maid, and raised
Awakening then to life and thought, . .
thou here ?
For when his voice she heard,
The dreadful past recurr'd,
Which dimly, like a dream of pain,
Till now with troubled sense confused
her brain.

10

And hath he spared us then ? she cried,
Half rising as she spake,
For hope and joy the sudden strength
supplied ; 110
In mercy hath he curb'd his cruel will,
That still thou livest ? But as thus she
said,
Impatient of that look of hope, her sire
Shook hastily his head ;
Oh ! he hath laid a Curse upon my life,
A clinging curse, quoth he ;
Hath sent a fire into my heart and brain,
A burning fire, for ever there to be !
The Winds of Heaven must never
breathe on me ;
The Rains and Dews must never fall on
me ; 120

Water must mock my thirst and shrink
from me ;
The common Earth must yield no fruit
to me ;
Sleep, blessed Sleep ! must never light
on me ;
And Death, who comes to all, must fly
from me,
And never, never set Ladurlad free.

11

This is a dream ! exclaim'd the in-
credulous maid,
Yet in her voice the while a fear exprest,
Which in her larger eye was manifest.
This is a dream ! she rose and laid her
hand
Upon her father's brow, to try the
charm ; 130
He could not bear the pressure there ; . .
he shrunk, . .
He warded off her arm,
As though it were an enemy's blow, he
smote
His daughter's arm aside.
Her eye glanced down, his mantle she
espied
And caught it up ; . . Oh misery !
Kailyal cried, [yet
He bore me from the river-depths, and
His garment is not wet !

IV. THE DEPARTURE

1

RECLINED beneath a Cocoa's feathery
shade
Ladurlad lies,
And Kailyal on his lap her head hath
laid,
To hide her streaming eyes.
The boatman, sailing on his easy way,
With envious eye beheld them where
they lay ;

For every herb and flower
Was fresh and fragrant with the early
      dew,   [hour,
Sweet sung the birds in that delicious
And the cool gale of morning as it blew,
Not yet subdued by day's increasing
      power,   11
Ruffling the surface of the silvery stream,
Swept o'er the moisten'd sand, and
      rais'd no shower.
Telling their tale of love,
The boatman thought they lay
At that lone hour, and who so blest as
      they !

2

But now the Sun in heaven is high,
    The little songsters of the sky
    Sit silent in the sultry hour,
They pant and palpitate with heat ;
    Their bills are open languidly   21
    To catch the passing air ;
They hear it not, they feel it not,
It murmurs not, it moves not.
The boatman, as he looks to land,
Admires what men so mad to linger
      there,
For yonder Cocoa's shade behind them
      falls,
A single spot upon the burning sand.

3

There all the morning was Ladurlad laid,
Silent and motionless like one at ease ;
There motionless upon her father's knees
    Reclined the silent maid.   32
The man was still, pondering with steady
      mind,
    As if it were another's Curse,
    His own portentous lot ;
Scanning it o'er and o'er in busy thought,
As though it were a last night's tale of
      woe,
    Before the cottage door
    By some old beldam sung,

While young and old, assembled round,
  Listened, as if by witchery bound, 41
In fearful pleasure to her wondrous
      tongue.

4

Musing so long he lay, that all things
      seem
Unreal to his sense, even like a dream,
A monstrous dream of things which
      could not be.
That beating, burning brow, . . why it
    was now   [there
The height of noon, and he was lying
    In the broad sun, all bare !
What if he felt no wind ? the air was
      still.
    That was the general will   50
Of Nature, not his own peculiar doom ;
Yon rows of rice erect and silent stand,
  The shadow of the Cocoa's lightest
      plume
    Is steady on the sand.

5

Is it indeed a dream ? he rose to try,
  Impatient to the water side he went,
    And down he bent,
And in the stream he plunged his hasty
      arm
    To break the visionary charm.
With fearful eye and fearful heart, 60
  His daughter watch'd the event ;
    She saw the start and shudder,
    She heard the in-drawn groan,
For the Water knew Kehama's charm,
  The Water shrunk before his arm.
His dry hand moved about unmoisten'd
      there ;
As easily might that dry hand avail
    To stop the passing gale,
    Or grasp the impassive air.
    He is Almighty then !   70
Exclaim'd the wretched man in his
      despair ;

Air knows him, Water knows him ; Sleep
His dreadful word will keep ;
Even in the grave there is no rest for me,
Cut off from that last hope, . . the
wretch's joy ;
And Veeshnoo hath no power to save,
Nor Seeva to destroy,

6

Oh ! wrong not them ! quoth Kailyal,
Wrong not the Heavenly Powers !
Our hope is all in them : They are not
blind !   80
And lighter wrongs than ours,
And lighter crimes than his,
Have drawn the Incarnate down among
mankind.
Already have the Immortals heard our
cries,
And in the mercy of their righteousness
Beheld us in the hour of our distress !
She spake with streaming eyes,
Where pious love and ardent feeling
beam.
And turning to the Image, threw
Her grateful arms around it, . . It was
thou   90
Who savedst me from the stream !
My Marriataly, it was thou !
I had not else been here
To share my Father's Curse,
To suffer now, . . and yet to thank thee
thus !

7

Here then, the maiden cried, dear
Father, here
Raise our own Goddess, our divine
Preserver !
The mighty of the earth despise her rites,
She loves the poor who serve her.
Set up her Image here,   100
With heart and voice the guardian
Goddess bless,
For jealously would she resent
Neglect and thanklessness ; . .

Set up her Image here,
And bless her for her aid with tongue
and soul sincere.

8

So saying on her knees the maid
Began the pious toil.
Soon their joint labour scoops the easy
soil ;   [hand,
They raise the Image up with reverent
And round its rooted base they heap the
sand.   110
O Thou whom we adore,
O Marriataly, thee do I implore,
The virgin cried ; my Goddess, pardon
thou
The unwilling wrong, that I no more,
With dance and song,
Can do thy daily service, as of yore !
The flowers which last I wreathed around
thy brow,
Are withering there ; and never now
Shall I at eve adore thee,
And swimming round with arms out-
spread,   120
Poise the full pitcher on my head,
In dexterous dance before thee,
While underneath the reedy shed, at rest
My father sat the evening rites to view,
And blest thy name, and blest
His daughter too.

9

Then heaving from her heart a heavy sigh,
O Goddess ! from that happy home,
cried she,
The Almighty Man hath forced us !
And homeward with the thought un-
consciously   130
She turn'd her dizzy eye. . . But there
on high,
With many a dome, and pinnacle, and
spire,
The summits of the Golden Palaces
Blazed in the dark blue sky, aloft, like
fire.

Father, away ! she cried, away !
Why linger we so nigh ?
For not to him hath Nature given
The thousand eyes of Deity,
Always and every where with open
    sight,
        To persecute our flight !   140
Away . . away ! she said,
And took her father's hand, and like a
        child
He followed where she led.

V. THE SEPARATION

1

EVENING comes on : arising from the
    stream,
    Homeward the tall flamingo wings
        his flight ;
And where he sails athwart the setting
    beam,
    His scarlet plumage glows with deeper
        light.
The watchman, at the wish'd approach
    of night,
    Gladly forsakes the field, where he all
        day,
To scare the winged plunderers from
    their prey,
    With shout and sling, on yonder
        clay-built height,
        Hath borne the sultry ray.
    Hark ! at the Golden Palaces   10
        The Bramin strikes the hour.
For leagues and leagues around, the
    brazen sound
Rolls through the stillness of departing
    day,
    Like thunder far away.

2

Behold them wandering on their hope-
    less way,
    Unknowing where they stray,

Yet sure where'er they stop to find no
    rest.
    The evening gale is blowing,
    It plays among the trees ;
Like plumes upon a warrior's crest,
They see yon cocoas tossing to the
    breeze.   21
Ladurlad views them with impatient
    mind,
    Impatiently he hears
    The gale of evening blowing,
    The sound of waters flowing,
As if all sights and sounds combined
    To mock his irremediable woe ;
For not for him the blessed waters flow,
For not for him the gales of evening blow,
    A fire is in his heart and brain,   30
And Nature hath no healing for his pain.

3

    The Moon is up, still pale
    Amid the lingering light.
A cloud ascending in the eastern sky,
    Sails slowly o'er the vale,
And darkens round and closes in the
    night.
    No hospitable house is nigh,
No traveller's home the wanderers to
    invite ;
    Forlorn, and with long watching
        overworn,
The wretched father and the wretched
        child   40
    Lie down amid the wild.

4

    Before them full in sight,
A white flag flapping to the winds of night
Marks where the tiger seized a human
        prey.
    Far, far away with natural dread,
        Shunning the perilous spot,
    At other times abhorrent had they fled ;
        But now they heed it not.
Nothing they care ; the boding death-
        flag now

F

In vain for them may gleam and flutter
     there.   50
Despair and agony in him,
Prevent all other thought ;
And Kailyal hath no heart or sense for
     aught,
Save her dear father's strange and
     miserable lot.

5

There in the woodland shade,
Upon the lap of that unhappy maid,
     His head Ladurlad laid,
     And never word he spake ;
     Nor heaved he one complaining sigh,
Nor groaned he with his misery,   60
     But silently for her dear sake
     Endured the raging pain.
And now the moon was hid on high,
No stars were glimmering in the sky ;
She could not see her father's eye,
     How red with burning agony ;
Perhaps he may be cooler now,
She hoped, and long'd to touch his
     brow
With gentle hand, yet did not dare
To lay the painful pressure there. 70
Now forward from the tree she bent,
And anxiously her head she leant,
     And listen'd to his breath.
Ladurlad's breath was short and quick,
     Yet regular it came,
     And like the slumber of the sick,
     In pantings still the same.
Oh if he sleeps ! . . her lips unclose,
Intently listening to the sound,
That equal sound so like repose.   80
Still quietly the sufferer lies,
Bearing his torment now with resolute
     will ;
He neither moves, nor groans, nor sighs.
     Doth satiate cruelty bestow
     This little respite to his woe,
She thought, or are there Gods who look
     below ?

6

Perchance, thought Kailyal, willingly
     deceived,
Our Marriataly hath his pain relieved,
And she hath bade the blessed sleep
     assuage   89
His agony, despite the Rajah's rage,
That was a hope which fill'd her gushing
     eyes,
And made her heart in silent yearnings
     rise,
To bless the power divine in thankful-
     ness.
And yielding to that joyful thought
     her mind,
Backward the maid her aching head
     reclined
Against the tree, and to her father's
     breath   [ear.
In fear she hearken'd still with earnest
But soon forgetful fits the effort broke ;
In starts of recollection then she woke,
Till now benignant Nature over-
     came   100
The Virgin's weary and exhausted frame,
Nor able more her painful watch to keep,
She closed her heavy lids, and sunk to
     sleep.

7

Vain was her hope ! he did not rest from
     pain,
The Curse was burning in his brain ;
Alas ! the innocent maiden thought he
     slept,
But Sleep the Rajah's dread command-
     ment kept,
     Sleep knew Kehama's Curse.
The dews of night fell round them now,
They never bathed Ladurlad's brow,
     They knew Kehama's Curse.   111
     The night-wind is abroad,
Aloft it moves among the stirring trees ;
     He only heard the breeze, . .
No healing aid to him it brought,

It play'd around his head and touch'd
  him not,
    It knew Kehama's Curse.

8

Listening, Ladurlad lay in his despair,
If Kailyal slept, for wherefore should
  she share
Her father's wretchedness, which none
  could cure?   120
  Better alone to suffer; he must bear
The burden of his Curse, but why endure
. The unavailing presence of her grief?
  She too, apart from him, might find
    relief;
For dead the Rajah deem'd her, and
  as thus
Already she his dread revenge had fled,
So might she still escape and live secure.

9

    Gently he lifts his head,
  And Kailyal does not feel;   129
Gently he rises up, .. she slumbers still;
  Gently he steals away with silent
    tread.
Anon she started, for she felt him gone;
She call'd, and through the stillness of
  the night,
    His step was heard in flight.
Mistrustful for a moment of the sound,
She listens; till the step is heard no
    more;
But then she knows that he indeed is
    gone,
And with a thrilling shriek she rushes on.
The darkness and the wood impede her
    speed;
    She lifts her voice again,   140
Ladurlad! .. and again, alike in vain,
  And with a louder cry [away,
Straining its tone to hoarseness; .. far
    Selfish in misery,
He heard the call and faster did he fly.

10

She leans against that tree whose jutting
    bough
  Smote her so rudely. Her poor heart
    How audibly it panted,
  With sudden stop and start;
Her breath how short and painfully it
    came!   150
    Hark! all is still around her, ..
    And the night so utterly dark,
  She opened her eyes and she closed
    them,
And the blackness and blank were the
    same.

11

'Twas like a dream of horror, and she
    stood
  Half doubting whether all indeed
    were true.
A tiger's howl loud echoing through the
    wood,
  Roused her; the dreadful sound she
    knew,
And turn'd instinctively to what she
    fear'd.
  Far off the tiger's hungry howl was
    heard;   160
A nearer horror met the maiden's view,
  For right before her a dim form appear'd,
  A human form in that black night,
Distinctly shaped by its own lurid light,
  Such light as the sickly moon is seen
    to shed,
Through spell-raised fogs, a bloody
    baleful red.

12

That Spectre fix'd his eyes upon her full;
The light which shone in their accursed
    orbs
    Was like a light from Hell,
And it grew deeper, kindling with the
    view.   170
    She could not turn her sight

From that infernal gaze, which like
a spell
Bound her, and held her rooted to
the ground.
It palsied every power,
Her limbs avail'd her not in that dread
hour,
There was no moving thence.
Thought, memory, sense were gone :
She heard not now the tiger's nearer cry,
She thought not on her father now,
Her cold heart's blood ran back, 180
Her hand lay senseless on the bough it
clasp'd,
Her feet were motionless ;
Her fascinated eyes
Like the stone eye-balls of a statue fix'd,
Yet conscious of the sight that blasted
them.

13

The wind is abroad,
It opens the clouds ;
Scatter'd before the gale,
They skurry through the sky,
And the darkness retiring rolls over the
vale.   190
The Stars in their beauty come forth on
high,
And through the dark blue night
The Moon rides on triumphant, broad
and bright.
Distinct and darkening in her light,
Appears that Spectre foul,
The moon-beam gives his face and form
to sight,
The shape of man,
The living form and face of Arvalan ! . .
His hands are spread to clasp her.

14

But at that sight of dread the Maid
awoke ;   200
As if a lightning-stroke
Had burst the spell of fear,

Away she broke all franticly, and fled.
There stood a temple near beside the
way,
An open fane of Pollear, gentle God,
To whom the travellers for protection
pray.
With elephantine head and eye severe,
Here stood his image, such as when he
seiz'd
And tore the rebel Giant from the
ground,   209
With mighty trunk wreathed round
His impotent bulk, and on his tusks, on
high
Impaled upheld him between earth and
sky.

15

Thither the affrighted Maiden sped her
flight,
And she hath reach'd the place of
sanctuary ;
And now within the temple in despite,
Yea, even before the altar, in his
sight,
Hath Arvalan with flesh.y arm of might
Seized her.   That instant the insulted
God
Caught him aloft, and from his sinuous
grasp,   219
As if from some tort catapult let loose,
Over the forest hurl'd him all abroad.

16

O'ercome with dread,
She tarried not to see what heavenly
Power
Had saved her in that hour ;
Breathless and faint she fled.
And now her foot struck on the knotted
root
Of a broad manchineil, and there the
Maid
Fell senselessly beneath the deadly
shade.

VI. CASYAPA

1

SHALL this then be thy fate, O lovely
Maid,
Thus, Kailyal, must thy sorrows then
be ended ?
Her face upon the ground,
Her arms at length extended,
There like a corpse behold her laid
Beneath the deadly shade.
What if the hungry tiger, prowling by,
Should snuff his banquet nigh ?
Alas, Death needs not now his ministry ;
The baleful boughs hang o'er her,   10
The poison-dews descend.
What Power will now restore her ?
What God will be her friend ?

2

Bright and so beautiful was that fair
night,
It might have calm'd the gay amid
their mirth,
And given the wretched a delight in
tears.
One of the Glendoveers,
The loveliest race of all of heavenly
birth,
Hovering with gentle motion o'er the
earth,
Amid the moonlight air,   20
In sportive flight was floating round and
round,
Unknowing where his joyous way was
tending.
He saw the Maid where motionless she
lay,
And stoopt his flight descending,
And raised her from the ground.
Her heavy eye-lids are half closed,
Her cheeks are pale and livid like the
dead,
Down hang her loose arms lifelessly,
Down hangs her languid head.

3

With timely pity touch'd for one so fair,
The gentle Glendoveer   31
Press'd her thus pale and senseless to
his breast,
And springs aloft in air with sinewy wings,
And bears the Maiden there,
Where Himakoot, the holy Mount, on high
From mid-earth rising in mid-Heaven,
Shines in its glory like the throne of
Even.
Soaring with strenuous flight above,
He bears her to the blessed Grove,
Where in his ancient and august abodes,
There dwells old Casyapa, the Sire
of Gods.   41

4

The Father of the Immortals sate,
Where underneath the Tree of Life,
The Fountains of the Sacred River
sprung ;
The Father of the Immortals smiled
Benignant on his son.
Knowest thou, he said, my child,
Ereenia, knowest thou whom thou
bringest here,
A mortal to the holy atmosphere ?

EREENIA

I found her in the Groves of Earth,
Beneath a poison-tree,   51
Thus lifeless as thou seest her.
In pity have I brought her to these
bowers,
Not erring, Father ! by that smile ..
By that benignant eye !

CASYAPA

What if the Maid be sinful ? if her ways
Were ways of darkness, and her death
predoom'd
To that black hour of midnight, when
the Moon
Hath turn'd her face away,
Unwilling to behold   60
The unhappy end of guilt ?

EREENIA

Then what a lie, my Sire, were written
          here,   [died,
In these fair characters ! and she had
Sure proof of purer life and happier
          doom,   [Heaven,
Now in the moonlight, in the eye of
If I had left so fair a flower to fade.
But thou, . . all knowing as thou art,
     Why askest thou of me ?
O Father, oldest, holiest, wisest, best,
     To whom all things are plain,   70
     Why askest thou of me ?

CASYAPA

Knowest thou Kehama ?

EREENIA

The Almighty Man !
Who knows not him and his tremendous
          power ?
     The Tyrant of the Earth,
     The Enemy of Heaven !

CASYAPA

Fearest thou the Rajah ?

EREENIA

He is terrible !

CASYAPA

Yea, he is terrible ! such power hath he
     That hope hath enter'd Hell.   80
The Asuras and the spirits of the damn'd
Acclaim their Hero ; Yamen, with the
          might
     Of Godhead, scarce can quell
     The rebel race accurst :   [rise,
Half from their beds of torture they up-
And half uproot their chains.
Is there not fear in Heaven ?
The Souls that are in bliss suspend their
          joy ;
     The danger hath disturb'd
     The calm of Deity,   90
And Brama fears, and Veeshnoo turns
          his face
     In doubt toward Seeva's throne.

EREENIA

I have seen Indra tremble at his prayers,
And at his dreadful penances turn pale.
They claim and wrest from Seeva power
          so vast,
     That even Seeva's self,
The Highest, cannot grant and be secure.

CASYAPA

     And darest thou, Ereenia, brave
     The Almighty Tyrant's power ?

EREENIA

     I brave him, Father ! I ?   100

CASYAPA

Darest thou brave his vengeance ? . . For,
          if not,
     Take her again to earth,
Cast her before the tiger in his path,
Or where the death-dew-dropping tree
     May work Kehama's will.

EREENIA

Never !

CASYAPA

Then meet his wrath ! for He, even He,
Hath set upon this worm his wanton
          foot.

EREENIA

I knew her not, how wretched and how
          fair,
When here I wafted her. . . Poor Child
          of Earth,   110
Shall I forsake thee, seeing thee so fair,
So wretched ?   O my Father, let the
          Maid
     Dwell in the Sacred Grove !

CASYAPA

     That must not be,
For Force and Evil then would enter
          here ;   [sin,
Ganges, the holy stream which cleanseth
Would flow from hence polluted in
          its springs,   [death,
And they who gasp upon its banks in

Feel no salvation. Piety, and Peace,
And Wisdom, these are mine ; but not
the power 120
Which could protect her from the
Almighty Man ;
Nor when the spirit of dead Arvalan
Should persecute her here to glut his
rage,
To heap upon her yet more agony,
And ripen more damnation for himself.

EREENIA

Dead Arvalan ?

CASYAPA

All power to him, whereof
The disembodied spirit in its state
Of weakness could be made participant,
Kehama hath assign'd, until his days
Of wandering shall be number'd. 131

EREENIA

Look ! she drinks
The gale of healing from the blessed
Groves.
She stirs, and lo ! her hand
Hath touch'd the Holy River in its
source,
Who would have shrunk if aught impure
were nigh.

CASYAPA

The Maiden, of a truth, is pure from sin.

5

The waters of the Holy Spring
About the hand of Kailyal play ;
They rise, they sparkle, and they sing,
Leaping where languidly she lay, 141
As if with that rejoicing stir
The Holy Spring would welcome her.
The Tree of life which o'er her spread,
Benignant bow'd its sacred head,
And dropt its dews of healing ;
And her heart-blood at every breath,
Recovering from the strife of death,
Drew in new strength and feeling.
Behold her beautiful in her repose, 150

A life-bloom reddening now her dark-
brown cheek ;
And lo ! her eyes unclose,
Dark as the depth of Ganges' spring
profound
When night hangs over it,
Bright as the moon's refulgent beam,
That quivers on its clear up-sparkling
stream.

6

Soon she let fall her lids,
As one who, from a blissful dream
Waking to thoughts of pain,
Fain would return to sleep, and dream
again. 160
Distrustful of the sight,
She moves not, fearing to disturb
The deep and full delight.
In wonder fix'd, opening again her eye
She gazes silently,
Thinking her mortal pilgrimage was past,
That she had reach'd her heavenly home
of rest,
And these were Gods before her,
Or spirits of the blest.

7

Lo ! at Ereenia's voice. 170
A Ship of Heaven comes sailing down
the skies.
Where would'st thou bear her ? cries
The ancient Sire of Gods.
Straight to the Swerga, to my Bower of
Bliss,
The Glendoveer replies,
To Indra's own abodes.
Foe of her foe, were it alone for this
Indra should guard her from his ven-
geance there ;
But if the God forbear,
Unwilling yet the perilous strife to try,
Or shrinking from the dreadful Rajah's
might, . . 181
Weak as I am, O Father, even I
Stand forth in Seeva's sight.

8

Trust thou in him whate'er betide,
And stand forth fearlessly !
The Sire of Gods replied :
All that He wills is right, and doubt not
thou,
Howe'er our feeble scope of sight
May fail us now,
His righteous will in all things must be
done.   190
My blessing be upon thee, O my son !

VII. THE SWERGA

1

THEN in the Ship of Heaven, Ereenia
laid
The waking, wondering Maid ;
The Ship of Heaven, instinct with
thought, display'd
Its living sail, and glides along the sky.
On either side in wavy tide,
The clouds of morn along its path divide;
The Winds who swept in wild career on
high,   [force ;
Before its presence check their charmed
The Winds that loitering lagg'd along
their course,
Around the living Bark enamour'd play,
Swell underneath the sail, and sing
before its way.   11

2

That Bark, in shape, was like the
furrow'd shell
Wherein the Sea-Nymphs to their parent-
King,   [bring.
On festal day, their duteous offerings
Its hue ? . . Go watch the last green
light   [Night ;
Ere Evening yields the western sky to
Or fix upon the Sun thy strenuous sight
Till thou hast reach'd its orb of
chrysolite.

The sail from end to end display'd
Bent, like a rainbow, o'er the Maid.
An Angel's head, with visual eye,   21
Through trackless space, directs its
chosen way ;
Nor aid of wing, nor foot, nor fin,
Requires to voyage o'er the obedient
sky.
Smooth as the swan when not a breeze
at even
Disturbs the surface of the silver stream,
Through air and sunshine sails the Ship
of Heaven.

3

Recumbent there the Maiden glides
along
On her aërial way,
How swift she feels not, though the
swiftest wind   30
Had flagg'd in flight behind.
Motionless as a sleeping babe she lay,
And all serene in mind,
Feeling no fear ; for that etherial air
With such new life and joyance fill'd her
heart,
Fear could not enter there ;
For sure she deem'd her mortal part
was o'er,
And she was sailing to the heavenly
shore ;   [beside,
And that angelic form, who moved
Was some good Spirit sent to be her
guide.   40

4

Daughter of Earth ! therein thou deem'st
aright ;
And never yet did form more beautiful,
In dreams of night descending from
on high,
Bless the religious Virgin's gifted sight,
Nor like a vision of delight,
Rise on the raptured Poet's inward eye.
Of human form divine was he,

The immortal Youth of Heaven who
floated by,
Even such as that divinest form shall be
In those blest stages of our onward race,
When no infirmity,   51
Low thought, nor base desire, nor
wasting care,
Deface the semblance of our heavenly
sire.

5

The wings of Eagle or of Cherubim
Had seem'd unworthy him ;
Angelic power and dignity and grace
Were in his glorious pennons ; from the
neck
Down to the ankle reach'd their swelling
web
Richer than robes of Tyrian dye, that
deck
    Imperial Majesty :   60
Their colour like the winter's moonless
sky,
When all the stars of midnight's canopy
Shine forth ; or like the azure deep at
noon,
Reflecting back to heaven a brighter
blue.
Such was their tint when closed, but
when outspread,
    The permeating light
Shed through their substance thin a
varying hue ;
Now bright as when the rose,
Beauteous as fragrant, gives to scent
and sight
A like delight ; now like the juice that
flows   70
From Douro's generous vine ;
Or ruby when with deepest red it glows ;
Or as the morning clouds refulgent
shine,
When, at forthcoming of the Lord of
Day,
The Orient, like a shrine,

Kindles as it receives the rising ray,
    And heralding his way,
Proclaims the presence of the Power
divine.

6

Thus glorious were the wings   79
Of that celestial Spirit, as he went
Disporting through his native element.
    Nor these alone
The gorgeous beauties that they gave
to view ;
Through the broad membrane branched
a pliant bone,   [stem,
Spreading like fibres from their parent
Its veins like interwoven silver shone,
    Or as the chaster hue
Of pearls that grace some Sultan's
diadem.
Now with slow stroke and strong behold
him smite
The buoyant air, and now in gentler
flight,   90
On motionless wing expanded, shoot
along.

7

Through air and sunshine sails the Ship
of Heaven ;
    Far, far beneath them lies
The gross and heavy atmosphere of
earth ;
    And with the Swerga gales,
    The Maid of mortal birth
At every breath a new delight inhales.
And now toward its port the Ship of
Heaven,   [flight,
Swift as a falling meteor, shapes its
Yet gently as the dews of night that
gem,   100
And do not bend the hare-bell's
slenderest stem.
Daughter of Earth, Ereenia cried, alight ;
This is thy place of rest, the Swerga this,
    Lo, here my Bower of Bliss !

8

He furl'd his azure wings, which round
        him fold
Graceful as robes of Grecian chief of old.
The happy Kailyal knew not where
        to gaze ;
Her eyes around in joyful wonder roam,
Now turn'd upon the lovely Glendoveer,
Now on his heavenly home.   110

EREENIA

Here, Maiden, rest in peace,
And I will guard thee, feeble as I am.
The Almighty Rajah shall not harm
        thee here,
While Indra keeps his throne.

KAILYAL

Alas, thou fearest him !
Immortal as thou art, thou fearest him !
I thought that death had saved me from
        his power ;
Not even the dead are safe.

EREENIA

Long years of life and happiness,
        O Child of Earth be thine !   120
From death I sav'd thee, and from all
        thy foes
Will save thee, while the Swerga is
        secure.

KAILYAL

Not me alone, O gentle Deveta !
I have a Father suffering upon earth,
A persecuted, wretched, poor, good man,
        For whose strange misery
        There is no human help,
And none but I dare comfort him
        Beneath Kehama's Curse ;   129
O gentle Deveta, protect him too !

EREENIA

Come, plead thyself to Indra ! Words
        like thine
May win their purpose, rouse his slum-
        bering heart,

And make him yet put forth his arm to
        wield
The thunder, while the thunder is his
        own.

9

Then to the Garden of the Deity
        Ereenia led the Maid.
In the mid garden tower'd a giant Tree ;
Rock-rooted on a mountain-top, it grew,
        Rear'd its unrivall'd head on high,
And stretch'd a thousand branches o'er
        the sky,   140
Drinking with all its leaves celestial dew.
Lo ! where from thence as from a living
        well
        A thousand torrents flow !
For still in one perpetual shower,
Like diamond drops, etherial waters fell
From every leaf of all its ample bower.
        Rolling adown the steep
        From that aërial height,
Through the deep shade of aromatic
        trees,
Half-seen, the cataracts shoot their
        gleams of light,   150
        And pour upon the breeze
Their thousand voices ; far away the
        roar,
In modulations of delightful sound,
Half-heard and ever varying, floats
        around.
Below, an ample Lake expanded lies,
        Blue as the o'er-arching skies :
Forth issuing from that lovely Lake
A thousand rivers water Paradise.
Full to the brink, yet never overflowing,
They cool the amorous gales, which,
        ever blowing,   160
O'er their melodious surface love to
        stray ;
        Then winging back their way,
Their vapours to the parent Tree repay ;
And ending thus where they began,

And feeding thus the source from whence
    they came,
The eternal rivers of the Swerga ran,
For ever renovate, yet still the same.

10

On that ethereal lake, whose waters lie
Blue and transpicuous, like another sky,
The Elements had rear'd their King's
    abode   170
A strong controuling power their strife
    suspended,
And there their hostile essences they
    blended,
To form a Palace worthy of the God.
Built on the Lake, the waters were its
    floor ;
And here its walls were water arch'd
    with fire,
And here were fire with water vaulted
    o'er ;
And spires and pinnacles of fire
Round watery cupolas aspire,
And domes of rainbow rest on fiery
    towers ;
And roofs of flame are turreted around
With cloud, and shafts of cloud with
    flame are bound.   181
Here too the Elements for ever veer,
Ranging around with endless inter-
    changing ;
Pursued in love, and so in love pursuing,
In endless revolutions here they roll ;
For ever their mysterious work
    renewing;
The parts all shifting, still unchanged
    the whole.
Even we on earth at intervals descry
Gleams of the glory, streaks of flowing
    light,
Openings of heaven, and streams that
    flash at night   190
In fitful splendour, through the northern
    sky.

11

Impatient of delay, Ereenia caught
The Maid aloft, and spread his wings
    abroad,
And bore her to the presence of the God.
There Indra sate upon his throne
    reclined,
Where Devetas adore him ;
The lute of Nared, warbling on the wind,
All tones of magic harmony combined
    To sooth his troubled mind,
While the dark-eyed Apsaras danced
    before him.   200
In vain the God-musician play'd,
In vain the dark-eyed Nymphs of
    Heaven essay'd
To charm him with their beauties in the
    dance ;   [appear,
And when he saw the mortal Maid
Led by the heroic Glendoveer,
A deeper trouble fill'd his countenance.
What hast thou done, Ereenia, said the
    God,
    Bringing a mortal here ?
And while he spake his eye was on the
    Maid ;
The look he gave was solemn, not
    severe :   210
No hope to Kailyal it convey'd,
    And yet it struck no fear ;
There was a sad displeasure in his air,
    But pity too was there.

EREENIA

Hear me, O Indra ! On the lower earth
I found this child of man, by what
    mishap
I know not, lying in the lap of death.
Aloft I bore her to our Father's grove,
Not having other thought, than when
    the gales
Of bliss had heal'd her, upon earth again
To leave its lovely daughter.   Other
    thoughts   221
Arose, when Casyapa declared her fate ;

For she is one who groans beneath the
power
Of the dread Rajah, terrible alike
To men and Gods. His son, dead
Arvalan,   [power,
Arm'd with a portion, Indra, of thy
Already wrested from thee, persecutes
The Maid, the helpless one, the innocent.
What then behoved me but to waft
her here
To my own Bower of Bliss ? what other
choice ?   230
The Spirit of foul Arvalan not yet
Hath power to enter here ; here thou
art yet   [own.
Supreme, and yet the Swerga is thine

INDRA

No child of man, Ereenia, in the Bowers
Of Bliss may sojourn, till he hath put off
His mortal part ; for on mortality
Time and Infirmity and Death attend,
Close followers they, and in their mourn-
ful train
Sorrow and Pain and Mutability.
Did these find entrance here, we should
behold   240
Our joys, like earthly summers, pass
away.
Those joys perchance may pass ; a
stronger hand
May wrest my sceptre, and unparadise
The Swerga ; . . but, Ereenia, if we fall,
Let it be Fate's own arm that casts
us down :
We will not rashly hasten and provoke
The blow, nor bring ourselves the
ruin on.

EREENIA

Fear courts the blow, Fear brings the
ruin on.   [Destiny
Needs must the chariot-wheels of
Crush him who throws himself before
their track,   250
Patient and prostrate.

INDRA

All may yet be well.
Who knows but Veeshnoo will descend
and save,
Once more incarnate ?

EREENIA

Look not there for help,
Nor build on unsubstantial hope thy
trust.
Our Father Casyapa hath said he turns
His doubtful eye to Seeva, even as thou
Dost look to him for aid. But thine
own strength
Should for thine own salvation be put
forth ;   260
Then might the higher Powers
approving see
And bless the brave resolve. . . Oh, that
my arm
Could wield yon lightnings which play
idly there,
In inoffensive radiance round thy head !
The Swerga should not need a champion
now,   [vain !
Nor Earth implore deliverance still in

INDRA

Thinkest thou I want the will ? Rash
Son of Heaven,
What if my arm be feeble as thine own
Against the dread Kehama ? He went
on
Conquering in irresistible career, 270
Till his triumphant car had measured
o'er
The insufficient earth, and all the Kings
Of men received his yoke ; then had he
won
His will, to ride upon their necks elate,
And crown his conquests with the
sacrifice
That should, to men and gods, proclaim
him Lord   [World,
And Sovereign Master of the vassal
Sole Rajah, the Omnipotent below.

The steam of that portentous sacrifice
Arose to Heaven. Then was the hour to
  strike;   280
Then in the consummation of his pride,
His height of glory, then the thunder-
  bolt
Should have gone forth, and hurl'd him
  from his throne
Down to the fiery floor of Padalon,
To overlasting burnings, agony
Eternal, and remorse which knows no
  end.
That hour went by: grown impious in
  success,
By prayer and penances he wrested now
Such power from Fate, that soon, if
  Seeva turn not 289
His eyes on earth, and no Avatar save,
Soon will he seize the Swerga for his own,
Roll on through Padalon his chariot
  wheels,
Tear up the adamantine bolts which lock
The accurst Asuras to its burning floor,
And force the drink of Immortality
From Yamen's charge. . . Vain were it
  now to strive;
My thunder cannot pierce the sphere
  of power
Wherewith, as with a girdle, he is bound.

KAILYAL

Take me to earth, O gentle Deveta!
Take me again to earth! This is no
  place   300
Of rest for me! . . my Father still
  must bear
His curse. . he shall not bear it all alone;
Take me to earth, that I may follow
  him! . .
I do not fear the Almighty Man! the
  Gods [Powers
Are feeble here; but there are higher
Who will not turn their eyes from wrongs
  like ours;
Take me to earth, O gentle Deveta! . .

12

Saying thus she knelt, and to his knees
  she clung
And bow'd her head, in tears and
  silence praying.
Rising anon, around his neck she flung
Her arms, and there with folded
  hands she hung, 311
And fixing on the guardian Glendoveer
Her eyes, more eloquent than Angel's
  tongue, [here!
Again she cried, There is no comfort
I must be with my Father in his pain . .
Take me to earth, O Deveta, again!

13

Indra with admiration heard the Maid.
  O Child of Earth, he cried,
  Already in thy spirit thus divine,
  Whatever weal or woe betide, 320
Be that high sense of duty still thy guide,
And all good Powers will aid a soul like
  thine.
Then turning to Ereenia, thus he said,
Take her where Ganges hath its second
  birth,
Below our sphere, and yet above the
  earth; [power
There may Ladurlad rest beyond the
Of the dread Rajah, till the fated hour.

VIII. THE SACRIFICE

1

Dost thou tremble, O Indra, O God of
  the Sky,
Why slumber those thunders of thine?
  Dost thou tremble on high, . .
Wilt thou tamely the Swerga resign, . .
Art thou smitten, O Indra, with dread?
Or seest thou not, seest thou not, Monarch
  divine,
How many a day to Seeva's shrine
Kehama his victim hath led?
Nine and ninety days are fled,

Nine and ninety steeds have bled ; 10
One more, the rite will be complete,
One victim more, and this the dreadful
                    day.   [seat,
Then will the impious Rajah seize thy
And wrest the thunder-sceptre from thy
    sway.

Along the mead the hallow'd Steed
Yet bends at liberty his way ;
At noon his consummating blood will
    flow.
O day of woe ! above, below,
That blood confirms the Almighty
    Tyrant's reign !
Thou tremblest, O Indra, O God of the
    Sky,   20
Thy thunder is vain,
Thou tremblest on high for thy power !
But where is Veeshnoo at this hour,
But where is Seeva's eye ?
Is the Destroyer blind ?
Is the Preserver careless for mankind ?

2

Along the mead the hallow'd Steed
Still wanders wheresoe'er he will,
    O'er hill, or dale, or plain ;   29
No human hand hath trick'd that mane
From which he shakes the morning dew ;
His mouth has never felt the rein,
His lips have never froth'd the chain ;
For pure of blemish and of stain,
His neck unbroke to mortal yoke,
Like Nature free the Steed must be,
Fit offering for the Immortals he.
A year and day the Steed must stray
Wherever chance may guide his way,
    Before he fall at Seeva's shrine ; 40
The year and day have pass'd away,
Nor touch of man hath marr'd the rite
    divine.
And now at noon the Steed must bleed,
The perfect rite to-day must force the
    meed   [bestow ;
Which Fate reluctant shudders to

Then must the Swerga-God
Yield to the Tyrant of the world below ;
Then must the Devetas obey
The Rajah's rod, and groan beneath his
    hateful sway.

3

The Sun rides high ; the hour is nigh ;
    The multitude who long,   51
    Lest aught should mar the rite,
    In circle wide on every side,
    Have kept the Steed in sight,
Contract their circle now, and drive him
    on.   [court,
Drawn in long files before the Temple-
The Rajah's archers flank an ample
    space ;
Here, moving onward still, they drive
    him near,   [here.
Then, opening, give him way to enter

4

Behold him, how he starts and flings
    his head !   60
On either side in glittering order spread,
The archers ranged in narrowing lines
    appear ;
The multitude behind close up the rear
With moon-like bend, and silently await
    The aweful end,
The rite that shall from Indra wrest his
    power.
In front, with far-stretched walls, and
    many a tower,
Turret and dome and pinnacle elate,
The huge Pagoda seems to load the land :
    And there before the gate   70
The Bramin band expectant stand,
The axe is ready for Kehama's hand.

5

Hark ! at the Golden Palaces
The Bramin strikes the time !
One, two, three, four, a thrice-told
    chime,

And then again, one, two.
The bowl that in its vessel floats, anew
   Must fill and sink again,
   Then will the final stroke be due.
The Sun rides high, the noon is nigh,
   And silently, as if spell bound,   81
   The multitude expect the sound.

6

Lo! how the Steed, with sudden start,
Turns his quick head to every part;
Long files of men on every side appear.
The sight might well his heart affright,
   And yet the silence that is here
      Inspires a stranger fear;
   For not a murmur, not a sound
   Of breath or motion rises round,   90
No stir is heard in all that mighty crowd;
He neighs, and from the temple-wall
   The voice re-echoes loud,
Loud and distinct, as from a hill
Across a lonely vale, when all is still.

7

Within the temple, on his golden throne
Reclined, Kehama lies,
   Watching with steady eyes
The perfumed light that, burning bright,
   Metes out the passing hours.   100
On either hand his eunuchs stand,
Freshening with fans of peacock-plumes
   the air,
Which, redolent of all rich gums and
   flowers,
Seems, overcharged with sweets, to
   stagnate there.   [slow
Lo! the time-taper's flame ascending
Creeps up its coil toward the fated line;
Kehama rises and goes forth,
And from the altar, ready where it lies,
He takes the axe of sacrifice.

8

That instant from the crowd, with
   sudden shout,   110
   A Man sprang out

To lay upon the Steed his hand profane.
A thousand archers, with unerring eye,
   At once let fly,
And with their hurtling arrows fill the
   sky.
In vain they fall upon him fast as rain;
He bears a charmed life, which may
   defy
All weapons, .. and the darts that whizz
   around,
   As from an adamantine panoply
   Repell'd, fall idly to the ground.   120
Kehama clasp'd his hands in agony
And saw him grasp the hallow'd
   courser's mane,
   Spring up with sudden bound,
   And with a frantic cry,
And madman's gesture, gallop round
   and round.

9

They seize, they drag him to the Rajah's
   feet.
What doom will now be his, . . what
   vengeance meet
   Will he, who knows no mercy, now
      require?
The obsequious guards around, with
   blood-hound eye,
Look for the word, in slow-consuming
   fire,   130
By piece-meal death, to make the
   wretch expire,   [high,
Or hoist his living carcass, hook'd on
To feed the fowls and insects of the sky;
Or if aught worse inventive cruelty
To that remorseless heart of royalty
Might prompt, accursed instruments
   they stand
To work the wicked will with wicked
   hand.
   Far other thoughts were in the
   multitude;
Pity, and human feelings, held them
   still;

And stifled sighs and groans supprest
          were there,   140
And many a secret curse and inward
          prayer
Call'd on the insulted Gods to save
          mankind.
Expecting some new crime, in fear they
          stood,
Some horror which would make the
          natural blood
Start, with cold shudderings thrill the
          sinking heart,
Whiten the lip, and make the abhorrent
          eye
Roll back and close, prest in for agony.

10

How then fared he for whom the mighty
          crowd
Suffer'd in spirit thus, . . how then
          fared he ?
A ghastly smile was on his lip, his eye
Glared with a ghastly hope, as he drew
          nigh,   151
And cried aloud, Yes, Rajah ! it is I !
          And wilt thou kill me now ?
The countenance of the Almighty Man
Fell when he knew Ladurlad, and his
          brow
     Was clouded with despite, as one
          ashamed.
That wretch again ! indignant he ex-
          claim'd,
     And smote his forehead, and stood
          silently
Awhile in wrath : then, with ferocious
          smile,
     And eyes which seem'd to darken
          his dark cheek,   160
Let him go free ! he cried ; he hath
          his Curse,
And vengeance upon him can wreak
          no worse . .
But ye who did not stop him . . tremble
          ye !

11

He bade the archers pile their weapons
          there :
No manly courage fill'd the slavish band,
No sweetening vengeance roused a brave
          despair.
He call'd his horsemen then, and gave
          command
To hem the offenders in, and hew them
          down.   [rear'd,
Ten thousand scymitars at once up-
Flash up, like waters sparkling to the
          sun ;   170
A second time the fatal brands appear'd
Lifted aloft, . . they glitter'd then no
          more,
Their light was gone, their splendour
          quench'd in gore.
At noon the massacre begun,
And night closed in before the work of
          death was done.

IX. THE HOME-SCENE

1

THE steam of slaughter from that place
          of blood
     Spread o'er the tainted sky.
Vultures, for whom the Rajah's tyranny
So oft had furnish'd food, from far and
          nigh
Sped to the lure : aloft with joyful cry,
     Wheeling around, they hover'd over
          head ;
Or, on the temple perch'd, with greedy
          eye,
     Impatient watch'd the dead.
Far off the tigers, in the inmost wood,
Heard the death shriek, and snuff'd the
          scent of blood ;   10
They rose, and through the covert went
          their way,
Couch'd at the forest edge, and waited
          for their prey.

2

He who had sought for death went
wandering on,
The hope which had inspired his heart
was gone,
Yet a wild joyance still inflamed his face,
A smile of vengeance, a triumphant glow.
Where goes he ? . . Whither should
Ladurlad go !
Unwittingly the wretch's footsteps trace
Their wonted path toward his dwelling -
place ;
And wandering on, unknowing where, 20
He starts like one surprised at finding
he is there.

3

Behold his lowly home,
By yonder broad-bough'd plane o'er-
shaded :
There Marriataly's Image stands,
And there the garland twined by
Kailyal's hands
Around its brow hath faded.
The peacocks, at their master's sight,
Quick from the leafy thatch alight,
And hurry round, and search the ground,
And veer their glancing necks from side
to side,   30
Expecting from his hand
Their daily dole which erst the Maid
supplied,
Now all too long denied.

4

But as he gazed around,
How strange did all accustom'd sights
appear !
How differently did each familiar sound
Assail his alter'd ear !
Here stood the marriage bower,
Rear'd in that happy hour
When he, with festal joy and youthful
pride,   40
Had brought Yedillian home, his
beauteous bride.

Leaves not its own, and many a
borrow'd flower,
Had then bedeck'd it, withering ere the
night ;
But he who look'd from that auspicious
day
For years of long delight,
And would not see the marriage bower
decay,   [care,
There planted and nurst up, with daily
The sweetest herbs that scent the
ambient air,
And train'd them round to live and
flourish there.
Nor when dread Yamen's will   50
Had call'd Yedillian from his arms away
Ceased he to tend the marriage bower,
but still,
Sorrowing, had drest it like a pious rite
Due to the monument of past delight.

5

He took his wonted seat before the
door, . .
Even as of yore,
When he was wont to view with placid
eyes,
His daughter at her evening sacrifice.
Here were the flowers which she so
carefully
Did love to rear for Marriataly's brow ;
Neglected now,   61
Their heavy heads were drooping, over-
blown :
All else appear'd the same as heretofore,
All . . save himself alone ;
How happy then, . . and now a wretch
for evermore !

6

The market-flag which hoisted high,
From far and nigh,
Above yon cocoa grove is seen,
Hangs motionless amid the sultry sky.
Loud sounds the village drum ; a happy
crowd   70

Is there ; Ladurlad hears their distant
   voices,
But with their joy no more his heart
   rejoices ;   [fare,
And how their old companion now may
Little they know, and less they care ;
The torment he is doom'd to bear
Was but to them the wonder of a day,
A burthen of sad thoughts soon put
   away.

7

They knew not that the wretched man
   was near,   [ear,
And yet it seem'd, to his distemper'd
As if they wrong'd him with their merri-
   ment.   80
Resentfully he turn'd away his eyes,
   Yet turn'd them but to find
   Sights that enraged his mind
With envious grief more wild and over-
   powering.
The tank which fed his fields was there,
   and there
The large-leaved lotus on the waters
   flowering.
There, from the intolerable heat
   The buffaloes retreat ;
Only their nostrils raised to meet the air,
Amid the sheltering element they rest.
Impatient of the sight, he closed his
   eyes,   91
And bow'd his burning head, and in
   despair
Calling on Indra, .. Thunder-God ! he
   said,
Thou owest to me alone this day thy
   throne,
Be grateful, and in mercy strike me
   dead.

8

Despair had roused him to that hopeless
   prayer,
Yet thinking on the heavenly Powers,
   his mind

Drew comfort ; and he rose and gather'd
   flowers,
And twined a crown for Marriataly's
   brow ;
And taking then her wither'd garland
   down,   100
Replaced it with the blooming coronal.
Not for myself, the unhappy Father
   cried,
Not for myself, O Mighty One ! I pray,
   Accursed as I am beyond thy aid !
But, oh ! be gracious still to that dear
   Maid
Who crown'd thee with these garlands
   day by day,
And danced before thee aye at even-tide
   In beauty and in pride.
O Marriataly, wheresoe'er she stray
Forlorn and wretched, still be thou her
   guide !   110

9

A loud and fiendish laugh replied,
Scoffing his prayer. Aloft, as from the
   air,
The sound of insult came : he look'd,
   and there
The visage of dead Arvalan came forth,
Only his face amid the clear blue sky,
Withlong-drawnlips of insolentmockery,
   And eyes whose lurid glare
   Was like a sulphur fire,
Mingling with darkness ere its flames
   expire.

10

Ladurlad knew him well : enraged to
   see   120
   The cause of all his misery,
He stoop'd and lifted from the ground
A stake, whose fatal point was black
   with blood ;
The same wherewith his hand had dealt
   the wound,
When Arvalan, in hour with evil fraught,
For violation seized the shrieking Maid.

Thus arm'd, in act again to strike he
          stood,
And twice with inefficient wrath essay'd
To smite the impassive shade.
The lips of scorn their mockery-laugh
          renew'd,   130
And Arvalan put forth a hand and
          caught   [light,
The sunbeam, and condensing there its
Upon Ladurlad turn'd the burning
          stream.
Vain cruelty ! the stake
Fell in white ashes from his hold, but he
Endured no added pain ; his agony
Was full, and at the height ;
The burning stream of radiance nothing
          harm'd him ;
A fire was in his heart and brain,
And from all other flame   140
Kehama's Curse had charm'd him.

11

Anon the Spirit waved a second hand ;
Down rush'd the obedient whirlwind
          from the sky,
Scoop'd up the sand like smoke, and
          from on high,
Shed the hot shower upon Ladurlad's
          head.   there ;
Where'er he turns, the accursed Hand is
East, West, and North, and South, on
          every side
The Hand accursed waves in air to
          guide
The dizzying storm ; ears, nostrils, eyes,
          and mouth
It fills and choaks, and clogging every
          pore,   150
Taught him new torments might be
          yet in store.
Where shall he turn to fly ? behold his
          house   [bower,
In flames ! uprooted lies the marriage-
The Goddess buried by the sandy
          shower.

Blindly, with staggering step, he reels
          about,
And still the accursed Hand pursued,
And still the lips of scorn their mockery-
          laugh renew'd.

12

What, Arvalan ! hast thou so soon
          forgot   [defy
The grasp of Pollear ? Wilt thou still
The righteous Powers of heaven ? or
          know'st thou not   160
That there are yet superior Powers on
          high,   [flight,
Son of the Wicked ? . . Lo, in rapid
Ereenia hastens from the etherial height,
Bright is the sword celestial in his hand ;
Like lightning in its path athwart
          the sky,
He comes and drives, with angel-arm,
          the blow.
Oft have the Asuras, in the wars of
          Heaven,
Felt that keen sword by arm angelic
          driven,
And fled before it from the fields of light
Thrice through the vulnerable shade
The Glendoveer impels the griding
          blade,   171
The wicked Shade flies howling from his
          foe.
So let that Spirit foul
Fly, and for impotence of anger, howl,
Writhing with anguish, and his wounds
          deplore ;   [served,
Worse punishment hath Arvalan de-
And righteous Fate hath heavier doom
          in store.

13

Not now the Glendoveer pursues his
          flight ;
He bade the Ship of Heaven alight,
          And gently there he laid   180
The astonish'd Father by the happy
          Maid,

The Maid now shedding tears of deep
                                delight.   [eyes,
Beholding all things with incredulous
Still dizzy with the sand-storm, there
                        he lay,   [Bark
While sailing up the skies, the living
Through air and sunshine held its
            heavenly way.

X. MOUNT MERU

1

SWIFT through the sky the vessel of the
                                    Suras
Sails up the fields of ether like an Angel.
Rich is the freight, O Vessel, that thou
                            bearest !
Beauty and Virtue,
Fatherly cares and filial veneration,
Hearts which are proved and strength-
            en'd by affliction,
Manly resentment, fortitude and action,
            Womanly goodness ;
All with which Nature halloweth her
            daughters,
Tenderness, truth, and purity and
            meekness,   10
Piety, patience, faith and resignation,
            Love and devotement.
Ship of the Gods, how richly art thou
            laden !
Proud of the charge, thou voyagest
            rejoicing,
Clouds float around to honour thee, and
            Evening
            Lingers in heaven.

2

A Stream descends on Meru mountain ;
None hath seen its secret fountain ;
            It had its birth, so Sages say,
            Upon the memorable day   20
When Parvati presumed to lay,
            In wanton play,

Her hands, too venturous Goddess, in
            her mirth,
On Seeva's eyes, the light and life of
            Earth.
Thereat the heart of the Universe stood
            still :
The Elements ceased their influences ;
            the Hours
Stopt on the eternal round ; Motion
            and Breath,
Time, Change, and Life and Death,
In sudden trance opprest, forgot their
            powers.
A moment, and the dread eclipse was
            ended ;   30
But at the thought of Nature thus
            suspended,
The sweat on Seeva's forehead stood,
And Ganges thence upon the world
            descended,
The Holy River, the Redeeming Flood.

3

None hath seen its secret fountain ;
But on the top of Meru Mountain
Which rises o'er the hills of earth,
In light and clouds, it hath its mortal
            birth.
Earth seems that pinnacle to rear
Sublime above this worldly sphere, 40
Its cradle, and its altar, and its throne ;
And there the new-born River lies
Outspread beneath its native skies,
As if it there would love to dwell
            Alone and unapproachable.
Soon flowing forward, and resign'd
To the will of the Creating Mind,
It springs at once, with sudden leap,
Down from the immeasurable steep.
From rock to rock, with shivering force
            rebounding,   50
The mighty cataract rushes ; Heaven
            around,
Like thunder, with the incessant roar
            resounding,

And Meru's summit shaking with the
sound.
Wide spreads the snowy foam, the
sparkling spray
Dances aloft ; and ever there at
morning
The earliest sunbeams haste to wing
their way, [adorning ;
With rainbow wreaths the holy stream
And duly the adoring Moon at night
Sheds her white glory there,
And in the watery air   60
Suspends her halo-crowns of silver light.

4

A mountain-valley in its blessed breast
Receives the stream, which there
delights to lie,
Untroubled and at rest
Beneath the untainted sky.
There in a lovely lake it seems to sleep,
And thence through many a channel
dark and deep,
Their secret way the holy Waters wind,
Till, rising underneath the root
Of the Tree of Life on Hemakoot, 70
Majestic forth they flow to purify man-
kind.

5

Towards this Lake, above the nether
sphere,
The living Bark with angel eye
Directs its course along the obedient sky.
Kehama hath not yet dominion here ;
And till the dreaded hour,
When Indra by the Rajah shall be driven
Dethroned from Heaven,
Here may Ladurlad rest beyond his
power.

6

The living Bark alights ; the Glen-
doveer   80
Then lays Ladurlad by the blessed
Lake ; . .   [Daughter !
O happy Sire, and yet more happy

The etherial gales his agony aslake,
His daughter's tears are on his cheek,
His hand is in the water ;
The innocent man, the man opprest,
Oh joy ! . . hath found a place of rest
Beyond Kehama's sway ;
The Curse extends not here ; his pains
have pass'd away.

7

O happy Sire, and happy Daughter ! 90
Ye on the banks of that celestial water
Your resting place and sanctuary have
found.
What ! hath not then their mortal taint
defiled
The sacred solitary ground ?
Vain thought ! the Holy Valley smiled
Receiving such a Sire and Child ;
Ganges, who seem'd asleep to lie,
Beheld them with benignant eye,
And rippled round melodiously,
And roll'd her little waves, to meet
And welcome their beloved feet. 101
The gales of Swerga thither fled,
And heavenly odours there were shed
About, below, and overhead ;
And Earth rejoicing in their tread,
Hath built them up a blooming Bower,
Where every amaranthine flower
Its deathless blossom interweaves
With bright and undecaying leaves.

8

Three happy beings are there here, 110
The Sire, the Maid, the Glendoveer.
A fourth approaches, . . who is this
That enters in the Bower of Bliss ?
No form so fair might painter find
Among the daughters of mankind ;
For death her beauties hath refined,
And unto her a form hath given
Framed of the elements of Heaven ;
Pure dwelling place for perfect mind.
She stood and gazed on Sire and Child ;
Her tongue not yet had power to speak,

The tears were streaming down her
    cheek ;   122
And when those tears her sight beguiled,
And still her faltering accents fail'd,
The Spirit, mute and motionless,
Spread out her arms for the caress,
Made still and silent with excess
Of love and painful happiness.

9

The Maid that lovely form survey'd ;
Wistful she gazed, and knew her not,
But Nature to her heart convey'd 131
A sudden thrill, a startling thought,
A feeling many a year forgot,
Now like a dream anew recurring,
    As if again in every vein
Her mother's milk was stirring,
With straining neck and earnest eye
She stretch'd her hands imploringly,
As if she fain would have her nigh,
Yet fear'd to meet the wish'd embrace,
At once with love and awe opprest. 141
Not so Ladurlad ; he could trace,
Though brighten'd with angelic grace,
His own Yedillian's earthly face ;
He ran and held her to his breast !
Oh joy above all joys of Heaven,
By Death alone to others given,
This moment hath to him restored
The early-lost, the long-deplored.

10

They sin who tell us Love can die. 150
With life all other passions fly,
    All others are but vanity.
In Heaven Ambition cannot dwell,
Nor Avarice in the vaults of Hell ;
Earthly these passions of the Earth,
They perish where they have their birth;
    But Love is indestructible.
    Its holy flame for ever burneth,
From Heaven it came, to Heaven re-
    turneth ;
Too oft on Earth a troubled guest, 160
At times deceived, at times opprest,

It here is tried and purified,
Then hath in Heaven its perfect rest :
It soweth here with toil and care,
But the harvest time of Love is there.

11

Oh ! when a Mother meets on high
    The Babe she lost in infancy,
Hath she not then, for pains and fears,
    The day of woe, the watchful night,
For all her sorrow, all her tears, 170
    An over-payment of delight ?

12

A blessed family is this
Assembled in the Bower of Bliss !
Strange woe, Ladurlad, hath been thine,
And pangs beyond all human measure,
    And thy reward is now divine,
    A foretaste of eternal pleasure.
He knew indeed there was a day
When all these joys would pass away,
And he must quit this blest abode ; 180
And, taking up again the spell,
Groan underneath the baleful load,
And wander o'er the world again
Most wretched of the sons of men :
Yet was this brief repose, as when
A traveller in the Arabian sands,
Half-fainting on his sultry road,
Hath reach'd the water-place at last ;
And resting there beside the well,
Thinks of the perils he has past, 190
And gazes o'er the unbounded plain,
The plain which must be traversed still,
And drinks, .. yet cannot drink his fill ;
Then girds his patient loins again.
So to Ladurlad now was given
New strength, and confidence in heaven,
    And hope, and faith invincible.

13

For often would Ereenia tell
    Of what in elder days befell, 199
When other Tyrants in their might,
Usurp'd dominion o'er the earth ;
And Veeshnoo took a human birth,

Deliverer of the Sons of men,
And slew the huge Ermaccasen,
And piece-meal rent, with lion force,
 Errenen's accursed corse,
And humbled Baly in his pride;
And when the Giant Ravanen
Had borne triumphant from his side
Sita, the earth-born God's beloved bride,
Then from his island-kingdom, laugh'd
 to scorn   211
The insulted husband, and his power
 defied;   [hied,
How to revenge the wrong in wrath he
Bridging the sea before his dreadful way,
And met the hundred-headed foe,
And dealt him the unerring blow;
By Brama's hand the righteous lance
 was given,
And by that arm immortal driven,
It laid the mighty Tyrant low;
And Earth and Ocean, and high Heaven,
 Rejoiced to see his overthrow.   221
Oh! doubt not thou, Yedillian cried,
 Such fate Kehama will betide;
For there are Gods who look below,
 Seeva, the Avenger, is not blind,
Nor Veeshnoo careless for mankind.

14

Thus was Ladurlad's soul imbued
With hope and holy fortitude;
And Child and Sire, with pious mind,
 Alike resolved, alike resign'd,   230
Look'd onward to the evil day:
Faith was their comfort, Faith their
 stay;
They trusted woe would pass away,
And Tyranny would sink subdued,
 And Evil yield to Good.

15

Lovely wert thou, O Flower of Earth!
Above all flowers of mortal birth;
But foster'd in this blissful bower,
From day to day, and hour to hour,
 Lovelier grew the lovely flower. 240

O blessed, blessed company!
When men and heavenly spirits greet,
And they whom Death had sever'd meet,
And hold again communion sweet; . .
 O blessed, blessed company!

16

The Sun, careering round the sky,
 Beheld them with rejoicing eye,
 And bade his willing Charioteer
Relax his speed as they drew near;
Arounin check'd the rainbow reins,
The seven green coursers shook their
 manes,   251
And brighter rays around them threw;
 The Car of Glory in their view
More radiant, more resplendent grew;
And Surya[1], through his veil of light,
Beheld the Bower, and blest the sight.

17

The Lord of Night, as he sail'd by,
Stay'd his pearly boat on high;
And while around the blissful Bower
He bade the softest moonlight flow,
Linger'd to see that earthly flower,
 Forgetful of his Dragon foe,   262
Who, mindful of their ancient feud,
With open jaws of rage pursued.

18

There all good Spirits of the air,
 Suras and Devetas repair;
Aloft they love to hover there,
And view the flower of mortal birth
Here for her innocence and worth,
Transplanted from the fields of earth; . .
And him, who on the dreadful day
When Heaven was fill'd with consterna-
 tion,   272
And Indra trembled with dismay,
And for the sounds of joy and mirth,
Woe was heard and lamentation,
 Defied the Rajah in his pride,

[1] Surya, the Sun.

Though all in Heaven and Earth beside
Stood mute in dolorous expectation ;
And, rushing forward in that hour,
Saved the Swerga from his power. 280
Grateful for this they hover nigh,
And bless that blessed Company.

19

One God alone, with wanton eye,
Beheld them in their Bower ;
O ye, he cried, who have defied
The Rajah, will ye mock my power ?
'Twas Camdeo riding on his lory,
'Twas the immortal Youth of Love ;
If men below, and Gods above,
Subject alike, quoth he, have felt these
                    darts,   290
Shall ye alone, of all in story,
Boast impenetrable hearts ?
Hover here, my gentle lory,
Gently hover, while I see
To whom hath Fate decreed the glory,
To the Glendoveer or me.

20

Then in the dewy evening sky,
The bird of gorgeous plumery
Poised his wings and hover'd nigh.
It chanced at that delightful hour
Kailyal sate before the Bower,   301
On the green bank with amaranth sweet,
Where Ganges warbled at her feet.
Ereenia there, before the Maid,
His sails of ocean blue display'd ;
And sportive in her sight,
Moved slowly o'er the lake with gliding
                    flight ;
Anon with sudden stroke and strong,
In rapid course careering, swept along ;
Now shooting downward from his
                heavenly height,   310
Plunged in the deep below,
Then rising, soar'd again,
And shook the sparkling waters off like
                    rain,

And hovering o'er the silver surface hung.
At him young Camdeo bent the bow ;
With living bees the bow was strung,
The fatal bow of sugar-cane,
And flowers which would inflame the
                    heart
With their petals barb'd the dart.

21

The shaft, unerringly addrest,   320
Unerring flew, and smote Ereenia's
                    breast.
Ah, Wanton ! cried the Glendoveer,
Go aim at idler hearts,
Thy skill is baffled here !
A deeper love I bear that Maid divine,
A love that springeth from a higher will,
A holier power than thine !

22

A second shaft, while thus Ereenia cried,
Had Camdeo aim'd at Kailyal's side ;
But lo ! the Bees which strung his bow
Broke off, and took their flight. 331
To that sweet Flower of earth they wing
                    their way,
Around her raven tresses play,
And buzz about her with delight,
As if with that melodious sound,
They strove to pay their willing duty
To mortal purity and beauty.

23

Ah ! Wanton ! cried the Glendoveer,
No power hast thou for mischief here !
Choose thou some idler breast,   340
For these are proof, by nobler thoughts
                    possest.
Go, to thy plains of Matra go,
And string again thy broken bow !

24

Rightly Ereenia spake ; and ill had
                    thoughts
Of earthly love beseem'd the sanctuary
Where Kailyal had been wafted, that
                    the Soul

Of her dead Mother there might
    strengthen her,   [lore,
Feeding her with the milk of heavenly
And influxes of Heaven imbue her heart
    With hope and faith, and holy
        fortitude,   350
Against the evil day. Here rest a while
In peace, O father ! mark'd for misery
Above all sons of men ; O daughter !
    doom'd
For sufferings and for trials above all
Of women ; . . yet both favour'd,
        both beloved   [peace.
By all good Powers, rest here a while in

XI. THE ENCHANTRESS

1

WHEN from the sword by arm angelic
        driven,
Foul Arvalan fled howling, wild in pain,
His thin essential spirit, rent and riven
With wounds, united soon and heal'd
        again ;
Backward the accursed turn'd his eye
        in flight,   [then,
Remindful of revengeful thoughts even
And saw where, gliding through the
        evening light,
The Ship of Heaven sail'd upward
        through the sky,   [sight.
Then, like a meteor, vanish'd from his
Where should he follow ? vainly might
        he try   10
To trace through trackless air its rapid
        course,
Nor dared he that angelic arm defy,
Still sore and writhing from its dreaded
        force.

2

Should he the lust of vengeance lay
        aside ?
Too long had Arvalan in ill been train'd ;
Nurst up in power and tyranny and pride,

His soul the ignominious thought
        disdain'd.
Or to his mighty Father should he go,
    Complaining of defeature twice
        sustain'd,
And ask new powers to meet the im-
        mortal foe ? . .   20
Repulse he fear'd not, but he fear'd
        rebuke,
And shamed to tell him of his overthrow.
There dwelt a dread Enchantress in
        a nook   [been,
Obscure ; old helpmate she to him had
Lending her aid in many a secret sin ;
And there for counsel now his way
        he took.

3

She was a woman, whose unlovely youth,
    Even like a canker'd rose which none
        will cull,
Had wither'd on the stalk ; her heart
        was full
Of passions which had found no natural
        scope,   30
    Feelings which there had grown but
        ripen'd not,
    Desires unsatisfied, abortive hope,
Repinings which provoked vindictive
        thought :
These restless elements for ever wrought
Fermenting in her with perpetual stir,
And thus her spirit to all evil moved ;
She hated men because they loved not
        her,
    And hated women because they were
        loved.
And thus, in wrath and hatred and
        despair,
She tempted Hell to tempt her ; and
        resign'd   40
Her body to the Demons of the Air,
Wicked and wanton fiends, who where
        they will
Wander abroad, still seeking to do ill,

And take whatever vacant form they
find,   [left,
Carcase of man or beast that life hath
Foul instrument for them of fouler mind.
To these the Witch her wretched body
gave,
So they would wreak her vengeance on
mankind ;
She thus at once their mistress and
their slave ;
And they to do such service nothing
loth,   50
Obey'd her bidding, slaves and masters
both.

4

So from this cursed intercourse she
caught
Contagious power of mischief, and was
taught
Such secrets as are damnable to guess.
Is there a child whose little lovely ways
Might win all hearts, . . on whom his
parents gaze   [ness ?
Till they shed tears of joy and tender-
Oh ! hide him from that Witch's
withering sight !
Oh ! hide him from the eye of Lorrinite !
Her look hath crippling in it, and her
curse   60
All plagues which on mortality can light;
Death is his doom if she behold, . . or
worse, . .
Diseases loathsome and incurable,
And inward sufferings that no tongue
can tell.

5

Woe was to him, on whom that eye of
hate   [Fate,
Was bent ; for, certain as the stroke of
It did its mortal work, nor human arts
Could save the unhappy wretch, her
chosen prey ;
For gazing, she consumed his vital parts,
Eating his very core of life away. 70

The wine which from yon wounded palm
on high
Fills yonder gourd, as slowly it distils,
Grows sour at once if Lorrinite pass by.
The deadliest worm from which all
creatures fly
Fled from the deadlier venom of her eye;
The babe unborn, within its mother's
womb,
Started and trembled when the Witch
came nigh ;
And in the silent chambers of the tomb,
Death shudder'd her unholy tread to
hear,
And from the dry and mouldering bones
did fear   80
Force a cold sweat, when Lorrinite
was near.

6

Power made her haughty : by ambition
fired,
Ere long to mightier mischiefs she
aspired.
The Calis, who o'er Cities rule unseen,
Each in her own domain a Demon Queen,
And there adored with blood and
human life,
They knew her, and in their accurst
employ
She stirr'd up neighbouring states to
mortal strife.
Sani, the dreadful God, who rides abroad
Upon the King of the Ravens, to
destroy   90
The offending sons of men, when his
four hands
Were weary with their toil, would let
her do
His work of vengeance upon guilty lands;
And Lorrinite, at his commandment,
knew
When the ripe earthquake should be
loosed, and where   [air
To point its course. And in the baneful

The pregnant seeds of death he bade her
strew,
All deadly plagues and pestilence to
brew.
The Locusts were her army, and their
bands,
Where'er she turn'd her skinny finger,
flew.   100
The floods in ruin roll'd at her
commands:
And when, in time of drought, the
husbandman
Beheld the gather'd rain about to fall,
Her breath would drive it to the desert
sands,   [soil
While in the marshes' parch'd and gaping
The rice-roots by the searching Sun
were dried,
And in lean groups, assembled at the
side
Of the empty tank, the cattle dropt
and died;   [wide
And Famine, at her bidding, wasted
The wretched land, till, in the public
way,   110
Promiscuous where the dead and dying
lay,
Dogs fed on human bones in the open
light of day.

7

Her secret cell the accursed Arvalan,
In quest of vengeance, sought, and thus
began.

Mighty mother! mother wise!
Revenge me on my enemies.

LORRINITE

Comest thou, son, for aid to me?
Tell me who have injured thee,
Where they are, and who they be:
Of the Earth, or of the Sea,   120
Or of the aërial company?
Earth, nor Sea, nor Air is free
From the powers who wait on me,
And my tremendous witchery.

ARVALAN

She for whom so ill I sped,
Whom my Father deemeth dead,
Lives, for Marriataly's aid
From the water saved the Maid.
In hatred I desire her still,
And in revenge would have my will.
A Deveta with wings of blue,   131
And sword whose edge even now I rue,
In a Ship of Heaven on high,
Pilots her along the sky.
Where they voyage thou canst tell,
Mistress of the mighty spell.

8

At this the Witch, through shrivell'd
lips and thin,
Sent forth a sound half whistle and half
hiss.
Two winged Hands came in,
Armless and bodiless,   140
Bearing a globe of liquid crystal, set
In frame as diamond bright, yet black
as jet.   [night
A thousand eyes were quench'd in endless
To form that magic globe; for Lorrinite
Had, from their sockets, drawn the
liquid sight,
And kneaded it, with re-creating skill,
Into this organ of her mighty will.
Look in yonder orb, she cried,
Tell me what is there descried.

9

ARVALAN

A mountain top, in clouds of light
Enveloped, rises on my sight;   151
Thence a cataract rushes down,
Hung with many a rainbow crown;
Light and clouds conceal its head;
Below, a silver Lake is spread;
Upon its shores a Bower I see,
Fit home for blessed company.
See they come forward, . . one, two,
three, . .

The last a Maiden, . . it is she ! 159
The foremost shakes his wings of blue,
'Tis he whose sword even yet I rue ;
And in that other one I know
The visage of my deadliest foe.
Mother, let thy magic might
Arm me for the mortal fight ;
Helm and shield and mail afford,
Proof against his dreaded sword.
Then will I invade their seat,
Then shall vengeance be complete.

10

LORRINITE

Spirits who obey my will,   170
Hear him, and his wish fulfil !
So spake the mighty Witch, nor farther
spell
Needed ; anon a sound, like smother'd
thunder,
Was heard, slow rolling under ;
The solid pavement of the cell
Quaked, heaved, and cleft asunder,
And at the feet of Arvalan display'd,
Helmet and mail, and shield and
scymitar, were laid.

11

The Asuras, often put to flight
And scatter'd in the fields of light
By their foes' celestial might,   181
Forged this enchanted armour for the
fight.
'Mid fires intense did they anneal,
In mountain furnaces, the quivering
steel,   [hue,
Till, trembling through each deepening
It settled in a midnight blue ;
Last they cast it, to aslake,
In the penal icy lake.
Then they consign'd it to the Giant
brood ;
And while they forged the impenetrable
arms,   190

The Evil Powers, to oversee them, stood,
And there imbued
The work of Giant strength with magic
charms.
Foul Arvalan, with joy, survey'd
The crescent sabre's cloudy blade,
With deeper joy the impervious mail,
The shield and helmet of avail.
Soon did he himself array,
And bade her speed him on his way.

12

Then she led him to the den,   200
Where her chariot, night and day,
Stood harness'd ready for the way.
Two Dragons, yoked in adamant, convey
The magic car ; from either collar
sprung
An adamantine rib, which met in air,
O'er-arch'd, and crost and bent diverging
there,
And firmly in its arc upbore,
Upon their brazen necks, the seat of
power.
Arvalan mounts the car, and in his hand
Receives the magic reins from Lorrinite ;
The dragons, long obedient to command,
Their ample sails expand ;   212
Like steeds well-broken to fair lady's
hand,
They feel the reins of might,
And up the northern sky begin their
flight.

13

Son of the Wicked, doth thy soul delight
To think its hour of vengeance now is
nigh ?
Lo ! where the far-off light
Of Indra's palace flashes on his sight,
And Meru's heavenly summit shines on
high,   220
With clouds of glory bright,
Amid the dark-blue sky.
Already, in his hope, doth he espy,

Himself secure in mail of tenfold charms,
Ereenia writhing from the magic blade,
The Father sent to bear his Curse, . . the Maid
Resisting vainly in his impious arms.

14

Ah, Sinner ! whose anticipating soul
Incurs the guilt even when the crime is spared !
Joyous toward Meru's summit on he fared,   230
While the twin Dragons, rising as he guides,   [the pole.
With steady flight, steer northward for
Anon, with irresistible controul,
Force mightier far than his arrests their course ;
It wrought as though a Power unseen had caught
Their adamantine yokes to drag them on.
Straight on they bend their way, and now, in vain,
Upward doth Arvalan direct the rein ;
The rein of magic might avails no more,
Bootless its strength against that unseen Power   240
That in their mid career,
Hath seized the Chariot and the Charioteer.
With hands resisting, and down-pressing feet
Upon their hold insisting,
He struggles to maintain his difficult seat.
Seeking in vain with that strange Power to vie,
Their doubled speed the affrighted Dragons try.
Forced in a stream from whence was no retreat,
Strong as they are, behold them whirl'd along,
Headlong, with useless pennons, through the sky.   250

15

What Power was that, which, with resistless might,
Foil'd the dread magic thus of Lorrinite ?
'Twas all-commanding Nature . . They were here
Within the sphere of the adamantine rocks
Which gird Mount Meru round, as far below
That heavenly height where Ganges hath its birth
Involved in clouds and light,
So far above its roots of ice and snow.

16

On . . on they roll . . rapt headlong they roll on ; . .
The lost canoe, less rapidly than this,
Down the precipitous stream is whirl'd along   261
To the brink of Niagara's dread abyss.
On . . on they roll, and now, with shivering shock,
Are dash'd against the rock that girds the Pole.
Down from his shatter'd mail the unhappy Soul
Is dropt, . . ten thousand thousand fathoms down, . .
Till in an ice-rift, 'mid the eternal snow,
Foul Arvalan is stopt.   There let him howl,
Groan there, . . and there with unavailing moan,
For aid on his Almighty Father call.

17

All human sounds are lost   271
Amid those deserts of perpetual frost,
Old Winter's drear domain,
Beyond the limits of the living World,
Beyond Kehama's reign.

Of utterance and of motion soon bereft,
Frozen to the ice-rock, there behold him
lie,
Only the painful sense of Being left,
A Spirit who must feel, and cannot die,
Bleaching and bare beneath the polar
sky.   280

XII. THE SACRIFICE COMPLETED

1

O YE who, by the Lake
On Meru Mount, partake
The joys which Heaven hath destined
for the blest,
Swift, swift, the moments fly,
The silent hours go by,
And ye must leave your dear abode of
rest.
O wretched Man, prepare
Again thy Curse to bear !
Prepare, O wretched Maid, for farther
woe !
The fatal hour draws near,   10
When Indra's heavenly sphere
Must own the Tyrant of the World
below.
To-day the hundredth Steed,
At Seeva's shrine must bleed,
The dreadful sacrifice is full to-day ;
Nor man nor God hath power,
At this momentous hour,
Again to save the Swerga from his sway.
Fresh woes, O Maid divine,
Fresh trials must be thine :   20
And what must thou, Ladurlad, yet
endure !
But let your hearts be strong,
And rise against all wrong,
For Providence is just, and virtue is
secure.

2

They, little deeming that the fatal day
Was come, beheld where through the
morning sky
A Ship of Heaven drew nigh.
Onward they watch it steer its steady
flight ;
Till wondering, they espy   29
Old Casyapa, the Sire of Gods, alight.
But when Ereenia saw the Sire appear,
At that unwonted and unwelcome sight
His heart received a sudden shock of
fear :
Thy presence doth its doleful tidings tell,
O Father ! cried the startled Glendoveer,
The dreadful hour is near ! I know
it well !   [Gods
Not for less import would the Sire of
Forsake his ancient and august abodes.

3

Even so, serene the immortal Sire replies;
Soon like an earthquake will ye feel the
blow   40
Which consummates the mighty sacri-
fice :
And this World, and its Heaven, and all
therein,
Are then Kehama's. To the second ring
Of these seven Spheres, the Swerga-
King,
Even now, prepares for flight,
Beyond the circle of the conquer'd world,
Beyond the Rajah's might.
Ocean, that clips this inmost of the
Spheres,
And girds it round with everlasting roar,
Set like a gem appears   50
Within that bending shore.
Thither fly all the Sons of heavenly race :
I too forsake mine ancient dwelling-
place.   [go :
And now, O Child and Father, ye must
Take up the burthen of your woe,
And wander once again below.

With patient heart hold onward to the
end, . .
Be true unto yourselves, and bear in
mind   [friend ;
That every God is still the good Man's
And when the Wicked have their day
assign'd,   60
Then they who suffer bravely save
mankind.

1

Oh tell me, cried Ereenia, for from thee
Nought can be hidden, when the end
will be !
Seek not to know, old Casyapa replied,
What pleaseth Heaven to hide.
Dark is the abyss of Time,
But light enough to guide your steps is
given ;
Whatever weal or woe betide,
Turn never from the way of truth aside,
And leave the event, in holy hope, to
Heaven.   70
The moment is at hand, no more delay,
Ascend the etherial bark, and go your
way ;
And Ye, of heavenly nature, follow me.

5

The will of Heaven be done, Ladurlad
cried,
Nor more the man replied ;
But placed his daughter in the etherial
bark,
Then took his seat beside.
There was no word at parting, no adieu.
Down from that empyreal height they
flew :
One groan Ladurlad breathed, yet
utter'd not,   80
When, to his heart and brain,
The fiery Curse again like lightning shot.
And now on earth the Sire and Child
alight,
Up soar'd the Ship of Heaven, and
sail'd away from sight.

6

O ye immortal Bowers,
Where hitherto the Hours
Have led their dance of happiness for
aye,
With what a sense of woe
Do ye expect the blow,
And see your heavenly dwellers driven
away !   90
Lo ! where the sunnay-birds of graceful
mien,
Whose milk-white forms were seen,
Lovely as Nymphs, your ancient trees
between,
And by your silent springs,
With melancholy cry
Now spread unwilling wings ;
Their stately necks reluctant they
protend,
And through the sullen sky,
To other worlds, their mournful progress
bend.

7

The affrighted gales to-day   100
O'er their beloved streams no longer
play,
The streams of Paradise have ceased to
flow ;
The Fountain-Tree withholds its
diamond shower,
In this portentous hour. . .
This dolorous hour, . . this universal
woe.
Where is the Palace, whose far-flashing
beams,
With streaks and streams of ever-
varying light,
Brighten'd the polar night
Around the frozen North's extremest
shore ?
Gone like a morning rainbow, . . like
a dream, . .   110
A star that shoots and falls, and then is
seen no more.

8

Now! now!.. Before the Golden
        Palaces,
The Bramin strikes the inevitable hour.
The fatal blow is given,
That over Earth and Heaven
Confirms the Almighty Rajah in his
        power.
All evil Spirits then,
That roam the World about,
Or wander through the sky,
        Set up a joyful shout.   120
The Asuras and the Giants join the cry;
The damn'd in Padalon acclaim
Their hoped Deliverer's name;
Heaven trembles with the thunder-
        drowning sound;
Back starts affrighted Ocean from the
        shore,   [floor
And the adamantine vaults and brazen
Of Hell are shaken with the roar.
Up rose the Rajah through the con-
        quer'd sky,
To seize the Swerga for his proud abode;
Myriads of evil Genii round him fly, 130
As royally on wings of winds he rode,
And scaled high Heaven, triumphant
        like a God.

XIII. THE RETREAT

1

AROUND her Father's neck the Maiden
        lock'd
Her arms, when that portentous blow
        was given;   [uproar,
Clinging to him she heard the dread
And felt the shuddering shock which
        ran through Heaven;
Earth underneath them rock'd,
Her strong foundations heaving in com-
        motion,
Such as wild winds upraise in raving
        Ocean,
As though the solid base were rent
        asunder.   [sky,
And lo! where, storming the astonish'd
Kehama and his evil host ascend! 10
Before them rolls the thunder,
Ten thousand thousand lightnings
        round them fly,
Upward the longthening pageantries
        aspire,
Leaving from Earth to Heaven a widen-
        ing wake of fire.

2

When the wild uproar was at length
        allay'd,
And Earth recovering from the shock
        was still,
Thus to her father spake the imploring
        Maid: [borne
Oh! by the love which we so long have
Each other, and we ne'er shall cease to
        bear, ..
Oh! by the sufferings we have shared,
        And must not cease to share, .. 21
One boon I supplicate in this dread hour,
One consolation in this hour of woe!
Father, thou hast it in thy power,
Thou wilt not, Father, sure refuse me
        now   [know.
The only comfort my poor heart can

3

O dearest, dearest Kailyal! with a
        smile
Of tenderness and anguish, he replied,
O best beloved, and to be loved the best,
Best worthy, .. set thy duteous heart
        at rest.   30
I know thy wish, and let what will
        betide,
Ne'er will I leave thee wilfully again.
My soul is strengthen'd to endure its
        pain;   [guide;
Be thou in all my wanderings, still my
Be thou, in all my sufferings, at my side.

4

The Maiden, at those welcome words, imprest
A passionate kiss upon her father's cheek !   [seek
They look'd around them then as if to
Where they should turn, North, South, or East, or West,
Wherever to their vagrant feet seem'd best.   40
But, turning from the view her mournful eyes,   [cries,
Oh, whither should we wander, Kailyal
Or wherefore seek in vain a place of rest?
Have we not here the Earth beneath our tread,
Heaven overhead,
A brook that winds through this sequester'd glade,
And yonder woods, to yield us fruit and shade ?
The little all our wants require is nigh ;
Hope we have none ; . . why travel on in fear ?
We cannot fly from Fate, and Fate will find us here.   50

5

'Twas a fair scene wherein they stood,
A green and sunny glade amid the wood,
And in the midst an aged Banian grew.
It was a goodly sight to see
That venerable tree,
For o'er the lawn, irregularly spread,
Fifty straight columns propt its lofty head ;
And many a long depending shoot,
Seeking to strike its root,
Straight like a plummet, grew towards the ground.   60
Some on the lower boughs which crost their way,
Fixing their bearded fibres, round and round,   [wound ;
With many a ring and wild contortion

Some to the passing wind at times, with sway
Of gentle motion swung ;
Others of younger growth, unmoved, were hung
Like stone-drops from the cavern's fretted height ;
Beneath was smooth and fair to sight,
Nor weeds nor briars deform'd the natural floor,
And through the leafy cope which bower'd it o'er   70
Came gleams of chequer'd light.
So like a temple did it seem, that there
A pious heart's first impulse would be prayer.

6

A brook, with easy current, murmur'd near ;
Water so cool and clear   [well,
The peasants drink not from the humble
Which they with sacrifice of rural pride,
Have wedded to the cocoa-grove beside ;
Nor tanks of costliest masonry dispense
To those in towns who dwell,   80
The work of Kings, in their beneficence.
Fed by perpetual springs, a small lagoon,
Pellucid, deep and still, in silence join'd
And swell'd the passing stream. Like burnish'd steel
Glowing, it lay beneath the eye of noon ;
And when the breezes in their play,
Ruffled the darkening surface, then with gleam
Of sudden light, around the lotus stem
It rippled, and the sacred flowers that crown
The lakelet with their roseate beauty, ride   90
In easy waving rock'd, from side to side ;
And as the wind upheaves
Their broad and buoyant weight, the glossy leaves   [down.
Flap on the twinkling waters, up and

G

7

They built them here a bower, of jointed
           cane,   [long
Strong for the needful use, and light and
Was the slight framework rear'd, with
          little pain ;   [supply,
Lithe creepers, then, the wicker sides
And the tall jungle-grass fit roofing gave
    'Beneath the genial sky.   100
And here did Kailyal, each returning
          day,   [pay
Pour forth libations from the brook to
The Spirits of her Sires their grateful rite;
    In such libations pour'd in open
         glades,
Beside clear streams and solitary shades,
The Spirits of the virtuous dead delight.
And duly here, to Marriataly's praise,
    The Maid, as with an angel's voice
         of song,
      Poured her melodious lays
        Upon the gales of even,   110
And gliding in religious dance along,
Moved graceful as the dark-eyed Nymphs
       of Heaven,
Such harmony to all her steps was given.

8

Thus ever, in her Father's doating eye,
Kailyal perform'd the customary rite ;
He, patient of his burning pain the
       while,
Beheld her, and approved her pious toil ;
    And sometimes at the sight
      A melancholy smile
Would gleam upon his aweful coun-
         tenance.   120
He too by day and night, and every
       hour,
   Paid to a higher Power his sacrifice ;
   An offering, not of ghee, or fruit, and
       rice,
Flower-crown, or blood ; but of a heart
      subdued,
  A resolute, unconquer'd fortitude,

An agony represt, a will resign'd,
  To her, who, on her secret throne
      reclined,
Amid the Sea of Milk, by Veeshnoo's side,
Looks with an eye of mercy on mankind.
  By the Preserver, with his power
       endued,   130
There Voomdavee beholds this lower
         clime,   [good,
And marks the silent sufferings of the
To recompense them in her own good
      time.

9

O force of faith ! O strength of virtuous
      will !
Behold him in his endless martyrdom,
      Triumphant still !
The Curse still burning in his heart and
      brain,
     And yet doth he remain
   Patient the while, and tranquil, and
      content !
The pious soul hath framed unto itself
  A second nature, to exist in pain   141
    As in its own allotted element.

10

Such strength the will reveal'd had given
This holy pair, such influxes of grace,
That to their solitary resting place
They brought the peace of Heaven.
Yea, all around was hallow'd ! Danger,
      Fear,
Nor thought of evil ever enter'd here.
A charm was on the Leopard when he
      came
Within the circle of that mystic glade ;
Submiss he crouch'd before the heavenly
       maid,   151
And offer'd to her touch his speckled
       side ;   [head,
Or with arch'd back erect, and bending
And eyes half-closed for pleasure, would
      he stand,
Courting the pressure of her gentle hand.

11

Trampling his path through wood and
brake,
And canes which crackling fall before his
way, [play
And tassel-grass, whose silvery feathers
O'ertopping the young trees,
On comes the Elephant, to slake 160
His thirst at noon in yon pellucid springs.
Lo! from his trunk upturn'd, aloft he
flings
The grateful shower; and now
Plucking the broad-leaved bough
Of yonder plane, with wavey motion
slow,
Fanning the languid air,
He moves it to and fro.
But when that form of beauty meets his
sight,
The trunk its undulating motion stops,
From his forgetful hold the plane-branch
drops, 170
Reverent he kneels, and lifts his rational
eyes
To her as if in prayer;
And when she pours her angel voice in
song, [notes,
Entranced he listens to the thrilling
Till his strong temples, bathed with
sudden dews,
Their fragrance of delight and love
diffuse.

12

Lo! as the voice melodious floats
around,
The Antelope draws near,
The Tigress leaves her toothless cubs to
hear;
The Snake comes gliding from the secret
brake, 180
Himself in fascination forced along
By that enchanting song;
The antic Monkies, whose wild gambols
late,
When not a breeze waved the tall jungle
grass,
Shook the whole wood, are hush'd, and
silently
Hang on the cluster'd tree.
All things in wonder and delight are still;
Only at times the Nightingale is heard,
Not that in emulous skill that sweetest
bird
Her rival strain would try, 190
A mighty songster, with the Maid to vie;
She only bore her part in powerful
sympathy.

13

Well might they thus adore that heavenly
Maid!
For never Nymph of Mountain,
Or Grove, or Lake, or Fountain,
With a diviner presence fill'd the shade.
No idle ornaments deface
Her natural grace,
Musk-spot, nor sandal-streak, nor scarlet
stain,
Ear-drop nor chain, nor arm nor
ankle-ring, 200
Nor trinketry on front, or neck, or breast
Marring the perfect form: she seem'd
a thing
Of Heaven's prime uncorrupted work,
a child
Of early nature undefiled,
A daughter of the years of innocence.
And therefore all things loved her. When
she stood
Beside the glassy pool, the fish, that flies
Quick as an arrow from all other eyes,
Hover'd to gaze on her. The mother
bird,
When Kailyal's step she heard, 210
Sought not to tempt her from her secret
nest,
But hastening to the dear retreat,
would fly
To meet and welcome her benignant eye.

14

Hope we have none, said Kailyal to her
                    Sire.   [Maid
Said she aright ? and had the mortal
    No thoughts of heavenly aid, . .
No secret hopes her inmost heart to
                    move   [desire,
With longings of such deep and pure
As Vestal Maids, whose piety is love,
Feel in their ecstasies, when rapt above,
Their souls unto their heavenly Spouse
                    aspire ?   221
Why else so often doth that searching
                    eye
    Roam through the scope of sky ?
Why, if she sees a distant speck on high,
Starts there that quick suffusion to her
                    cheek ?
'Tis but the Eagle in his heavenly height;
Reluctant to believe, she hears his cry,
    And marks his wheeling flight,
Then pensively averts her mournful
                    sight.
Why ever else, at morn, that waking
                    sigh,   230
Because the lovely form no more is nigh
Which hath been present to her soul all
                    night ;
    And that injurious fear
Which ever, as it riseth, is represt,
Yet riseth still within her troubled
                    breast,   [veer !
That she no more shall see the Glendo-

15

Hath he forgotten me ? The wrong-
                    ful thought
Would stir within her, and though still
                    repell'd
    With shame and self-reproaches,
                    would recur.
Days after days unvarying come and go,
    And neither friend nor foe   241
Approaches them in their sequester'd
                    bower.

Maid of strange destiny ! but think not
                    thou
    Thou art forgotten now,
And hast no cause for farther hope or
                    fear ;
High-fated Maid, thou dost not know
What eyes watch over thee for weal and
                    woe !
    Even at this hour,
    Searching the dark decrees divine,
    Kehama, in the fulness of his power,
Perceives his thread of fate entwine with
                    thine.   251
The Glendoveer, from his far sphere,
With love that never sleeps, beholds thee
                    here,
And in the hour permitted will be near.
Dark Lorrinite on thee hath fix'd her
                    sight,
    And laid her wiles, to aid
Foul Arvalan when he shall next appear ;
For well she ween'd his Spirit would
                    renew   [hate ;
Old vengeance now, with unremitting
The Enchantress well that evil nature
                    knew,   260
The accursed Spirit hath his prey in
                    view ;
    And thus, while all their separate
                    hopes pursue,
All work, unconsciously, the will of Fate.

16

Fate work'd its own the while. A band
Of Yoguees, as they roam'd the land
Seeking a spouse for Jaga-Naut their
                    God,
    Stray'd to this solitary glade,
    And reach'd the bower wherein the
                    Maid abode.
Wondering at form so fair, they deem'd
                    the Power
Divine had led them to his chosen bride,
    And seized and bore her from her
                    Father's side.   271

XIV. JAGA-NAUT

1

Joy in the City of great Jaga-Naut!
Joy in the seven-headed Idol's shrine!
A virgin-bride his ministers have
          brought,
A mortal maid, in form and face divine,
  Peerless among all daughters of
          mankind;
Search'd they the world again from East
          to West,
    In endless quest,
  Seeking the fairest and the best,
No maid so lovely might they hope to
          find; . .
  For she hath breathed celestial air, 10
And heavenly food hath been her fare,
And heavenly thoughts and feelings give
          her face
    That heavenly grace.
Joy in the City of great Jaga-Naut,
Joy in the seven-headed Idol's shrine!
The fairest Maid his Yoguees sought,
A fairer than the fairest have they
          brought,
A maid of charms surpassing human
          thought,
    A maid divine.

2

Now bring ye forth the Chariot of the
          God!   20
    Bring him abroad,
That through the swarming City he may
          ride;
    And by his side
Place ye the Maid of more than mortal
          grace,
The Maid of perfect form and heavenly
          face;
Set her aloft in triumph, like a bride
    Upon the Bridal Car,
And spread the joyful tidings wide and
          far, . .

Spread it with trump and voice
That all may hear, and all who hear
          rejoice, . .   30
Great Jaga-Naut hath found his mate!
          the God
    Will ride abroad!
To-night will he go forth from his abode!
    Ye myriads who adore him,
    Prepare the way before him!

3

Uprear'd on twenty wheels elate,
Huge as a Ship, the Bridal Car appear'd;
Loud creak its ponderous wheels, as
          through the gate   [load.
A thousand Bramins drag the enormous
    There throned aloft in state,   40
The Image of the seven-headed God
Came forth from his abode; and at his
          side
    Sate Kailyal like a bride.
A bridal statue rather might she seem,
For she regarded all things like a dream,
Having no thought, nor fear, nor will,
          nor aught
Save hope and faith, that lived within
          her still.

4

O silent night, how have they startled
          thee
  With the brazen trumpet's blare;
And thou, O Moon! whose quiet light
          serene   50
Filleth wide heaven, and bathing hill
          and wood,   [flood.
Spreads o'er the peaceful valley like a
How have they dimm'd thee with the
          torches' glare,
Which round yon moving pageant flame
          and flare,
As the wild rout, with deafening song
          and shout,
    Fling their long flashes out,
That, like infernal lightnings, fire the air.

5

A thousand pilgrims strain
Arm, shoulder, breast and thigh, with
    might and main,
    To drag that sacred wain,   60
And scarce can draw along the enormous
    load,
Prone fall the frantic votaries in its road,
    And calling on the God,
Their self-devoted bodies there they lay
    To pave his chariot-way.
    On Jaga-Naut they call,
The ponderous Car rolls on, and crushes
    all.
Through flesh and bones it ploughs its
    dreadful path.
Groans rise unheard: the dying cry,
    And death and agony   70
Are trodden under foot by yon mad
    throng,
Who follow close, and thrust the deadly
    wheels along.

6

Pale grows the Maid at this accursed
    sight;
    The yells which round her rise
    Have roused her with affright,
And fear hath given to her dilated eyes
    A wilder light.
Where shall those eyes be turn'd? she
    knows not where!
    Downward they dare not look, for
        there
    Is death, and horror, and despair; 80
Nor can her patient looks to Heaven
    repair,
    For the huge Idol over her, in air,
Spreads his seven hideous heads, and
    wide
Extends their snaky necks on every side;
    And all around, behind, before,
    The Bridal Car, is the raging rout,
With frantic shout, and deafening roar,
    Tossing the torches' flames about.

And the double double peals of the drum
    are there,
And the startling burst of the trumpet's
    blare;   90
And the gong, that seems, with its
    thunders dread
To astound the living, and waken the
    dead.   [rent,
    The ear-strings throb as if they were
    And the eyelids drop as stunned
        and spent.   [fast,
Fain would the Maid have kept them
But open they start at the crack of the
    blast.

7

Where art thou, Son of Heaven, Ereenia!
    where
In this dread hour of horror and despair?
Thinking on him, she strove her fear to
    quell,
If he be near me, then will all be well;
    And, if he reck not for my misery,
Let come the worst, it matters not to
    me.   102
    Repel that wrongful thought,
O Maid! thou feelest, but believest it
    not;
It is thine own imperfect nature's fault
That lets one doubt of him arise within;
    And this the Virgin knew; and like
        a sin,
Repell'd the thought, and still believed
    him true;
And summon'd up her spirit to endure
    All forms of fear, in that firm trust
        secure.   110

8

She needs that faith, she needs that
    consolation,
For now the Car hath measured back its
    track
Of death, and hath re-enter'd now its
    station.

There, in the Temple-court with song
    and dance,
A harlot-band, to meet the Maid,
    advance.
The drum hath ceased its peals ; the
    trump and gong
Are still ; the frantic crowd forbear their
    yells ;
And sweet it was to hear the voice of
    song,
And the sweet music of their girdle-bells,
Armlets and anklets, that, with cheerful
    sound,   120
Symphonious tinkled as they wheel'd
    around.

9

They sung a bridal measure,
    A song of pleasure,
A hymn of joyaunce and of gratulation.
    Go, chosen One, they cried,
    Go, happy bride !
For thee the God descends in expecta-
    tion !
    For thy dear sake
He leaves his Heaven, O Maid of match-
    less charms !
Go, happy One, the bed divine partake,
    And fill his longing arms !   131
    Thus to the inner fane,
With circling dance and hymeneal strain,
    The astonish'd Maid they led,
And there they laid her on the bridal bed.
    Then forth they go, and close the
        Temple-gate,
And leave the wretched Kailyal to her
    fate.

10

Where art thou, Son of Heaven, Ereenia,
    where ?
From the loathed bed she starts, and
    in the air
Looks up, as if she thought to find him
    there ;   140

    Then, in despair,
Anguish and agony, and hopeless
    prayer,
Prostrate she laid herself upon the floor.
    There trembling as she lay,
    The Bramin of the fane advanced
    And came to seize his prey.
But as the abominable Priest drew nigh,
    A power invisible opposed his way ;
Starting, he utter'd wildly a death-cry,
And fell. At that the Maid all eagerly
    Lifted in hope her head ;   151
She thought her own deliverer had been
    near ;
When lo ! with other life re-animate,
    She saw the dead arise,
And in the fiendish joy within his eyes,
    She knew the hateful Spirit who
        look'd through
Their specular orbs, . . clothed in the
    flesh of man,
She knew the accursed soul of Arvalan.

11

Where art thou, Son of Heaven, Ereenia,
    where ?
But not in vain, with sudden shriek
    of fear,   160
She calls Ereenia now ; the Glendoveer
Is here ! Upon the guilty sight he burst
Like lightning from a cloud, and caught
    the accurst,
Bore him to the roof aloft, and on the
    floor
With vengeance dash'd him, quivering
    there in gore.
Lo ! from the pregnant air, . . heart-
    withering sight,
There issued forth the dreadful Lorrinite.
    Seize him ! the Enchantress cried ;
A host of Demons at her word appear,
And like tornado winds, from every side
At once they rush upon the Glendoveer.
Alone against a legion, little here   172
    Avails his single might,

Nor that celestial faulchion, which in
fight
So oft had put the rebel race to flight.
There are no Gods on earth to give
him aid ;
Hemm'd round, he is overpower'd, beat
down, and bound,
And at the feet of Lorrinite is laid.

12

Meantime the scatter'd members of the
slain,
Obedient to her mighty voice assum'd
Their vital form again,   181
And that foul Spirit upon vengeance
bent,
Fled to the fleshly tenement.
Lo ! here, quoth Lorrinite, thou seest
thy foe !
Him in the Ancient Sepulchres, below
The billows of the Ocean will I lay ;
Gods are there none to help him now,
and there
For Man there is no way.
To that dread scene of durance and
despair,
Asuras, bear your enemy ! I go 190
To chain him in the Tombs. Meantime
do thou,
Freed from thy foe, and now secure from
fear,
Son of Kehama, take thy pleasure here.

13

Her words the accursed race obey'd ;
Forth with a sound like rushing winds
they fled,
And of all aid from Earth or Heaven
bereft,
Alone with Arvalan the Maid was left.
But in that hour of agony, the Maid
Deserted not herself ; her very dread
Had calm'd her ; and her heart 200
Knew the whole horror, and its only
part.

Yamen, receive me undefiled ! she said,
And seized a torch, and fired the bridal
bed.
Up ran the rapid flames ; on every side
They find their fuel wheresoe'er they
spread ;
Thin hangings, fragrant gums, and
odorous wood,
That piled like sacrificial altars stood.
Around they run, and upward they
aspire,   [fire.
And, lo ! the huge Pagoda lined with

14

The wicked Soul, who had assumed
again   210
A form of sensible flesh for his foul will,
Still bent on base revenge and baffled
still,
Felt that corporeal shape alike to pain
Obnoxious as to pleasure : forth he
flew,   [flame ;
Howling and scorch'd by the devouring
Accursed Spirit ! Still condemn'd to rue,
The act of sin and punishment the same.
Freed from his loathsome touch, a
natural dread
Came on the self-devoted, and she drew
Back from the flames, which now toward
her spread,   220
And, like a living monster, seem'd to dart
Their hungry tongues toward their
shrinking prey.
Soon she subdued her heart ;
O Father ! she exclaim'd, there was
no way
But this ! And thou, Ereenia, who for
me   [pany.
Sufferest, my soul shall bear thee com-

15

So having said, she knit
Her body up to work her soul's desire,
And rush at once among the thickest
fire.

A sudden cry withheld her, . . Kailyal,
      stay !   230
Child ! Daughter ! I am here ! the
      voice exclaims,
And from the gate, unharm'd, through
      smoke and flames,
Like as a God, Ladurlad made his way ;
Wrapt his preserving arms around,
      and bore
His Child, uninjured, o'er the burning
      floor.

XV. THE CITY OF BALY

1

KAILYAL

Ereenia !

LADURLAD

Nay, let no reproachful thought
Wrong his heroic heart ! The Evil
      Powers
Have the dominion o'er this wretched
      World,   [here.
And no good Spirit now can venture

KAILYAL

Alas, my Father ! he hath ventured
      here,
And saved me from one horror. But the
      Powers
Of Evil beat him down, and bore away
To some dread scene of durance and
      despair ;
The Ancient Tombs, methought their
      mistress said,   10
Beneath the ocean-waves ; no way for
      Man
Is there ; and Gods, she boasted, there
      are none
On Earth to help him now.

LADURLAD

Is that her boast ?
And hath she laid him in the Ancient
      Tombs,

Relying that the Waves will guard him
      there ?   [ness,
Short-sighted are the eyes of Wicked-
And all its craft but folly. Oh my child !
The Curses of the Wicked are upon me,
   And the immortal Deities, who see 20
And suffer all things for their own wise
      end,
Have made them blessings to us !

KAILYAL

Then thou knowest
Where they have borne him ?

LADURLAD

To the Sepulchres
Of the Ancient Kings, which Baly in his
      power
Made in primeval times ; and built
      above them
A City, like the Cities of the Gods,
Being like a God himself. For many an
      age
Hath Ocean warr'd against his Palaces,
Till, overwhelm'd, they lie beneath the
      waves,   31
Not overthrown, so well the aweful Chief
Had laid their deep foundations. Rightly
      said
The Accursed, that no way for man was
      there,
But not like man am I !

2

Up from the ground the Maid exultant
      sprung,
And clapp'd her happy hands in attitude
Of thanks to Heaven, and flung
Her arms around her Father's neck, and
      stood
Struggling awhile for utterance, with
      excess   40
Of hope and pious thankfulness.
Come . . come ! she cried, Oh let us not
      delay, . .   [away !
He is in torments there, . . away ! . .

3

Long time they travell'd on ; at dawn
        of day
Still setting forward with the earliest
        light,
    Nor ceasing from their way
    Till darkness closed the night.
Short refuge from the noontide heat,
Reluctantly compell'd, the Maiden took,
    And ill her indefatigable feet   50
    Could that brief respite brook.
Hope kept her up, and her intense desire
Supports that heart which ne'er at
        danger quails,
    Those feet which never tire,
    That frame which never fails.

4

Their talk was of the City of the days
Of old, Earth's wonder once, and of the
        fame
Of Baly its great founder, . . he whose
        name
In ancient story and in poet's praise,
Liveth and flourisheth for endless
        glory,   60
    Because his might
Put down the wrong, and aye upheld
        the right.
Till for ambition, as old sages tell,
At length the universal Monarch fell :
For he too, having made the World his
        own,
    Then in his pride, had driven
•   The Devetas from Heaven,
And seized triumphantly the Swerga
        throne.
The Incarnate came before the Mighty
        One,
In dwarfish stature, and in mien obscure ;
    The sacred cord he bore,   71
And ask'd, for Brama's sake, a little
        boon,   [more.
. Three steps of Baly's ample reign, no

Poor was the boon required, and poor
        was he
Who begg'd, . . a little wretch it seem'd
        to be ;   [prayer.
But Baly ne'er refused a suppliant's
    He on the Dwarf cast down
A glance of pity in contemptuous mood,
    And bade him take the boon,
    And measure where he would.   80

5

    Lo, Son of giant birth,
I take my grant ! the Incarnate Power
        replies.
With his first step he measured o'er
        the Earth,
    The second spann'd the skies.
    Three paces thou hast granted,
Twice have I set my footstep, Veeshnoo
        cries,
    Where shall the third be planted ?

6

Then Baly knew the God, and at his feet,
In homage due, he laid his humbled head.
Mighty art thou, O Lord of Earth
        and Heaven,   90
    Mighty art thou ! he said,
Be merciful, and let me be forgiven.
He ask'd for mercy of the Merciful,
    And mercy for his virtue's sake was
        shown.
For though he was cast down to Padalon,
    Yet there, by Yamen's throne,
Doth Baly sit in majesty and might,
    To judge the dead, and sentence them
        aright.
And forasmuch as he was still the friend
Of righteousness, it is permitted him,
Yearly, from those drear regions to
        ascend,   101
And walk the Earth, that he may hear
        his name
Still hymn'd and honour'd by the
        grateful voice
Of humankind, and in his fame rejoice.

7

Such was the talk they held upon their
way,
Of him to whose old City they were
bound ;   [day
And now, upon their journey, many a
Had risen and closed, and many a
week gone round,
And many a realm and region had they
pass'd,
When now the Ancient Towers appear'd
at last.   110

8

Their golden summits in the noon-day
light,
Shone o'er the dark green deep that
roll'd between,
For domes, and pinnacles, and spires
were seen
Peering above the sea, . . a mournful
sight !
Well might the sad beholder ween
from thence
What works of wonder the devouring
wave
Had swallow'd there, when monuments
so brave
Bore record of their old magnificence.
And on the sandy shore, beside the
verge
Of Ocean, here and there, a rock-hewn
fane   120
Resisted in its strength the surf and
surge
That on their deep foundations beat in
vain.
In solitude the Ancient Temples stood,
Once resonant with instrument and
song,
And solemn dance of festive multitude ;
Now as the weary ages pass along,
Hearing no voice save of the Ocean flood,
Which roars for ever on the restless
shores ;

Or, visiting their solitary caves,
The lonely sound of winds, that moan
around   130
Accordant to the melancholy waves.

9

With reverence did the travellers see
The works of ancient days, and silently
Approach the shore.   Now on the
yellow sand,
Where round their feet the rising surges
part,
They stand.   Ladurlad's heart
Exulted in his wondrous destiny.
To Heaven he raised his hand
In attitude of stern heroic pride ;
Oh what a power, he cried,   140
Thou dreadful Rajah, doth thy curse
impart !
I thank thee now ! . . Then turning
to the Maid,
Thou seest how far and wide
Yon Towers extend, he said,
My search must needs be long.   Mean-
time the flood
Will cast thee up thy food, . .
And in the Chambers of the Rock by
night,
Take thou thy safe abode.
No prowling beast to harm thee, or
affright,
Can enter there ; but wrap thyself with
care   150
From the foul Birds obscene that thirst
for blood ;
For in such caverns doth the Bat delight
To have its haunts. Do thou with stone
and shout,
Ere thou liest down at evening, scare
them out,
And in this robe of mine involve thy
feet.
Duly commend us both to Heaven
in prayer,   [sweet !
Be of good heart, and may thy sleep be

10

So saying, he put back his arm, and gave
The cloth which girt his loins, and press'd
          her hand
With fervent love, then from the sand
Advanced into the sea ; the coming
                    Wave   161
Which knew Kehama's curse, before his
          way
Started, and on he went as on dry land,
And still around his path the waters
          parted.
She stands upon the shore, where sea-
          weeds play,
Lashing her polish'd ankles, and the
          spray   [fled,
Which off her Father, like a rainbow,
Falls on her like a shower ; there Kailyal
          stands,
And sees the billows rise above his head.
She at the startling sight forgot the
          power   170
The Curse had given him, and held forth
          her hands
Imploringly, . . her voice was on the
          wind,
And the deaf Ocean o'er Ladurlad closed.
Soon she recall'd his destiny to mind,
And shaking off that natural fear,
          composed
Her soul with prayer, to wait the event
          resign'd.

11

Alone, upon the solitary strand,
The lovely one is left ; behold her go,
Pacing with patient footsteps, to and fro,
          Along the bending sand.   180
Save her, ye Gods ! from Evil Powers,
          and here
From man she need not fear :
For never Traveller comes near
These aweful ruins of the days of yore,
Nor fisher's bark, nor venturous mariner,
          Approach the sacred shore.

All day, she walk'd the beach, at night
          she sought
The Chamber of the Rock ; with stone
          and shout
Assail'd the Bats obscene, and scared
          them out ;
Then in her Father's robe involved her
          feet,   190
And wrapt her mantle round to guard
          her head,
And laid her down ; the rock was
          Kailyal's bed,   [sky,
Her chamber-lamps were in the starry
The winds and waters were her lullaby.

12

Be of good heart, and may thy sleep be
          sweet,
Ladurlad said : . . Alas ! that cannot be
To one whose days are days of misery.
How often did she stretch her hands to
          greet
Ereenia, rescued in the dreams of night !
How oft amid the vision of delight,
Fear in her heart all is not as it seems ;
Then from unsettled slumber start, and
          hear   202
The Winds that moan above, the Waves
          below !
Thou hast been call'd, O Sleep ! the
          friend of Woe,   [so.
But 'tis the happy who have call'd thee

13

Another day, another night are gone,
A second passes, and a third wanes on.
So long she paced the shore,
So often on the beach she took her stand,
That the wild Sea-Birds knew her, and
          no more   210
Fled, when she pass'd beside them on
          the strand.   [light
Bright shine the golden summits in the
Of the noon-sun, and lovelier far by
          night   [shed :
Their moonlight glories o'er the sea they

Fair is the dark-green deep : by night
and day
Unvex'd with storms, the peaceful
billows play,
As when they closed above Ladurlad's
head ;
The firmament above is bright and clear ;
The sea-fowl, lords of water, air, and
land,
Joyous alike upon the wing appear,
Or when they ride the waves, or walk
the sand ;   221
Beauty and light and joy are every
where ;
There is no sadness and no sorrow here,
Save what that single human breast
contains,
But oh ! what hopes, and fears, and
pains are there !

14

Seven miserable days the expectant
Maid,
From earliest dawn till evening, watch'd
the shore ;
Hope left her then ; and in her heart
she said,   [more.
Never should she behold her Father

XVI. THE ANCIENT
SEPULCHRES

1

WHEN the broad Ocean on Ladurlad's
head
Had closed and arch'd him o'er,
With steady tread he held his way
Adown the sloping shore.
The dark green waves with emerald hue,
Imbue the beams of day,
And on the wrinkled sand below,
Rolling their mazy network to and fro,
Light shadows shift and play.   9
The hungry Shark, at scent of prey,

Toward Ladurlad darted ;
Beholding then that human form erect,
How like a God the depths he trod,
Appall'd the monster started,
And in his fear departed.
Onward Ladurlad went with heart elate,
And now hath reach'd the Ancient
City's gate.

2

Wondering he stood awhile to gaze
Upon the works of elder days.
The brazen portals open stood,   20
Even as the fearful multitude
Had left them, when they fled
Before the rising flood.
High over-head, sublime,
The mighty gateway's storied roof was
spread,
Dwarfing the puny piles of younger time.
With the deeds of days of yore
That ample roof was sculptured o'er,
And many a godlike form there met his
his eye,
And many an emblem dark of mystery.
Through these wide portals oft had
Baly rode   31
Triumphant from his proud abode,
When, in his greatness, he bestrode
The Aullay, hugest of four-footed kind,
The Aullay-Horse, that in his force,
With elephantine trunk, could bind
And lift the elephant, and on the wind
Whirl him away, with sway and swing,
Even like a pebble from the practised
sling.

3

Those streets which never, since the
days of yore,   40
By human footstep had been visited,
Those streets which never more
A human foot shall tread,
Ladurlad trod.   In sun-light and sea-
green,
The thousand Palaces were seen

Of that proud City, whose superb abodes
Seem'd rear'd by Giants for the immortal
        Gods.   [stand,
How silent and how beautiful they
Like things of Nature ! the eternal
        rocks
Themselves not firmer. Neither hath
        the sand   50
Drifted within their gates and choak'd
        their doors,
Nor slime defiled their pavements and
        their floors.
Did then the Ocean wage
His war for love and envy, not in rage,
O thou fair City, that he spared thee
        thus ?
Art thou Varounin's capital and court,
Where all the Sea-Gods for delight
        resort,
A place too godlike to be held by us,
The poor degenerate children of the
        Earth ?
So thought Ladurlad, as he look'd
        around,   60
Weening to hear the sound
Of Mermaid's shell, and song
Of choral throng from some imperial
        hall,
Wherein the Immortal Powers at
        festival,
Their high carousals keep ;
But all is silence dread,
Silence profound and dead,
The everlasting stillness of the Deep.

4

Through many a solitary street,
And silent market-place, and lonely
        square,   70
Arm'd with the mighty Curse, behold
        him fare.   [fane
And now his feet attain that royal
Where Baly held of old his aweful reign.
What once had been the Gardens
        spread around,

Fair Gardens, once which wore per-
        petual green,
Where all sweet flowers through all the
        year were found,
And all fair fruits were through all
        seasons seen ;
A place of Paradise, where each device
Of omulous Art with Nature strove to vie;
        And Nature on her part,   80
Call'd forth new powers wherewith to
        vanquish Art.   [eye,
The Swerga-God himself, with envious
Survey'd those peerless gardens in their
        prime ;
Nor ever did the Lord of Light,
Who circles Earth and Heaven upon
        his way,   [sight
Behold from eldest time a goodlier
Than were the groves which Baly, in
        his might,
Made for his chosen place of solace
        and delight.

5

It was a Garden still beyond all price,
Even yet it was a place of Paradise ;
For where the mighty Ocean could not
        spare,   91
There had he with his own creation,
Sought to repair his work of devasta-
        tion.
And here were coral bowers,
And grots of madrepores,
And banks of sponge, as soft and fair to
        eye
As e'er was mossy bed
Whereon the Wood Nymphs lie
With languid limbs in summer's sultry
        hours.
Here too were living flowers   100
Which, like a bud compacted,
Their purple cups contracted,
And now in open blossom spread,
Stretch'd like green anthers many a
        seeking head.

And arborets of jointed stone were
          there,
And plants of fibres fine, as silkworm's
          thread ;   [hair
Yea, beautiful as Mermaid's golden
Upon the waves dispread.
Others that, like the broad banana
          growing,
Raised their long wrinkled leaves of
          purple hue,   110
Like streamers wide out-flowing.
And whatsoe'er the depths of Ocean
          hide
From human eyes, Ladurlad there
          espied,
Trees of the deep, and shrubs and
          fruits and flowers,
          As fair as ours,
Wherewith the Sea-Nymphs love their
          locks to braid,
When to their father's hall, at festival
Repairing they, in emulous array,
          Their charms display,
To grace the banquet, and the solemn
          day.   120

6

The golden fountains had not ceased
          to flow :
And where they mingled with the
          briny Sea,
There was a sight of wonder and
          delight,
To see the fish, like birds in air,
          Above Ladurlad flying.
Round those strange waters they repair,
Their scarlet fins outspread and plying.
They float with gentle hovering there ;
And now upon those little wings,
          As if to dare forbidden things,   130
          With wilful purpose bent,
Swift as an arrow from a bow,
They shoot across, and to and fro,
In rapid glance, like lightning go
Through that unwonted element.

7

Almost in scenes so wondrous fair,
          Ladurlad had forgot
The mighty cause which led him there ;
          His busy eye was every where,
          His mind had lost all thought ;   140
His heart, surrender'd to the joys
          Of sight, was happy as a boy's.
But soon the awakening thought
          recurs
Of him who in the Sepulchres,
Hopeless of human aid, in chains is
          laid ;
And her who on the solitary shore,
By night and day her weary watch
          will keep,
Till she shall see them issuing from
          the deep.

8

Now hath Ladurlad reach'd the Court
Of the great Palace of the King ; its
          floor   150
Was of the marble rock ; and there
          before
          The imperial door,
A mighty Image on the steps was
          seen,
Of stature huge, of countenance serene.
A crown and sceptre at his feet were
          laid ;
          One hand a scroll display'd,
The other pointed there, that all might
          see ;
          My name is Death, it said,
In mercy have the Gods appointed me.
Two brazen gates beneath him night
          and day   160
Stood open ; and within them you
          behold
Descending steps, which in the living
          stone
          Were hewn, a spacious way
Down to the Chambers of the Kings
          of old.

9

Trembling with hope, the adventurous
man descended.
The sea-green light of day
Not far along the vault extended ;
But where the slant reflection ended,
Another light was seen
Of red and fiery hue,   170
That with the water blended,
And gave the secrets of the Tombs to
view.

10

Deep in the marble rock, the Hall
Of Death was hollow'd out, a chamber
wide,
Low-roof'd, and long ; on either side,
Each in his own alcove, and on his
throne,   [hand
The Kings of old were seated : in his
Each held the sceptre of command,
From whence, across that scene of
endless night,
A carbuncle diffused its everlasting
light.   180

11

So well had the embalmers done their
part   [imbue
With spice and precious unguents to
The perfect corpse, that each had still
the hue
Of living man, and every limb was still
Supple and firm and full, as when of
yore
Its motion answer'd to the moving will.
The robes of royalty which once they
wore,
Long since had moulder'd off and left
them bare :   [there,
Naked upon their thrones behold them
Statues of actual flesh, . . a fearful
sight !   190
Their large and rayless eyes
Dimly reflecting to that gem-born light,

Glazed, fix'd, and meaningless, . . yet,
open wide,
Their ghastly balls belied
The mockery of life in all beside.

12

But if amid these chambers drear,
Death were a sight of shuddering and
of fear,
Life was a thing of stranger horror
here.
For at the farther end, in yon alcove,
Where Baly should have lain, had he
obey'd   200
Man's common lot, behold Ereenia laid.
Strong fetters link him to the rock ;
his eye
Now rolls and widens, as with effort
vain
He strives to break the chain,
Now seems to brood upon his misery.
Before him couch'd there lay
One of the mighty monsters of the
deep,
Whom Lorrinite encountering on the
way,
There station'd, his perpetual guard
to keep ;
In the sport of wanton power, she
charm'd him there,   210
As if to mock the Glendoveer's despair.

13

Upward his form was human, save
that here
The skin was cover'd o'er with scale
on scale
Compact, a panoply of natural mail.
His mouth, from ear to ear,
Weapon'd with triple teeth, extended
wide,
And tusks on either side ;
A double snake below, he roll'd
His supple length behind in many
a sinuous fold.

14

With red and kindling eye, the Beast
    beholds   220
A living man draw nigh,
And rising on his folds,
In hungry joy awaits the expected
    feast,
His mouth half-open, and his teeth
    unsheath'd.   [arms
Then on he sprung, and in his scaly
Seized him, and fasten'd on his neck,
    to suck,
With greedy lips the warm life-blood :
    and sure   [charms,
But for the mighty power of magic
As easily as, in the blithesome hour
Of spring, a child doth crop the
    meadow-flower,   230
Piecemeal those claws
Had rent their victim, and those armed
    jaws   [stood,
Snapt him in twain.   Naked Ladurlad
Yet fearless and unharm'd in this
    dread strife,
So well Kehama's Curse had charm'd
    his fated life.

15

He too, . . for anger, rising at the
    sight
Of him he sought, in such strange
    thrall confined,
With desperate courage fired Ladur-
    lad's mind, . .
He too unto the fight himself addrest,
And grappling breast to breast,   240
With foot firm-planted stands,
And seized the monster's throat with
    both his hands.
Vainly, with throttling grasp, he prest
    The impenetrable scales ;
And lo ! the Guard rose up, and round
    his foe,
With gliding motion, wreath'd his
    lengthening coils,

Then tighten'd all their folds with
    stress and strain.
Nought would the raging Tiger's
    strength avail   [toils ;
If once involved within those mighty
The arm'd Rhinoceros, so clasp'd, in
    vain   250
Had trusted to his hide of rugged mail,
His bones all broken, and the breath
    of life
Crush'd from the lungs, in that un-
    equal strife.   [break
Again, and yet again, he sought to
The impassive limbs ; but when the
    Monster found
His utmost power was vain,
A moment he relax'd in every round,
Then knit his coils again with closer
    strain,
And, bearing forward, forced him to
    the ground.

16

Ereenia groan'd in anguish at the sight
Of this dread fight : once more the
    Glendoveer   261
Essay'd to break his bonds, and fear
For that brave father who had sought
    him here,
Stung him to wilder strugglings. From
    the rock
He raised himself half-up, with might
    and main
Pluck'd at the adamantine chain,
And now with long and unrelaxing
    strain,
In obstinate effort of indignant strength,
    Labour'd and strove in vain ;
Till his immortal sinews fail'd at length ;
And yielding, with an inward groan,
    to fate,   271
Despairingly, he let himself again
Fall prostrate on his prison-bed of
    stone,   [weight.
Body and chain alike with lifeless

17

Struggling they lay in mortal fray
All day, while day was in our upper
    sphere,
    For light of day
And natural darkness never entered
    here ;
  All night, with unabated might,
 They waged the unremitting fight.
  A second day, a second night, 281
With furious will they wrestled still.
The third came on, the fourth is gone ;
    Another comes, another goes,
    And yet no respite, no repose !
But day and night, and night and day,
  Involv'd in mortal strife they lay ;
  Six days and nights have pass'd
     away,
And still they wage, with mutual rage,
  The unremitting fray.   290
With mutual rage their war they wage,
  But not with mutual will :
For when the seventh morning came,
The monster's worn and wearied frame
  In this strange contest fails ;
  And weaker, weaker, every hour,
 He yields beneath strong Nature's
    power,
  For now the Curse prevails.

18

Sometimes the Beast sprung up to bear
  His foe aloft ; and trusting there 300
    To shake him from his hold,
Relax'd the rings that wreath'd him
    round ;
But on his throat Ladurlad hung
  And weigh'd him to the ground ;
  And if they sink, or if they float,
Alike with stubborn clasp he clung,
    Tenacious of his grasp ;
For well he knew with what a power,
  Exempt from Nature's laws, 309
The Curse had arm'd him for this hour ;
And in the monster's gasping jaws,

And in his hollow eye,
  Well could Ladurlad now descry
  The certain signs of victory.

19

And now the Beast no more can keep
His painful watch ; his eyes, opprest,
  Are fainting for their natural sleep ;
His living flesh and blood must rest,
  The Beast must sleep or die.
Then he, full faint and languidly, 320
Unwreathes his rings and strives to fly,
  And still retreating, slowly trails
  His stiff and heavy length of scales.
    But that unweariable foe,
  With will relentless follows still :
No breathing time, no pause of fight
He gives, but presses on his flight ;
Along the vaulted chambers, and the
    ascent
Up to the emerald-tinted light of day,
    He harasses his way,   330
Till lifeless, underneath his grasp,
    The huge Sea-Monster lay.

20

That obstinate work is done ; Ladur-
    lad cried,
    One labour yet remains !
    And thoughtfully he eyed
  Ereenia's ponderous chains ;
And with faint effort, half-despairing,
    tried
The rivets deep in-driven.   Instinc-
    tively,
As if in search of aid, he look'd around :
  Oh, then how gladly, in the near
    alcove,   340
Fallen on the ground its lifeless Lord
    beside,
  The crescent scymitar he spied,
Whose cloudy blade, with potent spells
    imbued,
  Had lain so many an age unhurt in
    solitude.

21

Joyfully springing there
He seized the weapon, and with eager
        stroke
Hew'd at the chain; the force was
        dealt in vain,
For not as if through yielding air
Pass'd the descending scymitar,
Its deaden'd way the heavy water
        broke;   350
Yet it bit deep. Again, with both his
        hands,
He wields the blade, and dealt a surer
        blow.
The baser metal yields
To that fine edge, and lo! the
        Glendoveer
Rises and snaps the half-sever'd links,
        and stands
Freed from his broken bands.

XVII. BALY

1

THIS is the appointed night,
The night of joy and consecrated mirth,
When from his judgement-seat in
        Padalon,
By Yamen's throne,
Baly goes forth, that he may walk the
        Earth
Unseen, and hear his name
Still hymn'd and honour'd by the
        grateful voice
Of humankind, and in his fame rejoice.
Therefore from door to door, and
        street to street,
        With willing feet,   10
Shaking their firebrands, the glad
        children run;
Baly! great Baly! they acclaim,
Where'er they run they bear the mighty
        name,

Where'er they meet,
Baly! great Baly! still their choral
        tongues repeat.
Therefore at every door the votive
        flame
Through pendant lanterns sheds its
        painted light,
And rockets hissing upward through the
        sky,
Fall like a shower of stars
From Heaven's black canopy.   20
Therefore, on yonder mountain's
        templed height,
The brazen caldron blazes through
        the night.
Huge as a Ship that travels the main
        sea
Is that capacious brass; its wick as tall
As is the mast of some great admiral.
Ten thousand votaries bring
Camphor and ghee to feed the sacred
        flame;
And while, through regions round, the
        nations see
Its fiery pillar curling high in heaven,
Baly! great Baly! they exclaim,   30
For ever hallowed be his blessed name!
Honour and praise to him for ever
        more be given!

2

Why art not thou among the festive
        throng,
Baly, O righteous Judge! to hear thy
        fame?
Still, as of yore, with pageantry and
        song,
The glowing streets along,
They celebrate thy name;
Baly! great Baly! still
The grateful habitants of Earth
        acclaim,
Baly! great Baly! still   40
The ringing walls and echoing towers
        proclaim.

From yonder mountain the portentous
flame
Still blazes to the nations as before ;
All things appear to human eyes the
same,
As perfect as of yore ;
To human eyes, .. but how unlike to
thine !
Thine which were wont to see
The Company divine,
That with their presence came to
honour thee !
For all the blessed ones of mortal birth
Who have been clothed with immor-
tality,   51
From the eight corners of the Earth,
From the Seven Worlds assembling, all
Wont to attend thy solemn festival.
Then did thine eyes behold
The wide air peopled with that glorious
train ;
Now may'st thou seek the blessed
ones in vain,
For Earth and Air are now beneath
the Rajah's reign.

3

Therefore the righteous Judge hath
walk'd the Earth
In sorrow and in solitude to-night.   60
The sound of human mirth
To him is no delight ;
He turns away from that ungrateful
sight,
Hallowed not now by visitants divine,
And there he bends his melancholy
way
Where, in yon full-orb'd Moon's
refulgent light,
The Golden Towers of his old City
shine
Above the silver sea. The ancient Chief
There bent his way in grief,
As if sad thoughts indulged would
work their own relief.   70

4

There he beholds upon the sand
A lovely Maiden in the moonlight stand.
The land-breeze lifts her locks of jet,
The waves around her polish'd ankles
play,
Her bosom with the salt sea-spray is
wet ;
Her arms are cross'd, unconsciously,
to fold
That bosom from the cold,
While statue-like she seems her watch
to keep,
Gazing intently on the restless deep.

5

Seven miserable days had Kailyal
there,   80
From earliest dawn till evening watch'd
the deep ;
Six nights within the chamber of the
rock,
Had laid her down, and found in
prayer
That comfort which she sought in vain
from sleep.
But when the seventh night came,
Never should she behold her father
more,
The wretched Maiden said in her
despair ;
Yet would not quit the shore,
Nor turn her eyes one moment from
the sea ;
Never before   90
Had Kailyal watch'd it so impatiently,
Never so eagerly had hoped before,
As now when she believed, and said all
hope was o'er.

6

Beholding her, how beautiful she stood,
In that wild solitude,
Baly from his invisibility
Had issued then, to know her cause
of woe ;

But that in the air beside her, he espied
Two Powers of Evil for her hurt allied,
Foul Arvalan and dreadful Lorrinite.
Walking in darkness him they could not
          see   101
And marking with what demon-like
          delight
They kept their innocent prey in sight,
He waits, expecting what the end
          may be.

7

She starts; for lo! where floating
          many a rood,
A Monster, hugest of the Ocean brood,
Weltering and lifeless, drifts toward
          the shore.
Backward she starts in fear before the
          flood,
    And, when the waves retreat,
They leave their hideous burthen at
         her feet.   110

8

She ventures to approach with timid
          tread,
She starts, and half draws back in
          fear,
Then stops, and stretches out her
          head,
To see if that huge Beast indeed be
          dead.
Now growing bold, the Maid advances
          near,
Even to the margin of the ocean-flood.
Rightly she reads her Father's victory,
And lifts her joyous hands exultingly
    To Heaven in gratitude.
Then spreading them toward the Sea,
While pious tears bedim her streaming
         eyes,   121
Come! come! my Father, come to me,
    Ereenia, come! she cries,
Lo! from the opening deep they rise,
And to Ladurlad's arms the happy
         Kailyal flies.

9

She turn'd from him, to meet with
        beating heart,
    The Glendoveer's embrace.
Now turn to me, for mine thou art!
Foul Arvalan exclaim'd; his loathsome
        face
    Came forth, and from the air,   130
    In fleshly form, he burst.
Always in horror and despair
Had Kailyal seen that form and face
        accurst,
But yet so sharp a pang had ne'er
Shot with a thrill like death through
        all her frame,
As now when on her hour of joy the
        Spectre came.

10

    Vain is resistance now,
The fiendish laugh of Lorrinite is heard;
    And at her dreadful word,
    The Asuras once again appear,   140
And seize Ladurlad and the Glendoveer.

11

    Hold your accursed hands!
A voice exclaim'd, whose dread com-
        mands   [Padalon;
Were fear'd through all the vaults of
And there among them, in the mid-
        night air,
The presence of the mighty Baly shone.
He, making manifest his mightiness,
Put forth on every side an hundred
        arms,
And seized the Sorceress; maugre all
        her charms,
Her and her fiendish ministers he
        caught   150
With force as uncontroulable as fate;
And that unhappy Soul, to whom
The Almighty Rajah's power availeth not
Living to avert, nor dead to mitigate
        His righteous doom.

12

Help, help, Kehama ! Father, help !
                            he cried,
But Baly tarried not to abide
That mightier Power ; with irresistible
                            feet
He stampt and cleft the Earth ; it
                        open'd wide,
And gave him way to his own Judge-
                        ment-seat.   160
Down, like a plummet, to the World
                    below
He sunk, and bore his prey
To punishment deserved, and endless
                    woe.

XVIII. KEHAMA'S DESCENT

1

THE Earth, by Baly's feet divided,
Closed o'er his way as to the Judge-
                        ment-seat
        He plunged and bore his prey.
Scarce had the shock subsided,
When, darting from the Swerga's
                    heavenly heights,
Kehama, like a thunderbolt, alights.
In wrath he came, a bickering flame
Flash'd from his eyes which made the
                    moonlight dim,
And passion forcing way from every
                    limb,
Like furnace-smoke, with terrors wrapt
                    him round.   10
Furious he smote the ground ;
Earth trembled underneath the dread-
                    ful stroke,
        Again in sunder riven ;
He hurl'd in rage his whirling weapon
                    down.
But lo ! the fiery sheckra to his feet
Return'd, as if by equal force re-
                    driven,

And from the abyss the voice of Baly
                        came :
    Not yet, O Rajah, hast thou won
            The realms of Padalon !
Earth and the Swerga are thine own,
        But, till Kehama shall subdue
                    the throne   21
Of Hell, in torments Yamen holds his
                    son.

2

Fool that he is ! . . in torments let
                    him lie !
Kehama, wrathful at his son, replied.
            But what am I,
That thou should'st brave me ? . .
                    kindling in his pride
            The dreadful Rajah cried.
Ho ! Yamen ! hear me.   God of
                    Padalon,
            Prepare thy throne,
        And let the Amreeta cup   30
Be ready for my lips, when I anon
Triumphantly shall take my seat
                    thereon,
And plant upon thy neck my royal feet.

3

In voice like thunder thus the Rajah
                    cried,
    Impending o'er the abyss, with
                menacing hand
Put forth, as in the action of command,
And eyes that darted their red anger
                    down.
Then drawing back he let the earth
                    subside,
And, as his wrath relax'd, survey'd,
Thoughtfully and silently, the mortal
                    Maid.   40
Her eye the while was on the farthest
                    sky,
    Where up the ethereal height
Ereenia rose and pass'd away from
                    sight.

Never had she so joyfully
Beheld the coming of the Glendoveer,
Dear as he was and he deserved to be,
As now she saw him rise and disap-
          pear.
Come now what will, within her heart
          said she,
For thou art safe, and what have I to
          fear ?

4

Meantime the Almighty Rajah, late 50
In power and majesty and wrath array'd,
Had laid his terrors by
And gazed upon the Maid.
Pride could not quit his eye,
Nor that remorseless nature from his
          front
Depart; yet whoso had beheld him then
Had felt some admiration mix'd with
          dread,
And might have said,
That sure he seem'd to be the King
          of Men !
Less than the greatest that he could not
          be,   60
Who carried in his port such might
          and majesty.

5

In fear no longer for the Glendoveer,
Now towards the Rajah Kailyal turn'd
          her eyes
As if to ask what doom awaited her.
But then surprise,
Even as with fascination held them
          there,
So strange a thing it seem'd to see the
          change
Of purport in that all-commanding
          brow,
Which thoughtfully was bent upon her
          now.
Wondering she gazed, the while her
          Father's eye   70

Was fix'd upon Kehama haughtily ;
It spake defiance to him, high disdain,
Stern patience unsubduable by pain,
And pride triumphant over agony.

6

Ladurlad, said the Rajah, thou and I
Alike have done the work of Destiny,
Unknowing each to what the impulse
          tended ;
But now that over Earth and Heaven
          my reign
Is stablish'd, and the ways of Fate are
          plain
Before me, here our enmity is ended.
I take away thy Curse . . As thus he
          said,   81
The fire which in Ladurlad's heart and
          brain
Was burning, fled, and left him free
          from pain.
So rapidly his torments were departed,
That at the sudden ease he started,
As with a shock, and to his head
          His hands up-fled.
As if he felt through every failing limb
The power and sense of life forsaking
          him.

7

Then turning to the Maid, the Rajah
          cried,   90
O Virgin, above all of mortal birth
Favour'd alike in beauty and in worth,
And in the glories of thy destiny,
Now let thy happy heart exult with
          pride,
For Fate hath chosen thee
To be Kehama's bride,
To be the Queen of Heaven and Earth,
And of whatever Worlds beside
Infinity may hide . . For I can see
The writing which, at thy nativity,
All-knowing Nature wrought upon thy
          brain,   101

In branching veins, which to the gifted
eye
Map out the mazes of futurity.
There is it written, Maid, that thou
and I,
Alone of human kind a deathless pair,
Are doom'd to share
The Amreeta-drink divine
Of immortality.   Come, Maiden mine !
High-fated One, ascend the subject
sky,
 And by Kehama's side 110
Sit on the Swerga throne, his equal
bride.

8

 Oh never, . . never, . . Father !
  Kailyal cried ;
It is not as he saith, . . it cannot be !
  I ! . . I, his bride !
Nature is never false ; he wrongeth her !
My heart belies such lines of destiny.
There is no other true interpreter !

9

At that reply, Kehama's darkening
brow
Bewray'd the anger which he yet
suppress'd ;
Counsel thy daughter ! tell her thou art
 now 120
Free from thy Curse, he said, and bid
her bow
In thankfulness to Fate's benign behest.
Bid her her stubborn will restrain,
For Destiny at last must be obey'd,
And tell her, while obedience is delay'd,
Thy Curse will burn again.

10

She needeth not my counsel, he replied,
And idly, Rajah, dost thou reason thus
Of destiny ! for though all other
 things 129
Were subject to the starry influencings,
And bow'd submissive to thy tyranny,

The virtuous heart and resolute mind
are free.
Thus in their wisdom did the Gods
decree
When they created man.   Let come
 what will, [ill,
This is our rock of strength ; in every
Sorrow, oppression, pain and agony,
The spirit of the good is unsubdued,
And, suffer as they may, they triumph
still.

11

Obstinate fools ! exclaim'd the Mighty
One,
Fate and my pleasure must be done,
 And ye resist in vain ! 141
Take your fit guerdon till we meet
again !
So saying, his vindictive hand he flung
Towards them, fill'd with curses ;
 then on high
Aloft he sprung, and vanish'd through
the Sky.

XIX.   MOUNT CALASAY

1

The Rajah, scattering curses as he rose,
Soar'd to the Swerga, and resumed his
throne.
Not for his own redoubled agony,
Which now through heart and brain
 With renovated pain,
Rush'd to its seat, Ladurlad breathes
that groan,
That groan is for his child ; he groan'd
to see
That she was stricken now with
leprosy,
Which as the enemy vindictive fled,
O'er all her frame with quick con-
tagion spread. 10

She, wondering at events so passing
    strange,
  And fill'd with hope and fear,
And joy to see the Tyrant disappear,
And glad expectance of her Glendoveer,
Perceived not in herself the hideous
    change.
His burning pain, she thought, had
    forced the groan
Her father breathed ; his agonies alone
Were present to her mind ; she clasp'd
    his knees,
Wept for his Curse, and did not feel
    her own.

2

Nor when she saw her plague, did her
    good heart,   20
True to itself, even for a moment fail.
Ha, Rajah ! with disdainful smile she
    cries,
Mighty and wise and wicked as thou art,
Still thy blind vengeance acts a friendly
    part.
Shall I not thank thee for this scurf
    and scale   [ness,
Of dire deformity, whose loathsome-
Surer than panoply of strongest mail,
Arms me against all foes ? Oh, better so,
  Better such foul disgrace,
  Than that this innocent face   30
Should tempt thy wooing ! That I
    need not dread ;
  Nor ever impious foe
Will offer outrage now, nor farther woe
Will beauty draw on my unhappy head,
Safe through the unholy world may
    Kailyal go.

3

  Her face in virtuous pride
    Was lifted to the skies,
As him and his poor vengeance she
    defied ;

But earthward, when she ceased, she
    turn'd her eyes,
  As if she thought to hide   40
The tear which in her own despite
    would rise.
Did then the thought of her own
    Glendoveer
  Call forth that natural tear ?
    Was it a woman's fear,
A thought of earthly love which
    troubled her ?
Like yon thin cloud amid the moon-
    light sky
  That flits before the wind
  And leaves no trace behind,
The womanly pang pass'd over Kailyal's
    mind.
This is a loathsome sight to human eye.
Half-shrinking at herself the Maiden
    thought ;   50
Will it be so to him ? Oh surely not !
  The immortal Powers, who see
Through the poor wrappings of
         mortality,   [within,
Behold the soul, the beautiful soul,
Exempt from age and wasting maladies,
And undeform'd, while pure and free
    from sin.
This is a loathsome sight to human eyes,
  But not to eyes divine,
Ereenia, Son of Heaven, oh not to
    thine !   60

4

The wrongful thought of fear, the
    womanly pain
Had pass'd away, her heart was calm
    again.   [see
She raised her head, expecting now to
    The Glendoveer appear;
  Where hath he fled, quoth she,
That he should tarry now ? Oh ! had
    she known
Whither the adventurous son of Heaven
    was flown,

Strong as her spirit was, it had not
              borne
The appalling thought, nor dared to
        hope for his return.

5

For ho in search of Seeva's throne was
              gone,   70
      To tell his tale of wrong;
  In search of Seeva's own abode
The Glendoveer began his heavenly
              road.   [skies
O wild emprize! above the farthest
        He hoped to rise!
Him who is throned beyond the reach
        of thought,
The Alone, the Inaccessible, he sought.
O wild emprize! for when in days of
              yore,
For proud pre-eminence of power,
Brama and Veeshnoo, wild with rage
        contended,   80
      And Seeva, in his might,
      Their dread contention ended;
      Before their sight
In form a fiery column did he tower,
Whose head above the highest height
        extended,
Whose base below the deepest depth
        descended.
  Downward, its depth to sound
Veeshnoo a thousand years explored
      The fathomless profound,
    And yet no base he found: 90
      Upward, to reach its head,
Ten myriad years the aspiring Brama
        soar'd,
      And still, as up he fled,
Above him still the Immeasurable
        spread.   *
    The rivals own'd their Lord,
    And trembled and adored.
How shall the Glendoveer attain
What Brama and what Veeshnoo sought
        in vain?

6

Ne'er did such thought of lofty daring
              enter
    Celestial Spirit's mind.   O wild
              adventure   100
That throne to find, for he must leave
              behind
  This World, that in the centre,
Within its salt-sea girdle, lies confined;
Yea the Seven Earths that, each with
        its own ocean,
  Ring clasping ring, compose the
        mighty round.
    What power of motion,
  In less than endless years shall bear
        him there,
    Along the limitless extent,
To the utmost bound of the remotest
        spheres?
    What strength of wing   110
Suffice to pierce the Golden Firmament
    That closes all within?
  Yet he hath pass'd the measureless
        extent
And pierced the Golden Firmament;
For Faith hath given him power, and
        Space and Time
Vanish before that energy sublime.
    Nor doth eternal Night
And outer Darkness check his resolute
        flight;
By strong desire through all he makes
        his way,
  Till Seeva's Seat appears, .. behold
        Mount Calasay!   120

7

Behold the Silver Mountain! round
        about
  Seven ladders stand, so high, the
        aching eye,
    Seeking their tops in vain amid
        the sky,
  Might deem they led from earth to
        highest Heaven.

Ages would pass away,
And worlds with age decay,
Ere one whose patient feet from ring
 to ring
Must win their upward way,
Could reach the summit of Mount
 Calasay.
But that strong power that nerved his
 wing, 130
That all-surmounting will,
Intensity of faith and holiest love,
Sustain'd Ereenia still,
And he hath gain'd the plain, the
 sanctuary above.

8

Lo, there the Silver Bell,
That, self-sustain'd, hangs buoyant in
 the air !
Lo ! the broad Table there, too bright
 For mortal sight,
From whose four sides the bordering
 gems unite
 Their harmonising rays, 140
In one mid fount of many-colour'd light.
The stream of splendour, flashing as
 it flows,
Plays round, and feeds the stem of yon
 celestial Rose ! [declare
Where is the Sage whose wisdom can
The hidden things of that mysterious
 flower, [to bear ?
That flower which serves all mysteries
The sacred Triangle is there,
Holding the Emblem which no tongue
 may tell ;
Is this the Heaven of Heavens, where
 Seeva's self doth dwell ?

9

Here first the Glendoveer 150
Felt his wing flag, and paused upon
 his flight. [here
Was it that fear came over him, when
He saw the imagined throne appear ?

Not so, for his immortal sight
Endured the Table's light ;
Distinctly he beheld all things around,
And doubt and wonder rose within his
 mind
That this was all he found.
Howbeit he lifted up his voice and
 spake.
There is oppression in the World below ;
Earth groans beneath the yoke ; yea,
 in her woe, 161
She asks if the Avenger's eye is blind ?
Awake, O Lord, awake !
Too long thy vengeance sleepeth. Holiest
 One ! [sake,
Put thou thy terrors on for mercy's
And strike the blow, in justice to
 mankind !

10

So as he pray'd, intenser faith he felt,
His spirit seem'd to melt
With ardent yearnings of increasing
 love ;
 Upward he turn'd his eyes 170
As if there should be something yet
 above ; [cries ;
Let me not, Seeva, seek in vain ! he
Thou art not here, . . for how should
 these contain thee ?
Thou art not here, . . for how should
 I sustain thee ?
But thou, where'er thou art,
Canst hear the voice of prayer,
Canst read the righteous heart.
Thy dwelling who can tell,
Or who, O Lord, hath seen thy secret
 throne ?
 But thou art not alone, 180
Not unapproachable !
O all-containing Mind,
Thou who art every where,
Whom all who seek shall find,
Hear me, O Seeva ! hear the sup-
 pliant's prayer !

11

So saying, up he sprung,
And struck the Bell, which self-sus-
pended hung
Before the mystic Rose.
From side to side the silver tongue
Melodious swung, and far and wide
Soul-thrilling tones of heavenly music
rung.   191
Abash'd, confounded,
It left the Glendoveer ; . . yea all
astounded
In overpowering fear and deep dismay ;
For when that Bell had sounded,
The Rose, with all the mysteries it
surrounded,
The Bell, the Table, and Mount Calasay,
The holy Hill itself, with all thereon,
Even as a morning dream before the day
Dissolves away, they faded and were
gone.   200

12

Where shall he rest his wing, where
turn for flight,
For all around is Light,
Primal, essential, all-pervading Light !
Heart cannot think, nor tongue declare,
Nor eyes of Angel bear
That Glory unimaginably bright ;
The Sun himself had seem'd
A speck of darkness there,
Amid that Light of Light !

13

Down fell the Glendoveer,   210
Down through all regions, to our
mundane sphere
He fell ; but in his ear [heard,
A Voice, which from within him came, was
The indubitable word
Of Him to whom all secret things are
known :   [throne.
Go, ye who suffer, go to Yamen's
He hath the remedy for every woe ;
He setteth right whate'er is wrong below.

XX. THE EMBARKATION

1

Down from the Heaven of Heavens
Ereenia fell
Precipitate, yet imperceptible
His fall, nor had he cause nor thought
of fear ;
And when he came within this mundane
sphere,
And felt that Earth was near,
The Glendoveer his azure wings
expanded,
And, sloping down the sky
Toward the spot from whence he
sprung on high,
There on the shore he landed.

2

Kailyal advanced to meet him,   10
Not moving now as she was wont to
greet him,
Joy in her eye and in her eager pace ;
With a calm smile of melancholy pride
She met him now, and turning half aside
Her warning hand repell'd the dear
embrace.

3

Strange things, Ereenia, have befallen
us here,
The Virgin said ; the Almighty Man
hath read
The lines which, traced by Nature on
my brain,
There to the gifted eye
Make all my fortunes plain,   20
Mapping the mazes of futurity.
He sued for peace, for it is written there
That I with him the Amreeta cup
must share ;
Wherefore he bade me come, and by
his side
Sit on the Swerga throne, his equal
bride.

I need not tell thee what reply was
          given ;
My heart, the sure interpreter of Heaven,
          His impious words belied.
Thou seest his poor revenge ! So
          having said,
One look she glanced upon her leprous
          stain   30
Indignantly, and shook
Her head in calm disdain.

4

O Maid of soul divine !
O more than ever dear,
And more than ever mine,
Replied the Glendoveer ;
He hath not read, be sure, the mystic
          ways
Of Fate ; almighty as he is, that maze
Hath mock'd his fallible sight.
Said he the Amreeta-cup ? So far aright
The Evil One may see ; for Fate
          displays   41
Her hidden things in part, and part
          conceals,
Baffling the wicked eye
Alike with what she hides, and what
          reveals,
When with unholy purpose it would pry
Into the secrets of futurity.
So may it be permitted him to see
Dimly the inscrutable decree ;
For to the World below,
Where Yamen guards the Amreeta, we
          must go ;   50
Thus Seeva hath express'd his will,
          even he   [he saith,
The Holiest hath ordain'd it ; there,
All wrongs shall be redrest
By Yamen, by the righteous Power of
          Death.

5

Forthwith the Father and the fated
          Maid,
And that heroic Spirit, who for them

Such flight had late essay'd,
The will of Heaven obey'd.
They went their way along the road
That leads to Yamen's dread abode.

6

Many a day hath pass'd away   61
Since they began their arduous way,
Their way of toil and pain ;
And now their weary feet attain
The Earth's remotest bound,
Where outer Ocean girds it round.
But not like other Oceans this ;
Rather it seem'd a drear abyss,
Upon whose brink they stood.
Oh ! scene of fear ! the travellers hear
          The raging of the flood ;   71
They hear how fearfully it roars,
But clouds of darker shade than night
For ever hovering round those shores,
Hide all things from their sight ;
The Sun upon that darkness pours
          His unavailing light,
Nor ever Moon nor Stars display,
Through the thick shade, one guiding
          ray
To show the perils of the way.   80

7

There in a creek a vessel lay,
Just on the confines of the day,
It rode at anchor in its bay,
These venturous pilgrims to convey
          Across that outer Sea.
Strange vessel sure it seem'd to be,
And all unfit for such wild sea !
For through its yawning side the wave
Was oozing in ; the mast was frail,
And old and torn its only sail.   90
How may that crazy vessel brave
The billows that in wild commotion
          For ever roar and rave ?
How hope to cross the dreadful Ocean
O'er which eternal shadows dwell,
Whose secrets none return to tell !

8

Well might the travellers fear to enter !
But summon'd once on that adventure,
　　For them was no retreat.
　　Nor boots it with reluctant feet　100
　　To linger on the strand ;
　　　Aboard ! aboard !
An aweful voice, that left no choice,
　　Sent forth its stern command,
　　　Aboard ! aboard !
The travellers hear that voice in fear,
And breathe to Heaven an inward
　　　　prayer,
And take their seats in silence there.

9

Self-hoisted then, behold the sail
　　Expands itself before the gale ;　110
Hands, which they cannot see, let slip
　　The cable of that fated ship ;
The land breeze sends her on her way,
And lo ! they leave the living light of
　　　　day !

XXI. THE WORLD'S END

1

SWIFT as an arrow in its flight
The Ship shot through the incumbent
　　　　night ;
　　And they have left behind
The raging billows and the roaring wind,
　　The storm, the darkness, and all
　　　　mortal fears ;
　　　And lo ! another light
　　　To guide their way appears,
　　　The light of other spheres.

2

That instant from Ladurlad's heart
　　　　and brain
The Curse was gone ; he feels again
Fresh as in youth's fair morning, and
　　　　the Maid　11
　　Hath lost her leprous stain.

The Tyrant then hath no dominion here,
Starting she cried ;　O happy, happy
　　　　hour !
　　We are beyond his power !
　Then raising to the Glendoveer,
　With heavenly beauty bright, her
　　　　angel face,
Turn'd not reluctant now, and met his
　　　dear embrace.

3

Swift glides the Ship with gentle motion
　　Across that calm and quiet ocean ;　20
　　That glassy sea which seem'd to be
　　　The mirror of tranquillity.
Their pleasant passage soon was o'er,
　　The Ship hath reach'd its destined
　　　　shore ;
　　A level belt of ice which bound,
　　As with an adamantine mound,
The waters of the sleeping Ocean round.
　　Strange forms were on the strand
Of earth-born spirits slain before their
　　　　time ;
Who wandering over sea and sky and
　　　　land,　30
Had so fulfill'd their term ; and now
　　　　were met
Upon this icy belt, a motley band,
　　Waiting their summons at the
　　　　appointed hour,
When each before the Judgement-seat
　　　　must stand,
　　And hear his doom from Baly's
　　　righteous power.

4

Foul with habitual crimes, a hideous
　　　　crew
Were there, the race of rapine and of
　　　　blood.
Now having overpass'd the mortal flood,
　　Their own deformity they knew,
　　And knew the meed that to their
　　　deeds was due.　40

Therefore in fear and agony they stood,
Expecting when the Evil Messenger
Among them should appear.   But with
          their fear
     A hope was mingled now ;
O'er the dark shade of guilt a deeper hue
It threw, and gave a fiercer character
To the wild eye and lip and sinful brow.
They hoped that soon Kehama would
          subdue
The inexorable God and seize his throne,
     Reduce the infernal World to his
          command,   50
     And with his irresistible right hand,
     Redeem them from the vaults of
          Padalon.

                    5

Apart from these a milder company,
The victims of offences not their own,
Look'd when the appointed Messenger
          should come ;
Gather'd together some, and some alone
     Brooding in silence on their future
          doom.
Widows whom, to their husbands'
          funeral fire,   [pyre,
Force or strong error led, to share the
As to their everlasting marriage-bed :
     And babes, by sin unstain'd,   61
     Whom erring parents vow'd
To Ganges, and the holy stream pro-
          faned   [unordain'd
With that strange sacrifice, rite
By Law, by sacred Nature unallow'd :
Others more hapless in their destiny,
Scarce having first inhaled their vital
          breath,
     Whose cradles from some tree
     Unnatural hands suspended,
     Then left, till gentle Death,   70
Coming like Sleep, their feeble moan-
          ings ended ;
     Or for his prey the ravenous Kite
          descended ;

Or marching like an army from their
          caves,
     The Pismires blacken'd o'er, then
          bleach'd and bare
     Left their unharden'd bones to fall
          asunder there.

                    6

Innocent Souls ! thus set so early free
From sin and sorrow and mortality,
Their spotless spirits all creating Love
Received into its universal breast.
     Yon blue serene above   80
Was their domain ; clouds pillow'd
          them to rest :
     The Elements on them like nurses
          tended,
     And with their growth ethereal
          substance blended.
Less pure than these is that strange
          Indian bird,   [bill,
Who never dips in earthly streams her
But, when the sound of coming
          showers is heard,
Looks up, and from the clouds receives
          her fill.
Less pure the footless fowl of Heaven,
          that never   [ever
Rest upon earth, but on the wing for
Hovering o'er flowers, their fragrant
          food inhale,   90
Drink the descending dew upon its way,
And sleep aloft while floating on the gale.

                    7

And thus these innocents in yonder sky
     Grow and are strengthen'd, while the
          allotted years
     Perform their course ; then hither-
          ward they fly,
     Being free from moral taint, so free
          from fears,
A joyous band, expecting soon to soar
     To Indra's happy spheres,   98
And mingle with the blessed company
Of heavenly spirits there for ever more.

8

A Gulph profound surrounded
This icy belt; the opposite side
With highest rocks was bounded;
But where their heads they hide,
Or where their base is founded,
None could espy. Above all reach of
            sight
They rose, the second Earth was on
            their height,   [night.
Their feet were fix'd in everlasting

9

So deep the Gulph, no eye
Could plum its dark profundity, 110
Yet all its depth must try; for this
            the road
To Padalon, and Yamen's dread abode.
And from below continually
Ministrant Demons rose and caught
The Souls whose hour was come;
Then with their burthen fraught,
Plunged down, and bore them to
            receive their doom.

10

Then might be seen who went in hope,
            and who
Trembled to meet the meed
Of many a foul misdeed, as wild they
            threw   120
Their arms retorted from the Demons'
            grasp,
And look'd around, all eagerly, to seek
For help, where help was none; and
            strove for aid
To clasp the nearest shade;
Yea, with imploring looks and horrent
            shriek,   [bending,
Even from one Demon to another
With hands extending,
Their mercy they essay'd.
Still from the verge they strain,
And from the dreadful gulph avert their
            eyes,   130

In vain; down plunge the Demons, and
            their cries
Feebly, as down they sink, from that
            profound arise.

11

What heart of living man could,
            undisturb'd,   [there
Dear sight so sad as this! What wonder
If Kailyal's lip were blanch'd with
            inmost dread !
The chill which from that icy belt
Struck through her, was less keen than
            what she felt
With her heart's blood through every
            limb dispread.
Close to the Glendoveer she clung,
And clasping round his neck her
            trembling hands,   140
She closed her eyes, and there in
            silence hung.

12

Then to Ladurlad said the Glendoveer,
These Demons, whom thou seest, the
            ministers
Of Yamen, wonder to behold us here;
But for the dead they come, and not
            for us :   [thus,
Therefore albeit they gaze upon thee
Have thou no fear.
A little while thou must be left alone,
Till I have borne thy daughter down,
And placed her safely by the throne
Of him who keeps the Gate of Padalon.

13

Then taking Kailyal in his arms, he
            said,   152
Be of good heart, Beloved ! it is I
Who bear thee. Saying this, his wings
            he spread,
Sprung upward in the sky, and poised
            his flight,
Then plunged into the Gulph, and
            sought the World of Night.

XXII. THE GATE OF PADALON

1

THE strong foundations of this inmost
Earth
Rest upon Padalon.   That icy Mound
Which girt the mortal Ocean round,
Reach'd the profound, . .
Ice in the regions of the upper air,
Crystal midway, and adamant below,
Whose strength sufficed to bear
The weight of all this upper World of
ours,   [of Woe.
And with its rampart closed the Realm
Eight gates hath Padalon ; eight
heavenly Powers   10
Have them in charge, each alway at
his post,
Lest from their penal caves the
accursed host,
Maugre the might of Baly and the God,
Should break, and carry ruin all abroad.

2

Those gates stand ever open, night and
day,
And Souls of mortal men
For ever throng the way.
Some from the dolorous den,
Children of sin and wrath, return no
more :
They, fit companions of the Spirits
accurst,   20
Are doom'd, like them in baths of fire
immerst,
Or weltering upon beds of molten ore,
Or stretch'd upon the brazen floor,
Are fasten'd down with adamantine
chains ;
While, on their substance inconsumable,
Leeches of fire for ever hang and pull,
And worms of fire for ever gnaw their
food,
That, still renew'd,
Freshens for ever their perpetual pains.

3

Others there were whom Baly's voice
condemn'd,   30
By long and painful penance, to atone
Their fleshly deeds.   Them, from the
Judgement-throne,
Dread Azyoruca, where she sat involved
In darkness as a tent, received, and
dealt
To each the measure of his punishment ;
Till, in the central springs of fire, the
Will
Impure is purged away ; and the
freed soul,
Thus fitted to receive a second birth,
Embodied once again, revisits Earth.

4

But they whom Baly's righteous voice
absolved,   40
And Yamen, viewing with benignant
eye,
Dismiss'd to seek their heritage on high.
How joyfully they leave this gloomy
bourne,
The dread sojourn
Of Guilt and twin-born Punishment
and Woe,
And wild Remorse, here link'd with
worse Despair !
They to the eastern Gate rejoicing go :
The Ship of Heaven awaits their
coming there,   [light
And on they sail, greeting the blessed
Through realms of upper air,   50
Bound for the Swerga once ; but now
no more
Their voyage rests upon that happy
shore,   [might
Since Indra, by the dreadful Rajah's
Compell'd, hath taken flight ;
On to the second World their way
they wend,
And there, in trembling hope, await
the doubtful end.

5

For still in them doth hope pre-
dominate,
Faith's precious privilege, when higher
Powers   [hours.
Give way to fear in these portentous
Behold the Wardens eight,   60
Each silent at his gate
Expectant stands ; they turn their
anxious eyes
Within, and, listening to the dizzy din
Of mutinous uproar, each in all his
hands   [fight.
Holds all his weapons, ready for the
For, hark ! what clamorous cries
Upon Kehama, for deliverance, call !
Come, Rajah ! they exclaim, too long
we groan
In torments. Come, Deliverer !
yonder throne
Awaits thee. . . Now, Kehama !
Rajah, now !   70
Earthly Almighty, wherefore tarriest
thou ? . .
Such were the sounds that rung, in
wild uproar,
O'er all the echoing vaults of Padalon ;
And as the Asuras from the Brazen
floor,   [to rise,
Struggling against their fetters, strove
Their clashing chains were heard, and
shrieks and cries,
With curses mix'd, against the Fiends
who urge,
Fierce on their rebel limbs, the avenging
scourge.

6

These were the sounds which, at the
southern gate,
Assail'd Ereenia's ear ; alighting here
He laid before Neroodi's feet the Maid,
Who, pale and cold with fear,   81
Hung on his neck, well-nigh a lifeless
weight.

7

Who and what art thou ? cried the
Guardian Power,
Sight so unwonted wondering to
behold, . .
O Son of Light !
Who comest here at this portentous
hour,
When Yamen's throne
Trembles, and all our might can scarce
keep down
The rebel race from seizing Padalon, . .
Who and what art thou ? and what
wild despair,   91
Or wilder hope, from realms of upper air,
Tempts thee to bear
This mortal Maid to our forlorn abodes?
Fitter for her, I ween, the Swerga
bowers,
And sweet society of heavenly Powers,
Than this, . . a doleful scene,
Even in securest hours.
And whither would ye go ?
Alas ! can human or celestial ear,
Unmadden'd, hear   101
The shrieks and yellings of infernal woe?
Can living flesh and blood
Endure the passage of the fiery flood !

8

Lord of the Gate, replied the Glendoveer,
We come obedient to the will of Fate ;
And haply doom'd to bring
Hope and salvation to the Infernal
King,
For Seeva sends us here,
Even He to whom futurity is known,
The Holiest, bade us go to Yamen's
throne.   111
Thou seest my precious charge ;
Under thy care, secure from harm, I
leave her,
While I ascend to bear her father down.
Beneath the shelter of thine arm
receive her !

9

Then quoth he to the Maid,
Be of good cheer, my Kailyal! dearest
                                dear,
In faith subdue thy dread ;
Anon I shall be here. So having said,
Aloft with vigorous bound the Glen-
                        doveer   120
Sprung in celestial might,
And soaring up, in spiral circles, wound
His indefatigable flight.

10

But as he thus departed,
The Maid, who at Neroodi's feet was
                            lying,
Like one entranced or dying,
Recovering strength from sudden
                    terror, started ;   [sight,
And gazing after him with straining
And straining arms, she stood,
        As if in attitude   130
To win him back from flight.
Yea, she had shaped his name
For utterance, to recall and bid him
                        stay,   [shame
Nor leave her thus alone ; but virtuous
Represt the unbidden sounds upon
                    their way ;
And calling faith to aid,
Even in this fearful hour, the pious Maid
Collected courage, till she seem'd to be
Calm and in hope, such power hath
                        piety.
Before the Giant Keeper of the Gate
She crost her patient arms, and at his
                        feet,   141
        Prepar'd to meet
The aweful will of Fate with equal mind,
She took her seat resign'd.

11

Even the stern trouble of Neroodi's brow
Relax'd as he beheld the valiant Maid.
Hope, long unfelt till now,

Rose in his heart reviving, and a smile
Dawn'd in his brightening countenance,
                        the while
He gazed on her with wonder and
                        delight.   150
The blessing of the Powers of Padalon,
Virgin, be on thee ! said the admiring
                        God ;   [birth,
And blessed be the hour that gave thee
                    Daughter of Earth !
For thou to this forlorn abode hast
                        brought
Hope, who too long hath been a
                    stranger here.
And surely for no lamentable lot
        Nature, that erreth not,
To thee that heart of fortitude hath
                        given,
Those eyes of purity, that face of
                        love ; . .   160
If thou beëst not the inheritrix of
                        Heaven,
        There is no truth above.

12

Thus as Neroodi spake, his brow severe
Shone with an inward joy ; for sure
                    he thought
When Seeva sent so fair a creature here,
        In this momentous hour,
Ere long the World's deliverance would
                    be wrought,
And Padalon escape the Rajah's power.
With pious mind the Maid, in humble
                    guise
Inclined, received his blessing silently,
        And raised her grateful eyes   171
        A moment, then again   [high
Abased them at his presence. Hark ! on
The sound of coming wings ! . . her
                    anxious ears
Have caught the distant sound.   Ereenia
                        brings
His burthen down ! Upstarting from
                    her seat,

How joyfully she rears
Her eager head ! and scarce upon the
          ground   [found,
Ladurlad's giddy feet their footing
When, with her trembling arms, she
          claspt him round.   180
No word of greeting,
Nor other sign of joy at that strange
          meeting ;
Expectant of their fate,
Silent, and hand in hand,
Before the Infernal Gate,
The Father and his pious Daughter stand.

13

Then to Neroodi said the Glendoveer,
No Heaven-born Spirit e'er hath visited
This region drear and dread ; but I,
          the first
Who tread your World accurst.   190
Lord of the Gate, to whom these
          realms are known,
Direct our fated way to Yamen's
          throne.

14

Bring forth my Chariot, Carmala !
          quoth then
The Keeper of the way.
It was the Car wherein
On Yamen's festal day,
When all the Powers of Hell attend
          their King,
Yearly to Yamenpur did he repair
To pay his homage there.
Poised on a single wheel, it moved
          along,   200
Instinct with motion ; by what won-
          drous skill
Compact, no human tongue could tell,
Nor human wit devise ; but on that
          wheel,
Moving or still,
As if with life indued,
The Car miraculous supported stood.

15

Then Carmala brought forth two
          mantles, white
As the swan's breast, and bright as
          mountain snow,
When from the wintry sky
The sun, late rising, shines upon the
          height.   210
And rolling vapours fill the vale below.
Not without pain the unaccustom'd
          sight
That brightness could sustain ;
For neither mortal stain,
Nor parts corruptible, remain,
Nor aught that time could touch, or
          force destroy,
In that pure web whereof the robes
          were wrought ;   [tried,
So long had it in tenfold fires been
And blanch'd, and to that brightness
          purified.
          Apparell'd thus, alone,   220
Children of Earth, Neroodi cried,
In safety may ye pass to Yamen's
          throne.   [blood
Thus only can your living flesh and
Endure the passage of the fiery flood.

16

Of other frame, O son of Heaven, art
          thou !
Yet hast thou now to go
Through regions which thy heavenly
          mould will try.
Glories unutterably bright, I know,
And beams intense of empyrean light,
Thine eye divine can bear : but fires
          of woe,   230
The sight of torments, and the cry
Of absolute despair,
Might not these things dismay thee on
          thy flight,
And thy strong pennons flag and fail
          thee there ?   [thou art
Trust not thy wings, celestial thoug[h]

Nor thy good heart, which horror might
                  assail
            And pity quail,
Pity in these abodes of no avail ;
But take thy seat this mortal pair
                  beside,
And Carmala the infernal Car will
                  guide.   240
Go, and may happy end your way
            betide !   [roll'd on.
So, as he spake, the self-moved Car
And lo ! they pass the Gate of Padalon.

XXIII. PADALON

1

WHOE'ER hath loved with venturous
                  step to tread
            The chambers dread
Of some deep cave, and seen his taper's
                  beam
Lost in the arch of darkness overhead,
            And mark'd its gleam,
Playing afar upon the sunless stream,
            Where from their secret bed,
And course unknown and inaccessible,
            The silent waters well ;
Whoe'er hath trod such caves of endless
                  night,   10
He knows, when measuring back the
                  gloomy way,
With what delight refresh'd his eye
Perceives the shadow of the light of
                  day,   [it falls
Through the far portal slanting, where
Dimly reflected on the watery walls ;
            How heavenly seems the sky ;
And how, with quicken'd feet, he
                  hastens up,
            Eager again to greet
The living World and blessed sunshine
                  there,
            And drink, as from a cup   20
Of joy, with thirsty lips, the open air.

2

Far other light than that of day there
                  shone
Upon the travellers, entering Padalon.
They too in darkness enter'd on their
                  way,
            But, far before the Car,
A glow, as of a fiery furnace light,
Fill'd all before them.   'Twas a light
                  which made
Darkness itself appear
A thing of comfort, and the sight,
                  dismay'd,
Shrunk inward from the molten
                  atmosphere.   30
Their way was through the adaman-
                  tine rock   [side
Which girt the World of Woe ; on either
Its massive walls arose, and overhead
Arch'd the long passage ; onward as
                  they ride,
With stronger glare the light around
                  them spread ;
            And lo ! the regions dread,
The World of Woe before them,
                  opening wide.

3

            There rolls the fiery flood,
Girding the realms of Padalon around.
            A sea of flame it seem'd to be,   40
            Sea without bound ;
For neither mortal nor immortal sight,
            Could pierce across through that
                  intensest light.
            A single rib of steel,
Keen as the edge of keenest scymitar,
Spann'd this wide gulph of fire.   The
                  infernal Car
Roll'd to the Gulph, and on its single
                  wheel
Self-balanced, rose upon that edge of
                  steel.   [head,
Red-quivering float the vapours over-
The fiery gulph beneath them spread.

Tosses its billowing blaze with rush
  and roar ;   51
Steady and swift the self-moved
  Chariot went,
Winning the long ascent,
Then, downward rolling, gains the
  farther shore.

4

But, oh ! what sounds and sights of woe,
What sights and sounds of fear,
Assail the mortal travellers here !
Their way was on a causey straight
  and wide,
Where penal vaults on either side were
  seen,
  Ranged like the cells wherein   60
Those wondrous winged alchemists
  infold
  Their stores of liquid gold.
Thick walls of adamant divide
The dungeons ; and from yonder
  circling flood,
Off-streams of fire through secret
  channels glide,
And wind among them, and in each
  provide
  An everlasting food
Of rightful torments for the accursed
  brood.

5

These were the rebel race, who in their
  might
Confiding impiously, would fain have
  driven   70
The Deities supreme from highest
  Heaven :
But by the Suras, in celestial fight,
  Opposed and put to flight,
Here, in their penal dens, the accursed
  crew,
Not for its crime, but for its failure, rue
Their wild ambition.   Yet again they
  long
  The contest to renew,

And wield their arms again in happier
  hour ;
  And with united power,
Following Kehama's triumph, to press
  on   80
From World to World, and Heaven
  to Heaven, and Sphere
To Sphere, till Hemakoot shall bo
  their own,
And Meru-Mount, and Indra's Swerga-
  Bowers,
  And Brama's region, where the
    heavenly Hours   [day.
Weave the vast circle of his age-long
Even over Veeshnoo's empyreal seat
They trust the Rajah shall extend
  their sway,
And that the seven-headed Snake,
  whereon
The strong Preserver sets his con-
  quering feet,
Will rise and shake him headlong from
  his throne,   90
  When, in their irresistible array,
Amid the Milky Sea they force their
  way.
Even higher yet their frantic thoughts
  aspire ;
Yea, on their beds of torment as they
  lie,
The highest, holiest Seeva, they defy,
And tell him they shall have anon
  their day,
When they will storm his realm, and
  seize Mount Calasay.

6

  Such impious hopes torment
  Their raging hearts, impious and
    impotent ;
And now, with unendurable desire
And lust of vengeance, that, like in-
  ward fire,   101
Doth aggravate their punishment,
  they rave

Upon Kehama ; him the accursed rout
Acclaim ; with furious cries and
    maddening shout
They call on him to save ;
    Kehama ! they exclaim ;
Thundering the dreadful echo rolls
    about,
And Hell's whole vault repeats
    Kehama's name.

7

Over these dens of punishment, the host
Of Padalon maintain eternal guard,
Keeping upon the walls their vigilant
    ward.   111
    At every angle stood
A watch-tower, the decurion Demon's
    post,
Where raised on high he view'd with
    sleepless eye
His trust, that all was well. And over
    these,   [Hell,
Such was the perfect discipline of
Captains of fifties and of hundreds held
Authority, each in his loftier tower ;
And chiefs of legions over them had
    power ;
And thus all Hell with towers was
    girt around.   120
    Aloft the brazen turrets shone
    In the red light of Padalon ;
    And on the walls between,
Dark moving, the infernal Guards
    were seen,
Gigantic Demons, pacing to and fro ;
    Who ever and anon,
Spreading their crimson pennons,
    plunged below,
Faster to rivet down the Asuras' chains,
And with the snaky scourge and fiercer
    pains,
Repress their rage rebellious. Loud
    around,   130
In mingled sound, the echoing lash,
    the clash

Of chains, the ponderous hammer's
    iron stroke,
With execrations, groans, and shrieks
    and cries
Combined, in one wild dissonance,
    arise ;
    And through the din there broke,
Like thunder heard through all the
    warring winds,
The dreadful name. Kehama, still
    they rave,
    Hasten and save !
Now, now, Deliverer ! now, Kehama,
    now !
Earthly Almighty, wherefore tarriest
    thou ?   140

8

    Oh, if that name abhorr'd,
    Thus utter'd, could well nigh
Dismay the Powers of Hell, and daunt
    their Lord,
How fearfully to Kailyal's ear it came !
She, as the Car roll'd on its rapid way,
Bent down her head, and closed her
    eyes for dread ;
And deafening, with strong effort
    from within,
    Her ears against the din,
Cover'd and press'd them close with
    both her hands.
Sure if the mortal Maiden had not fed
On heavenly food, and long been
    strengthened   151
With heavenly converse for such end
    vouchsafed,
Her human heart had fail'd, and she
    had died
Beneath the horrors of this aweful hour.
    But Heaven supplied a power
Beyond her earthly nature, to the
    measure
    Of need infusing strength ;
And Fate, whose secret and unerring
    pleasure

Appointed all, decreed
An ample meed and recompense at
                    length.   160
High-fated Maid, the righteous hour
    is nigh!
The all-embracing Eye
Of Retribution still beholdeth thee;
Bear onward to the end. O Maid.
    courageously!

9

On roll'd the Car, and lo! afar
Upon its height the towers of Yamenpur
    Rise on the astonish'd sight.
Behold the infernal City, Yamen's seat
Of empire, in the midst of Padalon,
    Where the eight causeys meet.   170
There on a rock of adamant it stood,
    Resplendent far and wide,
    Itself of solid diamond edified,
And all around it roll'd the fiery flood.
Eight bridges arch'd the stream; huge
    piles of brass
Magnificent, such structures as beseem
The Seat and Capital of such great God,
Worthy of Yamen's own august abode.
A brazen tower and gateway at each
    end
Of each was raised, where Giant
                    Wardens stood,   180
Station'd in arms the passage to defend,
That never foe might cross the fiery
    flood.

10

Oh what a gorgeous sight it was to see
The Diamond City blazing on its height
With more than mid-sun splendour,
    by the light
    Of its own fiery river!
Its towers and domes and pinnacles
    and spires,
Turrets and battlements, that flash
    and quiver
Through the red restless atmosphere
    for ever;

And hovering over head,   190
The smoke and vapours of all Padalon,
Fit firmament for such a world, were
    spread,
With surge and swell, and everlasting
                    motion,   [ocean.
Heaving and opening like tumultuous

11

Nor were there wanting there
Such glories as beseem'd such region
    well;
For though with our blue heaven and
    genial air
The firmament of Hell might not
    compare,
As little might our earthly tempests vie
With the dread storms of that infernal
                    sky,   200
Whose clouds of all metallic elements
    Sublimed were full. For, when its
    thunder broke,
Not all the united World's artillery,
    In one discharge, could equal that
    loud stroke;
And though the Diamond Towers and
    Battlements
Stood firm upon their adamantine rock,
Yet while it vollied round the vault of
                    Hell,   [shock,
Earth's solid arch was shaken with the
And Cities in one mighty ruin fell.
Through the red sky terrific meteors
                    scour;   210
Huge stones come hailing down; or
    sulphur-shower,
Floating amid the lurid air like snow,
    Kindles in its descent,
And with blue fire-drops rains on all
    below.
At times the whole supernal element
Igniting, burst in one large sheet of
    flame,
    And roar'd as with the sound
Of rushing winds, above, below, around;

Anon the flame was spent, and overhead
A heavy cloud of moving darkness
    spread.   220

12

Straight to the brazen bridge and gate
The self-moved Chariot bears its
    mortal load.
    At sight of Carmala,
On either side the Giant guards divide,
And give the chariot way.
Up yonder winding road it rolls along,
Swift as the bittern soars on spiral wing,
And lo ! the Palace of the Infernal
    King !

13

Two forms inseparable in unity
Hath Yamen ; even as with hope or
    fear   230
The Soul regardeth him doth he appear ;
    For hope and fear
At that dread hour, from ominous
    conscience spring,
And err not in their bodings.   There-
    fore some,
They who polluted with offences come,
    Behold him as the King
Of Terrors, black of aspect, red of eye,
Reflecting back upon the sinful mind,
Heighten'd with vengeance, and with
    wrath divine
    Its own inborn deformity.   240
But to the righteous Spirit how benign
    His aweful countenance,
Where, tempering justice with parental
    love,
Goodness and heavenly grace
And sweetest mercy shine ! Yet is he still
Himself the same, one form, one face,
    one will ;   [one ;
And these his twofold aspects are but
And change is none
In him, for change in Yamen could
    not be,
    The Immutable is he.   250

14

    He sat upon a marble sepulchre
    Massive and huge, where at the
        Monarch's feet,
The righteous Baly had his Judgement-
        seat.   [stood ;
A Golden Throne before them vacant
Three human forms sustain'd its pon-
        derous weight,
With lifted hands outspread, and
    shoulders bow'd
    Bending beneath the load.
A fourth was wanting.   They were of
    the hue
Of coals of fire ; yet were they flesh
    and blood,
    And living breath they drew ;   260
And their red eye-balls roll'd with
    ghastly stare,
As thus, for their misdeeds, they stood
    tormented there.

15

On steps of gold those living Statues
    stood,
Who bore the Golden Throne.   A cloud
    behind   [light
Immovable was spread ; not all the
Of all the flames and fires of Padalon
    Could pierce its depth of night.
There Azyoruca veil'd her aweful form
In those eternal shadows : there she
    sate,
And as the trembling Souls, who crowd
    around   270
The Judgement-seat, received the
    doom of fate,
Her giant arms, extending from the
    cloud,
Drew them within the darkness.   Mov-
    ing out   [rout,
To grasp and bear away the innumerous
For ever and for ever thus were seen
The thousand mighty arms of that
    dread Queen.

16

Here, issuing from the car, the Glen-
doveer
Did homage to the God, then raised
his head.
Suppliants we come, he said,
I need not tell thee by what wrongs
opprest,   280
For nought can pass on earth to thee
unknown ;
Sufferers from tyranny we seek for rest,
And Seeva bade us go to Yamen's
throne ;
Here, he hath said, all wrongs shall be
redrest.
Yamen replied, Even now the hour
draws near,
When Fate its hidden ways will
manifest.
Not for light purpose would the Wisest
send
His suppliants here, when we, in doubt
and fear,
The aweful issue of the hour attend.
Wait ye in patience and in faith the
end !   290

XXIV. THE AMREETA

1

So spake the King of Padalon, when,
lo !   [Hell,
The voice of lamentation ceased in
And sudden silence all around them fell,
Silence more wild and terrible
Than all the infernal dissonance before.
Through that portentous stillness, far
away,
Unwonted sounds were heard, ad-
vancing on
And deepening on their way ;
For now the inexorable hour
Was come, and, in the fulness of his
power,   10

Now that the dreadful rites had all
been done,
Kehama from the Swerga hasten'd
down,
To seize upon the throne of Padalon.

2

He came in all his might and majesty,
With all his terrors clad, and all his
pride ;
And, by the attribute of Deity,
Which he had won from Heaven, self-
multiplied,
The Almighty Man appear'd on every
side.
In the same indivisible point of time,
At the eight Gates he stood at once,
and beat   20
The Warden-Gods of Hell beneath his
feet ;
Then, in his brazen Cars of triumph,
straight,
At the same moment, drove through
every gate.
By Aullays, hugest of created kind,
Fiercest, and fleeter than the viewless
wind,
His Cars were drawn, ten yokes of
ten abreast, . .
What less sufficed for such almighty
weight ?
Eight bridges from the fiery flood arose
Growing before his way ; and on he goes,
And drives the thundering Chariot
wheels along,   30
At once o'er all the roads of Padalon.

3

Silent and motionless remain
The Asuras on their bed of pain,
Waiting, with breathless hope, the
great event.
All Hell was hush'd in dread,
Such awe that omnipresent coming
spread ;

Nor had its voice been heard, though
     all its rout
Innumerable had lifted up one shout ;
Nor if the infernal firmament
     Had in one unimaginable burst   40
Spent its collected thunders, had the
     sound,
Been audible, such louder terrors went
Before his forms substantial.   Round
          about   [wide,
The presence scattered lightnings far and
     That quench'd on every side,
With their intensest blaze, the feebler fire
Of Padalon, even as the stars go out,
     When, with prodigious light,
Some blazing meteor fills the astonish'd
     night.

4

     The Diamond City shakes !   50
     The adamantine Rock
     Is loosen'd with the shock !
From its foundation moved, it heaves
     and quakes ;   [dust ;
The brazen portals crumbling fall to
     Prone fall the Giant Guards
     Beneath the Aullays crush'd ;
On, on, through Yamenpur, their
     thundering feet
Speed from all points to Yamen's
     Judgement-seat.
And lo ! where multiplied,
Behind, before him, and on every side,
Wielding all weapons in his countless
     hands,   61
Around the Lord of Hell Kehama
     stands !
Then too the Lord of Hell put forth
     his might :
Thick darkness, blacker than the
     blackest night,
Rose from their wrath, and veil'd
     The unutterable fight.
The power of Fate and Sacrifice
     prevail'd,

     And soon the strife was done.
Then did the Man-God re-assume
     His unity, absorbing into one   70
The consubstantiate shapes ; and as
     the gloom
Opened, fallen Yamen on the ground
     was seen,
His neck beneath the conquering
     Rajah's feet,
     Who on the marble tomb
     Had his triumphal seat.

5

Silent the Man-Almighty sate ;
     a smile
Gleam'd on his dreadful lips, the
     while
Dallying with power, he paused from
     following up
His conquest, as a man in social hour
     Sips of the grateful cup,   80
Again and yet again with curious
     taste
Searching its subtle flavour ere he
     drink :
Even so Kehama now torbore his
     haste ;
Having within his reach whate'er he
     sought,
On his own haughty power he seem'd
     to muse,
Pampering his arrogant heart with
     silent thought.
Before him stood the Golden Throne
     in sight,
Right opposite ; he could not choose
     but see
Nor seeing choose but wonder.   Who
     are ye
Who bear the Golden Throne tor-
     mented there ?   90
He cried ; for whom doth Destiny
     prepare
The Imperial Seat, and why are ye
     but Three ?

6

FIRST STATUE

I of the Children of Mankind was first,
Me miserable ! who, adding store to
      store,   [accurst,
Heapt up superfluous wealth ; and now
For ever I the frantic crime deplore.

SECOND STATUE

I o'er my Brethren of Mankind the first
Usurping power, set up a throne sublime,
A King and Conqueror : therefore
      thus accurst,   99
For ever I in vain repent the crime.

THIRD STATUE

I on the Children of Mankind the first,
In God's most holy name, imposed a tale
Of impious falsehood ; therefore thus
      accurst,
For ever I in vain the crime bewail.

7

Even as thou here beholdest us,
Here we have stood, tormented thus,
Such countless ages, that they seem
      to be
Long as eternity,
And still we are but Three.
A Fourth will come to share   110
Our pain, at yonder vacant corner bear
His portion of the burthen, and compleat
The Golden Throne for Yamen's
      Judgement-seat.   [be
Thus hath it been appointed : he must
Equal in guilt to us, the guilty Three.
Kehama, come ! too long we wait for
      thee !

8

Thereat, with one accord,
The Three took up the word, like
      choral song,
Come Rajah ! Man-God ! Earth's
      Almighty Lord !
Kehama, come ! we wait for thee too
      long.   120

9

A short and sudden laugh of won-
      dering pride   [reply
Burst from him in his triumph : to
Scornful he deign'd not ; but with
      alter'd eye
Wherein some doubtful meaning
      seem'd to lie,   [cried,
He turn'd to Kailyal. Maiden, thus he
I need not bid thee see
How vain it is to strive with Fate's
      decree,   [from me,
When hither thou hast fled to fly
And lo ! even here thou find'st me at
      thy side.
Mine thou must be, being doom'd
      with me to share   130
The Amreeta-cup of immortality ;
   Yea, by Myself I swear,
It hath been thus appointed. Joyfully
Join then thy hand and heart and will
      with mine,
Nor at such glorious destiny repine,
Nor in thy folly more provoke my
      wrath divine.

10

She answer'd ; I have said. It must
      not be !
Almighty as thou art,
Thou hast put all things underneath
      thy feet ;
But still the resolute heart   140
And virtuous will are free.
Never, oh ! never, . . never . . can
      there be   [me.
Communion, Rajah, between thee and

11

Once more, quoth he, I urge, and once
      alone.
Thou seest yon Golden Throne,
Where I anon shall set thee by my side ;
Take thou thy seat thereon,
Kehama's willing bride,

And I will place the Kingdoms of the
World
    Beneath thy Father's feet,   150
Appointing him the King of mortal
men :
    Else underneath that Throne,
The Fourth supporter he shall stand
and groan ;
Prayers will be vain to move my
mercy then.

12

Again the Virgin answer'd, I have said !
Ladurlad caught her in his proud
embrace,
    While on his neck she hid
    In agony her face.

13

Bring forth the Amreeta-cup ! Kehama
cried   159
To Yamen, rising sternly in his pride.
It is within the Marble Sepulchre,
The vanquish'd Lord of Padalon replied,
Bid it be open'd. Give thy treasure up !
Exclaim'd the Man-Almighty to the
Tomb.
    And at his voice and look
The massy fabric shook, and open'd
wide.
A huge Anatomy was seen reclined
Within its marble womb. Give me
the Cup !
Again Kehama cried ; no other charm
Was needed than that voice of stern
command.   170
From his repose the ghastly form arose,
Put forth his bony and gigantic arm,
And gave the Amreeta to the Rajah's
hand.
Take ! drink ! with accents dread the
Spectre said,
For thee and Kailyal hath it been
assign'd,
Ye only of the Children of Mankind.

14

Then was the Man-Almighty's heart
elate ;
This is the consummation ! he exclaim'd ;
Thus have I triumphed over Death
and Fate.   179
Now, Seeva ! look to thine abode !
Henceforth, on equal footing we engage,
Alike immortal now, and we shall wage
    Our warfare, God to God !
    Joy fill'd his impious soul,
And to his lips he raised the fatal bowl.

15

Thus long the Glendoveer had stood
Watching the wonders of the eventful
hour,
    Amazed but undismay'd ; for in his
heart
Faith, overcoming fear, maintain'd its
power.
Nor had that faith abated, when the
God   190
Of Padalon was beaten down in fight ;
For then he look'd to see the heavenly
might   [now
Of Seeva break upon them. But when
He saw the Amreeta in Kehama's hand,
    An impulse which defied all self-
command
    In that extremity
Stung him, and he resolved to seize
the cup,
And dare the Rajah's force in Seeva's
sight.
    Forward he sprung to tempt the
unequal fray,
    When lo ! the Anatomy,   200
With warning arm, withstood his
desperate way,
And from the Golden Throne the fiery
Three
Again, in one accord, renew'd their
song,   [long.
Kehama, come ! we wait for thee too

16

O fool of drunken hope and frantic
•   vice !
Madman ! to seek for power beyond thy
          scope
Of knowledge, and to deem
Less than Omniscience could suffice
To wield Omnipotence ! O fool,
          to dream
That immortality could be   210
The meed of evil ! . . yea thou hast it
          now,
Victim of thine own wicked heart's
          device,
Thou hast thine object now, and now
          must pay the price.

17

He did not know the holy mystery
Of that divinest cup, that as the lips
Which touch it, even such its quality,
Good or malignant : Madman ! and
          he thinks
The blessed prize is won, and joyfully
          he drinks.

18

Then Seeva open'd on the Accursed One
His Eye of Anger : upon him alone
The wrath-beam fell. He shudders . .
          but too late ;   221
          The deed is done,
The dreadful liquor works the will of
          Fate.
Immortal he would be,
Immortal he is made ; but through
          his veins
Torture at once and immortality,
A stream of poison doth the Amreeta
          run,
And while within the burning anguish
          flows,
His outward body glows
Like molten ore, beneath the avenging
          Eye,   230
Doom'd thus to live and burn eternally.

19

The fiery Three,
Beholding him, set up a fiendish cry,
          A song of jubilee ;   [long
Come, Brother, come ! they sung ; too
          Have we expected thee,
          Henceforth we bear no more
The unequal weight ; Come, Brother,
          we are Four !

20

Vain his almightiness, for mightier pain
Subdued all power ; pain ruled supreme
          alone ;   240
And yielding to the bony hand
The unemptied cup, he moved toward
          the Throne,   [stand.
And at the vacant corner took his
Behold the Golden Throne at length
          complete,   [ment-seat.
And Yamen silently ascends the Judge-

21

For two alone, of all mankind, to me
The Amreeta Cup was given,
          Then said the Anatomy ;
The Man hath drunk, the Woman's
          turn is next.
Come, Kailyal, come, receive thy doom,
          And do the Will of Heaven ! . .   251
Wonder, and Fear, and Awe at once
          perplext
The mortal Maiden's heart, but over all
          Hope rose triumphant. With a
          trembling hand,
          Obedient to his call,
She took the fated Cup ; and, lifting up
Her eyes, where holy tears began to swell,
          Is it not your command,
Ye heavenly Powers ? as on her knees
          she fell,
          The pious Virgin cried ;   260
Ye know my innocent will, my heart
          sincere,
          Ye govern all things still,
          And wherefore should I fear !

22

She said, and drank.   The Eye of
Mercy beam'd
Upon the Maid : a cloud of fragrance
steam'd
Like incense-smoke, as all her mortal
frame
Dissolved beneath the potent agency
Of that mysterious draught ; such
quality,
From her pure touch, the fated Cup
partook.
Like one entranced she knelt,   270
Feeling her body melt
Till all but what was heavenly pass'd
away :
Yet still she felt
Her Spirit strong within her, the same
heart,
With the same loves, and all her
heavenly part
Unchang'd, and ripen'd to such perfect
state   [Earth,
In this miraculous birth, as here on
Dimly our holiest hopes anticipate.

23

Mine ! mine ! with rapturous joy
Ereenia cried,
Immortal now, and yet not more
divine ;   280
Mine, mine, . . for ever mine !
The immortal Maid replied,
For ever, ever, thine !

24

Then Yamen said, O thou to whom
by Fate,
Alone of all mankind, this lot is given,
Daughter of Earth, but now the Child
of Heaven !
Go with thy heavenly Mate,
Partaker now of his immortal bliss ;
Go to the Swerga Bowers,
And there recall the hours   290
Of endless happiness.

25

But that sweet Angel, for she still
retain'd
Her human loves and human piety,
As if reluctant at the God's commands,
Linger'd, with anxious eye
Upon her Father fix'd, and spread her
hands
Toward him wistfully.
Go ! Yamen said, nor cast that look
behind
Upon Ladurlad at this parting hour,
For thou shalt find him in thy Mother's
Bower.   300

26

The Car, for Carmala his word obey'd,
Moved on, and bore away the
Maid,
While from the Golden Throne the
Lord of Death
With love benignant on Ladurlad
smiled,
And gently on his head his blessing
laid.
As sweetly as a Child,
Whom neither thought disturbs nor
care encumbers,
Tired with long play, at close of
summer day,
Lies down and slumbers,
Even thus as sweet a boon of sleep
partaking,   310
By Yamen blest, Ladurlad sunk to
rest.
Blessed that sleep ! more blessed was
the waking !
For on that night a heavenly morning
broke,
The light of heaven was round him
when he woke,
And in the Swerga, in Yedillian's
Bower,
All whom he loved he met, to part no
more.

RODERICK,
THE LAST OF THE GOTHS:
A TRAGIC POEM.

'Tanto acrior apud majores, sicut virtutibus gloria, ita flagitiis poenitentia, fuit. Sed haec aliaque, ex veteri memoria petita, quotiens res locusque exempla recti, aut solatia mali, poscet, haud absurde memorabimus.'—*Taciti Hist.* lib. iii. c. 51.

TO
GROSVENOR CHARLES BEDFORD,
THIS POEM IS INSCRIBED,
IN LASTING MEMORIAL OF A LONG AND UNINTERRUPTED FRIENDSHIP,
BY HIS OLD SCHOOLFELLOW,
ROBERT SOUTHEY.

.. 'As the ample Moon,
In the deep stillness of a summer even
Rising behind a thick and lofty Grove,
Burns like an unconsuming fire of light
In the green trees; and kindling on all sides
Their leafy umbrage, turns the dusky veil
Into a substance glorious as her own,
Yea, with her own incorporated, by power
Capacious and serene: Like power abides
In Man's celestial Spirit; Virtue thus
Sets forth and magnifies herself; thus feeds
A calm, a beautiful and silent fire,
From the incumbrances of mortal life,
From error, disappointment, .. nay from guilt;
And sometimes, so relenting Justice wills,
From palpable oppressions of Despair.'
Wordsworth.

PREFACE.

THE history of the Wisi-Goths for some years before their overthrow is very imperfectly known. It is, however, apparent, that the enmity between the royal families of Chindasuintho and Wamba was one main cause of the destruction of the kingdom, the latter party having assisted in betraying their country to the Moors for the gratification of their own revenge. Theodofred and Favila were younger sons of King Chindasuintho; King Witiza, who was of Wamba's family, put out the eyes of Theodofred, and murdered Favila, at the instigation of that Chieftain's wife, with whom he lived in adultery. Pelayo, the son of Favila, and afterwards the founder of the Spanish monarchy, was driven into exile. Roderick, the son of Theodofred, recovered the throne, and put out Witiza's eyes in vengeance for his father; but he spared Orpas, the brother of the tyrant, as being a Priest, and Ebba and Sisibert, the two sons of Witiza, by Pelayo's mother. It may be convenient thus briefly to premise these circumstances of an obscure portion of history, with which few readers can be supposed to be familiar; and a list of the principal persons who are introduced, or spoken of, may as properly be prefixed to a Poem as to a Play.

WITIZA, ... King of the Wisi-Goths; dethroned and blinded by Roderick.
THEODOFRED, .. son of King Chindasuintho, blinded by King Witiza.
FAVILA, ... his brother; put to death by Witiza.
The Wife of Favila, Witiza's adulterous mistress.

(*These four persons are dead before the action of the poem commences.*)

RODERICK, ... the last King of the Wisi-Goths: son of Theodofred.
PELAYO, ... the founder of the Spanish Monarchy: son of Favila.
GAUDIOSA, ... his wife.
GUISLA, ... his sister.
FAVILA, ... his son.
HERMESIND, ... his daughter.
RUSILLA, ... widow of Theodofred, and mother of Roderick.
COUNT PEDRO, } powerful Lords of Can-
COUNT EUDON, } tabria.
ALPHONSO, ... Count Pedro's son, afterwards King.
URBAN, ... Archbishop of Toledo.
ROMANO, ... a Monk of the Caulian Schools, near Merida.
ABDALAZIZ, ... the Moorish Governor of Spain.
EGILONA, ... formerly the wife of Roderick, now of Abdalaziz.

ABULCACEM, .. }
ALCAHMAN, .. }
AYUB, ... } Moorish Chiefs.
IBRAHIM, ... }
MAGUED, ... }
ORPAS, ... brother to Witiza, and formerly Archbishop of Seville, now a renegade.
SISIBERT, ... } sons of Witiza and of
EBBA, ... } Pelayo's mother.
NUMACIAN, ... a renegade, governor of Gegio.
COUNT JULIAN, . a powerful Lord among the Wisi-Goths, now a renegade.
FLORINDA, ... his daughter, violated by King Roderick.

ADOSINDA, ... daughter of the Governor of Auria.
ODOAR, ... Abbot of St. Felix.
SIVERIAN, ... Roderick's foster-father.
FAVINIA, ... Count Pedro's wife.

The four latter persons are imaginary. All the others are mentioned in history. I ought, however, to observe that Romano is a creature of monkish legends; that the name of Pelayo's sister has not been preserved; and that that of Roderick's mother, Ruscilo, has been altered to Rusilla, for the sake of euphony.

RODERICK, THE LAST OF THE GOTHS.

I. RODERICK AND ROMANO

LONG had the crimes of Spain cried out to Heaven;
At length the measure of offence was full.
Count Julian call'd the invaders; not because
Inhuman priests with unoffending blood
Had stain'd their country; not because
a yoke
Of iron servitude oppress'd and gall'd
The children of the soil; a private wrong
Roused the remorseless Baron. Mad to wreak
His vengeance for his violated child
On Roderick's head, in evil hour for Spain, 10

For that unhappy daughter and himself,
Desperate apostate .. on the Moors he call'd;
And like a cloud of locusts, whom the South
Wafts from the plains of wasted Africa,
The Musselmen upon Iberia's shore
Descend. A countless multitude they came;
Syrian, Moor, Saracen, Greek renegade,
Persian and Copt and Tatar, in one bond
Of erring faith conjoin'd, .. strong in the youth
And heat of zeal, .. a dreadful brotherhood, 20
In whom all turbulent vices were let loose;

While Conscience, with their impious
  creed accurst,
Drunk as with wine, had sanctified to
  them
All bloody, all abominable things.

Thou, Calpe, saw'st their coming;
  ancient Rock
Renown'd, no longer now shalt thou be
  call'd
From Gods and Heroes of the years of
  yore,
Kronos, or hundred-handed Briareus,
Bacchus or Hercules; but doom'd to bear
The name of thy new conqueror, and
  thenceforth   30
To stand his everlasting monument.
Thou saw'st the dark-blue waters flash
  before
Their ominous way, and whiten round
  their keels;
Their swarthy myriads darkening o'er
  thy sands.
There on the beach the Misbelievers
  spread
Their banners, flaunting to the sun and
  breeze;
Fair shone the sun upon their proud
  array,
White turbans, glittering armour, shields
  engrail'd
With gold, and scymitars of Syrian steel;
And gently did the breezes, as in sport,
Curl their long flags outrolling, and
  display   41
The blazon'd scrolls of blasphemy. Too
  soon
The gales of Spain from that unhappy land
Wafted, as from an open charnel-house,
The taint of death; and that bright
  sun, from fields
Of slaughter, with the morning dew drew
  up
Corruption through the infected atmo-
  sphere.

Then fell the kingdom of the Goths;
  their hour
Was come, and Vengeance, long with-
  held, went loose.   49
Famine and Pestilence had wasted them,
And Treason, like an old and eating sore,
Consumed the bones and sinews of their
  strength,
And worst of enemies, their Sins were
  arm'd
Against them. Yet the sceptre from
  their hands
Pass'd not away inglorious, nor was
  shame
Left for their children's lasting heritage;
Eight summer days, from morn till
  latest eve,
The fatal fight endured, till perfidy
Prevailing to their overthrow, they sunk
Defeated, not dishonour'd. On the
  banks   60
Of Chrysus, Roderick's royal car was
  found,
His battle-horse Orelio, and that helm
Whose horns, amid the thickest of the fray
Eminent, had mark'd his presence. Did
  the stream
Receive him with the undistinguish'd
  dead,
Christian and Moor, who clogg'd its
  course that day?
So thought the Conqueror, and from
  that day forth,
Memorial of his perfect victory,
He bade the river bear the name of Joy.
So thought the Goths; they said no
  prayer for him,   70
For him no service sung, nor mourning
  made,
But charged their crimes upon his head,
  and curs'd
His memory.
            Bravely in that eight-days' fight
The King had striven, . . for victory
  first, while hope

Remain'd, then desperately in search
of death.
The arrows pass'd him by to right and
left,
The spear-point pierced him not, the
scymitar
Glanced from his helmet. Is the shield
of Heaven,
Wretch that I am, extended over me ?
Cried Roderick ; and he dropt Orelio's
reins,   80
And threw his hands aloft in frantic
prayer, . .
Death is the only mercy that I crave,
Death soon and short, death and forget-
fulness !
Aloud he cried ; but in his inmost heart
There answer'd him a secret voice, that
spake
Of righteousness and judgement after
death,
And God's redeeming love, which fain
would save
The guilty soul alive. 'Twas agony,
And yet 'twas hope ; . . a momentary
light,
That flash'd through utter darkness on
the Cross   90
To point salvation, then left all within
Dark as before. Fear, never felt till
then,
Sudden and irresistible as stroke
Of lightning, smote him. From his
horse he dropt,
Whether with human impulse, or by
Heaven
Struck down, he knew not ; loosen'd
from his wrist
The sword-chain, and let fall the sword,
whose hilt
Clung to his palm a moment ere it fell,
Glued there with Moorish gore. His
royal robe,   99
His horned helmet and enamell'd mail,
He cast aside, and taking from the dead

A peasant's garment, in those weeds
involved
Stole, like a thief in darkness, from the
field.

. Evening closed round to favour him.
All night
He fled, the sound of battle in his ear
Ringing, and sights of death before his
eyes,
With forms more horrible of eager fiends
That seem'd to hover round, and gulphs
of fire
Opening beneath his feet. At times the
groan
Of some poor fugitive, who, bearing
with him   110
His mortal hurt, had fallen beside the
way,
Roused him from these dread visions,
and he call'd
In answering groans on his Redeemer's
name,
That word the only prayer that pass'd
his lips
Or rose within his heart. Then would
he see
The Cross whereon a bleeding Saviour
hung,
Who call'd on him to come and cleanse
his soul
In those all-healing streams, which from
his wounds,
As from perpetual springs, for ever
flow'd.
No hart e'er panted for the water-
brooks   120
As Roderick thirsted there to drink and
live ;
But Hell was interposed ; and worse
than Hell . .
Yea to his eyes more dreadful than the
fiends
Who flock'd like hungry ravens round
his head, . .

Florinda stood between, and warn'd
    him off
With her abhorrent hands, .. that agony
Still in her face, which, when the deed
    was done,
Inflicted on her ravisher the curse
That it invoked from Heaven. .. Oh
    what a night
Of waking horrors! Nor when morning
    came   130
Did the realities of light and day
Bring aught of comfort; wheresoe'er
    he went
The tidings of defeat had gone before;
And leaving their defenceless homes to
    seek
What shelter walls and battlements
    might yield,
Old men with feeble feet, and tottering
    babes,
And widows with their infants in their
    arms,
Hurried along. Nor royal festival,
Nor sacred pageant, with like multitudes
E'er fill'd the public way. All whom
    the sword   140
Had spared were here; bed-rid infirmity
Alone was left behind; the cripple plied
His crutches, with her child of yester-
    day
The mother fled, and she whose hour
    was come
Fell by the road.
            Less dreadful than this view
Of outward suffering which the day
    disclosed,
Had night and darkness seem'd to
    Roderick's heart,
With all their dread creations. From
    the throng
He turn'd aside, unable to endure
This burthen of the general woe; nor
    walls,   150
Nor towers, nor mountain fastnesses he
    sought,

A firmer hold his spirit yearn'd to find,
A rock of surer strength. Unknowing
    where,
Straight through the wild he hasten'd
    on all day,
And with unslacken'd speed was travel-
    ling still
When evening gather'd round. Seven
    days from morn
Till night he travell'd thus; the forest
    oaks,
The fig-grove by the fearful husbandman
Forsaken to the spoiler, and the vines,
Where fox and household dog together
    now   160
Fed on the vintage, gave him food; the
    hand
Of Heaven was on him, and the agony
Which wrought within, supplied a
    strength beyond
All natural force of man.
                    When the eighth eve
Was come, he found himself on Ana's
    banks,
Fast by the Caulian Schools. It was
    the hour
Of vespers, but no vesper bell was heard,
Nor other sound, than of the passing
    stream,
Or stork, who flapping with wide wing
    the air,
Sought her broad nest upon the silent
    tower.   170
Brethren and pupils thence alike had
    fled
To save themselves within the embattled
    walls
Of neighbouring Merida. One aged
    Monk
Alone was left behind; he would not
    leave
The sacred spot beloved, for having
    served
There from his childhood up to ripe old
    age

God's holy altar, it became him now,
He thought, before that altar to await
The merciless misbelievers, and lay
 down
His life, a willing martyr. So he staid
When all were gone, and duly fed the
 lamps, 181
And kept devotedly the altar drest,
And duly offer'd up the sacrifice.
Four days and nights he thus had pass'd
 alone,
In such high mood of saintly fortitude,
That hope of Heaven became a heavenly
 joy;
And now at evening to the gate he went
If he might spy the Moors, . . for it
 seem'd long
To tarry for his crown.
     Before the Cross
Roderick had thrown himself; his body
 raised, 190
Half kneeling, half at length he lay; his
 arms
Embraced its foot, and from his lifted
 face
Tears streaming down bedew'd the
 senseless stone.
He had not wept till now, and at the
 gush
Of these first tears, it seem'd as if his
 heart,
From a long winter's icy thrall let loose,
Had open'd to the genial influences
Of Heaven. In attitude, but not in act
Of prayer he lay; an agony of tears
Was all his soul could offer. When the
 Monk 200
Beheld him suffering thus, he raised him
 up,
And took him by the arm, and led him in;
And there before the altar, in the name
Of Him whose bleeding image there was
 hung,
Spake comfort, and adjured him in that
 name

There to lay down the burthen of his
 sins.
Lo! said Romano, I am waiting here
The coming of the Moors, that from their
 hands
My spirit may receive the purple robe
Of martyrdom, and rise to claim its
 crown. 210
That God who willeth not the sinner's
 death
Hath led thee hither. Threescore years
 and five,
Even from the hour when I, a five-years'
 child,
Enter'd the schools, have I continued
 here
And served the altar: not in all those
 years
Hath such a contrite and a broken heart
Appear'd before me. O my brother,
 Heaven
Hath sent thee for thy comfort, and for
 mine,
That my last earthly act may reconcile
A sinner to his God.
     Then Roderick knelt 220
Before the holy man, and strove to
 speak.
Thou seest, he cried, . . thou seest, . .
 but memory
And suffocating thoughts repress'd the
 word,
And shudderings, like an ague fit, from
 head
To foot convulsed him; till at length,
 subduing
His nature to the effort, he exclaim'd,
Spreading his hands and lifting up his
 face,
As if resolved in penitence to bear
A human eye upon his shame, . . Thou
 seest
Roderick the Goth! That name would
 have sufficed 230
To tell its whole abhorred history:

He not the less pursued, . . the ravisher,
The cause of all this ruin ! Having said,
In the same posture motionless he knelt,
Arms straighten'd down, and hands out-
    spread, and eyes
Raised to the Monk, like one who from
    his voice
Awaited life or death.
                    All night the old man
Pray'd with his penitent, and minister'd
Unto the wounded soul, till he infused
A healing hope of mercy that allay'd 240
Its heat of anguish. But Romano saw
What strong temptations of despair
    beset,
And how he needed in this second birth,
Even like a yearling child, a fosterer's
    care.
Father in Heaven, he cried, thy will be
    done !
Surely I hoped that I this day should
    sing
Hosannahs at thy throne ; but thou
    hast yet
Work for thy servant here. He girt his
    loins,
And from her altar took with reverent
    hands
Our Lady's image down: In this, quoth
    he,   250
We have our guide and guard and com-
    forter,
The best provision for our perilous way.
Fear not but we shall find a resting-
    place,
The Almighty's hand is on us.
                    They went forth,
They cross'd the stream, and when
    Romano turn'd
For his last look toward the Caulian
    towers,
Far off the Moorish standards in the
    light
Of morn were glittering, where the
    miscreant host

Toward the Lusitanian capital
To lay their siege advanced ; the eastern
    breeze   260
Bore to the fearful travellers far away
The sound of horn and tambour o'er the
    plain.
All day they hasten'd, and when evening
    fell
Sped toward the setting sun, as if its line
Of glory came from Heaven to point
    their course.
But feeble were the feet of that old man
For such a weary length of way ; and
    now
Being pass'd the danger (for in Merida
Sacaru long in resolute defence
Withstood the tide of war,) with easier
    pace   270
The wanderers journey'd on ; till having
    cross'd
Rich Tagus, and the rapid Zezere,
They from Albardos' hoary height
    beheld
Pine-forest, fruitful vale, and that fair
    lake
Where Alcoa, mingled there with Baza's
    stream,
Rests on its passage to the western sea,
That sea the aim and boundary of their
    toil.

    The fourth week of their painful
        pilgrimage
Was full, when they arrived where from
    the land
A rocky hill, rising with steep ascent,
O'erhung the glittering beach ; there
    on the top   281
A little lowly hermitage they found,
And a rude Cross, and at its foot a
    grave,
Bearing no name, nor other monument.
Where better could they rest than here,
    where faith
And secret penitence and happiest death

Had bless'd the spot, and brought good
    Angels down,
And open'd as it were a way to Heaven ?
Behind them was the desert, offering
    fruit
And water for their need : on either
    side   290
The white sand sparkling to the sun ; in
    front,
Great Ocean with its everlasting voice,
As in perpetual jubilee, proclaim'd,
The wonders of the Almighty, filling
    thus
The pauses of their fervent orisons.
Where better could the wanderers rest
    than here ?

II. RODERICK IN SOLITUDE

TWELVE months they sojourn'd in their
    solitude,
And then beneath the burthen of old age
Romano sunk. No brethren were there
    here
To spread the sackcloth, and with ashes
    strew
That penitential bed, and gather round
To sing his requiem, and with prayer
    and psalm
Assist him in his hour of agony.
He lay on the bare earth, which long
    had been
His only couch ; beside him Roderick
    knelt,
Moisten'd from time to time his
    blacken'd lips,   10
Received a blessing with his latest
    breath,
Then closed his eyes, and by the name-
    less grave
Of the fore-tenant of that holy place
Consign'd him earth to earth.
              Two graves are here,
And Roderick transverse at their feet
    began

To break the third. In all his intervals
Of prayer, save only when he search'd
    the woods
And fill'd the water-cruise, he labour'd
    there ;
And when the work was done and he
    had laid
Himself at length within its narrow sides
And measured it, he shook his head to
    think   21
There was no other business now for
    him.
Poor wretch, thy bed is ready, he
    exclaim'd,
And would that night were come ! . . It
    was a task,
All gloomy as it was, which had beguiled
The sense of solitude ; but now he felt
The burthen of the solitary hours :
The silence of that lonely hermitage
Lay on him like a spell ; and at the
    voice
Of his own prayers, he started half
    aghast.   30
Then too as on Romano's grave he sate
And pored upon his own, a natural
    thought
Arose within him, . . well might he have
    spared
That useless toil ; the sepulchre would
    be
No hiding place for him ; no Christian
    hands
Were here who should compose his
    decent corpse
And cover it with earth. There he
    might drag
His wretched body at its passing hour,
But there the Sea-Birds of her heritage
Would rob the worm, or peradventure
    seize,   40
Ere death had done its work, their
    helpless prey.
Even now they did not fear him : when
    he walk'd

Beside them on the beach, regardlessly
They saw his coming; and their whirring
    wings
Upon the height had sometimes fann'd
    his cheek,
As if, being thus alone, humanity
Had lost its rank, and the prerogative
Of man were done away.
             For his lost crown
And sceptre never had he felt a thought
Of pain; repentance had no pangs to
    spare   50
For trifles such as these, . . the loss of
    these
Was a cheap penalty; . . that he had
    fallen
Down to the lowest depth of wretched-
    ness,
His hope and consolation. But to lose
His human station in the scale of
    things, . .
To see brute nature scorn him, and
    renounce
Its homage to the human form divine; . .
Had then Almighty vengeance thus
    reveal'd
His punishment, and was he fallen
    indeed
Below fallen man, below redemption's
    reach, . .   60
Made lower than the beasts, and like the
    beasts
To perish! . . Such temptations troubled
    him
By day, and in the visions of the night;
And even in sleep he struggled with the
    thought,
And waking with the effort of his
    prayers
The dream assail'd him still.
               A wilder form
Sometimes his poignant penitence as-
    sumed,
Starting with force revived from inter-
    vals

Of calmer passion, or exhausted rest;
When floating back upon the tide of
    thought   70
Remembrance to a self-excusing strain
Beguiled him, and recall'd in long array
The sorrows and the secret impulses
Which to the abyss of wretchedness and
    guilt
Led their unwary victim. The evil hour
Return'd upon him, when reluctantly
Yielding to worldly counsel his assent,
In wedlock to an ill-assorted mate
He gave his cold unwilling hand: then
    came   79
The disappointment of the barren bed,
The hope deceived, the soul dissatisfied,
Home without love, and privacy from
    which
Delight was banish'd first, and peace too
    soon
Departed. Was it strange that when
    he met
A heart attuned, . . a spirit like his own,
Of lofty pitch, yet in affection mild,
And tender as a youthful mother's joy, . .
Oh was it strange if at such sympathy
The feelings which within his breast
    repell'd
And chill'd had shrunk, should open
    forth like flowers   90
After cold winds of night, when gentle
    gales
Restore the genial sun? If all were
    known,
Would it indeed be not to be forgiven? . .
(Thus would he lay the unction to his
    soul,)
If all were truly known, as Heaven knows
    all,
Heaven that is merciful as well as just, . .
A passion slow and mutual in its growth,
Pure as fraternal love, long self-con-
    ceal'd,
And when confess'd in silence, long
    controll'd;

Treacherous occasion, human frailty,
 fear   100
Of endless separation, worse than
 death, . .
The purpose and the hope with which
 the Fiend
Tempted, deceived, and madden'd him ;
 . . but then
As at a new temptation would he start,
Shuddering beneath the intolerable
 shame,
And clench in agony his matted hair ;
While in his soul the perilous thought
 . . . arose,
How easy 'twere to plunge where yonder
 waves
Invited him to rest.
     Oh for a voice
Of comfort, . . for a ray of hope from
 Heaven !   110
A hand that from these billows of despair
May reach and snatch him ere he sink
 engulph'd !
At length, as life when it hath lain long
 time
Oppress'd beneath some grievous mal-
 ady,
Seems to rouse up with re-collected
 strength,
And the sick man doth feel within him-
 self
A second spring ; so Roderick's better
 mind
Arose to save him. Lo ! the western sun
Flames o'er the broad Atlantic ; on the
 verge
Of glowing ocean rests ; retiring then
Draws with it all its rays, and sudden
 night   121
Fills the whole cope of heaven. The
 penitent
Knelt by Romano's grave, and falling
 prone,
Clasp'd with extended arms the funeral
 mould.

Father ! he cried ; Companion ! only
 friend,
When all beside was lost ! thou too art
 gone,
And the poor sinner whom from utter
 death
Thy providential hand preserved, once
 more
Totters upon the gulph. I am too weak
For solitude, . . too vile a wretch to bear
This everlasting commune with myself.
The Tempter hath assail'd me ; my own
 heart   132
Is leagued with him ; Despair hath laid
 the nets
To take my soul, and Memory like a
 ghost,
Haunts me, and drives me to the toils.
 O Saint,
While I was blest with thee, the her-
 mitage
Was my sure haven ! Look upon me
 still,
For from thy heavenly mansion thou
 canst see
The suppliant ; look upon thy child in
 Christ,
Is there no other way for penitence ? 140
I ask not martyrdom ; for what am I
That I should pray for triumphs, the
 fit meed
Of a long life of holy works like thine ;
Or how should I presumptuously aspire
To wear the heavenly crown resign'd by
 thee,
For my poor sinful sake ? Oh point me
 thou
Some humblest, painfulest, severest
 path, . .
Some new austerity, unheard of yet
In Syrian fields of glory, or the sands
Of holiest Egypt. Let me bind my
 brow   150
With thorns, and barefoot seek Jeru-
 salem,

Tracking the way with blood; there
day by day
Inflict upon this guilty flesh the scourge,
Drink vinegar and gall, and for my bed
Hang with extended limbs upon the
Cross,
A nightly crucifixion ! .. any thing
Of action, difficulty, bodily pain,
Labour, and outward suffering, .. any
thing
But stillness and this dreadful solitude !
Romano ! Father ! let me hear thy
voice   160
In dreams, O sainted Soul ! or from the
grave
Speak to thy penitent; even from the
grave
Thine were a voice of comfort.
                        Thus he cried,
Easing the pressure of his burthen'd
heart
With passionate prayer; thus pour'd
his spirit forth,
Till with the long impetuous effort spent
His spirit fail'd, and laying on the grave
His weary head as on a pillow, sleep
Fell on him.   He had pray'd to hear
a voice
Of consolation, and in dreams a voice
Of consolation came.   Roderick, it
said, . .   171
Roderick, my poor, unhappy, sinful
child,
Jesus have mercy on thee ! . . Not if
Heaven
Had opened, and Romano, visible
In his beatitude, had breathed that
prayer ; . .
Not if the grave had spoken, had it
pierced
So deeply in his soul, nor wrung his heart
With such compunctious visitings, nor
given
So quick, so keen a pang.   It was that
voice

Which sung his fretful infancy to sleep
So patiently; which soothed his child-
ish griefs,   181
Counsell'd, with anguish and prophetic
tears,
His headstrong youth.   And lo ! his
Mother stood
Before him in the vision ; in those weeds
Which never from the hour when to the
grave
She follow'd her dear lord Theodofred
Rusilla laid aside ; but in her face
A sorrow that bespake a heavier load
At heart, and more unmitigated woe, ..
Yea a more mortal wretchedness than
when   190
Witiza's ruffians and the red-hot brass
Had done their work, and in her arms
she held
Her eyeless husband ; wiped away the
sweat
Which still his tortures forced from
every pore ;
Cool'd his scorch'd lids with medicinal
herbs,
And pray'd the while for patience for
herself
And him, and pray'd for vengeance too,
and found
Best comfort in her curses.   In his
dream,
Groaning he knelt before her to beseech
Her blessing, and she raised her hands
to lay   200
A benediction on him.   But those hands
Were chain'd, and casting a wild look
around,
With thrilling voice she cried, Will no
one break
These shameful fetters ? Pedro, Theu-
demir,
Athanagild, where are ye ? Roderick's
arm
Is wither'd ; .. Chiefs of Spain, but
where are ye ?

And thou, Pelayo, thou our surest hope,
Dost thou too sleep ? . . Awake, Pelayo !
. . up ! . .
Why tarriest thou, Deliverer ? . . But
with that
She broke her bonds, and lo ! her form
was changed !　　　210
Radiant in arms she stood ! a bloody
Cross
Gleam'd on her breast-plate, in her
shield display'd
Erect a lion ramp'd ; her helmed head
Rose like the Berecynthian Goddess
crown'd
With towers, and in her dreadful hand
the sword
Red as a fire-brand blazed. Anon the
tramp
Of horsemen, and the din of multitudes
Moving to mortal conflict, rang around ;
The battle-song, the clang of sword and
shield,
War-cries and tumult, strife and hate
and rage,　　　220
Blasphemous prayers, confusion, agony,
Rout and pursuit and death ; and over
all
The shout of victory. . . Spain and
Victory !
Roderick, as the strong vision master'd
him,
Rush'd to the fight rejoicing : starting
then,
As his own effort burst the charm of
sleep,
He found himself upon that lonely grave
In moonlight and in silence. But the
dream
Wrought in him still ; for still he felt
his heart
Pant, and his wither'd arm was trem-
bling still ;　　　230
And still that voice was in his ear which
call'd
On Jesus for his sake.

Oh, might he hear
That actual voice ! and if Rusilla
lived, . .
If shame and anguish for his crimes not
yet
Had brought her to the grave, . . sure
she would bless
Her penitent child, and pour into his
heart
Prayers and forgiveness, which, like
precious balm,
Would heal the wounded soul. Nor to
herself
Less precious, or less healing, would the
voice
That spake forgiveness flow. She wept
her son　　　240
For ever lost, cut off with all the weight
Of unrepented sin upon his head,
Sin which had weigh'd a nation down . .
what joy
To know that righteous Heaven had in
its wrath
Remember'd mercy, and she yet might
meet
The child whom she had borne, redeem'd,
in bliss.
The sudden impulse of such thoughts
confirmed
That unacknowledged purpose, which
till now
Vainly had sought its end. He girt his
loins,
Laid holiest Mary's image in a cleft　250
Of the rock, where, shelter'd from the
elements,
It might abide till happier days came on,
From all defilement safe ; pour'd his
last prayer
Upon Romano's grave, and kiss'd the
earth
Which cover'd his remains, and wept
as if
At long leave-taking, then began his
way.

III. ADOSINDA

'Twas now the earliest morning; soon
the Sun,
Rising above Albardos, pour'd his light
Amid the forest, and with ray aslant
Entering its depth, illumed the branch-
less pines,
Brighten'd their bark, tinged with a
redder hue
Its rusty stains, and cast along the floor
Long lines of shadow, where they rose
erect
Like pillars of the temple. With slow
foot
Roderick pursued his way; for peni-
tence,
Remorse which gave no respite, and
the long   10
And painful conflict of his troubled soul,
Had worn him down. Now brighter
thoughts arose,
And that triumphant vision floated still
Before his sight with all her blazonry,
Her castled helm, and the victorious
sword
That flash'd like lightning o'er the field
of blood.
Sustain'd by thoughts like these, from
morn till eve
He journey'd, and drew near Leyria's
walls.
'Twas even-song time, but not a bell was
heard;
Instead thereof, on her polluted towers,
Bidding the Moors to their unhallow'd
prayer,   21
The cryer stood, and with his sonorous
voice
Fill'd the delicious vale where Lena winds
Thro' groves and pastoral meads. The
sound, the sight
Of turban, girdle, robe, and scymitar,
And tawny skins, awoke contending
thoughts

Of anger, shame, and anguish in the
Goth;
The face of human-kind so long unseen
Confused him now, and through the
streets he went
With haggèd mien, and countenance
like one   30
Crazed or bewilder'd. All who met him
turn'd,
And wonder'd as he pass'd. One stopt
him short,
Put alms into his hand, and then desired
In broken Gothic speech, the moon-
struck man
To bless him. With a look of vacancy
Roderick received the alms; his wan-
dering eye
Fell on the money, and the fallen King,
Seeing his own royal impress on the
piece,
Broke out into a quick convulsive voice,
That seem'd like laughter first, but
ended soon   40
In hollow groans supprest; the Mussel-
man
Shrunk at the ghastly sound, and
magnified
The name of Allah as he hasten'd on.
A Christian woman spinning at her door
Beheld him, and, with sudden pity
touch'd,
She laid her spindle by, and running in
Took bread, and following after call'd
him back,
And placing in his passive hands the
loaf,
She said, Christ Jesus for his mother's
sake
Have mercy on thee! With a look that
seem'd   50
Like idiotcy he heard her, and stood
still,
Staring awhile; then bursting into tears
Wept like a child, and thus relieved his
heart,

Full even to bursting else with swelling
　　thoughts.
So through the streets, and through the
　　northern gate
Did Roderick, reckless of a resting-
　　place,
With feeble yet with hurried step pursue
His agitated way ; and when he reach'd
The open fields, and found himself alone
Beneath the starry canopy of Heaven,
The sense of solitude, so dreadful late,
Was then repose and comfort.   There
　　he stopt   62
Beside a little rill, and brake the loaf ;
And shedding o'er that long untasted
　　food
Painful but quiet tears, with grateful soul
He breathed thanksgiving forth, then
　　made his bed
On heath and myrtle.
　　　　　　　But when he arose
At day-break and pursued his way, his
　　heart
Felt lighten'd that the shock of mingling
　　first
Among his fellow-kind was overpast ; 70
And journeying on, he greeted whom
　　he met
With such short interchange of benison
As each to other gentle travellers give,
Recovering thus the power of social
　　speech
Which he had long disused.   When
　　hunger prest
He ask'd for alms : slight supplication
　　served ;
A countenance so pale and woe-begone
Moved all to pity ; and the marks it
　　bore
Of rigorous penance and austerest life,
With something too of majesty that still
Appear'd amid the wreck, inspired a
　　sense   81
Of reverence too.   The goat-herd on
　　the hills

Open'd his scrip for him ; the babe in
　　arms,
Affrighted at his visage, turn'd away,
And clinging to the mother's neck in
　　tears
Would yet again look up, and then again
Shrink back, with cry renew'd.   The
　　bolder imps
Sporting beside the way, at his approach
Brake off their games for wonder, and
　　stood still
In silence ; some among them cried, A
　　Saint !   90
The village matron when she gave him
　　food
Besought his prayers ; and one en-
　　treated him
To lay his healing hands upon her child,
For with a sore and hopeless malady
Wasting, it long had lain, . . and sure,
　　she said,
He was a man of God.
　　　　　　　　Thus travelling on
He pass'd the vale where wild Arunca
　　pours
Its wintry torrents ; and the happier
　　site
Of old Conimbrica, whose ruin'd towers
Bore record of the fierce Alani's wrath.
Mondego too he cross'd, not yet re-
　　nown'd   101
In poets' amorous lay ; and left behind
The walls at whose foundation pious
　　hands
Of Priest and Monk and Bishop meekly
　　toil'd, . .
So had the insulting Arian given com-
　　mand.
Those stately palaces and rich domains
Were now the Moor's, and many a weary
　　age
Must Coimbra wear the misbeliever's
　　yoke,
Before Fernando's banner through her
　　gate

Shall pass triumphant, and her hallow'd
    Mosque   110
Behold the hero of Bivar receive
The knighthood which he glorified so oft
In his victorious fields.   Oh, if the years
To come might then have risen on
    Roderick's soul,
How had they kindled and consoled his
    heart ! . .
What joy might Douro's haven then
    have given,
Whence Portugal, the faithful and the
    brave,
Shall take her name illustrious ! . . what,
    those walls
Where Mumadona one day will erect
Convent and town and towers, which
    shall become   120
The cradle of that famous monarchy !
What joy might these prophetic scenes
    have given, . .
What ample vengeance on the Mussel-
    man,
Driven out with foul defeat, and made
    to feel
In Africa the wrongs he wrought to
    Spain ;
And still pursued by that relentless
    sword,
Even to the farthest Orient, where his
    power
Received its mortal wound.
               O years of pride !
In undiscoverable futurity,
Yet unevolved, your destined glories
    lay ;   130
And all that Roderick in these fated
    scenes
Beheld, was grief and wretchedness, . .
    the waste
Of recent war, and that more mournful
    calm
Of joyless, helpless, hopeless servitude.
'Twas not the ruin'd walls of church or
    tower,

Cottage or hall or convent, black with
    smoke ;
'Twas not the unburied bones, which
    where the dogs
And crows had strewn them, lay amid
    the field
Bleaching in sun or shower, that wrung
    his heart
With keenest anguish : 'twas when he
    beheld   140
The turban'd traitor show his shameless
    front
In the open eye of Heaven, . . the
    renegade,
On whose base brutal nature unredeem'd
Even black apostacy itself could stamp
No deeper reprobation, at the hour
Assign'd fall prostrate ; and unite the
    names
Of God and the Blasphemer, . . impious
    prayer, . .
Most impious, when from unbelieving
    lips
The accursèd utterance came.   Then
    Roderick's heart
With indignation burnt, and then he
    long'd   150
To be a King again, that so, for Spain
Betray'd and his Redeemer thus re-
    nounced,
He might inflict due punishment, and
    make
These wretches feel his wrath.   But
    when he saw
The daughters of the land, . . who, as
    they went
With cheerful step to church, were wont
    to show
Their innocent faces to all passers' eyes
Freely, and free from sin as when they
    look'd
In adoration and in praise to Heaven, . .
Now mask'd in Moorish mufflers, to the
    Mosque   160
Holding uncompanied their jealous way,

His spirit seem'd at that unhappy sight
To die away within him, and he too
Would fain have died, so death could
bring with it
Entire oblivion.

Rent with thoughts like these
He reach'd that city, once the seat
renown'd
Of Suevi kings, where, in contempt of
Rome
Degenerate long, the North's heroic race
Raised first a rival throne; now from
its state
Of proud regality debased and fallen. 170
Still bounteous nature o'er the lovely
vale,
Where like a Queen rose Bracara august,
Pour'd forth her gifts profuse; perennial
springs
Flow'd for her habitants, and genial
suns,
With kindly showers to bless the happy
clime,
Combined in vain their gentle influences;
For patient servitude was there, who
bow'd
His neck beneath the Moor, and silent
grief
That eats into the soul. The walls and
stones
Seem'd to reproach their dwellers;
stately piles 180
Yet undecayed, the mighty monuments
Of Roman pomp, Barbaric palaces,
And Gothic halls, where haughty Barons
late
Gladden'd their faithful vassals with the
feast
And flowing bowl, alike the spoiler's now.

Leaving these captive scenes behind,
he crost
Cavado's silver current, and the banks
Of Lima, through whose groves in after
years,

Mournful yet sweet, Diogo's amorous
lute
Prolong'd its tuneful echoes. But when
now 190
Beyond Arnoya's tributary tide,
He came where Minho roll'd its ampler
stream
By Auria's ancient walls, fresh horrors
met
His startled view; for prostrate in the
dust
Those walls were laid, and towers and
temples stood
Tottering in frightful ruins, as the flame
Had left them black and bare; and
through the streets,
All with the recent wreck of war
bestrewn,
Helmet and turban, scymitar and sword,
Christian and Moor in death pro-
miscuous lay 200
Each where they fell; and blood-flakes,
parch'd and crack'd
Like the dry slime of some receding
flood;
And half-burnt bodies, which allured
from far
The wolf and raven, and to impious food
Tempted the houseless dog.

A thrilling pang,
A sweat like death, a sickness of the soul,
Came over Roderick. Soon they pass'd
away,
And admiration in their stead arose,
Stern joy, and inextinguishable hope,
With wrath, and hate, and sacred ven-
geance now 210
Indissolubly link'd. O valiant race,
O people excellently brave, he cried,
True Goths ye fell, and faithful to the
last;
Though overpower'd, triumphant, and
in death
Unconquer'd! Holy be your memory!
Bless'd and glorious now and evermore

Be your heroic names ! . . Led by the
  sound,
As thus he cried aloud, a woman came
Toward him from the ruins. For the
  love
Of Christ, she said, lend me a little while
Thy charitable help ! . . Her words, her
  voice,   221
Her look, more horror to his heart con-
  vey'd
Than all the havoc round : for though
  she spake
With the calm utterance of despair, in
  tones
Deep-breathed and low, yet never
  sweeter voice
Pour'd forth its hymns in ecstasy to
  Heaven.
Her hands were bloody, and her gar-
  ments stain'd
With blood, her face with blood and
  dust defiled.
Beauty and youth, and grace and
  majesty,
Had every charm of form and feature
  given ;   230
But now upon her rigid countenance
Severest anguish set a fixedness
Ghastlier than death.
            She led him through the streets
A little way along, where four low walls,
Heapt rudely from the ruins round,
  enclosed
A narrow space : and there upon the
  ground
Four bodies, decently composed, were
  laid,
Though horrid all with wounds and
  clotted gore ;
A venerable ancient, by his side
A comely matron, for whose middle age,
(If ruthless slaughter had not inter-
  vened,)   241
Nature it seem'd, and gentle Time,
  might well

Have many a calm declining year in store ;
The third an armëd warrior, on his breast
An infant, over whom his arms were
  cross'd.
There, . . with firm eye and steady
  countenance
Unfaltering, she addrest him, . . there
  they lie,
Child, Husband, Parents, . . Adosinda's
  all !
I could not break the earth with these
  poor hands,
Nor other tomb provide, . . but let that
  pass !   250
Auria itself is now but one wide tomb
For all its habitants :—What better
  grave ?
What worthier monument ? . . Oh cover
  not
Their blood, thou Earth ! and ye, ye
  blessëd Souls
Of Heroes and of murder'd Innocents,
Oh never let your everlasting cries
Cease round the Eternal Throne, till the
  Most High
For all these unexampled wrongs hath
  given
Full, . . over-flowing vengeance !
                        While she spake
She raised her lofty hands to Heaven,
  as if   260
Calling for justice on the Judgement-
  seat ;
Then laid them on her eyes, and leaning
  on
Bent o'er the open sepulchre.
                        But soon
With quiet mien collectedly, like one
Who from intense devotion, and the act
Of ardent prayer, arising, girds himself
For this world's daily business, . . she
  arose,
And said to Roderick, Help me now to
  raise
The covering of the tomb.

With half-burnt planks,
Which she had gather'd for this funeral
    use,   270
They roof'd the vault, then, laying
    stones above,
They closed it down ; last, rendering all
    secure,
Stones upon stones they piled, till all
    appeared
A huge and shapeless heap. Enough,
    she cried ;
And taking Roderick's hands in both her
    own,
And wringing them with fervent thank-
    fulness,
May God shew mercy to thee, she
    exclaim'd,
When most thou needest mercy ! Who
    thou art
I know not ; not of Auria, . . for of all
Her sons and daughters, save the one
    who stands   280
Before thee, not a soul is left alive.
But thou hast render'd to me, in my
    hour
Of need, the only help which man could
    give.
What else of consolation may be found
For one so utterly bereft, from Heaven
And from myself must come. For deem
    not thou
That I shall sink beneath calamity :
This visitation, like a lightning-stroke,
Hath scathed the fruit and blossom of
    my youth ;
One hour hath orphan'd me, and
    widow'd me,   290
And made me childless. In this
    sepulchre
Lie buried all my earthward hopes and
    fears,
All human loves and natural charities ; . .
All womanly tenderness, all gentle
    thoughts,
All female weakness too, I bury here,

Yea, all my former nature. There
    remain
Revenge and death : . . the bitterness
    of death
Is past, and Heaven already hath
    vouchsafed
A foretaste of revenge.
                    Look here ! she cried,
And drawing back, held forth her
    bloody hands, . .   300
'Tis Moorish ! . . In the day of massacre,
A captain of Alcahman's murderous
    host
Reserved me from the slaughter. Not
    because
My rank and station tempted him with
    thoughts
Of ransom, for amid the general waste
Of ruin all was lost ; . . Nor yet, be sure,
That pity moved him, . . they who from
    this race
Accurst for pity look, such pity find
As ravenous wolves show the defenceless
    flock.
My husband at my foot had fallen ; my
    babe, . .   310
Spare me that thought, O God ! . . and
    then . . even then
Amid the maddening throes of agony
Which rent my soul, . . when if this
    solid Earth
Had open'd and let out the central fire
Before whose all-involving flames wide
    Heaven
Shall shrivel like a scroll and be con-
    sumed,
The universal wreck had been to me
Relief and comfort ; . . even then this
    Moor
Turn'd on me his libidinous eyes, and
    bade   319
His men reserve me safely for an hour
Of dalliance, . . me ! . . me in my agonies !
But when I found for what this mis-
    creant child

I

Of Hell had snatch'd me from the
butchery,
The very horror of that monstrous
thought
Saved me from madness; I was calm
at once, ..
Yea comforted and reconciled to life:
Hatred became to me the life of life,
Its purpose and its power.
              The glutted Moors
At length broke up.   This hell-dog
turn'd aside
Toward his home; we travell'd fast and
far,   330
Till by a forest edge at eve he pitched
His tents. I wash'd and ate at his
command,
Forcing revolted nature; I composed
My garments and bound up my scatter'd
hair;
And when he took my hand, and to his
couch
Would fain have drawn me, gently I
retired
From that abominable touch, and said,
Forbear to-night I pray thee, for this
day
A widow, as thou seest me, am I made;
Therefore, according to our law, must
watch   340
And pray to-night.   The loathsome
villain paused
Ere he assented, then laid down to rest;
While at the door of the pavilion, I
Knelt on the ground, and bowed my
face to earth;
But when the neighbouring tents had
ceased their stir,
The fires were out, and all were fast
asleep,
Then I arose.   The blessed Moon from
Heaven
Lent me her holy light. I did not pray
For strength, for strength was given me
as I drew

The scymitar, and standing o'er his
couch,   350
Raised it in both my hands with steady
aim
And smote his neck.   Upward, as from
a spring
When newly open'd by the husbandman,
The villain's life-blood spouted.   Twice
I struck,
So making vengeance sure;   then,
praising God,
Retired amid the wood, and measured
back
My patient way to Auria, to perform
This duty which thou seest.
            As thus she spake,
Roderick intently listening had forgot
His crown, his kingdom, his calamities,
His crimes, .. so like a spell upon the
Goth   361
Her powerful words prevail'd. With
open lips,
And eager ear, and eyes which, while
they watch'd
Her features, caught the spirit that she
breathed,
Mute and enrapt he stood, and motion-
less;
The vision rose before him; and that
shout,
Which, like a thunder-peal, victorious
Spain
Sent through the welkin, rung within
his soul
Its deep prophetic echoes.   On his brow
The pride and power of former majesty
Dawn'd once again, but changed and
purified: 371
Duty and high heroic purposes
Now hallow'd it, and as with inward light
Illumed his meagre countenance austere

Awhile in silence Adosinda stood,
Reading his alter'd visage and the
thoughts

Which thus transfigured him. Ay, she
    exclaim'd,
My tale hath moved thee! it might
    move the dead,
Quicken captivity's dead soul, and
    rouse
This prostrate country from her mortal
    trance: 380
Therefore I live to tell it; and for this
Hath the Lord God Almighty given to
    me
A spirit not mine own and strength from
    Heaven;
Dealing with me as in the days of old
With that Bethulian Matron when she
    saved
His people from the spoiler. What
    remains
But that the life which he hath thus
    preserved
I consecrate to him? Not veil'd and
    vow'd
To pass my days in holiness and peace;
Nor yet between sepulchral walls
    immured,   390
Alive to penitence alone; my rule
He hath himself prescribed, and hath
    infused
A passion in this woman's breast,
    wherein
All passions and all virtues are com-
    bined;
Love, hatred, joy, and anguish, and
    despair,
And hope, and natural piety, and faith,
Make up the mighty feeling. Call it not
Revenge! thus sanctified and thus
    sublimed,
Tis duty, 'tis devotion. Like the grace
Of God, it came and saved me; and in
    it   400
Spain must have her salvation. In thy
    hands
Here, on the grave of all my family,
    make my vow.

        She said, and kneeling down,
Placed within Roderick's palms her
    folded hands.
This life, she cried, I dedicate to God,
Therewith to do him service in the way
Which he hath shown. To rouse the
    land against
This impious, this intolerable yoke, ..
To offer up the invader's hateful
    blood, ..
This shall be my employ, my rule and
    rite,   410
Observances and sacrifice of faith;
For this I hold the life which he hath
    given,
A sacred trust; for this, when it shall
    suit
His service, joyfully will lay it down.
So deal with me as I fulfil the pledge,
O Lord my God, my Saviour and my
    Judge.

    Then rising from the earth, she spread
    her arms,
And looking round with sweeping eyes
    exclaim'd,
Auria, and Spain, and Heaven receive
    the vow!

IV. THE MONASTERY OF
ST. FELIX

THUS long had Roderick heard her
    powerful words
In silence, awed before her: but his
    heart
Was fill'd the while with swelling sym-
    pathy,
And now with impulse not to be re-
    strain'd
The feeling overpower'd him. Hear
    me too,
Auria, and Spain, and Heaven! he
    cried; and thou

Who risest thus above mortality,
Sufferer and patriot, saint and heroine,
The servant and the chosen of the Lord,
For surely such thou art, . . receive in
    me   10
The first-fruits of thy calling.   Kneeling
    then,
And placing as he spake his hand in hers,
As thou hast sworn, the royal Goth
    pursued,
Even so I swear ; my soul hath found
    at length
Her rest and refuge ; in the invader's
    blood
She must efface her stains of mortal sin,
And in redeeming this lost land, work out
Redemption for herself.   Herein I place
My penance for the past, my hope to
    come,
My faith and my good works ; here offer
    up   20
All thoughts and passions of mine in-
    most heart,
My days and night, . . this flesh, this
    blood, this life,
Yea this whole being, do I here devote
For Spain.   Receive the vow, all Saints
    in Heaven,
And prosper its good end ! . . Clap now
    your wings,
The Goth with louder utterance as he
    rose
Exclaim'd, . . clap now your wings
    exultingly,
Ye ravenous fowl of Heaven ; and in
    your dens
Set up, ye wolves of Spain, a yell of joy ;
For, lo ! a nation hath this day been
    sworn   30
To furnish forth your banquet ; for a
    strife
Hath been commenced, the which from
    this day forth
Permits no breathing-time, and knows
    no end

Till in this land the last invader bow
His neck beneath the exterminating
    sword.

Said I not rightly ? Adosinda cried ;
The will which goads me on is not mine
    own,
'Tis from on high, . . yea, verily of
    Heaven !
But who art thou who hast profess'd
    with me,
My first sworn brother in the appointed
    rule ?   40
Tell me thy name.
                    Ask any thing but that !
The fallen King replied.   My name was
    lost
When from the Goths the sceptre pass'd
    away.
The nation will arise regenerate ;
Strong in her second youth and beauti-
    ful,
And like a spirit which hath shaken off
The clog of dull mortality, shall Spain
Arise in glory.   But for my good name
No resurrection is appointed here.
Let it be blotted out on earth : in
    Heaven   50
There shall be written with it penitence,
And grace, and saving faith, and such
    good deeds
Wrought in atonement, as my soul this
    day
Hath sworn to offer up.
                    Then be thy name
She answer'd, Maccabee, from this day
    forth :
For this day art thou born again ; and
    like
Those brethren of old times, whose holy
    names
Live in the memory of all noble hearts
For love and admiration, ever young, .
So for our native country, for her
    hearths

And altars, for her cradles and her
  graves,
Hast thou thyself devoted. Let us now
Each to our work. Among the neigh-
  bouring hills,
I to the vassals of my father's house;
Thou to Visonia. Tell the Abbot there
What thou hast seen at Auria; and with
  him
Take counsel who of all our Baronage
Is worthiest to lead on the sons of Spain,
And wear upon his brow the Spanish
  crown.
Now, brother, fare thee well! we part
  in hope,   70
And we shall meet again, be sure, in joy.

So saying, Adosinda left the King
Alone amid the ruins. There he stood,
As when Elisha, on the farther bank
Of Jordan, saw that elder prophet mount
The fiery chariot, and the steeds of fire,
Trampling the whirlwind, bear him up
  the sky:
Thus gazing after her did Roderick
  stand;
And as the immortal Tishbite left
  behind
His mantle and prophetic power, even
  so   80
Had her inspiring presence left infused
The spirit which she breathed. Gazing
  he stood,
As at a heavenly visitation there
Vouchsafed in mercy to himself and
  Spain;
And when the heroic mourner from his
  sight
Had pass'd away, still reverential awe
Held him suspended there and motion-
  less.
Then turning from the ghastly scene of
  death
Up murmuring Lona, he began toward
The holy Bierzo his obedient way. 90

Sil's ample stream he crost, where
  through the vale
Of Orras, from that sacred land it bears
The whole collected waters; northward
  then,
Skirting the heights of Aguiar, he
  reach'd
That consecrated pile amid the wild,
Which sainted Fructuoso in his zeal
Rear'd to St. Felix, on Visonia's banks.

In commune with a priest of age
  mature,
Whose thoughtful visage and majestic
  mien
Bespake authority and weight of care,
Odoar, the venerable Abbot, sate, 101
When ushering Roderick in, the Porter
  said,
A stranger came from Auria, and re-
  quired
His private ear. From Auria? said the
  old man,
Comest thou from Auria, brother? I
  can spare
Thy painful errand then, .. we know the
  worst.

Nay, answer'd Roderick, but thou hast
  not heard
My tale. Where that devoted city lies
In ashes, 'mid the ruins and the dead
I found a woman, whom the Moors had
  borne   110
Captive away; but she, by Heaven
  inspired
And her good heart, with her own arm
  had wrought
Her own deliverance, smiting in his tent
A lustful Moorish miscreant, as of yore
By Judith's holy deed the Assyrian fell.
And that same spirit which had
  strengthen'd her
Work'd in her still. Four walls with
  patient toil

She rear'd, wherein, as in a sepulchre,
With her own hands she laid her mur-
    der'd babe,
Her husband and her parents, side by
    side;   120
And when we cover'd in this shapeless
    tomb,
There on the grave of all her family,
Did this courageous mourner dedicate
All thoughts and actions of her future
    life
To her poor country.   For she said, that
    Heaven
Supporting her, in mercy had vouch-
    safed
A foretaste of revenge; that, like the
    grace
Of God, revenge had saved her; that in it
Spain must have her salvation; and
    henceforth
That passion, thus sublimed and sancti-
    fied,   130
Must be to all the loyal sons of Spain
The pole-star of their faith, their rule
    and rite,
Observances and worthiest sacrifice.
I took the vow, unworthy as I am,
Her first sworn follower in the appointed
    rule;
And then we parted; she among the hills
To rouse the vassals of her father's
    house:
I at her bidding hitherward, to ask
Thy counsel, who of our old Baronage
Shall place upon his brow the Spanish
    crown.   140

    The Lady Adosinda ?   Odoar cried.
Roderick made answer, So she call'd
    herself.

    Oh, none but she ! exclaim'd the good
    old man,
Clasping his hands, which trembled as
    he spake

In act of pious passion raised to
    Heaven, . .
Oh, none but Adosinda ! . . none but
    she, . .
None but that noble heart, which was
    the heart
Of Auria while it stood, its life and
    strength,
More than her father's presence, or the
    arm
Of her brave husband, valiant as he was.
Hers was the spirit which inspired old
    age,   151
Ambitious boyhood, girls in timid youth,
And virgins in the beauty of their spring,
And youthful mothers, doting like her-
    self
With ever-anxious love : She breathed
    through all
That zeal and that devoted faithfulness,
Which to the invader's threats and
    promises
Turn'd a deaf ear alike; which in the
    head
And flood of prosperous fortune check'd
    his course,
Repell'd him from the walls, and when
    at length   160
His overpowering numbers forced their
    way,
Even in that uttermost extremity
Unyielding, still from street to street,
    from house
To house, from floor to floor, maintain'd
    the fight :
Till by their altars falling, in their doors,
And on their household hearths, and by
    their beds
And cradles, and their fathers' sepul-
    chres,
This noble army, gloriously revenged,
Embraced their martyrdom.   Heroic
    souls !
Well have ye done, and righteously
    discharged   170

Your arduous part! Your service is
    perform'd,
Your earthly warfare done! Ye have
    put on
The purple robe of everlasting peace!
Ye have received your crown! Ye bear
    the palm
Before the throne of Grace!
             With that he paused,
Checking the strong emotions of his soul.
Then with a solemn tone addressing
    him
Who shared his secret thoughts, thou
    knowest, he said,
O Urban, that they have not fallen in
    vain;
For by this virtuous sacrifice they
    thinn'd   180
Alcahman's thousands; and his broken
    force,
Exhausted by their dear-bought victory,
Turn'd back from Auria, leaving us to
    breathe
Among our mountains yet. We lack
    not here
Good hearts, nor valiant hands. What
    walls or towers
Or battlements are like these fastnesses,
These rocks and glens and everlasting
    hills?
Give but that Aurian spirit, and the
    Moors
Will spend their force as idly on these
    holds,
As round the rocky girdle of the land 190
The wild Cantabrian billows waste their
    rage.
Give but that spirit! . . Heaven hath
    given it us,
If Adosinda thus, as from the dead,
Be granted to our prayers!
             And who art thou,
Said Urban, who hast taken on thyself
This rule of warlike faith? Thy coun-
    tenance

And those poor weeds bespeak a life ere
    this
Devoted to austere observances.

Roderick replied, I am a sinful man,
One who in solitude hath long deplored
A life mis-spent; but never bound by
    vows,   201
Till Adosinda taught me where to find
Comfort, and how to work forgiveness
    out.
When that exalted woman took my vow,
She call'd me Maccabee; from this day
    forth
Be that my earthly name. But tell me
    now,
Whom shall we rouse to take upon his
    head
The crown of Spain? Where are the
    Gothic Chiefs?
Sacaru, Theudemir, Athanagild,
All who survived that eight days'
    obstinate fight,   210
When clogg'd with bodies Chrysus scarce
    could force
Its bloody stream along? Witiza's sons,
Bad offspring of a stock accurst, I know,
Have put the turban on their recreant
    heads.
Where are your own Cantabrian Lords?
    I ween,
Eudon, and Pedro, and Pelayo now
Have ceased their rivalry. If Pelayo
    live,
His were the worthy heart and rightful
    hand
To wield the sceptre and the sword of
    Spain.

Odoar and Urban eyed him while he
    spake,   220
As if they wonder'd whose the tongue
    might be
Familiar thus with Chiefs and thoughts
    of state.

They scann'd his countenance, but not
  a trace
Betray'd the Royal Goth: sunk was
  that eye
Of sovereignty, and on the emaciate
  cheek
Had penitence and anguish deeply
  drawn
Their furrows premature, . . forestalling
  time,
And shedding upon thirty's brow more
  snows
Than threescore winters in their natural
  course
Might else have sprinkled there.   It
  seems indeed   230
That thou hast pass'd thy days in
  solitude,
Replied the Abbot, or thou would'st not
  ask
Of things so long gone by.   Athanagild
And Theudemir have taken on their
  necks
The yoke.   Sacaru play'd a nobler part.
Long within Merida did he withstand
The invader's hot assault; and when
  at length,
Hopeless of all relief, he yielded up
The gates, disdaining in his father's land
To breathe the air of bondage, with a
  few   240
Found faithful till the last, indignantly
Did he toward the ocean bend his way,
And shaking from his feet the dust of
  Spain,
Took ship, and hoisted sail through seas
  unknown
To seek for freedom.   Our Cantabrian
  Chiefs
All have submitted, but the wary Moor
Trusteth not all alike: At his own Court
He holds Pelayo, as suspecting most
That calm and manly spirit; Pedro's
  son
There too is held as hostage, and secures

His father's faith;   Count Eudon is
  despised,   251
And so lives unmolested.   When he
  pays
His tribute, an uncomfortable thought
May then perhaps disturb him: . . or
  more like
He meditates how profitable 'twere
To be a Moor; and if apostacy
Were all, and to be unbaptized might
  serve, . .
But I waste breath upon a wretch like
  this;
Pelayo is the only hope of Spain,
Only Pelayo.
                 If, as we believe,   260
Said Urban then, the hand of Heaven is
  here,
And dreadful though they be, yet for
  wise end
Of good, these visitations do its work;
And dimly as our mortal sight may scan
The future, yet methinks my soul
  descries
How in Pelayo should the purposes
Of Heaven be best accomplished.   All
  too long,
Here in their own inheritance, the sons
Of Spain have groan'd beneath a foreign
  yoke.
Punic and Roman, Kelt, and Goth, and
  Greek: 270
This latter tempest comes to sweep
  away
All proud distinctions which com-
  mingling blood
And time's long course have fail'd to
  efface; and now
Perchance it is the will of Fate to rear
Upon the soil of Spain a Spanish throne,
Restoring in Pelayo's native line
The sceptre to the Spaniard.
                          Go thou, then,
And seek Pelayo at the Conqueror's
  court.

Tell him the mountaineers are unsub-
    dued;
The precious time they needed hath
    been gain'd   280
By Auria's sacrifice, and all they ask
Is him to guide them on. In Odoar's
    name
And Urban's, tell him that the hour is
    come.

Then pausing for a moment, he pur-
    sued,
The rule which thou hast taken on thy-
    self
Toledo ratifies: 'tis meet for Spain,
And as the will divine, to be received,
Observed, and spread abroad. Come
    hither thou,
Who for thyself hast chosen the good
    part;
Let me lay hands on thee, and conse-
    crate   290
Thy life unto the Lord.
                Me! Roderick cried;
Me! sinner that I am!.. and while he
    spake
His wither'd cheek grew paler, and his
    limbs
Shook. As thou goest among the
    infidels,
Pursued the Primate, many thou wilt
    find
Fallen from the faith; by weakness
    some betray'd,
Some led astray by baser hope of gain,
And haply too by ill example led
Of those in whom they trusted. Yet
    have these
Their lonely hours, when sorrow, or the
    touch   300
Of sickness, and that aweful power
    divine
Which hath its dwelling in the heart of
    man,
Life of his soul, his monitor and judge,

Move them with silent impulse; but
    they look
For help, and finding none to succour
    them,
The irrevocable moment passeth by.
Therefore, my brother, in the name of
    Christ
Thus I lay hands on thee, that in His
    name
Thou with His gracious promises may'st
    raise
The fallen, and comfort those that are in
    need,   310
And bring salvation to the penitent.
Now, brother, go thy way: the peace
    of God
Be with thee, and his blessing prosper us!

V. RODERICK AND SIVERIAN

BETWEEN St. Felix and the regal seat
Of Abdalazis, ancient Cordoba,
Lay many a long day's journey inter-
    posed;
And many a mountain range hath
    Roderick crost,
And many a lovely vale, ere he beheld
Where Betis, winding through the un-
    bounded plain,
Roll'd his majestic waters. There at eve,
Entering an inn, he took his humble seat
With other travellers round the crack-
    ling hearth,
Where heath and cistus gave their
    flagrant flame.   10
That flame no longer, as in other times,
Lit up the countenance of easy mirth
And light discourse: the talk which
    now went round
Was of the grief that press'd on every
    heart;
Of Spain subdued; the sceptre of the
    Goths
Broken; their nation and their name
    effaced;

Slaughter and mourning, which had
    left no house
Unvisited; and shame, which set its
    mark
On every Spaniard's face. One who
    had seen
His sons fall bravely at his side,
    bewail'd   20
The unhappy chance which, rescuing
    him from death,
Left him the last of all his family;
Yet he rejoiced to think that none who
    drew
Their blood from him remain'd to wear
    the yoke,
Be at the miscreant's beck, and propa-
    gate
A breed of slaves to serve them. Here
    sate one
Who told of fair possessions lost, and
    babes
To goodly fortunes born, of all bereft.
Another for a virgin daughter mourn'd,
The lewd barbarian's spoil. A fourth
    had seen   30
His only child forsake him in his age,
And for a Moor renounce her hope in
    Christ.
His was the heaviest grief of all, he said;
And clenching as he spake his hoary
    locks,
He cursed King Roderick's soul.
                 Oh curse him not!
Roderick exclaim'd, all shuddering as
    he spake.
Oh, for the love of Jesus, curse him not!
Sufficient is the dreadful load of guilt
That lies upon his miserable soul!
O brother, do not curse that sinful soul,
Which Jesus suffer'd on the cross to
    save!   41

But then an old man, who had sate
    thus long
A silent listener, from his seat arose,

And moving round to Roderick took his
    hand;
Christ bless thee, brother, for that
    Christian speech,
He said; and shame on me that any
    tongue
Readier than mine was found to utter it!
His own emotion fill'd him while he
    spake,
So that he did not feel how Roderick's
    hand
Shook like a palsied limb; and none
    could see   50
How, at his well-known voice, the
    countenance
Of that poor traveller suddenly was
    changed,
And sunk with deadlier paleness; for
    the flame
Was spent, and from behind him, on the
    wall
High hung, the lamp with feeble glim-
    mering play'd.

Oh it is ever thus! the old man
    pursued,
The crimes and woes of universal Spain
Are charged on him; and curses which
    should aim
At living heads, pursue beyond the grave
His poor unhappy soul! As if his sin 60
Had wrought the fall of our old
    monarchy!
As if the Musselmen in their career
Would ne'er have overleapt the gulph
    which parts .
Iberia from the Mauritanian shore,
If Julian had not beckon'd them! . .
    Alas!
The evils which drew on our overthrow,
Would soon by other means have
    wrought their end,
Though Julian's daughter should have
    lived and died
A virgin vow'd and veil'd.

Touch not on that,
Shrinking with inward shiverings at the
thought,   70
The penitent exclaim'd. Oh, if thou
lovest
The soul of Roderick, touch not on that
deed !
God in his mercy may forgive it him,
But human tongue must never speak his
name
Without reproach and utter infamy,
For that abhorred act. Even thou . .
But here
Siverian taking up the word, brake off
Unwittingly the incautious speech.
Even I,
Quoth he, who nursed him in his father's
hall, . .
Even I can only for that deed of shame
Offer in agony my secret prayers.   81
But Spain hath witness'd other crimes
as foul :
Have we not seen Favila's shameless
wife,
Throned in Witiza's ivory car, parade
Our towns with regal pageantry, and bid
The murderous tyrant in her husband's
blood
Dip his adulterous hand ? Did we not
see
Pelayo, by that bloody king's pursuit,
And that unnatural mother, from the
land
With open outcry, like an outlaw'd
thief,   90
Hunted ? And saw ye not, Theodofred,
As through the streets I guided his dark
steps,
Roll mournfully toward the noon-day
sun
His blank and senseless eye-balls ?
Spain saw this,
And suffer'd it ! . . I seek not to excuse
The sin of Roderick. Jesu, who beholds
The burning tears I shed in solitude,

Knows how I plead for him in midnight
prayer.
But if, when he victoriously revenged
The wrongs of Chindasuintho's house,
his sword   100
Had not for mercy turn'd aside its edge,
Oh what a day of glory had there been
Upon the banks of Chrysus ! Curse not
him,
Who in that fatal conflict to the last
So valiantly maintain'd his country's
cause ;
But if your sorrow needs must have its
vent
In curses, let your imprecations strike
The caitiffs, who, when Roderick's
horned helm
Rose eminent amid the thickest fight,
Betraying him who spared and trusted
them,   110
Forsook their King, their Country, and
their God,
And gave the Moor his conquest.
                         Ay ! they said,
These were Witiza's hateful progeny ;
And in an evil hour the unhappy King
Had spared the viperous brood. With
that they talk'd
How Sisibert and Ebba through the land
Guided the foe : and Orpas, who had
cast
The mitre from his renegado brow,
Went with the armies of the infidels ;
And how in Hispalis, even where his
hands   120
Had minister'd so oft the bread of life,
The circumcised apostate did not shame
To shew in open day his turban'd head.
The Queen too, Egilona, one exclaim'd ;
Was she not married to the enemy,
The Moor, the Misbeliever ? What a
heart
Were hers, that she could pride and
plume herself
To rank among his herd of concubines,

Having been what she had been! And
who could say
How far domestic wrongs and discon-
tent   130
Had wrought upon the King!.. Hereat
the old man,
Raising beneath the knit and curly brow
His mournful eyes, replied, This I can
tell,
That that unquiet spirit and unblest,
Though Roderick never told his sorrows,
drove
Rusilla from the palace of her son.
She could not bear to see his generous
mind
Wither beneath the unwholesome in-
fluence,
And cankering at the core.   And I know
well,
That oft when she deplored his barren
bed,   140
The thought of Egilona's qualities
Came like a bitter medicine for her grief,
And to the extinction of her husband's
line,
Sad consolation, reconciled her heart.

But Roderick, while they communed
thus, had ceased
To hear, such painfulest anxiety
The sight of that old venerable man
Awoke.   A sickening fear came over
him:
The hope which led him from his her-
mitage
Now seem'd for ever gone, for well he
knew   150
Nothing but death could break the ties
which bound
That faithful servant to his father's
house.
She then for whose forgiveness he had
yearn'd,
Who in her blessing would have given
and found

The peace of Heaven, . . she then was
to the grave
Gone down disconsolate at last; in this
Of all the woes of her unhappy life
Unhappiest, that she did not live to see
God had vouchsafed repentance to her
child.
But then a hope arose that yet she lived;
The weighty cause which led Siverian
here .   161
Might draw him from her side; better
to know
The worst than fear it.   And with that
he bent
Over the embers, and with head half
raised
Aslant, and shadow'd by his hand, he
said,
Where is King Roderick's mother?
lives she still?

God hath upheld her, the old man
replied;
She bears this last and heaviest of her
griefs,
Not as she bore her husband's wrongs,
when hope
And her indignant heart supported her;
But patiently, like one who finds from
Heaven   171
A comfort which the world can neither
give
Nor take away. . . Roderick inquired no
more;
He breathed a silent prayer in gratitude,
Then wrapt his cloak around him, and
lay down
Where he might weep unseen.
                        When morning came,
Earliest of all the travellers he went
forth,
And linger'd for Siverian by the way,
Beside a fountain, where the constant
fall   179
Of water its perpetual gurgling made,

To the wayfaring or the musing man
Sweetest of all sweet sounds. The
    Christian hand,
Whose general charity for man and
    beast
Built it in better times, had with a cross
Of well-hewn stone crested the pious
    work,
Which now the misbelievers had cast
    down,
And broken in the dust it lay defiled.
Roderick beheld it lying at his feet,
And gathering reverently the fragments
    up,
Placed them within the cistern, and
    restored   190
With careful collocation its dear form, . .
So might the waters, like a crystal
    shrine,
Preserve it from pollution. Kneeling
    then,
O'er the memorial of redeeming love
He bent, and mingled with the fount his
    tears,
And pour'd his spirit to the Crucified.

    A Moor came by, and seeing him,
    exclaim'd,
Ah, Kaffer! worshipper of wood and
    stone,
God's curse confound thee! And as
    Roderick turn'd
His face, the miscreant spurn'd him with
    his foot   200
Between the eyes. The indignant King
    arose,
And fell'd him to the ground. But then
    the Moor
Drew forth his dagger, rising as he cried,
What, darest thou, thou infidel and slave,
Strike a believer? and he aim'd a blow
At Roderick's breast. But Roderick
    caught his arm,
And closed, and wrench'd the dagger
    from his hold, . .

Such timely strength did those emaciate
    limbs
From indignation draw, . . and in his
    neck
With mortal stroke he drove the
    avenging steel   210
Hilt deep. Then, as the thirsty sand
    drank in
The expiring miscreant's blood, he
    look'd around
In sudden apprehension, lest the Moors
Had seen them; but Siverian was in
    sight,
The only traveller, and he smote his
    mule
And hasten'd up. Ah, brother! said
    the old man,
Thine is a spirit of the ancient mould!
And would to God a thousand men like
    thee
Had fought at Roderick's side on that
    last day
When treason overpower'd him! Now,
    alas!   220
A manly Gothic heart doth ill accord
With these unhappy times. Come, let
    us hide
This carrion, while the favouring hour
    permits.

    So saying he alighted. Soon they
    scoop'd
Amid loose-lying sand a hasty grave,
And levell'd over it the easy soil.
Father, said Roderick, as they journey'd
    on,
Let this thing be a seal and sacrament
Of truth between us: Wherefore should
    there be
Concealment between two right Gothic
    hearts   230
In evil days like ours? What thou hast
    seen
Is but the first fruit of the sacrifice,
Which on this injured and polluted soil,

As on a bloody altar, I have sworn
To offer to insulted Heaven for Spain,
Her vengeance and her expiation. This
Was but a hasty act, by sudden wrong
Provoked : but I am bound for Cordoba,
On weighty mission from Visonia sent,
To breathe into Pelayo's ear a voice 240
Of spirit-stirring power, which, like the
   trump
Of the Arch-angel, shall awake dead
   Spain.
The northern mountaineers are unsub-
   dued ;
They call upon Pelayo for their chief ;
Odoar and Urban tell him that the hour
Is come. Thou too, I ween, old man,
   art charged
With no light errand, or thou wouldst
   not now
Have left the ruins of thy master's house.

Who art thou ? cried Siverian, as he
   search'd
The wan and wither'd features of the
   King.   250
The face is of a stranger, but thy voice
Disturbs me like a dream.
                Roderick replied,
Thou seest me as I am, . . a stranger ;
   one
Whose fortunes in the general wreck
   were lost,
His name and lineage utterly extinct,
Himself in mercy spared, surviving all ; . .
In mercy, that the bitter cup might heal
A soul diseased. Now, having cast the
   slough
Of old offences, thou beholdest me
A man new born ; in second baptism
   named,   260
Like those who in Judea bravely raised
Against the Heathen's impious tyranny
The banner of Jehovah, Maccabee ;
So call me. In that name hath Urban
   laid

His consecrating hands upon my head ;
And in that name have I myself for Spain
Devoted. Tell me now why thou art
   sent
To Cordoba ; for sure thou goëst not
An idle gazer to the Conqueror's court.

Thou judgest well, the old man replied.
   I too   270
Seek the Cantabrian Prince, the hope of
   Spain,
With other tidings charged, for other
   end
Design'd, yet such as well may work
   with thine.
My noble Mistress sends me to avert
The shame that threats his house. The
   renegade
Numacian, he who for the infidels
Oppresses Gegio, insolently woos
His sister. Moulded in a wicked womb,
The unworthy Guisla hath inherited
Her Mother's leprous taint ; and will-
   ingly   280
She to the circumcised and upstart
   slave,
Disdaining all admonishment, gives ear.
The Lady Gaudiosa sees in this,
With the quick foresight of maternal
   care,
The impending danger to her husband's
   house,
Knowing his generous spirit ne'er will
   brook
The base alliance. Guisla lewdly sets
His will at nought ; but that vile rene-
   gade,
From hatred, and from avarice, and
   from fear,   289
Will seek the extinction of Pelayo's line.
This too my venerable Mistress sees ;
Wherefore these valiant and high-
   minded dames
Send me to Cordoba ; that if the Prince
Cannot by timely interdiction stop

The irrevocable act of infamy,
He may at least to his own safety look,
Being timely warn'd.
       Thy Mistress sojourns then
With Gaudiosa, in Pelayo's hall ?
Said Roderick. 'Tis her natural home,
    rejoin'd
Siverian : Chindasuintho's royal race
Have ever shared one lot of weal or woe :
And she who hath beheld her own fair
    shoot,   301
The goodly summit of that ancient tree,
Struck by Heaven's bolt, seeks shelter
    now beneath
The only branch of its majestic stem
That still survives the storm.
       Thus they pursued
Their journey, each from other gathering
    store
For thought, with many a silent interval
Of mournful meditation, till they saw
The temples and the towers of Cordoba
Shining majestic in the light of eve. 310
Before them Betis roll'd his glittering
    stream,
In many a silvery winding traced afar
Amid the ample plain. Behind the
    walls
And stately piles which crown'd its
    margin, rich
With olives, and with sunny slope of
    vines,
And many a lovely hamlet interspersed,
Whose citron bowers were once the
    abode of peace,
Height above height, receding hills were
    seen
Imbued with evening hues ; and over all
The summits of the dark sierra rose, 320
Lifting their heads amid the silent sky.
The traveller who with a heart at ease
Had seen the goodly vision, would have
    loved
To linger, seeking with insatiate sight
To treasure up its image, deep impress'd,

A joy for years to come. O Cordoba,
Exclaim'd the old man, how princely are
    thy towers,
How fair thy vales, thy hills how beauti-
    ful !
The sun who sheds on thee his parting
    smiles   329
Sees not in all his wide career a scene
Lovelier, nor more exuberantly blest
By bounteous earth and heaven. The
    very gales
Of Eden waft not from the immortal
    bowers
Odours to sense more exquisite, than
    these
Which, breathing from thy groves and
    gardens, now
Recall in me such thoughts of bitterness.
The time has been when happy was
    their lot
Who had their birthright here ; but
    happy now
Are they who to thy bosom are gone
    home,
Because they feel not in their graves
    the feet   340
That trample upon Spain. 'Tis well
    that age
Hath made me like a child, that I can
    weep :
My heart would else have broken, over-
    charged,
And I, false servant, should lie down to
    rest
Before my work is done.
       Hard by their path,
A little way without the walls, there
    stood
An edifice, whereto, as by a spell,
Siverian's heart was drawn. Brother,
    quoth he,
'Tis like the urgency of our return
Will brook of no retardment ; and this
    spot   350
It were a sin if I should pass, and leave

Unvisited. Beseech you turn with me,
The while I offer up one duteous prayer.

Roderick made no reply.   He had not
  dared
To turn his face toward those walls ; but
  now
He follow'd where the old man led the
  way.
Lord ! in his heart the silent sufferer
  said,
Forgive my feeble soul, which would
  have shrunk
From this, . . for what am I that I should
  put   359
The bitter cup aside ! O let my shame
And anguish be accepted in thy sight !

VI. RODERICK IN TIMES PAST

THE mansion whitherward they went,
  was one
Which in his youth Theodofred had
  built :
Thither had he brought home in happy
  hour
His blooming bride ; there fondled on
  his knee
The lovely boy she bore him.   Close
  beside,
A temple to that Saint he rear'd, who
  first,
As old tradition tells, proclaim'd to
  Spain
The gospel-tidings ; and in health and
  youth,
There mindful of mortality, he saw
His sepulchre prepared. Witiza took 10
For his adulterous leman and himself
The stately pile : but to that sepulchre,
When from captivity and darkness
  death
Enlarged him, was Theodofred con-
  sign'd ;

For that unhappy woman, wasting then
Beneath a mortal malady, at heart
Was smitten, and the Tyrant at her
  prayer
This poor and tardy restitution made.
Soon the repentant sinner follow'd him ;
And calling on Pelayo ere she died, 20
For his own wrongs, and for his father's
  death,
Implored forgiveness of her absent
  child, . .
If it were possible he could forgive
Crimes black as hers, she said.   And by
  the pangs
Of her remorse, . . by her last agonies, . .
The unutterable horrors of her death, . .
And by the blood of Jesus on the cross
For sinners given, did she beseech his
  prayers
In aid of her most miserable soul.
Thus mingling sudden shrieks with
  hopeless vows,   30
And uttering franticly Pelayo's name,
And crying out for mercy in despair,
Here had she made her dreadful end,
  and here
Her wretched body was deposited.
That presence seem'd to desecrate the
  place :
Thenceforth the usurper shunn'd it with
  the heart
Of conscious guilt ; nor could Rusilla bear
These groves and bowers, which, like
  funereal shades,
Oppress'd her with their monumental
  forms :
One day of bitter and severe delight, 40
When Roderick came for vengeance, she
  endured,
And then for ever left her bridal halls.

Oh when I last beheld yon princely
  pile,
Exclaim'd Siverian, with what other
  thoughts

Full, and elate of spirit, did I pass
Its joyous gates! The weedery which
    through
The interstices of those neglected courts
Uncheck'd had flourish'd long, and
    seeded there,
Was trampled then and bruised beneath
    the feet
Of thronging crowds. Here drawn in
    fair array,   50
The faithful vassals of my master's
    house,
Their javelins sparkling to the morning
    sun,
Spread their triumphant banners; high-
    plumed helms
Rose o'er the martial ranks, and pran-
    cing steeds
Made answer to the trumpet's stirring
    voice;
While yonder towers shook the dull
    silence off
Which long to their deserted walls had
    clung,
And with redoubling echoes swell'd the
    shout
That hail'd victorious Roderick. Louder
    rose
The acclamation, when the dust was
    seen   60
Rising beneath his chariot-wheels far off;
But nearer as the youthful hero came,
All sounds of all the multitude were
    hush'd,
And from the thousands and ten
    thousands here,
Whom Cordoba and Hispalis sent
    forth,..
Yea whom all Baetica, all Spain pour'd
    out
To greet his triumph, .. not a whisper
    rose
To Heaven, such awe and reverence
    master'd them,
Such expectation held them motionless.

Conqueror and King he came; but with
    no joy   70
Of conquest, and no pride of sovereignty
That day display'd; for at his father's
    grave
Did Roderick come to offer up his vow
Of vengeance well perform'd. Three
    coal-black steeds
Drew on his ivory chariot: by his side,
Still wrapt in mourning for the long-
    deceased,
Rusilla sate; a deeper paleness blanch'd
Her faded countenance, but in her eye
The light of her majestic nature shone.
Bound, and expecting at their hands
    the death   80
So well deserved, Itiza follow'd them;
Aghast and trembling, first he gazed
    around,
Wildly from side to side; then from the
    face
Of universal execration shrunk,
Hanging his wretched head abased;
    and poor
Of spirit, with unmanly tears deplored
His fortune, not his crimes. With
    bolder front,
Confiding in his priestly character,
Came Orpas next; and then the spurious
    race
Whom in unhappy hour Favila's wife 90
Brought forth for Spain. O mercy ill
    bestow'd,
When Roderick, in compassion for their
    youth,
And for Pelayo's sake, forbore to crush
The brood of vipers!
                Err perchance he might,
Replied the Goth, suppressing as he
    spake
All outward signs of pain, though every
    word
Went like a dagger to his bleeding
    heart; ..
But sure, I ween, that error is not placed

Among his sins.   Old man, thou mayest regret
The mercy ill deserved, and worse return'd,   100
But not for this wouldst thou reproach the King!

Reproach him! cried Siverian; . . I reproach
My child, . . my noble boy, . . whom every tongue
Bless'd at that hour, . . whose love fill'd every heart
With joy, and every eye with joyful tears!
My brave, my beautiful, my generous boy!
Brave, beautiful, and generous as he was,
Never so brave, so beautiful, so great
As then, . . not even on that glorious day,
When on the field of victory, elevate 110
Amid the thousands who acclaim'd him King,
Firm on the shield above their heads upraised,
Erect he stood, and waved his bloody sword. . .
Why dost thou shake thy head as if in doubt?
I do not dream, nor fable! Ten short years
Have scarcely pass'd away, since all within
The Pyrenean hills, and the three seas
Which girdle Spain, echoed in one response
The acclamation from that field of fight. . .
Or doth aught ail thee, that thy body quakes   120
And shudders thus?
                                   'Tis but a chill, replied
The King, in passing from the open air
Under the shadow of this thick-set grove.

Oh! if this scene awoke in thee such thoughts
As swell my bosom here, the old man pursued,
Sunshine, or shade, and all things from without,
Would be alike indifferent. Gracious God,
Only but ten short years, . . and all so changed!
Ten little years since in yon court he check'd
His fiery steeds. The steeds obey'd his hand,   130
The whirling wheels stood still, and when he leapt
Upon the pavement, the whole people heard,
In their deep silence, open-ear'd, the sound.
With slower movement from the ivory seat
Rusilla rose, her arm, as down she stept,
Extended to her son's supporting hand;
Not for default of firm or agile strength,
But that the feeling of that solemn hour
Subdued her then, and tears bedimm'd her sight.
Howbeit when to her husband's grave she came,   140
On the sepulchral stone she bow'd her head
Awhile; then rose collectedly, and fix'd
Upon the scene her calm and steady eye.
Roderick, . . oh when did valour wear a form
So beautiful, so noble, so august?
Or vengeance, when did it put on before
A character so aweful, so divine?
Roderick stood up, and reaching to the tomb
His hands, my hero cried, Theodofred!
Father! I stand before thee once again,
According to thy prayer, when kneeling down   151

Between thy knees I took my last fare-
   well ;
And vow'd by all thy sufferings, all thy
   wrongs,
And by my mother's days and nights of
   woe,
Her silent anguish, and the grief which
   then
Even from thee she did not seek to hide,
That if our cruel parting should avail
To save me from the Tyrant's jealous
   guilt,
Surely should my avenging sword fulfil
Whate'er he omen'd. Oh that time,
   I cried,   160
Would give the strength of manhood to
   this arm,
Already would it find a manly heart
To guide it to its purpose ! And I swore
Never again to see my father's face,
Nor ask my mother's blessing, till I
   brought,
Dead or in chains, the Tyrant to thy feet.
Boy as I was, before all Saints in
   Heaven,
And highest God, whose justice slum-
   bereth not,
I made the vow. According to thy
   prayer,
In all things, O my father, is that vow
Perform'd, alas too well ! for thou didst
   pray,   171
While looking up I felt the burning tears
Which from thy sightless sockets
   stream'd, drop down, . .
That to thy grave, and not thy living
   feet,
The oppressor might be led. Behold
   him there, . .
Father ! Theodofred ! no longer now
In darkness, from thy heavenly seat
   look down,
And see before thy grave thine enemy
In bonds, awaiting judgement at my
   hand !

Thus while the hero spake, Witiza
   stood   180
Listening in agony, with open mouth,
And head half-raised, toward his sen-
   tence turn'd ;
His eye-lids stiffen'd and pursed up, . .
   his eyes
Rigid, and wild, and wide ; and when
   the King
Had ceased, amid the silence which
   ensued,
The dastard's chains were heard, link
   against link
Clinking. At length upon his knees he
   fell,
And lifting up his trembling hands,
   outstretch'd
In supplication, . . Mercy ! he ex-
   claim'd, . .
Chains, dungeons, darkness, . . any
   thing but death ! . .   190
I did not touch his life.
                 Roderick replied,
His hour, whenever it had come, had
   found
A soul prepared : he lived in peace with
   Heaven,
And life prolong'd for him, was bliss
   delay'd.
But life, in pain and darkness and de-
   spair,
For thee, all leprous as thou art with
   crimes,
Is mercy... Take him hence, and let him
   see
The light of day no more !
                 Such Roderick was
When last I saw these courts, . . his
   theatre
Of glory ; . . such when last I visited   200
My master's grave ! Ten years have
   hardly held
Their course, . . ten little years . . break,
   break, old heart . .
Oh, why art thou so tough !

As thus he spake
They reach'd the church. The door
before his hand
Gave way; both blinded with their
tears, they went
Straight to the tomb; and there
Siverian knelt,
And bow'd his face upon the sepulchre,
Weeping aloud; while Roderick, over-
power'd,
And calling upon earth to cover him,
Threw himself prostrate on his father's
grave.   210

Thus as they lay, an aweful voice in
tones
Severe address'd them. Who are ye, it
said,
That with your passion thus, and on
this night,
Disturb my prayers? Starting they
rose; there stood
A man before them of majestic form
And stature, clad in sackcloth, bare of
foot,
Pale, and in tears, with ashes on his
head.

VII. RODERICK AND PELAYO

'Twas not in vain that on her absent
son,
Pelayo's mother from the bed of death
Call'd for forgiveness, and in agony
Besought his prayers; all guilty as she
was,
Sure he had not been human, if that cry
Had fail'd to pierce him. When he
heard the tale
He bless'd the messenger, even while his
speech
Was faltering, . . while from head to
foot he shook
With icy feelings from his inmost heart

Effused. It changed the nature of his
woe,   10
Making the burthen more endurable :
The life-long sorrow that remain'd,
became
A healing and a chastening grief, and
brought
His soul, in close communion, nearer
Heaven.
For he had been her first-born, and the
love
Which at her breast he drew, and from
her smiles,
And from her voice of tenderness
imbibed,
Gave such unnatural horror to her
crimes,
That when the thought came over him,
it seem'd
As if the milk which with his infant life
Had blended, thrill'd like poison
through his frame.   21
It was a woe beyond all reach of hope,
Till with the dreadful tale of her remorse
Faith touch'd his heart; and ever from
that day
Did he for her who bore him, night and
morn,
Pour out the anguish of his soul in
prayer :
But chiefly as the night return'd, which
heard
Her last expiring groans of penitence,
Then through the long and painful
hours, before
The altar, like a penitent himself,   30
He kept his vigils; and when Roderick's
sword
Subdued Witiza, and the land was free,
Duly upon her grave he offer'd up
His yearly sacrifice of agony
And prayer. This was the night, and
he it was
Who now before Siverian and the King
Stood up in sackcloth.

The old man, from fear
Recovering and from wonder, knew
    him first.
It is the Prince ! he cried, and bending
    down
Embraced his knees.   The action and
    the word   40
Awaken'd Roderick ; he shook off the
    load
Of struggling thoughts, which pressing
    on his heart,
Held him like one entranced ; yet, all
    untaught
To bend before the face of man, confused
Awhile he stood, forgetful of his part.
But when Siverian cried, My Lord, my
    Lord,
Now God be praised that I have found
    thee thus,
My Lord and Prince, Spain's only hope
    and mine !
Then Roderick, echoing him, exclaim'd,
    My Lord
And Prince, Pelayo ! . . and approaching
    near,   50
He bent his knee obeisant : but his head
Earthward inclined ; while the old man,
    looking up
From his low gesture to Pelayo's face,
Wept at beholding him for grief and joy.

Siverian ! cried the chief, . . of whom
    hath Death
Bereaved me, that thou comest to
    Cordoba ? . .
Children, or wife ? . . Or hath the merci-
    less scythe
Of this abhorr'd and jealous tyranny
Made my house desolate at one wide
    sweep ?

They are as thou couldst wish, the
    old man replied,   60
Wert thou but lord of thine own house
    again,

And Spain were Spain once more.   A
    tale of ill
I bear, but one that touches not the
    heart
Like what thy fears forbode.   The
    renegade
Numacian woos thy sister, and she lends
To the vile slave, unworthily, her ear :
The Lady Gaudiosa hath in vain
Warn'd her of all the evils which await
A union thus accurst :   she sets at
    nought
Her faith, her lineage, and thy certain
    wrath.   70

    Pelayo hearing him, remain'd awhile
Silent ;   then turning to his mother's
    grave, . .
O thou poor dust, hath then the infec-
    tious taint
Survived thy dread remorse, that it
    should run
In Guisla's veins ? he cried ; . . I should
    have heard
This shameful sorrow any where but
    here ! . .
Humble thyself, proud heart ;   thou,
    gracious Heaven,
Be merciful ! . . it is the original flaw, . .
And what are we ? . . a weak unhappy
    race,
Born to our sad inheritance of sin   80
And death ! . . He smote his forehead as
    he spake,
And from his head the ashes fell, like
    snow
Shaken from some dry beech-leaves,
    when a bird
Lights on the bending spray.   A little
    while
In silence, rather than in thought, he
    stood
Passive beneath the sorrow :   turning
    then,
And what doth Gaudiosa counsel me ?

He ask'd the old man; for she hath
   ever been
My wise and faithful counsellor. . . He
   replied,
The Lady Gaudiosa bade me say   90
She sees the danger which on every part
Besets her husband's house . . Here she
   had ceased;
But when my noble Mistress gave in
   charge,
How I should tell thee that in evil times
The bravest counsels ever are the best;
Then that high-minded Lady thus re-
   join'd,
Whatever be my Lord's resolve, he
   knows
I bear a mind prepared.
            Brave spirits! cried
Pelayo, worthy to remove all stain
Of weakness from their sex! I should
   be less   100
Than man, if, drawing strength where
   others find
Their hearts most open to assault of fear,
I quail'd at danger. Never be it said
Of Spain, that in the hour of her distress
Her women were as heroes, but her men
Perform'd the woman's part.
            Roderick at that
Look'd up, and taking up the word,
   exclaim'd,
O Prince, in better days the pride of
   Spain,
And prostrate as she lies, her surest
   hope,
Hear now my tale. The fire which
   seem'd extinct   110
Hath risen revigorate: a living spark
From Auria's ashes, by a woman's hand
Preserved and quicken'd, kindles far
   and wide
The beacon-flame o'er all the Asturian
   hills.
There hath a vow been offer'd up,
   which binds

Us and our children's children to the
   work
Of holy hatred. In the name of Spain
That vow hath been pronounced and
   register'd
Above, to be the bond whereby we
   stand
For condemnation or acceptance..
   Heaven   120
Received the irrevocable vow, and Earth
Must witness its fulfilment, Earth and
   Heaven
Call upon thee, Pelayo! Upon thee
The spirits of thy royal ancestors
Look down expectant; unto thee, from
   fields
Laid waste, and hamlets burnt, and
   cities sack'd,
The blood of infancy and helpless age
Cries out; thy native mountains call
   for thee,
Echoing from all their armèd sons thy
   name.
And deem not thou that hot impatience
   goads   130
Thy countrymen to counsels immature.
Odoar and Urban from Visonia's banks
Send me, their sworn and trusted mes-
   senger,
To summon thee, and tell thee in their
   name
That now the hour is come: For sure
   it seems,
Thus saith the Primate, Heaven's high
   will to rear
Upon the soil of Spain a Spanish throne,
Restoring in thy native line, O Prince,
The sceptre to the Spaniard. Worthy
   son
Of that most ancient and heroic race, 140
Which with unweariable endurance still
Hath striven against its mightier
   enemies,
Roman or Carthaginian, Greek or Goth;
So often by superior arms oppress'd,

More often by superior arts beguiled ;
Yet amid all its sufferings, all the waste
Of sword and fire remorselessly employ'd,
Unconquer'd and unconquerable still ; . .
Son of that injured and illustrious stock,
Stand forward thou, draw forth the
 sword of Spain,   150
Restore them to their rights, too long
 withheld,
And place upon thy brow the Spanish
 crown.

When Roderick ceased, the princely
 Mountaineer
Gazed on the passionate orator awhile,
With eyes intently fix'd, and thoughtful
 brow ;
Then turning to the altar, he let fall
The sackcloth robe, which late with
 folded arms
Against his heart was prest ; and
 stretching forth
His hands toward the crucifix, ex-
 claim'd,
My God and my Redeemer ! where but
 here,   160
Before thy aweful presence, in this garb,
With penitential ashes thus bestrewn,
Could I so fitly answer to the call
Of Spain ; and for her sake, and in thy
 name,
Accept the Crown of Thorns she proffers
 me !

And where but here, said Roderick in
 his heart,
Could I so properly, with humbled knee
And willing soul, confirm my forfeiture ? . .
The action follow'd on that secret
 thought :
He knelt, and took Pelayo's hand, and
 cried,   170
First of the Spaniards, let me with this
 kiss

Do homage to thee here, my Lord and
 King ! . .
With voice unchanged and steady coun-
 tenance
He spake ; but when Siverian follow'd
 him,
The old man trembled as his lips pro-
 nounced
The faltering vow ; and rising he ex-
 claim'd,
God grant thee, O my Prince, a better fate
Than thy poor kinsman's, who in hap-
 pier days   •
Received thy homage here ! Grief
 choak'd his speech,
And, bursting into tears, he sobb'd
 aloud.   180
Tears too adown Pelayo's manly cheek
Roll'd silently. Roderick alone ap-
 pear'd
Unmoved and calm ; for now the royal
 Goth
Had offer'd his accepted sacrifice,
And therefore in his soul he felt that
 peace
Which follows painful duty well per-
 form'd, . .
Perfect and heavenly peace, . . the peace
 of God.

VIII. ALPHONSO

FAIN would Pelayo have that hour
 obey'd
The call, commencing his adventurous
 flight,
As one whose soul impatiently endured
His country's thraldom, and in daily
 prayer
Imploring her deliverance, cried to
 Heaven,
How long, O Lord, how long ! . . But
 other thoughts
Curbing his spirit, made him yet awhile

Sustain the weight of bondage. Him alone,
Of all the Gothic baronage, the Moors
Watch'd with regard of wary policy, . .
Knowing his powerful name, his noble mind,   11
And how in him the old Iberian blood,
Of royal and remotest ancestry,
From undisputed source flow'd unde-filed ;
His mother's after-guilt attainting not
The claim legitimate he derived from her,
Her first-born in her time of innocence.
He too of Chindasuintho's regal line
Sole remnant now, drew after him the love
Of all true Goths, uniting in himself 20
Thus by this double right, the general heart
Of Spain.   For this the renegado crew,
Wretches in whom their conscious guilt and fear
Engender'd cruellest hatred, still ad-vised
The extinction of Pelayo's house ; but most
The apostate Prelate, in iniquity
Witiza's genuine brother as in blood,
Orpas, pursued his life. He never ceased
With busy zeal, true traitor, to infuse
His deadly rancour in the Moorish chief ;
Their only danger, ever he observed, 31
Was from Pelayo ; root his lineage out,
The Caliph's empire then would be secure,
And universal Spain, all hope of change
Being lost, receive the Prophet's con-quering law.
Then did the Arch-villain urge the Moor at once
To cut off future peril, telling him
Death was a trusty keeper, and that none

E'er broke the prison of the grave.   But here
Keen malice overshot its mark : the Moor,   40
Who from the plunder of their native land
Had bought the recreant crew that join'd his arms,
Or cheaplier with their own possessions bribed
Their sordid souls, saw through the flimsy show
Of policy wherewith they sought to cloak
Old enmity, and selfish aims : he scorn'd
To let their private purposes incline
His counsels, and believing Spain sub-dued,
Smiled, in the pride of power and victory,
Disdainful at the thought of farther strife.   50
Howbeit he held Pelayo at his court,
And told him that until his countrymen
Submissively should lay their weapons down,
He from his children and paternal hearth
Apart must dwell ; nor hope to see again
His native mountains and their vales beloved,
Till all the Asturian and Cantabrian hills
Had bow'd before the Caliph ; Cordoba
Must be his nightly prison till that hour.
This night, by special favour from the Moor   60
Ask'd and vouchsafed, he pass'd without the walls,
Keeping his yearly vigil ; on this night
Therefore the princely Spaniard could not fly,
Being thus in strongest bonds by honour held ;
Nor would he by his own escape expose
To stricter bondage, or belike to death,

Count Pedro's son.   The ancient enmity
Of rival houses from Pelayo's heart
Had, like a thing forgotten, pass'd away;
He pitied child and parent, separated 70
By the stern mandate of unfeeling
power,
And almost with a father's eyes beheld
The boy, his fellow in captivity.
For young Alphonso was in truth an heir
Of nature's largest patrimony : rich
In form and feature, growing strength
of limb,
A gentle heart, a soul affectionate,
A joyous spirit fill'd with generous
thoughts,
And genius heightening and ennobling
all ;
The blossom of all manly virtues made
His boyhood beautiful.   Shield, gracious
Heaven, 81
In this ungenial season perilous, . .
Thus would Pelayo sometimes breathe
in prayer
The aspirations of prophetic hope, . .
Shield, gracious Heaven, the blooming
tree ! and let
This goodly promise, for thy people's
sake,
Yield its abundant fruitage.
            When the Prince,
With hope and fear and grief and shame
disturb'd,
And sad remembrance, and the shadowy
light
Of days before him, thronging as in
dreams, 90
Whose quick succession fill'd and over-
power'd
Awhile the unresisting faculty,
Could in the calm of troubled thoughts
subdued
Seek in his heart for counsel, his first
care
Was for the boy ; how best they might
evade

The Moor, and renegade's more watchful
eye ;
And leaving in some unsuspicious guise
The city, through what unfrequented
track
Safeliest pursue with speed their dan-
gerous way.
Consumed in cares like these, the fleet-
ing hours 100
Went by.   The lamps and tapers now
grew pale,
And through the eastern window slant-
ing fell
The roseate ray of morn.   Within those
walls
Returning day restored no cheerful
sounds
Or joyous motions of awakening life;
But in the stream of light the speckled
motes,
As if in mimickry of insect play,
Floated with mazy movement.   Sloping
down
Over the altar pass'd the pillar'd beam,
And rested on the sinful woman's grave
As if it enter'd there, a light from
Heaven. 111
So be it ! cried Pelayo, even so !
As in a momentary interval,
When thought expelling thought, had
left his mind
Open and passive to the influxes
Of outward sense, his vacant eye was
there, . .
So be it, Heavenly Father, even so !
Thus may thy vivifying goodness shed
Forgiveness there ; for let not thou the
groans
Of dying penitence, nor my bitter
prayers 120
Before thy mercy-seat, be heard in vain !
And thou, poor soul, who from the
dolorous house
Of weeping and of pain, dost look to me
To shorten and assuage thy penal term,

Pardon me that these hours in other
   thoughts
And other duties than this garb, this
   night
Enjoin, should thus have pass'd ! Our
   mother-land
Exacted of my heart the sacrifice ;
And many a vigil must thy son perform
Henceforth in woods and mountain
   fastnesses,   130
And tented fields, outwatching for her
   sake
The starry host, and ready for the work
Of day, before the sun begins his course.

   The noble Mountaineer, concluding
   then
With silent prayer the service of the
   night,
Went forth. Without the porch await-
   ing him
He saw Alphonso, pacing to and fro
With patient step and eye reverted oft.
He, springing forward when he heard
   the door
Move on its heavy hinges, ran to him,
And welcomed him with smiles of youth-
   ful love.   141
I have been watching yonder moon,
   quoth he,
How it grew pale and paler as the sun
Scatter'd the flying shades ; but woe is
   me,
For on the towers of Cordoba the while
That baleful crescent glitter'd in the
   morn,
And with its insolent triumph seem'd
   to mock
The omen I had found. . . Last night
   I dreamt
That thou wert in the field in arms for
   Spain,
And I was at thy side : the infidels   150
Beset us round, but we with our good
   swords

Hew'd out a way. Methought I stabb'd
   a Moor
Who would have slain thee ; but with
   that I woke
For joy, and wept to find it but a dream.

   Thus as he spake a livelier glow o'er-
   spread
His cheek, and starting tears again
   suffused
The brightening lustre of his eyes. The
   Prince
Regarded him a moment steadfastly,
As if in quick resolve ; then looking
   round
On every side with keen and rapid
   glance,   160
Drew him within the church. Alphonso's
   heart
Throbb'd with a joyful boding as he
   mark'd
The calmness of Pelayo's countenance
Kindle with solemn thoughts, expressing
   now
High purposes of resolute hope. He
   gazed
All eagerly to hear what most he wish'd.
If, said the Prince, thy dream were
   verified,
And I indeed were in the field in arms
For Spain, . . wouldst thou be at
   Pelayo's side ? . .
If I should break these bonds, and fly
   to rear   170
Our country's banner on our native hills,
Wouldst thou, Alphonso, share my
   dangerous flight,
Dear boy, . . and wilt thou take thy lot
   with me
For death, or for deliverance ?
                    Shall I swear ?
Replied the impatient boy ; and laying
   hand
Upon the altar, on his knee he bent,
Looking towards Pelayo with such joy

Of reverential love, as if a God
Were present to receive the eager vow.
Nay, quoth Pelayo : what hast thou to
  do   180
With oaths ? . . Bright emanation as
  thou art,
It were a wrong to thy unsullied soul,
A sin to nature, were I to require
Promise or vow from thee ! Enough for
  me
That thy heart answers to the stirring
  call.
Alphonso, follow thou in happy faith
Alway the indwelling voice that counsels
  thee ;
And then, let fall the issue as it may,
Shall all thy paths be in the light of
  Heaven,
The peace of Heaven be with thee in all
  hours.   190

How then, exclaim'd the boy, shall I
  discharge
The burthen of this happiness, . . how ease
My overflowing soul ! . . Oh, gracious
  God,
Shall I behold my mother's face again, . .
My father's hall, . . my native hills and
  vales,
And hear the voices of their streams
  again, . .
And free as I was born amid those scenes
Beloved, maintain my country's free-
  dom there, . .
Or, failing in the sacred enterprise,
Die as becomes a Spaniard ? . . Saying
  thus,   200
He lifted up his hands and eyes toward
The image of the Crucified, and cried,
O Thou who didst with thy most pre-
  cious blood
Redeem us, Jesu ! help us while we seek
Earthly redemption from this yoke of
  shame
And misbelief and death.

The noble boy
Then rose, and would have knelt again
  to clasp
Pelayo's knees, and kiss his hand in act
Of homage ; but the Prince, preventing
  this,
Bent over him in fatherly embrace,   210
And breathed a fervent blessing on his
  head.

IX. FLORINDA

THERE sate a woman like a supplicant,
Muffled and cloak'd, before Pelayo's
  gate,
Awaiting when he should return that
  morn.
She rose at his approach, and bow'd her
  head,
And, with a low and trembling utterance,
Besought him to vouchsafe her speech
  within
In privacy.   And when they were alone,
And the doors closed, she knelt and
  claspt his knees,
Saying, a boon ! a boon ! This night,
  O Prince,
Hast thou kept vigil for thy mother's
  soul :   10
For her soul's sake, and for the soul of
  him
Whom once, in happier days, of all man-
  kind
Thou heldest for thy chosen bosom
  friend,
Oh for the sake of his poor suffering soul,
Refuse me not !
            How should I dare refuse,
Being thus adjured ? he answer'd. Thy
  request
Is granted, woman, . . be it what it may
So it be lawful, and within the bounds
Of possible achievement : . . aught unfit
Thou wouldst not with these adjurations
  seek.   20

But who thou art, I marvel, that dost
touch
Upon that string, and ask in Roderick's
name ! . .
She bared her face, and, looking up,
replied,
Florinda ! . . Shrinking then, with both
her hands
She hid herself, and bow'd her head
abased
Upon her knee, . . as one who, if the
grave
Had oped beneath her, would have
thrown herself,
Even like a lover, in the arms of Death.

Pelayo stood confused : he had not
seen
Count Julian's daughter since in
Roderick's court,   30
Glittering in beauty and in innocence,
A radiant vision, in her joy she moved ;
More like a poet's dream, or form divine,
Heaven's prototype of perfect woman-
hood,
So lovely was the presence, . . than a
thing
Of earth and perishable elements.
Now had he seen her in her winding-
sheet,
Less painful would that spectacle have
proved ;
For peace is with the dead, and piety
Bringeth a patient hope to those who
mourn   40
O'er the departed ; but this alter'd face,
Bearing its deadly sorrow character'd,
Came to him like a ghost, which in the
grave
Could find no rest. He, taking her cold
hand,
Raised her, and would have spoken ;
but his tongue
Fail'd in its office, and could only speak
In under tones compassionate her name.

The voice of pity soothed and melted
her ;
And when the Prince bade her be com-
forted,
Proffering his zealous aid in whatsoe'er
Might please her to appoint, a feeble
smile   51
Pass'd slowly over her pale countenance,
Like moonlight on a marble statue.
Heaven
Requite thee, Prince ! she answer'd.
All I ask
Is but a quiet resting-place, wherein
A broken heart, in prayer and humble
hope,
May wait for its deliverance. Even this
My most unhappy fate denies me here.
Griefs which are known too widely and
too well
I need not now remember. I could
bear   60
Privation of all Christian ordinances,
The woe which kills hath saved me too,
and made
A temple of this ruin'd tabernacle,
Wherein redeeming God doth not dis-
dain
To let his presence shine. And I could
bear
To see the turban on my father's brow,..
Sorrow beyond all sorrows, . . shame of
shames, ..
Yet to be borne, while I with tears of
blood,
And throes of agony, in his behalf
Implore and wrestle with offended
Heaven.   70
This I have borne resign'd : but other ills
And worse assail me now ; the which
to bear,
If to avoid be possible, would draw
Damnation down. Orpas, the perjured
Priest,
The apostate Orpas, claims me for his
bride.

Obdurate as he is, the wretch profanes
My sacred woe, and woos me to his bed,
The thing I am, . . the living death thou
    seest !

    Miscreant ! exclaim'd Pelayo. Might
    I meet
That renegado, sword to scymitar,   80
In open field, never did man approach
The altar for the sacrifice in faith
More sure, than I should hew the villain
    down !
But how should Julian favour his
    demand ? . .
Julian, who hath so passionately loved
His child, so dreadfully revenged her
    wrongs !

    Count Julian, she replied, hath none
    but me,
And it hath, therefore, been his heart's
    desire
To see his ancient line by me preserved.
This was their covenant when in fatal
    hour   90
For Spain, and for themselves, in traitor-
    ous bond
Of union they combined. My father,
    stung
To madness, only thought of how to
    make
His vengeance sure ; the Prelate, calm
    and cool,
When he renounced his outward faith in
    Christ,
Indulged at once his hatred of the King,
His inbred wickedness, and a haughty
    hope,
Versed as he was in treasons, to direct
The invaders by his secret policy,
And at their head, aided by Julian's
    power,   100
Reign as a Moor upon that throne to
    which
The priestly order else had barr'd his way.

The African hath conquer'd for himself ;
But Orpas coveteth Count Julian's
    lands,
And claims to have the covenant per-
    form'd.
Friendless, and worse than fatherless,
    I come
To thee for succour. Send me secretly, . .
For well I know all faithful hearts must
    be
At thy devotion, . . with a trusty guide
To guard me on the way, that I may
    reach   110
Some Christian land, where Christian
    rites are free,
And there discharge a vow, alas ! too
    long,
Too fatally delay'd. Aid me in this
For Roderick's sake, Pelayo ! and thy
    name
Shall be remember'd in my latest prayer.

    Be comforted ! the Prince replied ;
    but when
He spake of comfort, twice did he break
    off
The idle words, feeling that earth had
    none
For grief so irremediable as hers.
At length he took her hand, and pressing
    it,   120
And forcing through involuntary tears
A mournful smile affectionate, he said,
Say not that thou art friendless while
    I live !
Thou couldst not to a readier ear have
    told
Thy sorrows, nor have ask'd in fitter hour
What for my country's honour, for my
    rank,
My faith, and sacred knighthood, I am
    bound
In duty to perform ; which not to do
Would show me undeserving of the
    names

Of Goth, Prince, Christian, even of Man.
   This day,   130
Lady, prepare to take thy lot with me,
And soon as evening closes meet me here.
Duties bring blessings with them, and
   I hold
Thy coming for a happy augury,
In this most awful crisis of my fate.

X. RODERICK AND FLORINDA

WITH sword and breast-plate, under
   rustic weeds
Conceal'd, at dusk Pelayo pass'd the
   gate,
Florinda following near, disguised alike.
Two peasants on their mules they
   seem'd, at eve
Returning from the town.   Not distant
   far,
Alphonso by the appointed orange-
   grove,
With anxious eye and agitated heart,
Watch'd for the Prince's coming.
   Eagerly
At every foot-fall through the gloom he
   strain'd
His sight, nor did he recognize him when
The Chieftain thus accompanied drew
   nigh ;   11
And when the expected signal called
   him on,
Doubting this female presence, half in
   fear
Obey'd the call.   Pelayo too perceived
The boy was not alone ; he not for that
Delay'd the summons, but lest need
   should be,
Laying hand upon his sword, toward
   him bent
In act soliciting speech, and low of voice
Enquired if friend or foe.   Forgive me,
   cried
Alphonso, that I did not tell thee this, 20

Full as I was of happiness, before.
'Tis Hoya, servant of my father's house,
Unto whose dutiful care and love, when
   sent
To this vile bondage, I was given in
   charge.
How could I look upon my father's face
If I had in my joy deserted him,
Who was to me found faithful ?.. Right !
   replied
The Prince ;   and viewing him with
   silent joy,
Blessed the Mother, in his heart he said,
Who gave thee birth !   but sure of
   womankind   30
Most blessed she whose hand her happy
   stars
Shall link with thine !   and with that
   thought the form
Of Hermesind, his daughter, to his soul
Came in her beauty.
            Soon by devious tracks
They turn'd aside.   The favouring
   moon arose,
To guide them on their flight through
   upland paths
Remote from frequentage, and dales
   retired,
Forest and mountain glen.   Before their
   feet
The fire-flies, swarming in the woodland
   shade,
Sprung up like sparks, and twinkled
   round their way ;   40
The timorous blackbird, starting at their
   step,
Fled from the thicket with shrill note of
   fear ;
And far below them in the peopled dell,
When all the soothing sounds of eve had
   ceased,
The distant watch-dog's voice at times
   was heard,
Answering the nearer wolf.   All through
   the night

Among the hills they travell'd silently;
Till when the stars were setting, at what
    hour
The breath of Heaven is coldest, they
    beheld
Within a lonely grove the expected fire,
Where Roderick and his comrade
    anxiously   51
Look'd for the appointed meeting.
    Halting there,
They from the burthen and the bit
    relieved
Their patient bearers, and around the
    fire
Partook of needful food and grateful
    rest.

Bright rose the flame replenish'd; it
    illumed
The cork-tree's furrow'd rind, its rifts
    and swells
And redder scars, .. and where its aged
    boughs
O'erbower'd the travellers, cast upon
    the leaves
A floating, grey, unrealizing gleam. 60
Alphonso, light of heart, upon the heath
Lay carelessly dispread, in happy
    dreams
Of home; his faithful Hoya slept beside.
Years and fatigue to old Siverian
    brought
Easy oblivion; and the Prince himself,
Yielding to weary nature's gentle will,
Forgot his cares awhile. Florinda sate
Beholding Roderick with fix'd eyes in-
    tent,
Yet unregardant of the countenance
Whereon they dwelt; in other thoughts
    absorb'd,   70
Collecting fortitude for what she yearn'd,
Yet trembled to perform. Her steady
    look
Disturb'd the Goth, albeit he little
    ween'd

What agony awaited him that hour.
Her face, well nigh as changed as his,
    was now
Half hidden, and the lustre of her eye
Extinct; nor did her voice awaken in
    him
One startling recollection when she spake,
So altered were its tones.
               Father, she said,
All thankful as I am to leave behind 80
The unhappy walls of Cordoba, not less
Of consolation doth my heart receive
At sight of one to whom I may disclose
The sins which trouble me, and at his
    feet
Lay down repentantly, in Jesu's name,
The burthen of my spirit. In his name
Hear me, and pour into a wounded soul
The balm of pious counsel... Saying thus,
She drew toward the minister ordain'd,
And kneeling by him, Father, dost thou
    know   90
The wretch who kneels beside thee?
    she enquired.
He answered, Surely we are each to each
Equally unknown.
            Then said she, Here thou seest
One who is known too fatally for all, ..
The daughter of Count Julian... Well it
    was
For Roderick that no eye beheld him
    now;
From head to foot a sharper pang than
    death
Thrill'd him; his heart, as at a mortal
    stroke,
Ceased from its functions: his breath
    fail'd, and when
The power of life recovering set its
    springs   100
Again in action, cold and clammy sweat
Starting at every pore suffused his
    frame.
Their presence help'd him to subdue
    himself;

For else, had none been nigh, he would
    have fallen
Before Florinda prostrate on the earth,
And in that mutual agony belike
Both souls had taken flight. She mark'd
    him not;
For having told her name, she bow'd her
    head,
Breathing a short and silent prayer to
    Heaven,   109
While, as a penitent, she wrought herself
To open to his eye her hidden wounds.

Father, at length she said, all tongues
    amid
This general ruin shed their bitterness
On Roderick, load his memory with
    reproach,
And with their curses persecute his
    soul. . .
Why shouldst thou tell me this? ex-
    claim'd the Goth,
From his cold forehead wiping as he spake
The death-like moisture: . . Why of
    Roderick's guilt
Tell me? Or thinkest thou I know it
    not?
Alas! who hath not heard the hideous
    tale   120
Of Roderick's shame! Babes learn it
    from their nurses,
And children, by their mothers unre-
    proved,
Link their first execrations to his name.
Oh, it hath caught a taint of infamy,
That, like Iscariot's, through all time
    shall last,
Reeking and fresh for ever!
                    There! she cried,
Drawing her body backward where she
    knelt,
And stretching forth her arms with head
    upraised, . .
There! it pursues me still! . . I came to
    thee,

Father, for comfort, and thou heapest
    fire   130
Upon my head.   But hear me patiently,
And let me undeceive thee; self-abased,
Not to arraign another, do I come; . .
I come a self-accuser, self-condemn'd
To take upon myself the pain deserved;
For I have drunk the cup of bitterness,
And having drunk therein of heavenly
    grace,
I must not put away the cup of shame.

Thus as she spake she falter'd at the
    close,
And in that dying fall her voice sent forth
Somewhat of its original sweetness.
    Thou! . .   141
Thou self-abased! exclaim'd the as-
    tonish'd King; . .
Thou self-condemn'd! . . The cup of
    shame for thee!
Thee . . thee, Florinda! . . But the very
    excess
Of passion check'd his speech, restrain-
    ing thus
From farther transport, which had
    haply else
Master'd him; and he sate like one
    entranced,
Gazing upon that countenance so fallen,
So changed: her face, raised from its
    muffler now,
Was turn'd toward him, and the fire-
    light shone   150
Full on its mortal paleness; but the shade
Conceal'd the King.
              She roused him from the spell
Which held him like a statue motionless.
Thou too, quoth she, dost join the
    general curse,
Like one who when he sees a felon's
    grave,
Casting a stone there as he passes by,
Adds to the heap of shame.   Oh what
    are we,

Frail creatures as we are, that we should sit
In judgement man on man! and what were we,
If the All-merciful should mete to us   160
With the same rigorous measure wherewithal
Sinner to sinner metes! But God beholds
The secrets of the heart, . . therefore his name
Is Merciful.   Servant of God, see thou
The hidden things of mine, and judge thou then
In charity thy brother who hath fallen. . .
Nay, hear me to the end! I loved the King, . .
Tenderly, passionately, madly loved him.
Sinful it was to love a child of earth
With such entire devotion as I loved   170
Roderick, the heroic Prince, the glorious Goth!
And yet methought this was its only crime,
The imaginative passion seem'd so pure:
Quiet and calm like duty, hope nor fear
Disturb'd the deep contentment of that love;
He was the sunshine of my soul, and like
A flower, I lived and flourish'd in his light.
Oh bear not with me thus impatiently!
No tale of weakness this, that in the act
Of penitence, indulgent to itself,   180
With garrulous palliation half repeats
The sin it ill repents.   I will be brief,
And shrink not from confessing how the love
Which thus began in innocence, betray'd
My unsuspecting heart; nor me alone,
But him, before whom, shining as he shone

With whatsoe'er is noble, whatsoe'er
Is lovely, whatsoever good and great,
I was as dust and ashes, . . him, alas!
This glorious being, this exalted Prince,
Even him, with all his royalty of soul,
Did this ill-omen'd, this accursèd love,
To his most lamentable fall betray   193
And utter ruin.   Thus it was: The King,
By counsels of cold statesmen ill-advised,
To an unworthy mate had bound himself
In politic wedlock.   Wherefore should I tell
How Nature upon Egilona's form,
Profuse of beauty, lavishing her gifts,
Left, like a statue from the graver's hands,   200
Deformity and hollowness beneath
The rich external?   For the love of pomp
And emptiest vanity, hath she not incurr'd
Tho grief and wonder of good men, tho gibes
Of vulgar ribaldry, the reproach of all;
Profaning the most holy sacrament
Of marriage, to become chief of the wives
Of Abdalaziz, of the Infidel,
The Moor, the tyrant-enemy of Spain!
All know her now; but they alone who knew   210
What Roderick was can judge his wretchedness,
To that light spirit and unfeeling heart
In hopeless bondage bound.   No children rose
From this unhappy union, towards whom
The springs of love within his soul confined
Might flow in joy and fulness; nor was he
One, like Witiza, of the vulgar crew,

Who in promiscuous appetite can find
All their vile nature seeks.   Alas for
   man !
Exuberant health diseases him, frail
   worm !   220
And the slight bias of untoward chance
Makes his best virtue from the even line,
With fatal declination, swerve aside
Ay, thou mayest groan for poor mor-
   tality, . .
Well, Father, mayest thou groan !
                          My evil fate
Made me an inmate of the royal house,
And Roderick found in me, if not a heart
Like his, . . for who was like the heroic
   Goth ? . .
One which at least felt his surpassing
   worth,
And loved him for himself. . . A little yet
Bear with me, reverend Father, for I
   touch   231
Upon the point, and this long prologue
   goes,
As justice bids, to palliate his offence,
Not mine.   The passion, which I fondly
   thought
Such as fond sisters for a brother feel,
Grew day by day, and strengthen'd in
   its growth,
Till the beloved presence had become
Needful as food or necessary sleep,
My hope, light, sunshine, life, and every
   thing.
Thus lapt in dreams of bliss, I might
   have lived   240
Contented with this pure idolatry,
Had he been happy :   but I saw and
   knew
The inward discontent and household
   griefs
Which he subdued in silence; and alas !
Pity with admiration mingling then,
Alloy'd and lower'd and humanized my
   love,
Till to the level of my lowliness

It brought him down ;   and in this
   treacherous heart
Too often the repining thought arose,
That if Florinda had been Roderick's
   Queen,   250
Then might domestic peace and happi-
   ness
Have bless'd his home and crown'd our
   wedded loves.
Too often did that sinful thought recur,
Too feebly the temptation was repell'd.

   See, Father, I have probed my inmost
   soul ;
Have search'd to its remotest source the
   sin ;
And tracing it through all its specious
   forms
Of fair disguisement, I present it now,
Even as it lies before the eye of God,
Bare and exposed, convicted and con-
   demn'd.   260
One eve, as in the bowers which over-
   hang
The glen where Tagus rolls between his
   rocks
I roam'd alone, alone I met the King.
His countenance was troubled, and his
   speech
Like that of one whose tongue to light
   discourse
At fits constrain'd, betrays a heart
   disturb'd :
I too, albeit unconscious of his thoughts,
With anxious looks' reveal'd what
   wandering words
In vain essay'd to hide.   A little while
Did this oppressive intercourse endure,
Till our eyes met in silence, each to each
Telling their mutual tale, then con-
   sciously   272
Together fell abash'd.   He took my hand
And said, Florinda, would that thou
   and I
Earlier had met ! oh what a blissful lot

Had then been mine, who might have
found in thee
The sweet companion and the friend
endear'd,
A fruitful wife and crown of earthly joys!
Thou too shouldst then have been of
womankind
Happiest, as now the loveliest. . . And
with that,   280
First giving way to passion first dis-
closed,
He press'd upon my lips a guilty kiss, . .
Alas! more guiltily received than given.
Passive and yielding, and yet self-
reproach'd,
Trembling I stood, upheld in his em-
brace;
When coming steps were heard, and
Roderick said,
Meet me to-morrow, I beseech thee, here,
Queen of my heart! Oh meet me here
again,
My own Florinda, meet me here again! . .
Tongue, eye, and pressure of the impas-
sion'd hand   290
Solicited and urged the ardent suit,
And from my hesitating hurried lips
The word of promise fatally was drawn.
O Roderick, Roderick! hadst thou told
me all
Thy purpose at that hour, from what
a world
Of woe had thou and I. . . The bitterness
Of that reflection overcame her then,
And choak'd her speech. But Roderick
sate the while
Covering his face with both his hands
close-prest,
His head bow'd down, his spirit to such
point   300
Of sufferance knit, as one who patiently
Awaits the uplifted sword.
                      Till now, said she,
Resuming her confession, I had lived,
If not in innocence, yet self-deceived,

And of my perilous and sinful state
Unconscious. But this fatal hour re-
veal'd
To my awakening soul her guilt and
shame;
And in those agonies with which remorse,
Wrestling with weakness and with
cherish'd sin,
Doth triumph o'er the lacerated heart,
That night . . that miserable night . .
I vow'd,   311
A virgin dedicate, to pass my life
Immured; and, like redeemed Magdalen,
Or that Egyptian penitent [1], whose tears
Fretted the rock, and moisten'd round
her cave
The thirsty desert, so to mourn my fall.
The struggle ending thus, the victory
Thus, as I thought, accomplish'd, I be-
lieved
My soul was calm, and that the peace of
Heaven
Descended to accept and bless my vow;
And in this faith, prepared to consum-
mate   321
The sacrifice, I went to meet the King.
See, Father, what a snare had Satan laid!
For Roderick came to tell me that the
Church
From his unfruitful bed would set him
free,
And I should be his Queen.
                      O let me close
The dreadful tale! I told him of my
vow;
And from sincere and scrupulous piety,
But more, I fear me, in that desperate
mood
Of obstinate will perverse, the which,
with pride   330
And shame and self-reproach, doth
sometimes make
A woman's tongue, her own worst enemy,

[1] St. Mary the Egyptian (S.).

Run counter to her dearest heart's
    desire, . .
In that unhappy mood did I resist
All his most earnest prayers to let the
    power
Of holy Church, never more rightfully
Invoked, he said, than now in our behalf,
Release us from our fatal bonds. He
    urged
With kindling warmth his suit, like one
    whose life
Hung on the issue; I dissembled not 340
My cruel self-reproaches, nor my grief,
Yet desperately maintain'd the rash
    resolve ;
Till in the passionate argument he grew
Incensed, inflamed, and madden'd or
    possess'd, . .
For Hell too surely at that hour pre-
    vail'd,
And with such subtile toils enveloped him,
That even in the extremity of guilt
No guilt he purported, but rather meant
An amplest recompence of life-long love
For transitory wrong, which fate per-
    verse,   350
Thus madly he deceived himself, com-
    pell'd,
And therefore stern necessity excused.
Here then, O Father, at thy feet I own
Myself the guiltier ; for full well I knew
These were his thoughts, but vengeance
    master'd me,
And in my agony I cursed the man
Whom I loved best.
                Dost thou recall that curse?
Cried Roderick, in a deep and inward
    voice,
Still with his head depress'd, and
    covering still
His countenance.   Recall it ! she ex-
    claim'd ;   360
Father, I come to thee because I gave
The reins to wrath too long, . . because
    I wrought

His ruin, death, and infamy. . . O God,
Forgive the wicked vengeance thus in-
    dulged,
As I forgive the King ! . . But teach me
    now
What reparation more than tears and
    prayers
May now be made ; . . how shall I vindi-
    cate
His injured name, and take upon my-
    self . . . .
Daughter of Julian, firmly he replied,
Speak not of that, I charge thee ! On
    his fame   370
The Ethiop dye, fixed ineffaceably,
For ever will abide ; so it must be,
So should be : 'tis his rightful punish-
    ment ;
And if to the full measure of his sin
The punishment hath fallen, the more
    our hope
That through the blood of Jesus he may
    find
That sin forgiven him.
                Pausing then, he raised
His hand, and pointed where Siverian lay
Stretch'd on the heath. To that old
    man, said he,
And to the mother of the unhappy Goth,
Tell, if it please thee, . . not what thou
    hast pour'd   381
Into my secret ear, but that the child
For whom they mourn with anguish
    unallay'd,
Sinn'd not from vicious will, or heart
    corrupt,
But fell by fatal circumstance betray'd.
And if in charity to them thou sayest
Something to palliate, something to
    excuse
An act of sudden frenzy when the Fiend
O'ercame him, thou wilt do for Roderick
All he could ask thee, all that can be
    done   390
On earth, and all his spirit could endure.

Venturing towards her an imploring
　　look,
Wilt thou join with me for his soul in
　　prayer ?
He said, and trembled as he spake.
　　That voice
Of sympathy was like Heaven's influence,
Wounding at once and comforting the
　　soul.
O Father, Christ requite thee ! she ex-
　　claim'd ;
Thou hast set free the springs which
　　withering griefs
Have closed too long.　Forgive me, for
　　I thought　　　　　　　　　　　399
Thou wert a rigid and unpitying judge ;
One whose stern virtue, feeling in itself
No flaw of frailty, heard impatiently
Of weakness and of guilt.　I wrong'd
　　thee, Father ! . .
With that she took his hand, and kissing
　　it,
Bathed it with tears.　Then in a firmer
　　speech,
For Roderick, for Count Julian and
　　myself,
Three wretchedest of all the human race,
Who have destroyed each other and
　　ourselves,
Mutually wrong'd and wronging, let us
　　pray !

XI.　COUNT PEDRO'S CASTLE

Twelve weary days with unremitting
　　speed,
Shunning frequented tracks, the tra-
　　vellers
Pursued their way ; the mountain path
　　they chose,
The forest or the lonely heath wide-
　　spread,
Where cistus shrubs sole-seen exhaled
　　at noon

Their fine balsamic odour all around ;
Strew'd with their blossoms, frail as
　　beautiful,
The thirsty soil at eve ; and when the
　　sun
Relumed the gladden'd earth, opening
　　anew
Their stores exuberant, prodigal as frail,
Whiten'd again the wilderness.　They
　　left　　　　　　　　　　　　　　11
The dark Sierra's skirts behind, and
　　cross'd
The wilds where Ana in her native hills
Collects her sister springs, and hurries on
Her course melodious amid loveliest
　　glens,
With forest and with fruitage over-
　　bower'd.
These scenes profusely blest by Heaven
　　they left,
Where o'er the hazel and the quince the
　　vine
Wide-mantling spreads ; and clinging
　　round the cork
And ilex, hangs amid their dusky leaves
Garlands of brightest hue, with redden-
　　ing fruit　　　　　　　　　　　21
Pendant, or clusters cool of glassy green.
So holding on o'er mountain and o'er
　　vale,
Tagus they cross'd where midland on
　　his way
The King of Rivers rolls his stately
　　stream ;
And rude Alverches wide and stony bed,
And Duero distant far, and many a
　　stream
And many a field obscure, in future war
For bloody theatre of famous deeds
Foredoom'd ; and deserts where in
　　years to come　　　　　　　　　30
Shall populous towns arise, and crested
　　towers
And stately temples rear their heads on
　　high.

Cautious with course circuitous they shunn'd
The embattled city, which in eldest time
Thrice-greatest Hermes built, so fables say,
Now subjugate, but fated to behold
Ere long the heroic Prince (who passing now
Unknown and silently the dangerous track,
Turns thither his regardant eye) come down
Victorious from the heights, and bear abroad   40
Her banner'd Lion, symbol to the Moor
Of rout and death through many an age of blood.
Lo, there the Asturian hills ! Far in the west,
Huge Rabanal and Foncebadon huge,
Pre-eminent, their giant bulk display,
Darkening with earliest shade the distant vales
Of Leon, and with evening premature.
Far in Cantabria eastward, the long line
Extends beyond the reach of eagle's eye,
When buoyant in mid-heaven the bird of Jove   50
Soars at his loftiest pitch.   In the north, before
The travellers the Erbasian mountains rise,
Bounding the land beloved, their native land.

How then, Alphonso, did thy eager soul
Chide the slow hours and painful way, which seem'd
Lengthening to grow before their lagging pace !
Youth of heroic thought and high desire,
'Tis not the spur of lofty enterprize
That with unequal throbbing hurries now

The unquiet heart, now makes it sink dismay'd ;   60
'Tis not impatient joy which thus disturbs
In that young breast the healthful spring of life ;
Joy and ambition have forsaken him,
His soul is sick with hope   So near his home,
So near his mother's arms ; . . alas ! perchance
The long'd-for meeting may be yet far off
As earth from heaven.   Sorrow in these long months
Of separation may have laid her low ;
Or what if at his flight the bloody Moor
Hath sent his ministers of slaughter forth,   70
And he himself should thus have brought the sword
Upon his father's head ? . . Sure Hoya too
The same dark presage feels, the fearful boy
Said in himself ; or wherefore is his brow
Thus overcast with heaviness, and why
Looks he thus anxiously in silence round ?

    Just then that faithful servant raised his hand,
And turning to Alphonso with a smile,
He pointed where Count Pedro's towers far off
Peer'd in the dell below ; faint was the smile,   80
And while it sate upon his lips, his eye
Retain'd its troubled speculation still.
For long had he look'd wistfully in vain,
Seeking where far or near he might espy
From whom to learn if time or chance had wrought
Change in his master's house : but on the hills

Nor goat-herd could he see, nor traveller,
Nor huntsman early at his sports afield,
Nor angler following up the mountain
   glen
His lonely pastime; neither could he
   hear   90
Carol, or pipe, or shout of shepherd's boy,
Nor woodman's axe, for not a human
   sound
Disturb'd the silence of the solitude.

Is it the spoiler's work? At yonder
   door
Behold the favourite kidling bleats un-
   heard;
The next stands open, and the sparrows
   there
Boldly pass in and out. Thither he
   turn'd
To seek what indications were within;
The chesnut-bread was on the shelf,
   the churn,
As if in haste forsaken, full and fresh;
The recent fire had moulder'd on the
   hearth;   101
And broken cobwebs mark'd the whiter
   space
Where from the wall the buckler and
   the sword
Had late been taken down. Wonder at
   first
Had mitigated fear, but Hoya now
Return'd to tell the symbols of good
   hope,
And they prick'd forward joyfully. Ere
   long,
Perceptible above the ceaseless sound
Of yonder stream, a voice of multitudes,
As if in loud acclaim, was heard far off;
And nearer as they drew, distincter
   shouts   111
Came from the dell, and at Count Pedro's
   gate
The human swarm were seen, .. a motley
   group,

Maids, mothers, helpless infancy, weak
   age,
And wondering children and tumultuous
   boys,
Hot youth and resolute manhood
   gather'd there,
In uproar all. Anon the moving mass
Falls in half circle back, a general cry
Bursts forth, exultant arms are lifted up,
And caps are thrown aloft, as through
   the gate   120
Count Pedro's banner came. Alphonso
   shriek'd
For joy, and smote his steed and gallop'd
   on.

Fronting the gate the standard-bearer
   holds
His precious charge. Behind the men
   divide
In order'd files; green boyhood presses
   there,
And waning eld, pleading a youthful
   soul,
Intreats admission. All is ardour here,
Hope and brave purposes and minds
   resolved.
Nor where the weaker sex is left apart
Doth aught of fear find utterance,
   though perchance   130
Some paler cheeks might there be seen,
   some eyes
Big with sad bodings, and some natural
   tears.
Count Pedro's war-horse in the vacant
   space
Strikes with impatient hoof the trodden
   turf,
And gazing round upon the martial show,
Proud of his stately trappings, flings his
   head,
And snorts and champs the bit, and
   neighing shrill
Wakes the near echo with his voice of
   joy.

The page beside him holds his master's
spear
And shield and helmet.   In the castle-
gate   140
Count Pedro stands, his countenance
resolved
But mournful, for Favinia on his arm
Hung, passionate with her fears, and held
him back.
Go not, she cried, with this deluded
crew !
She hath not, Pedro, with her frantic
words
Bereft thy faculty, . . she is crazed with
grief,
And her delirium hath infected these :
But, Pedro, thou art calm ; thou dost
not share
The madness of the crowd ; thy sober
mind
Surveys the danger in its whole extent,
And sees the certain ruin, . . for thou
know'st   151
I know thou hast no hope.   Unhappy
man,
Why then for this most desperate enter-
prize
Wilt thou devote thy son, thine only
child ?
Not for myself I plead, nor even for
thee ;
Thou art a soldier, and thou canst not
fear
The face of death ; and I should wel-
come it
As the best visitant whom Heaven could
send.
Not for our lives I speak then, . . were
they worth
The thought of preservation ; . . Nature
soon   160
Must call for them ; the sword that
should cut short
Sorrow's slow work were merciful to
us.

But spare Alphonso ! there is time and
hope
In store for him.   O thou who gavest
him life,
Seal not his death, his death and mine at
once !

   Peace ! he replied :   thou know'st
there is no choice,
I did not raise the storm ; I cannot turn
Its course aside ! but where yon banner
goes
Thy Lord must not be absent ! Spare
me then,
Favinia, lest I hear thy honour'd name
Now first attainted with deserved re-
proach.   171
The boy is in God's hands.   He who of
yore
Walk'd with the sons of Judah in the
fire,
And from the lion's den drew Daniel
forth
Unhurt, can save him, . . if it be his
will.

   Even as he spake, the astonish'd
troop set up
A shout of joy which rung through all
the hills.
Alphonso heeds not how they break
their ranks
And gather round to greet him ; from
his horse
Precipitate and panting off he springs.
Pedro grew pale, and trembled at his
sight ;   181
Favinia claspt her hands, and looking
up
To Heaven as she embraced the boy,
exclaim'd,
Lord God, forgive me for my sinful
fears ;
Unworthy that I am, . . my son, my
son !

XII. THE VOW

ALWAYS I knew thee for a generous foe,
Pelayo! said the Count, and in our time
Of enmity, thou too, I know, didst feel
The feud between us was but of the house,
Not of the heart. Brethren in arms henceforth
We stand or fall together: nor will I
Look to the event with one misgiving thought, . .
That were to prove myself unworthy now
Of Heaven's benignant providence, this hour,
Scarcely by less than miracle, vouch-safed.   10
I will believe that we have days in store
Of hope, now risen again as from the dead, . .
Of vengeance, . . of portentous victory, . .
Yea, maugre all unlikelihoods, . . of peace.
Let us then here indissolubly knit
Our ancient houses, that those happy days,
When they arrive, may find us more than friends,
And bound by closer than fraternal ties.
Thou hast a daughter, Prince, to whom my heart
Yearns now, as if in winning infancy 20
Her smiles had been its daily food of love.
I need not tell thee what Alphonso is, . .
Thou know'st the boy!
                    Already had that hope,
Replied Pelayo, risen within my soul.
O Thou, who in thy mercy from the house
Of Moorish bondage hast deliver'd us,
Fulfil the pious purposes for which
Here, in thy presence, thus we pledge our hands !

Strange hour to plight espousals ! yielding half
To superstitious thoughts, Favinia cried,
And these strange witnesses ! . . The times are strange,   31
With thoughtful speech composed her Lord replies,
And what thou seest accords with them. This day
Is wonderful ; nor could auspicious Heaven
With fairer or with fitter omen gild
Our enterprize, when strong in heart and hope
We take the field, preparing thus for works
Of piety and love. Unwillingly
I yielded to my people's general voice,
Thinking that she who with her power-ful words   40
To this excess had roused and kindled them,
Spake from the spirit of her griefs alone,
Not with prophetic impulse. Be that sin
Forgiven me ! and the calm and quiet faith
Which, in the place of incredulity,
Hath fill'd me, now that seeing I believe,
Doth give of happy end to righteous cause
A presage, not presumptuous, but assured.

Then Pedro told Pelayo how from vale
To vale the exalted Adosinda went,   50
Exciting sire and son, in holy war
Conquering or dying, to secure their place
In Paradise : and how reluctantly,
And mourning for his child by his own act
Thus doom'd to death, he bade with heavy heart

His banner be brought forth.   Devoid
alike
Of purpose and of hope himself, he
meant
To march toward the western Mountaineers,
Where Odoar by his counsel might
direct
Their force conjoin'd.   Now, said he,
we must haste   60
To Cangas, there, Pelayo, to secure,
With timely speed, I trust in God, thy
house.

Then looking to his men, he cried,
Bring forth
The armour which in Wamba's wars I
wore. . .
Alphonso's heart leapt at the auspicious
words.
Count Pedro mark'd the rising glow of
joy, . .
Doubly to thee, Alphonso, he pursued,
This day above all other days is blest,
From whence as from a birth-day thou
wilt date
Thy life in arms !
                    Rejoicing in their task,   70
The servants of the house with emulous
love
Dispute the charge.   One brings the
cuirass, one
The buckler ; this exultingly displays
The sword, his comrade lifts the helm on
high :
The greaves, the gauntlets they divide ;
a spur
Seems now to dignify the officious hand
Which for such service bears it to his
Lord.
Greek artists in the imperial city forged
That splendid armour, perfect in their
craft ;
With curious skill they wrought it,
framed alike   80

To shine amid the pageantry of war,
And for the proof of battle.   Many a
time
Alphonso from his nurse's lap had
stretch'd
His infant hands toward it eagerly,
Where gleaming to the central fire it
hung
High in the hall ; and many a time had
wish'd
With boyish ardour, that the day were
come
When Pedro to his prayers would grant
the boon,
His dearest heart's desire.   Count Pedro
then
Would smile, and in his heart rejoice to
see   90
The noble instinct manifest itself.
Then too Favinia with maternal pride
Would turn her eyes exulting to her
Lord,
And in that silent language bid him mark
His spirit in his boy ; all danger then
Was distant, and if secret forethought
faint
Of manhood's perils, and the chance of
war,
Hateful to mothers, pass'd across her
mind,
The ill remote gave to the present hour
A heighten'd feeling of secure delight.

No season this for old solemnities,   101
For wassailry and sport ; . . the bath,
the bed,
The vigil, . . all preparatory rites
Omitted now, . . here in the face of
Heaven,
Before the vassals of his father's house,
With them in instant peril to partake
The chance of life or death, the heroic
boy
Dons his first arms ; the coated scales of
steel

Which o'er the tunic to his knees depend,
The hose, the sleeves of mail; bare-
  headed then   110
He stood. But when Count Pedro took
  the spurs
And bent his knee in service to his son,
Alphonso from that gesture half drew
  back,
Starting in reverence, and a deeper hue
Spread o'er the glow of joy which flush'd
  his cheeks.
Do thou the rest, Pelayo! said the
  Count;
So shall the ceremony of this hour
Exceed in honour what in form it lacks.
The Prince from Hoya's faithful hand
  received
The sword; he girt it round the youth,
  and drew   120
And placed it in his hand; unsheathing
  then
His own good falchion, with its burnish'd
  blade
He touch'd Alphonso's neck, and with
  a kiss
Gave him his rank in arms.
                    Thus long the crowd
Had look'd intently on, in silence
  hush'd;
Loud and continuous now with one
  accord,
Shout following shout, their acclamations
  rose;
Blessings were breathed from every
  heart, and joy,
Powerful alike in all, which as with force
Of an inebriating cup inspired   130
The youthful, from the eye of age drew
  tears.
The uproar died away, when standing
  forth,
Roderick with lifted hand besought a
  pause
For speech, and moved towards the
  youth. I too,

Young Baron, he began, must do my
  part;
Not with prerogative of earthly power,
But as the servant of the living God,
The God of Hosts. This day thou
  promisest
To die when honour calls thee for thy
  faith,
For thy liege Lord, and for thy native
  land;   140
The duties which at birth we all con-
  tract,
Are by the high profession of this hour
Made thine especially. Thy noble
  blood,
The thoughts with which thy childhood
  hath been fed,
And thine own noble nature more than
  all,
Are sureties for thee. But these dread-
  ful times
Demand a farther pledge; for it hath
  pleased
The Highest, as he tried his Saints of old,
So in the fiery furnace of his wrath
To prove and purify the sons of Spain;
And they must knit their spirits to the
  proof,   151
Or sink, for ever lost. Hold forth thy
  sword,
Young Baron, and before thy people
  take
The vow which, in Toledo's sacred name,
Poor as these weeds bespeak me, I am
  here
To minister with delegated power.

With reverential awe was Roderick
  heard
By all, so well authority became
That mien and voice and countenance
  austere.
Pelayo with complacent eye beheld 160
The unlook'd-for interposal, and the
  Count

Bends toward Alphonso his approving
   head.
The youth obedient loosen'd from his
   belt
The sword, and looking, while his heart
   beat fast,
To Roderick, reverently expectant stood.

O noble youth, the Royal Goth pur-
   sued,
Thy country is in bonds ; an impious foe
Oppresses her ; he brings with him
   strange laws,
Strange language, evil customs, and
   false faith,
And forces them on Spain. Swear that
   thy soul   170
Will make no covenant with these
   accursed,
But that the sword shall be from this
   day forth
Thy children's portion, to be handed
   down
From sire to son, a sacred heritage,
Through every generation, till the work
Be done, and this insulted land hath
   drunk
In sacrifice, the last invader's blood !

Bear witness, ancient Mountains !
   cried the youth,
And ye, my native Streams, who hold
   your course
For ever ; . . this dear Earth, and yonder
   Sky,   180
Be witness ! for myself I make the vow,
And for my children's children. Here
   . I stand
Their sponsor, binding them in sight of
   Heaven,
As by a new baptismal sacrament,
To wage hereditary holy war,
Perpetual, patient, persevering war,
Till not one living enemy pollute
The sacred soil of Spain.

So as he ceased,
While yet toward the clear blue firma-
   ment
His eyes were raised, he lifted to his lips
The sword, with reverent gesture bending
   then   191
Devoutly kiss'd its cross.

And ye ! exclaimed
Roderick, as turning to the assembled
   troop
He motion'd with authoritative hand, . .
Ye children of the hills and sons of Spain!

Through every heart the rapid feeling
   ran, . .
For us ! they answer'd all with one
   accord,
And at the word they knelt : People
   and Prince,
The young and old, the father and the
   son,
At once they knelt ; with one accord
   they cried,   200
For us, and for our seed ! with one accord
They cross'd their fervent arms, and
   with bent head
Inclined toward that aweful voice from
   whence
The inspiring impulse came. The Royal
   Goth
Made answer, I receive your vow for
   Spain
And for the Lord of Hosts : your cause
   is good,
Go forward in his spirit and his strength.

Ne'er in his happiest hours had
   Roderick
With such commanding majesty dis-
   pensed
His princely gifts, as dignified him now,
When with slow movement, solemnly
   upraised,   211
Toward the kneeling troop he spread
   his arms,

As if the expanded soul diffused itself,
And carried to all spirits with the act
Its effluent inspiration. Silently
The people knelt, and when they rose, such awe
Held them in silence, that the eagle's cry,
Who far above them, at her highest flight
A speck scarce visible, gyred round and round,
Was heard distinctly; and the moun-
tain stream,   220
Which from the distant glen sent forth its sounds
Wafted upon the wind, grew audible
In that deep hush of feeling, like the voice
Of waters in the stillness of the night.

XIII. COUNT EUDON

THAT aweful silence still endured, when one,
Who to the northern entrance of the vale
Had turn'd his casual eye, exclaim'd,
The Moors ! ..
For from the forest verge a troop were seen
Hastening toward Pedro's hall. Their forward speed
Was check'd when they beheld his ban-
ner spread,
And saw his order'd spears in prompt array
Marshall'd to meet their coming. But the pride
Of power and insolence of long com-
mand
Prick'd on their Chief presumptuous :
We are come   10
Late for prevention, cried the haughty Moor,

But never time more fit for punishment !
These unbelieving slaves must feel and know
Their master's arm ! . . On, faithful Musselmen,
On .. on, .. and hew down the rebellious dogs ! . .
Then as he spurr'd his steed, Allah is great !
Mahommed is his Prophet ! he exclaim'd,
And led the charge.
                Count Pedro met the Chief
In full career ; he bore him from his horse
A full spear's length upon the lance transfix'd ;   20
Then leaving in his breast the mortal shaft,
Pass'd on, and breaking through the turban'd files
Open'd a path. Pelayo, who that day
Fought in the ranks afoot, for other war
Yet unequipp'd, pursued and smote the foe,
But ever on Alphonso at his side
Retain'd a watchful eye. The gallant boy
Gave his good sword that hour its earliest taste
Of Moorish blood, . . that sword whose hungry edge
Through the fair course of all his glorious life   30
From that auspicious day, was fed so well.
Cheap was the victory now for Spain achieved ;
For the first fervour of their zeal inspired
The Mountaineers, . . the presence of their Chiefs,
The sight of all dear objects, all dear ties,
The air they breathed, the soil whereon they trod,
Duty, devotion, faith, and hope and joy.
And little had the misbelievers ween'd

In such impetuous onset to receive
A greeting deadly as their own intent ;
Victims they thought to find, not men
    prepared   41
And eager for the fight ; their confidence
Therefore gave way to wonder, and dis-
    may
Effected what astonishment began.
Scatter'd before the impetuous Moun-
    taineers,
Buckler and spear and scymitar they
    dropt,
As in precipitate route they fled before
The Asturian sword : the vales and hills
    and rocks
Received their blood, and where they
    fell the wolves
At evening found them.
          From the fight apart 50
Two Africans had stood, who held in
    charge
Count Eudon. When they saw their
    countrymen
Falter, give way, and fly before the foe,
One turn'd toward him with malignant
    rage,
And saying, Infidel ! thou shalt not live
To join their triumph ! aim'd against his
    neck
The moony falchion's point. His com-
    rade raised
A hasty hand and turn'd its edge aside,
Yet so that o'er the shoulder glancing
    down
It scarr'd him as it pass'd. The mur-
    derous Moor,   60
Not tarrying to secure his vengeance,
    fled ;
While he of milder mood, at Eudon's feet
Fell and embraced his knees. The
    mountaineer
Who found them thus, withheld at
    Eudon's voice
His wrathful hand, and led them to his
    Lord.

Count Pedro and Alphonso and the
    Prince
Stood on a little rocky eminence
Which overlook'd the vale.   Pedro had
    put
His helmet off, and with sonorous horn
Blew the recall ; for well he knew what
    thoughts,   70
Calm as the Prince appear'd and undis-
    turb'd,
Lay underneath his silent fortitude ;
And how at this eventful juncture speed
Imported more than vengeance.   Thrice
    he sent
The long-resounding signal forth, which
    rung
From hill to hill, re-echoing far and
    wide.
Slow and unwillingly his men obey'd
The swelling horn's reiterated call ;
Repining that a single foe escaped
The retribution of that righteous hour.
With lingering step reluctant from the
    chase   81
They turn'd, . . their veins full-swoln,
    their sinews strung
For battle still, their hearts unsatisfied ;
Their swords were dropping still with
    Moorish blood,
And where they wiped their reeking
    brows, the stain
Of Moorish gore was left.   But when
    they came
Where Pedro, with Alphonso at his side,
Stood to behold their coming, then they
    press'd
All emulous, with gratulation round,
Extolling for his deeds that day dis-
    play'd   90
The noble boy. Oh! when had Heaven,
    they said,
With such especial favour manifest
Illustrated a first essay in arms !
They bless'd the father from whose loins
    he sprung,

The mother at whose happy breast he
   fed ;
And pray'd that their young hero's fields
   might be
Many, and all like this.
             Thus they indulged
The honest heart, exuberant of love,
When that loquacious joy at once was
   check'd,
For Eudon and the Moor were brought
   before   100
Count Pedro. Both came fearfully and
   pale,
But with a different fear : the African
Felt at this crisis of his destiny
Such apprehension as without reproach
Might blanch a soldier's cheek, when life
   and death
Hang on another's will, and helplessly
He must abide the issue. But the
   thoughts
Which quail'd Count Eudon's heart, and
   made his limbs
Quiver, were of his own unworthiness,
Old enmity, and that he stood in power
Of hated and hereditary foes.   111
I came not with them willingly ! he
   cried,
Addressing Pedro and the Prince at once,
Rolling from each to each his restless
   eyes
Aghast, . . the Moor can tell I had no
   choice ;
They forced me from my castle : . . in
   the fight
They would have slain me : . . see I
   bleed ! The Moor
Can witness that a Moorish scymitar
Inflicted this : . . he saved me from worse
   hurt : . .
I did not come in arms : . . he knows it
   all ; . .   120
Speak, man, and let the truth be known
   to clear
My innocence !

          Thus as he ceased, with fear
And rapid utterance panting open-
   mouth'd,
Count Pedro half represt a mournful
   smile,
Wherein compassion seem'd to mitigate
His deep contempt. Methinks, said he,
   the Moor
Might with more reason look himself to
   find
An intercessor, than be call'd upon
To play the pleader's part. Didst thou
   then save   129
The Baron from thy comrades ?
                   Let my Lord
Show mercy to me, said the Mussulman,
As I am free from falsehood. We were
   left,
I and another, holding him in charge ;
My fellow would have slain him when he
   saw
How the fight fared : I turn'd the
   scymitar
Aside, and trust that life will be the
   meed
For life by me preserved.
               Nor shall thy trust,
Rejoin'd the Count, be vain. Say
   farther now,
From whence ye came ? . . your orders
   what ? . . what force   139
In Gegio ? and if others like yourselves
Are in the field ?
            The African replied,
We came from Gegio, order'd to secure
This Baron on the way, and seek thee
   here
To bear thee hence in bonds. A mes-
   senger
From Cordoba, whose speed denoted
   well
He came with urgent tidings, was the
   cause
Of this our sudden movement. We
   went forth

Three hundred men; an equal force
    was sent   148
For Cangas, on like errand as I ween.
Four hundred in the city then were left.
If other force be moving from the south,
I know not, save that all appearances
Denote alarm and vigilance.
                    The Prince
Fix'd upon Eudon then his eye severe;
Baron, he said, the die of war is cast;
What part art thou prepared to take?
    against,
Or with the oppressor?
           Not against my friends, . .
Not against you! . . the irresolute wretch
    replied,
Hasty, yet faltering in his fearful speech:
But . . have ye weigh'd it well? . . It is
    not yet   160
Too late, . . their numbers, . . their vic-
    torious force,
Which hath already trodden in the dust
The sceptre of the Goths : . . the throne
    destroy'd, . .
Our towns subdued, . . our country
    overrun, . .
The people to the yoke of their new
    Lords
Resign'd in peace. . . Can I not me-
    diate? . .
Were it not better through my agency
To gain such terms, . . such honourable
    terms. . .

    Terms! cried Pelayo, cutting short at
    once
That dastard speech, and checking, ere
    it grew   170
Too powerful for restraint, the incipient
    wrath
Which in indignant murmurs breathing
    round,
Rose like a gathering storm, learn thou
    what terms
Asturias, this day speaking by my voice,

Doth constitute to be the law between
Thee and thy Country. Our portentous
    age,
As with an earthquake's desolating force,
Hath loosen'd and disjointed the whole
    frame
Of social order, and she calls not now
For service with the force of sovereign
    will.   180
That which was common duty in old
    times,
Becomes an arduous, glorious virtue now;
And every one, as between Hell and
    Heaven,
In free election must be left to chuse.
Asturias asks not of thee to partake
The cup which we have pledged; she
    claims from none
The dauntless fortitude, the mind
    resolved,
Which only God can give; . . therefore
    such peace
As thou canst find where all around is
    war,
She leaves thee to enjoy. But think
    not, Count,   190
That because thou art weak, one valiant
    arm,
One generous spirit must be lost to Spain!
The vassal owes no service to the Lord
Who to his Country doth acknowledge
    none.
The summons which thou hast not heart
    to give,
I and Count Pedro over thy domains
Will send abroad; the vassals who were
    thine
Will fight beneath our banners, and our
    wants
Shall from thy lands, as from a patri-
    mony
Which hath reverted to the common
    stock,   200
Be fed: such tribute, too, as to the
    Moors

Thou renderest, we will take : it is the
    price
Which in this land for weakness must
    be paid
While evil stars prevail.   And mark me,
    Chief !
Fear is a treacherous counsellor ! I know
Thou thinkëst that beneath his horses'
    hoofs
The Moor will trample our poor numbers
    down ;
But join not, in contempt of us and
    Heaven,
His multitudes ! for if thou shouldst be
    found
Against thy country, on the readiest
    tree   210
Those recreant bones shall rattle in the
    wind,
When the birds have left them bare.
               As thus he spake,
Count Eudon heard and trembled :
    every joint
Was loosen'd, every fibre of his flesh
Thrill'd, and from every pore effused,
    cold sweat
Clung on his quivering limbs.   Shame
    forced it forth,
Envy, and inward consciousness, and
    fear
Predominant, which stifled in his heart
Hatred and rage.   Before his livid lips
Could shape to utterance their essay'd
    reply,   220
Compassionately Pedro interposed.
Go, Baron, to the Castle, said the Count ;
There let thy wound be look'd to, and
    consult
Thy better mind at leisure.   Let this
    Moor
Attend upon thee there, and when thou
    wilt,
Follow thy fortunes. . . To Pelayo then
He turn'd, and saying, All-too-long, O
    Prince,

Hath this unlook'd-for conflict held thee
    here, . .
He bade his gallant men begin their
    march.

    Flush'd with success, and in aus-
    picious hour,   230
The Mountaineers set forth.   Blessings
    and prayers
Pursued them at their parting, and the
    tears
Which fell were tears of fervour, not of
    grief.
The sun was verging to the western
    slope
Of Heaven, but they till midnight
    travell'd on ;
Renewing then at early dawn their way,
They held their unremitting course from
    morn
Till latest eve, such urgent cause im-
    pell'd ;
And night had closed around, when to
    the vale
Where Sella in her ampler bed receives
Pionia's stream they came.   Massive
    and black   241
Pelayo's castle there was seen ; its lines
And battlements against the deep blue
    sky
Distinct in solid darkness visible.
No light is in the tower.   Eager to know
The worst, and with that fatal certainty
To terminate intolerable dread,
He spurr'd his courser forward.   All his
    fears
Too surely are fulfill'd, . . for open
    stand
The doors, and mournfully at times
    a dog   250
Fills with his howling the deserted hall.
A moment overcome with wretchedness,
Silent Pelayo stood ! recovering then,
Lord God, resign'd he cried, thy will be
    done !

XIV. THE RESCUE

Count, said Pelayo, Nature hath
    assign'd
Two sovereign remedies for human
    grief ;
Religion, surest, firmest, first and best,
Strength to the weak and to the wounded
    balm ;
And strenuous action next.   Think not
    I came
With unprovided heart.   My noble wife,
In the last solemn words, the last fare-
    well
With which she charged her secret mes-
    senger,
Told me that whatsoe'er was my resolve,
She bore a mind prepared.   And well
    I know   10
The evil, be it what it may, hath found
In her a courage equal to the hour.
Captivity, or death, or what worse pangs,
She in her children may be doom'd to
    feel,
Will never make that steady soul repent
Its virtuous purpose.   I too did not
    cast
My single life into the lot, but knew
These dearer pledges on the die were set ;
And if the worst have fallen, I shall but
    bear
That in my breast, which, with trans-
    figuring power   20
Of piety, makes chastening sorrow take
The form of hope, and sees, in Death,
    the friend
And the restoring Angel.   We must rest
Perforce, and wait what tidings night
    may bring,
Haply of comfort.   Ho there ! kindle
    fires,
And see if aught of hospitality
Can yet within these mournful walls be
    found !

Thus   while   he   spake,   lights   were
    descried far off
Moving among the trees, and coming
    sounds
Were heard as of a distant multitude. 30
Anon a company of horse and foot,
Advancing in disorderly array,
Came up the vale, before them and
    beside
Their torches flashed on Sella's rippling
    stream ;
Now gleam'd through chesnut groves,
    emerging now,
O'er their huge boughs and radiated
    leaves
Cast broad and bright a transitory glare.
That sight inspired with strength the
    mountaineers ;
All sense of weariness, all wish for
    rest
At once were gone ; impatient in desire
Of second victory alert they stood ;   41
And when the hostile symbols, which
    from far
Imagination to their wish had shaped,
Vanish'd in nearer vision, high-wrought
    hope
Departing, left the spirit pall'd and
    blank.
No turban'd race, no sons of Africa
Were they who now came winding up
    the vale,
As waving wide before their horses' feet
The torch-light floated, with its hovering
    glare
Blackening the incumbent and sur-
    rounding night.   50
Helmet and breast-plate glitter'd as
    they came,
And spears erect ; and nearer as they
    drew
Were the loose folds of female garments
    seen
On those who led the company.   Who
    then

Had stood beside Pelayo, might have
heard
The beating of his heart.
                    But vainly there
Sought he with wistful eye the well-
known forms
Beloved ; and plainly might it now be
seen
That from some bloody conflict they
return'd
Victorious, . . for at every saddle-bow 60
A gory head was hung. Anon they
stopt,
Levelling in quick alarm their ready
spears.
Hold ! who goes there ? cried one. A
hundred tongues
Sent forth with one accord the glad reply,
Friends and Asturians. Onward moved
the lights, . .
The people knew their Lord.
                    Then what a shout
Rung through the valley ! From their
clay-built nests,
Beneath the overbrowing battlements,
Now first disturb'd, the affrighted mar-
tins flew,
And uttering notes of terror short and
shrill,   70
Amid the yellow glare and lurid smoke
Wheel'd giddily. Then plainly was it
shown
How well the vassals loved their generous
Lord,
How like a father the Asturian Prince
Was dear. They crowded round ; they
claspt his knees ;
They snatch'd his hand ; they fell upon
his neck, . .
They wept ; . . they blest Almighty
Providence,
Which had restored him thus from
bondage free ;
God was with them and their good cause,
they said ;

His hand was here. . . His shield was
over them, . .   80
His spirit was abroad, . . His power dis-
play'd :
And pointing to their bloody trophies
then,
They told Pelayo there he might behold
The first-fruits of the harvest they should
soon
Reap in the field of war ! Benignantly,
With voice and look and gesture, did the
Prince
To these warm greetings of tumultuous
joy
Respond ; and sure if at that moment
aught
Could for a while have overpower'd
those fears
Which from the inmost heart o'er all his
frame   90
Diffused their chilling influence, worthy
pride,
And sympathy of love and joy and
hope,
Had then possess'd him wholly. Even
now
His spirit rose ; the sense of power, the
sight
Of his brave people, ready where he led
To fight their country's battles, and the
thought
Of instant action, and deliverance, . .
If Heaven, which thus far had protected
him,
Should favour still, . . revived his heart,
and gave
Fresh impulse to its spring. In vain
he sought   100
Amid that turbulent greeting to enquire
Where Gaudiosa was, his children where,
Who call'd them to the field, who cap-
tain'd them ;
And how these women, thus with arms
and death
Environ'd, came amid their company ?

For yet, amid the fluctuating light
And tumult of the crowd, he knew them
      not.

Guisla was one. The Moors had
      found in her
A willing and concerted prisoner.
Gladly to Gegio, to the renegade   110
On whom her loose and shameless love
      was bent,
Had she set forth ; and in her heart she
      cursed
The busy spirit, who, with powerful call
Rousing Pelayo's people, led them on
In quick pursual, and victoriously
Achieved the rescue, to her mind per-
      verse
Unwelcome as unlook'd for. With dis-
      may
She recognized her brother, dreaded now
More than he once was dear ; her coun-
      tenance
Was turn'd toward him, . . not with
      eager joy   120
To court his sight, and meeting its first
      glance,
Exchange delightful welcome, soul with
      soul ;
Hers was the conscious eye, that cannot
      chuse
But look to what it fears. She could
      not shun
His presence, and the rigid smile con-
      strain'd,
With which she coldly drest her features,
      ill
Conceal'd her inward thoughts, and the
      despite
Of obstinate guilt and unrepentant
      shame.
Sullenly thus upon her mule she sate,
Waiting the greeting which she did not
      dare   130
Bring on.   But who is she that at her
      side,

Upon a stately war-horse eminent,
Holds the loose rein with careless hand ?
      A helm
Presses the clusters of her flaxen hair ;
The shield is on her arm ; her breast is
      mail'd ;
A sword-belt is her girdle, and right
      well
It may be seen that sword hath done
      its work
To-day, for upward from the wrist her
      sleeve
Is stiff with blood.   An unregardant eye,
As one whose thoughts were not of
      earth, she cast   140
Upon the turmoil round.   One coun-
      tenance
So strongly mark'd, so passion-worn
      was there,
That it recall'd her mind. Ha ! Mac-
      cabee !
Lifting her arm, exultingly she cried,
Did I not tell thee we should meet in joy ?
Well, Brother, hast thou done thy part,
      . . I too
Have not been wanting ! Now be His
      the praise,
From whom the impulse came !
                        That startling call,
That voice so well remember'd, touch'd
      the Goth
With timely impulse now ; for he had
      seen   150
His Mother's face, . . and at her sight,
      the past
And present mingled like a frightful
      dream,
Which from some dread reality derives
Its deepest horror.   Adosinda's voice
Dispersed the waking vision. Little
      deem'd
Rusilla at that moment that the child,
For whom her supplications day and night
Were offer'd, breathed the living air.
      Her heart

Was calm; her placid countenance,
  though grief
Deeper than time had left its traces
  there,   160
Retain'd its dignity serene; yet when
Siverian, pressing through the people,
  kiss'd
Her reverend hand, some quiet tears ran
  down.
As she approach'd the Prince, the crowd
  made way
Respectful. The maternal smile which
  bore
Her greeting, from Pelayo's heart at
  once
Dispell'd its boding. What he would
  have asked
She knew, and bending from her palfrey
  down,
Told him that they for whom he look'd
  were safe,
And that in secret he should hear the
  rest.   170

XV. RODERICK AT CANGAS

How calmly gliding through the dark-
  blue sky
The midnight Moon ascends! Her
  placid beams
Through thinly scatter'd leaves and
  boughs grotesque,
Mottle with mazy shades the orchard
  slope;
Here, o'er the chesnut's fretted foliage
  grey
And massy, motionless they spread;
  here shine
Upon the crags, deepening with blacker
  night
Their chasms; and there the glittering
  argentry
Ripples and glances on the confluent
  streams.   9

A lovelier, purer light than that of day
Rests on the hills; and oh how awefully
Into that deep and tranquil firmament
The summits of Auseva rise serene!
The watchman on the battlements par-
  takes
The stillness of the solemn hour; he
  feels
The silence of the earth, the endless
  sound
Of flowing water soothes him, and the
  stars,
Which in that brightest moon-light well-
  nigh quench'd,
Scarce visible, as in the utmost depth
Of yonder sapphire infinite, are seen,
Draw on with elevating influence   21
Toward eternity the attemper'd mind.
Musing on worlds beyond the grave he
  stands,
And to the Virgin Mother silently
Prefers her hymn of praise.
                        The mountaineers
Before the castle, round their mouldering
  fires,
Lie on the hearth outstretch'd. Pelayo's
  hall
Is full, and he upon his careful couch
Hears all around the deep and long-
  drawn breath
Of sleep: for gentle night hath brought
  to these   30
Perfect and undisturb'd repose, alike
Of corporal powers and inward faculty.
Wakeful the while he lay, yet more by
  hope
Than grief or anxious thoughts pos-
  sess'd, .. though grief
For Guisla's guilt, which freshen'd in
  his heart
The memory of their wretched mother's
  crime,
Still made its presence felt, like the dull
  sense
Of some perpetual inward malady;

And the whole peril of the future lay
Before him clearly seen.   He had heard
   all ;   40
How that unworthy sister, obstinate
In wrong and shameless, rather seem'd
   to woo
The upstart renegado than to wait
His wooing ; how, as guilt to guilt led
   on,
Spurning at gentle admonition first,
When Gaudiosa hopelessly forbore
From farther counsel, then in sullen
   mood
Resentful, Guisla soon began to hate
The virtuous presence before which she
   felt
Her nature how inferior, and her fault 50
How foul.   Despiteful thus she grew,
   because
Humbled yet unrepentant.   Who could
   say
To what excess bad passions might impel
A woman thus possess'd ? She could not
   fail
To mark Siverian's absence, for what
   end
Her conscience but too surely had di-
   vined ;
And Gaudiosa, well aware that all
To the vile paramour was thus made
   known,
Had to safe hiding-place with timely
   fear
Removed her children.   Well the event
   had proved   60
How needful was that caution ; for at
   night
She sought the mountain solitudes, and
   morn
Beheld Numacian's soldiers at the gate.
Yet did not sorrow in Pelayo's heart
For this domestic shame prevail that
   hour,
Nor gathering danger weigh his spirit
   down.

The anticipated meeting put to flight
These painful thoughts ; to-morrow will
   restore
All whom his heart holds dear ; his wife
   beloved,
No longer now remember'd for regret, 70
Is present to his soul with hope and joy ;
His inward eye beholds Favila's form
In opening youth robust, and Hermesind,
His daughter, lovely as a budding rose ;
Their images beguile the hours of night,
Till with the earliest morning he may
   seek
Their secret hold.
            The nightingale not yet
Had ceased her song, nor had the early
   lark
Her dewy nest forsaken, when the Prince
Upward beside Pionia took his way   80
Toward Auseva.   Heavily to him,
Impatient for the morrow's happiness,
Long night had linger'd, but it seem'd
   more long
To Roderick's aching heart.   He too
   had watch'd
For dawn, and seen the earliest break of
   day,
And heard its earliest sounds; and when
   the Prince
Went forth, the melancholy man was
   seen
With pensive pace upon Pionia's side
Wandering alone and slow.   For he had
   left
The wearying place of his unrest, that
   morn   90
With its cold dews might bathe his
   throbbing brow,
And with its breath allay the feverish
   heat
That burnt within.   Alas ! the gales of
   morn
Reach not the fever of a wounded heart !
How shall he meet his Mother's eye, how
   make

His secret known, and from that voice
  revered
Obtain forgiveness, . . all that he has
  now
To ask, ere on the lap of earth in peace
He lay his head resign'd ? In silent
  prayer
He supplicated Heaven to strengthen
  him   100
Against that trying hour, there seeking
  aid
Where all who seek shall find ; and thus
  his soul
Received support, and gather'd forti-
  tude,
Never than now more needful, for the
  hour
Was nigh. He saw Siverian drawing
  near,
And with a dim but quick foreboding met
The good old man ; yet when he heard
  him say,
My Lady sends to seek thee, like a knell
To one expecting and prepared for
  death,
But fearing the dread point that hastens
  on,   110
It smote his heart. He follow'd silently
And knit his suffering spirit to the proof.

He went resolved to tell his Mother all,
Fall at her feet, and drinking the last
  dregs
Of bitterness, receive the only good
Earth had in store for him. Resolved
  for this
He went ; yet was it a relief to find
That painful resolution must await
A fitter season, when no eye but Heaven's
Might witness to their mutual agony. 120
Count Julian's daughter with Rusilla
  sate ;
Both had been weeping, both were pale,
  but calm.
With head as for humility abased

Roderick approach'd, and bending, on
  his breast
He cross'd his humble arms. Rusilla rose
In reverence to the priestly character,
And with a mournful eye regarding him,
Thus she began. Good Father, I have
  heard
From my old faithful servant and true
  friend,
Thou didst reprove the inconsiderate
  tongue,   130
That in the anguish of its spirit pour'd
A curse upon my poor unhappy child.
O Father Maccabee, this is a hard world,
And hasty in its judgements ! Time has
  been,
When not a tongue within the Pyrenees
Dared whisper in dispraise of Roderick's
  name,
Lest, if the conscious air had caught the
  sound,
The vengeance of the honest multitude
Should fall upon the traitorous head, or
  brand
For life-long infamy the lying lips. 140
Now if a voice be raised in his behalf,
'Tis noted for a wonder, and the man
Who utters the strange speech shall be
  admired
For such excess of Christian charity.
Thy Christian charity hath not been
  lost ; . .
Father, I feel its virtue : . . it hath been
Balm to my heart ; . . with words and
  grateful tears, . .
All that is left me now for gratitude, . .
I thank thee, and beseech thee in thy
  prayers
That thou wilt still remember Roderick's
  name.   150

  Roderick so long had to this hour
  look'd on,
That when the actual point of trial
  came,

Torpid and numb'd it found him ; cold
    he grew,
And as the vital spirits to the heart
Retreated, o'er his wither'd countenance,
Deathy and damp, a whiter paleness
    spread.
Unmoved the while, the inward feeling
    seem'd,
Even in such dull insensibility
As gradual age brings on, or slow disease,
Beneath whose progress lingering life
    survives   160
The power of suffering. Wondering
    at himself,
Yet gathering confidence, he raised his
    eyes,
Then slowly shaking as he bent his head,
O venerable Lady, he replied,
If aught may comfort that unhappy
    soul,
It must be thy compassion, and thy
    prayers.
She whom he most hath wrong'd, she
    who alone
On earth can grant forgiveness for his
    crime,
She hath forgiven him ; and thy
    blessing now
Were all that he could ask, . . all that
    could bring   170
Profit or consolation to his soul,
If he hath been, as sure we may believe,
A penitent sincere.
                    Oh had he lived,
Replied Rusilla, never penitence
Had equall'd his ! full well I know his
    heart,
Vehement in all things. He would on
    himself
Have wreak'd such penance as had
    reach'd the height
Of fleshly suffering . . yea, which being
    told
With its portentous rigour should have
    made

The memory of his fault, o'erpower'd
    and lost   180
In shuddering pity and astonishment,
Fade like a feebler horror.   Otherwise
Seem'd good to Heaven. I murmur not,
    nor doubt
The boundless mercy of redeeming love.
For sure I trust that not in his offence
Harden'd and reprobate was my lost
    son,
A child of wrath, cut off ! . . that dread-
    ful thought,
Not even amid the first fresh wretched-
    ness,
When the ruin burst around me like a
    flood,
Assail'd my soul.   I ever deem'd his
    fall   190
An act of sudden madness ; and this day
Hath in unlook'd-for confirmation given
A livelier hope, a more assuréd faith.
Smiling benignant then amid her tears,
She took Florinda by the hand, and
    said,
I little thought that I should live to bless
Count Julian's daughter !   She hath
    brought to me
The last, the best, the only comfort
    earth
Could minister to this afflicted heart,
And my grey hairs may now unto the
    grave   200
Go down in peace.
                    Happy, Florinda cried,
Are they for whom the grave hath peace
    in store !
The wrongs they have sustain'd, the
    woes they bear,
Pass not that holy threshold, where
    Death heals
The broken heart.   O Lady, thou
    may'st trust
In humble hope, through Him who on
    the Cross
Gave his atoning blood for lost mankind,

To meet beyond the grave thy child
     forgiven.
I too with Roderick there may inter-
     change
Forgiveness.   But the grief which
     wastes away   210
This mortal frame, hastening the happy
     hour
Of my enlargement, is but a light part
Of what my soul endures ! . . that grief
     hath lost
Its sting : . . I have a keener sorrow
     here, . .
One which, . . but God forefend that dire
     event, . .
May pass with me the portals of the grave,
And with a thought, like sin which can-
     not die,
Embitter Heaven.   My father hath
     renounced
His hope in Christ ! It was his love for me
Which drove him to perdition. . . I was
     born   220
To ruin all who loved me, . . all I loved !
Perhaps I sinn'd in leaving him ; . . that
     fear
Rises within me to disturb the peace
Which I should else have found.
               To Roderick then
The pious mourner turn'd her suppliant
     eyes :
O Father, there is virtue in thy prayers! . .
I do beseech thee offer them to Heaven
In his behalf ! For Roderick's sake, for
     mine,
Wrestle with Him whose name is Merci-
     ful,
That Julian may with penitence be
     touch'd,   230
And clinging to the Cross, implore that
     grace
Which ne'er was sought in vain.   For
     Roderick's sake
And mine, pray for him ! We have been
     the cause

Of his offence ! What other miseries
May from that same unhappy source
     have risen,
Are earthly, temporal, reparable all ; . .
But if a soul be lost through our mis-
     deeds,
That were eternal evil ! Pray for him,
Good Father Maccabee, and be thy
     prayers
More fervent, as the deeper is the crime.

     While thus Florinda spake, the dog
     who lay   241
Before Rusilla's feet, eyeing him long
And wistfully, had recognized at length,
Changed as he was and in those sordid
     weeds,
His royal master.   And he rose and
     lick'd
His wither'd hand, and earnestly look'd
     up
With eyes whose human meaning did
     not need
The aid of speech ; and moan'd, as if at
     once
To court and chide the long-withheld
     caress.
A feeling uncommix'd with sense of
     guilt   250
Or shame, yet painfulest, thrill'd through
     the King ;
But he to self-controul now long inured,
Represt his rising heart, nor other tears,
Full as his struggling bosom was, let fall
Than seem'd to follow on Florinda's
     words.
Looking toward her then, yet so that still
He shunn'd the meeting of her eye, he
     said,
Virtuous and pious as thou art, and ripe
For Heaven, O Lady, I must think the
     man
Hath not by his good Angel been cast off
For whom thy supplications rise.   The
     Lord   261

Whose justice doth in its unerring course
Visit the children for the sire's offence,
Shall He not in his boundless mercy hear
The daughter's prayer, and for her sake restore
The guilty parent ? My soul shall with thine
In earnest and continual duty join. . .
How deeply, how devoutly, He will know
To whom the cry is raised.
                        Thus having said,
Deliberately, in self-possession still, 270
Himself from that most painful interview
Dispeeding, he withdrew. The watchful dog
Follow'd his footsteps close. But he retired
Into the thickest grove ; there yielding way
To his o'erburthen'd nature, from all eyes
Apart, he cast himself upon the ground,
And threw his arms around the dog, and cried,
While tears stream'd down, Thou, Theron, then hast known
Thy poor lost master, . . Theron, none but thou !

XVI. COVADONGA

MEANTIME Pelayo up the vale pursued
Eastward his way, before the sun had climb'd
Auseva's brow, or shed his silvering beams
Upon Europa's summit, where the snows
Through all revolving seasons hold their seat.
A happy man he went, his heart at rest,
Of hope and virtue and affection full,
To all exhilarating influences

Of earth and heaven alive. With kindred joy
He heard the lark, who from her airy height,   10
On twinkling pinions poised, pour'd forth profuse,
In thrilling sequence of exuberant song,
As one whose joyous nature overflow'd
With life and power, her rich and rapturous strain.
The early bee, buzzing along the way,
From flower to flower, bore gladness on its wing
To his rejoicing sense ; and he pursued,
With quicken'd eye alert, the frolic hare,
Where from the green herb in her wanton path
She brush'd away the dews. For he long time,   20
Far from his home and from his native hills,
Had dwelt in bondage ; and the mountain breeze,
Which he had with the breath of infancy
Inhaled, such impulse to his heart restored,
As if the seasons had roll'd back, and life
Enjoy'd a second spring.
                        Through fertile fields
He went, by cots with pear-trees overbower'd,
Or spreading to the sun their trelliced vines ;
Through orchards now, and now by thymy banks,
Where wooden hives in some warm nook were hid   30
From wind and shower ; and now thro' shadowy paths,
Where hazels fringed Pionia's vocal stream ;
Till where the loftier hills to narrower bound
Confine the vale, he reach'd those huts remote

Which should hereafter to the noble
  line
Of Soto origin and name impart:
A gallant lineage, long in fields of war
And faithful chronicler's enduring page
Blazon'd: but most by him illustrated,
Avid of gold, yet greedier of renown,   40
Whom not the spoils of Atabalipa
Could satisfy insatiate,[1] nor the fame
Of that wide empire overthrown appease;
But he to Florida's disastrous shores
In evil hour his gallant comrades led,
Through savage woods and swamps, and
  hostile tribes,
The Apalachian arrows, and the snares
Of wilier foes, hunger, and thirst, and
  toil;
Till from ambition's feverish dream the
  touch
Of Death awoke him; and when he had
  seen   50
The fruit of all his treasures, all his toil,
Foresight, and long endurance, fade
  away,
Earth to the restless one refusing rest,
In the great river's midland bed he left
His honour'd bones.
                 A mountain rivulet,
Now calm and lovely in its summer
  course,
Held by those huts its everlasting way
Towards Pionia. They whose flocks
  and herds
Drink of its water call it Deva. Here
Pelayo southward up the ruder vale   60
Traced it, his guide unerring. Amid
  heaps
Of mountain wreck, on either side
  thrown high,
The wide-spread traces of its wintry
  might,
The tortuous channel wound; o'er beds
  of sand

Here silently it flows; here from the
  rock
Rebutted, curls and eddies; plunges here
Precipitate; here roaring among crags,
It leaps and foams and whirls and
  hurries on.
Grey alders here and bushy hazels hid
The mossy side; their wreath'd and
  knotted feet   70
Bared by the current, now against its
  force
Repaying the support they found, up-
  held
The bank secure. Here, bending to
  the stream,
The birch fantastic stretch'd its rugged
  trunk,
Tall and erect, from whence, as from
  their base,
Each like a tree, its silver branches grew.
The cherry here hung for the birds of
  heaven
Its rosy fruit on high. The elder there
Its purple berries o'er the water bent,
Heavily hanging. Here, amid the
  brook,   80
Grey as the stone to which it clung, half
  root,
Half trunk, the young ash rises from the
  rock;
And there its parent lifts a lofty head,
And spreads its graceful boughs; the
  passing wind
With twinkling motion lifts the silent
  leaves,
And shakes its rattling tufts.
                        Soon had the Prince
Behind him left the farthest dwelling-
  place
Of man; no fields of waving corn were
  here,
Nor wicker storehouse for the autumnal
  grain;
Vineyard, nor bowery fig, nor fruitful
  grove;   90

[1] Hernando de Soto (S.).

Only the rocky vale, the mountain stream,
Incumbent crags, and hills that over hills
Arose on either hand, here hung with woods,
Here rich with heath, that o'er some smooth ascent
Its purple glory spread, or golden gorse;
Bare here, and striated with many a hue,
Scored by the wintry rain; by torrents here
Riven, and with overhanging rocks abrupt.
Pelayo, upward as he cast his eyes
Where crags loose-hanging o'er the narrow pass   100
Impended, there beheld his country's strength
Insuperable, and in his heart rejoiced.
Oh that the Musselman were here, he cried,
With all his myriads! While thy day endures,
Moor! thou may'st lord it in the plains; but here
Hath Nature for the free and brave prepared
A sanctuary, where no oppressor's power,
No might of human tyranny can pierce.

The tears which started then sprang not alone   109
From lofty thoughts of elevating joy;
For love and admiration had their part,
And virtuous pride. Here then thou hast retired,
My Gaudiosa! in his heart he said;
Excellent woman! ne'er was richer boon
By fate benign to favour'd man indulged,
Than when thou wert before the face of Heaven
Given me to be my children's mother, brave

And virtuous as thou art! Here thou hast fled,
Thou who wert nurst in palaces, to dwell
In rocks and mountain caves! . . The thought was proud,   120
Yet not without a sense of inmost pain;
For never had Pelayo till that hour
So deeply felt the force of solitude.
High over head the eagle soar'd serene,
And the grey lizard on the rocks below
Bask'd in the sun: no living creature else
In this remotest wilderness was seen;
Nor living voice was there, . . only the flow
Of Deva, and the rushing of its springs
Long in the distance heard, which nearer now,   130
With endless repercussion deep and loud,
Throbb'd on the dizzy sense.
                    The ascending vale,
Long straiten'd by the narrowing mountains, here
Was closed. In front a rock, abrupt and bare,
Stood eminent, in height exceeding far
All edifice of human power, by King
Or Caliph, or barbaric Sultan rear'd,
Or mightier tyrants of the world of old,
Assyrian or Egyptian, in their pride;
Yet far above, beyond the reach of sight,
Swell after swell, the heathery mountain rose.   141
Here, in two sources, from the living rock
The everlasting springs of Deva gush'd.
Upon a smooth and grassy plat below,
By Nature there as for an altar drest,
They join'd their sister stream, which from the earth
Well'd silently. In such a scene rude man
With pardonable error might have knelt,
Feeling a present Deity, and made
His offering to the fountain Nymph devout.   150

The arching rock disclosed above the
    springs
A cave, where hugest son of giant birth,
That o'er of old in forest of romance
'Gainst knights and ladies waged dis-
    courteous war,
Erect within the portal might have stood.
The broken stone allow'd for hand and
    foot
No difficult ascent, above the base
In height a tall man's stature, measured
    thrice.
No holier spot than Covadonga Spain
Boasts in her wide extent, though all her
    realms   160
Be with the noblest blood of martyrdom
In elder or in later days enrich'd,
And glorified with tales of heavenly aid
By many a miracle made manifest;
Nor in the heroic annals of her fame
Doth she show forth a scene of more
    renown.
Then, save the hunter, drawn in keen
    pursuit
Beyond his wonted haunts, or shepherd's
    boy,
Following the pleasure of his straggling
    flock,
None knew the place.
                Pelayo, when he saw   170
Those glittering sources and their sacred
    cave,
Took from his side the bugle silver-tipt,
And with a breath long drawn and slow
    expired
Sent forth that strain, which, echoing
    from the walls
Of Cangas, wont to tell his glad return
When from the chace he came.   At the
    first sound
Favila started in the cave, and cried,
My father's horn! . . A sudden flush
    suffused
Hermesind's cheek, and she with
    quicken'd eye

Look'd eager to her mother silently; 180
But Gaudiosa trembled and grew pale,
Doubting her sense deceived.   A second
    time
The bugle breathed its well-known notes
    abroad;
And Hermesind around her mother's
    neck
Threw her white arms, and earnestly
    exclaim'd,
'Tis he ! . . But when a third and broader
    blast
Rung in the echoing archway, ne'er did
    wand,
With magic power endued, call up a
    sight
So strange, as sure in that wild solitude
It seem'd, when from the bowels of the
    rock   190
The mother and her children hasten'd
    forth;
She in the sober charms and dignity
Of womanhood mature, nor verging yet
Upon decay; in gesture like a Queen,
Such inborn and habitual majesty
Ennobled all her steps, . . or Priestess,
    chosen
Because within such faultless work of
    Heaven
Inspiring Deity might seem to make
Its habitation known. . . Favila such
In form and stature as the Sea Nymph's
    son,   200
When that wise Centaur from his cave
    well-pleased
Beheld the boy divine his growing
    strength
Against some shaggy lionet essay,
And fixing in the half-grown mane his
    hands,
Roll with him in fierce dalliance inter-
    twined.
But like a creature of some higher sphere
His sister came; she scarcely touch'd
    the rock,

So light was Hermesind's aërial speed.
Beauty and grace and innocence in her
In heavenly union shone.   One who had
　　held   210
The faith of elder Greece, would sure
　　have thought
She was some glorious nymph of seed
　　divino,
Oread or Dryad, of Diana's train
The youngest and the loveliest : yea,
　　she seem'd
Angel, or soul beatified, from realms
Of bliss, on errand of parental love
To earth re-sent, . . if tears and trem-
　　bling limbs
With such celestial natures might con-
　　sist.

　　Embraced by all, in turn embracing
　　each,   219
The husband and the father for awhile
Forgot his country and all things beside :
Life hath few moments of such pure
　　delight,
Such foretaste of the perfect joy of
　　Heaven.
And when the thought recurr'd of suffer-
　　ings past,
Perils which threaten'd still, and ardu-
　　ous toil
Yet to be undergone, remember'd griefs
Heighten'd the present happiness ; and
　　hope
Upon the shadows of futurity
Shone like the sun upon the morning
　　mists,
When driven before his rising rays they
　　roll,   230
And melt and leave the prospect bright
　　and clear.

　　When now Pelayo's eyes had drunk
　　their fill
Of love from those dear faces, he went
　　up

To view the hiding-place.   Spacious it
　　was
As that Sicilian cavern in the hill
Wherein earth-shaking Neptune's giant
　　son
Duly at eve was wont to fold his flock,
Ere the wise Ithacan, over that brute
　　force
By wiles prevailing, for a life-long night
Seel'd his broad eye.   The healthful air
　　had here   240
Free entrance, and the cheerful light of
　　heaven ;
But at the end, an opening in the floor
Of rock disclosed a wider vault below,
Which never sun-beam visited, nor
　　breath
Of vivifying morning came to cheer.
No light was there but that which from
　　above
In dim reflection fell, or found its way,
Broken and quivering, through the
　　glassy stream,
Where through the rock it gush'd.   That
　　shadowy light
Sufficed to show, where from their secret
　　bed   250
The waters issued ; with whose rapid
　　course,
And with whose everlasting cataracts
Such motion to the chill damp atmo-
　　sphere
Was given, as if the solid walls of rock
Were shaken with the sound.
　　　　　　　　　　　　Glad to respire
The upper air, Pelayo hasten'd back
From that drear den.   Look ! Herme-
　　sind exclaim'd,
Taking her father's hand, thou hast not
　　seen
My chamber : . . See ! . . did ever ring-
　　dove chuse
In so secure a nook her hiding-place, 260
Or build a warmer nest ?   'Tis fragrant
　　too,

As warm, and not more sweet than soft;
  for thyme
And myrtle with the elastic heath are
  laid,
And, over all, this dry and pillowy
  moss. . .
Smiling she spake. Pelayo kiss'd the
  child,
And, sighing, said within himself, I trust
In Heaven, whene'er thy May of life is
  come,
Sweet bird, that thou shalt have a
  blither bower !
Fitlier, he thought, such chamber might
  beseem   269
Some hermit of Hilarion's school austere,
Or old Antonius, he who from the hell
Of his bewilder'd phantasy saw fiends
In actual vision, a foul throng grotesque
Of all horrific shapes and forms obscene
Crowd in broad day before his open eyes.
That feeling cast a momentary shade
Of sadness o'er his soul. But deeper
  thoughts,
If he might have foreseen the things to
  come,
Would there have fill'd him; for within
  that cave
His own remains were one day doom'd
  to find   280
Their final place of rest; and in that spot,
Where that dear child with innocent
  delight
Had spread her mossy couch, the
  sepulchre
Shall in the consecrated rock be hewn,
Where with Alphonso, her beloved lord,
Laid side by side, must Hermesind par-
  take
The everlasting marriage-bed, when he,
Leaving a name perdurable on earth,
Hath changed his earthly for a heavenly
  crown.
Dear child, upon that fated spot she
  stood,   290

In all the beauty of her opening youth,
In health's rich bloom, in virgin inno-
  cence,
While her eyes sparkled and her heart
  o'erflow'd
With pure and perfect joy of filial love.

Many a slow century since that day
  hath fill'd
Its course, and countless multitudes
  have trod
With pilgrim feet that consecrated cave;
Yet not in all those ages, amid all
The untold concourse, hath one breast
  been swoln
With such emotions as Pelayo felt   300
That hour. O Gaudiosa, he exclaim'd,
And thou couldst seek for shelter here,
  amid
This aweful solitude, in mountain caves !
Thou noble spirit ! Oh when hearts like
  thine
Grow on this sacred soil, would it not be
In me, thy husband, double infamy,
And tenfold guilt, if I despair'd of Spain ?
In all her visitations, favouring Heaven
Hath left her still the unconquerable
  mind ;
And thus being worthy of redemption,
  sure   310
Is she to be redeem'd.
                     Beholding her
Through tears he spake, and prest upon
  her lips
A kiss of deepest love. Think ever thus,
She answer'd, and that faith will give
  the power
In which it trusts. When to this moun-
  tain hold
These children, thy dear images, I
  brought,
I said within myself, where should they
  fly
But to the bosom of their native hills ?
I brought them here as to a sanctuary,

Where, for the temple's sake, the in-
dwelling God   320
Would guard his supplicants. O my
dear Lord,
Proud as I was to know that they were
thine,
Was it a sin if I almost believed,
That Spain, her destiny being link'd
with theirs,
Must save the precious charge ?
                            So let us think,
The Chief replied, so feel and teach and
act.
Spain is our common parent : let the
sons
Be to the parent true, and in her
strength
And Heaven, their sure deliverance
they will find.

XVII. RODERICK AND SIVERIAN

O HOLIEST Mary, Maid and Mother !
thou
In Covadonga, at thy rocky shrine,
Hast witness'd whatsoe'er of human bliss
Heart can conceive most perfect ! Faith-
ful love,
Long crost by envious stars, hath there
attain'd
Its crown, in endless matrimony given ;
The youthful mother there hath to the
font
Her first-born borne, and there, with
deeper sense
Of gratitude for that dear babe redeem'd
From threatening death, return'd to
pay her vows.   10
But ne'er on nuptial, nor baptismal day,
Nor from their grateful pilgrimage dis-
charged,
Did happier group their way down
Deva's vale

Rejoicing hold, than this blest family,
O'er whom the mighty Spirit of the
Land
Spread his protecting wings. The chil-
dren, free
In youthhead's happy season from all
cares
That might disturb the hour, yet
capable
Of that intense and unalloy'd delight
Which childhood feels when it enjoys
again   20
The dear parental presence long de-
prived ;
Nor were the parents now less bless'd
than they,
Even to the height of human happiness ;
For Gaudiosa and her Lord that hour
Let no misgiving thoughts intrude ; she
fix'd
Her hopes on him, and his were fix'd on
Heaven ;
And hope in that courageous heart
derived
Such rooted strength and confidence
assured
In righteousness, that 'twas to him like
faith . .
An everlasting sunshine of the soul,   30
Illumining and quickening all its powers.

But on Pionia's side meantime a heart
As generous, and as full of noble
thoughts,
Lay stricken with the deadliest bolts of
grief.
Upon a smooth grey stone sate Roderick
there ;
The wind above him stirr'd the hazel
boughs,
And murmuring at his feet the river ran.
He sate with folded arms and head de-
clined
Upon his breast feeding on bitter
thoughts,

Till nature gave him in the exhausted
    sense   40
Of woe a respite something like repose ;
And then the quiet sound of gentle winds
And waters with their lulling consonance
Beguiled him of himself. Of all within
Oblivious there he sate, sentient alone
Of outward nature, . . of the whispering
    leaves
That soothed his ear, . . the genial
    breath of Heaven
That fann'd his cheek, . . the stream's
    perpetual flow,
That, with its shadows and its glancing
    lights,
Dimples and thread-like motions in-
    finite,   50
For ever varying and yet still the same,
Like time toward eternity, ran by.
Resting his head upon his master's knees,
Upon the bank beside him Theron lay.
What matters change of state and cir-
    cumstance,
Or lapse of years, with all their dread
    events,
To him ? What matters it that Roderick
    wears
The crown no longer, nor the sceptre
    wields ? . .
It is the dear-loved hand, whose friendly
    touch
Had flatter'd him so oft ; it is the voice,
At whose glad summons to the field so
    oft   61
From slumber he had started, shaking off
Dreams of the chace, to share the actual
    joy ;
The eye, whose recognition he was wont
To watch and welcome with exultant
    tongue.

A coming step, unheard by Roderick,
    roused
His watchful ear, and turning he beheld
Siverian. Father, said the good old man,

As Theron rose and fawn'd about his
    knees,
Hast thou some charm, which draws
    about thee thus   70
The hearts of all our house, . . even to
    the beast
That lacks discourse of reason, but too
    oft,
With uncorrupted feeling and dumb
    faith,
Puts lordly man to shame ? . . The King
    replied,
'Tis that mysterious sense by which
    mankind
To fix their friendships and their loves
    are led,
And which with fainter influence doth
    extend
To such poor things as this. As we
    put off
The cares and passions of this fretful
    world,
It may be too that we thus far approach
To elder nature, and regain in part   81
The privilege through sin in Eden lost.
The timid hare soon learns that she may
    trust
The solitary penitent, and birds
Will light upon the hermit's harmless
    hand.

Thus Roderick answer'd in excursive
    speech,
Thinking to draw the old man's mind
    from what
Might touch him else too nearly, and
    himself
Disposed to follow on the lure he threw,
As one whom such imaginations led   90
Out of the world of his own miseries.
But to regardless ears his words were
    given,
For on the dog Siverian gazed the while,
Pursuing his own thoughts. Thou hast
    not felt,

Exclaim'd the old man, the earthquake
  and the storm ;
The kingdom's overthrow, the wreck of
  Spain,
The ruin of thy royal master's house,
Have reach'd not thee ! . . Then turning
  to the King,
When the destroying enemy drew nigh
Toledo, he continued, and we fled   100
Before their fury, even while her grief
Was fresh, my Mistress would not leave
  behind
This faithful creature.   Well we knew
  she thought
Of Roderick then, although she named
  him not ;
For never since the fatal certainty
Fell on us all, hath that unhappy name,
Save in her prayers, been known to pass
  her lips
Before this day.   She names him now,
  and weeps ;
But now her tears are tears of thankful-
  ness,   109
For blessed hath thy coming been to her
And all who loved the King.
                  His faltering voice
Here fail'd him, and he paused : re-
  covering soon,
When that poor injured Lady, he pur-
  sued,
Did in my presence to the Prince absolve
The unhappy King. . .
              Absolve him ! Roderick cried,
And in that strong emotion turn'd his
  face
Sternly toward Siverian, for the sense
Of shame and self-reproach drove from
  his mind
All other thoughts.   The good old man
  replied,
Of human judgements humanly I speak.
Who knows not what Pelayo's life hath
  been ?   121
Not happier in all dear domestic ties,

Than worthy for his virtue of the bliss
Which is that virtue's fruit ; and yet
  did he
Absolve, upon Florinda's tale, the King.
Siverian, thus he said, what most I
  hoped,
And still within my secret heart believed,
Is now made certain.   Roderick hath
  been
More sinn'd against than sinning.   And
  with that
He clasp'd his hands, and, lifting them
  to Heaven,   130
Cried, Would to God that he were yet
  alive !
For not more gladly did I draw my
  sword
Against Witiza in our common cause,
Than I would fight beneath his banners
  now,
And vindicate his name !
              Did he say this ?
The Prince ? Pelayo ? in astonishment
Roderick exclaim'd. . . He said it, quoth
  the old man.
None better knew his kinsman's noble
  heart,
None loved him better, none bewail'd
  him more :   139
And as he felt, like me, for his reproach
A deeper grief than for his death, even so
He cherish'd in his heart the constant
  thought
Something was yet untold, which, being
  known,
Would palliate his offence, and make the
  fall
Of one till then so excellently good,
Less monstrous, less revolting to belief,
More to be pitied, more to be forgiven.

  While thus he spake, the fallen King
  felt his face
Burn, and his blood flow fast.   Down
  guilty thoughts !

Firmly he said within his soul ; lie still,
Thou heart of flesh ! I thought thou
    hadst been quell'd,   151
And quell'd thou shalt be ! Help me,
    O my God,
That I may crucify this inward foe !
Yea, thou hast help'd me, Father ! I am
    strong,
O Saviour, in thy strength.
                 As he breath'd thus
His inward supplications, the old man
Eyed him with frequent and unsteady
    looks.
He had a secret trembling on his lips,
And hesitated, still irresolute
In utterance to embody the dear hope :
Fain would he have it strengthen'd and
    assured   161
By this concording judgement, yet he
    fear'd
To have it chill'd in cold accoil. At
    length
Venturing, he brake with interrupted
    speech
The troubled silence. Father Maccabee,
I cannot rest till I have laid my heart
Open before thee. When Pelayo wish'd
That his poor kinsman were alive to rear
His banner once again, a sudden
    thought . .
A hope . . a fancy . . what shall it be
    call'd ?   170
Possess'd me, that perhaps the wish
    might see
Its glad accomplishment, . . that
    Roderick lived,
And might in glory take the field once
    more
For Spain. . . I see thou startest at the
    thought !
Yet spurn it not with hasty unbelief,
As though 'twere utterly beyond the
    scope
Of possible contingency. I think
That I have calmly satisfied myself

How this is more than idle fancy, more
Than mere imaginations of a mind   180
Which from its wishes builds a baseless
    faith.
His horse, his royal robe, his horned
    helm,
His mail and sword were found upon the
    field ;
But if King Roderick had in battle
    fallen,
That sword, I know, would only have
    been found
Clench'd in the hand which, living,
    knew so well
To wield the dreadful steel ! Not in the
    throng
Confounded, nor amid the torpid stream,
Opening with ignominious arms a way
For flight, would he have perish'd !
    Where the strife   190
Was hottest, ring'd about with slaugh-
    ter'd foes,
Should Roderick have been found : by
    this sure mark
Ye should have known him, if nought
    else remain'd,
That his whole body had been gored
    with wounds,
And quill'd with spears, as if the Moors
    had felt
That in his single life the victory lay,
More than in all the host !
                 Siverian's eyes
Shone with a youthful ardour while he
    spake,
His gathering brow grew stern, and as
    he raised
His arm, a warrior's impulse character'd
The impassion'd gesture. But the King
    was calm   201
And heard him with unchanging coun-
    tenance ;
For he had taken his resolve, and felt
Once more the peace of God within his
    soul,

As in that hour when by his father's
grave
He knelt before Pelayo.
                    Soon the old man
Pursued in calmer tones, . . Thus much
I dare
Believe, that Roderick fell not on that
day
When treason brought about his over-
throw.
If yet he live, for sure I think I know 210
His noble mind, 'tis in some wilderness,
Where, in some savage den inhumed,
he drags
The weary load of life, and on his flesh
As on a mortal enemy, inflicts
Fierce vengeance with immitigable hand.
Oh that I knew but where to bend my
way
In his dear search! my voice perhaps
might reach
His heart, might reconcile him to himself,
Restore him to his mother ere she dies,
His people and his country : with the
sword,   220
Them and his own good name should he
redeem.
Oh might I but behold him once again
Leading to battle these intrepid bands,
Such as he was, . . yea rising from his fall
More glorious, more beloved! Soon
I believe
Joy would accomplish then what grief
hath fail'd
To do with this old heart, and I should die
Clasping his knees with such intense
delight,
That when I woke in Heaven, even
Heaven itself
Could have no higher happiness in store.

    Thus fervently he spake, and copious
tears   231
Ran down his cheeks. Full oft the
Royal Goth,

Since he came forth again among man-
kind,
Had trembled lest some curious eye
should read
His lineaments too closely; now he long'd
To fall upon the neck of that old man,
And give his full heart utterance. But
the sense
Of duty, by the pride of self-controul
Corroborate, made him steadily repress
His yearning nature. Whether Roderick
live,   240
Paying in penitence the bitter price
Of sin, he answered, or if earth hath
given
Rest to his earthly part, is only known
To him and Heaven. Dead is he to the
world ;
And let not these imaginations rob
His soul of thy continual prayers, whose
aid
Too surely, in whatever world, he needs.
The faithful love that mitigates his fault,
Heavenward addrest, may mitigate his
doom.
Living or dead, old man, be sure his
soul, . .   250
It were unworthy else, . . doth hold with
thine
Entire communion! Doubt not he relies
Firmly on thee, as on a father's love,
Counts on thy offices, and joins with thee
In sympathy and fervent act of faith,
Though regions, or though worlds,
should intervene.
Lost as he is, to Roderick this must be
Thy first, best, dearest duty; next must
be
To hold right onward in that noble path
Which he would counsel, could his voice
be heard.   260
Now therefore aid me, while I call upon
The Leaders and the People, that thi[s]
day
We may acclaim Pelayo for our King.

XVIII. THE ACCLAMATION

Now, when from Covadonga, down the
    vale
Holding his way, the princely moun-
    taineer
Came with that happy family in sight
Of Cangas and his native towers, far off
He saw before the gate, in fair array,
The assembled land. Broad banners
    were display'd,
And spears were sparkling to the sun,
    shields shone,
And helmets glitter'd, and the blairing
    horn,
With frequent sally of impatient joy,
Provoked the echoes round. Well he
    areeds,   10
From yonder ensigns and augmented
    force,
That Odoar and the Primate from the
    west
Have brought their aid ; but wherefore
    all were thus
Instructed as for some great festival,
He found not, till Favila's quicker eye
Catching the ready buckler, the glad boy
Leapt up, and clapping his exultant
    hands,
Shouted, King ! King ! my father shall
    be King
This day ! Pelayo started at the word,
And the first thought which smote him
    brought a sigh   20
For Roderick's fall ; the second was of
    hope,
Deliverance for his country, for himself
Enduring fame, and glory for his line.
That high prophetic forethought gather'd
    strength,
As looking to his honour'd mate, he
    read
Her soul's accordant augury ; her eyes
Brighten'd ; the quicken'd action of the
    blood
Tinged with a deeper hue her glowing
    cheek,
And on her lips there sate a smile which
    spake
The honourable pride of perfect love, 30
Rejoicing, for her husband's sake, to
    share
The lot he chose, the perils he defied,
The lofty fortune which their faith
    foresaw.

Roderick, in front of all the assembled
    troops,
Held the broad buckler, following to the
    end
That steady purpose to the which his
    zeal
Had this day wrought the Chiefs. Tall
    as himself,
Erect it stood beside him, and his hands
Hung resting on the rim. This was an
    hour
That sweeten'd life, repaid and recom-
    pensed   40
All losses ; and although it could not
    heal
All griefs, yet laid them for awhile to rest.
The active agitating joy that fill'd
The vale, that with contagious influence
    spread
Through all the exulting mountaineers,
    that gave
New ardour to all spirits, to all breasts
Inspired fresh impulse of excited hope,
Moved every tongue, and strengthen'd
    every limb, . .
That joy which every man reflected saw
From every face of all the multitude, 50
And heard in every voice, in every sound,
Reach'd not the King. Aloof from
    sympathy,
He from the solitude of his own soul
Beheld the busy scene. None shared or
    knew
His deep and incommunicable joy ;

None but that heavenly Father, who
    alone
Beholds the struggles of the heart, alone
Sees and rewards the secret sacrifice.

  Among the chiefs conspicuous, Urban
    stood,
He whom, with well-weigh'd choice, in
    arduous time,   60
To arduous office the consenting Church
Had call'd when Sindered fear-smitten
    fled ;
Unfaithful shepherd, who for life alone
Solicitous, forsook his flock, when most
In peril and in suffering they required
A pastor's care.   Far off at Rome he
    dwells
In ignominious safety, while the Church
Keeps in her annals the deserter's name,
But from the service which with daily
    zeal
Devout her ancient prelacy recalls,   70
Blots it, unworthy to partake her
    prayers.
Urban, to that high station thus being
    call'd,
From whence disanimating fear had
    driven
The former primate, for the general weal
Consulting first, removed with timely
    care
The relics and the written works of
    Saints,
Toledo's choicest treasure prized beyond
All wealth, their living and their dead
    remains ;
These to the mountain fastnesses he
    bore   79
Of unsubdued Cantabria, there deposed,
One day to be the boast of yet unbuilt
Oviedo, and the dear idolatry
Of multitudes unborn.   To things of
    state
Then giving thought mature, he held
    advice

With Odoar, whom of counsel competent
And firm of heart he knew.   What then
    they plann'd,
Time and the course of over-ruled events
To earlier act had ripen'd, than their
    hope
Had ever in its gladdest dream pro-
    posed ;
And here by agents unforeseen, and
    means   90
Beyond the scope of foresight brought
    about,
This day they saw their dearest heart's
    desire
Accorded them :   All-able Providence
Thus having ordered all, that Spain this
    hour
With happiest omens, and on surest
    base,
Should from its ruins rear again her
    throne.

  For acclamation and for sacring now
One form must serve, more solemn for
    the breach
Of old observances, whose absence here
Deeplier impress'd the heart, than all
    display   100
Of regal pomp and wealth pontifical,
Of vestments radiant with their gems,
    and stiff
With ornature of gold ;   the glittering
    train,
The long procession, and the full-voiced
    choir.
This day the forms of piety and war,
In strange but fitting union must com-
    bine.
Not in his alb and cope and orary
Came Urban now, nor wore he mitre
    here,
Precious or auriphrygiate ;   bare of
    head
He stood, all else in arms complete, and
    o'er   110

His gorget's iron rings the pall was
  thrown
Of wool undyed, which on the Apostle's
  tomb
Gregory had laid, and sanctified with
  prayer ;
That from the living Pontiff and the
  dead
Replete with holiness, it might impart
Doubly derived its grace   One Page
  beside
Bore his broad-shadow'd helm ; an-
  other's hand
Held the long spear, more suited in these
  times
For Urban, than the crosier richly
  wrought
With silver foliature, the elaborate work
Of Grecian or Italian artist, train'd 121
In the eastern capital, or sacred Rome,
Still o'er the West predominant, though
  fallen.
Better the spear befits the shepherd's
  hand
When robbers break the fold. Now he
  had laid
The weapon by, and held a natural cross
Of rudest form, unpeel'd, even as it grew
On the near oak that morn.
                    Mutilate alike
Of royal rites was this solemnity.
Where was the rubied crown, the sceptre
  where,   130
And where the golden pome, the proud
  array
Of ermines, aureate vests, and jewelry,
With all which Leuvigild for after kings
Left, ostentatious of his power ? The
  Moor
Had made his spoil of these, and on the
  field
Of Xeres, where contending multitudes
Had trampled it beneath their bloody
  feet,
The standard of the Goths forgotten lay

Defiled, and rotting there in sun and
  rain.
Utterly is it lost ; nor evermore   140
Herald or antiquary's patient search
Shall from forgetfulness avail to save
Those blazon'd arms, so fatally of old
Renown'd through all the affrighted
  Occident.
That banner, before which imperial Rome
First to a conqueror bow'd her head
  abased ;
Which when the dreadful Hun, with all
  his powers,
Came like a deluge rolling o'er the world,
Made head, and in the front of battle
  broke
His force, till then resistless ; which so
  oft   150
Had with alternate fortune braved the
  Frank :
Driven the Byzantine from the farthest
  shores
Of Spain, long lingering there, to final
  flight ;
And of their kingdoms and their name
  despoil'd
The Vandal, and the Alan, and the
  Sueve ;
Blotted from human records is it now
As it had never been. So let it rest
With things forgotten ! But Oblivion
  ne'er
Shall cancel from the historic roll, nor
  Time,
Who changeth all, obscure that fated
  sign,   160
Which brighter now than mountain
  snows at noon
To the bright sun displays its argent
  field.

Rose not the vision then upon thy
  soul,
O Roderick, when within that argent
  field

Thou saw'st the rampant Lion, red as if
Upon some noblest quarry he had roll'd,
Rejoicing in his satiate rage, and drunk
With blood and fury ? Did the auguries
Which open'd on thy spirit bring with
   them
A perilous consolation, deadening heart
And soul, yea worse than death, .. that
   thou through all   171
Thy chequer'd way of life, evil and good,
Thy errors and thy virtues, hadst but
   been
The poor mere instrument of things
   ordain'd, ..
Doing or suffering, impotent alike
To will or act, .. perpetually bemock'd
With semblance of volition, yet in all
Blind worker of the ways of destiny !
That thought intolerable, which in the
   hour
Of woe indignant conscience had re-
   pell'd   180
As little might it find reception now,
When the regenerate spirit self-approved
Beheld its sacrifice complete. With
   faith
Elate, he saw the banner'd Lion float
Refulgent, and recall'd that thrilling
   shout
Which he had heard when on Romano's
   grave
The joy of victory woke him from his
   dream,
And sent him with prophetic hope to
   work
Fulfilment of the great events ordain'd,
There in imagination's inner world   190
Prefigured to his soul.
              Alone, advanced
Before the ranks, the Goth in silence
   stood,
While from all voices round, loquacious
   joy
Mingled its buzz continuous with the
   blast

Of horn, shrill pipe, and tinkling cym-
   bals' clash,
And sound of deafening drum.   But
   when the Prince
Drew nigh, and Urban with the cross
   upheld
Stept forth to meet him, all at once were
   still'd
With instantaneous hush ; as when the
   wind,
Before whose violent gusts the forest
   oaks,   200
Tossing like billows their tempestuous
   heads,
Roar like a raging sea, suspends its force,
And leaves so dead a calm that not a
   leaf
Moves on the silent spray.   The passing
   air
Bore with it from the woodland undis-
   turb'd
The ringdove's wooing, and the quiet
   voice
Of waters warbling near.
                 Son of a race
Of Heroes and of Kings ! the Primate
   thus
Address'd him, Thou in whom the
   Gothic blood,
Mingling with old Iberia's, hath restored
To Spain a ruler of her native line,   211
Stand forth, and in the face of God and
   man
Swear to uphold the right, abate the
   wrong,
With equitable hand, protect the Cross
Whereon thy lips this day shall seal
   their vow,
And underneath that hallow'd symbol,
   wage
Holy and inextinguishable war
Against the accursëd nation that usurps
Thy country's sacred soil !
               So speak of me   219
Now and for ever, O my countrymen !

Replied Pelayo; and so deal with me
Here and hereafter, thou, Almighty
  God,
In whom I put my trust!
                    Lord God of Hosts,
Urban pursued, of Angels and of Men
Creator and Disposer, King of Kings,
Ruler of Earth and Heaven, . . look
  down this day,
And multiply thy blessings on the head
Of this thy servant, chosen in thy
  sight!
Be thou his counsellor, his comforter,
His hope, his joy, his refuge, and his
  strength;   230
Crown him with justice, and with forti-
  tude,
Defend him with thine all-sufficient
  shield,
Surround him every where with the
  right hand
Of thine all-present power, and with the
  might
Of thine omnipotence, send in his aid
Thy unseen Angels forth, that potently
And royally against all enemies
He may endure and triumph! Bless the
  land
O'er which he is appointed; bless thou
  it
With the waters of the firmament, the
  springs   240
Of the low-lying deep, the fruits which
  Sun
And Moon mature for man, the precious
  stores
Of the eternal hills, and all the gifts
Of Earth, its wealth and fulness!
                              Then he took
Pelayo's hand, and on his finger placed
The mystic circlet. . . With this ring,
  O Prince,
To our dear Spain, who like a widow
  now
Mourneth in desolation, I thee wed:

For weal or woe thou takest her, till
  death
Dispart the union: Be it blest to her,
To thee, and to thy seed!   251
                    Thus when he ceased,
He gave the awaited signal. Roderick
  brought
The buckler: Eight for strength and
  stature chosen
Came to their honour'd office: Round
  the shield
Standing, they lower it for the Chief-
  tain's feet,
Then, slowly raised upon their shoulders,
  lift
The steady weight. Erect Pelayo
  stands,
And thrice he brandishes the burnish'd
  sword,
While Urban to the assembled people
  cries,
Spaniards, behold your King! The
  multitude   260
Then sent forth all their voice with glad
  acclaim,
Raising the loud *Real;* thrice did the
  word
Ring through the air, and echo from the
  walls
Of Cangas. Far and wide the thun-
  dering shout,
Rolling among reduplicating rocks,
Peal'd o'er the hills, and up the moun-
  tain vales.
The wild ass starting in the forest glade
Ran to the covert; the affrighted wolf
Skulk'd through the thicket to a closer
  brake;
The sluggish bear, awaken'd in his den,
Roused up and answer'd with a sullen
  growl,   271
Low-breathed and long; and at the
  uproar scared,
The brooding eagle from her nest took
  wing.

Heroes and Chiefs of old ! and ye who
    bore
Firm to the last your part in that dread
    strife,
When Julian and Witiza's viler race
Betray'd their country, hear ye from
    yon Heaven
The joyful acclamation which proclaims
That Spain is born again ! O ye who
    died
In that disastrous field, and ye who fell
Embracing with a martyr's love your
    death   281
Amid the flames of Auria ; and all ye
Victims innumerable, whose cries un-
    heard
On earth, but heard in Heaven, from
    all the land
Went up for vengeance ; not in vain ye
    cry
Before the eternal throne ! . . Rest
    innocent blood !
Vengeance is due, and vengeance will
    be given,
Rest innocent blood ! The appointed
    age is come !
The star that harbingers a glorious day
Hath risen ! Lo there the Avenger
    stands ! Lo there   290
He brandishes the avenging sword ! Lo
    there
The avenging banner spreads its argent
    field
Refulgent with auspicious light ! . .
    Rejoice,
O Leon, for thy banner is displayed,
Rejoice with all thy mountains, and thy
    vales
And streams ! And thou, O Spain,
    through all thy realms,
For thy deliverance cometh ! Even now,
As from all sides the miscreant hosts
    move on ; . .
From southern Betis ; from the western
    lands,

Where through redundant vales smooth
    Minho flows,   300
And Douro pours through vine-clad hills
    the wealth
Of Leon's gathered waters ; from the
    plains
Burgensian, in old time Vardulia call'd,
But in their castellated strength ere long
To be design'd Castille, a deathless
    name ;
From midland regions where Toledo
    reigns
Proud city on her royal eminence,
And Tagus bends his sickle round the
    scene
Of Roderick's fall ; from rich Rioja's
    fields ;
Dark Ebro's shores ; the walls of Sal-
    duba,   310
Seat of the Sedetanians old, by Rome
Caesarian and August denominate,
Now Zaragoza, in this later time
Above all cities of the earth renown'd
For duty perfectly perform'd ; . . East,
    West
And South, where'er their gather'd
    multitudes
Urged by the speed of vigorous tyranny,
With more than with commeasurable
    strength
Haste to prevent the danger, crush the
    hopes
Of rising Spain, and rivet round her neck
The eternal yoke, . . the ravenous fowls
    of heaven   321
Flock there presentient of their food
    obscene,
Following the accursed armies, whom
    too well
They know their purveyors long. Pursue
    their march,
Ominous attendants ! Ere the moon
    hath fill'd
Her horns, these purveyors shall become
    the prey,

And ye on Moorish not on Christian
flesh

Wearying your beaks, shall clog your
scaly feet

With foreign gore. Soon will ye learn
to know,

Followers and harbingers of blood, the
flag   330

Of Leon where it bids you to your
feast !

Terror and flight shall with that flag go
forth,

And Havoc and the Dogs of War and
Death.

Thou Covadonga with the tainted
stream

Of Deva, and this now rejoicing vale,

Soon its primitial triumphs wilt behold !

Nor shall the glories of the noon be
less

Than such miraculous promise of the
dawn :

Witness Clavijo, where the dreadful cry

Of Santiago, then first heard, o'er-
power'd   340

The Akbar, and that holier name blasphemed

By misbelieving lips ! Simancas, thou

Be witness ! And do ye your record
bear,

Tolosan mountains, where the Almo-
hade

Beheld his myriads scatter'd and destroy'd,

Like locusts swept before the stormy
North !

Thou too, Salado, on that later day

When Africa received her final foil,

And thy swoln stream incarnadined,
roll'd back

The invaders to the deep, . . there shall
they toss   350

Till on their native Mauritanian shore

The waves shall cast their bones to
whiten there.

XIX. RODERICK AND RUSILLA

WHEN all had been perform'd, the royal
Goth

Look'd up towards the chamber in the
tower

Where, gazing on the multitude below,

Alone Rusilla stood. He met her eye,

For it was singling him amid the crowd ;

Obeying then the hand which beckon'd
him,

He went with heart prepared, nor
shrinking now,

But arm'd with self-approving thoughts
that hour.

Entering in tremulous haste, he closed
the door,

And turn'd to clasp her knees ; but lo,
she spread   10

Her arms, and catching him in close
embrace,

Fell on his neck, and cried, My Son, my
Son ! . .

Ere long, controlling that first agony

With effort of strong will, backward she
bent,

And gazing on his head now shorn and
grey,

And on his furrow'd countenance, exclaim'd,

Still, still, my Roderick ! the same noble
mind !

The same heroic heart ! Still, still, my
Son ! . .

Changed, . . yet not wholly fallen, . . not
wholly lost,

He cried, . . not wholly in the sight of
Heaven   20

Unworthy, O my Mother, nor in thine !

She lock'd her arms again around his
neck,

Saying, Lord, let me now depart in
peace !

And bow'd her head again, and silently

Gave way to tears.

When that first force was spent,
And passion in exhaustment found
   relief, . .
I knew thee, said Rusilla, when the dog
Rose from my feet, and lick'd his
   master's hand.
All flash'd upon me then ; the instinc-
   tive sense
That goes unerringly where reason
   fails, . .   30
The voice, the eye, . . a mother's
   thoughts are quick, . .
Miraculous as it seem'd, . . Siverian's
   tale, . .
Florinda's, . . every action, . . every
   word, . .
Each strengthening each, and all con-
   firming all,
Reveal'd thee, O my Son ! but I re-
   strain'd
My heart, and yielded to thy holier will
The thoughts which rose to tempt a soul
   not yet
Wean'd wholly from the world.
           What thoughts ? replied
Roderick.   That I might see thee yet
   again
Such as thou wert, she answer'd ; not
   alone   40
To Heaven and me restored, but to
   thyself, . .
Thy Crown, . . thy Country, . . all within
   thy reach ;
Heaven so disposing all things, that the
   means
Which wrought the ill, might work the
   remedy.
Methought I saw thee once again the
   hope, . .
The strength, . . the pride of Spain ! The
   miracle
Which I beheld made all things possible.
I know the inconstant people, how their
   mind,
With every breath of good or ill report,

Fluctuates, like summer corn before the
   breeze ;   50
Quick in their hatred, quicker in their
   love,
Generous and hasty, soon would they
   redress
All wrongs of former obloquy. . . I
   thought
Of happiness restored, . . the broken
   heart
Heal'd, . . and Count Julian, for his
   daughter's sake,
Turning in thy behalf against the Moors
His powerful sword : . . all possibilities
That could be found or fancied, built
   a dream
Before me ; such as easiest might illude
A lofty spirit train'd in palaces,   60
And not alone amid the flatteries
Of youth with thoughts of high ambition
   fed
When all is sunshine, but through years
   of woe,
When sorrow sanctified their use, upheld
By honourable pride and earthly hopes.
I thought I yet might nurse upon my
   knee
Some young Theodofred, and see in him
Thy Father's image and thine own
   renew'd,
And love to think the little hand which
   there
Play'd with the bauble, should in after
   days   70
Wield the transmitted sceptre ; . . that
   through him
The ancient seed should be perpetuate, . .
That precious seed revered so long, desired
   desired
So dearly, and so wondrously preserved.

Nay, he replied, Heaven hath not
   with its bolts
Scathed the proud summit of the tree,
   and left

The trunk unflaw'd ; ne'er shall it clothe
its boughs
Again, nor push again its scyons forth,
Head, root, and branch, all mortified
alike ! . .
Long ere these locks were shorn had
I cut off   80
The thoughts of royalty ! Time might
renew
Their growth, as for Manoah's captive
son,
And I too on the miscreant race, like
him,
Might prove my strength regenerate ;
but the hour,
When, in its second best nativity,
My soul was born again through grace,
this heart
Died to the world. Dreams such as
thine pass now
Like evening clouds before me ; if I
think
How beautiful they seem, 'tis but to
feel
How soon they fade, how fast the night
shuts in.   90
But in that World to which my hopes
look on,
Time enters not, nor Mutability ;
Beauty and goodness are unfading
there ;
Whatever there is given us to enjoy,
That we enjoy for ever, still the same. . .
Much might Count Julian's sword
achieve for Spain
And me, but more will his dear daughter's
soul
Effect in Heaven ; and soon will she be
there
An Angel at the throne of Grace, to
plead
In his behalf and mine.
                    I knew thy heart, 100
She answer'd, and subdued the vain
desire.

It was the World's last effort. Thou
hast chosen
The better part. Yes, Roderick, even
on earth
There is a praise above the monarch's
fame,
A higher, holier, more enduring praise,
And this will yet be thine !
                    O tempt me not,
Mother ! he cried ; nor let ambition
take
That specious form to cheat us ! What
but this,
Fallen as I am, have I to offer Heaven ?
The ancestral sceptre, public fame, con-
tent   110
Of private life, the general good report,
Power, reputation, happiness, . . what-
e'er
The heart of man desires to constitute
His earthly weal, . . unerring Justice
claim'd
In forfeiture. I with submitted soul
Bow to the righteous law and kiss the
rod
Only while thus submitted, suffering
thus, . .
Only while offering up that name on
earth,
Perhaps in trial offer'd to my choice,
Could I present myself before thy sight ;
Thus only could endure myself, or fix 121
My thoughts upon that fearful pass,
where Death
Stands in the Gate of Heaven ! . . Time
passes on,
The healing work of sorrow is complete ;
All vain desires have long been weeded
out,
All vain regrets subdued ; the heart is
dead,
The soul is ripe and eager for her birth.
Bless me, my Mother ! and come when
it will
The inevitable hour, we die in peace.

So saying, on her knees he bow'd his
    head ;   130
She raised her hands to Heaven and
    blest her child ;
Then bending forward, as he rose, em-
    braced
And claspt him to her heart, and cried,
    Once more
Theodofred, with pride behold thy son !

XX. THE MOORISH CAMP

THE times are big with tidings ; every
    hour
From east and west and south the breath-
    less scouts
Bring swift alarums in ; the gathering
    foe,
Advancing from all quarters to one
    point,
Close their wide crescent.   Nor was aid
    of fear
To magnify their numbers needed now,
They came in myriads.   Africa had
    pour'd
Fresh shoals upon the coast of wretched
    Spain ;
Lured from their hungry deserts to the
    scene
Of spoil, like vultures to the battle-field,
Fierce, unrelenting, habited in crimes, 11
Like bidden guests the mirthful ruffians
    flock
To that free feast which in their Pro-
    phet's name
Rapine and Lust proclaim'd.   Nor were
    the chiefs
Of victory less assured, by long success
Elate, and proud of that o'erwhelming
    strength,
Which, surely they believed, as it had
    roll'd
Thus far uncheck'd would roll victorious
    on,

Till, like the Orient, the subjected West
Should bow in reverence at Mahommed's
    name ;   20
And pilgrims, from remotest Arctic
    shores,
Tread with religious feet the burning
    sands
Of Araby, and Mecca's stony soil.
Proud of his part in Roderick's over-
    throw,
Their leader Abulcacem came, a man
Immitigable, long in war renown'd.
Here Magued comes, who on the con-
    quered walls
Of Cordoba, by treacherous fear be-
    tray'd,
Planted the moony standard : Ibrahim
    here,
He, who by Genil and in Darro's vales, 30
Had for the Moors the fairest portion won
Of all their spoils, fairest and best main-
    tain'd,
And to the Alpuxarras given in trust
His other name, through them preserved
    in song.
Here too Alcahman, vaunting his late
    deeds
At Auria, all her children by the sword
Cut off, her bulwarks rased, her towers
    laid low,
Her dwellings by devouring flames con-
    sumed,
Bloody and hard of heart, he little
    ween'd,
Vain-boastful chief ! that from those
    fatal flames   40
The fire of retribution had gone forth
Which soon should wrap him round.
                        The renegades
Here too were seen, Ebba and Sisibert ;
A spurious brood, but of their parent's
    crimes
True heirs, in guilt begotten, and in ill
Train'd up.   The same unnatural rage
    that turn'd

Their swords against their country,
made them seek,
Unmindful of their wretched mother's
end,
Pelayo's life. No enmity is like
Domestic hatred. For his blood they
thirst, 50
As if that sacrifice might satisfy
Witiza's guilty ghost, efface the shame
Of their adulterous birth, and one crime
more
Crowning a hideous course, emancipate
Thenceforth their spirits from all earthly
fear.
This was their only care: but other
thoughts
Were rankling in that elder villain's
mind,
Their kinsman Orpas, he of all the crew
Who in this fatal visitation fell,
The foulest and the falsest wretch that
e'er 60
Renounced his baptism. From his
cherish'd views
Of royalty cut off, he coveted
Count Julian's wide domains, and hope-
less now
To gain them through the daughter, laid
his toils
Against the father's life, . . the instru-
ment
Of his ambition first, and now design'd
Its victim. To this end with cautious
hints,
At favouring season ventured, he pos-
sess'd
The leader's mind; then, subtly fos-
tering
The doubts himself had sown, with
bolder charge 70
He bade him warily regard the Count,
Lest underneath an outward show of
faith
The heart uncircumcised were Christian
still:

Else, wherefore had Florinda not obey'd
Her dear loved sire's example, and em-
braced
The saving truth ? Else, wherefore was
her hand,
Plighted to him so long, so long withheld,
Till she had found a fitting hour to fly
With that audacious Prince, who now
in arms,
Defied the Caliph's power; . . for who
could doubt 80
That in his company she fled, perhaps
The mover of his flight ? What if the
Count
Himself had plann'd the evasion which
he feign'd
In sorrow to condemn ? What if she went
A pledge assured, to tell the moun-
taineers
That when they met the Musselmen in
the heat
Of fight, her father passing to their side
Would draw the victory with him ? . .
Thus he breathed
Fiend like in Abulcacem's ear his
schemes
Of murderous malice; and the course
of things, 90
Ere long, in part approving his dis-
course,
Aided his aim, and gave his wishes
weight.
For scarce on the Asturian territory
Had they set foot, when, with the speed
of fear,
Count Eudon, nothing doubting that
their force
Would like a flood sweep all resistance
down,
Hasten'd to plead his merits; . . he
alone,
Found faithful in obedience through
reproach
And danger, when the madden'd multi-
tude

Hurried their chiefs along, and high and
    low   100
With one infectious frenzy seized, pro-
    voked
The invincible in arms.   Pelayo led
The raging crew, . . he doubtless the
    prime spring
Of all these perilous movements; and
    'twas said
He brought the assurance of a strong
    support,
Count Julian's aid, for in his company
From Cordoba, Count Julian's daughter
    came.

Thus Eudon spake before the assem-
    bled chiefs;
When instantly a stern and wrathful
    voice
Replied, I know Pelayo never made   110
That senseless promise ! He who raised
    the tale
Lies foully ; but the bitterest enemy
That ever hunted for Pelayo's life
Hath never with the charge of falsehood
    touch'd
His name.
            The Baron had not recognized
Till then, beneath the turban's shadow-
    ing folds,
Julian's swart visage, where the fiery
    skies
Of Africa, through many a year's long
    course,
Had set their hue inburnt.   Something
    he sought   119
In quick excuse to say of common fame,
Lightly believed and busily diffused,
And that no enmity had moved his
    speech
Repeating rumour's tale. Julian replied,
Count Eudon, neither for thyself nor me
Excuse is needed here.   The path I
    tread
Is one wherein there can be no return,

No pause, no looking back ! A choice
    like mine
For time and for eternity is made,
Once and for ever ! and as easily
The breath of vain report might build
    again   130
The throne which my just vengeance
    overthrew,
As in the Caliph and his Captain's mind
Affect the opinion of my well-tried
    truth.
The tidings which thou givest me of my
    child
Touch me more vitally ; bad though
    they be,
A secret apprehension of aught worse
Makes me with joy receive them.
                            Then the Count
To Abulcacem turn'd his speech, and
    said,
I pray thee, Chief, give me a messenger
By whom I may to this unhappy child
Dispatch a father's bidding, such as yet
May win her back.   What I would say
    requires   142
No veil of privacy ; before ye all
The errand shall be given.
                            Boldly he spake,
Yet wary in that show of open truth,
For well he knew what dangers girt him
    round
Amid the faithless race.   Blind with
    revenge,
For them in madness had he sacrificed
His name, his baptism, and his native
    land,
To feel, still powerful as he was, that life
Hung on their jealous favour.   But his
    heart   151
Approved him now, where love, too
    long restrain'd,
Resumed its healing influence, leading
    him
Right on with no misgiving.   Chiefs, he
    said,

Hear me, and let your wisdom judge
      between
Me and Prince Orpas ! . . Known it is to
      all,
Too well, what mortal injury provoked
My spirit to that vengeance which your
      aid
So signally hath given.   A covenant
We made when first our purpose we
      combined,   160
That he should have Florinda for his
      wife,
My only child, so should she be, I thought,
Revenged and honour'd best.   My
      word was given
Truly, nor did I cease to use all means
Of counsel or command, entreating her
Sometimes with tears, seeking some-
      times with threats
Of an offended father's curse to enforce
Obedience ; that, she said, the Christian
      law
Forbade, moreover she had vow'd her-
      self   169
A servant to the Lord. In vain I strove
To win her to the Prophet's saving faith,
Using perhaps a rigour to that end
Beyond permitted means, and to my
      heart,
Which loved her dearer than its own
      life-blood,
Abhorrent.   Silently she suffer'd all,
Or when I urged her with most vehe-
      mence,
Only replied, I knew her fix'd resolve,
And craved my patience but a little
      while
Till death should set her free.   Touch'd
      as I was,
I yet persisted, till at length to escape
The ceaseless importunity, she fled : 181
And verily I fear'd until this hour,
My rigour to some fearfuller resolve
Than flight, had driven my child. Chiefs,
      I appeal

To each and all, and Orpas to thyself
Especially, if, having thus essay'd
All means that law and nature have
      allow'd
To bend her will, I may not rightfully
Hold myself free, that promise being
      void
Which cannot be fulfill'd.

                     Thou sayest then, 190
Orpas replied, that from her false belief
Her stubborn opposition drew its force
I should have thought that from the
      ways corrupt
Of these idolatrous Christians, little care
Might have sufficed to wean a duteous
      child,
The example of a parent so beloved
Leading the way ; and yet I will not
      doubt
Thou didst enforce with all sincerity
And holy zeal upon thy daughter's mind
The truths of Islam.

                     Julian knit his brow, 200
And scowling on the insidious renegade
He answered, By what reasoning my
      poor mind
Was from the old idolatry reclaim'd,
None better knows than Seville's mitred
      chief,
Who first renouncing errors which he
      taught,
Led me his follower to the Prophet's
      pale.
Thy lessons I repeated as I could ;
Of graven images, unnatural vows,
False records, fabling creeds, and
      juggling priests,   209
Who, making sanctity the cloak of sin,
Laugh'd at the fools on whose credulity
They fatten'd.   To these arguments,
      whose worth
Prince Orpas, least of all men, should
      impeach,
I added, like a soldier bred in arms,
And to the subtleties of schools unused,

The flagrant fact, that Heaven with
victory,
Where'er they turn'd, attested and ap-
proved
The chosen Prophet's arms. If thou
wert still
The mitred Metropolitan, and I
Some wretch of Arian or of Hebrew race,
Thy proper business then might be to
pry,   221
And question me for lurking flaws of
faith.
We Musselmen, Prince Orpas, live be-
neath
A wiser law, which with the iniquities
Of thine old craft, hath abrogated this
Its foulest practice!
                    As Count Julian ceased,
From underneath his black and gather'd
brow
There went a look, which with these
wary words
Bore to the heart of that false renegade
Their   whole   envenom'd   meaning.
Haughtily   230
Withdrawing then his alter'd eyes, he
said,
Too much of this! return we to the sum
Of my discourse. Let Abulcacem say,
In whom the Caliph speaks, if with all
faith
Having essay'd in vain all means to win
My child's consent, I may not hold
henceforth
The covenant discharged.
                        The Moor replied,
Well hast thou said, and rightly may'st
assure
Thy daughter that the Prophet's holy
law
Forbids compulsion. Give thine errand
now;   240
The messenger is here.
                    Then Julian said,
Go to Pelayo, and from him entreat

Admittance to my child, where'er she be.
Say to her, that her father solemnly
Annuls   the   covenant   with   Orpas
pledged,
Nor with solicitations, nor with threats,
Will urge her more, nor from that
liberty
Of faith restrain her, which the Prophet's
law,
Liberal as Heaven from whence it came,
to all
Indulges. Tell her that her father says
His days are number'd, and beseeches
her   251
By that dear love, which from her in-
fancy
Still he hath borne her, growing as she
grew,
Nursed in our weal and strengthen'd in
our woe,
She will not in the evening of his life
Leave him forsaken and alone. Enough
Of sorrow, tell her, have her injuries
Brought on her father's head; let not
her act
Thus aggravate the burden. Tell her
too,
That when he pray'd her to return, he
wept   260
Profusely as a child; but bitterer tears
Than ever fell from childhood's eyes
were those
Which traced his hardy cheeks.
                        With faltering voice
He spake, and after he had ceased from
speech
His   lip   was   quivering   still. The
Moorish chief
Then to the messenger his bidding gave.
Say, cried he, to these rebel infidels,
Thus Abulcacem in the Caliph's name
Exhorteth them : Repent and be for-
given !
Nor think to stop the dreadful storm of
war,   270

Which conquering and to conquer must
    fulfil
Its destined circle, rolling eastward now
Back from the subjugated west, to sweep
Thrones and dominions down, till in the
    bond
Of unity all nations join, and Earth
Acknowledge, as she sees one Sun in
    heaven,
One God, one Chief, one Prophet, and
    one Law.
Jerusalem, the holy City, bows
To holier Mecca's creed; the Crescent
    shines
Triumphant o'er the eternal pyramids;
On the cold altars of the worshippers 281
Of Fire moss grows, and reptiles leave
    their slime;
The African idolatries are fallen,
And Europe's senseless gods of stone
    and wood
Have had their day. Tell these mis-
    guided men,
A moment for repentance yet is left,
And mercy the submitted neck will
    spare
Before the sword is drawn : but once
    unsheath'd,
Let Auria witness how that dreadful
    sword
Accomplisheth its work ! They little
    know   290
The Moors who hope in battle to with-
    stand
Their valour, or in flight escape their
    rage !
Amid our deserts we hunt down the birds
Of heaven, . . wings do not save them !
    Nor shall rocks,
And holds, and fastnesses, avail to save
These mountaineers. Is not the Earth
    the Lord's ?
And we, his chosen people, whom he
    sends
To conquer and possess it in his name ?

XXI. THE FOUNTAIN IN THE FOREST

The second eve had closed upon their
    march
Within the Asturian border, and the
    Moors
Had pitch'd their tents amid an open
    wood
Upon the mountain side. As day grew
    dim,
Their scatter'd fires shone with distincter
    light
Among the trees, above whose top the
    smoke
Diffused itself, and stain'd the evening
    sky.
Ere long the stir of occupation ceased,
And all the murmur of the busy host
Subsiding died away, as through the
    camp   10
The crier from a knoll proclaim'd the
    hour
For prayer appointed, and with sonorous
    voice,
Thrice in melodious modulation full,
Pronounced the highest name. There
    is no God
But God, he cried; there is no God but
    God !
Mahommed is the Prophet of the
    Lord !
Come ye to prayer ! to prayer ! The
    Lord is great !
There is no God but God ! . . Thus he
    pronounced
His ritual form, mingling with holiest
    truth
The audacious name accurs'd. The
    multitude   20
Made their ablutions in the mountain
    stream
Obedient, then their faces to the earth
Bent in formality of easy prayer

An arrow's flight above that mountain stream
There was a little glade, where underneath
A long smooth mossy stone a fountain rose.
An oak grew near, and with its ample boughs
O'ercanopied the spring; its fretted roots
Emboss'd the bank, and on their tufted bark
Grew plants which love the moisture and the shade;   30
Short ferns, and longer leaves of wrinkled green
Which bent toward the spring, and when the wind
Made itself felt, just touch'd with gentle dip
The glassy surface, ruffled ne'er but then,
Save when a bubble rising from the depth
Burst, and with faintest circles mark'd its place,
Or if an insect skimm'd it with its wing,
Or when in heavier drops the gather'd rain
Fell from the oak's high bower. The mountain roe,
When, having drank there, he would bound across,   40
Drew up upon the bank his meeting feet,
And put forth half his force. With silent lapse
From thence through mossy banks the water stole,
Then murmuring hasten'd to the glen below.
Diana might have loved in that sweet spot
To take her noontide rest; and when she stoopt
Hot from the chase to drink, well pleased had seen

Her own bright crescent, and the brighter face
It crown'd, reflected there.
　　　　　　Beside that spring
Count Julian's tent was pitch'd upon the glade;   50
There his ablutions Moor-like he perform'd,
And Moor-like knelt in prayer, bowing his head
Upon the mossy bank. There was a sound
Of voices at the tent when he arose,
And lo! with hurried step a woman came
Toward him; rightly then his heart presaged,
And ere he could behold her countenance,
Florinda knelt, and with uplifted arms
Embraced her sire. He raised her from the ground,
Kiss'd her, and clasp'd her to his heart, and said,   60
Thou hast not then forsaken me, my child!
Howe'er the inexorable will of Fate
May in the world which is to come, divide
Our everlasting destinies, in this
Thou wilt not, O my child, abandon me!
And then with deep and interrupted voice,
Nor seeking to restrain his copious tears,
My blessing be upon thy head, he cried,
A father's blessing! Though all faiths were false,
It should not lose its worth! . . She lock'd her hands   70
Around his neck, and gazing in his face
Through streaming tears, exclaim'd, Oh never more,
Here or hereafter, never let us part!
And breathing then a prayer in silence forth,
The name of Jesus trembled on her tongue.

Whom hast thou there ? cried Julian,
and drew back,
Seeing that near them stood a meagre
man
In humble garb, who rested with raised
hands
On a long staff, bending his head like
one
Who when he hears the distant vesper-
bell,   80
Halts by the way, and, all unseen of men,
Offers his homage in the eye of Heaven.
She answered, Let not my dear father
frown
In anger on his child ! Thy messenger
Told me that I should be restrain'd no
more
From liberty of faith, which the new law
Indulged to all ; how soon my hour
might come
I knew not, and although that hour will
bring
Few terrors, yet methinks I would not
be
Without a Christian comforter in death.

A Priest ! exclaimed the Count, and
drawing back,   91
Stoopt for his turban that he might not
lack
Some outward symbol of apostacy ;
For still in war his wonted arms he wore,
Nor for the scymitar had changed the
sword
Accustomed to his hand. He covered
now
His short grey hair, and under the white
folds
His swarthy brow, which gather'd as he
rose,
Darken'd. Oh frown not thus ! Flor-
inda said,
A kind and gentle counsellor is this, 100
One who pours balm into a wounded
soul,

And mitigates the griefs he cannot heal.
I told him I had vow'd to pass my days
A servant of the Lord, yet that my
heart,
Hearing the message of thy love, was
drawn
With powerful yearnings back. Follow
thy heart, . .
It answers to the call of duty here,
He said, nor canst thou better serve the
Lord
Than at thy father's side.
                         Count Julian's brow,
While thus she spake, insensibly relax'd.
A Priest, cried he, and thus with even
hand   111
Weigh vows and natural duty in the
scale ?
In what old heresy hath he been train'd?
Or in what wilderness hath he escaped
The domineering Prelate's fire and
sword ?
Come hither, man, and tell me who
thou art !

    A sinner, Roderick, drawing nigh,
replied ;
Brought to repentance by the grace of
God,
And trusting for forgiveness through the
blood
Of Christ in humble hope.
                         A smile of scorn 120
Julian assumed, but merely from the
lips
It came ; for he was troubled while he
gazed
On the strong countenance and thought-
ful eye
Before him. A new law hath been
proclaim'd,
Said he, which overthrows in its career
The Christian altars of idolatry.
What think'st thou of the Prophet ? . .
                                    Roderick

Made answer, I am in the Moorish camp,
And he who asketh is a Musselman.
How then should I reply ? . . Safely,
    rejoin'd   130
The renegade, and freely may'st thou
    speak
To all that Julian asks.   Is not the yoke
Of Mecca easy, and its burden light ? . .
Spain hath not found it so, the Goth
    replied,
And groaning, turn'd away his coun-
    tenance.

Count Julian knit his brow, and stood
    awhile
Regarding him with meditative eye
In silence.   Thou art honest too! he
    cried ;
Why 'twas in quest of such a man as this
That the old Grecian search'd by lantern
    light   140
In open day the city's crowded streets,
So rare he deem'd the virtue.   Honesty
And sense of natural duty in a Priest !
Now for a miracle, ye Saints of Spain !
I shall not pry too closely for the wires,
For, seeing what I see, ye have me now
In the believing mood !

                    O blessed Saints,
Florinda cried, 'tis from the bitterness,
Not from the hardness of the heart, he
    speaks !
Hear him ! and in your goodness give
    the scoff   150
The virtue of a prayer !   So saying, she
    raised
Her hands in fervent action clasp'd to
    Heaven :
Then as, still clasp'd, they fell, toward
    her sire
She turn'd her eyes, beholding him
    through tears.
The look, the gesture, and that silent woe,
Soften'd her father's heart, which in this
    hour

Was open to the influences of love.
Priest, thy vocation were a blessed one,
Said Julian, if its mighty power were
    used
To lessen human misery, not to swell 160
The mournful sum, already all-too-great.
If, as thy former counsel should imply,
Thou art not one who would for his
    craft's sake
Fret with corrosives and inflame the
    wound,
Which the poor sufferer brings to thee
    in trust
That thou with virtuous balm wilt bind
    it up, . .
If, as I think, thou art not one of those
Whose villainy makes honest men turn
    Moors,
Thou then wilt answer with unbiass'd
    mind   169
What I shall ask thee, and exorcise thus
The sick and feverish conscience of my
    child,
From inbred phantoms, fiend-like, which
    possess
Her innocent spirit.   Children we are all
Of one great Father, in whatever clime
Nature or chance hath cast the seeds of
    life,
All tongues, all colours : neither after
    death
Shall we be sorted into languages
And tints, . . white, black, and tawny,
    Greek and Goth,
Northmen and offspring of hot Africa ;
The All-Father, He in whom we live and
    move,   180
He the indifferent Judge of all, regards
Nations, and hues, and dialects alike ;
According to their works shall they be
    judged,
When even-handed Justice in the scale
Their good and evil weighs.   All creeds,
    I ween,
Agree in this, and hold it orthodox.

Roderick, perceiving here that Julian
  paused,
As if he waited for acknowledgement
Of that plain truth, in motion of assent
Inclined his brow complacently, and
  said,   190
Even so: What follows ? . . This, re-
  sumed the Count,
That creeds like colours being but acci-
  dent,
Are therefore in the scale imponder-
  able ; . .
Thou seest my meaning ; . . that from
  every faith
As every clime, there is a way to Heaven,
And thou and I may meet in Paradise.

Oh grant it, God ! cried Roderick,
  fervently,
And smote his breast. Oh grant it,
  gracious God !
Through the dear blood of Jesus, grant
  that he
And I may meet before the Mercy-
  throne !   200
That were a triumph of Redeeming
  Love,
For which admiring Angels would renew
Their hallelujahs through the choir of
  Heaven !
Man ! quoth Count Julian, wherefore
  art thou moved
To this strange passion ? I require of
  thee
Thy judgement, not thy prayers !
          Be not displeased !
In gentle voice subdued the Goth
  replies ;
A prayer, from whatsoever lips it flow,
By thine own rule should find the way
  to Heaven,
So that the heart in its sincerity   210
Straight forward breathe it forth. I,
  like thyself,
Am all untrain'd to subtleties of speech,

Nor competent of this great argument
Thou openest; and perhaps shall answer
  thee
Wide of the words, but to the purport
  home.
There are to whom the light of gospel
  truth
Hath never reach'd ; of such I needs
  must deem
As of the sons of men who had their day
Before the light was given. But, Count,
  for those
Who, born amid the light, to darkness
  turn,   220
Wilful in error, . . I dare only say,
God doth not leave the unhappy soul
  without
An inward monitor, and till the grave
Open, the gate of mercy is not closed.

Priest-like ! the renegade replied, and
  shook
His head in scorn. What is not in the
  craft
Is error, and for error there shall be
No mercy found in Him whom yet ye
  name
The Merciful !
          Now God forbid, rejoin'd
The fallen King, that one who stands in
  need   230
Of mercy for his sins should argue thus
Of error ! Thou hast said that thou
  and I,
Thou dying in name a Musselman, and I
A servant of the Cross, may meet in
  Heaven.
Time was when in our fathers' ways we
  walk'd
Regardlessly alike ; faith being to
  each, . .
For so far thou hast reason'd rightly, . .
  like
Our country's fashion and our mother-
  tongue,

Of mere inheritance, . . no thing of choice
In judgement fix'd, nor rooted in the
    heart.   240
Me have the arrows of calamity
Sore stricken; sinking underneath the
    weight
Of sorrow, yet more heavily oppress'd
Beneath the burthen of my sins, I turn'd
In that dread hour to Him who from the
    Cross
Calls to the heavy-laden.   There I found
Relief and comfort; there I have my
    hope,
My strength and my salvation; there,
    the grave
Ready beneath my feet, and Heaven in
    view,
I to the King of Terrors say, Come,
    Death, . .   250
Come quickly ! Thou too wert a stricken
    deer,
Julian, . . God pardon the unhappy hand
That wounded thee ! . . but whither didst
    thou go
For healing ? Thou hast turn'd away
    from Him,
Who saith, Forgive as ye would be for-
    given ;
And that the Moorish sword might do
    thy work,
Received the creed of Mecca : with what
    fruit
For Spain, let tell her cities sack'd, her
    sons
Slaughter'd, her daughters than thine
    own dear child
More foully wrong'd, more wretched !
    For thyself,   260
Thou hast had thy fill of vengeance, and
    perhaps
The cup was sweet : but it hath left
    behind
A bitter relish ! Gladly would thy soul
Forget the past ; as little canst thou
    bear

To send into futurity thy thoughts :
And for this Now, what is it, Count, but
    fear . .
However bravely thou may'st bear thy
    front, . .
Danger, remorse, and stinging obloquy ?
One only hope, one only remedy,
One only refuge yet remains. . . My life
Is at thy mercy, Count ! Call, if thou
    wilt,   271
Thy men, and to the Moors deliver me !
Or strike thyself ! Death were from any
    hand
A welcome gift ; from thine, and in this
    cause,
A boon indeed ! My latest words on
    earth
Should tell thee that all sins may be
    effaced,
Bid thee repent, have faith, and be for-
    given !
Strike, Julian, if thou wilt, and send my
    soul
To intercede for thine, that we may meet,
Thou and thy child and I, beyond the
    grave.   280

    Thus Roderick spake, and spread his
    arms as if
He offer'd to the sword his willing breast,
With looks of passionate persuasion fix'd
Upon the Count, who in his first access
Of anger, seem'd as though he would
    have call'd
His guards to seize the Priest.   The
    attitude
Disarm'd him, and that fervent zeal
    sincere,
And more than both, the look and voice,
    which like
A mystery troubled him.   Florinda too
Hung on his arm with both her hands,
    and cried,   290
O father, wrong him not ! he speaks
    from God !

Life and salvation are upon his tongue!
Judge thou the value of that faith
    whereby,
Reflecting on the past, I murmur not,
And to the end of all look on with joy
Of hope assured!

        Peace, innocent! replied
The Count, and from her hold withdrew
    his arm.
Then with a gather'd brow of mournful-
    ness
Rather than wrath, regarding Roderick,
    said,
Thou preachest that all sins may be
    effaced: 300
Is there forgiveness, Christian, in thy
    creed
For Roderick's crime?.. For Roderick
    and for thee,
Count Julian, said the Goth, and as he
    spake
Trembled through every fibre of his
    frame,
The gate of Heaven is open. Julian
    threw
His wrathful hand aloft, and cried,
    Away!
Earth could not hold us both, nor can
    one Heaven
Contain my deadliest enemy and me!

  My father, say not thus! Florinda
    cried;
I have forgiven him! I have pray'd for
    him!   310
For him, for thee, and for myself I pour
One constant prayer to Heaven! In
    passion then
She knelt, and bending back, with arms
    and face
Raised toward the sky, the supplicant
    exclaim'd,
Redeemer, heal his heart! It is the grief
Which festers there that hath bewilder'd
    him!

Save him, Redeemer! by thy precious
    death
Save, save him, O my God! Then on her
    face
She fell, and thus with bitterness pur-
    sued
In silent throes her agonizing prayer. 320

  Afflict not thus thyself, my child, the
    Count
Exclaim'd; O dearest, be thou com-
    forted;
Set but thy heart at rest, I ask no more!
Peace, dearest, peace!.. and weeping
    as he spake,
He knelt to raise her. Roderick also
    knelt;
Be comforted, he cried, and rest in faith
That God will hear thy prayers! they
    must be heard.
He who could doubt the worth of prayers
    like thine
May doubt of all things! Sainted as
    thou art   329
In sufferings here, this miracle will be
Thy work and thy reward!

             Then raising her,
They seated her upon the fountain's
    brink,
And there beside her sate. The moon
    had risen,
And that fair spring lay blacken'd half
    in shade,
Half like a burnish'd mirror in her light.
By that reflected light Count Julian saw
That Roderick's face was bathed with
    tears, and pale
As monumental marble. Friend, said he,
Whether thy faith be fabulous, or sent
Indeed from Heaven, its dearest gift to
    man,   340
Thy heart is true: and had the mitred
    Priest
Of Seville been like thee, or hadst thou
    held

The place he fill'd; . . but this is idle
   talk, . .
Things are as they will be ; and we, poor
   slaves,
Fret in the harness as we may, must
   drag
The Car of Destiny where'er she drives,
Inexorable and blind !
               Oh wretched man !
Cried Roderick, if thou seekest to assuage
Thy wounded spirit with that deadly
   drug,
Hell's subtlest venom ; look to thine
   own heart,   350
Where thou hast Will and Conscience
   to belie
This juggling sophistry, and lead thee
   yet
Through penitence to Heaven !
             Whate'er it be
That governs us, in mournful tone the
   Count
Replied, Fate, Providence, or Allah's will,
Or reckless Fortune, still the effect the
   same,
A world of evil and of misery !
Look where we will we meet it ; where-
   soe'er
We go we bear it with us.   Here we sit
Upon the margin of this peaceful spring,
And oh ! what volumes of calamity 361
Would be unfolded here, if either heart
Laid open its sad records ! Tell me not
Of goodness ! Either in some freak of
   power
This frame of things was fashion'd, then
   cast off
To take its own wild course, the sport
   of chance ;
Or the bad Spirit o'er the Good prevails,
And in the eternal conflict hath arisen
Lord of the ascendant !
            Rightly would'st thou say
Were there no world but this ! the Goth
   replied.   370

The happiest child of earth that e'er was
   mark'd
To be the minion of prosperity,
Richest in corporal gifts and wealth of
   mind,
Honour and fame attending him abroad,
Peace and all dear domestic joys at
   home,
And sunshine till the evening of his days
Closed in without a cloud, . . even such
   a man
Would from the gloom and horror of his
   heart
Confirm thy fatal thought, were this
   world all !
Oh ! who could bear the haunting
   mystery,   380
If death and retribution did not solve
The riddle, and to heavenliest harmony
Reduce the seeming chaos ! . . Here we
   see
The water at its well-head ; clear it is,
Not more transpicuous the invisible air ;
Pure as an infant's thoughts ; and here
   to life
And good directed all its uses serve.
The herb grows greener on its brink;
   sweet flowers
Bend o'er the stream that feeds their
   freshened roots ;
The red-breast loves it for his wintry
   haunts ;   390
And when the buds begin to open forth,
Builds near it with his mate their brood-
   ing nest ;
The thirsty stag with widening nostrils
   there
Invigorated draws his copious draught ;
And there amid its flags the wild-boar
   stands,
Nor suffering wrong nor meditating hurt.
Through woodlands wild and solitary
   fields
Unsullied thus it holds its bounteous
   course ;

But when it reaches the resorts of men,
The service of the city there defiles 400
The tainted stream ; corrupt and foul
it flows
Through loathsome banks and o'er a bed
impure,
Till in the sea, the appointed end to
which
Through all its way it hastens, 'tis
received,
And, losing all pollution, mingles there
In the wide world of waters. So is it
With the great stream of things, if all
were seen ;
Good the beginning, good the end shall
be,
And transitory evil only make
The good end happier. Ages pass away,
Thrones fall, and nations disappear, and
worlds 411
Grow old and go to wreck ; the soul
alone
Endures, and what she chuseth for her-
self,
The arbiter of her own destiny,
That only shall be permanent.
                              But guilt,
And all our suffering ? said the Count.
The Goth
Replied, Repentance taketh sin away,
Death remedies the rest. . . Soothed by
the strain
Of such discourse, Julian was silent then,
And sate contemplating. Florinda too
Was calm'd : If sore experience may be
thought 421
To teach the uses of adversity,
She said, alas! who better learn'd than I
In that sad school ! Methinks if ye
would know
How visitations of calamity
Affect the pious soul, 'tis shown ye
there !
Look yonder at that cloud, which through
the sky

Sailing alone, doth cross in her career
The rolling Moon ! I watch'd it as it
came,
And deem'd the deep opake would blot
her beams ; 430
But, melting like a wreath of snow, it
hangs
In folds of wavy silver round, and
clothes
The orb with richer beauties than her
own,
Then passing, leaves her in her light
serene.

Thus having said, the pious sufferer
sate,
Beholding with fix'd eyes that lovely
orb,
Till quiet tears confused in dizzy light
The broken moonbeams. They too by
the toil
Of spirit, as by travail of the day
Subdued, were silent, yielding to the
hour. 440
The silver cloud diffusing slowly pass'd,
And now into its airy elements
Resolved is gone ; while through the
azure depth
Alone in heaven the glorious Moon pur-
sues
Her course appointed, with indifferent
beams
Shining upon the silent hills around,
And the dark tents of that unholy host,
Who, all unconscious of impending fate,
Take their last slumber there. The
camp is still ;
The fires have moulder'd, and the breeze
which stirs 450
The soft and snowy embers, just lays
bare
At times a red and evanescent light,
Or for a moment wakes a feeble flame.
They by the fountain hear the stream
below,

Whose murmurs, as the wind arose or
    fell,
Fuller or fainter reach the ear attuned.
And now the nightingale, not distant far,
Began her solitary song; and pour'd
To the cold moon a richer, stronger
    strain
Than that with which the lyric lark
    salutes   460
The new-born day. Her deep and
    thrilling song
Seem'd with its piercing melody to reach
The soul, and in mysterious unison
Blend with all thoughts of gentleness
    and love.
Their hearts were open to the healing
    power
Of nature; and the splendour of the
    night,
The flow of waters, and that sweetest lay
Came to them like a copious evening
    dew
Falling on vernal herbs which thirst for
    rain.

XXII. THE MOORISH COUNCIL

Thus they beside the fountain sate, of
    food
And rest forgetful, when a messenger
Summon'd Count Julian to the Leader's
    tent.
In council there at that late hour he
    found
The assembled Chiefs, on sudden tidings
    call'd
Of unexpected weight from Cordoba.
Jealous that Abdalaziz had assumed
A regal state, affecting in his court
The forms of Gothic sovereignty, the
    Moors,
Whom artful spirits of ambitious mould
Stirr'd up, had risen against him in
    revolt: 11

And he who late had in the Caliph's
    name
Ruled from the Ocean to the Pyrenees,
A mutilate and headless carcass now,
From pitying hands received beside the
    road
A hasty grave, scarce hidden there from
    dogs
And ravens, nor from wintry rains
    secure.
She, too, who in the wreck of Spain
    preserved
Her queenly rank, the wife of Roderick
    first,
Of Abdalaziz after, and to both   20
Alike unhappy, shared the ruin now
Her counsels had brought on; for she
    had led
The infatuate Moor, in dangerous
    vauntery,
To these aspiring forms, . . so should he
    gain
Respect and honour from the Musselmen,
She said, and that the obedience of the
    Goths
Follow'd the sceptre. In an evil hour
She gave the counsel, and in evil hour
He lent a willing ear; the popular rage
Fell on them both; and they to whom
    her name   30
Had been a mark for mockery and
    reproach,
Shudder'd with human horror at her
    fate.
Ayub was heading the wild anarchy;
But where the cement of authority
Is wanting, all things there are dislocate:
The mutinous soldiery, by every cry
Of rumour set in wild career, were
    driven
By every gust of passion, setting up
One hour, what in the impulse of the
    next,
Equally unreasoning, they destroy'd:
    thus all   40

Was in misrule where uproar gave the
law,
And ere from far Damascus they could
learn
The Caliph's pleasure, many a moon
must pass.
What should be done ? should Abulca-
cem march
To Cordoba, and in the Caliph's name
Assume the power which to his rank in
arms
Rightly devolved, restoring thus the
reign
Of order ? or pursue with quicken'd speed
The end of this great armament, and
crush
Rebellion first, then to domestic ills 50
Apply his undivided mind and force
Victorious ? What in this emergency
Was Julian's counsel, Abulcacem ask'd.
Should they accomplish soon their enter-
prize ?
Or would the insurgent infidels prolong
The contest, seeking by protracted war
To weary them, and trusting in the
strength
Of these wild hills ?
        Julian replied, The Chief
Of this revolt is wary, resolute,
Of approved worth in war : a desperate
part   60
He for himself deliberately hath chosen,
Confiding in the hereditary love
Borne to him by these hardy moun-
taineers,
A love which his own noble qualities
Have strengthen'd so that every heart
is his.
When ye can bring them to the open
proof
Of battle, ye will find them in his cause
Lavish of life ; but well they know the
strength
Of their own fastnesses, the mountain
paths

Impervious to pursuit, the vantages 70
Of rock, and pass, and woodland, and
ravine ;
And hardly will ye tempt them to forego
These natural aids wherein they put
their trust
As in their stubborn spirit, each alike
Deem'd by themselves invincible, and so
By Roman found and Goth . . beneath
whose sway
Slowly persuaded rather than subdued
They came, and still through every
change retain'd
Their manners obstinate and barbarous
speech.
My counsel, therefore, is, that we secure
With strong increase of force the adja-
cent posts,   81
And chiefly Gegio, leaving them so
mann'd
As may abate the hope of enterprize
Their strength being told. Time in a
strife like this
Becomes the ally of those who trust in
him :
Make then with Time your covenant.
Old feuds
May disunite the chiefs : some may be
gain'd
By fair entreaty, others by the stroke
Of nature, or of policy, cut off.
This was the counsel which in Cordoba
I offer'd Abdalaziz : in ill hour   91
Rejecting it, he sent upon this war
His father's faithful friend ! Dark are
the ways
Of destiny ! had I been at his side
Old Muza would not now have mourn'd
his age
Left childless, nor had Ayub dared defy
The Caliph's represented power. The
case
Calls for thine instant presence, with
the weight
Of thy legitimate authority.

Julian, said Orpas, turning from
beneath   100
His turban to the Count a crafty eye,
Thy daughter is return'd; doth she not
    bring
Some tidings of the movements of the
    foe ?
The Count replied, When child and
    parent meet
First reconciled from discontents which
    wrung
The hearts of both, ill should their con-
    verse be
Of warlike matters ! There hath been
    no time
For such inquiries, neither should I think
To ask her touching that for which
    I know   109
She hath neither eye nor thought.
                        There was a time,
Orpas with smile malignant thus replied,
When in the progress of the Caliph's
    arms
Count Julian's daughter had an interest
Which touch'd her nearly ! But her
    turn is served,
And hatred of Prince Orpas may beget
Indifference to the cause.   Yet Destiny
Still guideth to the service of the faith
The wayward heart of woman; for as
    one
Delivered Roderick to the avenging
    sword,
So hath another at this hour betray'd
Pelayo to his fall.   His sister came 121
At nightfall to my tent a fugitive.
She tells me that on learning our
    approach
The rebel to a cavern in the hills
Had sent his wife and children, and with
    them
Those of his followers, thinking there
    conceal'd
They might be safe.   She, moved, by
    injuries

Which stung her spirit, on the way
    escaped,
And for revenge will guide us.   In
    reward
She asks her brother's forfeiture of lands
In marriage with Numacian : some-
        thing too   131
Touching his life, that for her services
It might be spared, she said ; . . an after-
    thought
To salve decorum, and if conscience wake
Serve as a sop: but when the sword shall
    smite
Pelayo and his dangerous race, I ween
That a thin kerchief will dry all the tears
The Lady Guisla sheds !
                        'Tis the old taint !
Said Julian mournfully ;   from her
    mother's womb
She brought the inbred wickedness
    which now   140
In ripe infection blossoms.   Woman,
    woman,
Still to the Goths art thou the instru-
    ment
Of overthrow ;   thy virtue and thy vice
Fatal alike to them !
                        Say rather, cried
The insidious renegade, that Allah thus
By woman punisheth the idolatry
Of those who raise a woman to the rank
Of godhead, calling on their Mary's name
With senseless prayers.   In vain shall
    they invoke
Her trusted succour now !   like silly
    birds   150
By fear betray'd, they fly into the toils ;
And this Pelayo, who in lengthen'd war
Baffling our force, has thought perhaps
    to reign
Prince of the Mountains, when we hold
    his wife
And offspring at our mercy, must him-
    self
Come to the lure.

Enough, the Leader said ;
This unexpected work of favouring Fate
Opens an easy way to our desires,
And renders farther counsel needless
  now.
Great is the Prophet whose protecting
  power   160
Goes with the faithful forth ! the rebels'
  days
Are number'd ; Allah hath deliver'd
  them
Into our hands !
                  So saying he arose ;
The Chiefs withdrew, Orpas alone
  remain'd
Obedient to his indicated will.
The event, said Abulcacem, hath ap-
  proved
Thy judgement in all points ; his
  daughter comes
At the first summons, even as thou
  saidst ;
Her errand with the insurgents done,
  she brings
Their well-concerted project back, a
  safe   170
And unexpected messenger ; . . the
  Moor, . .
The shallow Moor, . . must see and not
  perceive ;
Must hear and understand not ; yea
  must bear,
Poor easy fool, to serve their after mirth,
A part in his own undoing ! But just
  Heaven
With this unlook'd-for incident hath
  marr'd
Their complots, and the sword shall cut
  this web
Of treason.
              Well, the renegade replied,
Thou knowest Count Julian's spirit,
  quick in wiles,
In act audacious. Baffled now, he
  thinks   180

Either by instant warning to apprize
The rebels of their danger, or preserve
The hostages when fallen into our power,
Till secret craft contrive, or open force
Win their enlargement. Haply too he
  dreams
Of Cordoba, the avenger and the friend
Of Abdalaziz, in that cause to arm
Moor against Moor, preparing for him-
  self
The victory o'er the enfeebled con-
  querors.
Success in treason hath embolden'd him,
And power but serves him for fresh
  treachery, false   191
To Roderick first, and to the Caliph now.

    The guilt, said Abulcacem, is con-
  firm'd,
The sentence pass'd ; all that is now
  required
Is to strike sure and safely. He hath
  with him
A veteran force devoted to his will,
Whom to provoke were perilous ; nor
  less
Of peril lies there in delay : what course
Between these equal dangers should we
  steer ?

    They have been train'd beneath him
  in the wars   200
Of Africa, the renegade replied ;
Men are they who, from their youth up,
  have found
Their occupation and their joy in arms ;
Indifferent to the cause for which they
  fight,
But faithful to their leader, who hath
  won
By licence largely given, yet temper'd
  still
With exercise of firm authority,
Their whole devotion. Vainly should
  we seek

By proof of Julian's guilt to pacify
Such martial spirits, unto whom all
　　creeds   210
And countries are alike; but take away
The head, and forthwith their fidelity
Goes at the market price.   The act must
　　be
Sudden and secret; poison is too slow.
Thus it may best be done; the Moun-
　　taineers,
Doubtless, ere long will rouse us with
　　some spur
Of sudden enterprize: at such a time
A trusty minister approaching him
May smite him, so that all shall think
　　the spear
Comes from the hostile troops.
　　　　　　　　Right counsellor !
Cried Abulcacem, thou shalt have his
　　lands,   221
The proper meed of thy fidelity :
His daughter thou may'st take or leave.
　　Go now
And find a faithful instrument to put
Our purpose in effect ! . . And when 'tis
　　done,
The Moor, as Orpas from the tent with-
　　drew,
Muttering pursued, . . look for a like
　　reward
Thyself ! that restless head of wicked-
　　ness
In the grave will brood no treasons.
　　Other babes
Scream when the Devil, as they spring
　　to life,   230
Infects them with his touch; but thou
　　didst stretch
Thine arms to meet him, and like
　　mother's milk
Suck the congenial evil ! Thou hast
　　tried
Both laws, and were there aught to gain,
　　would st prove
A third as readily; but when thy sins

Are   weigh'd,   'twill   be   against   an
　　empty scale,
And neither Prophet will avail thee
　　then !

XXIII. THE VALE OF COVADONGA

THE camp is stirring, and ere day hath
　　dawn'd
The tents are struck.   Early they rise
　　whom hope
Awakens, and they travel fast with
　　whom
She goes companion of the way.   By
　　noon
Hath Abulcacem in his speed attain'd
The vale of Cangas.   Well the trusty
　　scouts
Observe his march, and fleet as moun-
　　tain roes,
From post to post with instantaneous
　　speed
The warning bear : none else is nigh;
　　the vale
Hath been deserted, and Pelayo's hall   10
Is open to the foe, who on the tower
Hoist their white signal-flag.   In Sella's
　　stream
The misbelieving multitudes perform,
With hot and hasty hand, their noon-
　　tide rite,
Then hurryingly repeat the Impostor's
　　prayer.
Here they divide; the Chieftain halts
　　with half
The host, retaining Julian and his men,
Whom where the valley widen'd he dis-
　　posed,
Liable to first attack, that so the deed
Of murder plann'd with Orpas might be
　　done.   20
The other force the Moor Alcahman led
Whom Guisla guided up Pionia's stream

Eastward to Soto. Ibrahim went with
    him,
Proud of Granada's snowy heights sub-
    dued,
And boasting of his skill in mountain
    war ;
Yet sure he deem'd an easier victory
Awaited him this day. Little, quoth
    he,
Weens the vain Mountaineer who puts
    his trust
In dens and rocky fastnesses, how close
Destruction is at hand ! Belike he
    thinks   30
The Humma's happy wings have sha-
    dow'd him,
And therefore Fate with royalty must
    crown
His chosen head ! Pity the scymitar
With its rude edge so soon should inter-
    rupt
The pleasant dream !
              There can be no escape
For those who in the cave seek shelter,
    cried
Alcahman ; yield they must, or from
    their holes
Like bees we smoke them out. The
    Chief perhaps
May reign awhile King of the wolves and
    bears,
Till his own subjects hunt him down, or
    kites   40
And crows divide what hunger may have
    left
Upon his ghastly limbs. Happier for
    him
That destiny should this day to our
    hands
Deliver him ; short would be his suffer-
    ings then ;
And we right joyfully should in one hour
Behold our work accomplish'd, and his
    race
Extinct.

              Thus these in mockery and in
    thoughts
Of bloody triumph, to the future blind,
Indulged the scornful vein ; nor deem'd
    that they
Whom to the sword's unsparing edge
    they doom'd,   50
Even then in joyful expectation pray'd
To Heaven for their approach, and at
    their post
Prepared, were trembling with excess
    of hope.
Here in these mountain straits the
    Mountaineer
Had felt his country's strength insuper-
    able ;
Here he had pray'd to see the Musselman
With all his myriads ; therefore had he
    look'd
To Covadonga as a sanctuary
Apt for concealment, easy of defence ;
And Guisla's flight, though to his heart
    it sent   60
A pang more poignant for their mother's
    sake,
Yet did it further in its consequence
His hope and project, surer than decoy
Well-laid, or best-concerted stratagem.
That sullen and revengeful mind, he
    knew,
Would follow to the extremity of guilt
Its long fore-purposed shame : the toils
    were laid,
And she who by the Musselmen full sure
Thought on her kindred her revenge to
    wreak,
Led the Moors in.
              Count Pedro and his son
Were hovering with the main Asturian
    force   71
In the wider vale to watch occasion
    there,
And with hot onset when the alarm
    began
Pursue the vantage. In the fated straits

Of Deva had the King disposed the rest :
Amid the hanging woods, and on the
    cliffs,
A long mile's length on either side its bed,
They lay. The lever and the axe and
    saw
Had skilfully been plied ; and trees and
    stones,
A dread artillery, ranged on crag and
    shelf   80
And steep descent, were ready at the
    word
Precipitate to roll resistless down.
The faithful maiden not more wistfully
Looks for the day that brings her lover
    home ; . .
Scarce more impatiently the horse en-
    dures
The rein, when loud and shrill the
    hunter's horn
Rings in his joyous ears, than at their
    post
The Mountaineers await their certain
    prey ;
Yet mindful of their Prince's order, oft
And solemnly enforced, with eagerness
Subdued by minds well-master'd, they
    expect   91
The appointed signal.
              Hand must not be raised,
Foot stirr'd, nor voice be utter'd, said
    the Chief,
Till the word pass : impatience would
    mar all.
God hath deliver'd over to your hands
His enemies and ours, so we but use
The occasion wisely. Not till the word
    pass
From man to man transmitted, ' In the
    name
Of God, for Spain and Vengeance !' let
    a hand
Be lifted ; on obedience all depends, 100
Their march below with noise of horse
    and foot

And haply with the clang of instruments,
Might drown all other signal, this is
    sure ;
But wait it calmly ; it will not be given
Till the whole line hath enter'd in the
    toils.
Comrades, be patient, so shall none
    escape
Who once set foot within these straits of
    death.
Thus had Pelayo on the Mountaineers
With frequent and impressive charge
    enforced
The needful exhortation. This alone
He doubted, that the Musselmen might
    see   III
The perils of the vale, and warily
Forbear to enter. But they thought to
    find,
As Guisla told, the main Asturian force
Seeking concealment there, no other aid
Soliciting from these their native hills ;
And that the babes and women having
    fallen
In thraldom, they would lay their
    weapons down,
And supplicate forgiveness for their
    sake.
Nor did the Moors perceive in what a
    strait   120
They enter'd ; for the morn had risen
    o'ercast,
And when the Sun had reach'd the
    height of heaven,
Dimly his pale and beamless orb was
    seen
Moving through mist. A soft and
    gentle rain,
Scarce heavier than the summer's even-
    ing dew,
Descended, . . through so still an atmo-
    sphere,
That every leaf upon the moveless trees
Was studded o'er with rain-drops
    bright and full,

None falling till from its own weight
o'erswoln   129
The motion came.
            Low on the mountain side
The fleecy vapour hung, and in its veil
With all their dreadful preparations
wrapt
The Mountaineers ; . . in breathless hope
they lay,
Some blessing God in silence for the
power
This day vouchsafed ; others with
fervency
Of prayer and vow invoked the Mother-
Maid,
Beseeching her that in this favouring
hour
She would be strongly with them. From
below
Meantime distinct they heard the pass-
ing tramp
Of horse and foot, continuous as the
sound   140
Of Deva's stream, and barbarous tongues
commixt
With laughter, and with frequent
shouts, . . for all
Exultant came, expecting sure success ;
Blind wretches over whom the ruin
hung !

They say, quoth one, that though the
Prophet's soul
Doth with the black-eyed Houris bathe
in bliss,
Life hath not left his body, which bears
up
By its miraculous power the holy tomb,
And holds it at Medina in the air
Buoyant between the temple's floor and
roof :   150
And there the Angels fly to him with
news
From East, West, North, and South, of
what befalls

His faithful people. If when he shall
hear
The tale of this day's work, he should
for joy
Forget that he is dead, and walk
abroad, . .
It were as good a miracle as when
He sliced the moon ! Sir Angel hear
me now,
Whoe'er thou be'st who are about to
speed
From Spain to Araby ! when thou hast
got
The Prophet's ear, be sure thou tellest
him   160
How bravely Ghauleb did his part to-
day,
And with what special reverence he
alone
Desired thee to commend him to his
grace ! . .
Fie on thee, scoffer that thou art !
replied
His comrade ; thou wilt never leave
these gibes
Till some commission'd arrow through
the teeth
Shall nail the offending tongue. Hast
thou not heard
How when our clay is leaven'd first with
life,
The ministering Angel brings it from
that spot
Whereon 'tis written in the eternal book
That soul and body must their parting
take,   171
And earth to earth return ? How
knowest thou
But that the Spirit who compounded
thee,
To distant Syria from this very vale
Bore thy component dust, and Azrael
here
Awaits thee at this hour ? . . Little
thought he

Who spake, that in that valley at that
hour
One death awaited both!
                    Thus they pursued
Toward the cave their inauspicious
way.
Weak childhood there and ineffective
age   180
In the chambers of the rock were placed
secure;
But of the women, all whom with the
babes
Maternal care detain'd not, were aloft
To aid in the destruction; by the side
Of fathers, brethren, husbands, sta-
tion'd there,
They watch and pray. Pelayo in the
cave
With the venerable Primate took his
post.
Ranged on the rising cliffs on either
hand,
Vigilant sentinels with eye intent
Observe his movements, when to take
the word   190
And pass it forward. He in arms com-
plete
Stands in the portal: a stern majesty
Reign'd in his countenance severe that
hour,
And in his eye a deep and dreadful joy
Shone, as advancing up the vale he
saw
The Moorish banners. God hath blinded
them!
He said; the measure of their crimes is
full!
O Vale of Deva, famous shalt thou be
From this day forth for ever; and to
these
Thy springs shall unborn generations
come   200
In pilgrimage, and hallow with their
prayers
The cradle of their native monarchy!

There was a stirring in the air, the sun
Prevail'd, and gradually the brightening
mist
Began to rise and melt. A jutting
crag
Upon the right projected o'er the
stream,
Not farther from the cave than a strong
hand
Expert, with deadly aim, might cast the
spear,
Or a strong voice, pitch'd to full com-
pass, make
Its clear articulation heard distinct. 210
A venturous dalesman, once ascending
there
To rob the eagle's nest, had fallen, and
hung
Among the heather, wondrously pre-
served:
Therefore had he with pious gratitude
Placed on that overhanging brow a
Cross,
Tall as the mast of some light fisher's
skiff,
And from the vale conspicuous. As the
Moors
Advanced, the Chieftain in the van was
seen,
Known by his arms, and from the crag
a voice
Pronounced his name, . . Alcahman!
hoa, look up,   220
Alcahman! As the floating mist drew
up,
It had divided there, and open'd round
The Cross; part clinging to the rock
beneath,
Hovering and waving part in fleecy
folds,
A canopy of silver light condensed
To shape and substance. In the midst
there stood
A female form, one hand upon the
Cross,

The other raised in menacing act ; below
Loose flow'd her raiment, but her
    breast was arm'd,
And helmeted her head. The Moor
    turn'd pale,   230
For on the walls of Auria he had seen
That well-known figure, and had well
    believed
She rested with the dead. What, hoa !
    she cried,
Alcahman ! In the name of all who fell
At Auria in the massacre, this hour
I summon thee before the throne of
    God
To answer for the innocent blood ! This
    hour,
Moor, Miscreant, Murderer, Child of
    Hell, this hour
I summon thee to judgement ! . . In the
    name
Of God ! for Spain and Vengeance !
              Thus she closed
Her speech ; for taking from the Pri-
    mate's hand   241
That oaken cross which at the sacring
    rites
Had served for crosier, at the cavern's
    mouth
Pelayo lifted it and gave the word.
From voice to voice on either side it
    pass'd
With rapid repetition, . . In the name
Of God ! for Spain and Vengeance !
    and forthwith
On either side along the whole defile
The Asturians shouting in the name of
    God,
Set the whole ruin loose ! huge trunks
    and stones,   250
And loosen'd crags, down down they
    roll'd with rush
And bound, and thundering force. Such
    was the fall
As when some city by the labouring
    earth

Heaved from its strong foundations is
    cast down,
And all its dwellings, towers, and
    palaces,
In one wide desolation prostrated.
From end to end of that long strait, the
    crash
Was heard continuous, and commixt
    with sounds
More dreadful, shrieks of horror and
    despair,
And death, . . the wild and agonizing
    cry   260
Of that whole host in one destruction
    whelm'd.
Vain was all valour there, all martial
    skill ;
The valiant arm is helpless now ; the
    feet
Swift in the race avail not now to save ;
They perish, all their thousands perish
    there, . .
Horsemen and infantry they perish
    all, . .
The outward armour and the bones
    within
Broken and bruised and crush'd. Echo
    prolong'd
The long uproar : a silence then ensued,
Through which the sound of Deva's
    stream was heard,   270
A lonely voice of waters, wild and
    sweet ;
The lingering groan, the faintly-utter'd
    prayer,
The louder curses of despairing death,
Ascended not so high. Down from the
    cave
Pelayo hastes, the Asturians hasten
    down,
Fierce and immitigable down they
    speed
On all sides, and along the vale of blood
The avenging sword did mercy's work
    that hour.

XXIV. RODERICK AND COUNT JULIAN

THOU hast been busy, Death ! this day, and yet
But half thy work is done ; the Gates of Hell
Are throng'd, yet twice ten thousand spirits more,
Who from their warm and healthful tenements
Fear no divorce, must ere the sun go down
Enter the world of woe ! the Gate of Heaven
Is open too, and Angels round the throne
Of Mercy on their golden harps this day
Shall sing the triumphs of Redeeming Love.

There was a Church at Cangas dedicate   10
To that Apostle unto whom his Lord
Had given the keys ; a humble edifice,
Whose rude and time-worn structure suited well
That vale among the mountains. Its low roof
With stone plants and with moss was overgrown,
Short fern, and richer weeds which from the eaves
Hung their long tresses down. White lichens clothed
The sides, save where the ivy spread, which bower'd
The porch, and clustering round the pointed wall,
Wherein two bells, each open to the wind,   20
Hung side by side, threaded with hairy shoots
The double nich ; and climbing to the cross,

Wreathed it and half conceal'd its sacred form
With bushy tufts luxuriant. Here in the font, . .
Borne hither with rejoicing and with prayers
Of all the happy land who saw in him
The lineage of their ancient Chiefs renew'd, . .
The Prince had been immersed : and here within
An oaken galilee, now black with age,
His old Iberian ancestors were laid.   30

Two stately oaks stood nigh, in the full growth
Of many a century. They had flourish'd there
Before the Gothic sword was felt in Spain,
And when the ancient sceptre of the Goths
Was broken, there they flourish'd still. Their boughs
Mingled on high, and stretching wide around,
Form'd a deep shade, beneath which canopy
Upon the ground Count Julian's board was spread,
For to his daughter he had left his tent
Pitch'd for her use hard by. He at the board   40
Sate with his trusted Captains, Gunderick,
Felix and Miro, Theudered and Paul,
Basil and Cottila, and Virimar,
Men through all fortunes faithful to their Lord,
And to that old and tried fidelity,
By personal love and honour held in ties
Strong as religious bonds. As there they sate,
In the distant vale a rising dust was seen,

And frequent flash of steel, . . the flying
    fight
Of men who, by a fiery foe pursued, 50
Put forth their coursers at full speed, to
    reach
The aid in which they trust. Up sprung
    the Chiefs,
And hastily taking helm and shield, and
    spear,
Sped to their post.
            Amid the chesnut groves
On Sella's side, Alphonso had in charge
To watch the foe; a prowling band
    came nigh,
Whom with the ardour of impetuous
    youth
He charged and followed them in close
    pursuit:
Quick succours join'd them; and the
    strife grew hot, 59
Ere Pedro hastening to bring off his son,
Or Julian and his Captains, . . bent alike
That hour to abstain from combat, (for
    by this
Full sure they deem'd Alcahman had
    secured
The easy means of certain victory,) . .
Could reach the spot. Both thus in
    their intent
According, somewhat had they now
    allay'd
The fury of the fight, though still spears
    flew,
And strokes of sword and mace were
    interchanged,
When passing through the troop a Moor
    came up
On errand from the Chief, to Julian
    sent; 70
A fatal errand fatally perform'd
For Julian, for the Chief, and for himself,
And all that host of Musselmen he
    brought;
For while with well-dissembled words
    he lured

The warrior's ear, the dexterous ruffian
    mark'd
The favouring moment and unguarded
    place,
And plunged a javelin in his side. The
    Count
Fell, but in falling called to Cottila,
Treachery! the Moor! the Moor! . .
    He too on whom
He call'd had seen the blow from whence
    it came, 80
And seized the murderer. Miscreant!
    he exclaim'd,
Who set thee on? The Musselman, who
    saw
His secret purpose baffled, undismayed,
Replies, What I have done is authorized;
To punish treachery and prevent worse
    ill
Orpas and Abulcacem sent me here;
The service of the Caliph and the Faith
Required the blow.
            The Prophet and the Fiend
Reward thee then! cried Cottila;
    meantime
Take thou from me thy proper earthly
    meed; 90
Villain! . . and lifting as he spake the
    sword,
He smote him on the neck: the tren-
    chant blade
Through vein and artery pass'd and
    yielding bone;
And on the shoulder, as the assassin
    dropt,
His head half-severed fell. The curse
    of God
Fall on the Caliph and the Faith and thee;
Stamping for anguish, Cottila pursued!
African dogs, thus is it ye requite
Our services? . . But dearly shall ye pay
For this day's work! . . O Fellow-
    soldiers, here, 100
Stretching his hands toward the host,
    he cried,

Behold your noble leader basely slain!
He who for twenty years hath led us forth
To war, and brought us home with victory,
Here he lies foully murdered, . . by the Moors, . .
Those whom he trusted, whom he served so well!
Our turn is next! but neither will we wait
Idly, nor tamely fall!

      Amid the grief,
Tumult, and rage, of those who gather'd round,
When Julian could be heard, I have yet life,   110
He said, for vengeance. Virimar, speed thou
To yonder Mountaineers, and tell their Chiefs
That Julian's veteran army joins this day
Pelayo's standard! The command devolves
On Gunderick. Fellow-soldiers, who so well
Redress'd the wrongs of your old General,
Ye will not let this death go unrevenged!..
Tears then were seen on many an iron cheek,
And groans were heard from many a resolute heart,
And vows with imprecations mix'd went forth,   120
And curses check'd by sobs. Bear me apart,
Said Julian, with a faint and painful voice,
And let me see my daughter ere I die.

 Scarce had he spoken when the pitying throng
Divide before her. Eagerly she came ;

A deep and fearful lustre in her eye,
A look of settled woe, . . pale, deadly pale,
Yet to no lamentations giving way,
Nor tears nor groans; . . within her breaking heart
She bore the grief, and kneeling solemnly   130
Beside him, raised her aweful hands to heaven,
And cried, Lord God! be with him in this hour!

Two things have I to think of, O my child,
Vengeance and thee; said Julian. For the first
I have provided : what remains of life
As best may comfort thee may so be best
Employ'd ; let me be borne within the church,
And thou, with that good man who follows thee,
Attend me there.

     Thus when Florinda heard
Her father speak, a gleam of heavenly joy   140
Shone through the anguish of her countenance.
O gracious God, she cried, my prayers are heard :
Now let me die! . . They raised him from the earth ;
He, knitting as they lifted him his brow,
Drew in through open lips and teeth firm-closed
His painful breath, and on the lance laid hand,
Lest its long shaft should shake the mortal wound.
Gently his men with slow and steady step
Their suffering burthen bore, and in the Church
Before the altar laid him down, his head
Upon Florinda's knees. . . Now, friends, said he,   151

Farewell. I ever hoped to meet my
    death
Among ye, like a soldier, . . but not
    thus !
Go, join the Asturians; and in after
    years,
When of your old commander ye shall
    talk,
How well he loved his followers, what he
    was
In battle, and how basely he was slain,
Let not the tale its fit completion lack,
But say how bravely was his death
    revenged.
Vengeance ! in that good word doth
    Julian make   160
His testament; your faithful swords
    must give
The will its full performance. Leave
    me now,
I have done with worldly things. Com-
    rades, farewell,
And love my memory !
           They with copious tears
Of burning anger, grief exasperating
Their rage, and fury giving force to grief,
Hasten'd to form their ranks against the
    Moors.
Julian meantime toward the altar turn'd
His languid eyes : That Image, is it not
St. Peter, he inquired, he who denied
His Lord and was forgiven ? . . Roderick
    rejoin'd,   171
It is the Apostle ; and may that same
    Lord,
O Julian, to thy soul's salvation bless
The seasonable thought !
           The dying Count
Then fix'd upon the Goth his earnest
    eyes.
No time, said he, is this for bravery,
As little for dissemblance. I would fain
Die in the faith wherein my fathers died,
Whereto they pledged me in mine in-
    fancy. . .

A soldier's habits, he pursued, have
    steel'd   180
My spirit, and perhaps I do not fear
This passage as I ought. But if to feel
That I have sinn'd, and from my soul
    renounce
The Impostor's faith, which never in
    that soul
Obtain'd a place, . . if at the Saviour's
    feet,
Laden with guilt, to cast myself and cry,
Lord, I believe ! help thou my un-
    belief ! . .
If this in the sincerity of death
Sufficeth, . . Father, let me from thy lips
Receive the assurances with which the
    Church   190
Doth bless the dying Christian.
           Roderick raised
His eyes to Heaven, and crossing on his
    breast
His open palms, Mysterious are thy ways
And merciful, O gracious Lord ! he cried,
Who to this end hast thus been pleased
    to lead
My wandering steps ! O Father, this thy
    son
Hath sinn'd and gone astray : but hast
    not Thou
Said, When the sinner from his evil ways
Turneth, that he shall save his soul
    alive,
And Angels at the sight rejoice in
    Heaven ?   200
Therefore do I, in thy most holy name,
Into thy family receive again
Him who was lost, and in that name
    absolve
The Penitent. . . So saying on the head
Of Julian solemnly he laid his hands.
Then to the altar tremblingly he turn'd,
And took the bread, and breaking it,
    pursued,
Julian ! receive from me the Bread of
    Life !

In silence reverently the Count partook
The reconciling rite, and to his lips 210
Roderick then held the consecrated cup.

   Me too! exclaim'd Florinda, who till
   then
Had listen'd speechlessly; Thou Man
   of God,
I also must partake! The Lord hath
   heard
My prayers! one sacrament, . . one
   hour, . . one grave, . .
One resurrection!
            That dread office done,
Count Julian with amazement saw the
   Priest
Kneel down before him. By the sacra-
   ment
Which we have here partaken, Roderick
   cried,
In this most aweful moment; by that
   hope, . . 220
That holy faith which comforts thee in
   death,
Grant thy forgiveness, Julian, ere thou
   diest!
Behold the man who most hath injured
   thee!
Roderick, the wretched Goth, the guilty
   cause
Of all thy guilt, . . the unworthy instru-
   ment
Of thy redemption, . . kneels before thee
   here,
And prays to be forgiven!
            Roderick! exclaim'd
The dying Count, . . Roderick! . . and
   from the floor
With violent effort half he raised him-
   self;
The spear hung heavy in his side, and
   pain 230
And weakness overcame him, that he fell
Back on his daughter's lap. O Death,
   cried he, . .

Passing his hand across his cold damp
   brow, . .
Thou tamest the strong limb, and con-
   querest
The stubborn heart! But yesterday
   I said
One Heaven could not contain mine
   enemy
And me: and now I lift my dying voice
To say, Forgive me, Lord, as I forgive
Him who hath done the wrong! . . He
   closed his eyes
A moment; then with sudden impulse
   cried, . . 240
Roderick, thy wife is dead, . . the Church
   hath power
To free thee from thy vows, . . the broken
   heart
Might yet be heal'd, the wrong redress'd,
   the throne
Rebuilt by that same hand which pull'd
   it down,
And these cursed Africans. . . Oh for a
   month
Of that waste life which millions mis-
   bestow! . .
His voice was passionate, and in his eye
With glowing animation while he spake
The vehement spirit shone: its effort
   soon
Was pass'd, and painfully with feeble
   breath 250
In slow and difficult utterance he pur-
   sued, . .
Vain hope, if all the evil was ordain'd,
And this wide wreck the will and work
   of Heaven,
We but the poor occasion! Death will
   make
All clear, and joining us in better worlds,
Complete our union there! Do for me now
One friendly office more: draw forth the
   spear,
And free me from this pain! . . Receive
   his soul,

Saviour! exclaim'd the Goth, as he per-
 form'd
The fatal service. Julian cried, O
 friend! . .   260
True friend! . . and gave to him his
 dying hand.
Then said he to Florinda, I go first,
Thou followest! . . kiss me, child! . . and
 now good night!
When from her father's body she arose,
Her cheek was flush'd, and in her eyes
 there beam'd
A wilder brightness. On the Goth she
 gazed
While underneath the emotions of that
 hour
Exhausted life gave way. O God! she
 said,
Lifting her hands, thou hast restored
 me all, . .
All . . in one hour! . . and round his neck
 she threw   270
Her arms and cried, My Roderick!
 mine in Heaven!
Groaning, he clasp'd her close, and in
 that act
And agony her happy spirit fled.

XXV. RODERICK IN BATTLE

Eight thousand men had to Asturias
 march'd
Beneath Count Julian's banner; the
 remains
Of that brave army which in Africa
So well against the Musselman made
 head,
Till sense of injuries insupportable,
And raging thirst of vengeance, over-
 threw
Their leader's noble spirit. To revenge
His quarrel, twice that number left their
 bones,
Slain in unnatural battle, on the field

Of Xeres, when the sceptre from the
 Goths   10
By righteous Heaven was reft. Others
 had fallen
Consumed in sieges, alway by the Moor
To the front of war opposed. The
 policy,
With whatsoever show of honour
 cloak'd,
Was gross, and this surviving band had
 oft
At their carousals, of the flagrant wrong,
Held such discourse as stirs the mount-
 ing blood,
The common danger with one discontent
Affecting chiefs and men. Nor had the
 bonds
Of rooted discipline and faith attach'd,
Thus long restrain'd them, had they not
 known well   21
That Julian in their just resentment
 shared,
And fix'd their hopes on him. Slight
 impulse now
Sufficed to make these fiery martialists
Break forth in open fury; and though
 first
Count Pedro listen'd with suspicious ear
To Julian's dying errand, deeming it
Some new decoy of treason, . . when he
 found
A second legate follow'd Virimar,
And then a third, and saw the turbu-
 lence   30
Of the camp, and how against the Moors
 in haste
They form'd their lines, he knew that
 Providence
This hour had for his country interposed,
And in such faith advanced to use the
 aid
Thus wondrously ordain'd. The eager
 Chiefs
Hasten to greet him, Cottila and Paul,
Basil and Miro, Theudered, Gunderick,

Felix, and all who held authority;
The zealous services of their brave host
They proffer'd, and besought him in-
    stantly   40
To lead against the African their force
Combined, and in good hour assail a foe
Divided, nor for such attack prepared.

While thus they communed, Roderick
    from the church
Came forth, and seeing Pedro, bent his
    way
Toward them.   Sirs, said he, the Count
    is dead;
He died a Christian, reconciled to
    Heaven,
In faith; and when his daughter had
    received
His dying breath, her spirit too took
    flight.   49
One sacrament, one death, united them;
And I beseech ye, ye who from the work
Of blood which lies before us may
    return, . .
If, as I think, it should not be my fate . .
That in one grave with Christian cere-
    monies
Ye lay them side by side.   In Heaven
    I ween
They are met through mercy: . . ill befall
    the man
Who should in death divide them ! . .
    Then he turn'd
His speech to Pedro in an under voice;
The King, said he, I know with noble
    mind
Will judge of the departed; Christian
    like   60
He died, and with a manly penitence:
They who condemn him most should
    call to mind
How grievous was the wrong which
    madden'd him;
Be that remember'd in his history,
And let no shame be offer'd his remains.

As Pedro would have answer'd, a loud
    cry
Of menacing imprecation from the troops
Arose; for Orpas, by the Moorish Chief
Sent to allay the storm his villainy
Had stirr'd, came hastening on a milk-
    white steed,   70
And at safe distance having check'd the
    rein,
Beckon'd for parley.   'Twas Orelio
On which he rode, Roderick's own
    battle-horse,
Who from his master's hand had wont
    to feed,
And with a glad docility obey
His voice familiar.   At the sight the
    Goth
Started, and indignation to his soul
Brought back the thoughts and feelings
    of old times.
Suffer me, Count, he cried, to answer
    him,
And hold these back the while ! Thus
    having said,   80
He waited no reply, but as he was,
Bareheaded, in his weeds, and all un-
    arm'd,
Advanced toward the renegade.   Sir
    Priest,
Quoth Orpas as he came, I hold no talk
With thee; my errand is with Gun-
    derick
And the Captains of the host, to whom
    I bring
Such liberal offers and clear proof . .
              The Goth,
Breaking with scornful voice his speech,
    exclaim'd,
What, could no steed but Roderick's
    serve thy turn ?
I should have thought some sleek and
    sober mule   90
Long train'd in shackles to procession
    pace,
More suited to my lord of Seville's use

Than this good war-horse, . . he who
    never bore
A villain, until Orpas cross'd his back ! . .
Wretch ! cried the astonish'd renegade,
    and stoopt,
Foaming with anger, from the saddle-
    bow
To reach his weapon.   Ere the hasty
    hand
Trembling in passion could perform its
    will,
Roderick had seized the reins.   How
    now, he cried,
Orelio ! old companion, . . my good
    horse, . .   100
Off with this recreant burthen ! . . And
    with that
He raised his hand, and rear'd and
    back'd the steed,
To that remember'd voice and arm of
    power
Obedient.   Down the helpless traitor
    fell
Violently thrown, and Roderick over
    him
Thrice led with just and unrelenting
    hand
The trampling hoofs.   Go join Witiza
    now,
Where he lies howling, the avenger cried,
And tell him Roderick sent thee !
                                   At that sight,
Count Julian's soldiers and the Asturian
    host   110
Set up a shout, a joyful shout, which
    rung
Wide through the welkin.   Their exult-
    ing cry
With louder acclamation was renew'd,
When from the expiring miscreant's
    neck they saw
That Roderick took the shield, and
    round his own
Hung it, and vaulted in the seat.   My
    horse !

My noble horse ! he cried, with flatter-
    ing hand
Patting his high-arch'd neck ! the rene-
    gade,
I thank him for't, hath kept thee
    daintily !
Orelio, thou art in thy beauty still,   120
Thy pride and strength ! Orelio, my
    good horse,
Once more thou bearest to the field thy
    Lord,
He who so oft hath fed and cherish'd
    thee,
He for whose sake, wherever thou wert
    seen,
Thou wert by all men honour'd.   Once
    again
Thou hast thy proper master ! Do thy
    part
As thou wert wont ; and bear him glori-
    ously,
My beautiful Orelio, . . to the last , . .
The happiest of his fields ! . . Then he
    drew forth
The scymitar, and waving it aloft,   130
Rode toward the troops ; its unaccus-
    tom'd shape
Disliked him ;   Renegade in all things !
    cried
The Goth, and cast it from him ; to the
    Chiefs
Then said, If I have done ye service
    here,
Help me, I pray you, to a Spanish
    sword !
The trustiest blade that e'er in Bilbilis
Was dipt, would not to-day be mis-
    bestowed
On this right hand ! . . Go some one,
    Gunderick cried,
And bring Count Julian's sword.   Who-
    e'er thou art,
The worth which thou hast shown
    avenging him   140
Entitles thee to wear it.   But thou goest

For battle unequipp'd; .. haste there and strip
Yon villain of his armour !
                    Late he spake,
So fast the Moors came on. It matters not,
Replied the Goth; there's many a mountaineer,
Who in no better armour cased this day
Than his wonted leathern gipion, will be found
In the hottest battle, yet bring off untouch'd
The unguarded life he ventures. ..
Taking then
Count Julian's sword, he fitted round his wrist   150
The chain, and eyeing the elaborate steel
With stern regard of joy, The African
Under unhappy stars was born, he cried,
Who tastes thy edge ! .. Make ready for the charge !
They come .. they come ! .. On, brethren, to the field ! ..
The word is Vengeance !
                    Vengeance was the word ;
From man to man, and rank to rank it pass'd,
By every heart enforced, by every voice
Sent forth in loud defiance of the foe.
The enemy in shriller sounds return'd
Their Akbar and the Prophet's trusted name.   161
The horsemen lower'd their spears, the infantry
Deliberately with slow and steady step
Advanced ; the bowstrings twang'd, and arrows hiss'd,
And javelins hurtled by. Anon the hosts
Met in the shock of battle, horse and man
Conflicting ; shield struck shield, and sword and mace
And curtle-axe on helm and buckler rung ;

Armour was riven, and wounds were interchanged,
And many a spirit from its mortal hold
Hurried to bliss or bale. Well did the Chiefs   171
Of Julian's army in that hour support
Their old esteem ; and well Count Pedro there
Enhanced his former praise ; and by his side,
Rejoicing like a bridegroom in the strife,
Alphonso through the host of infidels
Bore on his bloody lance dismay and death.
But there was worst confusion and uproar,
There widest slaughter and dismay, where, proud
Of his recover'd Lord, Orelio plunged
Through thickest ranks, trampling beneath his feet   181
The living and the dead. Where'er he turns
The Moors divide and fly. What man is this,
Appall'd they say, who to the front of war
Bareheaded offers thus his naked life ?
Replete with power he is, and terrible,
Like some destroying Angel ! Sure his lips
Have drank of Kaf's dark fountain, and he comes
Strong in his immortality ! Fly ! fly !
They said, this is no human foe ! .. Nor less   190
Of wonder fill'd the Spaniards when they saw
How flight and terror went before his way,
And slaughter in his path. Behold, cries one,
With what command and knightly ease he sits
The intrepid steed, and deals from side to side

His dreadful blows ! Not Roderick in his
power
Bestrode with such command and
majesty
That noble war-horse. His loose robe
this day
Is death's black banner, shaking from
its folds   199
Dismay and ruin. Of no mortal mould
Is he who in that garb of peace affronts
Whole hosts, and sees them scatter
where he turns !
Auspicious Heaven beholds us, and
some Saint
Revisits earth !
        Ay, cries another, Heaven
Hath ever with especial bounty blest
Above all other lands its favour'd Spain;
Chusing her children forth from all man-
kind
For its peculiar people, as of yore
Abraham's ungrateful race beneath the
Law.
Who knows not how on that most holy
night   210
When peace on Earth by Angels was
proclaim'd,
The light which o'er the fields of Bethle-
hem shone,
Irradiated whole Spain ? not just dis-
play'd,
As to the Shepherds, and again with-
drawn ;
All the long winter hours from eve till
morn
Her forests and her mountains and her
plains,
Her hills and valleys were embathed in
light,
A light which came not from the sun or
moon
Or stars, by secondary powers dispensed,
But from the fountain-springs the Light
of Light   220

Effluent. And wherefore should we not
believe
That this may be some Saint or Angel,
charged
To lead us to miraculous victory ?
Hath not the Virgin Mother oftentimes
Descending, clothed in glory, sanctified
With feet adorable our happy soil ? . .
Mark'd ye not, said another, how he cast
In wrath the unhallow'd scymitar
away,
And called for Christian weapon ? Oh
be sure
This is the aid of Heaven ! On, com-
rades, on !   230
A miracle to-day is wrought for Spain !
Victory and Vengeance ! Hew the mis-
creants down,
And spare not ! hew them down in
sacrifice !
God is with us ! his Saints are in the
field !
Victory ! miraculous Victory !
                Thus they
Inflamed with wild belief the keen desire
Of vengeance on their enemies abhorr'd.
The Moorish chief, meantime, o'erlook'd
the fight
From an eminence, and cursed the
renegade
Whose counsels sorting to such ill effect
Had brought this danger on. Lo, from
the East   241
Comes fresh alarm ! a few poor fugitives
Well-nigh with fear exanimate came up,
From Covadonga flying, and the rear
Of that destruction, scarce with breath
to tell
Their dreadful tale. When Abulcacem
heard,
Stricken with horror, like a man bereft
Of sense, he stood. O Prophet, he
exclaim'd,
A hard and cruel fortune hast thou
brought   249

This day upon thy servant! Must I then
Here with disgrace and ruin close a life
Of glorious deeds? But how should man
    resist
Fate's irreversible decrees, or why
Murmur at what must be? They who
    survive
May mourn the evil which this day
    begins:
My part will soon be done!.. Grief then
    gave way
To rage, and cursing Guisla, he pursued,
Oh that that treacherous woman were
    but here!
It were a consolation to give her
The evil death she merits!
                    That reward
She hath had, a Moor replied. For
    when we reach'd   261
The entrance of the vale, it was her
    choice
There in the farthest dwellings to be
    left,
Lest she should see her brother's face;
    but thence
We found her flying at the overthrow,
And visiting the treason on her head,
Pierced her with wounds... Poor ven-
    geance for a host
Destroyed! said Abulcacem in his soul.
Howbeit, resolving to the last to do
His office, he roused up his spirit. Go,
Strike off Count Eudon's head! he
    cried; the fear   271
Which brought him to our camp will
    bring him else
In arms against us now; For Sisibert
And Ebba, he continued thus in thought,
Their uncle's fate for ever bars all plots
Of treason on their part; no hope have
    they
Of safety but with us. He call'd them
    then
With chosen troops to join him in the
    front

Of battle, that by bravely making head,
Retreat might now be won. Then
    fiercer raged   280
The conflict, and more frequent cries of
    death,
Mingling with imprecations and with
    prayers,
Rose through the din of war.
                    By this the blood
Which Deva down her fatal channel
    pour'd,
Purpling Pionia's course, had reach'd
    and stain'd
The wider stream of Sella. Soon far off
The frequent glance of spears and gleam
    of arms
Were seen, which sparkled to the
    westering orb,
Where down the vale impatient to com-
    plete
The glorious work so well that day
    begun,   290
Pelayo led his troops. On foot they
    came,
Chieftains and men alike; the Oaken
    Cross
Triumphant borne on high, precedes
    their march,
And broad and bright the argent banner
    shone.
Roderick, who dealing death from side
    to side,
Had through the Moorish army now
    made way,
Beheld it flash, and judging well what
    aid
Approach'd, with sudden impulse that
    way rode,
To tell of what had pass'd,.. lest in the
    strife
They should engage with Julian's men,
    and mar   300
The mighty consummation. One ran on
To meet him fleet of foot, and having
    given

His tale to this swift messenger, the
Goth

Halted awhile to let Orelio breathe.

Siverian, quoth Pelayo, if mine eyes

Deceive me not, yon horse, whose reeking sides

Are red with slaughter, is the same on
whom

The apostate Orpas in his vauntery

Wont to parade the streets of Cordoba.

But thou shouldst know him best;
regard him well :   310

Is't not Orelio ?

               Either it is he,

The old man replied, or one so like to
him,

Whom all thought matchless, that
similitude

Would be the greater wonder. But
behold,

What man is he who in that disarray

Doth with such power and majesty
bestride

The noble steed, as if he felt himself

In his own proper seat ? Look how he
leans

To cherish him ; and how the gallant
horse

Curves up his stately neck, and bends
his head,   320

As if again to court that gentle touch,

And answer to the voice which praises
him.

Can it be Maccabee ? rejoin'd the King,

Or are the secret wishes of my soul

Indeed fulfill'd, and hath the grave
given up

Its dead ? . . So saying, on the old man
he turn'd

Eyes full of wide astonishment, which
told

The incipient thought that for incredible

He spake no farther. But enough had
pass'd,   329

For old Siverian started at the words

Like one who sees a spectre, and exclaim'd,

Blind that I was to know him not till
now !

My Master, O my Master !

               He meantime

With easy pace moved on to meet their
march.

King, to Pelayo he began, this day

By means scarce less than miracle, thy
throne

Is stablish'd, and the wrongs of Spain
revenged.

Orpas the accursed, upon yonder field

Lies ready for the ravens. By the
Moors

Treacherously slain, Count Julian will
be found   340

Before Saint Peter's altar ; unto him

Grace was vouchsafed ; and by that
holy power

Which at Visonia from the Primate's
hand

Of his own proper act to me was given,

Unworthy as I am, . . yet sure I think

Not without mystery as the event hath
shown, . .

Did I accept Count Julian's penitence,

And reconcile the dying man to Heaven.

Beside him hath his daughter fallen
asleep ;

Deal honourably with his remains, and
let   350

One grave with Christian rites receive
them both.

Is it not written that as the Tree falls
So it shall lie ?

           In this and all things else,

Pelayo answer'd, looking wistfully

Upon the Goth, thy pleasure shall be
done.

Then Roderick saw that he was known,
and turn'd

His head away in silence. But the old
man

Laid hold upon his bridle, and look'd up
In his master's face, weeping and
   silently.
Thereat the Goth with fervent pressure
   took   360
His hand, and bending down toward him
   said,
My good Siverian, go not thou this day
To war! I charge thee keep thyself
   from harm!
Thou art past the age for battles, and
   with whom
Hereafter should thy mistress talk of me
If thou wert gone? . . Thou seest I am
   unarm'd;
Thus disarray'd as thou beholdest me,
Clean through yon miscreant army have
   I cut
My way unhurt; but being once by
   Heaven
Preserved, I would not perish with the
   guilt   370
Of having wilfully provoked my death.
Give me thy helmet and thy cuirass! . .
   nay, . .
Thou wert not wont to let me ask in
   vain,
Nor to gainsay me when my will was
   known!
To thee methinks I should be still the
   King.

   Thus saying, they withdrew a little
   way
Within the trees. Roderick alighted
   there,
And in the old man's armour dight himself.
Dost thou not marvel by what wondrous
   chance,
Said he, Orelio to his master's hand 380
Hath been restored? I found the
   renegade
Of Seville on his back, and hurl'd him
   down

Headlong to the earth. The noble
   animal
Rejoicingly obey'd my hand to shake
His recreant burthen off, and trample out
The life which once I spared in evil hour.
Now let me meet Witiza's viperous sons
In yonder field, and then I may go rest
In peace, . . my work is done!
               And nobly done!
Exclaim'd the old man. Oh! thou art
   greater now   390
Than in that glorious hour of victory
When grovelling in the dust Witiza lay,
The prisoner of thy hand! . . Roderick
   replied,
O good Siverian, happier victory
Thy son hath now achieved! . . the
   victory
Over the world, his sins, and his despair.
If on the field my body should be found,
See it, I charge thee, laid in Julian's
   grave,
And let no idle ear be told for whom
Thou mournest. Thou wilt use Orelio
As doth beseem the steed which hath
   so oft   401
Carried a King to battle; . . he hath
   done
Good service for his rightful Lord to-
   day,
And better yet must do. Siverian, now
Farewell! I think we shall not meet
   again
Till it be in that world where never
   change
Is known, and they who love shall part
   no more.
Commend me to my mother's prayers,
   and say
That never man enjoy'd a heavenlier
   peace
Than Roderick at this hour. O faithful
   friend,   410
How dear thou art to me these tears
   may tell!

With that he fell upon the old man's
neck ;
Then vaulted in the saddle, gave the
reins,
And soon rejoin'd the host. On, com-
rades, on !
Victory and Vengeance ! he exclaim'd,
and took
The lead on that good charger, he alone
Horsed for the onset. They with one
consent
Gave all their voices to the inspiring cry,
Victory and Vengeance ! and the hills
and rocks
Caught the prophetic shout and roll'd
it round.   420
Count Pedro's people heard amid the
heat
Of battle, and return'd the glad acclaim.
The astonish'd Musselmen, on all sides
charged,
Hear that tremendous cry ; yet man-
fully
They stood, and every where with gallant
front
Opposed in fair array the shock of war.
Desperately they fought, like men ex-
pert in arms,
And knowing that no safety could be
found,
Save from their own right hands. No
former day   429
Of all his long career had seen their chief
Approved so well ; nor had Witiza's sons
Ever before this hour achieved in fight
Such feats of resolute valour. Sisibert
Beheld Pelayo in the field afoot,
And twice essay'd beneath his horse's
feet
To thrust him down. Twice did the
Prince evade
The shock, and twice upon his shield
received
The fratricidal sword. Tempt me no
more,

Son of Witiza, cried the indignant chief,
Lest I forget what mother gave thee
birth !   440
Go meet thy death from any hand but
mine !
He said, and turn'd aside. Fitliest from
me !
Exclaim'd a dreadful voice, as through
the throng
Orelio forced his way ; fitliest from me
Receive the rightful death too long with-
held !
'Tis Roderick strikes the blow ! And as
he spake,
Upon the traitor's shoulder fierce he
drove
The weapon, well-bestow'd. He in the
seat
Totter'd and fell. The Avenger has-
ten'd on
In search of Ebba ; and in the heat of
fight   450
Rejoicing and forgetful of all else,
Set up his cry as he was wont in youth,
Roderick the Goth ! . . his war-cry
known so well.
Pelayo eagerly took up the word,
And shouted out his kinsman's name
beloved,
Roderick the Goth ! Roderick and Vic-
tory !
Roderick and Vengeance ! Odoar gave
it forth ;
Urban repeated it, and through his ranks
Count Pedro sent the cry. Not from
the field
Of his great victory, when Witiza fell,
With louder acclamations had that
name   461
Been borne abroad upon the winds of
heaven.
The unreflecting throng, who yesterday,
If it had pass'd their lips, would with
a curse
Have clogg'd it, echoed it as if it came

From some celestial voice in the air,
   reveal'd
To be the certain pledge of all their
   hopes.
Roderick the Goth ! Roderick and Vic-
   tory !
Roderick and Vengeance ! O'er the field
   it spread,
All hearts and tongues uniting in the
   cry ;   470
Mountains and rocks and vales re-
   echoed round ;
And he, rejoicing in his strength, rode
   on,
Laying on the Moors with that good
   sword, and smote,
And overthrew, and scatter'd, and
   destroy'd,
And trampled down ; and still at every
   blow
Exultingly he sent the war-cry forth,
Roderick the Goth ! Roderick and Vic-
   tory !
Roderick and Vengeance !
            Thus he made his way,
Smiting and slaying through the as-
   tonish'd ranks,   479
Till he beheld, where on a fiery barb,
Ebba, performing well a soldier's part,
Dealt to the right and left his deadly
   blows.
With mutual rage they met. The
   renegade
Displays a scymitar, the splendid gift
Of Walid from Damascus sent ; its hilt
Emboss'd with gems, its blade of perfect
   steel,
Which, like a mirror sparkling to the
   sun
With dazzling splendour, flash'd. The
   Goth objects
His shield, and on its rim received the
   edge
Driven from its aim aside, and of its
   force   450

Diminish'd. Many a frustrate stroke
   was dealt
On either part, and many a foin and
   thrust
Aim'd and rebated ; many a deadly
   blow,
Straight, or reverse, delivered and
   repell'd.
Roderick at length with better speed
   hath reach'd
The apostate's turban, and through all
   its folds
The true Cantabrian weapon making way
Attain'd his forehead. Wretch ! the
   avenger cried,
It comes from Roderick's hand !
   Roderick the Goth,
Who spared, who trusted thee, and was
   betray'd !   500
Go tell thy father now how thou hast
   sped
With all thy treasons ! Saying thus he
   seized
The miserable, who, blinded now with
   blood,
Reel'd in the saddle ; and with sidelong
   step
Backing Orelio, drew him to the ground.
He shrieking, as beneath the horse's feet
He fell, forgot his late-learnt creed, and
   called
On Mary's name. The dreadful Goth
   pass'd on,
Still plunging through the thickest war,
   and still
Scattering, where'er he turn'd, the
   affrighted ranks.   510

O who could tell what deeds were
   wrought that day ;
Or who endure to hear the tale of rage,
Hatred, and madness, and despair, and
   fear,
Horror, and wounds, and agony, and
   death,

The cries, the blasphemies, the shrieks, and groans,
And prayers, which mingled with the din of arms
In one wild uproar of terrific sounds ;
While over all predominant was heard,
Reiterate from the conquerors o'er the field,
Roderick the Goth ! Roderick and Victory ! 520
Roderick and Vengeance ! . . Woe for Africa !
Woe for the circumcised ! Woe for the faith
Of the lying Ishmaelite that hour ! The Chiefs
Have fallen ; the Moors, confused and captainless,
And panic-stricken, vainly seek to escape
The inevitable fate. Turn where they will,
Strong in his cause, rejoicing in success,
Insatiate at the banquet of revenge,
The enemy is there ; look where they will,
Death hath environed their devoted ranks : 530
Fly where they will, the avenger and the sword
Await them, . . wretches ! whom the righteous arm
Hath overtaken ! . . Join'd in bonds of faith
Accurs'd, the most flagitious of mankind
From all parts met are here ; the apostate Greek,
The vicious Syrian, and the sullen Copt,
The Persian cruel and corrupt of soul,
The Arabian robber, and the prowling sons
Of Africa, who from their thirsty sands
Pray that the locusts on the peopled plain 540
May settle and prepare their way. Conjoined

Beneath an impious faith, which sanctifies
To them all deeds of wickedness and blood,
Yea, and halloos them on, . . here are they met
To be conjoin'd in punishment this hour.
For plunder, violation, massacre,
All hideous, all unutterable things.
The righteous, the immitigable sword
Exacts due vengeance now ! the cry of blood
Is heard : the measure of their crimes is full ; 550
Such mercy as the Moor at Auria gave,
Such mercy hath he found this dreadful hour !

The evening darken'd, but the avenging sword
Turn'd not away its edge till night had closed
Upon the field of blood. The Chieftains then
Blew the recall, and from their perfect work
Return'd rejoicing, all but he for whom
All look'd with most expectance. He full sure
Had thought upon that field to find his end
Desired, and with Florinda in the grave 560
Rest, in indissoluble union join'd.
But still where through the press of war he went
Half-arm'd, and like a lover seeking death,
The arrows pass'd him by to right and left,
The spear-point pierced him not, the scymitar
Glanced from his helmet ; he, when he beheld

The rout complete, saw that the shield
of Heaven
Had been extended over him once more,
And bowed before its will.   Upon the
banks
Of Sella was Orelio found, his legs   570
And flanks incarnadined, his poitral
smeared
With froth and foam and gore, his silver
mane
Sprinkled with blood, which hung on
every hair,
Aspersed like dew-drops; trembling
there he stood
From the toil of battle, and at times
sent forth
His tremulous voice far echoing loud
and shrill,
A frequent anxious cry, with which he
seem'd

To call the master whom he loved so
well,
And who had thus again forsaken him.
Siverian's helm and cuirass on the grass
Lay near; and Julian's sword, its hilt
and chain   581
Clotted with blood; but where was he
whose hand
Had wielded it so well that glorious
day ? . .
. . . . .
Days, months, and years, and genera-
tions pass'd,
And centuries held their course, before,
far off
Within a hermitage near Viseu's walls
A humble tomb was found, which bore
inscribed
In ancient characters King Roderick's
name.

SELECTED MINOR POEMS

THE HOLLY TREE

[First published in *The Morning Post*, Dec. 17, 1798, afterwards in *The Annual Anthology*, 1799, and in *Metrical Tales*, 1805.]

1

O READER ! hast thou ever stood to see
    The Holly Tree ?
The eye that contemplates it well per-
    ceives
    Its glossy leaves
Order'd by an intelligence so wise,
As might confound the Atheist's
    sophistries.

2

Below, a circling fence, its leaves are
    seen
    Wrinkled and keen ;
No grazing cattle through their prickly
    round
    Can reach to wound ;   10
But as they grow where nothing is to
    fear,
Smooth and unarm'd the pointless leaves
    appear.

3

I love to view these things with curious
    eyes,
    And moralize :
And in this wisdom of the Holly Tree
    Can emblems see
Wherewith perchance to make a pleasant
    rhyme,
One which may profit in the after time.

4

Thus, though abroad perchance I might
    appear
    Harsh and austere,   20

To those who on my leisure would in-
    trude
    Reserved and rude,
Gentle at home amid my friends I'd be
Like the high leaves upon the Holly
    Tree.

5

And should my youth, as youth is apt
    I know,
    Some harshness show,
All vain asperities I day by day
    Would wear away,
Till the smooth temper of my age should
    be
Like the high leaves upon the Holly
    Tree.   30

6

And as when all the summer trees are
    seen
    So bright and green,
The Holly leaves a sober hue display
    Less bright than they,
But when the bare and wintry woods we
    see,
What then so cheerful as the Holly
    Tree ?

7

So serious should my youth appear
    among
    The thoughtless throng,
So would I seem amid the young and
    gay
    More grave than they,   40
That in my age as cheerful I might be
As the green winter of the Holly Tree.

Westbury, 1798.

THE DEAD FRIEND

[Published in *The Annual Anthology*, 1799, and in *Metrical Tales*, 1805.]

1

NOT to the grave, not to the grave, my
    Soul,
    Descend to contemplate
The form that once was dear
The Spirit is not there
Which kindled that dead eye,
Which throbb'd in that cold heart,
Which in that motionless hand
    Hath met thy friendly grasp.
    The Spirit is not there !
It is but lifeless perishable flesh   10
That moulders in the grave ;
Earth, air, and water's ministering
      particles
    Now to the elements
    Resolved, their uses done.
Not to the grave, not to the grave, my
    Soul,
    Follow thy friend beloved,
    The spirit is not there !

2

Often together have we talk'd of death ;
    How sweet it were to see
All doubtful things made clear ;   20
How sweet it were with powers
    Such as the Cherubim,
To view the depth of Heaven !
O Edmund ! thou hast first
Begun the travel of Eternity !
    I look upon the stars,
    And think that thou art there,
Unfetter'd as the thought that follows
    thee.

3

And we have often said how sweet it
    were
With unseen ministry of angel power 30
    To watch the friends we loved.
    Edmund ! we did not err !

Sure I have felt thy presence ! Thou
    hast given
    A birth to holy thought,
Has kept me from the world unstain'd
    and pure.
    Edmund ! we did not err !
    Our best affections here
They are not like the toys of infancy ;
    The Soul outgrows them not ;
    We do not cast them off ;   40
    Oh if it could be so,
It were indeed a dreadful thing to die !

4

Not to the grave, not to the grave, my
    Soul,
    Follow thy friend beloved !
    But in the lonely hour,
    But in the evening walk,
Think that he companies thy solitude ;
    Think that he holds with thee
    Mysterious intercourse ;
And though remembrance wake a tear,
    There will be joy in grief.   51

Westbury, 1799.

TO MARY

[First published in *The Morning Post*, Oct. 20, 1803, under the title : ' Stanzas written after a Long Absence.']

MARY ! ten chequer'd years have past
Since we beheld each other last ;
Yet, Mary, I remember thee,
Nor canst thou have forgotten me.

The bloom was then upon thy face,
Thy form had every youthful grace ;
I too had then the warmth of youth,
And in our hearts was all its truth.

We conversed, were there others by,
With common mirth and random eye ;
But when escaped the sight of men,   11
How serious was our converse then !

Our talk was then of years to come,
Of hopes which ask'd a humble doom,
Themes which to loving thoughts might
    move,
Although we never spake of love.

At our last meeting sure thy heart
Was even as loth as mine to part ;
And yet we little thought that then
We parted . . not to meet again.   20

Long, Mary ! after that adieu,
My dearest day-dreams were of you ;
In sleep I saw you still, and long
Made you the theme of secret song.

When manhood and its cares came on,
The humble hopes of youth were gone ;
And other hopes and other fears
Effaced the thoughts of happier years.

Meantime through many a varied year
Of thee no tidings did I hear,   30
And thou hast never heard my name
Save from the vague reports of fame.

But then I trust detraction's lie
Hath kindled anger in thine eye ;
And thou my praise wert proud to see, . .
My name should still be dear to thee.

Ten years have held their course ; thus
    late
I learn the tidings of thy fate ;
A Husband and a Father now,
Of thee, a Wife and Mother thou.   40

And, Mary, as for thee I frame
A prayer which hath no selfish aim,
No happier lot can I wish thee
Than such as Heaven hath granted me.

London, 1802.

FUNERAL SONG, FOR THE PRINCESS CHARLOTTE OF WALES

[Published in *The Annual Register* for 1827 and in *Friendship's Offering* for 1828.]

In its summer pride array'd,
Low our Tree of Hope is laid !
Low it lies : . . in evil hour,
Visiting the bridal bower,
Death hath levell'd root and flower.
Windsor, in thy sacred shade,
(This the end of pomp and power !)
Have the rites of death been paid :
Windsor, in thy sacred shade
Is the Flower of Brunswick laid !   10

Ye whose relics rest around,
Tenants of this funeral ground !
Know ye, Spirits, who is come,
By immitigable doom
Summon'd to the untimely tomb ?
Late with youth and splendour crown'd,
Late in beauty's vernal bloom,
Late with love and joyaunce blest !
Never more lamented guest
Was in Windsor laid to rest.   20

Henry, thou of saintly worth,
Thou, to whom thy Windsor gave
Nativity and name, and grave ;
Thou art in this hallowed earth
Cradled for the immortal birth ;
Heavily upon his head
Ancestral crimes were visited :
He, in spirit like a child,
Meek of heart and undefiled,
Patiently his crown resign'd,   30
And fix'd on heaven his heavenly mind,
Blessing, while he kiss'd the rod,
His Redeemer and his God.
Now may he in realms of bliss
Greet a soul as pure as his.

Passive as that humble spirit,
Lies his bold dethroner too ;
A dreadful debt did he inherit
To his injured lineage due ;
Ill-starr'd prince, whose martial merit 40
His own England long might rue !
Mournful was that Edward's fame,
Won in fields contested well,
While he sought his rightful claim :
Witness Aire's unhappy water,
Where the ruthless Clifford fell ;
And when Wharfe ran red with
  slaughter,
On the day of Towton's field,
Gathering, in its guilty flood,
The carnage and the ill-spilt blood 50
That forty thousand lives could yield.
Cressy was to this but sport, . .
Poictiers but a pageant vain ;
And the victory of Spain
Seem'd a strife for pastime meant,
And the work of Agincourt
Only like a tournament ;
Half the blood which there was spent,
Had sufficed again to gain
Anjou and ill-yielded Maine, 60
Normandy and Aquitaine,
And Our Lady's ancient towers,
Maugre all the Valois' powers,
Had a second time been ours. . .
A gentle daughter of thy line,
Edward, lays her dust with thine.

Thou, Elizabeth, art here ;
Thou to whom all griefs were known ;
Who wert placed upon the bier
In happier hour than on the throne. 70
Fatal daughter, fatal mother,
Raised to that ill-omen'd station,
Father, uncle, sons, and brother,
Mourn'd in blood her elevation !
Woodville, in the realms of bliss,
To thine offspring thou may'st say,
Early death is happiness ;
And favour'd in their lot are they

Who are not left to learn below
That length of life is length of woe. 80
Lightly let this ground be prest ;
A broken heart is here at rest.

But thou, Seymour, with a greeting,
Such as sisters use at meeting,
Joy, and sympathy, and love,
Wilt hail her in the seats above.
Like in loveliness were ye,
By a like lamented doom,
Hurried to an early tomb.
While together, spirits blest, 90
Here your earthly relics rest,
Fellow angels shall ye be
In the angelic company.

Henry, too, hath here his part ;
At the gentle Seymour's side,
With his best beloved bride,
Cold and quiet, here are laid
The ashes of that fiery heart.
Not with his tyrannic spirit,
Shall our Charlotte's soul inherit ; 100
No, by Fisher's hoary head,—
By More, the learned and the good,—
By Katharine's wrongs and Boleyn's
  blood,—
By the life so basely shed
Of the pride of Norfolk's line,
By the axe so often red,
By the fire with martyrs fed,
Hateful Henry, not with thee
May her happy spirit be ! 109

And here lies one whose tragic name
A reverential thought may claim ;
That murder'd Monarch, whom the
  grave,
Revealing its long secret, gave
Again to sight, that we might spy
His comely face and waking eye !
There, thrice fifty years, it lay,
Exempt from natural decay,
Unclosed and bright, as if to say,

A plague, of bloodier, baser birth,   119
Than that beneath whose rage he bled,
Was loose upon our guilty earth ;—
Such awetul warning from the dead,
Was given by that portentous eye ;
Then it closed eternally.

Ye whose relics rest around,
Tenants of this funeral ground ;
Even in your immortal spheres,
What fresh yearnings will ye feel,
When this earthly guest appears !
Us she leaves in grief and tears ;   130
But to you will she reveal
Tidings of old England's weal ;
Of a righteous war pursued,
Long, through evil and through good,
With unshaken fortitude ;
Of peace, in battle twice achieved ;
Of her fiercest foe subdued,
And Europe from the yoke reliev'd,
Upon that Brabantine plain !
Such the proud, the virtuous story,   140
Such the great, the endless glory
Of her father's splendid reign !
He who wore the sable mail,
Might at this heroic tale,
Wish himself on earth again.

One who reverently, for thee,
Raised the strain of bridal verse,
Flower of Brunswick ! mournfully
Lays a garland on thy herse.

MY DAYS AMONG THE DEAD ARE PAST

1

My days among the Dead are past ;
   Around me I behold,
Where'er these casual eyes are cast,
   The mighty minds of old ;
My never-failing friends are they,
With whom I converse day by day.

2

With them I take delight in weal,
   And seek relief in woe ;
And while I understand and feel
   How much to them I owe,   10
My cheeks have often been bedew'd
With tears of thoughtful gratitude.

3

My thoughts are with the Dead, with them
   I live in long-past years,
Their virtues love, their faults condemn,
   Partake their hopes and fears,
And from their lessons seek and find
Instruction with an humble mind.

4

My hopes are with the Dead, anon
   My place with them will be,   20
And I with them shall travel on
   Through all Futurity ;
Yet leaving here a name, I trust,
That will not perish in the dust.

Keswick, 1818.

IMITATED FROM THE PERSIAN

[First published in *The Bijou* for 1828.]

Lord ! who art merciful as well as just,
Incline thine ear to me, a child of dust !
Not what I would, O Lord ! I offer thee,
   Alas ! but what I can.   [man,
Father Almighty, who hast made me
And bade me look to Heaven, for Thou
   art there,
Accept my sacrifice and humble prayer.
Four things which are not in thy
   treasury,
I lay before thee, Lord, with this peti-
   tion : . .
   My nothingness, my wants,   10
   My sins, and my contrition.

Lowther Castle, 1828.

THE CATARACT OF LODORE

DESCRIBED IN RHYMES FOR THE NURSERY

[Published in Joanna Baillie's *A Collection
of Poems, chiefly Manuscript*, 1823.]

' How does the Water
Come down at Lodore ? '
My little boy ask'd me
Thus, once on a time ;
And moreover he task'd me
To tell him in rhyme.
Anon at the word,
There first came one daughter
And then came another,
To second and third   10
The request of their brother,
And to hear how the water
Comes down at Lodore,
With its rush and its roar,
As many a time
They had seen it before.
So I told them in rhyme,
For of rhymes I had store :
And 'twas in my vocation
For their recreation   20
That so I should sing ;
Because I was Laureate
To them and the King.

From its sources which well
In the Tarn on the fell ;
From its fountains
In the mountains,
Its rills and its gills ;
Through moss and through brake,
It runs and it creeps   30
For awhile, till it sleeps
In its own little Lake.
And thence at departing,
Awakening and starting,
It runs through the reeds
And away it proceeds,
Through meadow and glade,
In sun and in shade,

And through the wood-shelter,
Among crags in its flurry,   40
Helter-skelter,
Hurry-scurry.
Here it comes sparkling,
And there it lies darkling ;
Now smoking and frothing
Its tumult and wrath in,
Till in this rapid race
On which it is bent,
It reaches the place
Of its steep descent.   50

The Cataract strong
Then plunges along,
Striking and raging
As if a war waging
Its caverns and rocks among :
Rising and leaping,
Sinking and creeping,
Swelling and sweeping,
Showering and springing,
Flying and flinging,   60
Writhing and ringing,
Eddying and whisking,
Spouting and frisking,
Turning and twisting,
Around and around
With endless rebound !
Smiting and fighting,
A sight to delight in ;
Confounding, astounding,
Dizzying and deafening the ear with its
          sound.   70

Collecting, projecting,
Receding and speeding,
And shocking and rocking,
And darting and parting,
And threading and spreading,
And whizzing and hissing,
And dripping and skipping,
And hitting and splitting,
And shining and twining,
And rattling and battling,   80
And shaking and quaking,

And pouring and roaring,
And waving and raving,
And tossing and crossing,
And flowing and going,
And running and stunning,
And foaming and roaming,
And dinning and spinning,
And dropping and hopping,
And working and jerking,   90
And guggling and struggling,
And heaving and cleaving,
And moaning and groaning;

And glittering and frittering,
And gathering and feathering,
And whitening and brightening,
And quivering and shivering,
And hurrying and skurrying,
And thundering and floundering;

Dividing and gliding and sliding,   100
And falling and brawling and sprawling,
And driving and riving and striving,
And sprinkling and twinkling and wrink-
     ling,   [rounding,
And sounding and bounding and
And bubbling and troubling and
     doubling,
And grumbling and rumbling and
     tumbling,   [tering;
And clattering and battering and shat-

Retreating and beating and meeting and
     sheeting,   [spraying,
Delaying and straying and playing and
Advancing and prancing and glancing
     and dancing,   110
Recoiling, turmoiling and toiling and
     boiling,
And gleaming and streaming and steam-
     ing and beaming,
And rushing and flushing and brushing
     and gushing,
And flapping and rapping and clapping
     and slapping,   [and twirling,
And curling and whirling and purling

And thumping and plumping and bump-
     ing and jumping,
And dashing and flashing and splashing
     and clashing;
And so never ending, but always
     descending,
Sounds and motions for ever and ever
     are blending,
All at once and all o'er, with a mighty
     uproar,   120
And this way the Water comes down at
     Lodore.

Keswick, 1820.

SONNETS

[The two following Sonnets were numbered
V and XV respectively among the Sonnets
as printed in the collected edition of 1837–
1838.   The first was published in *Poems*,
1797;   the second in *The Annual Anthology*,
1800.]

(1) THE EVENING RAINBOW

[Published in *Poems*, 1797.]

MILD arch of promise, on the evening sky
Thou shinest fair with many a lovely ray
Each in the other melting.   Much mine
     eye
Delights to linger on thee; for the day,
Changeful and many-weather'd, seem'd
     to smile
Flashing brief splendour through the
     clouds awhile,   [rain:
Which deepen'd dark anon and fell in
But pleasant is it now to pause, and view
Thy various tints of frail and watery hue,
And think the storm shall not return
     again.   10
Such is the smile that Piety bestows
On the good man's pale cheek, when he,
     in peace
Departing gently from a world of woes,
Anticipates the world where sorrows
     cease.

1794.

(2) WINTER

[Published in *The Annual Anthology*, 1800.]

A WRINKLED, crabbed man they picture
    thee,
Old Winter, with a rugged beard as grey
As the long moss upon the apple-tree;
Blue-lipt, an ice-drop at thy sharp blue
    nose,
Close muffled up, and on thy dreary way,
Plodding alone through sleet and drift-
    ing snows.

They should have drawn thee by the
    high-heapt hearth,
Old Winter! seated in thy great arm'd
    chair,
Watching the children at their Christ-
    mas mirth;
Or circled by them as thy lips declare 10
Some merry jest or tale of murder dire,
Or troubled spirit that disturbs the night,
Pausing at times to rouse the mouldering
    fire,
Or taste the old October brown and
    bright.

Westbury, 1799.

INSCRIPTIONS

[This and the four following inscriptions
were numbered respectively XI, XVIII,
XXX, XXXIII, and XXXVIII in the
Inscriptions as published in the collected
edition of 1837–1838.]

(1) IN A FOREST

[First published in *The Morning Post*,
April 13, 1799, afterwards in *The Annual
Anthology*, 1799, and in *Metrical Tales*, 1805.]

STRANGER! whose steps have reach'd
    this solitude,
Know that this lonely spot was dear to
    one
Devoted with no unrequited zeal
To Nature. Here, delighted he has
    heard

The rustling of these woods, that now
    perchance
Melodious to the gale of summer move;
And underneath their shade on yon
    smooth rock,
With grey and yellow lichens overgrown,
Often reclined; watching the silent flow
Of this perspicuous rivulet, that steals 10
Along its verdant course, . . till all
    around
Had fill'd his senses with tranquillity,
And ever soothed in spirit he return'd
A happier, better man. Stranger! per-
    chance,
Therefore the stream more lovely to
    thine eye
Will glide along, and to the summer gale
The woods wave more melodious.
    Cleanse thou then
The weeds and mosses from this letter'd
    stone.

Westbury, 1798.

(2) EPITAPH

HERE in the fruitful vales of Somerset
Was Emma born, and here the Maiden
    grew
To the sweet season of her womanhood
Beloved and lovely, like a plant whose
    leaf
And bud and blossom all are beautiful.
In peacefulness her virgin years were
    past;
And when in prosperous wedlock she
    was given,
Amid the Cumbrian mountains far away
She had her summer Bower. 'Twas
    like a dream
Of old Romance to see her when she
    plied   10
Her little skiff on Derwent's glassy lake;
The roseate evening resting on the hills,
The lake returning back the hues of
    heaven,

Mountains and vales and waters all
    imbued
With beauty, and in quietness ; and she,
Nymph-like, amid that glorious solitude
A heavenly presence, gliding in her joy.
But soon a wasting malady began
To prey upon her, frequent in attack,
Yet with such flattering intervals as
    mock   20
The hopes of anxious love, and most of all
The sufferer, self-deceived. During
    those days
Of treacherous respite, many a time
    hath he,
Who leaves this record of his friend,
    drawn back
Into the shadow from her social board,
Because too surely in her cheek he saw
The insidious bloom of death ; and
    then her smiles
And innocent mirth excited deeper grief
Than when long-look'd-for tidings came
    at last,
That, all her sufferings ended, she was
    laid   30
Amid Madeira's orange groves to rest.
O gentle Emma ! o'er a lovelier form
Than thine, Earth never closed ; nor
    e'er did Heaven
Receive a purer spirit from the world.

    Keswick, 1810.

(3) AT BARROSA

THOUGH the four quarters of the world
    have seen
The British valour proved triumphantly
Upon the French, in many a field far-
    famed,
Yet may the noble Island in her rolls
Of glory write Barrosa's name. For
    there,
Not by the issue of deliberate plans
Consulted well, was the fierce conflict
    won,

Nor by the leader's eye intuitive,
Nor force of either arm of war, nor art
Of skill'd artillerist, nor the discipline 10
Of troops to absolute obedience train'd ;
But by the spring and impulse of the
    heart,
Brought fairly to the trial, when all else
Seem'd, like a wrestler's garment,
    thrown aside ;
By individual courage and the sense
Of honour, their old country's, and
    their own,
There to be forfeited, or there upheld ; . .
This warm'd the soldier's soul, and gave
    his hand
The strength that carries with it victory.
More to enhance their praise, the day
    was fought   20
Against all circumstance ; a painful
    march,
Through twenty hours of night and day
    prolong'd,
Forespent the British troops ; and hope
    delay'd
Had left their spirits pall'd. But when
    the word
Was given to turn, and charge, and win
    the heights,
The welcome order came to them, like
    rain
Upon a traveller in the thirsty sands.
Rejoicing, up the ascent, and in the
    front
Of danger, they with steady step
    advanced,
And with the insupportable bayonet 30
Drove down the foe. The vanquish'd
    Victor saw
And thought of Talavera, and deplored
His eagle lost. But England saw well-
    pleased
Her old ascendency that day sustain'd ;
And Scotland, shouting over all her hills,
Among her worthies rank'd another
    Graham.

(4) EPITAPH

[Published in *The Literary Souvenir*, 1827, under the title of ' A Soldier's Epitaph '.]

STEEP is the soldier's path ; nor are the
   heights
Of glory to be won without long toil
And arduous efforts of enduring hope ;
Save when Death takes the aspirant by
   the hand,
And cutting short the work of years, at
   once
Lifts him to that conspicuous eminence.
Such fate was mine.—The standard of
   the Buffs
I bore at Albuhera, on that day
When, covered by a shower, and fatally
For friends misdeem'd, the Polish
   lancers fell   10
Upon our rear.   Surrounding me, they
   claim'd
My precious charge.—' Not but with
   life ! ' I cried,
And life was given for immortality.
The flag which to my heart I held, when
   wet
With that heart's blood, was soon
   victoriously
Regain'd on that great day.   In former
   times,
Marlborough beheld it borne at Rami-
   lies ;
For Brunswick and for liberty it waved
Triumphant at Culloden ; and hath seen
The lilies on the Caribbean shores   20
Abased before it.   Then too in the
   front
Of battle did it flap exultingly,
When Douro, with its wide stream inter-
   posed,
Saved not the French invaders from
   attack,
Discomfiture, and ignominious rout.
My name is Thomas : undisgraced have I

Transmitted it.   He who in days to
   come
May bear the honour'd banner to the
   field,
Will think of Albuhera, and of me.

(5) EPITAPH

[First published in *The Literary Souvenir*, 1828.]

TIME and the world, whose magnitude
   and weight
Bear on us in this Now, and hold us
   here
To earth enthrall'd, . . what are they in
   the Past ?
And in the prospect of the immortal Soul
How poor a speck ! Not here her
   resting-place,
Her portion is not here ; and happiest
   they
Who, gathering early all that Earth can
   give,
Shake off its mortal coil, and speed for
   Heaven.
Such fate had he whose relics moulder
   here.
Few were his years, but yet enough to
   teach   10
Love, duty, generous feelings, high
   desires,
Faith, hope, devotion : and what more
   could length
Of days have brought him ?   What,
   but vanity,
Joys frailer even than health or human
   life ;
Temptation, sin and sorrow, both too
   sure,
Evils that wound, and cares that fret
   the heart.
Repine not, therefore, ye who love the
   dead.

DEDICATION OF THE AUTHOR'S COLLOQUIES ON THE PROGRESS AND PROSPECTS OF SOCIETY

TO THE
MEMORY OF THE REVEREND
HERBERT HILL,

Formerly Student of Christ Church, Oxford; successively Chaplain to the British Factories at Porto and at Lisbon; and late Rector of Streatham; who was released from this life, Sept. 19, 1828, in the 80th year of his age.

Not upon marble or sepulchral brass
Have I the record of thy worth inscribed,
Dear Uncle! nor from Chantrey's chisel ask'd
A monumental statue, which might wear
Through many an age thy venerable form.
Such tribute, were I rich in this world's wealth,
Should rightfully be rendered, in discharge
Of grateful duty, to the world evinced
When testifying so by outward sign
Its deep and inmost sense.   But what I can   10
Is rendered piously, prefixing here
Thy perfect lineaments, two centuries
Before thy birth by Holbein's happy hand
Prefigured thus.   It is the portraiture
Of More, the mild, the learned, and the good;
Traced in that better stage of human life,
When vain imaginations, troublous thoughts,
And hopes and fears have had their course, and left
The intellect composed, the heart at rest,

Nor yet decay hath touch'd our mortal frame.   20
Such was the man whom Henry, of desert
Appreciant alway, chose for highest trust;
Whom England in that eminence approved;
Whom Europe honoured, and Erasmus loved.
Such was he ere heart-hardening bigotry
Obscured his spirit, made him with himself
Discordant, and contracting then his brow,
With sour defeature marr'd his countenance.
What he was, in his best and happiest time,
Even such wert thou, dear Uncle! such thy look   30
Benign and thoughtful; such thy placid mien;
Thine eye serene, significant and strong,
Bright in its quietness, yet brightening oft
With quick emotion of benevolence,
Or flash of active fancy, and that mirth
Which aye with sober wisdom well accords.
Nor ever did true Nature, with more nice
Exactitude, fit to the inner man
The fleshly mould, than when she stampt on thine
Her best credentials, and bestow'd on thee   40
An aspect, to whose sure benignity
Beasts with instinctive confidence could trust,
Which at a glance obtain'd respect from men,
And won at once good will from all the good.

Such as in semblance, such in word
and deed
Lisbon beheld him, when for many a year
The even tenour of his spotless life
Adorn'd the English Church, . . her
minister
In that strong hold of Rome's Idolatry,
To God and man approved. What
Englishman,　　50
Who in those peaceful days of Portugal
Resorted thither, curious to observe
Her cities, and the works and ways of
men,
But sought him, and from his abundant
stores
Of knowledge profited ? What stricken
one,
Sent thither to protract a living death,
Forlorn perhaps, and friendless else, but
found
A friend in him ? What mourners, . .
who had seen
The object of their agonizing hopes
In that sad cypress ground deposited, 60
Wherein so many a flower of British
growth,
Untimely faded and cut down, is laid,
In foreign earth compress'd, . . but bore
away
A life-long sense of his compassionate
care,
His Christian goodness ? Faithful shep-
herd he,
And vigilant against the wolves, who
there,
If entrance might be won, would
straight beset
The dying stranger, and with merciless
zeal
Bay the death-bed. In every family
Throughout his fold was he the welcome
guest,　　70
Alike to every generation dear,
The children's favourite, and the grand-
sire's friend,

Tried, trusted and beloved. So liberal
too
In secret alms, even to his utmost
means,
That they who served him, and who
saw in part
The channels where his constant bounty
ran,
Maugre their own uncharitable faith,
Believed him, for his works, secure of
Heaven.
It would have been a grief for me to
think
The features, which so perfectly
express'd　　80
That excellent mind, should irre-
trievably
From earth have pass'd away, existing
now
Only in some few faithful memories
Insoul'd, and not by any limner's skill
To be imbodied thence. A blessing
then
On him, in whose prophetic counterfeit
Preserved, the children now, who were
the crown
Of his old age, may see their father's
face,
Here to the very life pourtray'd, as
when
Spain's mountain passes, and her ilex
woods,　　90
And fragrant wildernesses, side by side,
With him I traversed, in my morn of
youth,
And gather'd knowledge from his full
discourse.
Often in former years I pointed out,
Well-pleased, the casual portrait, which
so well
Assorted in all points ; and haply since,
While lingering o'er this meditative
work,
Sometimes that likeness, not uncon-
sciously,

Hath tinged the strain ; and therefore,
   for the sake
Of this resemblance, are these volumes
   now   100
Thus to his memory properly inscribed.

O friend ! O more than father ! whom
   I found
Forbearing alway, alway kind ; to
   whom
No gratitude can speak the debt I owe ;
Far on their earthly pilgrimage advanced
Are they who knew thee when we drew
   the breath
Of that delicious clime ! The most are
   gone ;
And whoso yet survive of those who then
Were in their summer season, on the
   tree
Of life hang here and there like wintry
   leaves,   110
Which the first breeze will from the
   bough bring down.
I, too, am in the sear, the yellow leaf.
And yet, (no wish is nearer to my heart,)
One arduous labour more, as unto thee
In duty bound, full fain would I com-
   plete,
(So Heaven permit,) recording faithfully
The heroic rise, the glories, the decline,
Of that fallen country, dear to us,
   wherein
The better portion of thy days was
   pass'd ;
And where, in fruitful intercourse with
   thee,   120
My intellectual life received betimes
The bias it hath kept. Poor Portugal,
In us thou harbouredst no ungrateful
   guests !
We loved thee well ; Mother magnani-
   mous
Of mighty intellects and faithful hearts,..
For such in other times thou wert, nor
   yet

To be despair'd of, for not yet, me-
   thinks,
Degenerate wholly, . . yes, we loved
   thee well !
And in thy moving story, (so but life
Be given me to mature the gathered
   store   130
Of thirty years,) poet and politick,
And Christian sage, (only philosopher
Who from the Well of living water
   drinks
Never to thirst again,) shall find, I ween,
For fancy, and for profitable thought,
Abundant food.
          Alas ! should this be given,
Such consummation of my work will
   now
Be but a mournful close, the one being
   gone,
Whom to have satisfied was still to me
A pure reward, outweighing far all
   breath   140
Of public praise. O friend revered, O
   guide
And fellow-labourer in this ample field,
How large a portion of myself hath
   pass'd
With thee, from earth to Heaven !..
         Thus they who reach
Grey hairs die piecemeal. But in good
   old age
Thou hast departed ; not to be be-
   wail'd, ..
Oh no ! The promise on the Mount
   vouchsafed,
Nor abrogate by any later law
Reveal'd to man, . . that promise, as by
   thee
Full piously deserved, was faithfully 150
In thee fulfill'd, and in the land thy
   days
Were long. I would not, as I saw thee
   last,
For a king's ransom, have detain'd thee
   here, ..

Bent, like the antique sculptor's limb-
   less trunk,
By chronic pain, yet with thine eye
   unquench'd,
The ear undimm'd, the mind retentive
   still,
The heart unchanged, the intellectual
   lamp
Burning in its corporeal sepulchre.
No; not if human wishes had had power
To have suspended Nature's constant
   work,   160
Would they who loved thee have
   detain'd thee thus,
Waiting for death.
          That trance is over. Thou
Art enter'd on thy heavenly heritage;
And I, whose dial of mortality
Points to the eleventh hour, shall follow
   soon.
Meantime, with dutiful and patient
   hope,
I labour that our names conjoin'd may
   long
Survive, in honour one day to be held
Where old Lisboa from her hills o'er-
   looks
Expanded Tagus, with its populous
   shores   170
And pine woods, to Palmella's crested
   height:
Nor there alone; but in those rising
   realms
Where now the offsets of the Lusian tree
Push forth their vigorous shoots, . .
   from central plains,
Whence rivers flow divergent, to the
   gulph
Southward, where wild Parana disem-
   bogues
A sea-like stream; and northward, in
   a world
Of forests, where huge Orellana clips
His thousand islands with his thousand
   arms.

LITTLE BOOK, IN GREEN AND GOLD

[Printed by Southey's cousin and son-in-
law, Herbert Hill, in *Oliver Newman; With
Other Poetical Remains*, in 1845.]

LITTLE Book, in green and gold,
Thou art thus bedight to hold
ROBERT SOUTHEY'S Album Rhymes,
Wrung from him in busy times:
Not a few to his vexation,
By importune application;
Some in half-sarcastic strain,
More against than with the grain;
Other some, he must confess,
Bubbles blown in idleness;   10
Some in earnest, some in jest,
Good for little at the best:
Yet, because his Daughter dear
Would collect them fondly here,
Little Book, in gold and green,
Thou art not unfitly seen
Thus apparell'd for her pleasure,
Like the casket of a treasure.
Other owner, well I know,
Never more can prize thee so.   20

Little Book, when thou art old,
Time will dim thy green and gold.
Little Book, thou wilt outlive
The pleasure thou wert made to give:
Dear domestic recollections,
Home-born loves, and old affections,
Incommunicable they:
And when these have past away,
As perforce they must, from earth,
Where is then thy former worth?   30
Other value, then, I ween,
Little Book, may supervene,
Happily if unto some
Thou in due descent shouldst come,
Who would something find in thee
Like a relic's sanctity,

And in whom thou may'st awake,
For thy former owner's sake,
A pious thought, a natural sigh,
A feeling of mortality.   10

When those feelings, and that race,
Have in course of time given place,
Little worth, and little prized,
Disregarded or despised,
Thou wilt then be bought and sold,
In thy faded green and gold.
Then, unless some curious eye
Thee upon the shelf should spy,
Dust will gather on thee there,
And the worms, that never spare,   50
Feed their fill within, and hide,
Burrowing safely in thy side,
Till transfigured out they come
From that emblem of the tomb :
Or, by mould and damp consumed,
Thou to perish may'st be doom'd.

But if some collector find thee,
He will, as a prize, re-bind thee ;
And thou may'st again be seen
Gayly drest in gold and green.   60

9th September, 1831.

LINES WRITTEN IN THE ALBUM
OF ROTHA QUILLINAN

[Printed, like the preceding poem, with
Oliver Newman, in 1845].

ROTHA, after long delays,
Since thy book must cross the Raise,
Down I sit to turn a stave,
Be it gay or be it grave.

Wiser wish than what thy name
Prompts for thee I cannot frame ;
No where find a better theme
Than thy native namesake stream.
Lovelier river is there none
Underneath an English sun ;   10

From its source it issues bright
Upon hoar Hellvellyn's height,
Flowing where its summer voice
Makes the mountain herds rejoice ;
Down the dale it issues then,
Not polluted there by men ;
While its lucid waters take
Their pastoral course from lake to lake,
Please the eye in every part,
Lull the ear, and soothe the heart,   20
Till into Windermere sedate
They flow and uncontaminate.
Rotha, such from youth to age
Be thy mortal pilgrimage ;
Thus in childhood blithe and free,
Thus in thy maturity,
Blest and blessing, may it be ;
And a course, in welfare past,
Thus serenely close at last.

ODE

WRITTEN DURING THE NEGOTIATIONS
WITH BUONAPARTE, IN JANUARY,
1814

[First published in *The Courier*, Feb. 3,
1814, with a number of slight variations
from the present text. Republished in *The
Times*, April 21, 1814, in its present form.]

1

WHO counsels peace at this momentous
hour,
When God hath given deliverance to
the oppress'd,
And to the injured power ?
Who counsels peace, when Vengeance
like a flood
Rolls on, no longer now to be repress'd ;
When innocent blood
From the four corners of the world
cries out
For justice upon one accursed head ;
When Freedom hath her holy banners
spread   9

Over all nations, now in one just cause
United ; when with one sublime accord
Europe throws off the yoke abhorr'd,
And Loyalty and Faith and Ancient Laws
    Follow the avenging sword !

2

Woe, woe to England ! woe and endless
        shame,
    If this heroic land,
False to her feelings and unspotted fame,
Hold out the olive to the Tyrant's hand !
Woe to the world, if Buonaparte's throne
    Be suffer'd still to stand !   20
For by what names shall Right and
        Wrong be known, . .
What new and courtly phrases must
        we feign
For Falsehood, Murder, and all mon-
        strous crimes,
If that perfidious Corsican maintain
    Still his detested reign,
And France, who yearns even now to
        break her chain,
Beneath his iron rule be left to groan ?
No ! by the innumerable dead,
Whose blood hath for his lust of power
        been shed,
Death only can for his foul deeds atone ;
That peace which Death and Judgement
        can bestow,   31
That peace be Buonaparte's, . . that
        alone !

3

For sooner shall the Ethiop change his
        skin,
Or from the Leopard shall her spots
        depart,
Than this man change his old flagitious
        heart.
Have ye not seen him in the balance
        weigh'd,
And there found wanting ?   On the
        stage of blood

Foremost the resolute adventurer stood ;
    And when, by many a battle won,
He placed upon his brow the crown, 40
Curbing delirious France beneath his
        sway,
    Then, like Octavius in old time,
Fair name might he have handed down,
Effacing many a stain of former crime.
Fool ! should he cast away that
        bright renown !
Fool ! the redemption proffer'd should
        he lose !
When Heaven such grace vouchsafed
        him that the way
        To Good and Evil lay
    Before him, which to choose.

4

    But Evil was his Good,   50
For all too long in blood had he been
        nurst,
And ne'er was earth with verier tyrant
        curst.
    Bold man and bad,
Remorseless, godless, full of fraud
        and lies,
And black with murders and with
        perjuries,
Himself in Hell's whole panoply he clad ;
No law but his own headstrong will
        he knew,
No counsellor but his own wicked heart.
From evil thus portentous strength
        he drew,
And trampled under foot all human ties,
    All holy laws, all natural charities. 61

5

O France ! beneath this fierce Bar-
        barian's sway
Disgraced thou art to all succeeding
        times ;
Rapine, and blood, and fire have mark'd
        thy way,
    All loathsome, all unutterable crimes.

A curse is on thee, France ! from far
and wide
It hath gone up to Heaven. All lands
have cried
For vengeance upon thy detested head !
All nations curse thee, France ! for
wheresoe'er
In peace or war thy banner hath
been spread, 70
All forms of human woe have follow'd
there.
The Living and the Dead
Cry out alike against thee ! They who
bear,
Crouching beneath its weight, thine
iron yoke,
Join in the bitterness of secret prayer
The voice of that innumerable throng,
Whose slaughter'd spirits day and
night invoke
The Everlasting Judge of right and
wrong,
How long, O Lord ! Holy and Just,
how long !

6

A merciless oppressor hast thou been, 80
Thyself remorselessly oppress'd
meantime ;
Greedy of war, when all that thou
couldst gain
Was but to dye thy soul with deeper
crime,
And rivet faster round thyself the chain.
O blind to honour, and to interest
blind,
When thus in abject servitude resign'd
To this barbarian upstart, thou
couldst brave
God's justice, and the heart of human
kind !
Madly thou thoughtest to enslave the
world,
Thyself the while a miserable slave. 90
Behold the flag of vengeance is unfurl'd !

The dreadful armies of the North
advance ;
While England, Portugal, and Spain
combined,
Give their triumphant banners to the
wind,
And stand victorious in the fields of
France.

7

One man hath been for ten long
wretched years
The cause of all this blood and all these
tears ;
One man in this most aweful point
of time
Draws on thy danger, as he caused thy
crime.
Wait not too long the event, 100
For now whole Europe comes against
thee bent,
His wiles and their own strength the
nations know :
Wise from past wrongs, on future peace
intent,
The People and the Princes, with one
mind,
From all parts move against the general
foe :
One act of justice, one atoning blow,
One execrable head laid low,
Even yet, O France ! averts thy
punishment.
Open thine eyes ! too long hast thou
been blind ;
Take vengeance for thyself, and for
mankind ! 110

8

France ! if thou lovest thine ancient
fame,
Revenge thy sufferings and thy
shame !
By the bones which bleach on Jaffa's
beach ;

By the blood which on Domingo's shore
   Hath clogg'd the carrion-birds with
              gore ;
By the flesh which gorged the wolves
           of Spain,
Or stiffen'd on the snowy plain
        Of frozen Moscovy ;
By the bodies which lie all open to the
           sky,
Tracking from Elbe to Rhine the
       Tyrant's flight ;   120
By the widow's and the orphan's cry ;
By the childless parent's misery ;
By the lives which he hath shed ;
   By the ruin he hath spread ;
By the prayers which rise for curses on
           his head ;
Redeem, O France ! thine ancient
         fame,
Revenge thy sufferings and thy
         shame,
Open thine eyes! . . too long hast thou
         been blind ;
Take vengeance for thyself, and for
         mankind !

9

By those horrors which the night 130
Witness'd, when the torches' light
To the assembled murderers show'd
   Where the blood of Condé flow'd ;
By thy murder'd Pichegru's fame ;
By murder'd Wright, . . an English
         name ;
By murder'd Palm's atrocious doom ;
   By murder'd Hofer's martyrdom ;
Oh ! by the virtuous blood thus vilely
         spilt,
The Villain's own peculiar private
         guilt,
Open thine eyes ! too long hast thou
        been blind !   140
Take vengeance for thyself and for
        mankind !
Keswick.

BALLADS AND METRICAL TALES

THE MARCH TO MOSCOW

[First published in *The Courier*, June 23, 1814, and afterwards in 1837–1838, among the *Ballads and Metrical Tales*.]

1

THE Emperor Nap he would set off
   On a summer excursion to Moscow ;
The fields were green, and the sky was
        blue,
     Morbleu ! Parbleu !
What a pleasant excursion to Moscow !

2

Four hundred thousand men and more
   Must go with him to Moscow :
There were Marshals by the dozen,
     And Dukes by the score ;
Princes a few, and Kings one or two ; 10
While the fields are so green, and the
       sky so blue,
     Morbleu ! Parbleu !
What a pleasant excursion to Moscow !

3

There was Junot and Augereau,
    Heigh-ho for Moscow !
Dombrowsky and Poniatowsky,
    Marshal Ney, lack-a-day !
General Rapp and the Emperor Nap ;
    Nothing would do
While the fields were so green, and the
       sky so blue,   20
     Morbleu ! Parbleu !
    Nothing would do
    For the whole of this crew,
But they must be marching to Moscow.

4

The Emperor Nap he talk'd so big
   That he frighten'd Mr. Roscoe.
John Bull, he cries, if you'll be wise,
Ask the Emperor Nap if he will please
To grant you peace upon your knees,
   Because he is going to Moscow !   30

He'll make all the Poles come out of
their holes,
And beat the Russians and eat the
Prussians,
For the fields are green, and the sky is
blue,
Morbleu ! Parbleu !
And he'll certainly march to Moscow !

5

And Counsellor Brougham was all in
a fume
At the thought of the march to Moscow :
The Russians, he said, they were undone,
And the great Fee-Faw-Fum
Would presently come   40
With a hop, step, and jump unto London.
For as for his conquering Russia,
However some persons might scoff it,
Do it he could, and do it he would,
And from doing it nothing would come
but good,
And nothing could call him off it.
Mr. Jeffrey said so, who must certainly
know,
For he was the Edinburgh Prophet.
They all of them knew Mr. Jeffrey's
Review,
Which with Holy Writ ought to be
reckon'd :   50
It was through thick and thin to its
party true ;
Its back was buff, and its sides were blue,
Morbleu ! Parbleu !   [too.
It served them for Law and for Gospel

6

But the Russians stoutly they turned-to
Upon the road to Moscow.
Nap had to fight his way all through ;
They could fight, though they could not
parlez-vous,
But the fields were green, and the sky
was blue,
Morbleu ! Parbleu !   60
And so he got to Moscow.

7

He found the place too warm for him,
For they set fire to Moscow.
To get there had cost him much
ado,
And then no better course he
knew,
While the fields were green, and the sky
was blue,
Morbleu ! Parbleu !
But to march back again from
Moscow.

8

The Russians they stuck close to him
All on the road from Moscow.   70
There was Tormazow and Jemalow
And all the others that end in ow ;
Milarodovitch and Jaladovitch
And Karatschkowitch,
And all the others that end in itch ;
Schamscheff, Souchosaneff,
And Schepaleff,
And all the others that end in eff ;
Waciltschikoff, Kostomaroff,
And Tchoglokoff,   80
And all the others that end in off ;
Rajeffsky and Novereffsky
And Rieffsky,
And all the others that end in effsky ;
Oscharoffsky and Rostoffsky,
And all the others that end in offsky ;
And Platoff he play'd them off,
And Shouvaloff he shovell'd them off,
And Markoff he mark'd them off,
And Krosnoff he cross'd them off,   90
And Tuchkoff he touch'd them off,
And Boroskoff he bored them off,
And Kutousoff he cut them off,
And Parenzoff he pared them off,
And Worronzoff he worried them off,
And Doctoroff he doctor'd them off,
And Rodionoff he flogg'd them off.
And last of all an Admiral came,
A terrible man with a terrible name,

A name which you all know by sight
    very well ;   100
But which no one can speak, and no one
    can spell.   [might,
They stuck close to Nap with all their
They were on the left and on the right,
Behind and before, and by day and by
    night,
He would rather parlez-vous than fight ;
But he look'd white and he look'd blue,
    Morbleu ! Parbleu !
When parlez-vous no more would do,
    For they remember'd Moscow.

9

And then came on the frost and snow
    All on the road from Moscow.   111
The wind and the weather he found in
    that hour
Cared nothing for him nor for all
    his power ;
For him who, while Europe crouch'd
    under his rod,
Put his trust in his fortune, and not in
    his God.
Worse and worse every day the
    elements grew,   [so blue,
The fields were so white and the sky
    Sacrebleu ! Ventrebleu !
What a horrible journey from Moscow !

10

What then thought the Emperor Nap
    Upon the road from Moscow ?   121
Why, I ween he thought it small delight
To fight all day, and to freeze all night :
And he was besides in a very great fright,
For a whole skin he liked to be in ;
And so, not knowing what else to do,
When the fields were so white and the
    sky so blue,
    Morbleu ! Parbleu !
He stole away, I tell you true,
    Upon the road from Moscow.   130
'Tis myself, quoth he, I must mind most;
So the Devil may take the hindmost.

11

Too cold upon the road was he,
    Too hot had he been at Moscow ;
But colder and hotter he may be,
For the grave is colder than Muscovy :
And a place there is to be kept in view
Where the fire is red and the brimstone
    blue,
    Morbleu ! Parbleu !
    Which he must go to,   140
    If the Pope say true,
If he does not in time look about him ;
    Where his namesake almost
    He may have for his Host,
He has reckon'd too long without him ;
    If that host get him in Purgatory,
He won't leave him there alone with his
    glory ;
But there he must stay for a very
    long day,
For from thence there is no stealing
    away   149
As there was on the road from Moscow.

Keswick, 1813.

LORD WILLIAM

[First published in *The Morning Post*,
March 16, 1798, with the omission of
Stanza 23 ; afterwards in *Poems*, vol. ii,
1799.]

No eye beheld when William plunged
    Young Edmund in the stream,
No human ear but William's heard
    Young Edmund's drowning scream.

Submissive all the vassals own'd
    The murderer for their Lord,
And he as rightful heir possess'd
    The house of Erlingford.

The ancient house of Erlingford
    Stood in a fair domain,   10
And Severn's ample waters near
    Roll'd through the fertile plain.

And often the way-faring man
   Would love to linger there,
Forgetful of his onward road,
   To gaze on scenes so fair.

But never could Lord William dare
   To gaze on Severn's stream ;
In every wind that swept its waves
   He heard young Edmund's scream. 20

In vain at midnight's silent hour
   Sleep closed the murderer's eyes,
In every dream the murderer saw
   Young Edmund's form arise.

In vain by restless conscience driven
   Lord William left his home,
Far from the scenes that saw his guilt,
   In pilgrimage to roam ;

To other climes the pilgrim fled,
   But could not fly despair ;   30
He sought his home again, but peace
   Was still a stranger there.

Slow were the passing hours, yet swift
   The months appear'd to roll ;
And now the day return'd that shook
   With terror William's soul ;

A day that William never felt
   Return without dismay,
For well had conscience kalendar'd
   Young Edmund's dying day.   40

A fearful day was that ; the rains
   Fell fast with tempest roar,
And the swoln tide of Severn spread
   Far on the level shore.

In vain Lord William sought the feast,
   In vain he quaff'd the bowl,
And strove with noisy mirth to drown
   The anguish of his soul.

The tempest, as its sudden swell
   In gusty howlings came,   50
With cold and death-like feeling seem'd
   To thrill his shuddering frame.

Reluctant now, as night came on,
   His lonely couch he prest ;
And, wearied out, he sunk to sleep, . .
   To sleep . . but not to rest.

Beside that couch his brother's form,
   Lord Edmund, seem'd to stand,
Such and so pale as when in death
   He grasp'd his brother's hand ;   60

Such and so pale his face as when
   With faint and faltering tongue,
To William's care, a dying charge,
   He left his orphan son.

' I bade thee with a father's love
   My orphan Edmund guard ; . .
Well, William, hast thou kept thy charge
   Take now thy due reward.'

He started up, each limb convulsed
   With agonizing fear ;   70
He only heard the storm of night, . .
   'Twas music to his ear.

When lo ! the voice of loud alarm
   His inmost soul appals ;
' What ho ! Lord William, rise in haste !
   The water saps thy walls ! '

He rose in haste, beneath the walls
   He saw the flood appear ;   [now,
It hemm'd him round, 'twas midnight
   No human aid was near.   80

He heard a shout of joy, for now
   A boat approach'd the wall,
And eager to the welcome aid
   They crowd for safety all.

' My boat is small,' the boatman cried,
   ' 'Twill bear but one away ;
Come in, Lord William, and do ye
   In God's protection stay.'

Strange feeling fill'd them at his voice
   Even in that hour of woe,   90
That, save their Lord, there was not one
   Who wish'd with him to go.

But William leapt into the boat,
His terror was so sore ;
' Thou shalt have half my gold,' he cried,
' Haste . . haste to yonder shore.'

The boatman plied the oar, the boat
Went light along the stream ;
Sudden Lord William heard a cry
Like Edmund's drowning scream. 100

The boatman paused,'Methought I heard
A child's distressful cry ! '
' 'Twas but the howling wind of night,'
Lord William made reply.

' Haste . . haste . . ply swift and strong
the oar ;
Haste . . haste across the stream ! '
Again Lord William heard a cry
Like Edmund's drowning scream.

'I heard a child's distressful voice,'
The boatman cried again. 110
' Nay, hasten on . . the night is dark . .
And we should search in vain.'

' O God ! Lord William, dost thou know
How dreadful 'tis to die ?
And canst thou without pity hear
A child's expiring cry ?

' How horrible it is to sink
Beneath the closing stream,
To stretch the powerless arms in vain,
In vain for help to scream ! ' 120

The shriek again was heard : it came
More deep, more piercing loud ;
That instant o'er the flood the moon
Shone through a broken cloud ;

And near them they beheld a child ;
Upon a crag he stood,
A little crag, and all around
Was spread the rising flood.

The boatman plied the oar, the boat
Approach'd his resting-place ; 130
The moon-beam shone upon the child,
And show'd how pale his face.

' Now reach thine hand ! ' the boatman
cried,
' Lord William, reach and save ! '
The child stretch'd forth his little hands
To grasp the hand he gave.

Then William shriek'd ; the hands he
felt
Were cold and damp and dead !
He held young Edmund in his arms
A heavier weight than lead. 140

The boat sunk down, the murderer sunk
Beneath the avenging stream ;
He rose, he shriek'd, no human ear
Heard William's drowning scream.

Westbury, 1798.

THE WELL OF ST. KEYNE

[First published in *The Morning Post*,
Dec. 3, 1798; afterwards in *The Annual Anthology*, 1799, and in *Metrical Tales*, 1805.]

' I know not whether it be worth the
reporting, that there is in Cornwall, near the
parish of St. Neots, a Well, arched over with
the robes of four kinds of trees, withy, oak,
elm, and ash, dedicated to St. Keyne. The
reported virtue of the water is this, that
whether husband or wife come first to drink
thereof, they get the mastery thereby.'—
Fuller.

This passage in one of the folios of the
Worthy old Fuller, who, as he says, knew
not whether it were worth the reporting,
suggested the following Ballad : and the
Ballad has produced so many imitations
that it may be prudent here thus to assert
its originality, lest I should be accused hereafter of having committed the plagiarism
which has been practised upon it.

A WELL there is in the west country,
And a clearer one never was seen ;
There is not a wife in the west country
But has heard of the well of St. Keyne.

An oak and an elm-tree stand beside,
And behind doth an ash-tree grow,
And a willow from the bank above
Droops to the water below.

A traveller came to the Well of St. Keyne;
  Joyfully he drew nigh,   10
For from cock-crow he had been travelling,
  And there was not a cloud in the sky.

He drank of the water so cool and clear,
  For thirsty and hot was he,
And he sat down upon the bank
  Under the willow-tree.

There came a man from the house hard by
  At the Well to fill his pail;
On the Well-side he rested it,
  And he bade the Stranger hail.   20

Now art thou a bachelor, Stranger ?'
  quoth he,
  ' For an if thou hast a wife,
The happiest draught thou hast drank this day
  That ever thou didst in thy life.

' Or has thy good woman, if one thou hast,
  Ever here in Cornwall been ?
For an if she have, I'll venture my life
  She has drank of the Well of St. Keyne.'

' I have left a good woman who never was here,'
  The Stranger he made reply,   30
' But that my draught should be the better for that,
  I pray you answer me why ?'

' St. Keyne,' quoth the Cornish-man,
  ' many a time
Drank of this crystal Well,
And before the Angel summon'd her,
  She laid on the water a spell.

' If the Husband of this gifted Well
  Shall drink before his Wife,
A happy man thenceforth is he,
  For he shall be Master for life.   40

' But if the Wife should drink of it first, ..
  God help the Husband then !'
The Stranger stoopt to the Well of St. Keyne,
  And drank of the water again.

' You drank of the Well I warrant betimes ?'
  He to the Cornish-man said :
But the Cornish-man smiled as the Stranger spake,
  And sheepishly shook his head.

' I hasten'd as soon as the wedding was done,
  And left my Wife in the porch ;   50
But i' faith she had been wiser than me,
  For she took a bottle to Church.'
    Westbury, 1798.

THE BATTLE OF BLENHEIM

[First published in *The Morning Post*, August 9, 1798; afterwards in *The Annual Anthology*, 1800, and in *Metrical Tales*, 1805.]

1

It was a summer evening,
  Old Kaspar's work was done,
And he before his cottage door
  Was sitting in the sun,
And by him sported on the green
His little grandchild Wilhelmine.

2

She saw her brother Peterkin
  Roll something large and round,
Which he beside the rivulet
  In playing there had found ;   10
He came to ask what he had found,
That was so large, and smooth, and round.

3

Old Kaspar took it from the boy,
  Who stood expectant by ;
And then the old man shook his head,
  And, with a natural sigh,
' 'Tis some poor fellow's skull,' said he,
' Who fell in the great victory.

4

' I find them in the garden,
  For there's many here about ;   20
And often when I go to plough,
  The ploughshare turns them out !
For many thousand men,' said he,
  ' Were slain in that great victory.'

5

' Now tell us what 'twas all about,'
  Young Peterkin, he cries ;
And little Wilhelmine looks up
  With wonder-waiting eyes ;
' Now tell us all about the war,
  And what they fought each other for.' 30

6

' It was the English,' Kaspar cried,
  ' Who put the French to rout ;
But what they fought each other for,
  I could not well make out ;
But every body said,' quoth he,
  ' That 'twas a famous victory.

7

' My father lived at Blenheim then,
  Yon little stream hard by ;
They burnt his dwelling to the ground,
  And he was forced to fly ;   40
So with his wife and child he fled,
  Nor had he where to rest his head.

8

' With fire and sword the country round
  Was wasted far and wide,
And many a childing mother then,
  And new-born baby died ;
But things like that, you know, must be
  At every famous victory.

9

' They say it was a shocking sight
  After the field was won ;   50
For many thousand bodies here
  Lay rotting in the sun ;
But things like that, you know, must be
  After a famous victory.

10

' Great praise the Duke of Marlbro' won,
  And our good Prince Eugene.'
' Why 'twas a very wicked thing ! '
  Said little Wilhelmine.
' Nay . . nay . . my little girl,' quoth he,
  ' It was a famous victory.   60

11

' And every body praised the Duke
  Who this great fight did win.'
' But what good came of it at last ? '
  Quoth little Peterkin.
' Why that I cannot tell,' said he
  ' But 'twas a famous victory.'

  Westbury, 1798.

THE OLD WOMAN OF BERKELEY,
A BALLAD,

SHEWING HOW AN OLD WOMAN RODE
  DOUBLE, AND WHO RODE BEFORE
  HER.

[Published in *Poems*, vol. ii, 1799. The
history of this ballad is described by Southey
in the Preface to the Sixth Volume of the
Collected Edition of his Poems (vide pp. 13,
14).]

' A.D. 852. Circa dies istos, mulier quae-
dam malefica, in villa quae Berkeleia dicitur
degens, gulae amatrix ac petulantiae,
flagitiis modum usque in senium et auguriis
non ponens, usque ad mortem impudica per-
mansit. Haec die quadam cum sederet ad
prandium, cornicula quam pro delitiis pasce-
bat, nescio quid garrire coepit ; quo audito,
mulieris cultellus de manu excidit, simul et
facies pallescere coepit, et emisso rugitu,
Hodie, inquit, accipiam grande incommo-
dum, hodieque ad sulcum ultimum meum
pervenit aratrum.   Quo dicto, nuncius
doloris intravit ; muliere vero percunctata
ad quid veniret, Affero, inquit, tibi filii tui
obitum et totius familiae ejus ex subita
ruina interitum.   Hoc quoque dolore mulier
permota, lecto protinus decubuit graviter
infirmata ; sentiensque morbum subrepere
ad vitalia, liberos quos habuit superstites,
monachum videlicet et monacham, per
epistolam invitavit ; advenientes autem
voce singultiente alloquitur. Ego, inquit,
o pueri, meo miserabili fato daemoniacis

semper artibus inservivi; ego omnium vitiorum sentina, ego illecebrarum omnium fui magistra. Erat tamen mihi inter haec mala spes vestrae religionis, quae meam solidaret animam desperatam; vos expectabam propugnatores contra daemones, tutores contra saevissimos hostes. Nunc igitur quoniam ad finem vitae perveni, rogo vos per materna ubera, ut mea tentetis alleviare tormenta. Insuite me defunctam in corio cervino, ac deinde in sarcophago lapideo supponite, operculumque ferro et plumbo consotringite, ac demum lapidem tribus cathenis ferreis et fortissimis circundantes, clericos quinquaginta psalmorum cantores, et tot per tres dies presbyteros missarum celebratores applicate, qui feroces lenigent adversariorum incursus. Ita si tribus noctibus secura jacuero, quarta die me infodite humo.

'Factumque est ut praeceperat illis. Sed, proh dolor! nil preces, nil lacrymae, nil demum valuere cathenae. Primis enim duabus noctibus, cum chori psallentium corpori assistebant, advenientes Daemones ostium ecclesiae confregerunt ingenti obice clausum, extremasque cathenas negotio levi dirumpunt; media autem quae fortior erat, illibata manebat. Tertia autem nocte, circa gallicinium, strepitu hostium adventantium, omne monasterium visum est a fundamento moveri. Unus ergo daemonum, et vultu caeteris terribilior et statura eminentior, januas ecclesiae impetu violento concussas in fragmenta dejecit. Divexerunt clerici cum laicis, metu steterunt omnium capilli, et psalmorum concentus defecit. Daemon ergo gestu ut videbatur arroganti ad sepulchrum accedens, et nomen mulieris modicum ingeminans, surgere imperavit. Qua respondente, quod nequiret pro vinculis, Jam malo tuo, inquit, solveris; et protinus cathenam quae caeterorum ferocium daemonum deluserat, velut stuppeum vinculum rumpebat. Operculum etiam sepulchri pede depellens, mulierem palam omnibus ab ecclesia extraxit, ubi prae foribus niger equus superbe hinniens videbatur, uncis ferreis et clavis undique confixus, super quem misera mulier projecta, ab oculis assistentium evanuit. Audiebantur tamen clamores per quatuor fere miliaria horribiles, auxilium postulantes.

'Ista itaque quae retuli incredibilia non erunt, si legatur beati Gregorii dialogus, in quo refert, hominem in ecclesia sepultum, a daemonibus foras ejectum. Et apud Francos Carolus Martellus insignis vir fortitudinis, qui Saracenos Galliam ingressos, Hispaniam redire compulit, exactis vitae suae diebus, in ecclesia beati Dionysii legitur fuisse sepultus. Sed quia patrimonia, cum decimis omnium fere ecclesiarum Galliae, pro stipendio commilitonum suorum mutilaverat, miserabiliter a malignis spiritibus de sepulchro corporaliter avulsus, usque in hodiernum diem nusquam comparuit.'— *Matthew of Westminster.*

This story is also related by Olaus Magnus, and in the *Nuremberg Chronicle.* But William of Malmesbury seems to have been the original authority, and he had the story from an eye-witness. 'When I shall have related it,' he says, ' the credit of the narrative will not be shaken, though the minds of the hearers should be incredulous, for I have heard it from a man of such character *who would swear he had seen it,* that I should blush to disbelieve.'—SHARPE, *William of Malmesbury,* p. 264.

THE Raven croak'd as she sate at her meal,
And the Old Woman knew what he said,
And she grew pale at the Raven's tale,
And sicken'd and went to her bed.

' Now fetch me my children, and fetch them with speed,'
The Old Woman of Berkeley said,
' The Monk my son, and my daughter the Nun,
Bid them hasten or I shall be dead.'

The Monk her son, and her daughter the Nun,
Their way to Berkeley went,   10
And they have brought with pious thought
The holy sacrament.

The Old Woman shriek'd as they enter'd her door,
And she cried with a voice of despair,
' Now take away the sacrament,
For its presence I cannot bear ! '

Her lip it trembled with agony,
The sweat ran down her brow,
' I have tortures in store for evermore,
But spare me, my children, now ! '   20

Away they sent the sacrament,
    The fit it left her weak,
She look'd at her children with ghastly
        eyes,
    And faintly struggled to speak.

' All kind of sin I have rioted in,
    And the judgement now must be,
But I secured my children's souls,
    Oh! pray, my children, for me!

' I have 'nointed myself with infant's fat,
    The fiends have been my slaves,   30
From sleeping babes I have suck'd the
        breath,
And breaking by charms the sleep of
        death,
    I have call'd the dead from their
        graves.

' And the Devil will fetch me now in fire,
    My witchcrafts to atone;
And I who have troubled the dead man's
        grave
    Shall never have rest in my own.

' Bless, I entreat, my winding sheet,
    My children, I beg of you;
And with holy water sprinkle my shroud,
    And sprinkle my coffin too.   41

' And let me be chain'd in my coffin of
        stone,
    And fasten it strong, I implore,
With iron bars, and with three chains,
    Chain it to the church floor.

' And bless the chains and sprinkle them,
    And let fifty Priests stand round,
Who night and day the mass may say
    Where I lie on the ground.

' And see that fifty Choristers   50
    Beside the bier attend me,
And day and night by the tapers' light,
    With holy hymns defend me.

' Let the church bells all, both great and
        small,
    Be toll'd by night and day,
To drive from thence the fiends who
        come
    To bear my body away.

' And ever have the church door barr'd
    After the even-song;
And I beseech you, children dear,   60
    Let the bars and bolts be strong.

' And let this be three days and nights
    My wretched corpse to save;
Till the fourth morning keep me safe,
    And then I may rest in my grave.'

The Old Woman of Berkeley laid her
        down,
    And her eyes grew deadly dim,
Short came her breath, and the struggle
        of death
    Did loosen every limb.

They blest the old woman's winding
        sheet   70
    With rites and prayers due,
With holy water they sprinkled her
        shroud,
    And they sprinkled her coffin too.

And they chain'd her in her coffin of
        stone,
    And with iron barr'd it down,
And in the church with three strong
        chains
    They chain'd it to the ground.

And they blest the chains and sprinkled
        them,
    And fifty Priests stood round,
By night and day the mass to say   80
    Where she lay on the ground.

And fifty sacred Choristers
    Beside the bier attend her,
Who day and night by the tapers' light
    Should with holy hymns defend her.

To see the Priests and Choristers
It was a goodly sight,
Each holding, as it were a staff,
A taper burning bright.

And the church bells all, both great and
small, 90
Did toll so loud and long ;
And they have barr'd the church door
hard,
After the even-song.

And the first night the tapers' light
Burnt steadily and clear,
But they without a hideous rout
Of angry fiends could hear ;

A hideous roar at the church door
Like a long thunder peal ;
And the Priests they pray'd, and the
Choristers sung 100
Louder in fearful zeal.

Loud toll'd the bell, the Priests pray'd
well,
The tapers they burnt bright,
The Monk her son, and her daughter the
Nun,
They told their beads all night.

The cock he crew, the Fiends they flew
From the voice of the morning away ;
Then undisturb'd the Choristers sing,
And the fifty Priests they pray ;
As they had sung and pray'd all night,
They pray'd and sung all day. 111

The second night the tapers' light
Burnt dismally and blue,
And every one saw his neighbour's face
Like a dead man's face to view.

And yells and cries without arise
That the stoutest heart might shock,
And a deafening roaring like a cataract
pouring
Over a mountain rock.

The Monk and Nun they told their
beads 120
As fast as they could tell,
And aye as louder grew the noise
The faster went the bell.

Louder and louder the Choristers sung
As they trembled more and more,
And the Priests as they pray'd to heaven
for aid,
They smote their breasts full sore.

The cock he crew, the Fiends they flew
From the voice of the morning away ;
Then undisturb'd the Choristers sing, 130
And the fifty Priests they pray ;
As they had sung and pray'd all night,
They pray'd and sung all day.

The third night came, and the tapers'
flame
A frightful stench did make ;
And they burnt as though they had been
dipt
In the burning brimstone lake.

And the loud commotion, like the rush-
ing of ocean,
Grew momently more and more ;
And strokes as of a battering ram 140
Did shake the strong church door.

The bellmen, they for very fear
Could toll the bell no longer ;
And still as louder grew the strokes
Their fear it grew the stronger.

The Monk and Nun forgot their beads,
They fell on the ground in dismay ;
There was not a single Saint in heaven
To whom they did not pray.

And the Choristers' song, which late was
so strong, 150
Falter'd with consternation,
For the church did rock as an earth-
quake shock
Uplifted its foundation.

And a sound was heard like the trumpet's blast,
That shall one day wake the dead ;
The strong church door could bear no
    more,
And the bolts and the bars they fled ;

And the tapers' light was extinguish'd
    quite,
And the choristers faintly sung,
And the Priests dismay'd, panted and
    pray'd,   160
And on all Saints in heaven for aid
They call'd with trembling tongue.

And in He came with eyes of flame,
The Devil to fetch the dead,
And all the church with his presence
    glow'd
Like a fiery furnace red.

He laid his hand on the iron chains,
And like flax they moulder'd asunder,
And the coffin lid, which was barr'd so
    firm,
He burst with his voice of thunder.

And he bade the Old Woman of Berkeley
    rise,   171
And come with her Master away ;
A cold sweat started on that cold corpse,
At the voice she was forced to obey.

She rose on her feet in her winding sheet,
Her dead flesh quiver'd with fear,
And a groan like that which the Old
    Woman gave
Never did mortal hear.

She follow'd her Master to the church
    door,
There stood a black horse there ;   180
His breath was red like furnace smoke,
His eyes like a meteor's glare.

The Devil he flung her on the horse,
    And he leapt up before,   [went,
And away like the lightning's speed they
    And she was seen no more.

They saw her no more, but her cries
For four miles round they could hear,
And children at rest at their mothers'
    breast
Started, and scream'd with fear.   190

Hereford, 1798.

GOD'S JUDGEMENT ON A WICKED BISHOP

[First published in *The Morning Post*, Nov. 27, 1799; afterwards in *The Annual Anthology*, 1800, and in *Metrical Tales*, 1805.]

' Here followeth the History of HATTO, Archbichop of Mentz.

' It hapned in the year 914, that there was an exceeding great famine in Germany, at what time Otho, surnamed the Great, was Emperor, and one Hatto, once Abbot of Fulda, was Archbishop of Mentz, of the Bishops after Crescens and Crescentius the two and thirtieth, of the Archbishops after St. Bonifacius the thirteenth. This Hatto, in the time of this great famine afore-mentioned, when he saw the poor people of the country exceedingly oppressed with famine, assembled a great company of them together into a Barne, and, like a most accursed and mercilesse caitiffe, burnt up those poor innocent souls, that were so far from doubting any such matter, that they rather hoped to receive some comfort and relief at his hands. The reason that moved the prelat to commit that execrable impiety was, because he thought the famine would the sooner cease, if those unprofitable beggars that consumed more bread than they were worthy to eat, were dispatched out of the world. For he said that those poor folks were like to Mice, that were good for nothing but to devour corne. But God Almighty, the just avenger of the poor folks quarrel, did not long suffer this hainous tyranny, this most detestable fact, unpunished. For he mustered up an army of Mice against the Archbishop, and sent them to persecute him as his furious Alastors, so that they afflicted him both day and night, and would not suffer him to take his rest in any place. Whereupon the Prelate, thinking that he should be secure from the injury of Mice if he were in a certain tower, that standeth in the Rhine near to the towne, betook himself unto the said tower as to a safe refuge and sanctuary from his enemies, and locked himself in. But the innumerable troupes of Mice chased him continually very eagerly, and swumme unto him upon the top of the water to execute the just Judgment of God, and so at last he was most miserably devoured by those sillie creatures; who pursued him with such bitter hostility, that it is recorded they scraped and knawed out his very name from the walls and tapistry wherein it was written, after they had so cruelly devoured his body. Wherefore the tower wherein he was eaten up by the Mice is shewn to this day, for a perpetual monument to all succeeding ages of the barbarous and inhuman tyranny of this impious Prelate, being situate in a little green Island in the midst of the Rhine near to the towne of Bingen, and is commonly called in the German Tongue the MOWSE-TURN.'— *Coryat's Crudities*, pp. 571, 572.

Other authors who record this tale say that the Bishop was eaten by Rats.

The summer and autumn had been so wet,
That in winter the corn was growing yet,
Twas a piteous sight to see all around
The grain lie rotting on the ground.

Every day the starving poor
Crowded around Bishop Hatto's door,
For he had a plentiful last-year's store,
And all the neighbourhood could tell
His granaries were furnish'd well.

At last Bishop Hatto appointed a day 10
To quiet the poor without delay;
He bade them to his great Barn repair,
And they should have food for the winter there.

Rejoiced such tidings good to hear,
The poor folk flock'd from far and near;
The great Barn was full as it could hold
Of women and children, and young and old.

Then when he saw it could hold no more,
Bishop Hatto he made fast the door;
And while for mercy on Christ they call,
He set fire to the Barn and burnt them all. 21

'I'faith 'tis an excellent bonfire!' quoth he,
'And the country is greatly obliged to me,
For ridding it in these times forlorn
Of Rats that only consume the corn.'

So then to his palace returned he,
And he sat down to supper merrily,
And he slept that night like an innocent man;
But Bishop Hatto never slept again.

In the morning as he enter'd the hall 30
Where his picture hung against the wall,
A sweat like death all over him came,
For the Rats had eaten it out of the frame.

As he look'd there came a man from his farm—
He had a countenance white with alarm;
'My Lord, I open'd your granaries this morn,
And the Rats had eaten all your corn.'

Another came running presently,
And he was pale as pale could be,
'Fly! my Lord Bishop, fly,' quoth he,
'Ten thousand Rats are coming this way, .. 41
The Lord forgive you for yesterday!'

'I'll go to my tower on the Rhine,' replied he,
''Tis the safest place in Germany;
The walls are high and the shores are steep,
And the stream is strong and the water deep.'

Bishop Hatto fearfully hasten'd away,
And he crost the Rhine without delay,
And reach'd his tower, and barr'd with care
All the windows, doors, and loop-holes there. 50

He laid him down and closed his eyes ; ..
But soon a scream made him arise,
He started and saw two eyes of flame
On his pillow from whence the screaming
    came.

He listen'd and look'd ; . . it was only
    the Cat ;
But the Bishop he grew more fearful for
    that,
For she sat screaming, mad with fear
At the Army of Rats that were drawing
    near.

For they have swum over the river so
    deep,
And they have climb'd the shores so
    steep,   60
And up the Tower their way is bent,
To do the work for which they were sent.

They are not to be told by the dozen or
    score,
By thousands they come, and by myriads
    and more,
Such numbers had never been heard of
    before,
Such a judgement had never been
    witness'd of yore.

Down on his knees the Bishop fell,
And faster and faster his beads did he
    tell,
As louder and louder drawing near   69
The gnawing of their teeth he could hear.

And in at the windows and in at the
    door,
And through the walls helter-skelter
    they pour,
And down from the ceiling and up
    through the floor,
From the right and the left, from behind
    and before,
From within and without, from above
    and below,
And all at once to the Bishop they go.

They have whetted their teeth against
    the stones,
And now they pick the Bishop's bones ;
They gnaw'd the flesh from every limb,
For they were sent to do judgement on
    him !   80
Westbury, 1799.

THE INCHCAPE ROCK.

[First published in *The Morning Post*,
Oct. 19, 1803. The Ballad was reprinted,
with a number of unauthorized variations,
in *The Edinburgh Annual Register* for 1810,
without Southey's knowledge or consent.]

An old writer mentions a curious tradition
which may be worth quoting. ' By east the
Isle of May,' says he, ' twelve miles from all
land in the German seas, lyes a great hidden
rock, called Inchcape, very dangerous for
navigators, because it is overflowed everie
tide. It is reported in old times, upon the
saide rock there was a bell, fixed upon a tree
or timber, which rang continually, being
moved by the sea, giving notice to the saylers
of the danger. This bell or clocke was put
there and maintained by the Abbot of
Aberbrothok, and being taken down by a
sea pirate, a yeare therafter he perished upon
the same rocke, with ship and goodes, in the
righteous judgement of God.'—STODDART,
Remarks on Scotland.

No stir in the air, no stir in the sea,
The ship was still as she could be,
Her sails from heaven received no mo-
    tion,
Her keel was steady in the ocean.

Without either sign or sound of their
    shock
The waves flow'd over the Inchcape
    Rock ;
So little they rose, so little they fell,
They did not move the Inchcape Bell.

The Abbot of Aberbrothok
Had placed that bell on the Inchcape
    Rock ;   10
On a buoy in the storm it floated and
    swung,
And over the waves its warning rung.

When the Rock was hid by the surge's
   swell,
The mariners heard the warning bell;
And then they knew the perilous
   Rock,
And blest the Abbot of Aberbrothok.

The Sun in heaven was shining gay,
All things were joyful on that day;
The sea-birds scream'd as they wheel'd
   round,   19
And there was joyaunce in their sound.

The buoy of the Inchcape Bell was
   seen
A darker speck on the ocean green;
Sir Ralph the Rover walk'd his deck,
And he fixed his eye on the darker
   speck.

He felt the cheering power of spring,
It made him whistle, it made him
   sing;
His heart was mirthful to excess,
But the Rover's mirth was wickedness.

His eye was on the Inchcape float;
Quoth he, 'My men, put out the
   boat,   30
And row me to the Inchcape Rock,
And I'll plague the Abbot of Aber-
   brothok.'

The boat is lower'd, the boatmen row,
And to the Inchcape Rock they go;
Sir Ralph bent over from the boat,
And he cut the Bell from the Inchcape
   float.

Down sunk the Bell with a gurgling
   sound,
The bubbles rose and burst around;
Quoth Sir Ralph, 'The next who comes
   to the Rock   39
Won't bless the Abbot of Aberbrothok.'

Sir Ralph the Rover sail'd away,
He scour'd the seas for many a day;
And now grown rich with plunder'd
   store,
He steers his course for Scotland's shore.

So thick a haze o'erspreads the sky
They cannot see the Sun on high;
The wind hath blown a gale all day,
At evening it hath died away.

On the deck the Rover takes his stand,
So dark it is they see no land.   50
Quoth Sir Ralph, 'It will be lighter
   soon,
For there is the dawn of the rising
   Moon.'

'Canst hear,' said one, 'the breakers
   roar?
For methinks we should be near the
   shore.'
'Now where we are I cannot tell,
But I wish I could hear the Inchcape
   Bell.'

They hear no sound, the swell is strong;
Though the wind hath fallen they drift
   along,
Till the vessel strikes with a shivering
   shock,—
'Oh Christ! it is the Inchcape Rock!'

Sir Ralph the Rover tore his hair;   61
He curst himself in his despair;
The waves rush in on every side,
The ship is sinking beneath the tide.

But even in his dying fear
One dreadful sound could the Rover
   hear,
A sound as if with the Inchcape Bell,
The Devil below was ringing his knell.

Bristol, 1802.

QUEEN ORRACA
AND
THE FIVE MARTYRS OF MOROCCO

[First published in *The Morning Post*,
Sept .1, 1803. Afterwards published in *The
Edinburgh Annual Register* for 1808, and in
Ballantyne's *English Minstrelsy*, 1810.]

This Legend is related in the Chronicle of
Affonso II, and in the Historia Serafica of
Fr. Manoel da Esperança.

1

THE Friars five have girt their loins,
     And taken staff in hand;
And never shall those Friars again
     Hear mass in Christian land.

They went to Queen Orraca,
     To thank her and bless her then;
And Queen Orraca in tears
     Knelt to the holy men.

' Three things, Queen Orraca,
     We prophesy to you :   10
Hear us, in the name of God !
     For time will prove them true.

' In Morocco we must martyr'd be;
     Christ hath vouchsafed it thus :
We shall shed our blood for Him
     Who shed his blood for us.

' To Coimbra shall our bodies be
          brought,
     Such being the will divine;
That Christians may behold and feel
     Blessings at our shrine.   20

' And when unto that place of rest
     Our bodies shall draw nigh,
Who sees us first, the King or you,
     That one that night must die.

' Fare thee well, Queen Orraca !
     For thy soul a mass we will say,
Every day as long as we live,
     And on thy dying day.'

The Friars they blest her, one by one,
     Where she knelt on her knee,   30
And they departed to the land
     Of the Moors beyond the sea.

2

' What news, O King Affonso,
     What news of the Friars five ?
Have they preach'd to the Miramamolin;
     And are they still alive ? '

' They have fought the fight, O Queen !
     They have run the race ;
In robes of white they hold the palm
     Before the throne of Grace.   40

' All naked in the sun and air
     Their mangled bodies lie ;
What Christian dared to bury them,
     By the bloody Moors would die.'

3

' What news, O King Affonso,
     Of the Martyrs five what news ?
Doth the bloody Miramamolin
     Their burial still refuse ? '

' That on a dunghill they should rot,
     The bloody Moor decreed ;   50
That their dishonour'd bodies should
     The dogs and vultures feed :

' But the thunder of God roll'd over
          them,
     And the lightning of God flash'd round;
Nor thing impure, nor man impure,
     Could approach the holy ground.

' A thousand miracles appall'd
     The cruel Pagan's mind ;
Our brother Pedro brings them here,
     In Coimbra to be shrined.'   60

4

Every altar in Coimbra
     Is drest for the festival day ;
All the people in Coimbra
     Are dight in their richest array ;

Every bell in Coimbra
  Doth merrily, merrily, ring;
The Clergy and the Knights await,
  To go forth with the Queen and the
    King.

' Come forth, come forth, Queen Orraca!
  We make the procession stay.'   70
' I beseech thee, King Affonso,
  Go you alone to-day.

' I have pain in my head this morning,
  I am ill at heart also:
Go without me, King Affonso,
  For I am too faint to go.'

' The relics of the Martyrs five
  All maladies can cure;
They will requite the charity
  You shew'd them once, be sure: 80

' Come forth then, Queen Orraca!
  You make the procession stay:
It were a scandal and a sin
  To abide at home to-day.'

Upon her palfrey she is set,
  And forward then they go;
And over the long bridge they pass,
  And up the long hill wind slow.

' Prick forward, King Affonso,
  And do not wait for me;   90
To meet them close by Coimbra,
  It were discourtesy;

' A little while I needs must wait,
  Till this sore pain be gone; ..
I will proceed the best I can,
  But do you and your Knights prick
    on.'

The King and his Knights prick'd up
    the hill
  Faster than before;
The King and his Knights have topt the
    hill,
  And now they are seen no more.   100

As the King and his Knights went down
    the hill
  A wild boar crost the way;
' Follow him! follow him!' cried the
    King;
  ' We have time by the Queen's delay!'

A-hunting of the boar astray
  Is King Affonso gone:
Slowly, slowly, but straight the while,
  Queen Orraca is coming on.

And winding now the train appears
  Between the olive-trees: 110
Queen Orraca alighted then,
  And fell upon her knees.

The Friars of Alanquer came first,
  And next the relics past; ..
Queen Orraca look'd to see
  The King and his Knights come last.

She heard the horses tramp behind;
  At that she turn'd her face:
King Affonso and his Knights came up
  All panting from the chase.   120

' Have pity upon my poor soul,
  Holy Martyrs five!' cried she:
' Holy Mary, Mother of God,
  Virgin, pray for me!'

5

That day in Coimbra
  Many a heart was gay;
But the heaviest heart in Coimbra,
  Was that poor Queen's that day.

The festival is over,
  The sun hath sunk in the west;   130
All the people in Coimbra
  Have betaken themselves to rest.

Queen Orraca's Father Confessor
  At midnight is awake;
Kneeling at the Martyr's shrine,
  And praying for her sake.

Just at the midnight hour, when all
  Was still as still could be,
Into the Church of Santa Cruz,
  Came a saintly company :   140

All in robes of russet grey,
  Poorly were they dight ;
Each one girdled with a cord,
  Like a Friar Minorite.

But from those robes of russet grey,
  There flow'd a heavenly light ;
For each one was the blessed soul
  Of a Friar Minorite.

Brighter than their brethren,
  Among the beautiful band ;   150
Five were there who each did bear
  A palm branch in his hand.

He who led the brethren,
  A living man was he ;
And yet he shone the brightest
  Of all the company.

Before the steps of the altar,
  Each one bow'd his head ;
And then with solemn voice they sung
  The Service of the Dead.   160

' And who are ye, ye blessed Saints ? '
  The Father Confessor said ;
' And for what happy soul sing ye
  The Service of the Dead ? '

' These are the souls of our brethren in
    bliss,
  The Martyrs five are we :
And this is our father Francisco,
  Among us bodily !

' We are come hither to perform
  Our promise to the Queen ;   170
Go thou to King Affonso,
  And say what thou hast seen.'

There was loud knocking at the door,
  As the heavenly vision fled ;
And the porter called to the Confessor,
  To tell him the Queen was dead.
Bristol, 1803.

BROUGH BELLS

' The church at Brough is a pretty large
handsome ancient building. The steeple is
not so old, having been built about the year
1513, under the direction of Thomas Blenkinsop, of Helbeck, Esq. There are in it
four excellent bells, by much the largest in
the county, except the great bell at Kirkby
Thore. Concerning these bells at Brough,
there is a tradition that they were given by
one Brunskill, who lived upon Stanemore, in
the remotest part of the parish, and had
a great many cattle. One time it happened
that his Bull fell a bellowing, which in the
dialect of the country is called cruning, this
being the genuine Saxon word to denote that
vociferation. Thereupon he said to one of
his neighbours, "Hearest thou how loud
this bull crunes ? If these cattle should all
crune together, might they not be heard
from Brough hither ? " He answered,
" Yea." " Well, then," says Brunskill,
" I'll make them all crune together." And
he sold them all, and with the price thereof
he bought the said bells (or perhaps he might
get the old bells new cast and made larger).
There is a monument in the body of the
church, in the south wall, between the
highest and second window, and in which it
is said the said Brunskill was the last that
was interred.'—*Nicolson and Burn's History
and Antiquities of Westmoreland and Cumberland*, vol. i, p. 571.

ONE day to Helbeck I had stroll'd
  Among the Crossfell hills,
And resting in its rocky grove
  Sat listening to the rills ;

The while to their sweet undersong
  The birds sang blithe around,
And the soft west wind awoke the wood
  To an intermitting sound.

Louder or fainter as it rose,
  Or died away, was borne   10
The harmony of merry bells,
  From Brough that pleasant morn.

' Why are the merry bells of Brough,
  My friend, so few ? ' said I,
' They disappoint the expectant ear,
  Which they should gratify.

' One, two, three, four ; one, two, three,
   four ;
   'Tis still one, two, three, four.
Mellow and silvery are the tones ;
   But I wish the bells were more ! '   20

' What ! art thou critical ? ' quoth he ;
   ' Eschew that heart's disease
That seeketh for displeasure where
   The intent hath been to please.

' By those four bells there hangs a tale,
   Which being told, I guess,
Will make thee hear their scanty peal
   With proper thankfulness.

' Not by the Cliffords were they given,
   Nor by the Tuftons' line ;   30
Thou hearest in that peal the crune
   Of old John Brunskill's kine.

' On Stanemore's side one summer eve,
   John Brunskill sate to see
His herds in yonder Borrodale
   Come winding up the lea.

' Behind them on the lowland's verge,
   In the evening light serene,
Brough's silent tower, then newly built
   By Blenkinsop, was seen.   40

' Slowly they came in long array,
   With loitering pace at will ;
At times a low from them was heard,
   Far off, for all was still.

' The hills return'd that lonely sound
   Upon the tranquil air ;
The only sound it was, which then
   Awoke the echoes there.

' " Thou hear'st that lordly Bull of
   mine,
   Neighbour," quoth Brunskill then ;   50
" How loudly to the hills he crunes,
   That crune to him again.

' " Think'st thou if yon whole herd at
   once
   Their voices should combine,
Were they at Brough, that we might not
Hear plainly from this upland spot
   That cruning of the kine ? "

' " That were a crune, indeed,' replied
   His comrade, " which, I ween,
Might at the Spital well be heard,   60
   And in all dales between.

' " Up Mallerstang to Eden's springs
The eastern wind upon its wings
   The mighty voice would bear ;
And Appleby would hear the sound,
   Methinks, when skies are fair."

' " Then shall the herd," John Brunskill
   cried,
   " From yon dumb steeple crune,
And thou and I, on this hill-side,
   Will listen to their tune.   70

' " So while the merry Bells of Brough
   For many an age ring on,
John Brunskill will remember'd be,
   When he is dead and gone ;

' " As one who in his latter years,
   Contented with enough,
Gave freely what he well could spare
   To buy the Bells of Brough."

' Thus it hath proved : three hundred
   years
   Since then have pass'd away,   80
And Brunskill's is a living name
   Among us to this day.'

' More pleasure,' I replied, ' shall I
   From this time forth partake,
When I remember Helbeck woods,
   For old John Brunskill's sake.

' He knew how wholesome it would be,
   Among these wild wide fells,
And upland vales, to catch, at times,
   The sound of Christian bells ;   90

' What feelings and what impulses
    Their cadence might convey,
To herdsman or to shepherd boy,
Whiling in indolent employ
    The solitary day ;

' That when his brethren were convened
    To meet for social prayer,
He, too, admonish'd by the call,
    In spirit might be there.

' Or when a glad thanksgiving sound, 100
    Upon the winds of Heaven,
Was sent to speak a Nation's joy,
    For some great blessing given—

' For victory by sea or land,
    And happy peace at length ;
Peace by his country's valour won,
    And 'stablish'd by her strength ;

' When such exultant peals were borne
    Upon the mountain air,
The sound should stir his blood, and
    give   110
An English impulse there.'

Such thoughts were in the old man's
    mind,
    When he that eve look'd down
From Stanemore's side on Borrodale,
    And on the distant town.

And had I store of wealth, methinks,
    Another herd of kine,
John Brunskill, I would freely give,
    That they might crune with thine.

Keswick, 1828.

INSCRIPTION FOR A COFFEE-POT

[Printed in a note in *Selections, From the Letters of Robert Southey*, ed. J. W. Warter, vol. iv, pp. 203, 204.]

A GOLDEN medal was voted to me
By a certain Royal Society :
'Twas not a thing at which to scoff,
For fifty guineas was the cost thereof :
On one side a head of the king you
    might see,
And on the other was Mercury !
But I was scant of worldly riches,
And moreover the Mercury had no
    breeches ;
So, thinking of honour and utility
    too,
And having modesty also in view,   10
I sold this medal, (why should I not ?)
And with the money which for it
    I got,
I purchased this silver coffee-pot :
Which I trust my son will preserve with
    care,
To be handed down from heir to heir.
These verses are engraven here,
That the truth of the matter may
    appear,
And I hope the society will be so
    wise,
As in future to dress their Mercuries !

SONNETS

[As two of the Sonnets have been inserted among the Selected Minor Poems (pp. 349, 350), and three of those published in 1837–1838 have been omitted, it has been necessary to make some alteration in the numbering of those here printed. Where this has been done the number in brackets ( ) at the head of a sonnet denotes its number in the edition of 1837–1838.

Of the Sonnets printed below, numbers I to IV inclusive (as numbered in the present edition) were published in *Poems*, 1797 ; the remainder were published in *Metrical Tales*, 1805. Sonnets V, VI, VII, VIII, and XII were included in *The Annual Anthology*, 1799 ; Sonnets IX, X, XI, XIV, XV, appeared in *The Annual Anthology*, 1800.]

I (IV) CORSTON

As thus I stand beside the murmuring
    stream
And watch its current, memory here
    pourtrays
Scenes faintly form'd of half-forgotten
    days,
Like far-off woodlands by the moon's
    bright beam
Dimly descried, but lovely. I have
    worn
Amid these haunts the heavy hours
    away,
When childhood idled through the
    Sabbath-day ;
Risen to my tasks at winter's earliest
    morn ;
And when the summer twilight darken'd
    here,
Thinking of home, and all of heart for-
    lorn,   10
Have sigh'd and shed in secret many a
    tear.
Dream-like and indistinct those days
    appear,
As the faint sounds of this low brooklet,
    borne
Upon the breeze, reach fitfully the ear.

1794.

II (VI)

With many a weary step, at length I gain
Thy summit, Lansdown ; and the cool
    breeze plays
Gratefully round my brow, as hence
    I gaze
Back on the fair expanse of yonder
    plain.   [eye
'Twas a long way and tedious ; to the
Though fair the extended vale, and fair
    to view
The autumnal leaves of many a faded
    hue,
That eddy in the wild gust moaning by.
Even so it fared with life : in discontent
Restless through Fortune's mingled
    scenes I went . .   10
Yet wept to think they would return no
    more.
But cease, fond heart, in such sad
    thoughts to roam ;
For surely thou ere long shalt reach thy
    home,
And pleasant is the way that lies before.

1794.

III (VII)

Fair is the rising morn when o'er the sky
The orient sun expands his roseate ray,
And lovely to the musing poet's eye
Fades the soft radiance of departing day;
But fairer is the smile of one we love,
Than all the scenes in Nature's ample
    sway,
And sweeter than the music of the grove,
The voice that bids us welcome. Such
    delight,
Edith ! is mine, escaping to thy sight
From the cold converse of the indifferent
    throng :   10
Too swiftly then toward the silent night,
Ye hours of happiness, ye speed along,
Whilst I, from all the world's dull cares
    apart,   [heart.
Pour out the feelings of my burthen'd

1794.

IV (VIII)

How darkly o'er yon far-off mountain
    frowns
The gather'd tempest ! from that lurid
    cloud
The deep-voiced thunders roll, aweful
    and loud
Though distant ; while upon the misty
    downs   [rain.
Fast falls in shadowy streaks the pelting
I never saw so terrible a storm !
Perhaps some way-worn traveller in
    vain
Wraps his thin raiment round his
    shivering form,
Cold even as hope within him. I the
    while
Pause here in sadness, though the sun-
    beams smile   10
Cheerily round me. Ah ! that thus my
    lot   [sign'd,
Might be with Peace and Solitude as-
Where I might from some little quiet cot
Sigh for the crimes and miseries of man-
    kind.

1794.

V (IX)

[First published in *The Morning Post*,
May 29, 1799.]

O thou sweet Lark, who in the heaven
    so high   [fully,
Twinkling thy wings dost sing so joy-
I watch thee soaring with a deep delight,
And when at last I turn mine aching eye
That lags below thee in the Infinite,
Still in my heart receive thy melody.
O thou sweet Lark, that I had wings
    like thee !
Not for the joy it were in yon blue light
Upward to mount, and from my
    heavenly height
Gaze on the creeping multitude below ;
But that I soon would wing my eager
    flight   11
To that loved home where Fancy even
    now
Hath fled, and Hope looks onward
    through a tear,   [here.
Counting the weary hours that hold her
1798.

VI (X)

[First published in *The Morning Post*,
May 21, 1799.]

Thou lingerest, Spring ! still wintry is
    the scene,   [wear ;
The fields their dead and sapless russet
Scarce doth the glossy celandine appear
Starring the sunny bank, or early green
The elder yet its circling tufts put forth.
The sparrow tenants still the eaves-built
    nest   [breast
Where we should see our martin's snowy
Oft darting out. The blasts from the
    bleak north   [blow.
And from the keener east still frequent
Sweet Spring, thou lingerest ; and it
    should be so, . .   10
Late let the fields and gardens blossom
    out !   [is drest,
Like man when most with smiles thy face
'Tis to deceive, and he who knows ye
    best,   [doubt.
When most ye promise, ever most must

Westbury, 1799.

VII (XI)

[First published in *The Morning Post*,
November 23, 1798.]

Beware a speedy friend, the Arabian
    said,
And wisely was it he advised distrust :
The flower that blossoms earliest fades
    the first.   [head,
Look at yon Oak that lifts its stately
And dallies with the autumnal storm,
    whose rage   [it rose,
Tempests the great sea-waves ; slowly
Slowly its strength increased through
    many an age,
And timidly did its light leaves disclose,
As doubtful of the spring, their palest
    green.
They to the summer cautiously expand,
And by the warmer sun and season
    bland   11
Matured, their foliage in the grove is seen,
When the bare forest by the wintry blast
Is swept, still lingering on the boughs
    the last.

1798.

VIII (XII) TO A GOOSE

[First published in *The Morning Post*, January 10, 1799.]

IF thou didst feed on western plains of
   yore ;
Or waddle wide with flat and flabby feet
Over some Cambrian mountain's plashy
   moor ;
Or find in farmer's yard a safe retreat
From gipsy thieves, and foxes sly and
   fleet ;   [trace
If thy grey quills, by lawyer guided,
Deeds big with ruin to some wretched
   race,   [sweet,
Or love-sick poet's sonnet, sad and
Wailing the rigour of his lady fair ;
Or if, the drudge of housemaid's daily
   toil,   10
Cobwebs and dust thy pinions white
   besoil,   [care.
Departed Goose ! I neither know nor
But this I know, that we pronounced
   thee fine,   [wine.
Season'd with sage and onions, and port

London, 1798.

IX (XIII)

I MARVEL not, O Sun ! that unto thee
In adoration man should bow the knee,
And pour his prayers of mingled awe
   and love ;
For like a God thou art, and on thy way
Of glory sheddest with benignant ray,
Beauty, and life, and joyance from
   above.   [shroud,
No longer let these mists thy radiance
These cold raw mists that chill the com-
   fortless day ;
But shed thy splendour through the
   opening cloud
And cheer the earth once more. The
   languid flowers   10
Lie scentless, beaten down with heavy
   rain ;
Earth asks thy presence, saturate with
   showers ;
O Lord of Light ! put forth thy beams
   again,   [hours.
For damp and cheerless are the gloomy

Westbury, 1798.

X (XIV)

[First published in *The Morning Post*, December 28, 1798.]

FAIR be thy fortunes in the distant land,
Companion of my earlier years and
   friend !
Go to the Eastern world, and may the
   hand   [send.
Of Heaven its blessing on thy labour
And may I, if we ever more should meet,
See thee with affluence to thy native
   shore   [greet
Return'd : . . I need not pray that I may
The same untainted goodness as before.
Long years must intervene before that
   day ;
And what the changes Heaven to each
   may send,   10
It boots not now to bode : O early
   friend !
Assured, no distance e'er can wear away
Esteem long rooted, and no change
   remove   [love.
The dear remembrance of the friend we

1798.

XI (XVI)

[First published in *The Morning Post*, August 26, 1799.]

PORLOCK, thy verdant vale so fair to
   sight,
Thy lofty hills which fern and furze
   embrown,
The waters that roll musically down
Thy woody glens, the traveller with
   delight   [grey
Recalls to memory, and the channel
Circling its surges in thy level bay.
Porlock, I also shall forget thee not,
Here by the unwelcome summer rain
   confined ;
But often shall hereafter call to mind
How here, a patient prisoner, 'twas my
   lot   10
To wear the lonely, lingering close of day,
Making my Sonnet by the alehouse fire,
Whilst Idleness and Solitude inspire
Dull rhymes to pass the duller hours
   away.

August 9, 1799.

XII (XVII)

[First published in *The Morning Post*, December 14, 1798.]

STATELY yon vessel sails adown the tide,
To some far distant land adventurous
          bound ;
The sailors' busy cries from side to side
Pealing among the echoing rocks re
          sound :
A patient, thoughtless, much-enduring
          band,
Joyful they enter on their ocean way,
With shouts exulting leave their native
          land,   [day.
And know no care beyond the present
But is there no poor mourner left behind,
Who sorrows for a child or husband
          there ?   10
Who at the howling of the midnight
          wind   [prayer ?
Will wake and tremble in her boding
So may her voice be heard, and Heaven
          be kind !   [fair !
Go, gallant Ship, and be thy fortune

Westbury, 1799.

XIII (XVIII)

[First published in *The Morning Post*, December 1, 1798.]

O GOD ! have mercy in this dreadful
          hour
On the poor mariner ! in comfort here
Safe sheltered as I am, I almost fear
The blast that rages with resistless
          power.   [waves,
What were it now to toss upon the
The madden'd waves, and know no
          succour near ;
The howling of the storm alone to hear,
And the wild sea that to the tempest
          raves ;
To gaze amid the horrors of the night
And only see the billow's gleaming light ;
Then in the dread of death to think of
          her   11
Who, as she listens sleepless to the gale,
Puts up a silent prayer and waxes
          pale ? . .
O God ! have mercy on the mariner !

Westbury, 1799.

XIV (XIX)

[First published in *The Morning Post*, August 9, 1799.]

SHE comes majestic with her swelling
          sails,   [way
The gallant Ship ; along her watery
Homeward she drives before the favour-
          ing gales ;
Now flirting at their length the streamers
          play,   [breeze.
And now they ripple with the ruffling
Hark to the sailors' shouts ! the rocks
          rebound,   [sound.
Thundering in echoes to the joyful
Long have they voyaged o'er the distant
          seas,   [last,
And what a heart-delight they feel at
So many toils, so many dangers past, 10
To view the port desired, he only knows
Who on the stormy deep for many a day
Hath tost, aweary of his watery way,
And watch'd, all anxious, every wind
          that blows.

Westbury, 1799.

XV (XX)

FAREWELL my home, my home no
          longer now,
Witness of many a calm and happy day ;
And thou fair eminence, upon whose
          brow   [ray,
Dwells the last sunshine of the evening
Farewell ! These eyes no longer shall
          pursue
The western sun beyond the farthest
          height,   [light.
When slowly he forsakes the fields of
No more the freshness of the falling dew,
Cool and delightful, here shall bathe my
          head,
As from this western window dear, I
          lean,   10
Listening, the while I watch the placid
          scene,   [shed.
The martins twittering underneath the
Farewell, dear home ! where many a
          day has past
In joys whose loved remembrance long
          shall last.

Westbury, 1799.

LYRIC POEMS

TO CONTEMPLATION

[Published in *Poems*, 1797.]

Καὶ παγᾶς φιλέοιμι τὸν ἐγγύθεν ἦχον ἀκούειν,
Ἀ τέρπει ψοφέοισα τὸν ἀγρικόν, οὐγὶ
    ταράσσει.   MOSCHUS.

FAINT gleams the evening radiance
    through the sky,
    The sober twilight dimly darkens
    round ;
In short quick circles the shrill bat
    flits by,   [ground.
And the slow vapour curls along the

Now the pleased eye from yon lone cot-
    tage sees
On the green mead the smoke long-
    shadowing play ;   [spray
    The Red-breast on the blossom'd
    Warbles wild her latest lay ;
And lo ! the Rooks to yon high-tufted
    trees
Wing in long files vociferous their
    way.   10
Calm CONTEMPLATION, 'tis thy favourite
    hour !
    Come, tranquillizing Power !

I view thee on the calmy shore
When Ocean stills his waves to rest ;
Or when slow-moving on the surges
    hoar
    Meet with deep hollow roar
    And whiten o'er his breast ;
And when the Moon with softer radiance
    gleams,   [beams.
And lovelier heave the billows in her

When the low gales of evening moan
    along,   20
I love with thee to feel the calm cool
    breeze,   [among,
And roam the pathless forest wilds
Listening the mellow murmur of the
    trees   [on high,
Full-foliaged, as they wave their heads
And to the winds respond in symphony.

Or lead me where amid the tranquil
    vale
The broken streamlet flows in silver
    light ;
    And I will linger where the
    gale
    O'er the bank of violets sighs,
Listening to hear its soften'd sounds
    arise ;   30
And hearken the dull beetle's drowsy
    flight,
    And watch'd the tube-eyed
    snail
Creep o'er his long moon-glittering
    trail,
And mark where radiant through the
    night
Shines in the grass-green hedge the glow-
    worm's living light.

    Thee, meekest Power ! I love to
    meet,
    As oft with solitary pace
The ruin'd Abbey's hallowed rounds
    I trace,
    And listen to the echoings of my
    feet.
    Or on some half-demolish'd tomb,
Whose warning texts anticipate my
    doom,   41
    Mark the clear orb of night
Cast through the ivy'd arch a broken
    light.

    Nor will I not in some more gloomy
    hour
Invoke with fearless awe thine holier
    power,
    Wandering beneath the sacred
    pile
When the blast moans along the dark-
    some aisle,
    And clattering patters all
    around
    The midnight shower with dreary
    sound.

But sweeter 'tis to wander wild   50
By melancholy dreams beguiled,
While the summer moon's pale ray
Faintly guides me on my way
To some lone romantic glen
Far from all the haunts of men ;
Where no noise of uproar rude
Breaks the calm of solitude ;
But soothing Silence sleeps in all,
Save the neighbouring waterfall,
Whose hoarse waters falling near   60
Load with hollow sounds the ear,
And with down-dasht torrent white
Gleam hoary through the shades of
        night.

Thus wandering silent on and slow,
I'll nurse Reflection's sacred woe,
And muse upon the happier day
When Hope would weave her visions
        gay,
Ere Fancy, chill'd by adverse fate,
Left sad Reality my mate.

O CONTEMPLATION ! when to Memory's
        eyes   70
The visions of the long-past days
        arise,
Thy holy power imparts the best relief,
And the calm'd Spirit loves the joy of
        grief.

Bristol, 1792.

REMEMBRANCE

[First published in *The Morning Post*,
May 26, 1798 ; afterwards in *The Annual
Anthology*, 1799.]

The remembrance of Youth is a sigh.
                                ALI.

MAN hath a weary pilgrimage
As through the world he wends,
On every stage from youth to age
        Still discontent attends ;
With heaviness he casts his eye
        Upon the road before,
And still remembers with a sigh
        The days that are no more.

To school the little exile goes,
Torn from his mother's arms, . .   10
What then shall soothe his earliest
        woes,
When novelty hath lost its charms ?
Condemn'd to suffer through the day
        Restraints which no rewards repay,
And cares where love has no concern,
Hope lengthens as she counts the hours
        Before his wish'd return.
From hard controul and tyrant rules,
The unfeeling discipline of schools,
        In thought he loves to roam,   20
And tears will struggle in his eye
While he remembers with a sigh
        The comforts of his home.

Youth comes ; the toils and cares of life
        Torment the restless mind ;
Where shall the tired and harass'd heart
        Its consolation find ?
Then is not Youth, as Fancy tells,
        Life's summer prime of joy ?
Ah no ! for hopes too long delay'd 30
And feelings blasted or betray'd,
        Its fabled bliss destroy ;
And Youth remembers with a sigh
        The careless days of Infancy.

Maturer Manhood now arrives,
        And other thoughts come on,
But with the baseless hopes of Youth
        Its generous warmth is gone ;
Cold calculating cares succeed,
The timid thought, the wary deed, 40
        The dull realities of truth ;
Back on the past he turns his eye,
Remembering with an envious sigh
        The happy dreams of Youth.

So reaches he the latter stage
        Of this our mortal pilgrimage,
        With feeble step and slow ;
New ills that latter stage await,
And old Experience learns too late
        That all is vanity below.   50
Life's vain delusions are gone by
        Its idle hopes are o'er,
Yet age remembers with a sigh
        The days that are no more.

Westbury, 1798.

THE WIDOW

SAPPHICS

[Published in *Poems*, 1797.]

COLD was the night wind, drifting fast
        the snow fell,
Wide were the downs and shelterless and
        naked,
When a poor Wanderer struggled on her
        journey,
        Weary and way-sore.

Drear were the downs, more dreary her
        reflections ;
Cold was the night-wind, colder was her
        bosom :
She had no home, the world was all
        before her,
        She had no shelter.

Fast o'er the heath a chariot rattled by
        her,
' Pity me !' feebly cried the lonely
        wanderer ;   10
' Pity me, strangers ! lest with cold and
        hunger
        Here I should perish.

' Once I had friends,—though now by
        all forsaken !
Once I had parents,—they are now in
        Heaven !
I had a home once—I had once a hus-
        band—
        Pity me, strangers !

' I had a home once—I had once a
        husband—
I am a widow, poor and broken-
        hearted !'
Loud blew the wind, unheard was her
        complaining,
        On drove the chariot.   20

Then on the snow she laid her down to
        rest her ;
She heard a horseman, ' Pity me !' she
        groan'd out ;
Loud was the wind, unheard was her
        complaining,
        On went the horseman.

Worn out with anguish, toil and cold
        and hunger,
Down sunk the Wanderer, sleep had
        seized her senses ;
There did the traveller find her in the
        morning ;
        GOD had released her.

Bristol, 1795.

THE TRAVELLER'S RETURN

[Published in *The Annual Anthology*, 1799.]

SWEET to the morning traveller
    The song amid the sky,
Where twinkling in the dewy light
    The skylark soars on high.

And cheering to the traveller
    The gales that round him play,
When faint and heavily he drags
    Along his noon-tide way.

And when beneath the unclouded sun
    Full wearily toils he,   10
The flowing water makes to him
    A soothing melody.

And when the evening light decays,
    And all is calm around,
There is sweet music to his ear
    In the distant sheep-bell's sound.

But oh ! of all delightful sounds
    Of evening or of morn,
The sweetest is the voice of Love,
    That welcomes his return.   20

Westbury, 1798.

THE OLD MAN'S COMFORTS

AND HOW HE GAINED THEM

[First published in *The Morning Post*,
January 17, 1799; afterwards in *The Annual
Anthology*, 1799, and in *Metrical Tales*, 1805.]

YOU are old, Father William, the young
        man cried,
    The few locks which are left you are
        grey ;
You are hale, Father William, a hearty
        old man,
    Now tell me the reason, I pray.

In the days of my youth, Father William replied,
   I remember'd that youth would fly fast,
And abused not my health and my vigour at first,
   That I never might need them at last.

You are old, Father William, the young man cried,
   And pleasures with youth pass away;
And yet you lament not the days that are gone,   11
   Now tell me the reason, I pray.

In the days of my youth, Father William replied,
   I remember'd that youth could not last;
I thought of the future, whatever I did,
   That I never might grieve for the past.

You are old, Father William, the young man cried,
   And life must be hastening away;
You are cheerful, and love to converse upon death,
   Now tell me the reason, I pray.   20

I am cheerful, young man, Father William replied,
   Let the cause thy attention engage;
In the days of my youth I remember'd my God!
   And He hath not forgotten my age.

Westbury, 1799.

TO A SPIDER

[First published in *The Morning Post*, March 23, 1799; afterwards in *The Annual Anthology*, 1799, and in *Metrical Tales*, 1805.]

1

SPIDER! thou need'st not run in fear about
   To shun my curious eyes;
I won't humanely crush thy bowels out
   Lest thou should'st eat the flies;
Nor will I roast thee with a damn'd delight
Thy strange instinctive fortitude to see,
   For there is One who might
      One day roast me.

2

Thou art welcome to a Rhymer sore perplext,
   The subject of his verse;   10
There's many a one who on a better text
   Perhaps might comment worse.
Then shrink not, old Free-Mason, from my view,
   But quietly like me spin out the line;
   Do thou thy work pursue
      As I will mine.

3

Weaver of snares, thou emblemest the ways
   Of Satan, Sire of lies;
Hell's huge black Spider, for mankind he lays
   His toils, as thou for flies.   20
When Betty's busy eye runs round the room,
   Woe to that nice geometry, if seen!
   But where is He whose broom
      The earth shall clean?

4

Spider! of old thy flimsy webs were thought,
   And 'twas a likeness true,
To emblem laws in which the weak are caught,
   But which the strong break through:
And if a victim in thy toils is ta'en,
Like some poor client is that wretched fly;   30
   I'll warrant thee thou'lt drain
      His life-blood dry.

5

And is not thy weak work like human schemes
   And care on earth employ'd?
Such are young hopes and Love's delightful dreams
   So easily destroyed!
So does the Statesman, whilst the Avengers sleep,
Self-deem'd secure, his wiles in secret lay,
   Soon shall destruction sweep
      His work away.   40

6

Thou busy labourer ! one resemblance
        more
      May yet the verse prolong,
For, Spider, thou art like the Poet
        poor,
      Whom thou hast help'd in song.
Both busily our needful food to win,
We work, as Nature taught, with
        ceaseless pains :
      Thy bowels thou dost spin,
        I spin my brains.

Westbury, 1798.

THE EBB TIDE

[First published in *The Morning Post*,
June 25, 1799 ; afterwards in *The Annual
Anthology*, 1799, and in *Metrical Tales*,
1805.]

SLOWLY thy flowing tide
Came in, old Avon ! scarcely did mine
        eyes,
As watchfully I roam'd thy green-wood
        side,
      Perceive its gentle rise.

With many a stroke and strong
The labouring boatmen upward plied
        their oars,
Yet little way they made, though la-
        bouring long
      Between thy winding shores.

Now down thine ebbing tide
The unlabour'd boat falls rapidly along ;
The solitary helmsman sits to guide, 11
      And sings an idle song.

Now o'er the rocks that lay
So silent late, the shallow current roars ;
Fast flow thy waters on their seaward
        way
      Through wider-spreading shores.

Avon ! I gaze and know
The lesson emblem'd in thy varying way;
It speaks of human joys that rise so slow,
      So rapidly decay.   20

Kingdoms which long have stood,
And slow to strength and power attain'd
        at last,
Thus from the summit of high fortune's
        flood
      They ebb to ruin fast.

Thus like thy flow appears
Time's tardy course to manhood's envied
        stage ;
Alas ! how hurryingly the ebbing years
      Then hasten to old age !

Westbury, 1799.

THE COMPLAINTS OF THE POOR

[First published in *The Morning Post*,
June 29, 1798 ; afterwards in *Poems*, vol. ii,
1799.]

AND wherefore do the Poor complain ?
      The Rich Man ask'd of me ; . .
Come walk abroad with me, I said,
      And I will answer thee.

'Twas evening, and the frozen streets
      Were cheerless to behold,
And we were wrapt and coated well,
      And yet we were a-cold.

We met an old bare-headed man,
      His locks were thin and white ;   10
I ask'd him what he did abroad
      In that cold winter's night ;

The cold was keen indeed, he said,
      But at home no fire had he,
And therefore he had come abroad
      To ask for charity.

We met a young bare-footed child,
      And she begg'd loud and bold ;
I ask'd her what she did abroad
      When the wind it blew so cold ;   20

She said her father was at home,
      And he lay sick a-bed,
And therefore was it she was sent
      Abroad to beg for bread.

We saw a woman sitting down
      Upon a stone to rest,
She had a baby at her back
      And another at her breast ;

I ask'd her why she loiter'd there
  When the night-wind was so chill ; 30
She turn'd her head and bade the child
  That scream'd behind, be still ;

Then told us that her husband served,
  A soldier, far away,
And therefore to her parish she
  Was begging back her way.

We met a girl, her dress was loose
  And sunken was her eye,
Who with a wanton's hollow voice
  Address'd the passers-by ; 40

I ask'd her what there was in guilt
  That could her heart allure
To shame, disease, and late remorse ;
  She answer'd she was poor.

I turn'd me to the Rich Man then,
  For silently stood he, . .
You ask'd me why the Poor complain,
  And these have answer'd thee !

London, 1798.

TO A FRIEND

INQUIRING IF I WOULD LIVE OVER MY
YOUTH AGAIN

[First published in *The Morning Post*,
May 27, 1799 ; afterwards in *The Annual
Anthology*, 1799, and in *Metrical Tales*,
1805.]

1

Do I regret the past ?
  Would I again live o'er
The morning hours of life ?
Nay, William ! nay, not so !
In the warm joyance of the summer
        sun
I do not wish again
  The changeful April day.
Nay, William ! nay, not so !
  Safe haven'd from the sea,

I would not tempt again   10
  The uncertain ocean's wrath.
Praise be to Him who made me what
      I am,
  Other I would not be.

2

Why is it pleasant then to sit and talk
  Of days that are no more ?
When in his own dear home
  The traveller rests at last,
And tells how often in his wanderings
  The thought of those far off
Hath made his eyes o'erflow 20
  With no unmanly tears ;
  Delighted he recalls
Through what fair scenes his lingering
      feet have trod ;
But ever when he tells of perils past
  And troubles now no more,
His eyes are brightest, and a readier
      joy
Flows thankful from his heart.

3

No, William ! no, I would not live
      again
  The morning hours of life ;
  I would not be again 30
The slave of hope and fear ;
  I would not learn again
The wisdom by Experience hardly
      taught.

4

To me the past presents
  No object for regret ;
  To me the present gives
  All cause for full content.
The future ? . . it is now the cheerful
      noon,
And on the sunny-smiling fields I gaze
  With eyes alive to joy ; 40
When the dark night descends,
I willingly shall close my weary lids,
In sure and certain hope to wake again.

Westbury, 1798.

OCCASIONAL PIECES

I
ON A LANDSCAPE OF GASPAR POUSSIN

[Published in *Poems*, 1797.]

GASPAR! how pleasantly thy pictured scenes
Beguile the lonely hour! I sit and gaze
With lingering eye, till dreaming Fancy makes
The lovely landscape live, and the rapt soul
From the foul haunts of herded human-kind
Flies far away with spirit speed, and tastes
The untainted air, that with the lively hue
Of health and happiness illumes tho cheek
Of mountain Liberty. My willing soul
All eager follows on thy faery flights, 10
Fancy! best friend; whose blessed witcheries
With cheering prospects cheat the traveller
O'er the long wearying desert of the world.
Nor dost thou, Fancy! with such magic mock
My heart, as, demon-born, old Merlin knew,
Or Alquif, or Zarzafiel's sister sage,
Who in her vengeance for so many a year
Held in the jacinth sepulchre entranced
Lisuart the pride of Grecian chivalry.
Friend of my lonely hours! thou leadest me 20
To such calm joys as Nature, wise and good,
Proffers in vain to all her wretched sons, . .
Her wretched sons who pine with want amid
The abundant earth, and blindly bow
them down
Before the Moloch shrines of Wealth and Power,
Authors of Evil. Well it is sometimes
That thy delusions should beguile the heart,
Sick of reality. The little pile
That tops the summit of that craggy hill
Shall be my dwelling: craggy is the hill
And steep; yet through yon hazels up-ward leads 31
The easy path, along whose winding way
Now close embower'd I hear the unseen stream
Dash down, anon behold its sparkling foam
Gleam through the thicket; and ascend-ing on
Now pause me to survey the goodly vale
That opens on my prospect. Half way up
Pleasant it were upon some broad smooth rock
To sit and sun myself, and look below,
And watch the goatherd down yon high-bank path 40
Urging his flock grotesque; and bidding now
His lean rough dog from some near cliff go drive
The straggler; while his barkings loud and quick
Amid their tremulous bleat arising oft,
Fainter and fainter from the hollow road
Send their far echoes, till the waterfall,
Hoarse bursting from the cavern'd cliff beneath,
Their dying murmurs drown. A little yet

Onward, and I have gain'd the utmost
    height.
Fair spreads the vale below : I see the
    stream   50
Stream radiant on beneath the noon-
    tide sky.
A passing cloud darkens the bordering
    steep,
Where the town-spires behind the castle-
    towers
Rise graceful ; brown the mountain in
    its shade,
Whose circling grandeur, part by mists
    conceal'd,
Part with white rocks resplendent in the
    sun,
Should bound mine eyes, . . ay, and my
    wishes too,
For I would have no hope or fear
    beyond.
The empty turmoil of the worthless
    world,
Its vanities and vices would not vex 60
My quiet heart. The traveller, who
    beheld
The low tower of the little pile, might
    deem
It were the house of God ; nor would
    he err
So deeming, for that home would be the
    home
Of Peace and Love, and they would
    hallow it
To Him.   Oh, life of blessedness ! to
    reap
The fruit of honourable toil, and bound
Our wishes with our wants ! Delightful
    thoughts,
That soothe the solitude of weary Hope,
Ye leave her to reality awaked,   70
Like the poor captive, from some fleeting
    dream
Of friends and liberty and home
    restored,
Startled, and listening as the midnight
    storm
Beats hard and heavy through his
    dungeon bars.

    Bath, 1795.

II

WRITTEN ON CHRISTMAS DAY,
    1795

[Published in *Letters from Spain and
Portugal*, 1797.]

How many hearts are happy at this
    hour
In England ! Brightly o'er the cheerful
    hall
Flares the heaped hearth, and friends
    and kindred meet,
And the glad mother round her festive
    board
Beholds her children, separated long
Amid the wide world's ways, assembled
    now,
A sight at which affection lightens up
With smiles the eye that age has long
    bedimm'd.
I do remember when I was a child
How my young heart, a stranger then
    to care,   10
With transport leap'd upon this holy-
    day,
As o'er the house, all gay with ever-
    greens,
From friend to friend with joyful speed
    I ran,
Bidding a merry Christmas to them all.
Those years are past ; their pleasures
    and their pains
Are now like yonder convent-crested hill
That bounds the distant prospect, indis-
    tinct,
Yet pictured upon memory's mystic
    glass
In faint fair hues.   A weary traveller
    now
I journey o'er the desert mountain
    tracks   20
Of Leon, wilds all drear and comfortless,
Where the grey lizards in the noontide
    sun
Sport on the rocks, and where the goat-
    herd starts,
Roused from his sleep at midnight when
    he hears
The prowling wolf, and falters as he calls
On Saints to save.   Here of the friends
    I think
Who now, I ween, remember me, and fill

The glass of votive friendship. At the
    name
Will not thy cheek, Beloved, change its
    hue,
And in those gentle eyes uncall'd-for
    tears   30
Tremble ? I will not wish thee not to
    weep ;
Such tears are free from bitterness, and
    they
Who know not what it is sometimes to
    wake
And weep at midnight, are but instru-
    ments
Of Nature's common work. Yes, think
    of me,
My Edith, think that, travelling far
    away,
Thus I beguile the solitary hours
With many a day-dream, picturing
    scenes as fair
Of peace, and comfort, and domestic bliss
As ever to the youthful poet's eye   40
Creative Fancy fashion'd. Think of me,
Though absent, thine ; and if a sigh
    will rise,
And tears, unbidden, at the thought
    steal down,
Sure hope will cheer thee, and the happy
    hour
Of meeting soon all sorrow overpay.

III

WRITTEN AFTER VISITING

THE CONVENT OF ARRABIDA

NEAR SETUBAL

MARCH 22, 1796

[Published in *Letters from Spain and
Portugal*, 1797. The original version has
been largely rewritten.]

HAPPY the dwellers in this holy house :
For surely never worldly thoughts in-
    trude
On this retreat, this sacred solitude,
Where Quiet with Religion makes her
    home.
And ye who tenant such a goodly scene,
How should ye be but good, where all is
    fair,

And where the mirror of the mind re-
    flects
Serenest beauty ? O'er these mountain
    wilds
The insatiate eye with ever new delight
Roams raptured, marking now where to
    the wind   10
The tall tree bends its many-tinted
    boughs
With soft accordant sound ; and now
    the sport
Of joyous sea-birds o'er the tranquil
    deep,
And now the long-extending stream of
    light
Where the broad orb of day refulgent
    sinks
Beneath old Ocean's line. To have no
    cares
That eat the heart, no wants that to
    the earth
Chain the reluctant spirit, to be freed
From forced communion with the selfish
    tribe
Who worship Mammon,—yea, emanci-
    pate   20
From this world's bondage, even while
    the soul
Inhabits still its corruptible clay, . .
Almost, ye dwellers in this holy house,
Almost I envy you. You never see
Pale Misery's asking eye, nor roam about
Those huge and hateful haunts of
    crowded men,
Where Wealth and Power have built
    their palaces,
Fraud spreads his snares secure, man
    preys on man,
Iniquity abounds, and rampant Vice,
With an infection worse than mortal,
    taints   30
The herd of humankind.
                    I too could love,
Ye tenants of this sacred solitude,
Here to abide, and when the sun rides
    high
Seek some sequester'd dingle's coolest
    shade ;
And at the breezy hour, along the beach
Stray with slow step, and gaze upon the
    deep,
And while the breath of evening fann'd
    my brow,

And the wild waves with their con-
   tinuous sound
Soothed my accustom'd ear, think
   thankfully
That I had from the crowd withdrawn
   in time,   40
And found an harbour. . . Yet may
   yonder deep
Suggest a less unprofitable thought,
Monastic brethren. Would the mariner,
Though storms may sometimes swell the
   mighty waves,
And o'er the reeling bark with thun-
   dering crash
Impel the mountainous surge, quit
   yonder deep,
And rather float upon some tranquil sea,
Whose moveless waters never feel the
   gale,   [soul !
In safe stagnation ? Rouse thyself my
No season this for self-deluding dreams ;
It is thy spring-time ; sow, if thou
   would'st reap ;   51
Then, after honest labour, welcome rest,
In full contentment not to be enjoy'd
Unless when duly earn'd. O happy then
To know that we have walked among
   mankind
More sinn'd against than sinning !
   Happy then
To muse on many a sorrow overpast,
And think the business of the day is
   done,   [close,
And as the evening of our lives shall
The peaceful evening, with a Christian's
   hope   60
Expect the dawn of everlasting day.

   Lisbon, 1796.

IV

ON MY OWN MINIATURE PICTURE
TAKEN AT TWO YEARS OF AGE

[Published in *Poems*, 1797.]

AND I was once like this ! that glowing
   cheek
Was mine, those pleasure-sparkling
   eyes ; that brow
Smooth as the level lake, when not a
   breeze   [years
Dies o'er the sleeping surface ! . . Twenty

Have wrought strange alteration ! Of
   the friends
Who once so dearly prized this miniature,
And loved it for its likeness, some are
   gone
To their last home ; and some, estranged
   in heart,
Beholding me, with quick-averted
   glance   [hues
Pass on the other side. But still these
Remain unalter'd, and these features
   wear   11
The look of Infancy and Innocence.
I search myself in vain, and find no
   trace
Of what I was : those lightly arching
   lines
Dark and o'erhanging now ; and that
   sweet face
Settled in these strong lineaments ! . .
   There were
Who form'd high hopes and flattering
   ones of thee,
Young Robert ! for thine eye was quick
   to speak
Each opening feeling : should they not
   have known,
If the rich rainbow on a morning cloud
Reflects its radiant dyes, the husband-
   man   21
Beholds the ominous glory, and foresees
Impending storms ! . . They augured
   happily,
That thou didst love each wild and
   wondrous tale
Of faery fiction, and thine infant tongue
Lisp'd with delight the godlike deeds of
   Greece
And rising Rome ; therefore they
   deem'd, forsooth,
That thou shouldst tread Preferment's
   pleasant path.
Ill-judging ones ! they let thy little
   feet
Stray in the pleasant paths of Poesy, 30
And when thou shouldst have prest
   amid the crowd,
There didst thou love to linger out the
   day,
Loitering beneath the laurel's barren
   shade.   [wrong ?
SPIRIT OF SPENSER ! was the wanderer

   Bristol, 1796.

V
RECOLLECTIONS OF A DAY'S JOURNEY IN SPAIN

[Published in *Letters from Spain and Portugal*, 1797, under the title 'Retrospective Musings'. The original version has been practically rewritten.]

Now less delighted do I call to mind,
Land of Romance, thy wild and lovely
    scenes,
Than I beheld them first. Pleased I
    retrace
With memory's eye the placid Minho's
    course,
And catch its winding waters gleaming
    bright
Amid the broken distance. I review
Leon's wide wastes, and heights pre-
    cipitous,
Seen with a pleasure not unmix'd with
    dread,
As the sagacious mules along the brink
Wound patiently and slow their way
    secure;   10
And rude Galicia's hovels, and huge
    rocks
And mountains, where, when all beside
    was dim,
Dark and broad-headed the tall pines
    erect
Rose on the farthest eminence distinct,
Cresting the evening sky.
                        Rain now falls thick,
And damp and heavy is the unwhole-
    some air;
I by this friendly hearth remember Spain,
And tread in fancy once again the road,
Where twelve months since I held my
    way, and thought
Of England, and of all my heart held
    dear,   20
And wish'd *this* day were come.
                        The morning mist,
Well I remember, hover'd o'er the heath,
When with the earliest dawn of day we
    left
The solitary Venta.[1] Soon the Sun
Rose in his glory; scatter'd by the
    breeze

[1] Venta de Peralbanegas.

The thin fog roll'd away, and now
    emerged
We saw where Oropesa's castled hill
Tower'd dark, and dimly seen; and now
    we pass'd
Torvalva's quiet huts, and on our way
Paused frequently, look'd back, and
    gazed around,   30
Then journey'd on, yet turn'd and gazed
    again,
So lovely was the scene. That ducal
    pile
Of the Toledos now with all its towers
Shone in the sunlight. Half way up the
    hill,
Embower'd in olives, like the abode of
    Peace,
Lay Lagartina; and the cool fresh gale
Bending the young corn on the gradual
    slope
Play'd o'er its varying verdure. I beheld
A convent near, and could almost have
    thought
The dwellers there must needs be holy
    men,   40
For as they look'd around them all they
    saw
Was good.
        But when the purple eve came on,
How did the lovely landscape fill my
    heart!
Trees scatter'd among peering rocks
    adorn'd
The near ascent; the vale was over-
    spread
With ilex in its wintry foliage gay,
Old cork trees through their soft and
    swelling bark
Bursting, and glaucous olives, under-
    neath
Whose fertilizing influence the green herb
Grows greener, and with heavier ears
    enrich'd   50
The healthful harvest bends. Pellucid
    streams
Through many a vocal channel from the
    hills
Wound through the valley their melo-
    dious way;
And o'er the intermediate woods de-
    scried,
Naval-Moral's church tower announced
    to us

Our resting-place that night,—a wel-
  come mark ;
Though willingly we loiter'd to behold
In long expanse Plasencia's fertile plain,
And the high mountain range which
  bounded it,
Now losing fast the roseate hue that eve
Shed o'er its summit and its snowy
  breast,   61
For eve was closing now.   Faint and
  more faint
The murmurs of the goatherd's scat-
  ter'd flock
Were borne upon the air, and sailing
  slow
The broad-wing'd stork sought on the
  church tower top
His consecrated nest.   O lovely scenes !
I gazed upon you with intense delight,
And yet with thoughts that weigh the
  spirit down.
I was a stranger in a foreign land,
And knowing that these eyes should
  never more   70
Behold that glorious prospect, Earth
  itself
Appear'd the place of pilgrimage it is.

Bristol, Jan. 15, 1797.

VI

TO MARGARET HILL

WRITTEN FROM LONDON.   1798.

[Published in *Poems*, vol. ii, 1799, under
the title, ' Metrical Letter, Written from
London.']

MARGARET ! my Cousin, . . nay, you
  must not smile,
I love the homely and familiar phrase :
And I will call thee Cousin Margaret,
However quaint amid the measured
  line
The good old term appears.   Oh ! it
  looks ill
When delicate tongues disclaim old
  terms of kin,
Sir-ing and Madam-ing as civilly
As if the road between the heart and lips
Were such a weary and Laplandish
  way,

That the poor travellers came to the red
  gates   10
Half frozen.   Trust me, Cousin Mar-
  garet,
For many a day my memory hath
  play'd
The creditor with me on your account,
And made me shame to think that I
  should owe
So long the debt of kindness.   But in
  truth,
Like Christian on his pilgrimage, I bear
So heavy a pack of business, that
  albeit
I toil on mainly, in our twelve hours'
  race
Time leaves me distanced.   Loth indeed
  were I
That for a moment you should lay to
  me   20
Unkind neglect ; mine, Margaret, is a
  heart
That smokes not, yet methinks there
  should be some
Who know its genuine warmth.   I am
  not one
Who can play off my smiles and cour-
  tesies
To every Lady of her lap-dog tired
Who wants a play-thing ; I am no sworn
  friend
Of half-an-hour, as apt to leave as love ;
Mine are no mushroom feelings, which
  spring up
At once without a seed and take no
  root,
Wiseliest distrusted.   In a narrow
  sphere,   30
The little circle of domestic life,
I would be known and loved : the world
  beyond
Is not for me.   But, Margaret, sure
  I think
That you should know me well, for you
  and I
Grew up together, and when we look
  back
Upon old times, our recollections paint
The same familiar faces.   Did I wield
The wand of Merlin's magic, I would
  make
Brave witchcraft.   We would have a
  faery ship,

Ay, a new Ark, as in that other flood 40
Which swept the sons of Anak from the
  earth ;
The Sylphs should waft us to some
  goodly isle
Like that where whilom old Apollidon,
Retiring wisely from the troublous
  world,
Built up his blameless spell; and I would
  bid
The Sea Nymphs pile around their
  coral bowers,
That we might stand upon the beach,
  and mark
The far-off breakers shower their silver
  spray,
And hear the eternal roar, whose
  pleasant sound
Told us that never mariner should
  reach   50
Our quiet coast.   In such a blessed
  isle
We might renew the days of infancy,
And Life like a long childhood pass
  away,
Without one care. It may be, Margaret,
That I shall yet be gather'd to my
  friends ;
For I am not of those who live estranged
Of choice, till at the last they join their
  race
In the family-vault. If so, if I should
  lose,
Like my old friend the Pilgrim, this huge
  pack   59
So heavy on my shoulders, I and mine
Right pleasantly will end our pilgrimage.
If not, if I should never get beyond
This Vanity-town, there is another
  world
Where friends will meet. And often,
  Margaret,
I gaze at night into the boundless sky,
And think that I shall there be born
  again,
The exalted native of some better star ;
And, like the untaught American, I look
To find in Heaven the things I loved on
  earth.

VII
HISTORY

[First published in *The Morning Post*,
January 16, 1799; afterwards in *The Annual
Anthology*, 1800, and in *Metrical Tales*,
1805.]

THOU chronicle of crimes ! I'll read no
  more ;
For I am one who willingly would love
Ills fellow kind. O gentle Poesy,
Receive me from the court's polluted
  scenes,
From dungeon horrors, from the fields of
  war,
Receive me to your haunts, . . that I may
  nurse
My nature's better feelings, for my soul
Sickens at man's misdeeds !
          I spake, when lo !
There stood before me, in her majesty,
Clio, the strong-eyed Muse. Upon her
  brow   10
Sate a calm anger. Go, young man, she
  cried,
Sigh among myrtle bowers, and let thy
  soul
Effuse itself in strains so sorrowful sweet,
That love-sick Maids may weep upon
  thy page,
Soothed with delicious sorrow. Oh
  shame ! shame !
Was it for this I waken'd thy young
  mind ?
Was it for this I made thy swelling
  heart
Throb at the deeds of Greece, and thy
  boy's eye
So kindle when that glorious Spartan
  died ?
Boy ! boy ! deceive me not ! . . What
  if the tale   20
Of murder'd millions strike a chilling
  pang ;
What if Tiberius in his island stews,
And Philip at his beads, alike inspire
Strong anger and contempt ; hast thou
  not risen
With nobler feelings, . . with a deeper
  love
For freedom ? Yes, if righteously thy
  soul

Loathes the black history of human
   crimes
And human misery, let that spirit fill
Thy song, and it shall teach thee, boy !
   to raise
Strains such as Cato might have deign'd
   to hear,   30
As Sidney in his hall of bliss may love.

Westbury, 1798.

VIII

WRITTEN IMMEDIATELY AFTER READING THE SPEECH OF ROBERT EMMET

ON HIS TRIAL AND CONVICTION FOR HIGH
TREASON, SEPT., 1803

' LET no man write my epitaph ; let
   my grave
Be uninscribed, and let my memory rest
Till other times are come, and other men,
Who then may do me justice.' [1]
           Emmet, no !
No withering curse hath dried my spirit
   up,
That I should now be silent, . . that my
   soul
Should from the stirring inspiration
   shrink,
Now when it shakes her, and withhold
   her voice,
Of that divinest impulse never more
Worthy, if impious I withheld it now, 10
Hardening my heart.   Here, here in this
   free Isle,
To which in thy young virtue's erring
   zeal

[1] These were the words in his speech :
' Let there be no inscription upon my tomb.
Let no man write my epitaph. No man
can write my epitaph. I am here ready to
die. I am not allowed to vindicate my
character ; and when I am prevented from
vindicating myself, let no man dare to
calumniate me. Let my character and my
motives repose in obscurity and peace, till
other times and other men can do them
justice. Then shall my character be vindi-
cated ; then may my epitaph be written.
I HAVE DONE.'

Thou wert so perilous an enemy,
Here in free England shall an English
   hand
Build thy imperishable monument ;
O, . . to thine own misfortune and to
   ours,
By thine own deadly error so beguiled,
Here in free England shall an English
   voice
Raise up thy mourning-song.   For thou
   hast paid
The bitter penalty of that misdeed ; 20
Justice hath done her unrelenting part,
If she in truth be Justice who drives on,
Bloody and blind, the chariot wheels of
   death.

So young, so glowing for the general
   good,
Oh what a lovely manhood had been
   thine,
When all the violent workings of thy
   youth
Had pass'd away, hadst thou been wisely
   spared,
Left to the slow and certain influences
Of silent feeling and maturing thought.
How had that heart, . . that noble heart
   of thine,   30
Which even now had snapt one spell,
   which beat
With such brave indignation at the
   shame
And guilt of France, and of her mis-
   creant Lord,
How had it clung to England !   With
   what love,
What pure and perfect love, return'd
   to her,
Now worthy of thy love, the champion
   now
For freedom, . . yea, the only champion
   now,
And soon to be the Avenger.   But the
   blow
Hath fallen, the indiscriminating blow,
That for its portion to the Grave con-
   sign'd   40
Youth, Genius, generous Virtue.   Oh
   grief, grief !
Oh, sorrow and reproach ! Have ye to
   learn,
Deaf to the past, and to the future blind

Ye who thus irremissibly exact
The forfeit life, how lightly life is staked,
When in distemper'd times the feverish
    mind
To strong delusion yields ? Have ye to
    learn
With what a deep and spirit-stirring voice
Pity doth call Revenge ? Have ye no
    hearts
To feel and understand how Mercy
    tames   50
The rebel nature, madden'd by old
    wrongs,
And binds it in the gentle bands of love,
When steel and adamant were weak to
    hold
That Samson-strength subdued !
                Let no man write
Thy epitaph ! Emmet, nay ; thou
    shalt not go
Without thy funeral strain ! O young
    and good
And wise, though erring here, thou shalt
    not go
Unhonour'd nor unsung. And better
    thus
Beneath that indiscriminating stroke,
Better to fall, than to have lived to
    mourn,   60
As sure thou wouldst, in misery and
    remorse,
Thine own disastrous triumph ; to have
    seen,
If the Almighty at that aweful hour
Had turn'd away his face, wild Ignor-
    ance
Let loose, and frantic Vengeance, and
    dark Zeal,
And all bad passions tyrannous, and
    the fires
Of Persecution once again ablaze.
How had it sunk into thy soul to see,
Last curse of all, the ruffian slaves of
    France
In thy dear native country lording it ! 70
How happier thus, in that heroic mood
That takes away the sting of death, to
    die,   [given,
By all the good and all the wise for-
Yea, in all ages by the wise and good
To be remember'd, mourn'd, and
    honour'd still.

Keswick.

IX

VERSES

SPOKEN IN THE THEATRE AT OXFORD,
UPON THE INSTALLATION OF LORD
GRENVILLE

GRENVILLE, few years have had their
    course, since last
Exulting Oxford view'd a spectacle
Like this day's pomp ; and yet to those
    who throng'd
These walls, which echo'd then with
    Portland's praise,
What change hath intervened ! The
    bloom of spring
Is fled from many a cheek, where roseate
    joy
And beauty bloom'd ; the inexorable
    Grave
Hath claimed its portion ; and the
    band of youths,
Who then, collected here as in a port
From whence to launch on life's adven-
    turous sea,   10
Stood on the beach, ere this have found
    their lots
Of good or evil. Thus the lapse of years,
Evolving all things in its quiet course,
Hath wrought for them ; and though
    those years have seen
Fearful vicissitudes, of wilder change
Than history yet had learnt, or old
    romance
In wildest mood imagined, yet these too,
Portentous as they seem, not less have
    risen
Each of its natural cause the sure effect,
All righteously ordain'd. Lo ! king-
    doms wreck'd,   20
Thrones overturn'd, built up, then swept
    away
Like fabrics in the summer clouds, dis-
    persed
By the same breath that heap'd them ;
    rightful kings,
Who, from a line of long-drawn ancestry
Held the transmitted sceptre, to the axe
Bowing the anointed head ; or dragg'd
    away
To eat the bread of bondage ; or escaped

Beneath the shadow of Britannia's shield,
There only safe. Such fate have vicious courts,
Statesmen corrupt, and fear-struck policy,   30
Upon themselves drawn down; till Europe, bound
In iron chains, lies bleeding in the dust,
Beneath the feet of upstart tyranny:
Only the heroic Spaniard, he alone
Yet unsubdued in these degenerate days,
With desperate virtue, such as in old time
Hallow'd Saguntum and Numantia's name,
Stands up against the oppressor undismay'd.
So may the Almighty bless the noble race,
And crown with happy end their holiest cause !   40

Deem not these dread events the monstrous birth
Of chance ! And thou, O England, who dost ride
Serene amid the waters of the flood,
Preserving, even like the Ark of old,
Amid the general wreck, thy purer faith,
Domestic loves, and ancient liberty,
Look to thyself, O England ! for be sure,
Even to the measure of thine own desert,
The cup of retribution to thy lips
Shall soon or late be dealt ! . . a thought that well   50
Might fill the stoutest heart of all thy sons
With aweful apprehension. Therefore, they
Who fear the Eternal's justice, bless thy name,
Grenville, because the wrongs of Africa
Cry out no more to draw a curse from Heaven
On England !—for if still the trooping sharks
Track by the scent of death the accursed ship
Freighted with human anguish, in her wake
Pursue the chace, crowd round her keel, and dart

Toward the sound contending, when they hear   60
The frequent carcass from her guilty deck
Dash in the opening deep, no longer now
The guilt shall rest on England; but if yet
There be among her children, hard of heart
And sear'd of conscience, men who set at nought
Her laws and God's own word, upon themselves
Their sin be visited ! . . the red-cross flag,
Redeem'd from stain so foul, no longer now
Covereth the abomination.
                    This thy praise,
O Grenville, and while ages roll away   70
This shall be thy remembrance. Yea, when all
For which the tyrant of these abject times
Hath given his honourable name on earth,
His nights of innocent sleep, his hopes of heaven ;
When all his triumphs and his deeds of blood,
The fretful changes of his feverish pride,
His midnight murders and perfidious plots,
Are but a tale of years so long gone by,
That they who read distrust the hideous truth,
Willing to let a charitable doubt   80
Abate their horror ; Grenville, even then
Thy memory will be fresh among mankind ;
Afric with all her tongues will speak of thee,
With Wilberforce and Clarkson, he whom Heaven,
To be the apostle of this holy work,
Raised up and strengthen'd, and upheld through all
His arduous toil. To end the glorious task,
That blessed, that redeeming deed was thine :
Be it thy pride in life, thy thought in death,

Thy praise beyond the tomb. The
  statesman's fame   90
Will fade, the conqueror's laurel crown
  grow sere ;
Fame's loudest trump upon the ear of
  Time
Leaves but a dying echo ; they alone
Are held in everlasting memory,
Whose deeds partake of heaven. Long
  ages hence,
Nations unborn, in cities that shall rise
Along the palmy coast, will bless thy
  name ;
And Senegal and secret Niger's shore,
And Calabar, no longer startled then
With sounds of murder, will, like Isis
  now,   100
Ring with the songs that tell of Gren-
  ville's praise.

Keswick, 1810.

X
THANKSGIVING FOR VICTORY

[Written for Music, and composed by
Shield.]

GLORY to Thee in thine omnipotence,
O Lord, who art our shield and our
    defence,
    And dost dispense,
As seemeth best to thine unerring will
  (Which passeth mortal sense),
    The lot of Victory still ;
Edging sometimes with might the
    sword unjust ;
    And bowing to the dust
The rightful cause, that so much
    seeming ill
May thine appointed purposes fulfil ;
Sometimes, as in this late auspicious
    hour   11
    For which our hymns we raise,
Making the wicked feel thy present
    power ;
    Glory to thee and praise,
Almighty God, by whom our strength
    was given !
Glory to thee, O Lord of Earth and
    Heaven !

Keswick, 1815.

XI
STANZAS

WRITTEN IN LADY LONSDALE'S ALBUM,
  AT LOWTHER CASTLE, OCTOBER 13,
  1821

[First published in Joanna Baillie's *A
Collection of Poems, chiefly Manuscript*, in
1823.]

1

SOMETIMES in youthful years,
When in some ancient ruin I have
  stood,
Alone and musing, till with quiet tears
  I felt my cheeks bedew'd,
A melancholy thought hath made me
  grieve
For this our age, and humbled me in
  mind,
  That it should pass away and leave
  No monuments behind.

2

Not for themselves alone
Our fathers lived ; nor with a niggard
  hand   10
Raised they the fabrics of enduring
  stone,
  Which yet adorn the land ;
Their piles, memorials of the mighty
  dead,
Survive them still, majestic in decay ;
  But ours are like ourselves, I said,
  The creatures of a day.

3

With other feelings now,
Lowther ! have I beheld thy stately
  walls,
Thy pinnacles, and broad embattled
  brow,
  And hospitable halls.   20
The sun those wide-spread battlements
  shall crest,
And silent years unharming shall go by
  Till centuries in their course invest
  Thy towers with sanctity.

4

But thou the while shalt bear,
To after-times, an old and honour'd
     name,
And to remote posterity declare
     Thy Founder's virtuous fame.
Fair structure ! worthy the triumphant
     age
Of glorious England's opulence and
     power,   30
     Peace be thy lasting heritage,
     And happiness thy dower !

XII

STANZAS

ADDRESSED TO W. R. TURNER, ESQ., R.A.,
     ON HIS VIEW OF THE LAGO MAGGIORE
     FROM THE TOWN OF ARONA

[First published in *The Keepsake*, 1829.]

1

TURNER, thy pencil brings to mind
     a day
     When from Laveno and the Beuscer
     hill
I over Lake Verbanus held my way
     In pleasant fellowship, with wind at
     will ;
Smooth were the waters wide, the sky
     serene,
And our hearts gladden'd with the
     joyful scene ;

2

Joyful, . . for all things minister'd de-
     light, . .
     The lake and land, the mountains and
     the vales ;
The Alps their snowy summits rear'd in
     light,
     Tempering with gelid breath the
     summer gales ;   10
And verdant shores and woods refresh'd
     the eye
That else had ached beneath that bril-
     liant sky.

3

To that elaborate island were we bound
     Of yore the scene of Borromean
     pride, . .
Folly's prodigious work ; where all
     around,
     Under its coronet and self-belied,
Look where you will, you cannot choose
     but see
The obtrusive motto's proud ' Hu-
     MILITY ! '

4

Far off the Borromean saint was seen,
     Distinct though distant, o'er his native
     town,   20
Where his Colossus with benignant
     mien
Looks from its station on Arona down :
To it the inland sailor lifts his eyes,
From the wide lake, when perilous
     storms arise.

5

But no storm threaten'd on that
     summer-day ;
     The whole rich scene appear'd for
     joyance made ;
With many a gliding bark the mere was
     gay,
     The fields and groves in all their
     wealth array'd ;
I could have thought the Sun beheld
     with smiles
Those towns and palaces and populous
     isles.   30

6

From fair Arona, even on such a day,
     When gladness was descending like
     a shower,
Great painter, did thy gifted eye survey
     The splendid scene ; and, conscious
     of its power,
Well hath thine hand inimitable given
The glories of the lake, and land, and
     heaven.

Keswick, 1828.

XIII
ON A PICTURE BY J. M. WRIGHT, ESQ.

[First published in *The Keepsake* for 1829, under the title of ' Lucy and her Bird '.]

1

THE sky-lark hath perceived his prison-door
  Unclosed; for liberty the captive tries :
Puss eagerly hath watched him from the floor,
  And in her grasp he flutters, pants, and dies.

2

Lucy's own Puss, and Lucy's own dear Bird,
  Her foster'd favourites both for many a day,
That which the tender-hearted girl preferr'd,
  She in her fondness knew not sooth to say.

3

For if the sky-lark's pipe were shrill and strong,
  And its rich tones the thrilling ear might please,   10
Yet Pussybel could breathe a fireside song
  As winning, when she lay on Lucy's knees.

4

Both knew her voice, and each alike would seek
  Her eye, her smile, her fondling touch to gain :
How faintly then may words her sorrow speak,   [slain.
  When by the one she sees the other

5

The flowers fall scatter'd from her lifted hands ;
  A cry of grief she utters in affright ;
And self-condemn'd for negligence she stands   19
  Aghast and helpless at the cruel sight.

6

Come, Lucy, let me dry those tearful eyes ;
  Take thou, dear child, a lesson not unholy
From one whom nature taught to moralize
  Both in his mirth and in his melancholy.

7

I will not warn thee not to set thy heart
  Too fondly upon perishable things ;
In vain the earnest preacher spends his art
  Upon that theme ; in vain the poet sings.

8

It is our nature's strong necessity,
  And this the soul's unerring instincts tell :   30
Therefore I say, let us love worthily,
  Dear child, and then we cannot love too well.

9

Better it is all losses to deplore,
  Which dutiful affection can sustain,
Than that the heart should, in its inmost core,
  Harden without it, and have lived in vain.

10

This love which thou hast lavish'd, and the woe
  Which makes thy lip now quiver with distress,
Are but a vent, an innocent overflow,
  From the deep springs of female tenderness.   40

11

And something I would teach thee from the grief
  That thus hath fill'd those gentle eyes with tears,
The which may be thy sober, sure relief
  When sorrow visits thee in after years.

12

I ask not whither is the spirit flown
    That lit the eye which there in death
        is seal'd ;
Our Father hath not made that mystery
        known ;
    Needless the knowledge, therefore not
        reveal'd.

13

But didst thou know in sure and sacred
    truth,
    It had a place assign'd in yonder skies,
There through an endless life of joyous
        youth,   51
    To warble in the bowers of Paradise ;

14

Lucy, if then the power to thee were
    given
    In that cold form its life to re-engage,
Wouldst thou call back the warbler from
        its Heaven,
    To be again the tenant of a cage ?

15

Only that thou might'st cherish it again,
    Wouldst thou the object of thy love
        recall
To mortal life, and chance, and change,
        and pain,
    And death, which must be suffered
        once by all ?   60

16

Oh, no, thou say'st : oh, surely not, not
        so !
    I read the answer which those looks
        express :
For pure and true affection well I know
    Leaves in the heart no room for
        selfishness.

17

Such love of all our virtues is the gem ;
    We bring with us the immortal seed
        at birth :
Of heaven it is, and heavenly ; woe to
        them
    Who make it wholly earthly and of
        earth !

18

What we love perfectly, for its own sake
    We love and not our own, being ready
        thus   70
Whate'er self-sacrifice is ask'd, to make ;
    That which is best for it, is best for us.

19

O Lucy ! treasure up that pious
        thought !
    It hath a balm for sorrow's deadliest
        darts ;
And with true comfort thou wilt find it
        fraught,
    If grief should reach thee in thy heart
        of hearts.

Buckland, 1828.

XIV

TO CHARLES LAMB

ON THE REVIEWAL OF HIS ' ALBUM
VERSES ' IN ' THE LITERARY GAZETTE '

[Published in *The Times*, August 6, 1830.]

CHARLES LAMB, to those who know thee
        justly dear
For rarest genius, and for sterling
        worth,
Unchanging friendship, warmth of heart
        sincere,
And wit that never gave an ill thought
        birth,
Nor ever in its sport infix'd a sting ;
To us, who have admired and loved thee
        long,
It is a proud as well as pleasant thing
To hear thy good report, now borne
        along
Upon the honest breath of public praise:
We know that with the elder sons of
        song,   10
In honouring whom thou hast delighted
        still,
Thy name shall keep its course to after
        days.
The empty pertness, and the vulgar
        wrong,
The flippant folly, the malicious will,

Which have assailed thee, now, or
heretofore,
Find, soon or late, their proper meed of
shame ;
The more thy triumph, and our pride
the more,
When witling critics to the world pro-
claim,
In lead, their own dolt incapacity.
Matter it is of mirthful memory   20

To think, when thou wert early in the
field,
How doughtily small Jeffrey ran at thee
A-tilt, and broke a bulrush on thy shield.
And now, a veteran in the lists of fame,
I ween, old Friend ! thou art not worse
bested
When with a maudlin eye and drunken
aim   [head.
Dulness hath thrown *a jerdan* at thy

THE RETROSPECT

[Published in *Poems by Robert Lovell and
Robert Southey*, 1795. In its present form
the poem has been completely rewritten.]

ON as I journey through the vale of
years,
By hopes enliven'd, or deprest by
fears,
Allow me, Memory, in thy treasured
store,
To view the days that will return no
more.
And yes ! before thine intellectual
ray,
The clouds of mental darkness melt
away !
As when, at earliest day's awakening
dawn,
The hovering mists obscure the dewy
lawn,
O'er all the landscape spread their
influence chill,
Hang o'er the vale and wood, and
hide the hill,   10
Anon, slow-rising, comes the orb of
day,
Slow fade the shadowy mists and roll
away,
The prospect opens on the traveller's
sight,
And hills and vales and woods reflect the
living light.

O thou, the mistress of my future days,
Accept thy minstrel's retrospective
lays ;

To whom the minstrel and the lyre
belong,
Accept, my EDITH, Memory's pensive
song.
Of long-past days I sing, ere yet I knew
Or thought and grief, or happiness and
you ;   20
Ere yet my infant heart had learnt
to prove
The cares of life, the hopes and fears
of love.

Corston, twelve years in various
fortunes fled
Have pass'd with restless progress
o'er my head,
Since in thy vale beneath the master's
rule
I dwelt an inmate of the village
school.
Yet still will Memory's busy eye retrace
Each little vestige of the well-known
place ;
Each wonted haunt and scene of
youthful joy,
Where merriment has cheer'd the
careless boy ;   30
Well-pleased will fancy still the spot
survey
Where once he triumph'd in the boyish play,
Without one care where every morn
he rose,
Where every evening sunk to calm
repose.

Large was the house, though fallen
    in course of fate
From its old grandeur and manorial
    state.   [Squire
Lord of the manor, here the jovial
Once called his tenants round the
    crackling fire ;
Here while the glow of joy suffused
    his face,
He told his ancient exploits in the
    chase,   40
And, proud his rival sportsmen to
    surpass,
He lit again the pipe, and fill'd again
    the glass.

But now no more was heard at early
    morn   [horn ;
The echoing clangor of the huntsman's
No more the eager hounds with
    deepening cry
Leapt round him as they knew their
    pastime nigh ;
The Squire no more obey'd the
    morning call,
Nor favourite spaniels fill'd the sports-
    man's hall ;
For he, the last descendant of his race,
Slept with his fathers, and forgot the
    chase.   50
There now in petty empire o'er the
    school
The mighty master held despotic rule ;
Trembling in silence all his deeds we
    saw,   [law ;
His look a mandate, and his word a
Severe his voice, severe and stern his
    mien,
And wondrous strict he was, and won-
    drous wise, I ween.

Even now through many a long long
    year I trace
The hour when first with awe I view'd
    his face ;
Even now recall my entrance at the
    dome, . .
'Twas the first day I ever left my
    home !   60
Years intervening have not worn
    away
The deep remembrance of that
    wretched day,

Nor taught me to forget my earliest
    fears,   [tears ;
A mother's fondness, and a mother's
When close she prest me to her
    sorrowing heart,
As loth as even I myself to part ;
And I, as I beheld her sorrows flow,
With painful effort hid my inward
    woe.

But time to youthful troubles brings
    relief,
And each new object weans the child
    from grief.   70
Like April showers the tears of youth
    descend,   [end,
Suddenly they fall, and suddenly they
And fresher pleasure cheers the fol-
    lowing hour,
As brighter shines the sun after the
    April shower.

Methinks even now the interview I
    see,
The Mistress's glad smile, the Master's
    glee ;
Much of my future happiness they
    said,
Much of the easy life the scholars led,
Of spacious play-ground and of whole-
    some air,
The best instruction and the tenderest
    care ;   80
And when I followed to the garden-
    door
My father, till through tears I saw no
    more, . .
How civilly they sooth'd my parting
    pain,
And never did they speak so civilly
    again.

Why loves the soul on earlier years to
    dwell,
When Memory spreads around her
    saddening spell,
When discontent, with sullen gloom
    o'ercast,
Turns from the present and prefers
    the past ?
Why calls reflection to my pensive
    view
Each trifling act of infancy anew, 90

Each trifling act with pleasure pon-
  dering o'er,
Even at the time when trifles please
  no more ?
Yet is remembrance sweet, though
  well I know   [woe ;
The days of childhood are but days of
Some rude restraint, some petty
  tyrant sours
What else should be our sweetest
  blithest hours ;
Yet is it sweet to call those hours to
  mind, . .
Those easy hours for ever left behind ;
Ere care began the spirit to oppress,
When ignorance itself was happiness.

Such was my state in those remem-
  ber'd years   101
When two small acres bounded all my
  fears ;   [call
And therefore still with pleasure I re-
The tapestried school, the bright
  brown-boarded hall,
The murmuring brook, that every
  morning saw
The due observance of the cleanly
  law ;
The walnuts, where, when favour
  would allow,
Full oft I went to search each well-
  stript bough ;
The crab-tree, which supplied a secret
  hoard
With roasted crabs to deck the wintry
  board ;   110
These trifling objects then my heart
  possest,
These trifling objects still remain
  imprest ;   [hind
So when with unskill'd hand some idle
Carves his rude name within a sap-
  ling's rind,
In after years the peasant lives to see
The expanding letters grow as grows
  the tree ;
Though every winter's desolating
  sway
Shake the hoarse grove and sweep the
  leaves away,   [last,
That rude inscription uneffaced will
Unalter'd by the storm or wintry
  blast.   120

Oh while well pleased the letter'd
  traveller roams
Among old temples, palaces, and
  domes,
Strays with the Arab o'er the wreck
  of time
Where erst Palmyra's towers arose
  sublime,   [pride,
Or marks the lazy Turk's lethargic
And Grecian slavery on Ilyssus' side,
Oh be it mine, aloof from public
  strife,
To mark the changes of domestic life,
The alter'd scenes where once I bore
  a part,
Where every change of fortune strikes
  the heart ;   130
As when the merry bells with echoing
  sound
Proclaim the news of victory around,
Rejoicing patriots run the news to
  spread
Of glorious conquest and of thousands
  dead,
All join the loud huzzah with eager
  breath,
And triumph in the tale of blood and
  death ;
But if extended on the battle-plain,
Cut off in conquest some dear friend
  be slain,   [eye,
Affection then will fill the sorrowing
And suffering Nature grieve that one
  should die.   140

Cold was the morn, and bleak the
  wintry blast
Blew o'er the meadow, when I saw
  thee last.
My bosom bounded as I wander'd
  round
With silent step the long-remember'd
  ground,   [hour,
Where I had loiter'd out so many an
Chased the gay butterfly, and cull'd
  the flower,
Sought the swift arrow's erring course
  to trace,
Or with mine equals vied amid the
  chase.   [away
I saw the church where I had slept
The tedious service of the summer
  day ;   150

Or, hearing sadly all the preacher told,
In winter waked and shiver'd with
　　the cold.
Oft have my footsteps roam'd the
　　sacred ground
Where heroes, kings, and poets sleep
　　around ;
Oft traced the mouldering castle's
　　ivied wall,
Or aged convent tottering to its fall ;
Yet never had my bosom felt such
　　pain,　　　　　　　　　[again ;
As, Corston, when I saw thy scenes
For many a long-lost pleasure came
　　to view,
For many a long-past sorrow rose
　　anew ;　　　　　　　　　160
Where whilom all were friends I stood
　　alone,　　　　　　　　　[known.
Unknowing all I saw, of all I saw un-

There, where my little hands were
　　wont to rear
With pride the earliest salad of the
　　year ;

Where never idle weed to spring was
　　seen,
Rank thorns and nettles rear'd their
　　heads obscene.
Still all around and sad, I saw no more
The playful group, nor heard the
　　playful roar ;
There echoed round no shout of mirth
　　and glee,
It seem'd as though the world were
　　changed like me !　　　　170

Enough ! it boots not on the past
　　to dwell, . .　　　　　　[well !
Fair scene of other years, a long fare-
Rouse up, my soul ! it boots not to
　　repine,
Rouse up ! for worthier feelings should
　　be thine ;
Thy path is plain and straight, . . that
　　light is given, . .
Onward in faith, . . and leave the rest
　　to Heaven.

Oxford, 1794.

HYMN TO THE PENATES

' Remove far from me vanity and lies ; give me neither poverty nor riches ; feed
me with food convenient for me.'—THE WORDS OF AGUR.

OIKOI βέλτερον εἶναι, ἐπεὶ βλαβερὸν τὸ θύρηφι.—HESIOD.

[Published in *Poems*, 1797.]

YET one Song more ! one high and
　　solemn strain
Ere, Phoebus ! on thy temple's ruin'd
　　wall
I hang the silent harp : there may its
　　strings,
When the rude tempest shakes the aged
　　pile,
Make melancholy music. One song
　　more !
PENATES, hear me ! for to you I hymn
The votive lay ; whether, as sages deem,
Ye dwell in inmost Heaven, the Coun-
　　sellors
Of Jove ; or if, Supreme of Deities,
All things are yours, and in your holy
　　train　　　　　　　　　10

Jove proudly ranks, and Juno, white-
　　arm'd Queen,
And wisest of Immortals, the dread Maid
Athenian Pallas. Venerable Powers,
Hearken your hymn of praise ! Though
　　from your rites
Estranged, and exiled from your altars
　　long,
I have not ceased to love you, House-
　　hold Gods !
In many a long and melancholy hour
Of solitude and sorrow, hath my heart
With earnest longings pray'd to rest at
　　length
Beside your hallow'd hearth, . . for
　　Peace is there !　　　　20
Yes, I have loved you long ! I call on ye
Yourselves to witness with what holy
　　joy,

Shunning the common herd of human-
    kind,
I have retired to watch your lonely fires
And commune with myself : . . delight-
    ful hours,
That gave mysterious pleasure, made
    me know
Mine inmost heart, its weakness and its
    strength,
Taught me to cherish with devoutest care
Its deep unworldly feelings, taught me
    too
The best of lessons—*to respect myself.* 30

  Nor have I ever ceased to reverence
    you,
Domestic Deities ! from the first dawn
Of reason, through the adventurous
    paths of youth
Even to this better day, when on mine
    ear
The uproar of contending nations sounds
But like the passing wind, and wakes no
    pulse
To tumult. When a child . . (for still
    I love
To dwell with fondness on my childish
    years,)
When first, a little one, I left my home,
I can remember the first grief I felt, 40
And the first painful smile that clothed
    my front
With feelings not its own : sadly at
    night
I sat me down beside a stranger's hearth;
And when the lingering hour of rest was
    come,
First wet with tears my pillow. As I
    grew
In years and knowledge, and the course
    of time
Developed the young feelings of my
    heart,
When most I loved in solitude to rove
Amid the woodland gloom ; or where
    the rocks
Darken'd old Avon's stream, in the ivied
    cave   50
Recluse to sit and brood the future
    song, . .
Yet not the less, PENATES, loved I then
Your altars ; not the less at evening
    hour

Loved I beside the well-trimm'd fire to
    sit,
Absorb'd in many a dear deceitful dream
Of visionary joys, . . deceitful dreams, . .
And yet not vain ; for painting purest
    bliss,
They form'd to Fancy's mould her
    votary's heart.

  By Cherwell's sedgey side, and in the
    meads
Where Isis in her calm clear stream
    reflects   60
The willow's bending boughs, at early
    dawn,
In the noon-tide hour, and when the
    night-mist rose,
I have remember'd you ; and when the
    noise
Of lewd Intemperance on my lonely ear
Burst with loud tumult, as recluse I sate,
Musing on days when man should be
    redeem'd
From servitude, and vice, and wretched-
    ness,
I bless'd you, Household Gods ! because
    I loved
Your peaceful altars and serener rites.
Nor did I cease to reverence you, when
    driven   70
Amid the jarring crowd, an unfit man
To mingle with the world ; still, still my
    heart
Sigh'd for your sanctuary, and inly
    pined ;
And loathing human converse, I have
    stray'd
Where o'er the sea-beach chilly howl'd
    the blast,
And gazed upon the world of waves, and
    wish'd
That I were far beyond the Atlantic
    deep,
In woodland haunts, a sojourner with
    Peace.

  Not idly did the ancient poets dream,
Who peopled earth with Deities. They
    trod   80
The wood with reverence where the
    Dryads dwelt ;
At day's dim dawn or evening's misty
    hour

They saw the Oreads on their mountain haunts,
And felt their holy influence ; nor impure
Of thought, nor ever with polluted hands,
Touch'd they without a prayer the Naiad's spring ;
Nor without reverence to the River God
Cross'd in unhappy hour his limpid stream.
Yet was this influence transient ; such brief awe
Inspiring as the thunder's long loud peal   90
Strikes to the feeble spirit. Household Gods,
Not such your empire ! in your votaries' breasts
No momentary impulse ye awake ;
Nor fleeting, like their local energies,
The deep devotion that your fanes impart.
O ye whom Youth has wilder'd on your way,
Or Pleasure with her syren song hath lured,
Or Fame with spirit-stirring trump hath call'd
To climb her summits, .. to your Household Gods
Return ; for not in Pleasure's gay abodes,   100
Nor in the unquiet unsafe halls of Fame
Doth Happiness abide. O ye who grieve
Much for the miseries of your fellow-kind,
More for their vices ; ye whose honest eyes
Scowl on Oppression,—ye whose honest hearts
Beat high when Freedom sounds her dread alarm ;
O ye who quit the path of peaceful life
Crusading for mankind .. a spaniel race
That lick the hand that beats them, or tear all
Alike in frenzy ; to your Household Gods   110
Return ! for by their altars Virtue dwells,   [fires
And Happiness with her ; for by their

Tranquillity, in no unsocial mood,
Sits silent, listening to the pattering shower ;
For, so Suspicion sleep not at the gate
Of Wisdom, Falsehood shall not enter there.

As on the height of some huge eminence,
Reach'd with long labour, the wayfaring man
Pauses awhile, and gazing o'er the plain
With many a sore step travell'd, turns him then   120
Serious to contemplate the onward road,
And calls to mind the comforts of his home,
And sighs that he has left them, and resolves
To stray no more : I on my way of life
Muse thus, Penates, and with firmest faith
Devote myself to you. I will not quit,
To mingle with the crowd, your calm abodes,
Where by the evening hearth Contentment sits
And hears the cricket chirp ; where Love delights
To dwell, and on your altars lays his torch   130
That burns with no extinguishable flame.

Hear me, ye Powers benignant ! there is one
Must be mine inmate, .. for I may not choose
But love him. He is one whom many wrongs
Have sicken'd of the world. There was a time
When he would weep to hear of wickedness,
And wonder at the tale ; when for the opprest
He felt a brother's pity, to the oppressor
A good man's honest anger. His quick eye
Betray'd each rising feeling ; every thought   140
Leapt to his tongue. When first among mankind   [them,
He mingled, by himself he judged of

And loved and trusted them, to Wisdom
  deaf,
And took them to his bosom. False-
  hood met
Her unsuspecting victim, fair of front,
And lovely as Apega's sculptured form,
Like that false image caught his warm
  embrace,
And pierced his open breast. The
  reptile race
Clung round his bosom, and with viper
  folds
Encircling, stung the fool who foster'd
  them.   150
His mother was Simplicity, his sire
Benevolence; in earlier days he bore
His father's name; the world who in-
  jured him
Call him Misanthropy. I may not choose
But love him, Household Gods! for we
  grew up   [bred,
Together, and in the same school were
And our poor fortunes the same course
  have held,
Up to this hour.
        Penates! some there are
Who say, that not in the inmost heaven
  ye dwell,
Gazing with eye remote on all the ways
Of man, his Guardian Gods; wiselier
  they deem   161
A dearer interest to the human race
Links you, yourselves the Spirits of the
  Dead.
No mortal eye may pierce the invisible
  world,
No light of human reason penetrate
The depth where Truth lies hid. Yet to
  this faith
My heart with instant sympathy assents;
And I would judge all systems and all
  faiths
By that best touchstone, from whose
  test Deceit
Shrinks like the Arch-Fiend at Ithuriel's
  spear;   170
And Sophistry's gay glittering bubble
  bursts,
As at the spousals of the Nereid's son,
When that false Florimel, with her pro-
  totype
Set side by side, in her unreal charms,
Dissolved away.

        Nor can the halls of Heaven
Give to the human soul such kindred
  joy,
As hovering o'er its earthly haunts it
  feels,
When with the breeze it dwells around
  the brow
Of one beloved on earth; or when at
  night
In dreams it comes, and brings with it
  the Days   180
And Joys that are no more. Or when,
  perchance
With power permitted to alleviate ill
And fit the sufferer for the coming woe,
Some strange presage the Spirit breathes,
  and fills   [it
The breast with ominous fear, preparing
For sorrow, pours into the afflicted heart
The balm of resignation, and inspires
With heavenly hope. Even as a child
  delights
To visit day by day the favourite plant
His hand has sown, to mark its gradual
  growth,   190
And watch all-anxious for the promised
  flower;
Thus to the blest spirit in innocence
And pure affections like a little child,
Sweet will it be to hover o'er the friends
Beloved; then sweetest, if, as duty
  prompts,
With earthly care we in their breasts
  have sown
The seeds of Truth and Virtue, holy
  flowers
Whose odour reacheth Heaven.
           When my sick Heart
(Sick with hope long delay'd, than which
  no care
Weighs on the spirit heavier,) from itself
Seeks the best comfort, often have I
  deem'd   201
That thou didst witness every inmost
  thought,
SEWARD! my dear! dear friend! For
  not in vain,
O early summon'd on thy heavenly
  course,
Was thy brief sojourn here; me didst
  thou leave
With strengthen'd step to follow the
  right path,

Till we shall meet again. Meantime
I soothe
The deep regret of nature, with belief,
O EDMUND! that thine eye's celestial
ken
Pervades me now, marking with no
mean joy   210
The movements of the heart that loved
thee well!

Such feelings Nature prompts, and
hence your rites,
Domestic Gods! arose. When for his
son
With ceaseless grief Syrophanes bewail'd,
Mourning his age left childless, and his
wealth
Heapt for an alien, he with obstinate eye
Still on the imaged marble of the dead
Dwelt, pampering sorrow. Thither
from his wrath,
A safe asylum, fled the offending slave,
And garlanded the statue, and implored
His young lost lord to save. Remem-
brance then   221
Soften'd the father, and he loved to see
The votive wreath renew'd, and the rich
smoke
Curl from the costly censer slow and
sweet.
From Egypt soon the sorrow-soothing
rites
Divulging spread; before your idol
forms
By every hearth the blinded Pagan
knelt,
Pouring his prayers to these, and offer-
ing there
Vain sacrifice or impious, and sometimes
With human blood your sanctuary
defiled: 230
Till the first Brutus, tyrant-conquering
chief,
Arose; he first the impious rites put
down,   [died,
He fitliest, who for Freedom lived and
The friend of humankind. Then did
your feasts
Frequent recur and blameless; and
when came
The solemn festival,[1] whose happiest rites

[1] The Saturnalia.

Emblem'd Equality, the holiest truth,
Crown'd with gay garlands were your
statues seen,
To you the fragrant censer smoked, to
you
The rich libation flowed: vain sacrifice!
For not the poppy wreath nor fruits nor
wine   241
Ye ask, Penates! nor the altar cleansed
With many a mystic form; ye ask the
heart
Made pure, and by domestic Peace and
Love
Hallow'd to you.
               Hearken your hymn of praise,
Penates! to your shrines I come for rest,
There only to be found. Often at eve,
As in my wanderings I have seen far off
Some lonely light that spake of comfort
there,   249
It told my heart of many a joy of home,
When I was homeless. Often as I gazed
From some high eminence on goodly
vales
And cots and villages embower'd below,
The thought would rise that all to me
was strange
Amid the scene so fair, nor one small
spot
Where my tired mind might rest, and
call it *Home*.
There is a magic in that little word:
It is a mystic circle that surrounds
Comforts and virtues never known
beyond
The hallowed limit. Often has my
heart   260
Ached for that quiet haven! Haven'd
now,   [ness
I think of those in this world's wilder-
Who wander on and find no home of
rest
Till to the grave they go: them Poverty,
Hollow-eyed fiend, the child of Wealth
and Power,
Bad offspring of worst parents, aye
afflicts,
Cankering with her foul mildews the
chill'd heart; . .
Them Want with scorpion scourge
drives to the den
Of Guilt: . . them Slaughter for the
price of death

Throws to her raven brood. Oh, not on
them,   270
God of eternal Justice ! not on them
Let fall thy thunder !
          Household Deities !
Then only shall be Happiness on earth
When man shall feel your sacred power,
and love
Your tranquil joys ; then shall the city
stand
A huge void sepulchre, and on the site
Where fortresses and palaces have stood,
The olive grow, there shall the Tree of
Peace
Strike its roots deep and flourish. This
the state
Shall bless the race redeem'd of Man,
when Wealth   280
And Power and all their hideous progeny
Shall sink annihilate, and all mankind
Live in the equal brotherhood of love.

Heart-calming hope, and sure ! for
hitherward
Tend all the tumults of the troubled
world,
Its woes, its wisdom, and its wickedness
Alike ; . . so He hath will'd, whose will is
just.

    Meantime, all hoping and expecting
all
In patient faith, to you, Domestic Gods !
Studious of other lore than song, I
come.   290
Yet shall my Heart remember the past
years
With honest pride, trusting that not in
vain
Lives the pure song of Liberty and
Truth.

Bristol, 1796.

ENGLISH ECLOGUES

[The first three of the following Eclogues
were published in *Poems*, vol. ii, 1799,
Eclogue II under the title of 'The Funeral'.
Eclogue IV was published in *The Edinburgh
Annual Register*, 1808.]

THE following Eclogues, I believe, bear
no resemblance to any poems in our language. This species of composition has
become popular in Germany, and I was
induced to attempt it by what was told me
of the German Idylls by my friend Mr.
William Taylor of Norwich. So far, therefore, these pieces may be deemed imitations,
though I am not acquainted with the
German language at present, and have
never seen any translations or specimens in
this kind.

With bad Eclogues I am sufficiently
acquainted, from Tityrus and Corydon
down to our English Strephons and Thir-
sisses. No kind of poetry can boast of more
illustrious names, or is more distinguished
by the servile dulness of imitated nonsense.
Pastoral writers, 'more silly than their
sheep,' have, like their sheep, gone on in
the same track one after another. Gay
struck into a new path. His eclogues were
the only ones which interested me when

I was a boy, and did not know they were
burlesque. The subject would furnish
matter for an essay, but this is not the place
for it.

1799.

I

THE OLD MANSION-HOUSE

STRANGER

OLD friend ! why you seem bent on
parish duty,
Breaking the highway stones, . . and
'tis a task
Somewhat too hard methinks for age
like yours !

OLD MAN

Why yes ! for one with such a weight of
years
Upon his back ! . . I've lived here, man
and boy,
In this same parish, well nigh the full
age
Of man, being hard upon threescore and
ten.

I can remember sixty years ago
The beautifying of this mansion here,
When my late Lady's father, the old
   Squire,   10
Came to the estate.

STRANGER

      Why then you have outlasted
All his improvements, for you see they're
   making
Great alterations here.

OLD MAN

         Ay . . great indeed !
And if my poor old Lady could rise up . .
God rest her soul ! 'twould grieve her to
   behold
What wicked work is here.

STRANGER

        They've set about it
In right good earnest.   All the front is
   gone ;
Here's to be turf, they tell me, and a
   road
Round to the door.   There were some
   yew trees too
Stood in the court. . .

OLD MAN

      Ay, Master ! fine old trees !
Lord bless us! I have heard my father
   say   21
His grandfather could just remember
   back
When they were planted there.   It was
   my task
To keep them trimm'd, and 'twas a
   pleasure to me ;
All straight and smooth, and like a great
   green wall !
My poor old lady many a time would
   come
And tell me where to clip, for she had
   play'd
In childhood under them, and 'twas her
   pride
To keep them in their beauty.   Plague,
   I say,
On their new-fangled whimsies ! we
   shall have   30
A modern shrubbery here stuck full of
   firs

And your pert poplar trees ; . . I could
   as soon
Have plough'd my father's grave as cut
   them down !

STRANGER

But 'twill be lighter and more cheerful
   now ;
A fine smooth turf, and with a carriage
   road
That sweeps conveniently from gate to
   gate.
I like a shrubbery too, for it looks fresh ;
And then there's some variety about it.
In spring the lilac and the snow-ball
   flower,
And the laburnum with its golden
   strings   40
Waving in the wind : And when the
   autumn comes   [ash,
The bright red berries of the mountain-
With pines enough in winter to look
   green,
And show that something lives.   Sure
   this is better
Than a great hedge of yew, making it
   look   [ever
All the year round like winter, and for
Dropping its poisonous leaves from the
   under boughs
Wither'd and bare.

OLD MAN

      Ay ! so the new Squire thinks ;
And pretty work he makes of it ! What
   'tis   49
To have a stranger come to an old house!

STRANGER

It seems you know him not ?

OLD MAN

         No, Sir, not I.
They tell me he's expected daily now ;
But in my Lady's time he never came
But once, for they were very distant kin.
If he had play'd about here when a child
In that fore court, and eat the yew-
   berries,
And sate in the porch, threading the
   jessamine flowers
Which fell so thick, he had not had the
   heart
To mar all thus !

STRANGER

Come ! come ! all is not wrong ;
Those old dark windows. . .

OLD MAN

They're demolish'd too, . . 60
As if he could not see through casement
glass !
The very red-breasts, that so regular
Came to my Lady for her morning
crumbs,
Won't know the windows now !

STRANGER

Nay they were small,
And then so darken'd round with jessa-
mine,
Harbouring the vermin ; . . yet I could
have wish'd
That jessamine had been saved, which
canopied
And bower'd and lined the porch.

OLD MAN

It did one good
To pass within ten yards when 'twas in
blossom.
There was a sweet-briar too that grew
beside ; 70
My Lady loved at evening to sit there
And knit ; and her old dog lay at her
feet
And slept in the sun ; 'twas an old
favourite dog, . .
She did not love him less that he was old
And feeble, and he always had a place
By the fire-side : and when he died at
last
She made me dig a grave in the garden
for him.
For she was good to all ! a woeful day
'Twas for the poor when to her grave
she went !

STRANGER

They lost a friend then ?

OLD MAN

You're a stranger here, 80
Or you wouldn't ask that question. Were
they sick ?
She had rare cordial waters, and for herbs
She could have taught the Doctors.
Then at winter,

When weekly she distributed the bread
In the poor old porch, to see her and to
hear
The blessings on her ! and I warrant
them
They were a blessing to her when her
wealth
Had been no comfort else. At Christ-
mas, Sir !
It would have warm'd your heart if you
had seen
Her Christmas kitchen, . . how the
blazing fire 90
Made her fine pewter shine, and holly
boughs
So cheerful red, . . and as for misseltoe, . .
The finest bush that grew in the country
round
Was mark'd for Madam. Then her old
ale went
So bountiful about ! a Christmas cask,
And 'twas a noble one ! . . God help me,
Sir !
But I shall never see such days again.

STRANGER

Things may be better yet than you
suppose,
And you should hope the best.

OLD MAN

It don't look well, . .
These alterations, Sir ! I'm an old
man, 100
And love the good old fashions ; we
don't find
Old bounty in new houses. They've
destroy'd
All that my Lady loved ; her favourite
walk
Grubb'd up, . . and they do say that the
great row
Of elms behind the house, which meet
a-top,
They must fall too. Well ! well ! I did
not think
To live to see all this, and 'tis perhaps
A comfort I shan't live to see it long.

STRANGER

But sure all changes are not needs for
the worse,
My friend ?

OLD MAN

May-hap they mayn't, Sir ; ..
for all that   110
I like what I've been used to. I re-
member
All this from a child up, and now to
lose it,
'Tis losing an old friend. There's
nothing left
As 'twas ; .. I go abroad and only
meet
With men whose fathers I remember
boys ;
The brook that used to run before my
door,
That's gone to the great pond ; the
trees I learnt
To climb are down ; and I see nothing
now
That tells me of old times, .. except the
stones
In the churchyard. You are young,
Sir, and I hope   120
Have many years in store, .. but pray
to God
You mayn't be left the last of all your
friends.

STRANGER

Well ! well ! you've one friend more
than you're aware of.
If the Squire's taste don't suit with
yours, I warrant
That's all you'll quarrel with: walk in
and taste
His beer, old friend ! and see if your old
Lady
E'er broach'd a better cask. You did
not know me,
But we're acquainted now. 'Twould
not be easy
To make you like the outside; but
within,
That is not changed, my friend ! you'll
always find   130
The same old bounty and old welcome
there.

Westbury, 1798.

II

HANNAH

PASSING across a green and lonely lane
A funeral met our view. It was not here
A sight of every day, as in the streets
Of some great city, and we stopt and
ask'd
Whom they were bearing to the grave.
A girl,
They answer'd, of the village, who had
pined
Through the long course of eighteen
painful months
With such slow wasting, that the hour
of death
Came welcome to her. We pursued our
way
To the house of mirth, and with that
idle talk   10
Which passes o'er the mind and is forgot,
We wore away the time. But it was
eve
When homewardly I went, and in the air
Was that cool freshness, that dis-
colouring shade
Which makes the eye turn inward :
hearing then
Over the vale the heavy toll of death
Sound slow, it made me think upon the
dead ;
I question'd more, and learnt her mourn-
ful tale.

She bore unhusbanded a mother's
pains,
And he who should have cherish'd her,
far off   20
Sail'd on the seas. Left thus, a wretched
one,
Scorn made a mock of her, and evil
tongues
Were busy with her name. She had to
bear
The sharper sorrow of neglect from him
Whom she had loved too dearly. Once
he wrote,
But only once that drop of comfort
came
To mingle with her cup of wretchedness ;
And when his parents had some tidings
from him,

There was no mention of poor Hannah
    there,
Or 'twas the cold inquiry, more unkind
Than silence. So she pined and pined
    away,   31
And for herself and baby toil'd and
    toil'd ;
Nor did she, even on her death-bed, rest
From labour, knitting there with lifted
    arms,
Till she sunk with very weakness. Her
    old mother
Omitted no kind office, working for her,
Albeit her hardest labour barely earn'd
Enough to keep life struggling, and pro-
    long
The pains of grief and sickness. Thus
    she lay
On the sick bed of poverty, worn out
With her long suffering and those pain-
    ful thoughts   41
Which at her heart were rankling, and
    so weak,
That she could make no effort to express
Affection for her infant; and the child,
Whose lisping love perhaps had solaced
    her,
Shunn'd her as one indifferent. But
    she too
Had grown indifferent to all things of
    earth,
Finding her only comfort in the thought
Of that cold bed wherein the wretched
    rest.
There had she now, in that last home,
    been laid,   50
And all was over now, . . sickness and
    grief,
Her shame, her suffering, and her peni-
    tence, . .
Their work was done. The school-boys
    as they sport
In the churchyard, for awhile might
    turn away
From the fresh grave till grass should
    cover it ;
Nature would do that office soon ; and
    none
Who trod upon the senseless turf would
    think
Of what a world of woes lay buried there!

Burton, near Christ Church, 1797.

III

THE RUINED COTTAGE

AY, Charles ! I knew that this would
    fix thine eye ; . .
This woodbine wreathing round the
    broken porch,
Its leaves just withering, yet one
    autumn flower
Still fresh and fragrant ; and yon holly-
    hock
That through the creeping weeds and
    nettles tall
Peers taller, lifting, column-like, a stem
Bright with its roseate blossoms. I have
    seen
Many an old convent reverend in decay,
And many a time have trod the castle
    courts
And grass-green halls, yet never did
    they strike   10
Home to the heart such melancholy
    thoughts
As this poor cottage. Look ! its little
    hatch
Fleeced with that grey and wintry moss;
    the roof
Part moulder'd in, the rest o'ergrown
    with weeds,
House-leek, and long thin grass, and
    greener moss ;
So Nature steals on all the works of man,
Sure conqueror she, reclaiming to her-
    self
His perishable piles.
                I led thee here,
Charles, not without design ; for this
    hath been
My favourite walk even since I was a
    boy ;   20
And I remember, Charles, this ruin here,
The neatest comfortable dwelling-place !
That when I read in those dear books
    which first
Woke in my heart the love of poesy,
How with the villagers Erminia dwelt,
And Calidore for a fair shepherdess
Forsook his quest to learn the shepherd's
    lore,
My fancy drew from this the little hut
Where that poor princess wept her hope-
    less love,

Or where the gentle Calidore at eve   30
Led Pastorella home. There was not then
A weed where all these nettles overtop
The garden-wall; but sweet-briar, scenting sweet
The morning air; rosemary and marjoram,
All wholesome herbs; and then, that woodbine wreathed
So lavishly around the pillar'd porch
Its fragrant flowers, that when I pass'd this way,
After a truant absence hastening home,
I could not chuse but pass with slacken'd speed
By that delightful fragrance. Sadly changed   40
Is this poor cottage! and its dwellers, Charles!..
Theirs is a simple melancholy tale,..
There's scarce a village but can fellow it:
And yet, methinks, it will not weary thee,
And should not be untold.
                              A widow here
Dwelt with an orphan grandchild: just removed
Above the reach of pinching poverty,
She lived on some small pittance which sufficed,
In better times, the needful calls of life,
Not without comfort. I remember her
Sitting at even in that open doorway,   51
And spinning in the sun. Methinks I see her
Raising her eyes and dark-rimm'd spectacles
To see the passer-by, yet ceasing not
To twirl her lengthening thread; or in the garden,
On some dry summer evening, walking round
To view her flowers, and pointing as she lean'd
Upon the ivory handle of her stick,
To some carnation whose o'erheavy head
Needed support; while with the watering-pot   60
Joanna follow'd, and refresh'd and trimm'd   [child,
The drooping plant; Joanna, her dear

As lovely and as happy then as youth
And innocence could make her.
                              Charles, it seems
As though I were a boy again, and all
The mediate years with their vicissitudes
A half-forgotten dream. I see the Maid
So comely in her Sunday dress! her hair,
Her bright brown hair, wreathed in contracting curls;
And then her cheek! it was a red and white   70
That made the delicate hues of art look loathsome.
The countrymen who on their way to church
Were leaning o'er the bridge, loitering to hear
The bell's last summons, and in idleness
Watching the stream below, would all look up
When she pass'd by. And her old Grandam, Charles,..
When I have heard some erring infidel
Speak of our faith as of a gloomy creed,
Inspiring superstitious wretchedness,
Her figure has recurr'd; for she did love
The Sabbath-day; and many a time hath cross'd   81
These fields in rain and through the winter snows,
When I, a graceless boy, and cold of foot,
Wishing the weary service at its end,
Have wonder'd wherefore that good dame came there,
Who, if it pleased her, might have staid beside
A comfortable fire.
                              One only care
Hung on her aged spirit. For herself,
Her path was plain before her, and the close
Of her long journey near. But then her child   90
Soon to be left alone in this bad world,..
That was a thought which many a winter night
Had kept her sleepless: and when prudent love
In something better than a servant's state
Had placed her well at last, it was a pang
Like parting life to part with her dear girl.

One summer, Charles, when at the
   holidays
Return'd from school, I visited again
My old accustom'd walks, and found in
   them   99
A joy almost like meeting an old friend,
I saw the cottage empty, and the weeds
Already crowding the neglected flowers.
Joanna, by a villain's wiles seduced,
Had play'd the wanton, and that blow
   had reach'd
Her grandam's heart. She did not
   suffer long ;
Her age was feeble, and this mortal grief
Brought her grey hairs with sorrow to
   the grave.

I pass this ruin'd dwelling oftentimes,
And think of other days. It wakes in
   me
A transient sadness ; but the feelings,
   Charles,   110
Which ever with these recollections rise,
I trust in God they will not pass away.

Westbury, 1799.

IV
THE ALDERMAN'S FUNERAL

STRANGER

WHOM are they ushering from the
   world, with all
This pageantry and long parade of
   death ?

TOWNSMAN

A long parade, indeed, Sir, and yet here
You see but half ; round yonder bend
   it reaches
A furlong further, carriage behind
   carriage.

STRANGER

'Tis but a mournful sight, and yet the
   pomp
Tempts me to stand a gazer.

TOWNSMAN

             Yonder schoolboy
Who plays the truant, says the proclamation
Of peace was nothing to the show ; and
   even

The chairing of the members at election
Would not have been a finer sight than
   this ;   11
Only that red and green are prettier
   colours
Than all this mourning. There, Sir,
   you behold
One of the red-gown'd worthies of the
   city,
The envy and the boast of our ex-
   change ; . .
Ay, what was worth, last week, a good
   half-million,
Screw'd down in yonder hearse !

STRANGER

             Then he was born
Under a lucky planet, who to-day
Puts mourning on for his inheritance.

TOWNSMAN

When first I heard his death, that very
   wish   20
Leapt to my lips ; but now the closing
   scene
Of the comedy hath waken'd wiser
   thoughts ;
And I bless God, that, when I go to the
   grave,
There will not be the weight of wealth
   like his
To sink me down.

STRANGER

           The camel and the needle, . .
Is that then in your mind ?

TOWNSMAN

            Even so. The text
Is Gospel-wisdom. I would ride the
   camel, . .
Yea leap him flying, through the
   needle's eye,
As easily as such a pamper'd soul
Could pass the narrow gate.

STRANGER

           Your pardon, Sir, 30
But sure this lack of Christian charity
Looks not like Christian truth.

TOWNSMAN

Your pardon too, Sir,
If, with this text before me, I should
    feel
In the preaching mood ! But for these
    barren fig-trees,
With all their flourish and their leafiness,
We have been told their destiny and
    use,
When the axe is laid unto the root, and
    they
Cumber the earth no longer.

STRANGER

Was his wealth
Stored fraudfully, . . the spoil of orphans
    wrong'd,
And widows who had none to plead their
    right ?   40

TOWNSMAN

All honest, open, honourable gains,
Fair legal interest, bonds and mortgages,
Ships to the East and West.

STRANGER

Why judge you then
So hardly of the dead ?

TOWNSMAN

For what he left
Undone ; . . for sins, not one of which is
    written
In the Ten Commandments. He, I
    warrant him,
Believed no other Gods than those of
    the Creed ;
Bow'd to no idols, . . but his money-
    bags ;
Swore no false oaths, except at the cus-
    tom-house ;
Kept the Sabbath idle ; built a monu-
    ment   50
To honour his dead father ; did no
    murder ;
Never sustain'd an action for crim-con ;
Never pick'd pockets ; never bore false-
    witness ;
And never, with that all-commanding
    wealth,
Coveted his neighbour's house, nor ox,
    nor ass !

STRANGER

You knew him then it seems ?

TOWNSMAN

As all men know
The virtues of your hundred-thou-
    sanders ;
They never hide their lights beneath a
    bushel.

STRANGER

Nay, nay, uncharitable Sir ! for often
Doth bounty like a streamlet flow un-
    seen,   60
Freshening and giving life along its
    course.

TOWNSMAN

We track the streamlet by the brighter
    green
And livelier growth it gives ; . . but as
    for this . .
This was a pool that stagnated and
    stunk ;
The rains of heaven engendered nothing
    in it
But slime and foul corruption.

STRANGER

Yet even these
Are reservoirs whence public charity
Still keeps her channels full.

TOWNSMAN

Now, Sir, you touch
Upon the point. This man of half a
    million
Had all these public virtues which you
    praise :   70
But the poor man rung never at his
    door,
And the old beggar, at the public gate,
Who, all the summer long, stands hat in
    hand,
He knew how vain it was to lift an eye
To that hard face.   Yet he was always
    found
Among your ten and twenty pound
    subscribers,
Your benefactors in the newspapers.
His alms were money put to interest
In the other world, . . donations to keep
    open

A running charity account with heaven, . .   80
Retaining fees against the Last Assizes,
When, for the trusted talents, strict account
Shall be required from all, and the old Arch-Lawyer
Plead his own cause as plaintiff.

STRANGER

I must needs Believe you, Sir : . . these are your witnesses,
These mourners here, who from their carriages
Gape at the gaping crowd. A good March wind
Were to be pray'd for now, to lend their eyes
Some decent rheum ; the very hireling mute
Bears not a face more blank of all emotion   90
Than the old servant of the family !
How can this man have lived, that thus his death
Costs not the soiling one white handkerchief !

TOWNSMAN

Who should lament for him, Sir, in whose heart
Love had no place, nor natural charity ?
The parlour spaniel, when she heard his step,
Rose slowly from the hearth, and stole aside
With creeping pace ; she never raised her eyes
To woo kind words from him, nor laid her head
Upraised upon his knee, with fondling whine.   100
How could it be but thus ? Arithmetic

Was the sole science he was ever taught ;
The multiplication-table was his Creed,
His Pater-noster, and his Decalogue.
When yet he was a boy, and should have breathed
The open air and sunshine of the fields,
To give his blood its natural spring and play,
He in a close and dusky counting-house
Smoke-dried and sear'd and shrivell'd up his heart.
So from the way in which he was train'd up   110
His feet departed not ; he toil'd and moil'd,
Poor muck-worm ! through his three-score years and ten ;
And when the earth shall now be shovell'd on him,
If that which served him for a soul were still
Within its husk, 'twould still be dirt to dirt.

STRANGER

Yet your next newspapers will blazon him
For industry and honourable wealth
A bright example.

TOWNSMAN

Even half a million
Gets him no other praise. But come this way
Some twelve months hence, and you will find his virtues   120
Trimly set forth in lapidary lines,
Faith with her torch beside, and little Cupids
Dropping upon his urn their marble tears.

Bristol 1803.

THE DEVIL'S WALK

ADVERTISEMENT

AFTER the Devil's Thoughts had been published by Mr. Coleridge in the collection of his Poetical Works, and the statement with which he accompanied it, it might have been supposed that the joint authorship of that Siamese production had been sufficiently authenticated, and that no supposititious claim to it would again be advanced. The following extract, however, appeared in the *John Bull* of Feb. 14, 1830 :—

' In the *Morning Post* of Tuesday, we find the following letter :—

' " *To the Editor of the Morning Post.*

' " SIR,—Permit me to correct a statement which appeared in a recent number of the *John Bull*, wherein it is made to appear that Dr. Southey is the author of the Poem entitled *The Devil's Walk*. I have the means of settling this question ; since I possess the identical MS. copy of verses, as they were written by my uncle, the late Professor Porson, during an evening party at Dr. Beloe's.

' " I am Sir, your very obedient Servant,
' " R. C. PORSON.
' " *Bayswater Terrace*, Feb. 6, 1830."

' We are quite sure that Mr. Porson, the writer of the above letter, is convinced of the truth of the statement it contains ; but although *The Devil's Walk* is perhaps not a work of which either Mr. Southey or Mr. Porson need be very proud, we feel it due to ourselves to re-state the fact of its being from the pen of Mr. Southey. If we are wrong, Mr. Porson may apply to Mr. Southey ; for although Mr. Porson's eminent uncle is dead, the Poet Laureate is alive and merry.

' The Lines—Poem they can scarcely be called—were written by Mr. Southey, one morning before breakfast, the idea having struck him while he was shaving ; they were subsequently shown to Mr. Coleridge, who, we believe, pointed some of the stanzas, and perhaps added one or two.

' We beg to assure Mr. R. C. Porson that we recur to this matter out of no disrespect either to the memory of his uncle, which is not likely to be affected one way or another by the circumstance ; or to his own veracity, being, as we said, quite assured that he believes the statement he makes : our only object is to set ourselves right.'

⸱   ⸱   ⸱   ⸱   ⸱

' Our readers, perhaps, may smile at the following, which appears in yesterday's *Court Journal :*—

' " We have received a letter, signed ' W. Marshall,' and dated ' York ' ; claiming for its writer the long-contested authorship of those celebrated verses, which are known by the title of *The Devil's Walk on Earth,* and to which attention has lately been directed anew, by Lord Byron's imitation of them. There have been so many mystifications connected with the authorship of these clever verses, that, for any thing we know to the contrary, this letter may be only one more." '

⸱   ⸱   ⸱   ⸱   ⸱

A week afterwards there was the following notice :—' We cannot waste any more time about *The Devil's Walk.* We happen to *know* that it is Mr. Southey's ; but, as he is alive, we refer any body, who is not yet satisfied, to the eminent person himself— we do not mean the Devil—but the Doctor.'

The same newspaper contained the ensuing advertisement :—' On Tuesday next, uniform with Robert Cruikshank's Monsieur Tonson, price one shilling : The Devil's Walk, a Poem, by Professor Porson. With additions and variations by Southey and Coleridge ; illustrated by seven engravings from R. Cruikshank. London, Marsh and Miller, 137 Oxford Street ; and Constable and Co., Edinburgh.'

Professor Porson never had any part in these verses as a *writer*, and it is for the first time that he now appears in them as the *subject* of two or three stanzas written some few years ago, when the fabricated story of his having composed them during an evening party at Dr. Vincent's (for that was the original *habitat* of this falsehood) was revived. A friend of one of the authors, more jealous for him than he has ever been for himself, urged him then to put the matter out of doubt (for it was before Mr. Coleridge had done so) ; and as much to please that friend, as to amuse himself and his domestic circle, in a sportive mood, the part which relates the rise and progress of the Poem was thrown off, and that also touching the aforesaid Professor. The old vein having thus been opened, some other passages were added ; and so it grew to its present length.

THE DEVIL'S WALK

[First printed in *The Morning Post*, September 6, 1799. See Notes.]

1

FROM his brimstone bed at break of day
A walking the Devil is gone,
To look at his little snug farm of the World,
And see how his stock went on.

2

Over the hill and over the dale,
And he went over the plain ;
And backward and forward he swish'd his tail,
As a gentleman swishes a cane.

3

How then was the Devil drest ?
Oh, he was in his Sunday's best,   10
His coat was red and his breeches were blue,
And there was a hole where his tail came through.

4

A lady drove by in her pride,
In whose face an expression he spied
For which he could have kiss'd her ;
Such a flourishing, fine, clever creature was she,
With an eye as wicked as wicked can be,
I should take her for my Aunt, thought he,
If my dam had had a sister.

5

He met a lord of high degree,   20
No matter what was his name ;
Whose face with his own when he came to compare
The expression, the look, and the air,
And the character too, as it seem'd to a hair,—
Such a twin-likeness there was in the pair
That it made the Devil start and stare,
For he thought there was surely a looking-glass there,
But he could not see the frame.

6

He saw a Lawyer killing a viper
On a dunghill beside his stable ;   30
Ho ! quoth he, thou put'st me in mind
Of the story of Cain and Abel.

7

An Apothecary on a white horse
Rode by on his vocation ;
And the Devil thought of his old friend
Death in the Revelation.

8

He pass'd a cottage with a double coach-house,
A cottage of gentility !
And he own'd with a grin
That his favourite sin   40
Is pride that apes humility.

9

He saw a pig rapidly
    Down a river float;
The pig swam well, but every stroke
    Was cutting his own throat;

10

And Satan gave thereat his tail
    A twirl of admiration;
For he thought of his daughter War
    And her suckling babe Taxation.

11

Well enough, in sooth, he liked that
        truth,   50
    And nothing the worse for the jest;
But this was only a first thought
    And in this he did not rest:
Another came presently into his head,
And here it proved, as has often been
        said,
    That second thoughts are best.

12

For as Piggy plied with wind and tide,
    His way with such celerity,
And at every stroke the water dyed
With his own red blood, the Devil cried,
    Behold a swinish nation's pride   61
    In cotton-spun prosperity.

13

He walk'd into London leisurely,
    The streets were dirty and dim:
But there he saw Brothers the Prophet,
    And Brothers the Prophet saw him.[1]

14

He entered a thriving bookseller's shop;
    Quoth he, We are both of one college,
For I myself sate like a Cormorant once
    Upon the Tree of Knowledge.   70

15

As he passed through Cold-Bath Fields
        he look'd
    At a solitary cell;
And he was well-pleased, for it gave him
        a hint
    For improving the prisons of Hell.

[1] ' After this I was in a vision, having the
angel of God near me, and saw Satan walking leisurely into London.'—Brothers' Prophecies, part i, p. 41.

16

He saw a turnkey tie a thief's hands
    With a cordial tug and jerk;
Nimbly, quoth he, a man's fingers move
    When his heart is in his work.

17

He saw the same turnkey unfettering a
        man
    With little expedition;   80
And he chuckled to think of his dear
        slave trade,
And the long debates and delays that
        were made
    Concerning its abolition.

18

He met one of his favourite daughters
    By an Evangelical Meeting;
And forgetting himself for joy at her
        sight,
He would have accosted her outright,
    And given her a fatherly greeting.

19

But she tipt him a wink, drew back, and
        cried,
    Avaunt! my name's Religion!   90
And then she turn'd to the preacher
    And leer'd like a love-sick pigeon.

20

A fine man and a famous Professor was
        he,
As the great Alexander now may be,
    Whose fame not yet o'erpast is;
Or that new Scotch performer
Who is fiercer and warmer,
    The great Sir Arch-Bombastes.

21

With throbs and throes, and ahs and ohs,
    Far famed his flock for frightening;
And thundering with his voice, the
        while   101
    His eyes zigzag like lightning.

22

This Scotch phenomenon, I trow,
    Beats Alexander hollow;
Even when most tame
He breathes more flame
    Than ten Fire-Kings could swallow.

23

Another daughter he presently met :
  With music of fife and drum,
  And a consecrated flag,   110
  And shout of tag and rag,
  And march of rank and file,
Which had fill'd the crowded aisle
  Of the venerable pile,
From church he saw her come.

24

He call'd her aside, and began to chide,
  For what dost thou here ? said he ;
My city of Rome is thy proper home,
  And there's work enough there for
    thee.

25

  Thou hast confessions to listen,
    And bells to christen,   121
And altars and dolls to dress ;
    And fools to coax,
    And sinners to hoax,
And beads and bones to bless ;
    And great pardons to sell
    For those who pay well,
And small ones for those who pay less.

26

Nay, Father, I boast, that this is my
    post,
  She answered ; and thou wilt allow,
    That the great Harlot,   131
    Who is clothed in scarlet,
  Can very well spare me now.

27

Upon her business I am come here,
  That we may extend her powers ;
Whatever lets down this church that
    we hate,
  Is something in favour of ours.

28

You will not think, great Cosmocrat !
  That I spend my time in fooling ;
Many irons, my Sire, have we in the fire,
  And I must leave none of them
    cooling ;   141
For you must know state-councils here
  Are held which I bear rule in.

When my liberal notions
Produce mischievous motions,
There's many a man of good intent,
In either house of Parliament,
  Whom I shall find a tool in ;
And I have hopeful pupils too
  Who all this while are schooling.

29

Fine progress they make in our liberal
    opinions,   151
  My Utilitarians,
My all sorts of —inians
  And all sorts of —arians ;
  My all sorts of —ists,
And my Prigs and my Whigs
  Who have all sorts of twists
Train'd in the very way, I know,
Father, you would have them go ;
    High and low,   160
  Wise and foolish, great and small.
  March-of-Intellect-Boys all.

30

Well pleased wilt thou be at no very far
    day
  When the caldron of mischief boils,
  And I bring them forth in battle array
  And bid them suspend their broils,
That they may unite and fall on the
    prey,
    For which we are spreading our
      toils.
How the nice boys all will give mouth
    at the call,
  Hark away ! hark away to the
    spoils !   170
My Macs and my Quacks and my law-
    less-Jacks,
My Sheils and O'Connells, my pious
    Mac-Donnells,
  My joke-smith Sydney, and all of his
    kidney,
    My Humes and my Broughams,
      My merry old Jerry,
  My Lord Kings, and my Doctor
    Doyles !

31

At this good news, so great
  The Devil's pleasure grew,
That with a joyful swish he rent
  The hole where his tail came through.

32

His countenance fell for a moment   181
    When he felt the stitches go ;
Ah ! thought he, there's a job now
    That I've made for my tailor below.

33

Great news ! bloody news ! cried a news
    man ;
The Devil said, Stop, let me see !
Great news ? bloody news ? thought
    the Devil,
    The bloodier the better for me.

34

So he bought the newspaper, and no
    news
    At all for his money he had.   190
Lying varlet, thought he, thus to take in
    old Nick !
But it's some satisfaction, my lad,
To know thou art paid beforehand for
    the trick,
    For the sixpence I gave thee is bad.

35

And then it came into his head
    By oracular inspiration,
That what he had seen and what he had
    said,
    In the course of this visitation,
Would be published in the Morning Post
    For all this reading nation.   200

36

Therewith in second-sight he saw
    The place and the manner and time,
In which this mortal story
    Would be put in immortal rhyme.

37

That it would happen when two poets
    Should on a time be met,
In the town of Nether Stowey,
    In the shire of Somerset :

38

There while the one was shaving
    Would he the song begin ;   210
And the other when he heard it at
    breakfast,
    In ready accord join in.

39

So each would help the other
    Two heads being better than one ;
    And the phrase and conceit
    Would in unison meet,
And so with glee the verse flow free,
    In ding-dong chime of sing-song
    rhyme,
    Till the whole were merrily done.

40

And because it was set to the razor,
    Not to the lute or harp,   221
    Therefore it was that the fancy
Should be bright, and the wit be sharp.

41

But then, said Satan to himself,
    As for that said beginner,
Against my infernal Majesty
    There is no greater sinner.

42

He hath put me in ugly ballads
    With libellous pictures for sale ;
He hath scoff'd at my hoofs and my
    horns,   230
    And has made very free with my tail.

43

But this Mister Poet shall find
    I am not a safe subject for whim ;
For I'll set up a School of my own,
    And my Poets shall set upon him.

44

He went to a coffee-house to dine,
    And there he had soy in his dish ;
Having ordered some soles for his
    dinner,
    Because he was fond of flat fish.

45

They are much to my palate, thought
    he,   240
And now guess the reason who can,
Why no bait should be better than
    place,
    When I fish for a Parliament-man.

46

But the soles in the bill were ten shillings ;
    Tell your master, quoth he, what I
    say :
If he charges at this rate for all things,
    He must be in a pretty good way.

47

But mark ye, said he to the waiter,
    I'm a dealer myself in this line,
And his business, between you and me,
    Nothing like so extensive as mine. 251

48

Now soles are exceedingly cheap ;
    Which he will not attempt to deny,
When I see him at my fish-market,
    I warrant him, by and by.

49

As he went along the Strand
    Between three in the morning and
    four
He observed a queer-looking person
    Who stagger'd from Perry's door.

50

And he thought that all the world over
    In vain for a man you might seek, 261
Who could drink more like a Trojan
    Or talk more like a Greek.

51

The Devil then he prophesied
    It would one day be matter of talk,
    That with wine when smitten,
And with wit moreover being happily
    bitten,
This erudite bibber was he who had
    written
    The story of this walk.

52

A pretty mistake, quoth the Devil ;
    A pretty mistake I opine !   271
I have put many ill thoughts in his
    mouth,
    He will never put good ones in mine.

53

And whoever shall say that to Porson
    These best of all verses belong,
He is an untruth-telling whoreson,
    And so shall be call'd in the song

54

And if seeking an illicit connection with
    fame,
    Any one else should put in a claim,
    In this comical competition ;   280
That excellent poem will prove
    A man-trap for such foolish ambi-
    tion,
Where the silly rogue shall be caught by
    the leg,
    And exposed in a second edition.

55

Now the morning air was cold for
    him
Who was used to a warm abode ;
And yet he did not immediately wish
    To set out on his homeward road.

56

For he had some morning calls to
    make
    Before he went back to Hell ;   290
So, thought he, I'll step into a gaming-
    house,
    And that will do as well ;
But just before he could get to the
    door
    A wonderful chance befell.

57

For all on a sudden, in a dark place,
He came upon General ———'s burning
    face ;
    And it struck him with such conster-
    nation,
That home in a hurry his way did he
    take,
Because he thought by a slight mis-
    take
    'Twas the general conflagration.   300

INSCRIPTIONS

'The three utilities of Poetry: the praise of Virtue and Goodness, the memory of things remarkable, and to invigorate the Affections.'—*Welsh Triad.*

[As five of the inscriptions have been inserted among the Selected Minor Poems, it has been necessary in some instances to alter the numbering of those here printed. Where this has been done, a number in brackets ( ) at the head of an inscription denotes its number in the edition of 1837–1838.

Inscriptions I–VI inclusive were published in *Poems*, 1797. I, II, and III have been almost rewritten.]

I
FOR A COLUMN AT NEWBURY

CALLEST thou thyself a Patriot? . . On this field
Did Falkland fall, the blameless and the brave,
Beneath the banners of that Charles whom thou
Abhorrest for a Tyrant. Dost thou boast
Of loyalty? The field is not far off
Where in rebellious arms against his King
Hambden was kill'd, that Hambden at whose name
The heart of many an honest Englishman
Beats with congenial pride. Both uncorrupt,
Friends to their common country both, they fought,   10
They died in adverse armies. Traveller !
If with thy neighbour thou shouldst not accord,
Remember these, our famous countrymen,
And quell all angry and injurious thoughts.

Bristol, 1796.

II
FOR A CAVERN THAT OVERLOOKS THE RIVER AVON

ENTER this cavern, Stranger! Here awhile
Respiring from the long and steep ascent,
Thou may'st be glad of rest, and haply too
Of shade, if from the summer's westering sun
Shelter'd beneath this beetling vault of rock.
Round the rude portal clasping its rough arms
The antique ivy spreads a canopy,
From whose grey blossoms the wild bees collect
In autumn their last store. The Muses love   9
This spot; believe a Poet who hath felt
Their visitation here. The tide below
Rising or refluent scarcely sends its sound
Of waters up; and from the heights beyond
Where the high-hanging forest waves and sways,
Varying before the wind its verdant hues,
The voice is music here. Here thou may'st feel
How good, how lovely, Nature! And when hence
Returning to the city's crowded streets,
Thy sickening eye at every step revolts
From scenes of vice and wretchedness, reflect   20
That Man creates the evil he endures.

Bristol, 1796.

III

FOR A TABLET AT SILBURY-HILL

THIS mound in some remote and date-
    less day
Rear'd o'er a Chieftain of the Age of
    Hills,
May here detain thee, Traveller! from
    thy road
Not idly lingering. In his narrow house
Some warrior sleeps below, whose gal-
    lant deeds
Haply at many a solemn festival
The Scald hath sung; but perish'd is
    the song
Of praise, as o'er these bleak and barren
    downs
The wind that passes and is heard no
    more.
Go, Traveller, and remember when the
    pomp   10
Of earthly Glory fades, that one good
    deed,
Unseen, unheard, unnoted by mankind,
Lives in the eternal register of Heaven.

Bristol, 1796.

IV

FOR A MONUMENT IN THE NEW FOREST

THIS is the place where William's kingly
    power
Did from their poor and peaceful homes
    expel,
Unfriended, desolate, and shelterless,
The habitants of all the fertile track
Far as these wilds extend. He levell'd
    down
Their little cottages, he bade their
    fields
Lie waste, and forested the land, that so
More royally might he pursue his
    sports.
If that thine heart be human, Pas-
    senger!
Sure it will swell within thee, and thy
    lips   10

Will mutter curses on him. Think thou
    then
What cities flame, what hosts unsepul-
    chred
Pollute the passing wind, when raging
    Power
Drives on his blood-hounds to the chase
    of Man;
And as thy thoughts anticipate that
    day
When God shall judge aright, in charity
Pray for the wicked rulers of mankind.

Bristol, 1796.

V

FOR A TABLET ON THE BANKS OF A STREAM

STRANGER! awhile upon this mossy
    bank
Recline thee. If the Sun rides high, the
    breeze,
That loves to ripple o'er the rivulet,
Will play around thy brow, and the
    cool sound
Of running waters soothe thee. Mark
    how clear
They sparkle o'er the shallows, and
    behold
Where o'er their surface wheels with
    restless speed
Yon glossy insect, on the sand below
How its swift shadow flits. In solitude
The rivulet is pure, and trees and
    herbs   10
Bend o'er its salutary course refresh'd,
But passing on amid the haunts of
    men,
It finds pollution there, and rolls from
    thence
A tainted stream. Seek'st thou for
    HAPPINESS?
Go, Stranger, sojourn in the woodland
    cot
Of INNOCENCE, and thou shalt find her
    there.

Bristol, 1796.

VI

FOR THE CENOTAPH AT ERMENONVILLE

STRANGER! the MAN of NATURE lies
    not here :
Enshrin'd far distant by the Scoffer's[1]
    side
His relics rest, there by the giddy throng
With blind idolatry alike revered.
Wiselier directed have thy pilgrim feet
Explored the scenes of Ermenonville.
    ROUSSEAU
Loved these calm haunts of Solitude and
    Peace ;
Here he has heard the murmurs of the
    lake,
And the soft rustling of the poplar grove,
When o'er its bending boughs the pass-
    ing wind   10
Swept a grey shade.   Here, if thy breast
    be full,
If in thine eye the tear devout should
    gush,
His SPIRIT shall behold thee, to thine
    home
From hence returning, purified of heart.

Bristol, 1796.

VII

FOR A MONUMENT AT OXFORD

[First published in *The Oracle*, afterwards
in *The Annual Anthology*, 1799, and in
Metrical Tales, 1805.]

HERE Latimer and Ridley in the flames
Bore witness to the truth.   If thou hast
    walk'd
Uprightly through the world, just
    thoughts of joy
May fill thy breast in contemplating
    here
Congenial virtue.   But if thou hast
    swerved
From the straight path of even rectitude,
Fearful in trying seasons to assert
The better cause, or to forsake the
    worse

[1] Voltaire.

Reluctant, when perchance therein en-
    thrall'd
Slave to false shame, oh ! thankfully
    receive   10
The sharp compunctious motions that
    this spot
May wake within thee, and be wise in
    time,
And let the future for the past atone.

Bath, 1797.

VIII

FOR A MONUMENT IN THE VALE OF EWIAS

[First published in *The Morning Post*,
December 21, 1798 ; afterwards in *The
Annual Anthology*, 1799, and in *Metrical
Tales*, 1805.]

HERE was it, Stranger, that the patron
    Saint
Of Cambria pass'd his age of penitence,
A solitary man ; and here he made
His hermitage, the roots his food, his
    drink
Of Hodney's mountain stream.   Per-
    chance thy youth
Has read with eager wonder how the
    Knight
Of Wales in Ormandine's enchanted
    bower
Slept the long sleep : and if that in thy
    veins
Flow the pure blood of Britain, sure that
    blood
Hath flow'd with quicker impulse at the
    tale   10
Of David's deeds, when through the
    press of war
His gallant comrades follow'd his green
    crest
To victory. Stranger! Hatterill's moun-
    tain heights
And this fair vale of Ewias, and the
    stream
Of Hodney, to thine after-thoughts will
    rise
More grateful, thus associate with the
    name
Of David and the deeds of other days.

Bath, 1798.

IX

EPITAPH ON ALGERNON SIDNEY

[First published in *The Morning Post*, December 25, 1798 ; afterwards in *Metrical Tales*, 1805.]

HERE Sidney lies, he whom perverted law,
The pliant jury and the bloody judge,
Doom'd to a traitor's death. A tyrant
King
Required, an abject country saw and
shared
The crime. The noble cause of Liberty
He loved in life, and to that noble cause
In death bore witness. But his country
rose
Like Samson from her sleep, and broke
her chains,
And proudly with her worthies she en-
roll'd
Her murder'd Sidney's name. The
voice of man   10
Gives honour or destroys ; but earthly
power
Gives not, nor takes away, the self-
applause
Which on the scaffold suffering virtue
feels,
Nor that which God appointed its
reward.

Westbury, 1798.

X

EPITAPH ON KING JOHN

[First published in *The Morning Post*, May 28, 1798 ; afterwards in *The Annual Anthology*, 1799, and in *Metrical Tales*, 1805.]

JOHN rests below. A man more in-
famous
Never hath held the sceptre of these
realms,
And bruised beneath the iron rod of
Power
The oppressed men of England. Eng-
lishman !

Curse not his memory. Murderer as he
was,
Coward and slave, yet he it was who
sign'd
That Charter which should make thee
morn and night
Be thankful for thy birth-place : . .
Englishman !
That holy Charter, which, shouldst thou
permit
Force to destroy, or Fraud to under-
mine,   ■■
Thy children's groans will persecute thy
soul,
For they must bear the burthen of thy
crime.

Westbury, 1798.

XI (XII)

FOR A MONUMENT AT
TORDESILLAS

[Published in *Letters from Spain and Portugal*, 1797.]

SPANIARD ! if thou art one who bows
the knee
Before a despot's footstool, hie thee
hence !
This ground is holy : here Padilla died,
Martyr of Freedom. But if thou dost
love
Her cause, stand then as at an altar
here,
And thank the Almighty that thine
honest heart,
Full of a brother's feelings for mankind,
Revolts against oppression. Not un-
heard
Nor unavailing shall the grateful prayer
Ascend ; for honest impulses will rise, 10
Such as may elevate and strengthen
thee
For virtuous action. Relics silver-
shrined,
And chaunted mass, would wake within
the soul
Thoughts valueless and cold compared
with these.

Bristol, 1796.

XII (XIII)

FOR A COLUMN AT TRUXILLO

[Published in *Letters from Spain and Portugal*, 1797.]

PIZARRO here was born ; a greater name
The list of Glory boasts not. Toil and
    Pain,
Famine and hostile Elements, and
    Hosts
Embattled, fail'd to check him in his
    course,
Not to be wearied, not to be deterr'd,
Not to be overcome. A mighty realm
He over-ran, and with relentless arm
Slew or enslaved its unoffending sons,
And wealth, and power, and fame, were
    his rewards.
There is another world, beyond the
    Grave,   10
According to their deeds where men are
    judged.
O Reader ! if thy daily bread be earn'd
By daily labour, . . yea, however low,
However painful be thy lot assign'd,
Thank thou, with deepest gratitude, the
    God
Who made thee, that thou art not such
    as he.

Bristol, 1796.

XIII (XIV)

FOR THE CELL OF HONORIUS, AT THE CORK CONVENT, NEAR CINTRA

[First published in *The Morning Post*, November 5, 1798.]

HERE cavern'd like a beast Honorius
    pass'd
In self-affliction, solitude, and prayer,
Long years of penance. He had rooted
    out
All human feelings from his heart, and
    fled
With fear and loathing from all human
    joys.
Not thus in making known his will
    divine

Hath Christ enjoin'd. To aid the father-
    less,
Comfort the sick, and be the poor man's
    friend,
And in the wounded heart pour gospel-
    balm ;
These are the injunctions of his holy
    law,   10
Which whoso keeps shall have a joy on
    earth,
Calm, constant, still increasing, pre-
    luding
The eternal bliss of Heaven. Yet mock
    not thou,
Stranger, the Anchorite's mistaken zeal !
He painfully his painful duties kept,
Sincere though erring : Stranger, do
    thou keep
Thy better and thine easier rule as well.

Bristol, 1798.

XIV (XV)

FOR A MONUMENT AT TAUNTON

[First published in *The Morning Post*, July 6, 1799; afterwards in *The Annual Anthology*, 1799, and in *Metrical Tales*, 1805.]

THEY suffer'd here whom Jefferies
    doom'd to death
In mockery of all justice, when the
    Judge
Unjust, subservient to a cruel King,
Perform'd his work of blood. They
    suffer'd here
The victims of that Judge, and of that
    King ;
In mockery of all justice here they
    bled,
Unheard. But not unpitied, nor of
    God
Unseen, the innocent suffered ; not un-
    heard
The innocent blood cried vengeance ;
    for at length,
The indignant Nation in its power
    arose,   10
Resistless. Then that wicked Judge
    took flight,
Disguised in vain : . . not always is the
    Lord

Slow to revenge ! A miserable man
He fell beneath the people's rage, and
still
The children curse his memory. From
the throne
The obdurate bigot who commission'd
him,
Inhuman James, was driven. He lived
to drag
Long years of frustrate hope, he lived
to load
More blood upon his soul. Let tell the
Boyne,
Let Londonderry tell his guilt and
shame ;   20
And that immortal day when on thy
shores,
La Hogue, the purple ocean dash'd the
dead !

Westbury, 1798.

XV (XVI)

FOR A TABLET AT PENSHURST

[First published in *The Morning Post*,
December 7, 1798 ; afterwards in *The
Annual Anthology*, 1799, and in *Metrical
Tales*, 1805.]

ARE days of old familiar to thy mind,
O Reader ? Hast thou let the midnight
hour
Pass unperceived, whilst thou in fancy
lived
With high-born beauties and enamour'd
chiefs,
Sharing their hopes, and with a breath-
less joy
Whose expectation touch'd the verge of
pain,
Following their dangerous fortunes ? If
such lore
Hath ever thrill'd thy bosom, thou wilt
tread,
As with a pilgrim's reverential thoughts,
The groves of Penshurst. Sidney here
was born,   10
Sidney, than whom no gentler, braver
man
His own delightful genius ever feign'd,
Illustrating the vales of Arcady

With courteous courage and with loyal
loves.
Upon his natal day an acorn here
Was planted : it grew up a stately oak,
And in the beauty of its strength it
stood
And flourish'd, when his perishable part
Had moulder'd, dust to dust. That
stately oak
Itself hath moulder'd now, but Sidney's
fame   20
Endureth in his own immortal works.

Westbury, 1799.

XVI (XVII)

EPITAPH

THIS to a mother's sacred memory
Her son hath hallow'd. Absent many
a year
Far over sea, his sweetest dreams were
still
Of that dear voice which soothed his
infancy ;
And after many a fight against the Moor
And Malabar, or that fierce cavalry
Which he had seen covering the bound-
less plain,
Even to the utmost limits where the eye
Could pierce the far horizon, . . his first
thought
In safety was of her, who when she
heard   10
The tale of that day's danger, would
retire
And pour her pious gratitude to Heaven
In prayers and tears of joy. The lin-
gering hour
Of his return, long-look'd-for, came at
length,
And full of hope he reach'd his native
shore.
Vain hope that puts its trust in human
life !
For ere he came, the number of her days
Was full. O Reader, what a world
were this,
How unendurable its weight, if they
Whom Death hath sunder'd did not
meet again !   20

Keswick, 1810.

XVII (XIX)

FOR A MONUMENT AT ROLISSA

TIME has been when Rolissa was a
  name
Ignoble, by the passing traveller heard
And then forthwith forgotten ; now in
  war
It is renown'd.   For when to her
  ally,
In bondage by perfidious France op-
  press'd
England sent succour, first within this
  realm
The fated theatre of their long strife
Confronted, here the hostile nations
  met.
Laborde took here his stand ; upon yon
  point
Of Mount Saint Anna was his Eagle
  fix'd ;   10
The veteran chief, disposing well all
  aid
Of height and glen, possess'd the moun-
  tain straits,
A post whose strength thus mann'd and
  profited
Seem'd to defy the enemy and make
The vantage of assailing numbers
  vain.
Here, too, before the sun should bend
  his course
Adown the slope of heaven, so had their
  plans
Been timed, he look'd for Loison's army,
  rich
With spoils from Evora and Beja
  sack'd.
That hope the British Knight areeding
  well,   20
With prompt attack prevented ; and
  nor strength
Of ground, nor leader's skill nor
  discipline
Of soldiers practised in the ways of
  war,
Avail'd that day against the British
  arm.

Resisting long, but beaten from their
  stand,
The French fell back ; they join'd their
  greater host
To suffer fresh defeat, and Portugal
First for Sir Arthur wreathed her
  laurels here.

XVIII (XX)

FOR A MONUMENT AT VIMEIRO

THIS is Vimeiro ; yonder stream which
  flows
Westward through heathery highlands
  to the sea,
Is call'd Maceira, till of late a name,
Save to the dwellers of this peaceful
  vale,
Known only to the coasting mariner ;
Now in the bloody page of war in-
  scribed.
When to the aid of injured Portugal
Struggling against the intolerable yoke
Of treacherous France, England, her old
  ally,
Long tried and always faithful found,
  went forth,   10
The embattled hosts in equal strength
  array'd,
And equal discipline, encountered here.
Junot, the mock Abrantes, led the
  French,
And confident of skill so oft approved,
And vaunting many a victory, advanced
Against an untried foe.   But when the
  ranks
Met in the shock of battle, man to
  man,
And bayonet to bayonet opposed,
The flower of France, cut down along
  their line,
Fell like ripe grass before the mower's
  scythe,   20
For the strong arm and rightful cause
  prevail'd.
That day deliver'd Lisbon from the
  yoke,
And babes were taught to bless Sir
  Arthur's name.

XIX (XXI)
AT CORUÑA

WHEN from these shores the British
⠀⠀army first
Boldly advanced into the heart of Spain,
The admiring people who beheld its
⠀⠀march
Call'd it ' the Beautiful '. And surely
⠀⠀well
Its proud array, its perfect discipline,
Its ample furniture of war complete,
Its powerful horse, its men of British
⠀⠀mould,
All high in heart and hope, all of them-
⠀⠀selves
Assured, and in their leaders confident,
Deserved the title. Few short weeks
⠀⠀elapsed⠀⠀⠀⠀⠀⠀⠀⠀⠀⠀⠀⠀⠀⠀10
Ere hither that disastrous host return'd,
A fourth of all its gallant force con-
⠀⠀sumed
In hasty and precipitate retreat,
Stores, treasure, and artillery, in the
⠀⠀wreck
Left to the fierce pursuer, horse and man
Founder'd, and stiffening on the moun-
⠀⠀tain snows.
But when the exulting enemy ap-
⠀⠀proach'd
Boasting that he would drive into the
⠀⠀sea
The remnant of the wretched fugitives,
Here, ere they reach'd their ships, they
⠀⠀turn'd at bay.⠀⠀⠀⠀⠀⠀⠀⠀⠀⠀20
Then was the proof of British courage
⠀⠀seen ;
Against a foe far overnumbering them,
An insolent foe, rejoicing in pursuit,
Sure of the fruit of victory, whatso-
⠀⠀e'er
Might be the fate of battle, here they
⠀⠀stood,
And their safe embarkation, . . all they
⠀⠀sought,
Won manfully. That mournful day
⠀⠀avenged
Their sufferings, and redeem'd their
⠀⠀country's name ;
And thus Coruña, which in this retreat
Had seen the else indelible reproach⠀30
Of England, saw the stain effaced in
⠀⠀blood.

XX (XXII)
EPITAPH

HE who in this unconsecrated ground
Obtain'd a soldier's grave, hath left a
⠀⠀name
Which will endure in history : the
⠀⠀remains
Of Moore, the British General, rest below.
His early prowess Corsica beheld,
When, at Mozello, bleeding, through the
⠀⠀breach
He passed victorious ; the Columbian
⠀⠀isles
Then saw him tried ; upon the sandy
⠀⠀downs
Of Holland was his riper worth approved;
And leaving on the Egyptian shores his
⠀⠀blood,⠀⠀⠀⠀⠀⠀⠀⠀⠀⠀⠀⠀⠀⠀10
He gathered there fresh palms. High
⠀⠀in repute
A gallant army last he led to Spain,
In arduous times ; for moving in his
⠀⠀strength,
With all his mighty means of war com-
⠀⠀plete,
The Tyrant Buonaparte bore down all
Before him ; and the British Chief be-
⠀⠀held,
Where'er he look'd, rout, treason, and
⠀⠀dismay,
All sides with all embarrassments beset,
And danger pressing on. Hither he
⠀⠀came
Before the far out-numbering hosts of
⠀⠀France⠀⠀⠀⠀⠀⠀⠀⠀⠀⠀⠀⠀⠀20
Retreating to her ships, and close pur-
⠀⠀sued ;
Nor were there wanting men who coun-
⠀⠀sell'd him
To offer terms, and from the enemy
Purchase a respite to embark in peace,
At price of such abasement, . . even to
⠀⠀this,
Brave as they were, by hopelessness
⠀⠀subdued.
That shameful counsel Moore, in happy
⠀⠀hour
Remembering what was due to Eng-
⠀⠀land's name,
Refused : he fought, he conquer'd, and
⠀⠀he fell.

XXI (XXIII)

TO THE MEMORY OF PAUL BURRARD

MORTALLY WOUNDED IN THE BATTLE OF CORUÑA

[Published in *The Literary Souvenir* for 1826.]

MYSTERIOUS are the ways of Providence !—
Old men who have grown grey in camps, and wish'd,
And pray'd, and sought in battle to lay down
The burthen of their age, have seen the young
Fall round, themselves untouch'd ; and balls beside
The graceless and the unblest head have pass'd,
Harmless as hail, to reach some precious life,
For which clasp'd hands, and supplicating eyes,
Duly at morn and eve were raised to Heaven ;
And, in the depth and loneness of the soul   10
(Then boding all too truly), midnight prayers
Breathed from an anxious pillow wet with tears.
But blessed, even amid their grief, are they
Who, in the hour of visitation, bow
Beneath the unerring will, and look toward
Their Heavenly Father, merciful as just !
They, while they own his goodness, feel that whom
He chastens, them he loves. The cup he gives,
Shall they not drink it ? Therefore doth the draught
Resent of comfort in its bitterness,   20
And carry healing with it. What but this

Could have sustain'd the mourners who were left,
With life-long yearnings, to remember him
Whose early death this monumental verse
Records ? For never more auspicious hopes
Were nipt in flower, nor finer qualities
From goodliest fabric of mortality
Divorced, nor virtues worthier to adorn
The world transferr'd to heaven, than when, ere time
Had measured him the space of nineteen years,   30
Paul Burrard on Coruña's fatal field
Received his mortal hurt. Not unprepared
The heroic youth was found : for in the ways
Of piety had he been trained ; and what
The dutiful child upon his mother's knees
Had learnt, the soldier faithfully observed.
In chamber or in tent, the Book of God
Was his beloved manual ; and his life
Beseem'd the lessons which from thence he drew.
For, gallant as he was, and blithe of heart,   40
Expert of hand, and keen of eye, and prompt
In intellect, religion was the crown
Of all his noble properties. When Paul
Was by, the scoffer, self-abased, restrain'd
The license of his speech ; and ribaldry
Before his virtuous presence sate rebuked.
And yet so frank and affable a form
His virtue wore, that wheresoe'er he moved
A sunshine of good-will and cheerfulness
Enliven'd all around. Oh ! marvel not,   50
If, in the morning of his fair career,
Which promised all that honour could bestow
On high desert, the youth was summon'd hence !

His soul required no farther discipline,
Pure as it was, and capable of Heaven.
Upon the spot from whence he just had
seen
His General borne away, the appointed
ball
Reach'd him. But not on that Galli-
cian ground
Was it his fate, like many a British
heart,
To mingle with the soil: the sea re-
ceived "
His mortal relics, . . to a watery grave
Consign'd so near his native shore, so
near
His father's house, that they who loved
him best,
Unconscious of its import, heard the
gun
Which fired his knell.—Alas! if it were
known,
When, in the strife of nations, dreadful
Death
Mows down with indiscriminating
sweep
His thousands ten times told, . . if it
were known
What ties are sever'd then, what ripen-
ing hopes
Blasted, what virtues in their bloom cut
off;   70
How far the desolating scourge extends;
How wide the misery spreads; what
hearts beneath
Their grief are broken, or survive to
feel
Always the irremediable loss;
Oh! who of woman born could bear the
thought?
Who but would join with fervent piety
The prayer that asketh in our time for
peace?—
Nor in our time alone!—Enable us,
Father which art in heaven! but to
receive
And keep thy word: thy kingdom then
should come,   80
Thy will be done on earth; the victory
Accomplished over Sin as well as
Death,
And the great scheme of Providence
fulfill'd.

XXII (XXIV)

FOR THE BANKS OF THE DOURO

CROSSING in unexampled enterprise
This great and perilous stream, the
English host
Effected here their landing, on the day
When Soult from Porto with his troops
was driven.
No sight so joyful ever had been seen
From Douro's banks,   not when the
mountains sent
Their generous produce down, or home-
ward fleets
Entered from distant seas their port
desired;
Nor e'er were shouts of such glad
mariners
So gladly heard, as then the cannon's
peal,   10
And short sharp strokes of frequent
musketry,
By the delivered habitants that hour.
For they who beaten then and routed
fled
Before victorious England, in their day
Of triumph, had, like fiends let loose
from hell,
Fill'd yon devoted city with all forms
Of horror, all unutterable crimes;
And vengeance now had reach'd the
inhuman race
Accurst. Oh what a scene did Night
behold
Within those rescued walls, when festal
fires,   20
And torches, blazing through the bloody
streets,
Stream'd their broad light where horse
and man in death
Unheeded lay outstretch'd! Eyes which
had wept
In bitterness so long, shed tears of joy,
And from the broken heart thanksgiving
mix'd
With anguish rose to Heaven. Sir
Arthur then
Might feel how precious in a righteous
cause
Is victory, how divine the soldier's meed,
When grateful nations bless the aveng-
ing sword!

XXIII (XXV)
TALAVERA

FOR THE FIELD OF BATTLE

YON wide-extended town, whose roofs
 and towers
And poplar avenues are seen far off,
In goodly prospect over scatter'd woods
Of dusky ilex, boasts among its sons
Of Mariana's name, . . he who hath
 made
The splendid story of his country's wars
Through all the European kingdoms
 known.
Yet in his ample annals thou canst find
No braver battle chronicled, than here
Was waged, when Joseph of the stolen
 crown   10
Against the hosts of England and of
 Spain
His veteran armies brought. By
 veteran chiefs
Captain'd, a formidable force they came,
Full fifty thousand. Victor led them on,
A man grown grey in arms, nor e'er in
 aught
Dishonoured, till by this opprobrious
 cause.
He over rude Alverche's summer
 stream
Winning his way, made first upon the
 right
His hot attack, where Spain's raw levies,
 ranged
In double line, had taken their strong
 stand   20
In yonder broken ground, by olive
 groves
Cover'd and flank'd by Tagus. Soon
 from thence,
As one whose practised eye could appre-
 hend
All vantages in war, his troops he drew ;
And on this hill, the battle's vital point,
Bore with collected power, outnum-
 bering
The British ranks twice told. Such
 fearful odds
Were balanced by Sir Arthur's master
 mind
And by the British heart. Twice during
 night

The fatal spot they storm'd, and twice
 fell back,   30
Before the bayonet driven. Again at
 morn
They made their fiery onset, and again
Repell'd, again at noon renew'd the
 strife.
Yet was their desperate perseverance
 vain,
Where skill by equal skill was counter-
 vail'd,
And numbers by superior courage foil'd ;
And when the second night drew over
 them
Its sheltering cope, in darkness they
 retired,
At all points beaten. Long in the red
 page
Of war shall Talavera's famous name 40
Stand forth conspicuous. While that
 name endures,
Bear in thy soul, O Spain, the memory
Of all thou sufferedst from perfidious
 France,
Of all that England in thy cause achieved.

XXIV (XXVI)

FOR THE DESERTO DE BUSACO

READER, thou standest upon holy
 ground
Which Penitence hath chosen for itself,
And war disturbing the deep solitude
Hath left it doubly sacred. On these
 heights
The host of Portugal and England stood,
Arrayed against Massena, when the
 chief
Proud of Rodrigo and Almeida won,
Press'd forward, thinking the devoted
 realm
Full sure should fall a prey. He in his
 pride
Scorn'd the poor numbers of the English
 foe,   10
And thought the children of the land
 would fly
From his advance, like sheep before the
 wolf,
Scattering, and lost in terror. Ill he
 knew

The Lusitanian spirit ! Ill he knew
The arm, the heart of England ! Ill he
   knew
Her Wellington ! He learnt to know
   them here.
That spirit and that arm, that heart,
   that mind,
Here on Busaco gloriously display'd,
When hence repulsed the beaten boaster
   wound
Below, his course circuitous, and left 20
His thousands for the beasts and
   ravenous fowl.
The Carmelite who in his cell recluse
Was wont to sit, and from a skull receive
Death's silent lesson, wheresoe'er he
   walk
Henceforth may find his teachers. He
   shall find
The Frenchmen's bones in glen and
   grove, on rock
And height, where'er the wolves and
   carrion birds
Have strewn them, wash'd in torrents,
   bare and bleach'd
By sun and rain and by the winds of
   heaven.

XXV (XXVII)
FOR THE LINES OF TORRES VEDRAS

THROUGH all Iberia, from the Atlantic
   shores
To far Pyrene, Wellington hath left
His trophies ; but no monument records
To after-time a more enduring praise,
Than this which marks his triumph here
   attain'd
By intellect, and patience to the end
Holding through good and ill its course
   assign'd,
The stamp and seal of greatness. Here
   the chief
Perceived in foresight Lisbon's sure
   defence,
A vantage ground for all reverse pre-
   pared,   10
Where Portugal and England might
   defy
All strength of hostile numbers. Not
   for this

Of hostile enterprise did he abate,
Or gallant purpose : witness the proud
   day
Which saw Soult's murderous host from
   Porto driven ;
Bear witness Talavera, made by him
Famous for ever ; and that later fight,
When from Busaco's solitude the birds,
Then first affrighted in their sanctuary,
Fled from the thunders and the fires of
   war.   20
But when Spain's feeble counsels, in
   delay
As erring, as in action premature,
Had left him in the field without sup-
   port,
And Buonaparte, having trampled down
The strength and pride of Austria, this
   way turn'd
His single thought and undivided power,
Retreating hither the great General
   came ;
And proud Massena, when the boastful
   chief
Of plundered Lisbon dreamt, here found
   himself
Stopt suddenly in his presumptuous
   course.   30
From Ericeyra on the western sea,
By Mafra's princely convent, and the
   heights
Of Montichique, and Bucellas famed
For generous vines, the formidable
   works
Extending, rested on the guarded shores
Of Tagus, that rich river who received
Into his ample and rejoicing port
The harvests and the wealth of distant
   lands,
Secure, insulting with the glad display
The robber's greedy sight. Five months
   the foe   40
Beheld these lines, made inexpugnable
By perfect skill, and patriot feelings here
With discipline conjoin'd, courageous
   hands,
True spirits, and one comprehensive
   mind
All overseeing and pervading all.
Five months, tormenting still his heart
   with hope,
He saw his projects frustrated ; the
   power

Of the blaspheming tyrant whom he
served
Fail in the proof ; his thousands disappear,
In silent and inglorious war consumed ;
Till hence retreating, madden'd with
despite,   51
Here did the self-styled Son of Victory
leave,
Never to be redeem'd, that vaunted
name.

XXVI (XXVIII)
AT SANTAREM

FOUR months Massena had his quarters
here,
When by those lines deterr'd where
Wellington
Defied the power of France, but loth to
leave
Rich Lisbon yet unsack'd, he kept his
ground,
Till from impending famine, and the
force
Array'd in front, and that consuming
war
Which still the faithful nation, day and
night,
And at all hours was waging on his rear,
He saw no safety, save in swift retreat.
Then of his purpose frustrated, this
child
Of Hell, . . so fitlier than of Victory
call'd,   11
Gave his own devilish nature scope, and
let
His devilish army loose. The mournful
rolls
That chronicle the guilt of humankind
Tell not of aught more hideous than the
deeds
With which this monster and his kindred
troops
Track'd their inhuman way ; all cruel-
ties,
All forms of horror, all deliberate crimes,
Which tongue abhors to utter, ear to
hear.   19
Let this memorial bear Massena's name
For everlasting infamy inscribed.

XXVII (XXIX)
AT FUENTES D'ONORO

THE fountains of Onoro which give name
To this poor hamlet, were distain'd with
blood,
What time Massena, driven from Por-
tugal
By national virtue in endurance proved,
And England's faithful aid, against the
land
Not long delivered, desperately made
His last fierce effort here. That day,
bestreak'd
With slaughter Coa and Agueda ran,
So deeply had the open veins of war
Purpled their mountain feeders. Strong
in means,   10
With rest, and stores, and numbers rein-
forced,
Came the ferocious enemy, and ween'd
Beneath their formidable cavalry
To trample down resistance. But there
fought
Against them here, with Britons side by
side,
The children of regenerate Portugal,
And their own crimes, and all-beholding
Heaven.
Beaten, and hopeless thenceforth of
success
The inhuman Marshal, never to be
named
By Lusitanian lips without a curse   20
Of clinging infamy, withdrew and left
These Fountains famous for his over-
throw.

XXVIII (XXXI)
FOR A MONUMENT AT ALBUHERA

SEVEN thousand men lay bleeding on
these heights,
When Beresford in strenuous conflict
strove
Against a foe whom all the accidents
Of battle favoured, and who knew full
well
To seize all offers that occasion gave.
Wounded or dead, seven thousand here
were stretch'd,

And on the plain around a myriad
more,
Spaniard and Briton and true Portu-
gueze,
Alike approved that day ; and in the
cause
Of France, with her flagitious sons com-
pell'd,   10
Pole and Italian, German, Hollander,
Men of all climes and countries, hither
brought,
Doing and suffering, for the work of
war.
This point by her superior cavalry
France from the Spaniard won, the
elements
Aiding her powerful efforts ; here
awhile
She seem'd to rule the conflict ; and
from hence
The British and the Lusitanian arm
Dislodged with irresistible assault
The enemy, even when he deem'd the
day   20
Was written for his own. But not for
Soult,
But not for France was that day in the
rolls
Of war to be inscribed by Victory's
hand,
Not for the inhuman chief, and cause
unjust ;
She wrote for aftertimes in blood the
names
Of Spain and England, Blake and
Beresford.

XXIX (XXXII)

TO THE MEMORY OF SIR WILLIAM MYERS

SPANIARD or Portugueze ! tread rever-
ently
Upon a soldier's grave ; no common
heart
Lies mingled with the clod beneath thy
feet.
To honours and to ample wealth was
Myers
In England born ; but leaving friends
beloved,

And all allurements of that happy land,
His ardent spirit to the field of war
Impell'd him. Fair was his career. He
faced
The perils of that memorable day,
When through the iron shower and fiery
storm   10
Of death the dauntless host of Britain
made
Their landing at Aboukir ; then not
less
Illustrated, than when great Nelson's
hand,
As if insulted Heaven with its own
wrath
Had arm'd him, smote the miscreant
Frenchmen's fleet,
And with its wreck wide-floating many
a league
Strew'd the rejoicing shores. What
then his youth
Held forth of promise, amply was con-
firm'd
When Wellesley, upon Talavera's plain,
On the mock monarch won his coronet :
There when the trophies of the field
were reap'd   21
Was he for gallant bearing eminent
When all did bravely. But his valour's
orb
Shone brightest at its setting. On the
field
Of Albuhera he the fusileers
Led to regain the heights, and promised
them
A glorious day ; a glorious day was
given ;
The heights were gain'd, the victory
was achieved,
And Myers received from death his
deathless crown.
Here to Valverde was he borne, and
here   30
His faithful men amid this olive grove,
The olive emblem here of endless peace,
Laid him to rest. Spaniard or Portu-
gueze,
In your good cause the British soldier
fell ;
Tread reverently upon his honour'd
grave.

XXX (XXXIV)

FOR THE WALLS OF CIUDAD RODRIGO

HERE Craufurd fell, victorious, in the
  breach,
Leading his countrymen in that assault
Which won from haughty France these
  rescued walls;
And here intomb'd far from his native
  land
And kindred dust, his honour'd relics
  rest.
Well was he versed in war, in the Orient
  train'd
Beneath Cornwallis; then for many a
  year
Following through arduous and ill-fated
  fields
The Austrian banners; on the sea-like
  shores
Of Plata next, still by malignant stars 10
Pursued; and in that miserable retreat,
For which Coruña witness'd on her hills
The pledge of vengeance given. At
  length he saw,
Long woo'd and well deserved, the
  brighter face
Of Fortune, upon Coa's banks vouch-
  safed,
Before Almeida, when Massena found
The fourfold vantage of his numbers
  foil'd,
Before the Briton, and the Portugal,
There vindicating first his old renown,
And Craufurd's mind that day presiding
  there.   20
Again was her auspicious countenance
Upon Busaco's holy heights reveal'd;
And when by Torres Vedras, Welling-
  ton,
Wisely secure, defied the boastful
  French,
With all their power; and when Onoro's
  springs
Beheld that execrable enemy
Again chastised beneath the avenging
  arm.
Too early here his honourable course
He closed, and won his noble sepulchre.
Where should the soldier rest so worthily

As where he fell? Be thou his monu-
  ment,   31
O City of Rodrigo, yea be thou,
To latest time, his trophy and his tomb!
Sultans, or Pharaohs of the elder world,
Lie not in Mosque or Pyramid enshrined
Thus gloriously, nor in so proud a grave.

XXXI (XXXV)

TO THE MEMORY OF MAJOR GENERAL MACKINNON

SON of an old and honourable house,
Henry Mackinnon from the Hebrides
Drew his descent, but upon English
  ground
An English mother bore him. Dauphiny
Beheld the blossom of his opening years;
For hoping in that genial clime to save
A child of feebler frame, his parents
  there
Awhile their sojourn fix'd: and thus it
  chanced
That in that generous season, when the
  heart
Yet from the world is pure and unde-
  filed,   10
Napoleon Buonaparte was his friend.
The adventurous Corsican, like Henry,
  then
Young, and a stranger in the land of
  France,
Their frequent and their favour'd guest
  became,
Finding a cheerful welcome at all hours,
Kindness, esteem, and in the English
  youth
Quick sympathy of apprehensive mind
And lofty thought heroic. On the way
Of life they parted, not to meet again.
Each follow'd war, but, oh! how dif-
  ferently   20
Did the two spirits which till now had
  grown
Like two fair plants, it seem'd, of kin-
  dred seed,
Develope in that awful element!
For never had benignant nature
  shower'd
More bounteously than on Mackinnon's
  head

Her choicest gifts. Form, features, in-
tellect,
Were such as might at once command
and win
All hearts. In all relationships ap-
proved,
Son, brother, husband, father, friend,
his life
Was beautiful; and when in tented
fields,   30
Such as the soldier should be in the sight
Of God and man was he. Poor praise it
were
To speak his worth evinced upon the
banks
Of Douro, Talavera's trophied plain,
Busaco's summit, and what other days,
Many and glorious all, illustrated
His bright career. Worthier of him to
say
That in the midst of camps his manly
breast
Retain'd its youthful virtue; that he
walk'd
Through blood and evil uncontaminate,
And that the stern necessity of war 41
But nurtured with its painful discipline
Thoughtful compassion in that gentle
soul,
And feelings such as man should cherish
still
For all of woman born. He met his
death
When at Rodrigo on the breach he
stood
Triumphant; to a soldier's wish it came
Instant, and in the hour of victory.
Mothers and maids of Portugal, oh bring
Your garlands here, and strew his grave
with flowers;   50
And lead the children to his monument,
Grey-headed sires, for it is holy ground !
For tenderness and valour in his heart,
As in your own Nunalures, had made
Their habitation; for a dearer life
Never in battle hath been offered up,
Since in like cause and in unhappy day,
By Zutphen's walls the peerless Sidney
fell.
'Tis said that Buonaparte, when he
heard
How thus, among the multitude whose
blood   60

Cries out to Heaven upon his guilty
head,
His early friend had fallen, was touch'd
with grief.
If aught it may avail him, be that
thought,
That brief recurrence of humanity
In his hard heart, remember'd in his
hour.

XXXII (XXXVI)

FOR THE AFFAIR AT ARROYO MOLINOS

HE who may chronicle Spain's arduous
strife
Against the Intruder, hath to speak of
fields
Profuselier fed with blood, and victories
Borne wider on the wings of glad report ;
Yet shall this town, which from the
mill-stream takes
Its humble name, be storied as the spot
Where the vain Frenchman, insolent
too long
Of power and of success, first saw the
strength
Of England in prompt enterprize es-
sayed,
And felt his fortunes ebb, from that day
forth   10
Swept back upon the refluent tide of war.
Girard lay here, who late from Caceres,
Far as his active cavalry could scour,
Had pillaged and opprest the country
round ;
The Spaniard and the Portugueze he
scorn'd,
And deem'd the British soldiers all too
slow
To seize occasion, unalert in war,
And therefore brave in vain. In such
belief
Secure at night he laid him down to
sleep,
Nor dreamt that these disparaged
enemies   20
With drum and trumpet should in
martial charge
Sound his reveille. All day their march
severe

They held through wind and drenching
rain ; all night
The autumnal tempest unabating raged,
While in their comfortless and open
camp
They cheer'd themselves with patient
hope : the storm
Was their ally, and moving in the mist,
When morning open'd, on the astonish'd
foe
They burst. Soon routed horse and
foot, the French
On all sides scattering, fled, on every
side   30
Beset, and every where pursued, with
loss
Of half their numbers captured, their
whole stores,
And all their gather'd plunder. 'Twas
a day
Of surest omen, such as fill'd with joy
True English hearts. . .No happier peals
have e'er
Been roll'd abroad from town and vil-
lage tower
Than gladden'd then with their exultant
sound
Salopian vales ; and flowing cups were
brimm'd
All round the Wrekin to Sir Rowland's
name.

XXXIII (XXXVII)

WRITTEN IN AN UNPUBLISHED
VOLUME OF LETTERS AND
MISCELLANEOUS PAPERS, BY
BARRÉ CHARLES ROBERTS.

NOT often hath the cold insensate earth
Closed over such fair hopes, as when the
grave
Received young Barré's perishable part ;
Nor death destroyed so sweet a dream
of life.
Nature, who sometimes lavisheth her
gifts
With fatal bounty, had conferred on him
Even such endowments as parental love
Might in its wisest prayer have ask'd of
Heaven ;
An intellect that, choosing for itself

The better part, went forth into the
fields   10
Of knowledge, and with never-sated
thirst
Drank of the living springs ; a judge-
ment calm
And clear ; a heart affectionate ; a soul
Within whose quiet sphere no vanities
Or low desires had place. Nor were the
seeds
Of excellence thus largely given, and left
To struggle with impediment of clime
Austere, or niggard soil ; all circum-
stance
Of happy fortune was to him vouch-
safed ;
His way of life was as through garden-
walks   20
Wherein no thorns are seen, save such
as grow,
Types of our human state, with fruits
and flowers.
In all things favoured thus auspiciously,
But in his father most. An intercourse
So beautiful no former record shows
In such relationship displayed, where
through
Familiar friendship's perfect confidence,
The father's ever-watchful tenderness
Meets ever in the son's entire respect
Its due return devout, and playful love
Mingles with every thing, and sheds o'er
all   31
A sunshine of its own. Should we then
say
The parents purchased at too dear a cost
This deep delight, the deepest, purest joy
Which Heaven hath here assign'd us,
when they saw
Their child of hope, just in the May of
life,
Beneath a slow and cankering malady,
With irremediable decay consumed,
Sink to the untimely grave ? Oh, think
not thus !
Nor deem that such long anguish, and
the grief   40
Which in the inmost soul doth strike its
roots
There to abide through time, can over-
weigh
The blessings which have been, and yet
shall be !

Think not that He in Whom we live,
doth mock
Our dearest aspirations ! Think not
love,
Genius, and virtue should inhere alone
In mere mortality, and Earth put out
The sparks which are of Heaven ! We
are not left
In darkness, nor devoid of hope. The
Light
Of Faith hath risen to us : the van-
quish'd Grave   50
To us the great consolatory truth
Proclaim'd that He who wounds will
heal ; and Death,
Opening the gates of Immortality,
The spirits whom it hath dissevered here
In everlasting union re-unite.

Keswick, 1814.

XXXIV (XXXIX)
EPITAPH

SOME there will be to whom, as here they
read,
While yet these lines are from the chisel
sharp,
The name of Clement Francis, will recall
His countenance benign ; and some who
knew
What stores of knowledge and what
humble thoughts,
What wise desires, what cheerful piety,
In happy union form'd the character
Which faithfully impress'd his aspect
meek.
And others too there are, who in their
hearts
Will bear the memory of his worth en-
shrined,   10
For tender and for reverential thoughts,
When grief hath had its course, a life-
long theme.
A little while, and these, who to the
truth
Of this poor tributary strain could bear
Their witness, will themselves have
pass'd away,
And this cold marble monument present
Words which can then within no living
mind

Create the ideal form they once evoked ;
This, then, the sole memorial of the
dead.
So be it. Only that which was of earth
Hath perish'd, only that which was
infirm,   21
Mortal, corruptible, and brought with it
The seed connate of death. A place in
Time
Is given us, only that we may prepare
Our portion for Eternity : the Soul
Possesseth there what treasures for
itself,
Wise to salvation, it laid up in Heaven.
O Man, take thou this lesson from the
Grave !
There too all true affections shall revive,
To fade no more ; all losses be re-
stored,   30
All griefs be heal'd, all holy hopes ful-
fill'd.

INSCRIPTIONS FOR THE CALE-
DONIAN CANAL

[Published in *The Anniversary*, 1829.]

XXXV (XL)
1. AT CLACHNACHARRY

ATHWART the island here, from sea to
sea,
Between these mountain barriers, the
Great Glen
Of Scotland offers to the traveller,
Through wilds impervious else, an easy
path,
Along the shore of rivers and of lakes,
In line continuous, whence the waters
flow
Dividing east and west. Thus had they
held
For untold centuries their perpetual
course
Unprofited, till in the Georgian age
This mighty work was plann'd, which
should unite   10
The lakes, control the innavigable
streams,
And through the bowels of the land
deduce
A way, where vessels which must else
have braved

The formidable Cape, and have essayed
The perils of the Hyperborean Sea,
Might from the Baltic to the Atlantic
  deep
Pass and repass at will. So when the
  storm
Careers abroad, may they securely here,
Through birchen groves, green fields,
  and pastoral hills,
Pursue their voyage home. Humanity
May boast this proud expenditure, be-
  gun   21
By Britain in a time of arduous war ;
Through all the efforts and emergencies
Of that long strife continued, and
  achieved
After her triumph, even at the time
When national burdens bearing on the
  state
Were felt with heaviest pressure. Such
  expense
Is best economy. In growing wealth,
Comfort, and spreading industry, be-
  hold
The fruits immediate ! And, in days to
  come,   30
Fitly shall this great British work be
  named
With whatsoe'er of most magnificence,
For public use, Rome in her plenitude
Of power effected, or all-glorious Greece,
Or Egypt, mother-land of all the arts.

XXXVI (XLI)

2. AT FORT AUGUSTUS

THOU who hast reach'd this level where
  the glede,
Wheeling between the mountains in
  mid air,
Eastward or westward as his gyre in-
  clines,
Descries the German or the Atlantic Sea,
Pause here ; and, as thou seest the ship
  pursue
Her easy way serene, call thou to mind
By what exertions of victorious art
The way was open'd. Fourteen times
  upheaved,
The vessel hath ascended, since she
  changed

The salt sea water for the highland
  lymph ;   10
As oft in imperceptible descent
Must, step by step, be lower'd, before
  she woo
The ocean breeze again. Thou hast
  beheld
What basins, most capacious of their
  kind,
Enclose her, while the obedient element
Lifts or depones its burthen. Thou hast
  seen
The torrent hurrying from its native hills
Pass underneath the broad canal in-
  humed,
Then issue harmless thence ; the rivulet
Admitted by its intake peaceably,   20
Forthwith by gentle overfall discharged:
And haply too thou hast observed the
  herds
Frequent their vaulted path, uncon-
  scious they
That the wide waters on the long low
  arch
Above them, lie sustained. What other
  works
Science, audacious in emprize, hath
  wrought,
Meet not the eye, but well may fill the
  mind.
Not from the bowels of the land alone,
From lake and stream hath their diluvial
  wreck
Been scoop'd to form this navigable
  way ;   30
Huge rivers were controll'd, or from
  their course
Shoulder'd aside ; and at the eastern
  mouth,
Where the salt ooze denied a resting place,
There were the deep foundations laid,
  by weight
On weight immersed, and pile on pile
  down-driven,
Till steadfast as the everlasting rocks
The massive outwork stands. Contem-
  plate now
What days and nights of thought, what
  years of toil,
What inexhaustive springs of public
  wealth
The vast design required ; the immediate
  good,   40

The future benefit progressive still ;
And thou wilt pay thy tribute of due
    praise
To those whose counsels, whose decrees,
    whose care,
For after ages formed the generous
    work.

XXXVII (XLII)

3. At Banavie

Where these capacious basins, by the
    laws
Of the subjacent element receive
The ship, descending or upraised, eight
    times,
From stage to stage with unfelt agency
Translated ; fitliest may the marble here
Record the Architect's immortal name.
Telford it was, by whose presiding
    mind
The whole great work was plann'd and
    perfected ;
Telford, who o'er the vale of Cambrian
    Dee,
Aloft in air, at giddy height upborne, 10
Carried his navigable road, and hung
High o'er Menai's straits the bending
    bridge ;
Structures of more ambitious enterprize
Than minstrels in the age of old romance
To their own Merlin's magic lore
    ascribed.
Nor hath he for his native land per-
    form'd
Less in this proud design ; and where
    his piers
Around her coast from many a fisher's
    creek
Unshelter'd else, and many an ample
    port,
Repel the assailing storm ; and where
    his roads   20
In beautiful and sinuous line far seen,
Wind with the vale, and win the long
    ascent,
Now o'er the deep morass sustain'd, and
    now
Across ravine, or glen, or estuary,
Opening a passage through the wilds
    subdued.

XXXVIII (XLIII)

EPITAPH IN BUTLEIGH CHURCH

Divided far by death were they, whose
    names
In honour here united, as in birth,
This monumental verse records.   They
    drew
In Dorset's healthy vales their natal
    breath,
And from these shores beheld the ocean
    first,
Whereon in early youth with one accord
They chose their way of fortune ; to
    that course
By Hood and Bridport's bright example
    drawn,
Their kinsmen, children of this place,
    and sons
Of one, who in his faithful ministry 10
Inculcated within these hallow'd walls
The truths in mercy to mankind reveal'd.
Worthy were these three brethren each
    to add
New honours to the already honour'd
    name : `
But Arthur, in the morning of his day,
Perish'd amid the Caribbean sea,
When the Pomona, by a hurricane
Whirl'd, riven and overwhelm'd, with
    all her crew
Into the deep went down.   A longer
    date
To Alexander was assign'd, for hope, 20
For fair ambition, and for fond regret,
Alas, how short ! for duty, for desert,
Sufficing ; and while Time preserves the
    roll
Of Britain's naval feats, for good report,
A boy, with Cook he rounded the great
    globe ;
A youth, in many a celebrated fight
With Rodney had his part ; and having
    reach'd
Life's middle stage, engaging ship to
    ship,
When the French Hercules, a gallant
    foe,
Struck to the British Mars his three-
    striped flag,   30
He fell, in the moment of his victory.

Here his remains in sure and certain
hope
Are laid, until the hour when Earth and
Sea
Shall render up their dead.   One brother
yet
Survived, with Keppel and with Rodney
train'd
In battles, with the Lord of Nile ap-
proved,
Ere in command he worthily upheld
Old England's high prerogative.   In the
east,
The west, the Baltic and the Midland
seas,
Yea, wheresoever hostile fleets have
plough'd   40
The ensanguined deep, his thunders have
been heard,
His flag in brave defiance hath been
seen;
And bravest enemies at Sir Samuel's
name
Felt fatal presage in their inmost heart,
Of unavertible defeat foredoom'd.
Thus in the path of glory he rode on,
Victorious alway, adding praise to
praise;
Till full of honours, not of years, be-
neath
The venom of the infected clime he
sunk,
On Coromandel's coast, completing
there   50
His service, only when his life was spent.

To the three brethren, Alexander's
son
(Sole scion he in whom their line survived),
With English feeling, and the deeper
sense
Of filial duty, consecrates this tomb.

1827.

XXXIX (XLIV)

EPITAPH.

To Butler's venerable memory
By private gratitude for public worth
This monument is raised, here where
twelve years
Meekly the blameless Prelate exercised
His pastoral charge;   and whither,
though removed
A little while to Durham's wider See,
His mortal relics were convey'd to rest.
Born in dissent, and in the school of
schism
Bred, he withstood the withering in-
fluence
Of that unwholesome nurture.   To the
Church,   10
In strength of mind mature and judg-
ment clear,
A convert, in sincerity of heart
Seeking the truth, deliberately con-
vinced,
And finding there the truth he sought,
he came.
In honour must his high desert be
held
While there is any virtue, any praise;
For he it was whose gifted intellect
First apprehended, and developed first
The analogy connate, which in its course
And constitution Nature manifests   20
To the Creator's word and will divine;
And in the depth of that great argument
Laying his firm foundation, built there-
on
Proofs never to be shaken of the truths
Reveal'd from Heaven in mercy to man-
kind;
Allying thus Philosophy with Faith,
And finding in things seen and known,
the type
And evidence of those within the veil.

CARMEN TRIUMPHALE

FOR THE COMMENCEMENT OF THE YEAR 1814

' Illi justitiam confirmavere triumphi,
Praesentes docuere Deos.'—CLAUDIAN.

[Published together with *Carmina Aulica* in one volume in 1814. The first four
stanzas were published in *The Courier* for January 8, 1814. See also Note to the ' Ode
Written during the Negotiations with Buonaparte in January, 1814,' p. 755.
Some extracts from Southey's notes to this Ode are printed at the end of the poem.
They are of interest as illustrating the attitude of British political parties during the
war with Napoleon, and the mistaken calculations of the *Edinburgh Review*.]

I

IN happy hour doth he receive
The Laurel, meed of famous Bards of
yore,
Which Dryden and diviner Spenser
wore, . .
In happy hour, and well may he rejoice,
Whose earliest task must be
To raise the exultant hymn for victory,
And join a nation's joy with harp and
voice,   [wind,
Pouring the strain of triumph on the
Glory to God, his song, Deliverance
for Mankind !

II

Wake, lute and harp ! My soul take
up the strain !   10
Glory to God ! Deliverance for Man-
kind !
Joy, . . for all Nations, joy ! But
most for thee,
Who hast so nobly fill'd thy part
assign'd,   [land !
O England ! O my glorious native
For thou in evil days didst stand
Against leagued Europe all in arms
array'd,
Single and undismay'd,   .
Thy hope in Heaven and in thine own
right hand.
Now are thy virtuous efforts overpaid,
Thy generous counsels now their
guerdon find, . .   20
Glory to God ! Deliverance for
Mankind !

III

Dread was the strife, for mighty was
the foe
Who sought with his whole strength
thy overthrow.
The Nations bow'd before him ; some
in war
Subdued, some yielding to superior art ;
Submiss, they follow'd his victorious car.
Their Kings, like Satraps, waited
round his throne ;
For Britain's ruin and their own,
By force or fraud in monstrous league
combined.
Alone, in that disastrous hour,   30
Britain stood firm and braved his
power ;
Alone she fought the battles of mankind.

IV

O virtue which, above all former fame,
Exalts her venerable name !
O joy of joys for every British breast !
That with that mighty peril full in
view,   [true !
The Queen of Ocean to herself was
That no weak heart, no abject mind
possess'd
Her counsels, to abase her lofty crest, . .
(Then had she sunk in everlasting
shame),   40
But ready still to succour the op-
press'd,
Her Red Cross floated on the waves
unfurl'd,   [world
Offering Redemption to the groaning

V

First from his trance the heroic
Spaniard woke ;
His chains he broke,
And casting off his neck the treacherous
yoke,
He call'd on England, on his generous
foe :
For well he knew that wheresoe'er
Wise policy prevail'd, or brave despair,
Thither would Britain's liberal
succours flow,   50
Her arm be present there.
Then, too, regenerate Portugal
display'd
Her ancient virtue, dormant all-too-
long.
Rising against intolerable wrong,
On England, on her old ally, for aid
The faithful nation call'd in her
distress :
And well that old ally the call
obey'd,
Well was that faithful friendship then
repaid.

VI

Say from thy trophied field how well,
Vimeiro ! Rocky Douro tell !   60
And thou, Busaco, on whose sacred
height
The astonished Carmelite,
While those unwonted thunders shook
his cell,
Join'd with his prayers the fervour of
the fight.
Bear witness those old Towers,[1] where
many a day
Waiting with foresight calm the fitting
hour,
The Wellesley, gathering strength in
wise delay,
Defied the Tyrant's undivided
power.
Swore not the boastful Frenchman in
his might,   69
Into the sea to drive his Island-foe ?
Tagus and Zezere, in secret night,
Ye saw that host of ruffians take their
flight ![2]
And in the Sun's broad light
Onoro's Springs[3] beheld their over-
throw.

VII

Patient of loss, profuse of life,
Meantime had Spain endured the strife ;
And though she saw her cities yield,
Her armies scatter'd in the field,
Her strongest bulwarks fall ;   79
The danger undismay'd she view'd,
Knowing that nought could e'er appal
The Spaniards' fortitude.[4]
What though the Tyrant, drunk with
power,
Might vaunt himself, in impious hour,
Lord and Disposer of this earthly ball ?
Her cause is just, and Heaven is
over all.

VIII

Therefore no thought of fear debased
Her judgment, nor her acts disgraced.
To every ill, but not to shame resign'd,
All sufferings, all calamities she bore.
She bade the people call to mind   91
Their heroes of the days of yore,
Pelayo and the Campeador,[5]
With all who, once in battle strong,
Lived still in story and in song.
Against the Moor, age after age,
Their stubborn warfare did they wage ;
Age after age, from sire to son,
The hallowed sword was handed down ;
Nor did they from that warfare cease,
And sheathe that hallow'd sword in
peace,   101
Until the work was done.

IX

Thus, in the famous days of yore,
Their fathers triumph'd o'er the Moor.
They gloried in his overthrow,
But touch'd not with reproach his
gallant name ;
For fairly, and with hostile aim profest,
The Moor had rear'd his haughty crest,
An open, honourable foe ;
But as a friend the treacherous French-
man came,   110
And Spain received him as a guest.
Think what your fathers were !
she cried,
Think what ye are, in sufferings tried ;
And think of what your sons must
be . .
Even as ye make them . . slaves or free!

X

Strains such as these from Spain's
three seas,
And from the farthest Pyrenees,
Rung through the region. Vengeance
was the word ;
One impulse to all hearts at once was
given ;
From every voice the sacred cry was
heard, 120
And borne abroad by all the winds of
Heaven
Heaven too, to whom the Spaniards
look'd for aid,
A spirit equal to the hour bestow'd ;
And gloriously the debt they paid,
Which to their valiant ancestors they
owed ; [France
And gloriously against the power of
Maintain'd their children's proud
inheritance.
Their steady purpose no defeat could
move, [mind ;
No horrors could abate their constant
Hope had its source and resting-place
above, 130
And they, to loss of all on earth
resign'd,
Suffer'd, to save their country, and
mankind.
What strain heroic might suffice to tell,
How Zaragoza stood, and how she fell?
Ne'er since yon sun began his daily
round,
Was higher virtue, holier valour, found
Than on that consecrated ground.

XI

Alone the noble Nation stood,
When from Coruña, in the main,
The star of England set in blood. 140
Ere long on Talavera's plain,
That star resplendent rose again ;
And though that day was doom'd to be
A day of frustrate victory,
Not vainly bled the brave ;
For French and Spaniard there might
see [save ;
That England's arm was strong to
Fair promise there the Wellesley gave,
And well in sight of earth and Heaven
Did he redeem the pledge which there
was given. 150

XII

Lord of Conquest, heir of Fame,
From rescued Portugal he came.
Rodrigo's walls in vain oppose ;
In vain thy bulwarks, Badajoz ;
And Salamanca's heights proclaim
The Conqueror's praise, the Wellesley's
name.
Oh, had the sun stood still that
hour,
When Marmont and his broken
power
Fled from their field of shame !
Spain felt through all her realms the
electric blow ; 160
Cadiz in peace expands her gates
again ;
And Betis, who, to bondage long
resign'd,
Flow'd mournfully along the silent
plain,
Into her joyful bosom unconfined
Receives once more the treasures of
the main.

XIII

What now shall check the Wellesley,
when at length
Onward he goes, rejoicing in his
strength ?
From Douro, from Castille's extended
plain,
The foe, a numerous band,
Retire ; amid the heights which over-
hang 170
Dark Ebro's bed, they think to make
their stand.
He reads their purpose, and prevents
their speed ;
And still as they recede,
Impetuously he presses on their
way ;
Till by Vittoria's walls they stood at
bay,
And drew their battle up in fair array.

XIV

Vain their array, their valour vain
There did the practised Frenchman
find
A master arm, a master mind !
Behold his veteran army driven 180
Like dust before the breath of Heaven,

Q

Like leaves before the autumnal
wind !
Now, Britain, now thy brow with
laurels bind ;
Raise now the song of joy for rescued
Spain !
And Europe, take thou up the
awakening strain . .
Glory to God ! Deliverance for Man-
kind !

XV

From Spain the living spark went
forth :
The flame hath caught, the flame is
spread !
It warms, . . it fires the farthest North.
Behold ! the awaken'd Muscovite 190
Meets the Tyrant in his might ; [6]
The Brandenburg, at Freedom's call,
Rises more glorious from his fall ;
And Frederick, best and greatest of
the name,
Treads in the path of duty and of
fame.
See Austria from her painful trance
awake !
The breath of God goes forth, . . the
dry bones shake !
Up Germany ! . . with all thy nations
rise !
Land of the virtuous and the wise,
No longer let that free, that mighty
mind,   200
Endure its shame ! She rose as from
the dead,
She broke her chains upon the op-
pressor's head . . [7]
Glory to God ! Deliverance for Man-
kind !

XVI

Open thy gates, O Hanover ! display
Thy loyal banners to the day ;
Receive thy old illustrious line once
more !
Beneath an Upstart's yoke opprest,
Long hath it been thy fortune to
deplore
That line, whose fostering and paternal
sway
So many an age thy grateful children
blest.   210

The yoke is broken now : . . A
mightier hand
Hath dash'd, . . in pieces dash'd, . .
the iron rod.
To meet her Princes, the deliver'd
land
Pours her rejoicing multitudes abroad ;
The happy bells, from every town
and tower,
Roll their glad peals upon the joyful
wind ;
And from all hearts and tongues, with
one consent,
The high thanksgiving strain to heaven
is sent, . .
Glory to God ! Deliverance for
Mankind !

XVII

Egmont and Horn, heard ye that holy
cry,   220
Martyrs of Freedom, from your seats
in Heaven ?
And William the Deliverer, doth thine
eye
Regard from yon empyreal realm the
land
For which thy blood was given ?
What ills hath that poor Country
suffer'd long !
Deceived, despised, and plunder'd, and
oppress'd,
Mockery and insult aggravating
wrong !
Severely she her errors hath atoned,
And long in anguish groan'd,
Wearing the patient semblance of
despair,   230
While fervent curses rose with every
prayer :
In mercy Heaven at length its ear
inclined ;
The avenging armies of the North
draw nigh,
Joy for the injured Hollander ! . . the
cry
Of Orange rends the sky !
All hearts are now in one good cause
combined, . .
Once more that flag triumphant floats
on high, . .
Glory to God ! Deliverance for
Mankind !

XVIII

When shall the Dove go forth ? Oh
    when
Shall Peace return among the Sons of
    Men ?   240
Hasten benignant Heaven the blessed
    day !
    Justice must go before,
And Retribution must make plain the
    way ;
    Force must be crushed by Force,
The power of Evil by the power of
    Good,
Ere Order bless the suffering world
    once more,
    Or Peace return again.
Hold then right on in your auspicious
    course,
Ye Princes, and ye People, hold right
    on !
    Your task not yet is done :   250

Pursue the blow, . . ye know your
    foe, . .
Complete the happy work so well
    begun.
Hold on, and be your aim with all
    your strength
Loudly proclaim'd and steadily
    pursued ;
So shall this fatal Tyranny at length
Before the arms of Freedom fall
    subdued.
Then, when the waters of the flood
    abate,
The Dove her resting-place secure may
    find :
And France restored, and shaking off
    her chain,
Shall join the Avengers in the joyful
    strain,   260
    Glory to God ! Deliverance for
    Mankind !

NOTES TO CARMEN TRIUMPHALE

[1] Torres Vedras. *Turres Veteres*, . . a name so old as to have been given when the Latin tongue was the language of Portugal. This town is said to have been founded by the Turduli, a short time before the commencement of the Christian Æra.

In remembering the lines of Torres Vedras, the opinion of the wise men of the North ought not to be forgotten, ' If they (the French) do not make an effort to drive us out of Portugal, it is because we are better there than any where else. We fear they will not leave us on the Tagus many days longer than suits their own purposes.'— *Edinburgh Review*, No. XXVII, p. 263.

The opinion is delivered with happy precision of language : . . Our troops were indeed, to use the same neat and felicitous expression, ' better there than any where else.'

[2] No cruelties recorded in history exceed those which were systematically committed by the French during their retreat from Portugal. ' Their conduct,' (says Lord Wellington in his dispatch of the 14th of March, 1811,) ' throughout this retreat, has been marked by a barbarity seldom equalled, and never surpassed.

' Even in the towns of Torres Novas, Thomar, and Pernes, in which the head-quarters of some of the corps had been for four months, and in which the inhabitants had been induced by promises of good treatment to remain, they were plundered, and many of their houses destroyed on the night the enemy withdrew from their position ; and they have since burnt every town and village through which they have passed. The Convent of Alcobaça was burnt by order from the French head-quarters. The Bishop's Palace, and the whole town of Leyria, in which General Drouet had had his head-quarters, shared the same fate ; and there is not an inhabitant of the country, of any class or description, who has had any dealing or communication with the French army who has not had reason to repent of it, or to complain of them. This is the mode in which the promises have been performed, and the assurances have been fulfilled, which were held out in the proclamation of the French commander-in-chief, in which he told the inhabitants of Portugal, that he was not come to make war upon them, but with a powerful army of one hundred and ten thousand men to drive the English into the sea. It is to be hoped, that the example of what has occurred in this country will teach the people of this and other nations what value they ought to place on such promises and assurances, and that there is no security for life or for any thing that renders life valuable, except in decided resistance to the enemy.'

As exact an account of these atrocities was collected as it was possible to obtain, . . and that record will for ever make the French name detested in Portugal. In the single diocese of Coimbra, 2,909 persons, men, women, and children, were murdered, . . every one with some shocking circumstance of aggravated cruelty. . . ' Nem huma só das 2969 mortes commettidas pelo inimigo deixou de ser atroz e dolorosissima.' (Breve Memoria dos Estragos Causados no Bispado de Coimbra pelo Exercito Francez, commandado pelo General Massena. Extrahida das Enformaçoens que deram os Reverendos Parocos, e remettida a Junta dos Socorros da Subscripsam Britannica, pelo Reverendo Provisor Governador do mesmo Bispado, p. 12.) Some details are given in this brief Memorial. ' A de tel forfaits,' says J. J. Rousseau, ' celui qui détourne ses regards est un lâche, un déserteur de la justice : la véritable humanité les envisage pour les connoître, pour les juger, pour les détester.' (Le Lévite d'Ephraïm.) I will not, however, in this place repeat abominations which at once outrage humanity and disgrace human nature.

When the French, in 1792, entered Spire, some of them began to commit excesses which would soon have led to a general sack. Custine immediately ordered a captain, two officers, and a whole company to be shot. This dreadful example, he told the National Convention, he considered as the only means of saving the honour of the French nation, . . and it met with the approbation of the whole army. But the French armies had not then been systematically brutalized. It was reserved for Buonaparte to render them infamous, as well as to lead them to destruction.

The French soldier, says Capmany, is executioner and robber at the same time : he leaves the unhappy wretch who is delivered over to his mercy, naked to the skin, . . stripping off the clothes that they may not be torn by the musket-shot ! . . The pen falls from my hand, and I cannot proceed !

' Para que se junte á esta crueldad la mayor infamia, el soldado Frances es verdugo y ladron en una pieza ; dexa en cueros vivos al malaventurado que entregan á su discrecion, quitandole la ropa antes que los fusilazos se la destrozen. La pluma se cae de la mano, y no puede proseguir.'—Centinela, contra Franceses, P. ii, p. 35.

Yet the Edinburgh Review says, ' the hatred of the name of a Frenchman in Spain has been such as the reality will by no means justify ; and the detestation of the French government has, among the inferior orders, been carried to a pitch wholly unauthorized by its proceedings towards them.'—No. XXVII, p. 262. This passage might be read with astonishment, if any thing absurd, any thing mischievous, or any thing false, could excite surprise when it comes from that quarter.

[3] Fuentes d'Onoro. This name has sometimes been rendered Fountains of Honour, by an easy mistake, or a pardonable licence.

[4] ' The fate of Spain, we think, is decided, and that fine and misguided country has probably yielded, by this time, to the fate which has fallen on the greater part of continental Europe. Her European dominions have yielded already to the unrelaxing grasp of the insatiable conqueror.'—Edinburgh Review, No. XXVI, p. 298.

' The fundamental position which we ventured to lay down respecting the Spanish question was this : . . that the spirit of the people, however enthusiastic and universal, was in its nature more uncertain and shortlived, more likely to be extinguished by reverses, or to go out of itself amidst the delays of a protracted contest, than the steady, regular, moderate feeling which calls out disciplined troops, and marshals them under known leaders, and supplies them by systematic arrangements : . . a proposition so plain and obvious, that if it escaped ridicule as a truism, it might have been reasonably expected to avoid the penalties of heresy and paradox. The event has indeed woefully proved its truth.'—Edinburgh Review, No. XXVII, p. 246.

These gentlemen could see no principle of permanence in the character of the Spaniards, and no proof of it in their history; . . and they could discover no principle of dissolution in the system of Buonaparte ; . . a system founded upon force and falsehood, in direct opposition to the interest of his own subjects and to the feelings of human nature.

[5] The Cid, Rodrigo Diaz de Bivar.

[6] ' Ecce iterum Crispinus ! ' What says the Edinburgh Review concerning Russia ? ' Considering how little that power has shown itself capable of effecting for the salvation of Europe, . . how wretched the

state of its subjects is under the present government, .. how trifling an acquisition of strength the common enemy could expect to obtain from the entire possession of its resources, we acknowledge that we should contemplate with great composure any change which might lay the foundation of future improvement, and scatter the forces of France over the dominion of the Czars.'— No. XXVIII, p. 460.

This is a choice passage. The reasoning is worthy of the writer's judgement, the feeling perfectly consistent with his *liberality*, and the conclusion as consistent with his politics.

[7] Hear the Edinburgh Reviewer! 'It would be as chimerical to expect a mutiny among the vassal states of France who are the most impatient of her yoke, as amongst the inhabitants of Bourdeaux, or the conscripts of the year 1808 and 1809. In making this comparison, we are indeed putting the case much more strongly against France than the facts warrant, for with the exception of Holland, and the States into which the conscription has been introduced, either immediately, or by means of large requisitions of men made to their Govern ments,* the changes effected by the French invasion have been favourable to the individual happiness of the inhabitants †, so that the hatred of France is liable to con siderable diminution, inasmuch as the national antipathy and spirit of indepen dence are gradually undermined by the solid benefits which the change of masters has conferred.'—No. XXVIII, p. 458.

Great as a statesman, profound as a philosopher, amiable as an optimist of the Pangloss school, .. but not altogether for tunate as a Prophet!

* N.B. These little exceptions include all the countries which were annexed to the French Empire, all Italy, and all the States of the Confederation of the Rhine.

† Particularly the commercial part of them.

EPISTLE TO ALLAN CUNNINGHAM

[First published in *The Anniversary*, 1829.]

WELL, Heaven be thank'd! friend Allan, here I am,
Once more to that dear dwelling place return'd,
Where I have pass'd the whole mid stage of life,
Not idly, certes; not unworthily, ..
So let me hope: where Time upon my head
Hath laid his frore and monitory hand;
And when this poor frail earthly taber nacle
Shall be dissolved, .. it matters not how soon
Or late, in God's good time, .. where I would fain
Be gathered to my children, earth to earth.   10

Needless it were to say how willingly
I bade the huge metropolis farewell,
Its din, and dust, and dirt, and smoke, and smut,
Thames' water, paviour's ground, and London sky;
Weary of hurried days and restless nights,
Watchmen, whose office is to murder sleep
When sleep might else have weigh'd one's eyelids down,
Rattle of carriages, and roll of carts,
And tramp of iron hoofs; and worse than all, ..
Confusion being worse confounded then,
With coachmen's quarrels and with footmen's shouts,   21
My next-door neighbours, in a street not yet
Macadamized, (me miserable!) *at home*;
For then had we from midnight until morn
House-quakes, street-thunders, and door-batteries.
O Government! in thy wisdom and thy want,
Tax knockers; .. in compassion to the sick,
And those whose sober habits are not yet

Inverted, topsy-turvying night and day,
Tax them more heavily than thou hast
   charged   30
Armorial bearings and bepowder'd pates.
And thou, O Michael, ever to be praised,
Angelic among Taylors ! for thy laws
Antifuliginous, extend those laws
Till every chimney its own smoke con-
   sume,
And give thenceforth thy dinners un-
   lampoon'd.
Escaping from all this, the very whirl
Of mail-coach wheels bound outward
   from Lad-lane,
Was peace and quietness. Three hun-
   dred miles
Of homeward way seem'd to the body
   rest,   40
And to the mind repose.
               Donne [1] did not hate
More perfectly that city. Not for all
Its social, all its intellectual joys, . .
Which having touch'd, I may not con-
   descend
To name aught else the Demon of the
   place
Might for his lure hold forth ; . . not even
   for these
Would I forego gardens and green-field
   walks,
And hedge-row trees, and stiles, and
   shady lanes,
And orchards, were such ordinary scenes
Alone to me accessible as those   50
Wherein I learnt in infancy to love
The sights and sounds of Nature ; . .
   wholesome sights
Gladdening the eye that they refresh ;
   and sounds
Which, when from life and happiness
   they spring,
Bear with them to the yet unharden'd
   heart
A sense that thrills its cords of sym-
   pathy ;

[1] This poet begins his second Satire
thus :—

'Sir, though (I thank God for it) I do hate
Perfectly all this town, yet there's one state
In all ill things so excellently best,
That hate towards them breeds pity towards
   the rest.'

Or, when proceeding from insensate
   things,
Give to tranquillity a voice wherewith
To woo the ear and win the soul
   attuned ; . .   59
Oh not for all that London might bestow
Would I renounce the genial influences
And thoughts and feelings to be found
   where'er
We breathe beneath the open sky, and
   see
Earth's liberal bosom. Judge then by
   thyself,
Allan, true child of Scotland, . . thou
   who art
So oft in spirit on thy native hills,
And yonder Solway shores, . . a poet
   thou,
Judge by thyself how strong the ties
   which bind
A poet to his home ; when, . . making
   thus
Large recompense for all that haply else
Might seem perversely or unkindly
   done, . .   71
Fortune hath set his happy habitacle
Among the ancient hills, near mountain
   streams
And lakes pellucid, in a land sublime
And lovely as those regions of Romance
Where his young fancy in its day-dreams
   roam'd,
Expatiating in forests wild and wide,
Loëgrian, or of dearest Faery-land.

Yet, Allan, of the cup of social joy
No man drinks freelier, nor with heartier
   thirst,   80
Nor keener relish, where I see around
Faces which I have known and loved so
   long,
That when he prints a dream upon my
   brain
Dan Morpheus takes them for his
   readiest types.
And therefore in that loathed metro-
   polis
Time measured out to me some golden
   hours.
They were not leaden-footed while the
   clay
Beneath the patient touch of Chantrey's
   hand

Grew to the semblance of my lineaments.
Lit up in memory's landscape, like green
   spots   90
Of sunshine, are the mornings, when in
   talk
With him and thee, and Bedford (my
   true friend
Of forty years), I saw the work proceed,
Subject the while myself to no restraint,
But pleasureably in frank discourse
   engaged :
Pleased too, and with no unbecoming
   pride
To think this countenance, such as it is,
So oft by rascally mislikeness wrong'd,
Should faithfully to those who in his
   works
Have seen the inner man pourtray'd, be
   shown,   100
And in enduring marble should partake
Of our great sculptor's immortality.

I have been libell'd, Allan, as thou
   knowest,
Through all degrees of calumny ; but
   they
Who fix one's name for public sale
   beneath
A set of features slanderously unlike,
Are the worst libellers. Against the
   wrong
Which they inflict Time hath no remedy.
Injuries there are which Time redresseth
   best,
Being more sure in judgement, though
   perhaps   110
Slower in process even than the court
Where justice, tortoise-footed and mole-
   eyed,
Sleeps undisturb'd, fann'd by the lulling
   wings
Of harpies at their prey. We soon live
   down
Evil or good report, if undeserved.
Let then the dogs of Faction bark and
   bay,
Its bloodhounds, savaged by a cross of
   wolf,
Its full-bred kennel from the Blatant-
   beast ;
And from my lady's gay veranda, let
Her pamper'd lap-dog with his fetid
   breath   120

In bold bravado join, and snap and
   growl,
With petulant consequentialness elate,
There in his imbecility at once
Ridiculous and safe, though all give cry,
Whiggery's sleek spaniels, and its
   lurchers lean,
Its poodles by unlucky training marr'd,
Mongrel and cur and bob-tail, let them
   yelp
Till weariness and hoarseness shall at
   length
Silence the noisy pack ; meantime be
   sure
I will not stoop for stones to cast among
   them.   130
The foumarts and the skunks may be
   secure
In their own scent ; and for that viler
   swarm,
The vermin of the press, both those that
   skip,
And those that creep and crawl, I do not
   catch
And pin them for exposure on the page,
Their filth is their defence.
             But I appeal
Against the limner's and the graver's
   wrong ;
Their evil works survive them. Bilder-
   dijk,
Whom I am privileged to call my friend,
Suffering by graphic libels in likewise,
Gave his wrath vent in verse. Would I
   could give   141
The life and spirit of his vigorous Dutch,
As his dear consort hath transfused my
   strains
Into her native speech ; and made them
   known
On Rhine and Yssel, and rich Amstel's
   banks ;
And wheresoe'er the voice of Vondel still
Is heard, and still Antonides and Hooft
Are living agencies ; and Father Cats,
The household poet, teacheth in his
   songs
The love of all things lovely, all things
   pure :   150
Best poet, who delights the cheerful
   mind
Of childhood, stores with moral strength
   the heart

Of youth, with wisdom maketh mid-life
   rich,
And fills with quiet tears the eyes of age.

   Hear then in English rhyme how
     Bilderdijk
Describes his wicked portraits, one by
   one.

' A madman who from Bedlam hath
   broke loose ;
An honest fellow of the numskull race;
And pappyer-headed still, a very goose
   Staring with eyes agast and vacant
     face ;   160
A Frenchman who would mirthfully
   display
   On some poor idiot his malicious wit ;
And lastly, one who, train'd up in the
   way
Of worldly craft, hath not forsaken it,
But hath served Mammon with his
   whole intent,
   A thing of Nature's worst materials
     made,
Low-minded, stupid, base and insolent.
I, . . I, . . a Poet, . . have been thus
   pourtray'd.
Can ye believe that my true effigy
   Among these vile varieties is found ?
What thought, or line, or word, hath
   fallen from me   171
   In all my numerous works whereon
   to ground
The opprobrious notion ? Safely I may
   smile
   At these, acknowledging no likeness
   here.
But worse is yet to come ; so, soft
   awhile !
   For now in potter's earth must I
   appear,
And in such workmanship, that, sooth
   to say,
Humanity disowns the imitation,
And the dolt image is not worth its clay.
   Then comes there one who will to
   admiration   180
In plastic wax my perfect face present ;
   And what of his performance comes
   at last ?
Folly itself in every lineament !
   Its consequential features overcast

With the coxcombical and shallow laugh
   Of one who would, for condescension,
   hide,
Yet in his best behaviour, can but half
   Suppress the scornfulness of empty
   pride.'

' And who is Bilderdijk ? ' methinks
   thou sayest,
A ready question ; yet which, trust me,
   Allan,   190
Would not be ask'd, had not the curse
   that came
From Babel, clipt the wings of Poetry.
Napoleon ask'd him once with cold fix'd
   look,
' Art thou then in the world of letters
   known ? '
' I have deserved to be,' the Hollander
Replied, meeting that proud imperial
   look
With calm and proper confidence, and
   eye
As little wont to turn away abash'd
Before a mortal presence. He is one
Who hath received upon his constant
   breast   200
The sharpest arrows of adversity ;
Whom not the clamours of the multitude
Demanding in their madness and their
   might
Iniquitous things, could shake in his
   firm mind ;
Nor the strong hand of instant tyranny,
From the straight path of duty turn
   aside.
But who in public troubles, in the wreck
Of his own fortunes, in proscription,
   exile,
Want, obloquy, ingratitude, neglect,
And what severer trials Providence 210
Sometimes inflicteth, chastening whom
   it loves,
In all, through all, and over all, hath
   borne
An equal heart, as resolute toward
The world, as humbly and religiously
Beneath his heavenly Father's rod
   resign'd.
Right-minded, happy-minded, righteous
   man,
True lover of his country and his kind ;
In knowledge, and in inexhaustive stores

Of native genius rich ; philosopher,
Poet, and sage. The language of a
State   220
Interior In Illustrious deeds to none,
But circumscribed by narrow bounds,
and now
Sinking in irrecoverable decline,
Hath pent within its sphere a name
wherewith
Europe should else have rung from side
to side.

Such, Allan, is the Hollander to
whom
Esteem and admiration have attach'd
My soul, not less than pre-consent of
mind,
And gratitude for benefits, when being
A stranger, sick, and in a foreign
land,   230
He took me like a brother to his
house,
And ministered to me, and made a time
Which had been wearisome and careful
else,
So pleasurable, that in my kalendar
There are no whiter days. 'Twill be a
joy
For us to meet In Heaven, though we
should look
Upon each other's earthly face no more.
. . This is this world's complexion !
'cheerful thoughts
Bring sad thoughts to the mind,' and
these again
Give place to calm content, and stead-
fast hope,   240
And happy faith assured. . . Return we
now,
With such transition as our daily life
Imposes in its wholesome discipline,
To a lighter strain ; and from the gallery
Of the Dutch Poet's mis-resemblances
Pass into mine; where I shall show thee,
Allan,
Such an array of villainous visages,
That if among them all there were but
one
Which as a likeness could be proved
upon me,
It were enough to make me in mere
shame   250
Take up an alias, and forswear myself.

Whom have we first ? A dainty gen-
tleman,
His sleepy eyes half-closed, and coun-
tenance
To no expression stronger than might
suit
A simper, capable of being moved :
Sawney and sentimental ; with an air
So lack-thought and so lackadaisycal,
You might suppose the volume in his
hand
Must needs be Zimmermann on Solitude.

Then comes a jovial landlord, who
hath made it   260
Part of his trade to be the shoeing horn
For his commercial customers. God
Bacchus
Hath not a thirstier votary. Many a pipe
Of Porto's vintage hath contributed
To give his cheeks that deep carmine
engrain'd,
And many a runlet of right Nantes, I
ween,
Hath suffer'd percolation through that
trunk,
Leaving behind it in the boozey eyes
A swoln and red suffusion, glazed and
dim.

Our next is in the evangelical line, 270
A leaden-visaged specimen; demure,
Because he hath put on his Sunday's
face ;
Dull by formation, by complexion sad,
By bile, opinions, and dyspepsy sour.
One of the sons of Jack, . . I know not
which,
For Jack hath a most numerous pro-
geny, . .
Made up for Mr. Colburn's Magazine
This pleasant composite ; a bust sup-
plied
The features ; look, expression, char-
acter,
Are of the artist's fancy and free grace.
Such was that fellow's birth and parent-
age.   281
The rascal proved prolific ; one of his
breed,
By Docteur Pichot introduced in France,
Passes for Monsieur Sooté ; and
another, . .

An uglier miscreant too, .. the brothers
    Schumann
And their most cruel copper-scratcher
    Zschoch,
From Zwickau sent abroad through
    Germany.
I wish the Schumen and the copper-
    scratcher
No worse misfortune for their recom-
    pence,
Than to encounter such a cut-throat
    face   290
In the Black Forest or the Odenwald.

And now is there a third derivative
From Mr. Colburn's composite, which
    late
The Arch-Pirate Galignani hath pre-
    fix'd,
A spurious portrait to a faithless life,
And bearing lyingly the libell'd name
Of Lawrence, impudently there insculpt.

The bust that was the innocent fore-
    father
To all this base, abominable brood,
I blame not, Allan. 'Twas the work of
    Smith,   300
A modest, mild, ingenious man, and errs,
Where erring, only because over-true,
Too close a likeness for similitude ;
Fixing to every part and lineament
Its separate character, and missing thus
That which results from all.
                Sir Smug comes next ;
Allan, I own Sir Smug ! I recognize
That visage with its dull sobriety ;
I see it duly as the day returns,
When at the looking-glass with lather'd
    chin   310
And razor-weapon'd hand I sit, the face
Composed and apprehensively intent
Upon the necessary operation
About to be perform'd, with touch, alas,
Not always confident of hair-breadth
    skill.
Even in such sober sadness and con-
    strain'd
Composure cold, the faithful Painter's
    eye
Had fix'd me like a spell, and I could feel
My features stiffen as he glanced upon
    them.

And yet he was a man whom I loved
    dearly,   320
My fellow-traveller, my familiar friend,
My household guest. But when he
    look'd upon me,
Anxious to exercise his excellent art,
The countenance he knew so thoroughly
Was gone, and in its stead there gate
    Sir Smug.

Under the graver's hand, Sir Smug
    became
Sir Smouch, .. a son of Abraham. Now
    albeit,
For rather would I trace my lineage
    thence
Than with the oldest line of Peers or
    Kings
Claim consanguinity, that cast of fea-
    tures   330
Would ill accord with me, who in all
    forms
Of pork, baked, roasted, toasted, boil'd
    or broil'd,
Fresh, salted, pickled, seasoned, moist
    or dry,
Whether ham, bacon, sausage, souse or
    brawn,
Leg, bladebone, baldrib, griskin, chine,
    or chop,
Profess myself a genuine Philopig.

It was, however, as a Jew whose
    portion
Had fallen unto him in a goodly land
Of loans, of omnium, and of three per
    cents,
That Messrs. Percy of the Anecdote-
    firm   340
Presented me unto their customers.
Poor Smouch endured a worse judaiza-
    tion
Under another hand. In this next stage
He is on trial at the Old Bailey, charged
With dealing in base coin. That he is
    guilty
No Judge or Jury could have half a
    doubt
When they saw the culprit's face ; and
    he himself,
As you may plainly see, is comforted
By thinking he has just contrived to
    keep

Out of rope's reach, and will come off
   this time   350
For transportation.
        Stand thou forth for trial,
Now, William Darton, of the Society
Of Friends called Quakers; thou who
   in 4th month
Of the year 24, on Holborn Hill,
At No. 58., didst wilfully,
Falsely, and knowing it was falsely done,
Publish upon a card, as Robert Southey's,
A face which might be just as like Tom
   Fool's,
Or John, or Richard Any-body-else's!
What had I done to thee, thou William
   Darton,
That thou shouldst for the lucre of base
   gain,   361
Yea, for the sake of filthy fourpences,
Palm on my countrymen that face for
   mine?
O William Darton, let the Yearly
   Meeting
Deal with thee for that falseness! All
   the rest
Are traceable; Smug's Hebrew family;
The German who might properly adorn
A gibbet or a wheel, and Monsieur Sooté,
Sons of Fitzbust the Evangelical; .
I recognize all these unlikenesses,   370
Spurious abominations though they be,
Each filiated on some original;
But thou, Friend Darton, and .. observe
   me, man,
Only in courtesy, and *quasi* Quaker,
I call thee Friend ! .. hadst no original;
No likeness or unlikeness, *silhouette*,
Outline, or plaster, representing me,
Whereon to form thy misrepresentation.
If I guess rightly at the pedigree

Of thy bad groatsworth, thou didst get
   a barber   380
To personate my injured Laureateship;
An advertising barber, .. one who keeps
A bear, and when he puts to death poor
   Bruin
Sells his grease, fresh as from the carcass
   cut,
Pro bono publico, the price per pound
Twelve shillings and no more. From
   such a barber,
O unfriend Darton ! was that portrait
   made
I think, or peradventure from his block.

Next comes a minion worthy to be set
In a wooden frame; and here I might
   invoke   390
Avenging Nemesis, if I did not feel
Just now God Cynthius pluck me by
   the ear.
But, Allan, in what shape God Cynthius
   comes,
And wherefore he admonisheth me thus,
Nor thou nor I will tell the world; here-
   after
The commentators, my Malones and
   Reids,
May if they can. For in my gallery
Though there remaineth undescribed
   good store,
Yet ' of enough enough, and now no
   more,'
(As honest old George Gascoigne said
   of yore,)   400
Save only a last couplet to express
That I am always truly yours,

                    R. S.

Keswick, August, 1828.

MADOC.

'OMNE SOLUM FORTI PATRIA.'

TO

CHARLES WATKIN WILLIAMS WYNN,

THIS POEM

WAS ORIGINALLY INSCRIBED, IN 1805,

AS A TOKEN OF SIXTEEN YEARS OF UNINTERRUPTED FRIENDSHIP;

AND IS NOW RE-INSCRIBED WITH THE SAME FEELING,

AFTER AN INTERVAL OF THIRTY-TWO.

PREFACE TO THE FIRST EDITION

THE historical facts on which this Poem is founded may be related in a few words. On the death of Owen Gwyneth, king of North Wales, A.D. 1169, his children disputed the succession. Yorwerth, the elder, was set aside without a struggle, as being incapacitated by a blemish in his face. Hoel, though illegitimate, and born of an Irish mother, obtained possession of the throne for a while, till he was defeated and slain by David, the eldest son of the late king by a second wife. The conqueror, who then succeeded without opposition, slew Yorwerth, imprisoned Rodri, and hunted others of his brethren into exile. But Madoc, meantime, abandoned his barbarous country, and sailed away to the West in search of some better resting-place. The land which he discovered pleased him : he left there part of his people, and went back to Wales for a fresh supply of adventurers, with whom he again set sail, and was heard of no more. Strong evidence has been adduced that he reached America, and that his posterity exist there to this day, on the southern branches of the Missouri, retaining their complexion, their language, and, in some degree, their arts.

About the same time, the Aztecas, an American tribe, in consequence of certain calamities, and of a particular omen, forsook Aztlan, their own country, under the guidance of Yuhid-thiton. They became a mighty people, and founded the Mexican empire, taking the name of Mexicans, in honour of Mexitli, their tutelary god. Their emigration is here connected with the adventures of Madoc, and their superstition is represented as the same which their descendants practised, when discovered by the Spaniards. The manners of the Poem, in both its parts, will be found historically true. It assumes not the degraded title of Epic : and the question, therefore, is not whether the story is formed upon the rules of Aristotle, but whether it be adapted to the purposes of poetry.

Keswick, 1805.

' Three things must be avoided in Poetry ; the frivolous, the obscure, and the superfluous.

' The three excellencies of Poetry ; simplicity of language, simplicity of subject, and simplicity of invention.

' The three indispensable purities of Poetry ; pure truth, pure language, and pure manners.

' Three things should all Poetry be ; thoroughly erudite, thoroughly animated, and thoroughly natural.'—*Triads.*

COME, LISTEN TO A TALE OF TIMES OF OLD!
COME, FOR YE KNOW ME. I AM HE WHO SANG
THE MAID OF ARU, AND I AM HE WHO FRAMED
OF THALABA THE WILD AND WONDROUS SONG.
COME, LISTEN TO MY LAY, AND YE SHALL
    HEAR
HOW MADOC FROM THE SHORES OF BRITAIN
    SPREAD
THE ADVENTUROUS SAIL, EXPLORED THE
    OCEAN PATHS,
AND QUELLED BARBARIAN POWER, AND
    OVERTHREW
THE BLOODY ALTARS OF IDOLATRY,
AND PLANTED IN ITS FANES TRIUMPHANTLY
THE CROSS OF CHRIST. COME, LISTEN TO
    MY LAY!

MADOC IN WALES: PART I

I. THE RETURN TO WALES

FAIR blows the wind, . . the vessel drives
    along,
Her streamers fluttering at their length,
    her sails
All full, . . she drives along, and round
    her prow
Scatters the ocean spray. What feelings
    then
Fill'd every bosom, when the mariners,
After the peril of that weary way,
Beheld their own dear country! Here
    stands one
Stretching his sight toward the distant
    shore,
And as to well-known forms his busy
    joy
Shapes the dim outline, eagerly he
    points   10
The fancied headland and the cape and
    bay,
Till his eyes ache o'erstraining. This
    man shakes
His comrade's hand and bids him wel-
    come home,
And blesses God, and then he weeps
    aloud:
Here stands another, who in secret
    prayer
Calls on the Virgin and his patron Saint,
Renewing his old vows of gifts and
    alms
And pilgrimage, so he may find all well.
Silent and thoughtful and apart from all
Stood Madoc; now his noble enterprize
Proudly remembering, now in dreams of
    hope,   21
Anon of bodings full and doubt and fear.

Fair smiled the evening, and the
    favouring gale
Sung in the shrouds, and swift the
    steady bark
Rush'd roaring through the waves.
                    The sun goes down:
Far off his light is on the naked crags
Of Penmanmawr, and Arvon's ancient
    hills;
And the last glory lingers yet awhile,
Crowning old Snowdon's venerable head,
That rose amid his mountains. Now
    the ship   30
Drew nigh where Mona, the dark island,
    stretch'd
Her shore along the ocean's lighter line.
There through the mist and twilight,
    many a fire
Up-flaming stream'd upon the level sea
Red lines of lengthening light, which, far
    away
Rising and falling, flash'd athwart the
    waves.
Thereat full many a thought of ill dis-
    turb'd
Prince Madoc's mind; . . did some new
    conqueror seize
The throne of David? had the tyrant's
    guilt
Awaken'd vengeance to the deed of
    death?   40
Or blazed they for a brother's obsequies,
The sport and mirth of murder? . . Like
    the lights
Which there upon Aberfraw's royal walls
Are waving with the wind, the painful
    doubt
Fluctuates within him. . . Onward drives
    the gale, . .

On flies the bark ; . . and she hath
reach'd at length
Her haven, safe from her unequall'd
way !
And now, in louder and yet louder joy
Clamorous, the happy mariners all-hail
Their native shore, and now they leap to
land.   50

There stood an old man on the beach
to wait
The comers from the ocean ; and he
ask'd,
Is it the Prince ? And Madoc knew his
voice,
And turn'd to him and fell upon his
neck ;
For it was Urien who had foster'd him,
Had loved him like a child ; and Madoc
loved,
Even as a father loved he that old man.
My Sister ? quoth the Prince. . . Oh, she
and I
Have wept together, Madoc, for thy
loss, . .
That long and cruel absence ! . . She
and I,   60
Hour after hour and day by day, have
look'd
Toward the waters, and with aching eyes
And aching heart, sate watching every
sail.

And David and our brethren ? cried
the Prince,
As they moved on. . . But then old
Urien's lips
Were slow at answer ; and he spake,
and paused
In the first breath of utterance, as to
choose
Fit words for uttering some unhappy
tale.
More blood, quoth Madoc, yet ? Hath
David's fear
Forced him to still more cruelty ?
Alas . .   70
Woe for the house of Owen !
                          Evil stars,
Replied the old man, ruled o'er thy
brethren's birth.
From Dolwyddelan driven, his peaceful
home,

Poor Yorwerth sought the church's
sanctuary ;
The murderer follow'd ; . . Madoc, need
I say
Who sent the sword ? . . Llewelyn, his
brave boy,   [realm,
Where wanders he ? In this his rightful
Houseless and hunted ; richly would the
King
Gift the red hand that rid him of that
fear !
Ririd, an outlaw'd fugitive, as yet   80
Eludes his deadly purpose ; Rodri lives,
A prisoner he, . . I know not in what fit
Of natural mercy from the slaughter
spared.
Oh, if my dear old master saw the wreck
And scattering of his house ! . . that
princely race !
The beautiful band of brethren that
they were !

Madoc made no reply, . . he closed his
eyes,
Groaning. But Urien, for his heart was
full,
Loving to linger on the woe, pursued :
I did not think to live to such an hour 90
Of joy as this ! and often, when my sight
Turn'd dizzy from the ocean, overcome
With heavy anguish, Madoc, I have
prayed
That God would please to take me to his
rest.

So as he ceased his speech, a sudden
shout
Of popular joy awakened Madoc's ear ;
And calling then to mind the festal fires,
He ask'd their import. The old man
replied,
It is the giddy people merry-making
To welcome their new Queen ; unheed-
ing they   100
The shame and the reproach to the long
line
Of our old royalty ! . . Thy brother weds
The Saxon's sister.
                  What ! . . in loud reply
Madoc exclaim'd, hath he forgotten all ?
David ! King Owen's son, . . my father's
son, . .
He wed the Saxon, . . the Plantagenet !

Quoth Urien, He so doats, as she had
  dropt
Some philtre in his cup, to lethargize
The British blood that came from Owen's
  veins.
Three days his halls have echoed to the
  song   110
Of joyaunce.
              Shame! foul shame! that
  they should hear
Songs of such joyaunce! cried the
  indignant Prince:
Oh that my Father's hall, where I
  have heard
The songs of Corwen and of Keiriog's
  day,
Should echo this pollution! Will the
  chiefs
Brook this alliance, this unnatural tie?

There is no face but wears a courtly
  smile,
Urien replied: Aberfraw's ancient
  towers
Beheld no pride of festival like this,
No like solemnities, when Owen came
In conquest, and Gowalchmai struck the
  harp.   121
Only Goervyl, careless of the pomp,
Sits in her solitude, lamenting thee.

Saw ye not then my banner? quoth
  the Lord
Of Ocean; on the topmast-head it
  stood
To tell the tale of triumph; .. or did
  night
Hide the glad signal, and the joy hath
  yet
To reach her?
            Now had they almost attain'd
The palace portal. Urien stopt and
  said,
The child should know your coming; it
  is long   130
Since she hath heard a voice that to her
  heart
Spake gladness; .. none but I must tell
  her this.
So Urien sought Goervyl, whom he
  found
Alone and gazing on the moonlight
  sea.

Oh you are welcome, Urien! cried the
  maid
There was a ship came sailing hither-
  ward ..
I could not see his banner, for the night
Closed in so fast around her; but my
  heart
Indulged a foolish hope!
                    The old man replied,
With difficult effort keeping his heart
  down,   140
God in his goodness may reserve for us
That blessing yet! I have yet life enow
To trust that I shall live to see the day,
Albeit the number of my years well nigh
Be full.
        Ill-judging kindness! said the
  maid.
Have I not nursed for two long wretched
  years
That miserable hope, which every day
Grew weaker, like a baby sick to death,
Yet dearer for its weakness day by day!
No, never shall we see his daring bark!
I knew and felt it in the evil hour   151
When forth she fared! I felt it then!
  that kiss
Was our death parting! .. And she
  paused to curb
The agony: anon, .. But thou hast been
To learn their tidings, Urien? .. He
  replied,
In half-articulate words, .. They said,
  my child,
That Madoc lived, .. that soon he would
  be here.

She had received the shock of happiness:
Urien! she cried .. thou art not mocking
  me!
Nothing the old man spake, but spread
  his arms   160
Sobbing aloud. Goervyl from their hold
Started, and sunk upon her brother's
  breast.

Recovering first, the aged Urien said,
Enough of this, .. there will be time for
  this,
My children! better it behoves ye now
To seek the King. And, Madoc, I
  beseech thee,

Bear with thy brother ! gently bear with
    him,
My gentle Prince ! he is the headstrong
    slave
Of passions unsubdued ; he feels no tie
Of kindly love, or blood ; .. provoke him
    not,   170
Madoc ! .. It is his nature's malady.

    Thou good old man ! replied the
        Prince, be sure
I shall remember what to him is due,
What to myself ; for I was in my youth
Wisely and well train'd up; nor yet hath
    time
Effaced the lore my foster-father taught.

    Haste, haste ! exclaim'd Goervyl ; ..
        for her heart
Smote her in sudden terror at the thought
Of Yorwerth, and of Owen's broken
    house ; ..
I dread his dark suspicions !
                    Not for me
Suffer that fear, my sister ! quoth the
    Prince.   181
Safe is the straight and open way I
    tread ; .
Nor hath God made the human heart so
    bad
That thou or I should have a danger
    there.
So saying, they toward the palace gate
Went on, ere yet Aberfraw had received
The tidings of her wanderer's glad
    return.

II. THE MARRIAGE FEAST

THE guests were seated at the festal
    board ;
Green rushes strew'd the floor ; high in
    the hall
Was David ; Emma, in her bridal robe,
In youth, in beauty, by her husband's
    side
Sate at the marriage feast. The
    monarch raised
His eyes, he saw the mariner approach ;
Madoc ! he cried ; strong nature's
    impulses

Prevail'd, and with a holy joy he met
His brother's warm embrace.
                    With that what peals
Of exultation shook Aberfraw's tower !
How then re-echoing rang the home of
    Kings,   11
When from subdued Ocean, from the
    World
That he had first foreseen, he first had
    found,
Came her triumphant child ! The
    mariners,
A happy band, enter the clamorous hall ;
Friend greets with friend, and all are
    friends ; one joy
Fills with one common feeling every
    heart,
And strangers give and take the wel-
    coming
Of hand and voice and eye. That
    boisterous joy
At length allay'd, the board was spread
    anew,   20
Anew the horn was brimm'd, the central
    hearth
Built up anew for later revelries.
Now to the ready feast ! the seneschal
Duly below the pillars ranged the crew ;
Toward the guest's most honourable seat
The King himself led his brave brother ;
    .. then,
Eyeing the lovely Saxon as he spake,
Here, Madoc, see thy sister ! thou hast
    been
Long absent, and our house hath felt
    the while
Sad diminution ; but my arm at last 30
Hath rooted out rebellion from the land ;
And I have stablish'd now our ancient
    house,
Grafting a scyon from the royal tree
Of England on the sceptre ; so shall
    peace
Bless our dear country.
                    Long and happy years
Await my sovereigns ! thus the Prince
    replied,
And long may our dear country rest in
    peace !
Enough of sorrow hath our royal house
Known in the field of battles, .. yet we
    reap'd
The harvest of renown

Ay, . . many a day, 40
David replied, together have we led
The onset. . . Dost thou not remember,
brother,
How in that hot and unexpected charge
On Keiriog's bank, we gave the enemy
Their welcoming ?
            And Berwyn's after-strife !
Quoth Madoc, as the memory kindled
him :
The fool that day, who in his masque
attire
Sported before King Henry, wished in
vain
Fitlier habiliments of javelin-proof !
And yet not more precipitate that fool
Dropt his mock weapons, than the
archers cast   51
Desperate their bows and quivers-full
away,
When we leapt on, and in the mire and
blood
Trampled their banner !
            That, exclaimed the King,
That was a day indeed, which I may still
Proudly remember, proved as I have
been
In conflicts of such perilous assay,
That Saxon combat seem'd like woman's
war.
When with the traitor Hoel I did wage
The deadly battle, then was I in truth 60
Put to the proof ; no vantage-ground
was there,
Nor famine, nor disease, nor storms to
aid,
But equal, hard, close battle, man to
man,
Briton to Briton. By my soul, pursued
The tyrant, heedless how from Madoc's
eye
Flash'd the quick wrath like lightning, . .
though I knew
The rebel's worth, his prowess then
excited
Unwelcome wonder ; even at the last,
When stiff with toil and faint with
wounds, he raised
Feebly his broken sword, . .
            Then Madoc's grief
Found utterance ; Wherefore, David,
dost thou rouse   71
The memory now of that unhappy day,

That thou should'st wish to hide from
earth and heaven ?
Not in Aberfraw, . . not to me this tale !
Tell it the Saxon ! . . he will join thy
triumph,
He hates the race of Owen ! . . but I
loved
My brother Hoel, . . loved him ? . . that
ye knew !
I was to him the dearest of his kin,
And he my own heart's brother.
                    David's cheek
Grew pale and dark ; he bent his broad
black brow   80
Full upon Madoc's glowing countenance;
Art thou return'd to brave me ? to my
teeth
To praise the rebel bastard ? to insult
The royal Saxon, my affianced friend ?
I hate the Saxon ! Madoc cried ; not yet
Have I forgotten, how from Keiriog's
shame
Flying, the coward wreak'd his cruelty
On our poor brethren ! . . David, seest
thou never
Those eyeless spectres by thy bridal bed?
Forget that horror ? . . may the fire of
God   90
Blast my right hand, or ever it be link'd
With that accursed Plantagenet's !
                    The while,
Impatience struggled in the heaving
breast
Of David ; every agitated limb
Shook with ungovernable wrath ; the
page,
Who chafed his feet, in fear suspends his
task ;
In fear the guests gaze on him silently ;
His eyeballs flash'd, strong anger choked
his voice,
He started up. . . Him Emma, by the
hand   99
Gently retaining, held, with gentle words
Calming his rage. Goervyl too in tears
Besought her generous brother : he had
met
Emma's reproaching glance, and self-
reproved,
While the warm blood flush'd deeper o'er
his cheek,
Thus he replied ; I pray you pardon
me,

My Sister-Queen ! nay, you will learn to
love
This high affection for the race of Owen,
Yourself the daughter of his royal house
By better ties than blood.
     Grateful the Queen
Replied, by winning smile and eloquent
eye   110
Thanking the gentle Prince: a moment's
pause
Ensued ; Goervyl then with timely
speech
Thus to the wanderer of the waters
spake :
Madoc, thou hast not told us of the
world
Beyond the ocean and the paths of man.
A lovely land it needs must be, my
brother,
Or sure you had not sojourn'd there so
long,
Of me forgetful, and my heavy hours
Of grief and solitude and wretched
hope.
Where is Cadwallon ? for one bark
alone   120
I saw come sailing here.
     The tale you ask
Is long, Goervyl, said the mariner,
And I in truth am weary. Many moons
Have wax'd and waned, since from that
distant world,
The country of my dreams and hope and
faith,
We spread the homeward sail : a goodly
world,
My Sister ! thou wilt see its goodliness,
And greet Cadwallon there. . . But this
shall be
To-morrow's tale ; . . indulge we now
the feast ! . .
You know not with what joy we mariners
Behold a sight like this.
     Smiling he spake, 131
And turning, from the sewer's hand he
took
The flowing mead. David, the while,
relieved
From rising jealousies, with better eye
Regards his venturous brother. Let the
Bard,
Exclaim'd the King, give his accustom'd
lay ;

For sweet, I know, to Madoc is the song
He loved in earlier years.
     Then, strong of voice,
The officer proclaim'd the sovereign will,
Bidding the hall be silent ; loud he
spake,   140
And smote the sounding pillar with his
wand,
And hush'd the banqueters. The chief
of Bards
Then raised the ancient lay.
     Thee, Lord ! he sung,
O Father ! Thee, whose wisdom, Thee,
whose power,
Whose love, . . all love, all power, all
wisdom, Thou !
Tongue cannot utter, nor can heart con-
ceive.
He in the lowest depth of Being framed
The imperishable mind ; in every
change,
Through the great circle of progressive
life,
He guides and guards, till evil shall be
known,   150
And being known as evil, cease to be ;
And the pure soul, emancipate by Death,
The Enlarger, shall attain its end pre-
doom'd,
The eternal newness of eternal joy.

He left this lofty theme ; he struck the
harp
To Owen's praise, swift in the course of
wrath,
Father of Heroes. That proud day he
sung,
When from green Erin came the insulting host,
Lochlin's long burthens of the flood, and
they
Who left their distant homes in evil
hour,   160
The death-doom'd Normen. There was
heaviest toil,
There deeper tumult, where the dragon
race
Of Mona trampled down the humbled
head
Of haughty power ; the sword of
slaughter carved
Food for the yellow-footed fowl of
heaven,

And Menai's waters, burst with plunge
  on plunge,
Curling above their banks with tempest-
  swoll
Their bloody billows heaved.
                    The long-past days
Came on the mind of Madoc, as he heard
That song of triumph ; on his sun-burnt
  brow   170
Sate exultation : . . other thoughts arose,
As on the fate of all his gallant house
Mournful he mused ; oppressive memory
  swell'd
His bosom, over his fix'd eye-balls swam
The tear's dim lustre, and the loud-
  toned harp
Rung on his ear in vain ; . . its silence
  first
Roused him from dreams of days that
  were no more.

III. CADWALLON

THEN on the morrow, at the festal board,
The Lord of Ocean thus began his tale.

  My heart beat high when with the
    favouring wind
We sail'd away ; Aberfraw ! when thy
  towers,
And the huge headland of my mother
  isle,
Shrunk and were gone.
              But, Madoc, I would learn,
Quoth David, how this enterprize arose,
And the wild hope of worlds beyond the
  sea ;
For, at thine outset, being in the war,
I did not hear from vague and common
  fame   10
The moving cause. Sprung it from
  bardic lore,
The hidden wisdom of the years of old,
Forgotten long ? or did it visit thee
In dreams that come from Heaven ?
                    The Prince replied,
Thou shalt hear all ; . . but if, amid the
  tale,
Strictly sincere, I haply should rehearse
Aught to the King ungrateful, let my
  brother
Be patient with the involuntary fault.

I was the guest of Rhys at Dinevawr,
And there the tidings found me, that
  our sire   20
Was gather'd to his fathers : . . not alone
The sorrow came ; the same ill mes-
  senger
Told of the strife that shook our royal
  house,
When Hoel, proud of prowess, seized
  the throne
Which you, for elder claim and lawful
  birth,
Challenged in arms. With all a brother's
  love,
I on the instant hurried to prevent
The impious battle : . . all the day I sped ;
Night did not stay me on my eager
  way . .
Where'er I pass'd, new rumour raised
  new fear. . .   30
Midnight, and morn, and noon, I hur-
  ried on,
And the late eve was darkening when
  I reach'd
Arvon, the fatal field. . . The sight, the
  sounds,
Live in my memory now, . . for all was
  done !
For horse and horseman, side by side in
  death,
Lay on the bloody plain ; . . a host of
  men,
And not one living soul, . . and not one
  sound,
One human sound ; . . only the raven's
  wing,
Which rose before my coming, and the
  neigh
Of wounded horses, wandering o'er the
  plain.   40

  Night now was coming on ; a man
    approach'd
And bade me to his dwelling nigh at
  hand.
Thither I turn'd, too weak to travel
  more ;
For I was overspent with weariness,
And having now no hope to bear me up,
Trouble and bodily labour master'd me.
I ask'd him of the battle : . . who had
  fallen
He knew not, nor to whom the lot of war

Had given my father's sceptre.   Here,
    said he,
I came to seek if haply I might find   50
Some wounded wretch, abandon'd else
    to death.
My search was vain, the sword of civil
    war
Had bit too deeply.
            Soon we reach'd his home,
A lone and lowly dwelling in the hills,
By a grey mountain stream.   Beside the
    hearth
There sate an old blind man ; his head
    was raised
As he were listening to the coming
    sounds,
And in the fire-light shone his silver
    locks.
Father, said he who guided me, I bring
A guest to our poor hospitality ;   60
And then he brought me water from the
    brook,
And homely fare, and I was satisfied :
That done, he piled the hearth, and
    spread around
The rushes of repose.   I laid me down;
But worn with toil, and full of many
    fears,
Sleep did not visit me : the quiet sounds
Of nature troubled my distemper'd
    sense ;
My ear was busy with the stirring gale,
The moving leaves, the brook's per-
    petual flow.   69

So on the morrow languidly I rose,
And faint with fever : but a restless
    wish
Was working in me, and I said, My host,
Wilt thou go with me to the battle-field,
That I may search the slain ? for in the
    fray
My brethren fought ; and though with
    all my speed
I strove to reach them ere the strife
    began,
Alas, I sped too slow !
            Grievest thou for that ?
He answer'd, grievest thou that thou art
    spared
The shame and guilt of that unhappy
    strife,   79
Briton with Briton in unnatural war ?

Nay, I replied, mistake me not ! I came
To reconcile the chiefs ; they might
    have heard
Their brother's voice.
            Their brother's voice ? said he,
Was it not so ? . . And thou, too, art the
    son
Of Owen ! . . Yesternight I did not know
The cause there is to pity thee.   Alas,
Two brethren thou wilt lose when one
    shall fall ! . .
Lament not him whom death may save
    from guilt ;
For all too surely in the conqueror
Thou wilt find one whom his own fears
    henceforth   90
Must make to all his kin a perilous foe.

I felt as though he wrong'd my
    father's sons,
And raised an angry eye, and answer'd
    him, . .
My brethren love me.
            Then the old man cried,
Oh what is Princes' love ? what are the
    ties
Of blood, the affections growing as we
    grow,
If but ambition come ? . . Thou deemest
    sure
Thy brethren love thee ; . . ye have
    play'd together
In childhood, shared your riper hopes
    and fears,
Fought side by side in battle : . . they
    may be   100
Brave, generous, all that once their
    father was,
Whom ye, I ween, call virtuous.
            At the name,
With pious warmth, I cried, Yes, he was
    good,
And great, and glorious ! Gwyneth's
    ancient annals
Boast not a name more noble.   In the
    war
Fearless he was, . . the Saxon found him
    so ;
Wise was his counsel, and no supplicant
For justice ever from his palace-gate
Unrighted turn'd away.   King Owen's
    name   109
Shall live to after times without a blot !

There were two brethren once of kingly
line,
The old man replied; they loved each
other well,
And when the one was at his dying hour,
It then was comfort to him that he left
So dear a brother, who would duly pay
A father's duties to his orphan boy.
And sure he loved the orphan, and the
boy
With all a child's sincerity loved him,
And learnt to call him father: so the
years
Went on, till when the orphan gain'd
the age   120
Of manhood, to the throne his uncle
came.
The young man claim'd a fair inherit-
ance,
His father's lands; and . . mark what
follows, Prince !
At midnight he was seized, and to his
eyes
The brazen plate was held. . . He cried
aloud,
He look'd around for help, . . he only
saw
His Uncle's ministers, prepared to do
Their wicked work, who to the red hot
brass
Forced his poor eyes, and held the open
lids,   129
Till the long agony consumed the sense ;
And when their hold relax'd, it had
been worth
The wealth of worlds if he could then
have seen,
Dreadful to him and hideous as they
were,
Their ruffian faces ! . . I am blind, young
Prince,
And I can tell how sweet a thing it is
To see the blessed light !
                Must more be told ?
What farther agonies he yet endured ?
Or hast thou known the consummated
crime,
And heard Cynetha's fate ?
                A painful glow
Inflamed my cheek, and for my father's
crime   140
I felt the shame of guilt. The dark-
brow'd man

Beheld the burning flush, the uneasy
eye,
That knew not where to rest. Come !
we will search
The slain ! arising from his seat, he said.
I follow'd ; to the field of fight we went,
And over steeds and arms and men we
held
Our way in silence. Here it was, quoth
he,
The fiercest war was waged ; lo ! in
what heaps
Man upon man fell slaughter'd ! Then
my heart
Smote me, and my knees shook ; for
I beheld   150
Where, on his conquer'd foemen, Hoel
lay.

      He paused, his heart was full, and on
his tongue
The imperfect utterance died ; a general
gloom
Sadden'd the hall, and David's cheek
grew pale.
Commanding first his feelings, Madoc
broke
The oppressive silence.
                Then Cadwallon took
My hand, and, pointing to his dwelling,
cried,
Prince, go and rest thee there, for thou
hast need
Of rest ; . . the care of sepulture be mine.
Nor did I then comply, refusing rest, 160
Till I had seen in holy ground inearth'd
My poor lost brother. Wherefore, he
exclaim'd,
(And I was awed by his severer eye)
Wouldst thou be pampering thy dis-
tempered mind ?
Affliction is not sent in vain, young
man,
From that good God, who chastens
whom he loves.
Oh ! there is healing in the bitter cup !
Go yonder, and before the unerring will
Bow, and have comfort ! To the hut
I went,
And there beside the lonely mountain-
stream,   170
I veil'd my head, and brooded on the
past.

He tarried long ; I felt the hours pass
  by,
As in a dream of morning, when the
  mind,
Half to reality awaken'd, blends
With airy visions and vague phantasies
Her dim perception ; till at length his
  step
Aroused me, and he came. I question'd
  him,
Where is the body ? hast thou bade the
  priests
Perform due masses for his soul's re-
  pose ?

He answer'd me, The rain and dew of
  heaven   180
Will fall upon the turf that covers him,
And greener grass will flourish on his
  grave.
But rouse thee, Prince ! there will be
  hours enough
For mournful memory ; . . it befits thee
  now
Take counsel for thyself : . . the son of
  Owen
Lives not in safety here.
              I bow'd my head
Opprest by heavy thoughts : all wretch-
  edness
The present ; darkness on the future lay ;
Fearful and gloomy both. I answer'd
  not.

Hath power seduced thy wishes ? he
  pursued,   190
And wouldst thou seize upon thy father's
  throne ?
Now God forbid ! quoth I. Now God
  forbid !
Quoth he ; . . but thou art dangerous,
  Prince ! and what
Shall shield thee from the jealous arm
  of power ?
Think of Cynetha ! . . the unsleeping eye
Of justice hath not closed upon his
  wrongs ;
At length the avenging arm is gone
  abroad,
One woe is past, . . woe after woe comes
  on, . .
There is no safety here, . . here thou
  must be

The victim or the murderer ! Does thy
  heart   200
Shrink from the alternative ? . . look
  round ! . . behold
What shelter, . . whither wouldst thou
  fly for peace ?
What if the asylum of the Church were
  safe, . .
Were there no better purposes ordain'd
For that young arm, that heart of noble
  hopes ?
Son of our kings, . . of old Cassibelan,
Great Caratach, immortal Arthur's line,
Oh, shall the blood of that heroic race
Stagnate in cloister-sloth ? . . Or wouldst
  thou leave
Thy native isle, and beg in awkward
  phrase   210
Some foreign sovereign's charitable
  grace, . .
The Saxon or the Frank, . . and earn his
  gold,
The hireling in a war whose cause thou
  know'st not,
Whose end concerns not thee ?
              I sate and gazed,
Following his eye with wonder, as he
  paced
Before me to and fro, and listening still,
Though now he paced in silence. But
  anon,
The old man's voice and step awakened
  us
Each from his thought ; I will come out,
  said he,
That I may sit beside the brook, and
  feel   220
The comfortable sun. As forth he
  came,
I could not choose but look upon his face :
Gently on him had gentle nature laid
The weight of years ; all passions that
  disturb
Were pass'd away ; the stronger lines of
  grief
Soften'd and settled, till they told of
  grief
By patient hope and piety subdued :
His eyes, which had their hue and
  brightness left,
Fix'd lifelessly, or objectless they roll'd,
Nor moved by sense, nor animate with
  thought.   230

On a smooth stone beside the stream he
took
His wonted seat in the sunshine. Thou
hast lost
A brother, Prince, he said . . or the dull
ear
Of age deceived me. Peace be with his
soul !
And may the curse that lies upon the
house
Of Owen turn away ! Wilt thou come
hither,
And let me feel thy face ? . . I wondered
at him :
Yet while his hand perused my linea-
ments
Deep awe and reverence fill'd me. O my
God,
Bless this young man ! he cried ; a
perilous state   240
Is his ; . . but let not thou his father's
sins
Be visited on him !
                    I raised my eyes
Enquiring, to Cadwallon ; Nay, young
Prince,
Despise not thou the blind man's prayer !
he cried ;
It might have given thy father's dying
hour
A hope, that sure he needed . . for, know
thou,
It is the victim of thy father's crime,
Who asks a blessing on thee !
                              At his feet
I fell, and clasp'd his knees : he raised
me up ; . .
Blind as I was, a mutilated wretch, 250
A thing that nature owns not, I survived,
Loathing existence, and with impious
voice
Accused the will of heaven, and groan'd
for death.
Years pass'd away ; this universal blank
Became familiar, and my soul reposed
On God, and I had comfort in my
prayers.
But there were blessings for me yet in
store.
Thy father knew not, when his bloody
fear
All hope of an avenger had cut off,
How there existed then an unborn babe,

Child of my lawless love. Year after
year   261
I lived a lonely and forgotten wretch,
Before Cadwallon knew his father's fate,
Long years and years before I knew my
son ;
For never, till his mother's dying hour,
Learnt he his dangerous birth. He
sought me then ;
He woke my soul once more to human
ties ; . .
I hope he hath not wean'd my heart
from heaven,
Life is so precious now ! . .
                    Dear good old man !
And lives he still ? Goervyl ask'd, in
tears ;   270
Madoc replied, I scarce can hope to find
A father's welcome at my distant home.
I left him full of days, and ripe for death ;
And the last prayer Cynetha breathed
upon me
Went like a death-bed blessing to my
heart !

When evening came, toward the
echoing shore
I and Cadwallon walk'd together forth :
Bright with dilated glory shone the west ;
But brighter lay the ocean flood below,
The burnish'd silver sea, that heaved
and flash'd   280
Its restless rays, intolerably bright.
Prince, quoth Cadwallon, thou hast rode
the waves
In triumph, when the invaders felt
thine arm.
Oh what a nobler conquest might be
won,
There, . . upon that wide field ! . . What
meanest thou ?
I cried. . . That yonder waters are not
spread
A boundless waste, a bourne impass-
able ! . .
That man should rule the Elements ! . .
that there
Might manly courage, manly wisdom
find
Some happy isle, some undiscovered
shore,   290
Some resting place for peace. . . Oh that
my soul

Could seize the wings of Morning ! soon
    would I
Behold that other world, where yonder
    sun
Speeds now, to dawn in glory !
               As he spake,
Conviction came upon my startled mind,
Like lightning on the midnight traveller.
I caught his hand; .. Kinsman and guide
    and friend,
Yea, let us go together ! . . Down we
    sate,
Full of the vision on the echoing shore ;
One only object fill'd ear, eye, and
    thought :   300
We gazed upon the aweful world of
    waves,
And talk'd and dreamt of years that
    were to come.

IV. THE VOYAGE

NOT with a heart unmoved I left thy
    shores,
Dear native isle ! oh . . not without a
    pang,
As thy fair uplands lessen'd on the view,
Cast back the long involuntary look !
The morning cheer'd our outset ; gentle
    airs
Curl'd the blue deep, and bright the
    summer sun
Play'd o'er the summer ocean, when our
    barks
Began their way.
          And they were gallant barks,
As ever through the raging billows rode ;
And many a tempest's buffeting they
    bore.   10
Their sails all swelling with the eastern
    breeze,
Their tighten'd cordage clattering to
    the mast,
Steady they rode the main : the gale
    aloft
Sung in the shrouds, the sparkling
    waters hiss'd
Before, and froth'd and whiten'd far
    behind.
Day after day, with one auspicious wind,
Right to the setting sun we held our
    course.

My hope had kindled every heart ; they
    blest
The unvarying breeze, whose unabating
    strength
Still sped us onward ; and they said
    that Heaven   20
Favour'd the bold emprize.
               How many a time,
Mounting the mast-tower-top, with
    eager ken
They gazed, and fancied in the distant
    sky
Their promised shore, beneath the
    evening cloud,
Or seen, low lying, through the haze of
    morn.
I too with eyes as anxious watch'd the
    waves,
Though patient, and prepared for long
    delay ;
For not on wild adventure had I rush'd
With giddy speed, in some delirious fit
Of fancy ; but in many a tranquil hour
Weigh'd well the attempt, till hope
    matured to faith.   31
Day after day, day after day the same, ..
A weary waste of waters ! still the breeze
Hung heavy in our sails, and we held on
One even course : a second week was
    gone,
And now another past, and still the
    same,
Waves beyond waves, the interminable
    sea !
What marvel, if at length the mariners
Grew sick with long expectance ? I
    beheld
Dark looks of growing restlessness, I
    heard   40
Distrust's low murmurings ; nor avail'd
    it long
To see and not perceive. Shame had
    awhile
Represt their fear, till like a smother'd
    fire
It burst, and spread with quick con-
    tagion round,
And strengthen'd as it spread. They
    spake in tones
Which might not be mistaken ; .. They
    had done
What men dared do, ventured where
    never keel

Had cut the deep before : still all was
    sea,
The same unbounded ocean ! . . to pro-
    ceed
Were tempting heaven.
        I heard with feign'd surprise,
And, pointing then to where our fellow
    bark,   51
Gay with her fluttering streamers and
    full sails,
Rode, as in triumph, o'er the element,
I ask'd them what their comrades there
    would deem
Of those so bold ashore, who, when a day,
Perchance an hour, might crown their
    glorious toil,
Shrunk then, and coward-like return'd
    to meet
Mockery and shame ? True, they had
    ventured on
In seas unknown, beyond where ever
    man
Had plough'd the billows yet : more
    reason so   60
Why they should now, like him whose
    happy speed
Well nigh hath run the race, with higher
    hope
Press onward to the prize.   But late
    they said,
Marking the favour of the steady gale,
That Heaven was with us ; Heaven
    vouchsafed us still
Fair seas and favouring skies : nor need
    we pray
For other aid, the rest was in ourselves ;
Nature had given it, when she gave to
    man
Courage and constancy.
        They answer'd not,
Awhile obedient ;   but I saw with
    dread   70
The silent sullenness of cold assent.
Then, with what fearful eagerness I
    gazed
At earliest daybreak, o'er the distant
    deep !
How sick at heart with hope, when
    evening closed,
Gazed through the gathering shadows !
    . . but I saw
The sun still sink below the endless
    waves,

And still at morn, beneath the farthest
    sky,
Unbounded ocean heaved.   Day after
    day
Before the steady gale we drove along, . .
Day after day !   The fourth week now
    had pass'd ;   80
Still all around was sea, . . the eternal
    sea !
So long that we had voyaged on so fast,
And still at morning where we were at
    night,
And where we were at morn, at nightfall
    still,
The centre of that drear circumference,
Progressive, yet no change ! . . almost it
    seem'd
That we had pass'd the mortal bounds
    of space,
And speed was toiling in infinity.
My days were days of fear, my hours of
    rest
Were like a tyrant's slumber.   Sullen
    looks,   90
Eyes turn'd on me, and whispers meant
    to meet
My ear, and loud despondency, and talk
Of home, now never to be seen again, . .
I suffer'd these, dissembling as I could,
Till that avail'd no longer.   Resolute
The men came round me :   They had
    shown enough
Of courage now, enough of constancy ;
Still to pursue the desperate enterprize
Were impious madness !   they had
    deem'd, indeed,
That Heaven in favour gave the un-
    changing gale ; . .   100
More reason now to think offended God,
When man's presumptuous folly strove
    to pass
The fated limits of the world, had sent
His winds, to waft us to the death we
    sought.
Their lives were dear, they bade me
    know, and they
Many, and I, the obstinate, but one.
With that, attending no reply, they
    hail'd
Our fellow bark, and told their fix'd
    resolve.
A   shout of   joy   approved.   Thus,
    desperate now,

I sought my solitary cabin : there   110
Confused with vague tumultuous feel-
     ings lay,
And to remembrance and reflection lost,
Knew only I was wretched.
                    Thus entranced
Cadwallon found me ; shame, and grief,
     and pride,
And baffled hope, and fruitless anger
     swell'd
Within me.   All is over ! I exclaim'd ;
Yet not in me, my friend, hath time
     produced
These tardy doubts and shameful fickle-
     ness ;
I have not fail'd, Cadwallon ! Nay, he
     said,
The coward fears which persecuted me
Have shown what thou hast suffer'd.
     We have yet   121
One hope . . I pray'd them to proceed a
     day, . .
But one day more ; . . this little have
     I gain'd,
And here will wait the issue ; in yon bark
I am not needed, . . they are masters
     there.

One only day! . . The gale blew strong,
     the bark
Sped through the waters ; but the silent
     hours,
Who make no pause, went by ; and
     center'd still,
We saw the dreary vacancy of heaven
Close round our narrow view, when that
     brief term,   130
The last poor respite of our hopes, ex-
     pired.
They shorten'd sail, and call'd with
     coward prayer
For homeward winds.   Why, what poor
     slaves are we,
In bitterness I cried ;   the sport of
     chance ;
Left to the mercy of the elements,
Or the more wayward will of such as
     these,
Blind tools and victims of their destiny !
Yea, Madoc ! he replied, the Elements
Master indeed the feeble powers of man !
Not to the shores of Cambria will thy
     ships   140

Win back their shameful way ! . . or HE,
     whose will
Unchains the winds, hath bade them
     minister
To aid us, when all human hope was gone,
Or we shall soon eternally repose
From life's long voyage.
                    As he spake, I saw
The clouds hang thick and heavy o'er
     the deep,
And heavily, upon the long slow swell,
The vessel labour'd on the labouring sea.
The reef-points rattled on the shivering
     sail ;
At fits the sudden gust howl'd ominous,
Anon with unremitting fury raged ; 151
High roll'd the mighty billows, and the
     blast
Swept from their sheeted sides the
     showery foam.
Vain now were all the seamen's home-
     ward hopes,
Vain all their skill ! . . we drove before
     the storm.

'Tis pleasant, by the cheerful hearth,
     to hear
Of tempests and the dangers of the deep,
And pause at times, and feel that we are
     safe ;   158
Then listen to the perilous tale again,
And with an eager and suspended soul,
Woo terror to delight us. . . But to hear
The roaring of the raging elements, . .
To know all human skill, all human
     strength,
Avail not, . . to look round, and only see
The mountain wave incumbent with its
     weight
Of bursting waters o'er the reeling
     bark, . .
O God, this is indeed a dreadful thing !
And he who hath endured the horror once
Of such an hour, doth never hear the
     storm
Howl round his home, but he remembers
     it,   170
And thinks upon the suffering mariner.

Onward we drove : with unabating
     force
The tempest raged ; night added to the
     storm

New horrors, and the morn arose o'er-
    spread
With heavier clouds. The weary
    mariners
Call'd on Saint Cyric's aid; and I too
    placed
My hope on Heaven, relaxing not the
    while
Our human efforts. Ye who dwell at
    home,
Ye do not know the terrors of the main !
When the winds blow, ye walk along
    the shore, 180
And as the curling billows leap and toss,
Fable that Ocean's mermaid Shepherdess
Drives her white flocks afield, and warns
    in time   [warn'd
The wary fisherman. Gwenhidwy
When we had no retreat ! My secret
    heart
Almost had fail'd me. . . Were the
    Elements
Confounded in perpetual conflict here,
Sea, Air, and Heaven ? Or were we
    perishing,
Where at their source the Floods, for
    ever thus,
Beneath the nearer influence of the
    moon, 190
Labour'd in these mad workings ? Did
    the Waters
Here on their outmost circle meet the
    void,
The verge and brink of Chaos ? Or this
    Earth, . .
Was it indeed a living thing, . . its breath
The ebb and flow of Ocean ? and had we
Reach'd the storm rampart of its Sanc-
    tuary,
The insuperable boundary, raised to
    guard
Its mysteries from the eye of man pro-
    fane ?

    Three dreadful nights and days we
    drove along ;
The fourth the welcome rain came
    rattling down, 200
The wind had fallen, and through the
    broken cloud
Appeared the bright dilating blue of
    heaven.
Embolden'd now, I call'd the mariners: . .

Vain were it should we bend a home-
    ward course.
Driven by the storm so far ; they saw
    our barks,
For service of that long and perilous way
Disabled, and our food belike to fail.
Silent they heard, reluctant in assent ;
Anon, they shouted joyfully, . . I look'd
And saw a bird slow sailing overhead,
His long white pinions by the sunbeam
    edged 211
As though with burnish'd silver ; . .
    never yet
Heard I so sweet a music as his cry !

    Yet three days more, and hope more
    eager now,
Sure of the signs of land, . . weed-shoals,
    and birds
Who flock'd the main, and gentle airs
    which breathed,
Or seem'd to breathe, fresh fragrance
    from the shore,
On the last evening, a long shadowy line
Skirted the sea ; . . how fast the night
    closed in !
I stood upon the deck, and watch'd till
    dawn. 220
But who can tell what feelings fill'd my
    heart,
When like a cloud the distant land arose
Grey from the ocean, . . when we left the
    ship,
And cleft, with rapid oars, the shallow
    wave,
And stood triumphant on another world !

V. LINCOYA

MADOC had paused awhile ; but every
    eye
Still watch'd his lips, and every voice
    was hush'd.
Soon as I leapt ashore, pursues the Lord
Of Ocean, prostrate on my face I fell,
Kiss'd the dear earth, and pray'd with
    thankful tears.
Hard by a brook was flowing ; . . never
    yet,
Even from the gold-tipt horn of victory
With harp and song amid my father's
    hall,

Pledged I so sweet a draught, as lying
    there,
Beside that streamlet's brink ! . . to feel
    the ground,   10
To quaff the cool clear water, to inhale
The breeze of land, while fears and
    dangers past
Recurr'd and heighten'd joy, as summer
    storms
Make the fresh evening lovelier !
                  To the shore
The natives throng'd ; astonish'd, they
    beheld
Our winged barks, and gazed with
    wonderment
On the strange garb, the bearded coun-
    tenance
And the white skin, in all unlike them-
    selves.
I see with what enquiring eyes you ask
What men were they ? Of dark-brown
    colour, tinged   20
With sunny redness ; wild of eye ; their
    brows
So smooth, as never yet anxiety
Nor busy thought had made a furrow
    there ;
Beardless, and each to each of linea-
    ments
So like, they seem'd but one great
    family,
Their loins were loosely cinctured, all
    beside
Bare to the sun and wind ; and thus
    their limbs
Unmanacled display'd the truest forms
Of strength and beauty. Fearless sure
    they were,
And while they eyed us grasp'd their
    spears, as if,   30
Like Britain's injured but unconquer'd
    sons,
They too had known how perilous it was
To let a stranger, if he came in arms,
Set foot upon their land.
                  But soon the guise
Of men nor purporting nor fearing ill,
Gain'd confidence ; their wild distrust-
    ful looks
Assumed a milder meaning ; over one
I cast my mantle, on another's head
The velvet bonnet placed, and all was
    joy.

We now besought for food ; at once
    they read   40
Our gestures, but I cast a hopeless eye
On hills and thickets, woods, and
    marshy plains,
A waste of rank luxuriance all around.
Thus musing to a lake I follow'd them,
Left when the rivers to their summer
    course
Withdrew ; they scatter'd on its water
    drugs
Of such strange potency, that soon the
    shoals
Coop'd there by Nature prodigally kind,
Floated inebriate. As I gazed, a deer
Sprung from the bordering thicket ; the
    true shaft   50
Scarce with the distant victim's blood
    had stain'd
Its point, when instantly he dropt and
    died,
Such deadly juice imbued it ; yet on
    this
We made our meal unharm'd ; and
    I perceived
The wisest leech that ever in our world
Cull'd herbs of hidden virtue, was to
    these
A child in knowledge.
                  Sorrowing we beheld
The night come on ; but soon did night
    display
More wonders than it veil'd : innumer-
    ous tribes
From the wood-cover swarm'd, and
    darkness made   60
Their beauties visible ; one while they
    stream'd
A bright blue radiance upon flowers
    which closed
Their gorgeous colours from the eye of
    day ;
Now motionless and dark eluded search,
Self-shrouded ; and anon starring the
    sky
Rose like a shower of fire.
                  Our friendly hosts
Now led us to the hut, our that night's
    home,
A rude and spacious dwelling : twisted
    boughs,
And canes and withies formed the walls
    and roof ;

And from the unhewn trunks which
  pillar'd it, 70
Low nets of interwoven reeds were
  hung.
With shouts of honour here they
  gather'd round me,
Ungarmented my limbs, and in a net
With softest feathers lined, a pleasant
  couch,
They laid and left me.
          To our ships return'd,
After soft sojourn here we coasted on,
Insatiate of the wonders and the
  charms
Of earth and air and sea. Thy summer
  woods
Are lovely, O my mother isle! the birch
Light bending on thy banks, thy elmy
  vales, 80
Thy venerable oaks! .. But there, what
  forms
Of beauty clothed the inlands and the
  shore!
All these in stateliest growth, and mixt
  with these
Dark spreading cedar, and the cypress
  tall,
Its pointed summit waving to the wind
Like a long beacon flame; and loveliest
Amid a thousand strange and lovely
  shapes,
The lofty palm, that with its nuts sup-
  plied
Beverage and food; they edged the
  shore and crown'd
The far-off highland summits, their
  straight stems 90
Bare without leaf or bough, erect and
  smooth,
Their tresses nodding like a crested
  helm,
The plumage of the grove.
             Will ye believe
The wonders of the ocean? how its
  shoals
Sprang from the wave, like flashing
  light, .. took wing,
And twinkling with a silver glitterance,
Flew through the air and sunshine? yet
  were these
To sight less wondrous than the tribe
  who swam,
Following like fowlers with uplifted eye

Their falling quarry: .. language cannot
  paint 100
Their splendid tints; though in blue
  ocean seen,
Blue, darkly, deeply, beautifully blue,
In all its rich variety of shades,
Suffused with glowing gold.
          Heaven too had there
Its wonders: .. from a deep, black,
  heavy cloud,
What shall I say? .. a shoot, .. a trunk,
  .. an arm
Came down: .. yea! like a Demon's
  arm, it seized
The waters, Ocean smoked beneath its
  touch,
And rose like dust before the whirlwind's
  force.
But we sail'd onward over tranquil seas,
Wafted by airs so exquisitely mild, 111
That even to breathe became an act of
  will
And sense and pleasure. Not a cloud
  by day
With purple islanded the dark-blue
  deep;
By night the quiet billows heaved and
  glanced
Under the moon, .. that heavenly Moon!
  so bright,
That many a midnight have I paced the
  deck,
Forgetful of the hours of due repose
Yea till the Sun in his full majesty
Went forth, like God beholding his own
  works. 120

Once when a chief was feasting us on
  shore,
A captive served the food: I mark'd
  the youth,
For he had features of a gentler race;
And oftentimes his eye was fix'd on me,
With looks of more than wonder. We
  return'd
At evening to our ships; at night a voice
Came from the sea, the intelligible voice
Of earnest supplication; he had swum
To trust our mercy; up the side he
  sprang,
And look'd among the crew, and singling
  me 130
Fell at my feet. Such friendly tokenings

As our short commerce with the native
    tribes
Had taught, I proffer'd, and sincerity
Gave force and meaning to the half-
    learnt forms.
For one we needed who might speak for
    us ;
And well I liked the youth,—the open
    lines
Which character'd his face, the fearless
    heart,
Which gave at once and won full con-
    fidence.
So that night at my feet Lincoya slept.

When I display'd whate'er might
    gratify,   140
Whate'er surprise, with most delight he
    view'd
Our arms, the iron helm, the pliant mail,
The buckler strong to save ; and then
    he shook
The lance, and grasp'd the sword, and
    turn'd to me
With vehement words and gestures,
    every limb
Working with one strong passion ; and
    he placed
The falchion in my hand, and gave the
    shield,
And pointed south and west, that I
    should go
To conquer and protect ; anon he wept
Aloud, and clasp'd my knees, and falling
    fain   150
He would have kiss'd my feet.   Went
    we to shore ?
Then would he labour restlessly to show
A better place lay onward ; and in the
    sand,
To south and west he drew the line of
    coast,
And figured how a mighty river there
Ran to the sea.   The land bent west-
    ward soon,
And thus confirm'd we voyaged on to
    seek
The river inlet, following at the will
Of our new friend : and we learnt after
    him,
Well pleased and proud to teach, what
    this was call'd,   160
What that, with no unprofitable pains.

Nor light the joy I felt at hearing first
The pleasant accents of my native
    tongue,
Albeit in broken words and tones un-
    couth,
Come from these foreign lips.
                    At length we came
Where the great river, amid shoals and
    banks
And islands, growth of its own gathering
    spoils,
Through many a branching channel,
    wide and full,
Rush'd to the main.   The gale was
    strong ; and safe,
Amid the uproar of conflicting tides, 170
Our gallant vessels rode.   A stream as
    broad
And turbid, when it leaves the Land of
    Hills,
Old Severn rolls ; but banks so fair as
    these
Old Severn views not in his Land of
    Hills,
Nor even where his turbid waters swell
And sully the salt sea.
                    So we sail'd on
By shores now cover'd with impervious
    woods,
Now stretching wide and low, a reedy
    waste,
And now through vales where earth
    profusely pour'd
Her treasures, gather'd from the first of
    days.   180
Sometimes a savage tribe would wel-
    come us,
By wonder from their lethargy of life
Awaken'd ; then again we voyaged on
Through tracts all desolate, for days and
    days,
League after league, one green and
    fertile mead,
That fed a thousand herds.
                    A different scene
Rose on our view, of mount on mountain
    piled,
Which when I see again in memory,
Star-gazing Idris's stupendous seat
Seems dwarf'd, and Snowdon with its
    eagle haunts   190
Shrinks, and is dwindled like a Saxon
    hill.

Here with Cadwallon and a chosen
   band,
I left the ships. Lincoya guided us
A toilsome way among the heights ; at
   dusk
We reach'd the village skirts ; he bade
   us halt,
And raised his voice ; the elders of the
   land
Came forth, and led us to an ample hut,
Which in the centre of their dwellings
   stood,
The Stranger's House. They eyed us
   wondering,
Yet not for wonder ceased they to
   observe   200
Their hospitable rites ; from hut to hut
The tidings ran that strangers were
   arrived,
Fatigued and hungry and athirst; anon,
Each from his means supplying us, came
   food
And beverage such as cheers the weary
   man.

VI. ERILLYAB

At morning their high-priest Ayayaca
Came with our guide : the venerable
   man
With reverential awe accosted us,
For we, he ween'd, were children of a
   race
Mightier than they, and wiser, and by
   heaven
Beloved and favour'd more : he came
   to give
Fit welcome, and he led us to the Queen.
The fate of war had reft her of her realm;
Yet with affection and habitual awe,
And old remembrances, which gave
   their love   10
A deeper and religious character,
Fallen as she was, and humbled as they
   were,
Her faithful people still in all they could
Obey'd Erillyab. She too in her mind
Those recollections cherish'd, and such
   thoughts
As, though no hope allay'd their bitter-
   ness,
Gave to her eye a spirit and a strength,

And pride to features which belike had
   borne,
Had they been fashion'd by a happier
   fate,   19
Meaning more gentle and more womanly,
Yet not more worthy of esteem and love.
She sate upon the threshold of her hut ;
For in the palace where her sires had
   reign'd
The conqueror dwelt. Her son was at
   her side,
A boy now near to manhood ; by the
   door,
Bare of its bark, the head and branches
   shorn,
Stood a young tree with many a weapon
   hung,
Her husband's war-pole, and his monu-
   ment.
There had his quiver moulder'd, his
   stone-axe
Had there grown green with moss, his
   bow-string there   30
Sung as it cut the wind.
               She welcom'd us
With a proud sorrow in her mien ; fresh
   fruits
Were spread before us, and her gestures
   said
That when he lived whose hand was
   wont to wield
Those weapons, . . that in better days, . .
   that ere
She let the tresses of her widowhood
Grow wild, she could have given to
   guests like us
A worthier welcome. Soon a man ap-
   proach'd,
Hooded with sable, his half-naked limbs
Smear'd black ; the people at his sight
   drew round,   40
The women wail'd and wept, the
   children turn'd
And hid their faces on their mothers'
   knees.
He to the Queen addrest his speech, then
   look'd
Around the children, and laid hands on
   two,
Of different sexes but of age alike
Some six years each, who at his touch
   shriek'd out.
But then Lincoya rose, and to my feet

Led them, and told me that the con-
    querors claim'd
These innocents for tribute; that the
    Priest   49
Would lay them on the altar of his god,
Pluck out their little hearts in sacrifice,
And with his brotherhood in impious
    rites
Feast on their flesh ! . . I shudder'd,
    and my hand
Instinctively unsheathed the avenging
    sword,
As he with passionate and eloquent
    signs,
Eye-speaking earnestness and quivering
    lips,
Besought me to preserve himself, and
    those
Who now fell suppliant round me, . .
    youths and maids,
Grey-headed men, and mothers with
    their babes.

I caught the little victims up, I kiss'd
Their innocent cheeks, I raised my eyes
    to heaven,   61
I call'd upon Almighty God to hear
And bless the vow I made ; in our own
    tongue
Was that sworn promise of protection
    pledged . .
Impetuous feeling made no pause for
    thought.
Heaven heard the vow ; the suppliant
    multitude
Saw what was stirring in my heart ; the
    Priest,
With eye inflamed and rapid answer,
    raised
His menacing hand ; the tone, the
    bitter smile,
Interpreting his threat.
                Meanwhile the Queen, 70
With watchful eye and steady coun-
    tenance,
Had listen'd ; now she rose and to the
    Priest
Address'd her speech. Low was her
    voice and calm,
As one who spake with effort to subdue
Sorrow that struggled still ; but while
    she spake
Her features kindled to more majesty,

Her eye became more animate, her voice
Rose to the height of feeling ; on her son
She call'd, and from her husband's
    monument
His battle-axe she took ; and I could see
That when she gave the boy his father's
    arms,   81
She call'd his father's spirit to look on
And bless them to his vengeance.
                            Silently
The tribe stood listening as Erillyab
    spake.
The very Priest was awed: once he
    essayed
To answer ; his tongue fail'd him, and
    his lip
Grew pale and fell. He to his country-
    men
Of rage and shame and wonder full, re-
    turn'd,
Bearing no victims for their shrines
    accurst,
But tidings that the Hoamen had cast
    off   90
Their vassalage, roused to desperate
    revolt
By men in hue and speech and garment
    strange,
Who in their folly dared defy the power
Of Aztlan.
            When the King of Aztlan heard
The unlook'd-for tale, ere yet he roused
    his strength,
Or pitying our rash valour, or perhaps
Curious to see the man so bravely rash,
He sent to bid me to his court. Sur-
    prised,
I should have given to him no credulous
    faith,
But fearlessly Erillyab bade me trust 100
Her honourable foe. Unarm'd I went,
Lincoya with me to exchange our speech
So as he could, of safety first assured ;
For to their devilish idols he had been
A victim doom'd, and from the bloody
    rites
Flying been carried captive far away.

From early morning till the midnoon
    hour
We travell'd in the mountains ; then
    a plain
Open'd below, and rose upon the sight,

Like boundless ocean from a hill-top
 seen.   110
A beautiful and populous plain it was;
Fair woods were there and fertilizing
 streams,
And pastures spreading wide, and
 villages
In fruitful groves embower'd, and
 stately towns,
And many a single dwelling specking it,
As though for many a year the land had
 been
The land of peace. Below us, where the
 base
Of the great mountain to the level
 sloped,
A broad blue lake extended far and wide
Its waters, dark beneath the light of
 noon.   120
There Aztlan stood upon the farther
 shore:
Amid the shade of trees its dwellings
 rose,
Their level roofs with turrets set around,
And battlements all burnish'd white,
 which shone
Like silver in the sunshine. I beheld
The imperial city, her far-circling walls,
Her garden groves and stately palaces,
Her temple's mountain-size, her thou-
 sand roofs;
And when I saw her might and majesty
My mind misgave me then.
    We reach'd the shore:
A floating islet waited for me there, 131
The beautiful work of man. I set my
 feet
Upon green-growing herbs and flowers,
 and sate
Embower'd in odorous shrubs: four
 long light boats
Yoked to the garden, with accordant
 song,
And dip and dash of oar in harmony,
Bore me across the lake.
     Then in a car
Aloft by human bearers was I borne;
And through the city gate, and through
 long lines
Of marshall'd multitudes who throng'd
 the way,   140
We reach'd the palace court. Four
 priests were there;

Each held a burning censer in his hand,
And strew'd the precious gum as I drew
 nigh,
And held the steaming fragrance forth
 to me,
Honouring me like a god. They led me
 in,
Where on his throne the royal Azteca
Coanocotzin sate. Stranger, said he,
Welcome; and be this coming to thy
 weal!
A desperate warfare doth thy courage
 court;
But thou shalt see the people and the
 power   150
Whom thy deluded zeal would call to
 arms;
So may the knowledge make thee timely
 wise.
The valiant love the valiant. . . Come
 with me!
So saying he rose; we went together
 forth
To the Great Temple. 'Twas a huge
 square hill,
Or rather like a rock it seem'd, hewn out
And squared by patient labour. Never
 yet
Did our forefathers, o'er beloved chief
Fallen in his glory, heap a monument
Of that prodigious bulk, though every
 shield   160
Was laden for his grave, and every hand
Toil'd unremitting at the willing work
From morn till eve, all the long summer
 day.

The ascent was lengthened with pro-
 voking art,
By steps which led but to a wearying
 path
Round the whole structure; then
 another flight,
Another road around, and thus a third,
And yet a fourth, before we reach'd the
 height.
Lo, now, Coanocotzin cried, thou seest
The cities of this widely peopled plain;
And wert thou on yon farthest temple-
 top,   171
Yet as far onward wouldst thou see the
 land   [men.
Well husbanded like this, and full of

They tell me that two floating palaces
Brought thee and all thy people ; . .
   when I sound
The Tambour of the God, ten Cities hear
Its voice, and answer to the call in arms.

   In truth I felt my weakness, and the
     view
Had wakened no unreasonable fear,
But that a nearer sight had stirr'd my
   blood ;   180
For on the summit where we stood four
   Towers
Were piled with human skulls, and all
   around
Long files of human heads were strung
   to parch
And whiten in the sun. What then I
   felt
Was more than natural courage . . 'twas
   a trust
In more than mortal strength . . a faith
   in God, . .
Yea, inspiration from Him ! . . I ex-
   claim'd,
Not though ten Cities ten times told
   obey'd
The King of Aztlan's bidding, should
   I fear   189
The power of man !
      Art thou then more than man ?
He answered ; and I saw his tawny
   cheek
Lose its life-colour as the fear arose ;
Nor did I undeceive him from that fear,
For sooth I knew not how to answer him,
And therefore let it work. So not a
   word
Spake he, till we again had reach'd the
   court,
And I too went in silent thoughtfulness :
But then when, save Lincoya, there was
   none
To hear our speech, again did he renew
The query . . Stranger ! art thou more
   than man,   200
That thou shouldst set the power of man
   at nought ?

   Then I replied, Two floating palaces
Bore me and all my people o'er the seas.
When we departed from our mother-
   land,

The Moon was newly born ; we saw her
   wax
And wane, and witnessed her new birth
   again ;
And all that while, alike by day and
   night,
We travell'd through the sea, and
   caught the winds,
And made them bear us forward. We
   must meet
In battle, if the Hoamen are not freed
From your accursed tribute, . . thou
   and I,   211
My people and thy countless multitudes.
Your arrows shall fall from us as the
   hail
Leaps on a rock, . . and when ye smite
   with swords,
Not blood but fire shall follow from the
   stroke.
Yet think not thou that we are more
   than men !
Our knowledge is our power, and God
   our strength,
God, whose almighty will created thee,
And me, and all that hath the breath of
   life.
He is our strength ; . . for in His name
   I speak, . .   220
And when I tell thee that thou shalt not
   shed
The life of man in bloody sacrifice,
It is His holy bidding which I speak :
And if thou wilt not listen and obey,
When I shall meet thee in the battle-
   field,
It is His holy cause for which I fight,
And I shall have His power to vanquish
   thee !

   And thinkest thou our Gods are
   feeble ? cried
The King of Aztlan ; thinkest thou they
   lack
Power to defend their altars, and to
   keep   230
The kingdom which they gave us
   strength to win ?
The Gods of thirty nations have opposed
Their irresistible might, and they lie
   now
Conquer'd and caged and fetter'd at
   their feet.

That we who serve them are no coward
race,
Let prove the ample realm we won in
arms ;
And I their leader am not of the sons
Of the feeble ! As he spake, he reach'd
a mace,
The trunk and knotted root of some
young tree,
Such as old Albion and his monster-
brood   240
From the oak-forest for their weapons
pluck'd,
When father Brute and Corineus set
foot
On the White Island first. Lo this,
quoth he,
My club ! and he threw back his robe ;
and this
The arm that wields it ! . . 'Twas my
father's once :
Erillyab's husband, King Tepollomi,
He felt its weight. . . Did I not show
thee him ?
He lights me at my evening banquet.
There,
In very deed, the dead Tepollomi
Stood up against the wall, by devilish
art   250
Preserv'd ; and from his black and
shrivell'd hand
The steady lamp hung down.
           My spirit rose
At that abomination ; I exclaimed
Thou art of noble nature, and full fain
Would I in friendship plight my hand
with thine ;
But till that body in the grave be laid,
Till thy polluted altars be made pure,
There is no peace between us. May my
God,
Who, though thou know'st Him not, is
also thine,
And after death will be thy dreadful
Judge,   260
May it please Him to visit thee, and
shed
His mercy on thy soul. . . But if thy
heart
Be harden'd to the proof, come when
thou wilt !
I know thy power, and thou shalt then
know mine.

VII. THE BATTLE

Now then to meet the war ! Erillyab's
call
Roused all her people to revenge their
wrongs ;
And at Lincoya's voice, the mountain
tribes
Arose and broke their bondage. I mean-
time
Took counsel with Cadwallon and his
sire,
And told them of the numbers we must
meet,
And what advantage from the moun-
tain-straits
I thought, as in the Saxon wars, to win.
Thou saw'st their weapons then, Cad-
wallon said ;
Are they like these rude works of
ignorance,   10
Bone-headed shafts, and spears of wood,
and shields,
Strong only for such strife ?
           We had to cope
With wiser enemies, and abler arm'd.
What for the sword they wielded was
a staff
Set thick with stones athwart ; you
would have deem'd
The uncouth shape was cumbrous ; but
a hand
Expert, and practised to its use, could
drive
The sharpen'd flints with deadly impulse
down.
Their mail, if mail it may be call'd, was
woven
Of vegetable down, like finest flax,   20
Bleach'd to the whiteness of the new-
fallen snow,
To every bend and motion flexible,
Light as a warrior's summer-garb in
peace ;
Yet, in that lightest, softest, habergeon,
Harmless the sharp stone arrow-head
would hang.
Others, of higher office, were array'd
In feathery breast-plates of more gor-
geous hue
Than the gay plumage of the mountain-
cock,

Or pheasant's glittering pride. But
what were these,
Or what the thin gold hauberk, when
opposed   30
To arms like ours in battle ? What the
mail
Of wood fire-harden'd, or the wooden
helm,
Against the iron arrows of the South,
Against our northern spears, or battle-
axe,
Or good sword, wielded by a British
hand ?

Then, quoth Cadwallon, at the wooden
helm,
Of these weak arms the weakest, let the
sword
Hew, and the spear be thrust. The
mountaineers,
So long inured to crouch beneath their
yoke,
We will not trust in battle ; from the
heights   40
They with their arrows may annoy the
foe ;
And when our closer strife has won the
fray,
Then let them loose for havoc.
                          O my son,
Exclaim'd the blind old man, thou
counsellest ill !
Blood will have blood, revenge beget
revenge,
Evil must come of evil. We shall win,
Certes, a cheap and easy victory
In the first field ; their arrows from our
arms
Will fall, and on the hauberk and the
helm
The flint-edge blunt and break ; while
through their limbs,   50
Naked, or vainly fenced, the griding steel
Shall sheer its mortal way. But what
are we
Against a nation ? Other hosts will rise
In endless warfare, with perpetual fights
Dwindling our all-too-few ; or multi-
tudes
Will wear and weary us, till we sink sub-
dued
By the very toil of conquest. Ye are
strong ;

But he who puts his trust in mortal
strength
Leans on a broken reed. First prove
your power ;
Be in the battle terrible, but spare   60
The fallen, and follow not the flying foe :
Then may ye win a nobler victory,
So dealing with the captives as to fill
Their hearts with wonder, gratitude,
and awe,
That love shall mingle with their fear,
and fear
'Stablish the love, else wavering. Let
them see,
That as more pure and gentle is your
faith,
Yourselves are gentler, purer. Ye shall
be
As gods among them, if ye thus obey
God's precepts.
                    Soon the mountain
tribes, in arms   70
Rose at Lincoya's call : a numerous
host,
More than in numbers, in the memory
Of long oppression, and revengeful hope,
A formidable foe. I station'd them
Where at the entrance of the rocky
straits,
Secure themselves, their arrows might
command
The coming army. On the plain below
We took our stand, between the moun-
tain-base
And the green margin of the waters.
Soon
Their long array came on. Oh what
a pomp   80
And pride and pageantry of war was
there !
Not half so gaudied, for their May-day
mirth,
All wreathed and ribanded, our youths
and maids,
As these stern Aztecas in war attire !
The golden glitterance, and the feather-
mail,
More gay than glittering gold ; and
round the helm
A coronal of high upstanding plumes
Green as the spring grass in the sunny
shower ;
Or scarlet bright, as in the wintry wood

The cluster'd holly ; or of purple tint, ..
Whereto shall that be liken'd ? to what
    gem   91
Indiadem'd, . . what flower, . . what
    insect's wing ?
With war songs and wild music they
    came on,
We the while kneeling, raised with one
    accord
The hymn of supplication.
                  Front to front,
And now the embattled armies stood :
    a band
Of priests, all sable-garmented, ad-
    vanced ;
They piled a heap of sedge before our
    host,
And warn'd us, .. Sons of Ocean ! from
    the land
Of Aztlan, while ye may, depart in
    peace !   100
Before the fire shall be extinguish'd,
    hence !
Or, even as yon dry sedge amid the
    flame,
So ye shall be consumed . . The arid
    heap
They kindled, and the rapid flame ran
    up,
And blazed, and died away.   Then from
    his bow,
With steady hand, their chosen archer
    loosed
The Arrow of the Omen.   To its mark
The shaft of divination fled ; it smote
Cadwallon's plated breast ; the brittle
    point
Rebounded.   He, contemptuous of their
    faith,   110
Stoopt for the shaft, and while with
    zealous speed
To the rescue they rushed onward,
    snapping it
Asunder, toss'd the fragments back in
    scorn.

    Fierce was their onset ; never in the
    field
Encounter'd I with braver enemies.
Nor marvel ye, nor think it to their
    shame,
If soon they stagger'd, and gave way,
    and fled,

So many from so few ; they saw their
    darts
Recoil, their lances shiver, and their
    swords
Fall ineffectual, blunted with the blow.
Think ye no shame of Aztlan that they
    fled,   121
When the bowmen of Deheubarth plied
    so well
Their shafts with fatal aim ; through
    the thin gold
Or feather-mail, while Gwyneth's deep-
    driven spears
Pierced to the bone and vitals ; when
    they saw
The falchion, flashing late so lightning-
    like,
Quench'd in their own life-blood.   Our
    mountaineers
Shower'd from the heights, meantime,
    an arrowy storm,
Themselves secure ; and we who bore
    the brunt
Of battle, iron men, impassable,   130
Stood in our strength unbroken. Marvel
    not
If then the brave felt fear, already im-
    press'd
That day by ominous thoughts, to fear
    akin ;
For so it chanced, high Heaven ordain-
    ing so,
The King, who who should have led his
    people forth,
At the army-head, as they began their
    march,
Was with sore sickness stricken ; and
    the stroke
Came like the act and arm of very God,
So suddenly, and in that point of time.

    A gallant man was he who in his
    stead   140
That day commanded Aztlan : his long
    hair,
Tufted with many a cotton lock, pro-
    claim'd
Of princely prowess many a feat
    achieved
In many a field of fame.   Oft had he
    led
The Aztecas, with happy fortune, forth ;
Yet could not now Yuhidthiton inspire

His host with hope : he, not the less,
      that day,
True to his old renown, and in the hour
Of rout and ruin with collected mind,
Sounded his signals shrill, and in the
      voice   150
Of loud reproach and anger, and brave
      shame,
Call'd on the people . . But when nought
      avail'd,
Seizing the standard from the timid
      hand
Which held it in dismay, alone he turn'd,
For honourable death resolved, and
      praise
That would not die. Thereat the braver
      chiefs
Rallied, anew their signals rung around,
And Aztlan, seeing how we spared her
      flight,
Took heart, and roll'd the tide of battle
      back.
But when Cadwallon from the chieftain's
      grasp   160
Had cut the standard-staff away, and
      stunn'd
And stretch'd him at his mercy on the
      field,
Then fled the enemy in utter rout,
Broken and quell'd at heart.   One chief
      alone
Bestrode the body of Yuhidthiton,
Bareheaded did young Malinal bestride
His brother's body, wiping from his
      brow
With the shield-hand the blinding blood
      away,
And dealing franticly with broken sword
Obstinate wrath, the last resisting foe.
Him, in his own despite, we seized and
      saved.   171

Then in the moment of our victory,
We purified our hands from blood, and
      knelt,
And pour'd to heaven the grateful
      prayer of praise
And raised the choral psalm. Trium-
      phant thus
To the hills we went our way ; the
      mountaineers
With joy, and dissonant song, and antic
      dance ;

The captives sullenly, deeming that they
      went
To meet the certain death of sacrifice,
Yet stern and undismay'd.   We bade
      them know   180
Ours was a law of mercy and of love ;
We heal'd their wounds, and set the
      prisoners free.
Dear ye, quoth I, my bidding to your
      King ;
Say to him, Did the stranger speak to
      thee
The words of truth, and hath he proved
      his power ?
Thus saith the Lord of Ocean, in the
      name
Of God, Almighty, Universal God,
Thy Judge and mine, whose battles
      I have fought,
Whose bidding I obey, whose will I
      speak ;   189
Shed thou no more in impious sacrifice
The life of man ; restore unto the grave
The dead Tepollomi ; set this people
      free,
And peace shall be between us.
                        On the morrow
Came messengers from Aztlan, in reply.
Coanocotzin with sore malady
Hath, by the Gods, been stricken : will
      the Lord
Of Ocean visit his sick bed ? . . He told
Of wrath, and as he said, the vengeance
      came ;
Let him bring healing now, and 'stablish
      peace.

VIII. THE PEACE

AGAIN, and now with better hope, I
      sought
The city of the King ! there went with
      me
Iolo, old Iolo, he who knows
The virtue of all herbs of mount or vale,
Or greenwood shade, or quiet brooklet's
      bed ;
Whatever lore of science, or of song,
Sages and Bards of old have handed
      down.
Aztlan that day pour'd forth her
      swarming sons,

To wait my coming. Will he ask his
God
To stay the hand of anger ? was the
cry,   10
The general cry, . . and will he save the
King ?
Coanocotzin too had nurst that thought,
And the strong hope upheld him ; he
put forth
His hand, and raised a quick and anxious
eye, . .
Is it not peace and mercy ? . . thou art
come
To pardon and to save !
                    I answer'd him,
That power, O King of Aztlan, is not
mine !
Such help as human cunning can bestow,
Such human help I bring ; but health
and life
Are in the hand of God, who at his will
Gives or withdraws ; and what he wills
is best.   21
Then old Iolo took his arm, and felt
The symptom, and he bade him have
good hope,
For life was strong within him. So it
proved :
The drugs of subtle virtue did their
work ;
They quell'd the venom of the malady,
And from the frame expell'd it, . . that
a sleep
Fell on the King, a sweet and natural
sleep,
And from its healing he awoke refresh'd
Though weak, and joyful as a man who
felt   30
The peril pass'd away.
                    Ere long we spake
Of concord, and how best to knit the
bonds
Of lasting friendship. When we won
this land,
Coanocotzin said, these fertile vales
Were not, as now, with fruitful groves
embower'd,
Nor rich with towns and populous
villages,
Abounding, as thou seest, with life and
joy ;
Our fathers found bleak heath, and
desert moor,

Wild woodland, and savannahs wide
and waste,
Rude country of rude dwellers. From
our arms   40
They to the mountain fastnesses retired,
And long with obstinate and harassing
war
Provoked us, hoping not for victory,
Yet mad for vengeance ; till Tepollomi
Fell by my father's hand ; and with
their King,
The strength and flower of all their
youth cut off,
All in one desolating day, they took
The yoke upon their necks. What
wouldest thou
That to these Hoamen I should now
concede ?
Lord of the Ocean, speak !
                    Let them be free ! 50
Quoth I. I come not from my native
isle
To wage the war of conquest, and cast
out
Your people from the land which time
and toil
Have rightly made their own. The
land is wide ;
There is enough for all. So they be freed
From that accursed tribute, and ye shed
The life of man no more in sacrifice,
In the most holy name of God I say,
Let there be peace between us !
                    Thou hast won
Their liberty, the King replied : hence-
forth,   60
Free as they are, if they provoke the war,
Reluctantly will Aztlan raise her arm.
Be thou the peace-preserver. To what
else
Thou say'st, instructed by calamity,
I lend a humble ear ; but to destroy
The worship of my fathers, or abate
Or change one point, lies not within the
reach
And scope of kingly power. Speak thou
hereon
With those whom we hold holy, with the
sons
Of the Temple, they who commune
with the Gods ;   70
Awe them, for they awe me. So we
resolved

That when the bones of King Tepollomi
Had had their funeral honours, they
    and I
Should by the green-lake side, before
    the King,
And in the presence of the people, hold
A solemn talk.
            Then to the mountain-huts,
The bearer of good tidings, I return'd,
Loading the honourable train who bore
The relics of the King ; not parch'd and
    black,
As I had seen the unnatural corpse stand
    up,   80
In ghastly mockery of the attitude
And act of life, . . his bones had now been
    blanch'd
With decent reverence. Soon the moun-
    taineers
Saw the white deer-skin shroud ; the
    rumour spread ;
They gather'd round, and follow'd in
    our train.
Before Erillyab's hut the bearers laid
Their burden down. She, calm of
    countenance,
And with dry eye, albeit her hand the
    while
Shook like an agueish limb, unroll'd the
    shroud.
The multitude stood gazing silently, 90
The young and old alike all awed and
    hush'd
Under the holy feeling, . . and the
    hush
Was aweful ; that huge multitude so
    still,
That we could hear distinct the moun-
    tain-stream
Roll down its rocky channel far away.
And this was all ; sole ceremony this,
The sight of death and silence, . . till at
    length,
In the ready grave his bones were laid
    to rest.
'Twas in her hut and home, yea, under-
    neath
The marriage bed, the bed of widow-
    hood,   100
Her husband's grave was dug ; on
    softest fur
The bones were laid, with fur were
    covered o'er,

Then heap'd with bark and boughs, and,
    last of all,
Earth was to earth trod down.
                    And now the day
Appointed for our talk of peace was
    come.
On the green margin of the lake we met,
Elders, and Priests, and Chiefs ; the
    multitude
Around the Circle of the Council stood.
Then, in the midst, Coanocotzin rose,
And thus the King began : Pabas and
    Chiefs   110
Of Aztlan, hither ye are come to learn
The law of peace. The Lord of Ocean
    saith,
The Tribes whom he hath gathered
    underneath
The wings of his protection, shall be
    free ;
And in the name of his great God he
    saith,
That ye shall never shed in sacrifice
The blood of man. Are ye content ?
    that so
We may together here, in happy hour,
Bury the sword.
            Hereat a Paba rose,
And answer'd for his brethren : . . He
    hath won   120
The Hoamen's freedom, that their blood
    no more
Shall on our altars flow ; for this the
    Lord
Of Ocean fought, and Aztlan yielded it
In battle. But if we forego the rites
Of our forefathers, if we wrong the Gods,
Who give us timely sun and timely
    showers,
Their wrath will be upon us ; they will
    shut
Their ears to prayer, and turn away the
    eyes
Which watch for our well-doing, and
    withhold   129
The hands dispensing our prosperity.

Cynetha then arose, between his son
And me supported, rose the blind old
    man.
Ye wrong us, men of Aztlan, if ye deem
We bid ye wrong the Gods ; accurst
    were he

Who would obey such bidding, . . more
accurst
The wretch who should enjoin impiety.
It is the will of God which we make
known,
Your God and ours. Know ye not Him
who laid
The deep foundations of the earth, and
built
The arch of heaven, and kindled yonder
sun,   140
And breathed into the woods and waves
and sky
The power of life ?
        We know Him, they replied,
The great For-Ever One, the God of
Gods,
Ipalnemoani, He by whom we live !
And we too, quoth Ayayaca, we know
And worship the Great Spirit, who in
clouds
And storms, in mountain caves, and by
the fall
Of waters, in the woodland solitude,
And in the night and silence of the sky,
Doth make his being felt. We also
know,   150
And fear, and worship the Beloved One.

Our God, replied Cynetha, is the same,
The Universal Father. He to the first
Made his will known ; but when men
multiplied,
The Evil Spirits darken'd them, and sin
And misery came into the world, and
men
Forsook the way of truth, and gave to
stocks
And stones the incommunicable name.
Yet with one chosen, one peculiar Race,
The knowledge of their Father and their
God   160
Remain'd, from sire to son transmitted
down.
While the bewilder'd Nations of the
earth
Wander'd in fogs, and were in darkness
lost,
The light abode with them ; and when
at times
They sinn'd and went astray, the Lord
hath put
A voice into the mouths of holy men,

Raising up witnesses unto himself,
That so the saving knowledge of his
name
Might never fail ; nor the glad promise,
given
To our first parent, that at length his
sons,   170
From error, sin, and wretchedness re-
deem'd,
Should form one happy family of love.
Nor ever hath that light, howe'er be-
dimm'd,
Wholly been quench'd ; still in the
heart of man
A feeling and an instinct it exists,
His very nature's stamp and privilege,
Yea, of his life the life. I tell ye not,
O Aztecas ! of things unknown before ;
I do but waken up a living sense
That sleeps within ye ! Do ye love the
Gods   180
Who call for blood ? Doth the poor
sacrifice
Go with a willing step, to lay his life
Upon their altars ? . . Good must come
of good,
Evil of evil ; if the fruit be death,
The poison springeth from the sap and
root,
And the whole tree is deadly ; if the rites
Be evil, they who claim them are not
good,
Not to be worshipp'd then ; for to obey
The evil will is evil. Aztecas !
From the For-Ever, the Beloved One,
The Universal Only God I speak,   191
Your God and mine, our Father and our
Judge.
Hear ye his law, . . hear ye the perfect
law
Of love, ' Do ye to others, as ye would
That they should do to you ! ' He bids
us meet
To praise his name, in thankfulness and
joy ;
He bids us, in our sorrow, pray to him,
The Comforter. Love him, for he is
good !
Fear him, for he is just ! Obey his will,
For who can bear his anger !
                            While he spake,
They stood with open mouth, and
motionless sight,   201

Watching his countenance, as though
  tho voice
Were of a God ; for sure it seem'd that
  less
Than inspiration could not have infused
That eloquent passion in a blind man's
  face.
And when he ceased, all oyes at once
  woro turn'd
Upon the Pabas, waiting their reply,
If that to that acknowledged argument
Reply could be devised.   But they
  themselves,
Stricken by the truth, were silent ; and
  they look'd   210
Toward their chief and mouth-piece, the
  High Priest
Tezozomoc ; he too was pale and mute,
And when he gather'd up his strength
  to speak,
Speech fail'd him, his lip falter'd, and
  his eye
Fell utterly abash'd, and put to shame.
But in the Chiefs, and in the multitude,
And in the King of Aztlan, better
  thoughts
Were working; for the Spirit of the Lord
That day was moving in the heart of
  man.   219
Coanocotzin rose : Pabas, and Chiefs,
And men of Aztlan, ye have heard a talk
Of peace and love, and there is no reply.
Are ye content with what the Wise Man
  saith ?
And will ye worship God in that good
  way
Which God himself ordains ? If it be so,
Together here will we in happy hour
Bury the sword.
                 Tezozomoc replied,
This thing is new, and in the land till
  now
Unheard : . . what marvel, therefore, if
  we find
No ready answer ? Let our Lord the
  King   230
Do that which seemeth best.
                      Yuhidthiton,
Chief of the Chiefs of Aztlan, next arose.
Of all her numerous sons, could Aztlan
  boast
No mightier arm in battle, nor whose
  voice

To more attentive silence hush'd the
  hall
Of council.   When the Wise Man spake,
  quoth he,
I ask'd of mine own heart if it were so,
And, as he said, the living instinct there
Answer'd, and own'd the truth.   In
  happy hour,
() King of Aztlan, did tho Ocean Lord
Through the great waters hither wend
  his way ;   241
For sure he is the friend of God and man.

With that an uproar of assent arose
From the whole people, a tumultuous
  shout
Of universal joy and glad acclaim.
But when Coanocotzin raised his hand,
That he might speak, the clamour and
  the buz
Ceased, and the multitude, in tiptoe
  hope,
Attent and still, await the final voice.
Then said the Sovereign, Hear, O Az-
  tecas,   250
Your own united will ! From this day
  forth
No life upon the altar shall be shed,
No blood shall flow in sacrifice ; the rites
Shall all be pure, such as the blind Old
  Man,
Whom God hath taught,will teach.   This
  ye have will'd ;
And therefore it shall be !
                 The King hath said !
Like thunder the collected voice replied :
Let it be so !
             Lord of the Ocean, then
Pursued the King of Aztlan, we will now
Lay the war-weapon in the grave, and
  join   260
In right-hand friendship.   By our
  custom, blood
Should sanctify and bind the solemn act ;
But by what oath and ceremony thou
Shalt proffer, by the same will Aztlan
  swear.
Nor oath, nor ceremony, I replied,
O King, is needful.   To his own good
  word
The good and honourable man will act,
Oaths will not curb the wicked.   Here
  we stand

In the broad day-light; the For-Ever
    One,
The Every-Where beholds us. In his
    sight   270
We join our hands in peace : if e'er again
Should these right hands be raised in
    enmity,
Upon the offender will his judgement fall.

The grave was dug ; Coanocotzin laid
His weapon in the earth ; Erillyab's son,
Young Amalahta, for the Hoamen, laid
His hatchet there ; and there I laid the
    sword.

Here let me end.   What follow'd was
    the work
Of peace, no theme for story ; how we
    fix'd
Our sojourn in the hills, and sow'd our
    fields,   280
And, day by day, saw all things pros-
    pering.   [nounce
Thence have I come, Goervyl, to an-
The tidings of my happy enterprize ;
There I return, to take thee to our home.
I love my native land ; with as true love
As ever yet did warm a British heart,
Love I the green fields of the beautiful
    Isle,
My father's heritage ! But far away,
Where nature's booner hand has blest
    the earth,
My lot hath been assign'd ; beyond the
    seas   290
Madoc hath found his home ; beyond
    the seas
A country for his children hath he
    chosen,   [peace.
A land wherein their portion may be

IX. EMMA

BUT while Aberfraw echoed to the
    sounds
Of merriment and music, Madoc's heart
Mourn'd for his brethren. Therefore,
    when no ear
Was nigh, he sought the King, and said
    to him,
To-morrow, for Mathraval I set forth ;
Longer I must not linger here, to pass

The easy hours in feast and revelry,
Forgetful of my people far away.
I go to tell the tidings of success,
And seek new comrades. What if it
    should chance   10
That, for this enterprize, our brethren,
Foregoing all their hopes and fortunes
    here,
Would join my banner ?. . Let me send
    abroad
Their summons, O my brother ! so
    secure,
You may forgive the past, and once again
Will peace and concord bless our
    father's house.

Hereafter will be time enow for this,
The King replied ; thy easy nature sees
    not,
How, if the traitors for thy banner send
Their bidding round, in open war against
    me   20
Their own would soon be spread.   I
    charge thee, Madoc,
Neither to see nor aid these fugitives,
The shame of Owen's blood.
                            Sullen he spake,
And turn'd away ; nor farther commune
    now
Did Madoc seek, nor had he more en-
    dured ;
For bitter thoughts were rising in his
    heart,
And anguish, kindling anger.   In such
    mood
He to his sister's chamber took his way.
She sate with Emma, with the gentle
    Queen ;
For Emma had already learnt to love
The gentle maid.   Goervyl saw what
    thoughts   31
Troubled her brother's brow.   Madoc,
    she cried,
Thou hast been with the King, been
    rashly pleading
For Ririd and for Rodri !. . He replied,
I did but ask him little, . . did but say,
Belike our brethren would go forth with
    me,
To voluntary exile ; then, methought,
His fear and jealousy might well have
    ceased,
And all be safe.

And did the King refuse?
Quoth Emma: I will plead for them,
   quoth she,   40
With dutiful warmth and zeal will plead
   for them;
And surely David will not say me nay.

O sister! cried Goervyl, tempt him
   not!
Sister, you know him not! Alas, to
   touch
That perilous theme is, even in Madoc
   here,
A perilous folly. . . Sister, tempt him
   not!
You do not know the King!
                     But then a fear
Fled to the cheek of Emma, and her eye,
Quickening with wonder, turn'd toward
   the Prince,
As if expecting that his manly mind 50
Would mould Goervyl's meaning to a
   shape
Less fearful, would interpret and amend
The words she hoped she did not hear
   aright.
Emma was young; she was a sacrifice
To that cold king-craft, which, in mar-
   riage-vows
Linking two hearts, unknowing each of
   each,
Perverts the ordinance of God, and
   makes
The holiest tie a mockery and a curse.
Her eye was patient, and she spake in
   tones
So sweet and of so pensive gentleness,
That the heart felt them. Madoc! she
   exclaimed,   61
Why dost thou hate the Saxons? O my
   brother,
If I have heard aright, the hour will
   come
When the Plantagenet shall wish herself
Among her nobler, happier countrymen,
From these unnatural enmities escaped,
And from the vengeance they must call
   from Heaven!

Shame then suffused the Prince's
   countenance,
Mindful how, drunk in anger, he had
   given

His hatred loose. My sister Queen,
   quoth he,   70
Marvel not you that with my mother's
   milk
I suck'd that hatred in.   Have they not
   been
The scourge and the devouring sword of
   God,
The curse and pestilence which he hath
   sent
To root us from the land? Alas, our
   crimes
Have drawn this dolorous visitation
   down!
Our sun hath long been westering; and
   the night
And darkness and extinction are at
   hand.
We are a fallen people! . . From our-
   selves
The desolation and the ruin come;   80
In our own vitals doth the poison
   work. .
The House that is divided in itself,
How should it stand? . . A blessing on
   you, Lady!
But in this wretched family the strife
Is rooted all too deep; it is an old
And cankered wound, . . an eating,
   killing sore,
For which there is no healing. . . If the
   King
Should ever speak his fears, . . and sure
   to you
All his most inward thoughts he will
   make known, . .
Counsel him then to let his brethren
   share   90
My enterprize, to send them forth with
   me
To everlasting exile. . . She hath told you
Too hardly of the King; I know him
   well;
He hath a stormy nature; and what
   germs
Of virtue would have budded in his
   heart,
Cold winds have check'd, and blighting
   seasons nipt,
Yet in his heart they live. . . A blessing
   on you,
That you may see their blossom and
   their fruit!

X. MATHRAVAL

Now for Mathraval went Prince Madoc
  forth ;
O'er Menai's ebbing tide, up mountain-
  paths,
Beside grey mountain-stream, and lonely
  lake,
And through old Snowdon's forest-
  solitude,
He held right on his solitary way.
Nor paused he in that rocky vale, where
  oft
Up the familiar path, with gladder pace,
His steed had hastened to the well-
  known door, . .
That valley, o'er whose crags, and
  sprinkled trees,
And winding stream, so oft his eye had
  loved   10
To linger, gazing, as the eve grew dim,
From Dolwyddelan's Tower ; . . alas !
  from thence
As from his brother's monument, he
  turn'd
A loathing eye, and through the rocky
  vale
Sped on. From morn till noon, from
  noon till eve,
He travelled on his way : and when at
  morn
Again the Ocean Chief bestrode his
  steed,
The heights of Snowdon on his back-
  ward glance
Hung like a cloud in heaven. O'er
  heath and hill
And barren height he rode ; and darker
  now,   20
In loftier majesty thy mountain-seat,
Star-loving Idris, rose. Nor turn'd he
  now
Beside Kregennan, where his infant feet
Had trod Ednywain's hall ; nor loitered
  he
In the green vales of Powys, till he
  came
Where Warnway rolls its waters under-
  neath
Ancient Mathraval's venerable walls,
Cyveilioc's princely and paternal seat.

But Madoc sprung not forward now
  to greet
The chief he loved, for from Cyveilioc's
  hall   30
The voice of harp and song commingled
  came ;
It was that day the feast of victory
  there ;
Around the Chieftain's board the
  warriors sate ;
The sword and shield and helmet, on the
  wall
And round the pillars, were in peace
  hung up ;
And, as the flashes of the central fire
At fits arose, a dance of wavy light
Play'd o'er the reddening steel. The
  Chiefs, who late
So well had wielded in the work of war
Those weapons, sate around the board,
  to quaff   40
The beverage of the brave, and hear
  their fame.
Mathraval's Lord, the Poet and the
  Prince,
Cyveilioc stood before them, . . in his
  pride ;
His hands were on the harp, his eyes
  were closed,
His head, as if in reverence to receive
The inspiration, bent ; anon, he raised
His glowing countenance and brighter
  eye,
And swept with passionate hand the
  ringing harp.

Fill high the Hirlas Horn ! to Grufydd
  bear
Its frothy beverage, . . from his crimson
  lance   50
The invader fled ; . . fill high the gold-
  tipt Horn !
Heard ye in Maelor the step of war . .
The hastening shout . . the onset ? . .
  Did ye hear
The clash and clang of arms . . the battle-
  din,
Loud as the roar of Ocean, when the
  winds
At midnight are abroad ? . . the yell of
  wounds . .
The rage . . the agony ? . . Give to him
  the Horn

Whose spear was broken, and whose
    buckler pierced
With many a shaft, yet not the less he
    fought
And conquered; . . therefore let Ed-
    nyved share   60
The generous draught, give him the long
    blue Horn!
Pour out again, and fill again the spoil
Of the wild bull, with silver wrought of
    yore;
And bear the golden lip to Tudyr's hand,
Eagle of battle! For Moreiddig fill
The honourable Hirlas! . . Where are
    They?
Where are the noble Brethren? Wolves
    of war,
They kept their border well, they did
    their part,
Their fame is full, their lot is praise and
    song. . .
A mournful song to me, a song of woe! . .
Brave Brethren! for their honour brim
    the cup,   71
Which they shall quaff no more.
                         We drove away
The strangers from our land; profuse
    of life,
Our warriors rush'd to battle, and the
    Sun
Saw from his noontide fields their manly
    strife.
Pour thou the flowing mead! Cup-
    bearer, fill
The Hirlas! for hadst thou beheld the
    day
Of Llidom, thou hadst known how well
    the Chiefs
Deserve this honour now. Cyveilioc's
    shield
Were they in danger, when the Invader
    came;   80
Be praise and liberty their lot on earth,
And joy be theirs in heaven!
             ·   Here ceased the song;
Then from the threshold on the rush-
    strewn floor
Madoc advanced. Cyveilioc's eye was
    now
To present forms awake, but even as
    still
He felt his harp-chords throb with dying
    sounds,

The heat and stir and passion had not
    yet
Subsided in his soul. Again he struck
The loud-toned harp. . . Pour from the
    silver vase,
And brim the honourable Horn, and
    bear   99
The draught of joy to Madoc, . . he who
    first
Explored the desert ways of Ocean, first
Through the wide waste of sea and sky,
    held on
Undaunted, till upon another World,
The Lord and Conqueror of the Elements,
He set his foot triumphant? Fill for
    him
The Hirlas! fill the honourable Horn!
This for Mathraval is a happy hour,
When Madoc, her hereditary guest,
Appears within her honour'd walls
    again,   100
Madoc, the British Prince, the Ocean
    Lord,
Who never for injustice rear'd his arm;
Whose presence fills the heart of every
    foe
With fear, the heart of every friend with
    joy;
Give him the Hirlas Horn, fill, till the
    draught
Of joy shall quiver o'er the golden brim!
In happy hour the hero hath return'd!
In happy hour the friend, the brother
    treads
Cyveilioc's floor!
             He sprung to greet his guest;
The cordial grasp of fellowship was
    given;   110
So in Mathraval there was double joy
On that illustrious day; they gave their
    guest
The seat of honour, and they fill'd for
    him
The Hirlas Horn. Cyveilioc and his
    Chiefs,
All eagerly, with wonder-waiting eyes,
Look to the Wanderer of the Water's
    tale.
Nor mean the joy which kindled Madoc's
    brow,
When as he told of daring enterprize
Crown'd with deserved success. Intent
    they heard

Of all the blessings of that happier
   clime ;   120
And when the adventurer spake of soon
   return,
Each on the other gazed, as if to say,
Methinks it were a goodly lot to dwell
In that fair land in peace.
            Then said the Prince
Of Powys, Madoc, at an happy time
Thou hast toward Mathraval bent thy
   way :
For on the morrow, in the eye of light,
Our bards will hold their congress.
   Seekest thou
Comrades to share success ? proclaim
   abroad
Thine invitation there, and it will
   spread   130
Far as our fathers' ancient tongue is
   known.

Thus at Mathraval went the Hirlas
   round ;
A happy day was that ! Of other
   years
They talk'd, of common toils, and fields
   of war
Where they fought side by side ; of
   Corwen's scene
Of glory, and of comrades now no
   more : . .
Themes of delight, and grief which
   brought its joy.
Thus they beguiled the pleasant hours,
   while night
Waned fast away ; then late they laid
   them down,
Each on his bed of rushes, stretch'd
   around   140
The central fire.
         The Sun was newly risen
When Madoc join'd his host, no longer
   now
Clad as the conquering chief of Maelor,
In princely arms, but in his nobler
   robe,
The sky-blue mantle of the Bard,
   arrayed.
So for the place of meeting they set
   forth ;
And now they reach'd Melangell's lonely
   church.
Amid a grove of evergreens it stood,

A garden and a grove, where every
   grave
Was deck'd with flowers, or with un-
   fading plants   150
O'ergrown, sad rue, and funeral rose-
   mary.
Here Madoc paused. The morn is
   young, quoth he,
A little while to old remembrance given
Will not belate us. . . Many a year hath
   fled,
Cyveilioc, since you led me here, and
   told
The legend of the Saint. Come ! . . be
   not loth !
We will not loiter long. . . So soon to
   mount
The bark, which will for ever bear me
   hence,
I would not willingly pass by one spot
Which thus recalls the thought of other
   times,   160
Without a pilgrim's visit.
             Thus he spake,
And drew Cyveilioc through the church-
   yard porch,
To the rude image of Saint Monacel.
Dost thou remember, Owen, said the
   Prince,
When first I was thy guest in early
   youth,
That once, as we had wandered here at
   eve,
You told, how here a poor and hunted
   hare
Ran to the Virgin's feet, and look'd to
   her
For life ? . . I thought, when listening to
   the tale,
She had a merciful heart, and that her
   face   170
Must with a saintly gentleness have
   beam'd,
When beasts could read its virtue. Here
   we sate
Upon the jutting root of this old
   yeugh. . .
Dear friend ! so pleasant didst thou
   make those days,
That in my heart, long as my heart shall
   beat,
Minutest recollections still will live,
Still be the source of joy.

As Madoc spake,
His glancing eye fell on a monument,
Around whose base the rosemary
        droop'd down,
As yet not rooted well.   Sculptured
        above,   180
A warrior lay ; the shield was on his
        arm ;
Madoc approach'd, and saw the
        blazonry, . .
A sudden chill ran through him, as he
        read,
Here Yorwerth lies, . . it was his bro-
        ther's grave.

Cyveilioc took him by the hand : For
        this,
Madoc, was I so loth to enter here !
He sought the sanctuary, but close upon
        him
The murderers follow'd, and by yonder
        copse
The stroke of death was given.   All
        I could
Was done ; . . I saw him here consign'd
        to rest,   190
Daily due masses for his soul are sung,
And duly hath his grave been deck'd
        with flowers.

So saying, from the place of death he
        led
The silent Prince.   But lately, he pur-
        sued,
Llewelyn was my guest, thy favourite
        boy.
For thy sake and his own, it was my
        hope
That at Mathraval he would make his
        home :
He had not needed then a father's love.
But he, I know not on what enterprize,
Was brooding ever ; and those secret
        thoughts   200
Drew him away.   God prosper the
        brave boy !
It were a happy day for this poor land
If e'er Llewelyn mount his rightful
        throne.

XI. THE GORSEDD

THE place of meeting was a high hill-
        top,
Nor bower'd with trees nor broken by
        the plough,
Remote from human dwellings and the
        stir
Of human life, and open to the breath
And to the eye of Heaven.   In days of
        old,
There had the circling stones been
        planted ; there,
From earliest ages, the primeval lore,
Through Bard to Bard with reverence
        handed down :
They whom to wonder, or the love of
        song,
Or reverence of their fathers' ancient
        rites   10
Drew thither, stood without the ring of
        stones.
Cyveilioc entered to the initiate Bards,
Himself, albeit his hands were stain'd
        with war,
Initiate ; for the Order, in the lapse
Of years and in their nation's long de-
        cline
From the first rigour of their purity
Somewhat had fallen.   The Masters of
        the Song
Were clad in azure robes, for in that hue
Deduced from Heaven, which o'er a
        sinful world
Spreads its eternal canopy serene,   20
Meet emblem did the ancient Sages see
Of unity and peace and spotless truth.

Within the stones of Federation there,
On the green turf, and under the blue
        sky,
A noble band, the Bards of Britain
        stood,
Their heads in reverence bare, and bare
        of foot.
A deathless brotherhood !   Cyveilioc
        there,
Lord of the Hirlas ; Llywarc there was
        seen,
And old Cynddelow, to whose lofty song,
So many a time amid his father's court
Resigning up his soul, had Madoc given

The flow of feeling loose. But Madoc's
 heart;   32
Was full; old feelings and remem-
 brances,
And thoughts from which was no escape,
 arose;
He was not there to whose sweet lay, so
 oft,
With all a brother's fond delight, he
 lov'd
To listen, . . Hoel was not there ! . . the
 hand
That once so well, amid the triple chords,
Moved in the rapid maze of harmony,
It had no motion now; the lips were
 dumb   40
Which knew all tones of passion; and
 that heart,
That warm ebullient heart, was cold
 and still
Upon its bed of clay. He look'd around,
And there was no familiar countenance,
None but Cynddelow's face, which he
 had learnt
In childhood, and old age had set its
 mark,
Making unsightly alteration there.
Another generation had sprung up,
And made him feel how fast the days of
 man
Flow by, how soon their number is told
 out.   50
He knew not then that Llywarc's lay
 should give
His future fame; his spirit on the past
Brooding, beheld with no forefeeling joy
The rising sons of song, who there
 essay'd
Their eaglet flight. But there among
 the youth
In the green vesture of their earliest
 rank,
Or with the aspirants clad in motley
 garb,
Young Benvras stood; and, one whose
 favoured race
Heaven with the hereditary power had
 blest,
The old Gowalchmai's not degenerate
 child;   60
And there another Einion; gifted
 youths,
And heirs of immortality on earth,

Whose after-strains, through many a dis-
 tant age
Cambria shall boast, and love the songs
 that tell
The fame of Owen's house.
        There, in the eye
Of light and in the face of day, the rites
Began. Upon the stone of Covenant
First the sheathed sword was laid; the
 Master then
Upraised his voice, and cried, Let them
 who seek
The high degree and sacred privilege   70
Of Bardic science, and of Cimbric lore,
Here to the Bards of Britain make their
 claim !
Thus having said, the Master bade the
 youths
Approach the place of peace, and merit
 there
The Bard's most honourable name.
 With that,
Heirs and transmittors of the ancient
 light,
The youths advanced; they heard the
 Cimbric lore,
From earliest days preserved; they
 struck their harps,
And each in due succession raised the
 song.

 Last of the aspirants, as of greener
 years,   80
Young Caradoc advanced; his lip as yet
Scarce darken'd with its down, his flaxen
 locks
Wreathed in contracting ringlets waving
 low;
Bright were his large blue eyes, and
 kindled now
With that same passion that inflamed
 his cheek;
Yet in his cheek there was the sickliness
Which thought and feeling leave, wear-
 ing away
The hue of youth. Inclining on his
 harp,
He, while his comrades in probation song
Approved their claim, stood hearkening
 as it seem'd,   90
And yet like unintelligible sounds
He heard the symphony and voice
 attuned;

Even in such feelings as, all undefined,
Come with the flow of waters to the
    soul,
Or with the motions of the moonlight
    sky.
But when his bidding came, he at the
    call
Arising from that dreamy mood, ad-
    vanced,
Threw back his mantle, and began the
    lay.

    Where are the sons of Gavran? where
        his tribe
The faithful? following their beloved
    chief,   100
They the Green Islands of the Ocean
    sought ;
Nor human tongue hath told, nor
    human ear,
Since from the silver shores they went
    their way,
Hath heard their fortunes. In his
    crystal Ark,
Whither sail'd Merlin with his band of
    Bards,
Old Merlin, master of the mystic lore ?
Belike his crystal Ark, instinct with
    life,
Obedient to the mighty Master, reach'd
The Land of the Departed ; there, be-
    like,
They in the clime of immortality,   110
Themselves immortal, drink the gales of
    bliss,
Which o'er Flathinnis breathe eternal
    spring,
Blending whatever odours make the gale
Of evening sweet, whatever melody
Charms the wood-traveller. In their
    high roof'd halls
There, with the Chiefs of other days, feel
    they
The mingled joy pervade them ? . . Or
    beneath
The mid-sea waters, did that crystal
    Ark
Down to the secret depths of Ocean
    plunge
Its fated crew ? Dwell they in coral
    bowers   120
With Mermaid loves, teaching their
    paramours

The songs that stir the sea, or make the
    winds
Hush, and the waves be still ? In fields
    of joy
Have they their home, where central
    fires maintain
Perpetual summer, and an emerald
    light
Pervades the green translucent element?

    Twice have the sons of Britain left
        her shores,
As the fledged eaglets quit their native
    nest ;
Twice over ocean have her fearless sons
For ever sail'd away. Again they
    launch   130
Their vessels to the deep. . . Who mounts
    the bark ?
The son of Owen, the beloved Prince,
Who never for injustice rear'd his arm.
Respect his enterprize, ye Ocean
    Waves !
Ye Winds of Heaven, waft Madoc on
    his way !
The Waves of Ocean, and the Winds of
    Heaven,
Became his ministers, and Madoc found
The world he sought.
                Who seeks the better land ?
Who mounts the vessel for a world of
    peace ?
He who hath felt the throb of pride, to
    hear   140
Our old illustrious annals ; who was
    taught
To lisp the fame of Arthur, to revere
Great Caratach's unconquer'd soul, and
    call
That gallant chief his countryman, who
    led
The wrath of Britain from her chalky
    shores
To drive the Roman robber. He who
    loves
His country, and who feels his country's
    shame ;
Whose bones amid a land of servitude
Could never rest in peace ; who if he
    saw
His children slaves, would feel a pang in
    Heaven, . .   150
He mounts the bark, to seek for liberty.

Who seeks the better land ? The
wretched one
Whose joys are blasted all, whose heart
is sick,
Who hath no hope, to whom all change
is gain,
To whom remember'd pleasures strike
a pang
That only guilt should know, . . he
mounts the bark,
The Bard will mount the bark of banishment ;
The harp of Cambria shall in other
lands
Remind the Cambrian of his father's
fame ; . .
The Bard will seek the land of liberty,
The world of peace. . . O Prince, receive
the Bard !   161

He ceased the song.   His cheek, now
fever-flush'd,
Was turn'd to Madoc, and his asking
eye
Linger'd on him in hope : nor linger'd
long
The look expectant ; forward sprung
the Prince,
And gave to Caradoc the right-hand
pledge,
And for the comrade of his enterprize,
With joyful welcome, hail'd the joyful
Bard.

Nor needed now the Searcher of the
Sea
Announce his enterprize, by Caradoc
In song announced so well ; from man
to man   171
The busy murmur spread, while from
the Stone
Of Covenant the sword was taken up,
And from the Circle of the Ceremony
The Bards went forth, their meeting
now fulfill'd.
The multitude, unheeding all beside,
Of Madoc and his noble enterprize
Held stirring converse on their home-
ward way,
And spread abroad the tidings of a
Land,
Where Plenty dwelt with Liberty and
Peace.   180

XII. DINEVAWR

So in the court of Powys pleasantly,
With hawk and hound afield, and harp
in hall,
The days went by ; till Madoc, for his
heart
Was with Cadwallon, and in early spring
Must he set forth to join him over-sea,
Took his constrain'd farewell.   To
Dinevawr
He bent his way, whence many a time
with Rhys
Had he gone forth to smite the Saxon
foe.
The son of Owen greets his father's
friend
With reverential joy ; nor did the Lord
Of Dinevawr with cold or deaden'd
heart   11
Welcome the Prince he loved ; though
not with joy
Unmingled now, nor the proud con-
sciousness
Which in the man of tried and approved
worth
Could bid an equal hail.   Henry had
seen
The Lord of Dinevawr between his knees
Vow homage ; yea, the Lord of Dine-
vawr
Had knelt in homage to that Saxon king,
Who set a price upon his father's head,
That Saxon, on whose soul his mother's
blood   20
Cried out for vengeance.   Madoc saw
the shame
Which Rhys would fain have hidden,
and, in grief
For the degenerate land, rejoiced at
heart
That now another country was his home.

Musing on thoughts like these, did
Madoc roam
Alone along the Towy's winding shore.
The beavers in its bank had hollow'd
out
Their social place of dwelling, and had
damm'd
The summer-current with their perfect
art

Of instinct, erring not in means nor end.
But as the floods of spring had broken
  down   31
Their barrier, so its breaches unrepair'd
Were left ; and round the piles, which,
  deeper driven,
Still held their place, the eddying waters
  whirl'd.
Now in those habitations desolate
One sole survivor dwelt : him Madoc
  saw,
Labouring alone, beside his hermit
  house ;
And in that mood of melancholy
  thought, . .
For in his boyhood he had loved to
  watch
Their social work, and for he knew that
  man   40
In bloody sport had well-nigh rooted out
The poor community, . . the ominous
  sight
Became a grief and burthen.   Eve came
  on ;
The dry leaves rustled to the wind, and
  fell
And floated on the stream ; there was
  no voice
Save of the mournful rooks, who over-
  head
Wing'd their long line ; for fragrance of
  sweet flowers,
Only the odour of the autumnal
  leaves ; . .
All sights and sounds of sadness. . . And
  the place
To that despondent mood was minis-
  trant ; . .   50
Among the hills of Gwyneth and its
  wilds
And mountain glens, perforce he
  cherish'd still
The hope of mountain liberty ; they
  braced
And knit the heart and arm of hardi-
  hood ; . .
But here, in these green meads, by these
  low slopes
And hanging groves, attemper'd to the
  scene,
His spirit yielded.   As he loiter'd on,
There came toward him one in peasant
  garb,

And call'd his name ; . . he started at the
  sound,
For he had heeded not the man's ap-
  proach ;   60
And now that sudden and familiar voice
Came on him, like a vision.   So he stood
Gazing, and knew him not in the dim
  light,
Till he again cried, Madoc ! . . then he
  woke,
And knew the voice of Ririd, and sprang
  on,
And fell upon his neck, and wept for joy
And sorrow.
            O my brother ! Ririd cried,
Long, very long it is since I have heard
The voice of kindness ! . . Let me go
  with thee !
I am a wanderer in my father's land, . .
Hoel he kill'd, and Yorwerth hath he
  slain ;   71
Llewelyn hath not where to hide his
  head
In his own kingdom ; Rodri is in
  chains ; . .
Let me go with thee, Madoc, to some
  land
Where I may look upon the sun, nor
  dread
The light that may betray me ; where
  at night
I may not, like a hunted beast, rouse up,
If the leaves rustle over me.
                            The Lord
Of Ocean struggled with his swelling
  heart.
Let me go with thee ? . . but thou didst
  not doubt   80
Thy brother ? . . Let thee go ? . . with
  what a joy,
Ririd, would I collect the remnant left, . .
The wretched remnant now of Owen's
  house,
And mount the bark of willing banish-
  ment,
And leave the tyrant to his Saxon
  friends,
And to his Saxon yoke ! . . I urged him
  thus,
Curb'd down my angry spirit, and be-
  sought
Only that I might bid our brethren
  come,

And share my exile ; . . and he spurn'd
my prayer ! . .
Thou hast a gentle pleader at his court ;
She may prevail ; till then abide thou
here ; . .   91
But not in this, the garb of fear and
guilt.
Come thou to Dinevawr, . . assume thy-
self ; . .
The good old Rhys will bid thee wel-
come there,
And the great Palace, like a sanctuary,
Is safe. If then Queen Emma's plea
should fail,
My timely bidding hence shall summon
thee,
When I shall spread the sail. . . Nay,
hast thou learnt
Suspicion ? . . Rhys is noble, and no
deed   99
Of treachery ever sullied his fair fame !

Madoc then led his brother to the hall
Of Rhys. I bring to thee a supplicant,
O King, he cried ; thou wert my father's
friend !
And till our barks be ready in the
spring,
I know that here the persecuted son
Of Owen will be safe.
                        A welcome guest !
The old warrior cried ; by his good
father's soul,
He is a welcome guest at Dinevawr !
And rising as he spake, he pledged his
hand
In hospitality. . . How now ! quoth he,
This raiment ill beseems the princely
son   111
Of Owen ! . . Ririd at his words was led
Apart ; they wash'd his feet, they gave
to him
Fine linen as beseem'd his royal race,
The tunic of soft texture woven well,
The broider'd girdle, the broad mantle
edged
With fur, and flowing low, the bonnet
last,
Form'd of some forest martin's costly
spoils.
The Lord of Dinevawr sat at the dice
With Madoc, when he saw him thus
array'd,.   120

Returning to the hall.   Ay ! this is
well !
The noble Chief exclaim'd : 'tis as of
yore,
When in Aberfraw, at his father's
board,
We sat together, after we had won
Peace and rejoicing with our own right
hands,
By Corwen, where, commixt with Saxon
blood,
Along its rocky channel the dark Dee
Roll'd darker waters. . . Would that all
his house
Had, in their day of trouble, thought of
me,
And honour'd me like this ! David
respects   130
Deheubarth's strength, nor would re-
spect it less,
When such protection leagued its cause
with Heaven.

I had forgot his messenger ! quoth he,
Arising from the dice. Go, bid him
here !
He came this morning at an ill-starr'd
hour,
To Madoc he pursued ; my lazy grooms
Had let the hounds play havoc in my
flock,
And my old blood was chafed. I'faith,
the King
Hath chosen well his messenger : . . he
saw
That in such mood, I might have ren-
der'd him   140
A hot and hasty answer, and hath
waited,
Perhaps to David's service and to
mine,
My better leisure.
                        Now the Messenger
Enter'd the hall ; Goagan of Powys-
land,
He of Caer-Einion was it, who was
charged
From Gwyneth to Deheubarth ; a brave
man
Of copious speech. He told the royal son
Of Gryffidd, the descendant of the line
Of Rhys-ab-Tudyr mawr, that he
came there   149

From David, son of Owen, of the stock
Of kingly Cynan. I am sent, said he,
With friendly greeting; and as I receive
Welcome and honour, so, in David's
    name,
Am I to thank the Lord of Dinevawr.

    Tell on! quoth Rhys, the purport and
        the cause
Of this appeal?
                Of late, some fugitives
Came from the South to Mona, whom
    the King
Received with generous welcome. Some
    there were
Who blamed his royal goodness; for
    they said,
These were the subjects of a rival
    Prince,   160
Who, peradventure, would with no such
    bounty
Cherish a northern suppliant. This they
    urged,
I know not if from memory of old feuds,
Better forgotten, or in envy. Moved
Hereby, King David swore he would not
    rest
Till he had put the question to the
    proof,
Whether with liberal honour the Lord
    Rhys
Would greet his messenger; but none
    was found
Of all who had instill'd that evil doubt,
Ready to bear the embassy: I heard it,
And did my person tender, . . for I
    knew   171
The nature of Lord Rhys of Dinevawr.

    Well! quoth the Chief, Goagan of
        Powys-land,
This honourable welcome that thou
    seekest
Wherein may it consist?
                        In giving me,
Goagan of Powys-land replied, a horse
Better than mine, to bear me home; a
    suit
Of seemly raiment, and ten marks in
    coin,
With raiment and two marks for him
    who leads
My horse's bridle.

                        For his sake, said Rhys,
Who sent thee, thou shalt have the
    noblest steed   181
In all my studs, . . I double thee the
    marks,
And give the raiment threefold. More
    than this, . .
Say thou to David, that the guests who
    sit
At board with me, and drink of my own
    cup,
Are Madoc and Lord Ririd. Tell the
    King,
That thus it is Lord Rhys of Dinevawr
Delighteth to do honour to the sons
Of Owen, of his old and honour'd friend.

XIII. LLEWELYN

FAREWELL, my brother, cried the Ocean
    Chief;
A little while farewell! as through the
    gate
Of Dinevawr he pass'd, to pass again
That hospitable threshold never more.
And thou too, O thou good old man, true
    friend
Of Owen, and of Owen's house, farewell!
'Twill not be told me, Rhys, when thy
    grey hairs
Are to the grave gone down; but often-
    times
In the distant world I shall remember
    thee,
And think that, come thy summons
    when it may,   10
Thou wilt not leave a braver man
    behind. . .
Now God be with thee, Rhys!
                        The old Chief paused
A moment ere he answer'd, as for pain;
Then shaking his hoar head, I never yet
Gave thee this hand unwillingly before!
When for a guest I spread the board, my
    heart
Will think on him, whom ever with
    most joy
It leapt to welcome: should I lift again
The spear against the Saxon, . . for old
    Rhys
Hath that within him yet, that could
    uplift   20

The Cimbric spear, . . I then shall wish
    his aid,
Who oft has conquer'd with me : when
    I kneel
In prayer to Heaven, an old man's
    prayer shall beg
A blessing on thee !
            Madoc answer'd not,
But press'd his hand in silence, then
    sprang up
And spurr'd his courser on. A weary
    way,
Through forest and o'er fell, Prince
    Madoc rode ;
And now he skirts the bay whose reck-
    less waves
Roll o'er the plain of Gwaelod : fair
    fields
And busy towns and happy villages, 30
They overwhelm'd in one disastrous
    day ;
For they by their eternal siege had
    sapp'd
The bulwark of the land, while Seithenyn
Took of his charge no thought, till in his
    sloth
And riotous cups surprised, he saw the
    waves
Roll like an army o'er the levell'd
    mound.
A supplicant in other courts, he mourn'd
His crime and ruin ; in another's court
The kingly harp of Garanhir was heard,
Wailing his kingdom wreck'd ; and
    many a Prince,   40
Warn'd by the visitation, sought and
    gain'd
A saintly crown, Tyneio, Merini,
Boda and Brenda and Aëlgyvarch,
Gwynon and Celynin and Gwynodyl.

    To Bardsey was the Lord of Ocean
        bound ;
Bardsey, the holy Islet, in whose soil
Did many a Chief and many a Saint
    repose,
His great progenitors. He mounts the
    skiff ;
Her canvass swells before the breeze, the
    sea
Sings round her sparkling keel, and soon
    the Lord   50
Of Ocean treads the venerable shore.

There was not, on that day, a speck
    to stain
The azure heaven; the blessed Sun alone
In unapproachable divinity
Career'd, rejoicing in his fields of light.
How beautiful, beneath the bright blue
    sky,   .
The billows heave ! one glowing green
    expanse,
Save where along the bending line of
    shore
Such hue is thrown, as when the pea-
    cock's neck
Assumes its proudest tint of amethyst,
Embathed in emerald glory. All the
    flocks   61
Of Ocean are abroad : like floating
    foam
The sea-gulls rise and fall upon the
    waves ;
With long protruded neck the cor-
    morants
Wing their far flight aloft, and round
    and round
The plovers wheel, and give their note
    of joy.
It was a day that sent into the heart
A summer feeling : even the insect
    swarms
From their dark nooks and coverts
    issued forth,
To sport through one day of existence
    more ;   70
The solitary primrose on the bank
Seem'd now as though it had no cause
    to mourn
Its bleak autumnal birth ; the Rocks,
    and Shores,
The Forest and the everlasting Hills,
Smiled in that joyful sunshine, . . they
    partook
The universal blessing.
            To this Isle,
Where his forefathers were to dust con-
    sign'd,
Did Madoc come for natural piety,
Ordering a solemn service for their souls.
Therefore for this the Church that day
    was drest :   80
For this the Abbot, in his alb arrayed,
At the high altar stood ; for this infused,
Sweet incense from the waving thuri-
    bule

Rose like a mist, and the grey brother-
hood
Chaunted the solemn mass. And now
on high
The mighty Mystery had been elevate,
And now around the graves the brethren
In long array proceed : each in his hand,
Tall as the staff of some wayfaring man,
Bears the brown taper, with their day-
light flames   90
Dimming the cheerful day. Before the
train
The Cross is borne, where, fashion'd to
the life
In shape and size and ghastly colouring,
The aweful Image hangs. Next, in its
shrine
Of gold and crystal, by the Abbot held,
The mighty Mystery came ; on either
hand
Three Monks uphold above, on silver
wands,
The purple pall. With holy water next
A father went, therewith from hyssop
branch
Sprinkling the graves ; the while, with
one accord,   100
The solemn psalm of mercy all entoned.

Pure was the faith of Madoc, though
his mind
To all this pomp and solemn circum-
stance
Yielded a willing homage. But the
place
Was holy ; . . the dead air, which under-
neath
Those arches never felt the healthy sun,
Nor the free motion of the elements,
Chilly and damp, infused associate awe :
The sacred odours of the incense still
Floated ; the daylight and the taper-
flames   110
Commingled, dimming each, and each
bedimm'd ;
And as the slow procession paced along,
Still to their hymn, as if in symphony,
The regular foot-fall sounded : swelling
now,
Their voices in one chorus, loud and deep,
Rung through the echoing aisles ; and
when it ceased,
The silence of that huge and sacred pile

Came on the heart. What wonder if the
Prince
Yielded his homage there ? the in-
fluences
Of that sweet autumn day made every
sense   120
Alive to every impulse, . . and beneath
The stones whereon he stood, his an-
cestors
Were mouldering, dust to dust. Father !
quoth he,
When now the rites were ended, . . far
away
It hath been Madoc's lot to pitch his
tent
On other shores ; there, in a foreign
land,
Far from my father's burial-place, must I
Be laid to rest ; yet would I have my
name
Be held with theirs in memory. I be-
seech you,
Have this a yearly rite for evermore, 130
As I will leave endowment for the same,
And let me be remember'd in the prayer.
The day shall be a holy day with me,
While I do live ; they who come after
me
Will hold it holy ; it will be a bond
Of love and brotherhood, when all be-
side
Hath been dissolved ; and though wide
ocean rolls
Between my people and their mother
Isle,
This shall be their communion. They
shall send,
Link'd in one sacred feeling at one hour,
In the same language, the same prayer
to Heaven,   141
And each remembering each in piety,
Pray for the other's welfare.
                                    The old man
Partook that feeling, and some pious
tears
Fell down his aged cheek. Kinsman
and son,
It shall be so ! said he ; and thou shalt
be
Remember'd in the prayer : nor then
alone ;
But till my sinking sands be quite run
out,

This feeble voice shall, from its solitude,
Go up for thee to Heaven!
⠀⠀⠀⠀⠀⠀And now the bell
Rung out its cheerful summons; to the
⠀⠀hall,⠀⠀⠀⠀⠀⠀⠀⠀151
In seemly order, pass the brotherhood:
The serving-men wait with the ready
⠀⠀ewer;
The place of honour to the Prince is
⠀⠀given,
The Abbot's right-hand guest; the
⠀⠀viands smoke,
The horn of ale goes round: and now,
⠀⠀the cates
Removed, for days of festival reserved,
Comes choicer beverage, clary, hippocras,
And mead mature, that to the goblet's
⠀⠀brim
Sparkles and sings and smiles. It was
⠀⠀a day⠀⠀⠀⠀⠀⠀⠀160
Of that allowable and temperate mirth
Which leaves a joy for memory. Madoc
⠀⠀told
His tale; and thus, with question and
⠀⠀reply
And cheerful intercourse, from noon till
⠀⠀nones
The brethren sate; and when the quire
⠀⠀was done,
Renew'd their converse till the vesper
⠀⠀bell.

But then the Porter call'd Prince
⠀⠀Madoc out,
To speak with one, he said, who from
⠀⠀the land
Had sought him and required his private
⠀⠀ear.
Madoc in the moonlight met him: in his
⠀⠀hand⠀⠀⠀⠀⠀⠀⠀170
The stripling held an oar, and on his
⠀⠀back,
Like a broad shield, the coracle was
⠀⠀hung.
Uncle! he cried, and with a gush of
⠀⠀tears,
Sprung to the glad embrace.
⠀⠀⠀⠀⠀⠀⠀⠀O my brave boy!
Llewelyn! my dear boy! with stifled
⠀⠀voice,
And interrupted utterance, Madoc cried;
And many times he claspt him to his
⠀⠀breast,

And many times drew back and gazed
⠀⠀upon him,
Wiping the tears away which dimm'd
⠀⠀the sight,
And told him how his heart had yearn'd
⠀⠀for him,⠀⠀⠀⠀⠀⠀⠀180
As with a father's love, and bade him
⠀⠀now
Forsake his lonely haunts and come with
⠀⠀him,
And sail beyond the seas and share his
⠀⠀fate.

No! by my God! the high-hearted
⠀⠀youth replied,
It never shall be said Llewelyn left
His father's murderer on his father's
⠀⠀throne!
I am the rightful king of this poor
⠀⠀land...
Go thou, and wisely go; but I must
⠀⠀stay,
That I may save my people. Tell me,
⠀⠀Uncle,⠀⠀⠀⠀⠀⠀⠀189
The story of thy fortunes; I can hear it
Here in this lonely Isle, and at this hour,
Securely.
⠀⠀⠀⠀⠀⠀Nay, quoth Madoc, tell me first
Where are thy haunts and coverts, and
⠀⠀what hope
Thou hast to bear thee up? Why goest
⠀⠀thou not
To thy dear father's friend in Powys-
⠀⠀land,
There at Mathraval would Cyveilioc give
A kinsman's welcome; or at Dinevawr,
The guest of honour shouldst thou be
⠀⠀with Rhys;
And he belike from David might obtain
Some recompence, though poor.
⠀⠀⠀⠀⠀⠀⠀⠀⠀What recompence?
Exclaim'd Llewelyn; what hath he to
⠀⠀give,⠀⠀⠀⠀⠀⠀⠀201
But life for life? and what have I to
⠀⠀claim
But vengeance, and my father Yor-
⠀⠀werth's throne?
If with aught short of this my soul could
⠀⠀rest,
Would I not through the wide world
⠀⠀follow thee,
Dear Uncle! and fare with thee, well
⠀⠀or ill,

And show to thine old age the tenderness
My childhood found from thee ! .. What hopes I have
Let time display. Have thou no fear for me !
My bed is made within the ocean caves,
Of sea-weeds, bleach'd by many a sun and shower ;   211
I know the mountain dens, and every hold
And fastness of the forest ; and I know, ..
What troubles him by day and in his dreams, ..
There's many an honest heart in Gwyneth yet !
But tell me thine adventure ; that will be
A joy to think of in long winter nights,
When stormy billows make my lullaby.

So as they walk'd along the moonlight shore,
Did Madoc tell him all ; and still he strove,   220
By dwelling on that noble end and aim,
That of his actions was the heart and life,
To win him to his wish. It touch'd the youth ;
And when the Prince had ceased, he heaved a sigh,
Long-drawn and deep, as if regret were there.
No, no ! he cried, it must not be ! lo yonder
My native mountains, and how beautiful
They rest in the moonlight ! I was nurst among them ;
They saw my sports in childhood, they have seen
My sorrows, they have saved me in the hour   230
Of danger ; .. I have vow'd, that as they were
My cradle, they shall be my monument ! ..
But we shall meet again, and thou wilt find me,
When next thou visitest thy native Isle,
King in Aberfraw !
                    Never more, Llewelyn,
Madoc replied, shall I behold the shores

Of Britain, nor will ever tale of me
Reach the Green Isle again.   With fearful care   238
I chuse my little company, and leave
No traces of our path, where Violence,
And bloody Zeal, and bloodier Avarice
Might find their blasting way.
                    If it be so, ..
And wise is thy resolve, the youth replied,
Thou wilt not know my fate ; .. but this be sure,
It shall not be inglorious.   I have in me
A hope from Heaven. .. Give me thy blessing, Uncle !

    Llewelyn, kneeling on the sand, embraced
His knees, with lifted head and streaming eyes
Listening.   He rose, and fell on Madoc's neck,
And clasp'd him, with a silent agony, ..
Then launch'd his coracle, and took his way,   251
A lonely traveller on the moonlight sea.

XIV. LLAIAN

Now hath Prince Madoc left the holy Isle,
And homeward to Aberfraw, through the wilds
Of Arvon, bent his course.   A little way
He turn'd aside, by natural impulses
Moved, to behold Cadwallon's lonely hut.
That lonely dwelling stood among the hills,
By a grey mountain-stream ; just elevate
Above the winter torrents did it stand,
Upon a craggy bank ; an orchard slope
Arose behind, and joyous was the scene
In early summer, when those antic trees
Shone with their blushing blossoms, and the flax   12
Twinkled beneath the breeze its liveliest green.
But save the flax-field and that orchard slope,

All else was desolate, and now it wore
One sober hue ; the narrow vale which
   wound
Among the hills was grey with rocks,
   that peer'd
Above its shallow soil ; the mountain
   side
Was loose with stones bestrewn, which
   oftentimes
Clattered adown the steep, beneath the
   foot   20
Of straggling goat dislodged ; or
   tower'd with crags,
One day, when winter's work hath
   loosen'd them,
To thunder down. All things assorted
   well
With that grey mountain hue ; the low
   stone lines,
Which scarcely seem'd to be the work of
   man,
The dwelling rudely rear'd with stones
   unhewn,
The stubble flax, the crooked apple-trees
Grey with their fleecy moss and missel-
   toe,
The white-bark'd birch now leafless, and
   the ash
Whose knotted roots were like the rifted
   rock,   30
Through which they forced their way.
   Adown the vale,
Broken by stones and o'er a stony bed,
Roll'd the loud mountain-stream.
           When Madoc came,
A little child was sporting by the brook,
Floating the fallen leaves, that he might
   see them
Whirl in the eddy now, and now be
   driven
Down the descent, now on the smoother
   stream
Sail onward far away. But when he
   heard
The horse's tramp, he raised his head
   and watch'd
The Prince, who now dismounted and
   drew nigh.   40
The little boy still fix'd his eyes on him,
His bright blue eyes ; the wind just
   moved the curls
That cluster'd round his brow ; and so
   he stood,

His rosy cheeks still lifted up to gaze
In innocent wonder. Madoc took his
   hand,
And now had ask'd his name, and if he
   dwelt
There in the hut, when from that
   cottage-door
A woman came, who, seeing Madoc, stopt,
With such a fear, . . for she had cause
   for fear, . .
As when a bird returning to her nest, 50
Turns to a tree beside, if she behold
Some prying boy too near the dear
   retreat.
Howbeit, advancing soon, she now ap-
   proach'd
The approaching Prince, and timidly
   enquired,
If on his wayfare he had lost the track,
That thither he had strayed. Not so,
   replied
The gentle Prince ; but having known
   this place,
And its old habitants, I came once more
To see the lonely hut among the hills.
Hath it been long your dwelling ?
          Some few years
Here we have dwelt, quoth she, my
   child and I,   61
Will it please you enter, and partake
   such fare
As we can give ? Still timidly she spake,
But gathering courage from the gentle
   mien
Of him with whom she conversed.
   Madoc thank'd
Her friendly proffer, and toward the hut
They went, and in his arms he took the
   boy.
Who is his father ? said the Prince, but
   wish'd
The word unutter'd ; for thereat her
   cheek
Was flush'd with sudden heat and
   manifest pain ;   70
And she replied, He perish'd in the war.

   They enter'd now her home ; she
   spread the board,
And set before her guest soft curds, and
   cheese
Of curd-like whiteness, with no foreign
   die

Adulterate, and what fruits the orchard
     gave,
And that old British beverage which
     the bees
Had toil'd to purvey all the summer
     long.
Three years, said Madoc, have gone by,
     since here
I found a timely welcome, overworn
With toil and sorrow and sickness : . .
     three long years !   80
'Twas when the battle had been waged
     hard by,
Upon the plain of Arvon.
                    She grew pale,
Suddenly pale ; and seeing that he
     mark'd
The change, she told him, with a feeble
     voice,
That was the fatal fight which widow'd
     her.

O Christ, cried Madoc, 'tis a grief to
     think
How many a gallant Briton died that
     day,
In that accursed strife ! I trod the field
When all was over, . . I beheld them
     heap'd . .
Ay, like ripe corn within the reaper's
     reach,   90
Strewn round the bloody spot where
     Hoel lay ;
Brave as he was, himself cut down at
     last,
Oppress'd by numbers, gash'd with
     wounds, yet still
Clenching in his dead hand the broken
     sword ! . .
But you are moved, . . you weep at what
     I tell.
Forgive me, that renewing my own grief,
I should have waken'd yours ! Did you
     then know
Prince Hoel ?
               She replied, Oh no ! my lot
Was humble, and my loss a humble one ;
Yet was it all to me ! They say, quoth
     she, . .   100
And, as she spake, she struggled to bring
     forth
With painful voice the interrupted
     words, . .

They say Prince Hoel's body was not
     found ;
But you who saw him dead perchance
     can tell
Where he was laid, and by what friendly
     hand.

Even where he fell, said Madoc, is his
     grave ;
For he who buried him was one whose
     faith
Reck'd not of boughten prayers, nor
     passing bell.
There is a hawthorn grows beside the
     place,
A solitary tree, nipt by the winds,   110
That it doth seem a fitting monument
For one untimely slain. . . But wherefore
     dwell we
On this ungrateful theme ?
                    He took a harp
Which stood beside, and passing o'er its
     chords
Made music. At the touch the child
     drew nigh,
Pleased by the sound, and leant on
     Madoc's knee,
And bade him play again. So Madoc
     play'd,
For he had skill in minstrelsy, and
     raised
His voice, and sung Prince Hoel's lay of
     love.

I have harness'd thee, my Steed of
     shining grey,   120
And thou shalt bear me to the dear
     white walls.
I love the white walls by the verdant
     bank,
That glitter in the sun, where Bashful-
     ness
Watches the silver sea-mew sail along.
I love that glittering dwelling, where we
     hear
The ever-sounding billows ; for there
     dwells
The shapely Maiden, fair as the sea-
     spray,
Her cheek as lovely as the apple flower,
Or summer evening's glow. I pine for
     her ;
In crowded halls my spirit is with her ;

Through the long sleepless night I think
on her;   131
And happiness is gone, and health is lost,
And fled the flush of youth, and I am pale
As the pale ocean on a sunless morn.
I pine away for her, yet pity her,
That she should spurn so true a love as
mine.

He ceased, and laid his hand upon the
child, . .
And didst thou like the song ? The child
replied, . .
Oh yes ! it is a song my mother loves,
And so I love it too. He stoopt and
kiss'd   140
The boy, who still was leaning on his
knee,
Already grown familiar. I should like
To take thee with me, quoth the Ocean
Lord,
Over the seas.
            Thou art Prince Madoc, then ! . .
The mother cried, . . thou art indeed the
Prince !
That song . . that look . . and at his feet
she fell,
Crying . . Oh take him, Madoc ! save
the child !
Thy brother Hoel's orphan !
                Long it was
Ere that in either agitated heart
The tumult could subside. One while
the Prince   150
Gazed on the child, tracing intently
there
His brother's lines ; and now he caught
him up,
And kiss'd his cheek, and gazed again
till all
Was dim and dizzy, . . then blest God,
and vow'd
That he should never need a father's
love.

At length when copious tears had now
relieved
Her burthen'd heart, and many a broken
speech
In tears had died away, O Prince, she
cried,
Long hath it been my dearest prayer to
heaven,

That I might see thee once, and to thy
love   160
Commit this friendless boy ! For many
a time,
In phrase so fond did Hoel tell thy worth
That it hath waken'd misery in me
To think I could not as a sister claim
Thy love ! and therefore was it that till
now
Thou knew'st me not ; for I entreated
him
That he would never let thy virtuous eye
Look on my guilt, and make me feel my
shame.
Madoc, I did not dare to see thee then,
Thou wilt not scorn me now, . . for I
have now   170
Forgiven myself ; and, while I here
perform'd
A mother's duty in this solitude,
Have felt myself forgiven.
                With that she clasp'd
His hand, and bent her face on it and
wept.
Anon collecting she pursued, . . My name
Is Llaian : by the chance of war I fell
Into his power, when all my family
Had been cut off, all in one hour of blood.
He saved me from the ruffian's hand, he
sooth'd
With tenderest care my sorrow. . . You
can tell   180
How gentle he could be, and how his eyes,
So full of life and kindliness, could win
All hearts to love him. Madoc, I was
young ;
I had no living friend ; . . and when I
gave
This infant to his arms, when with such
joy
He view'd it o'er and o'er again, and
press'd
A father's kiss upon its cheek, and turn'd
To me, and made me feel more deeply
yet
A mother's deep delight, . . oh ! I was
proud
To think my child in after years should
say,   190
Prince Hoel was his father !
                Thus I dwelt
In the white dwelling by the verdant
bank, . .

Though not without my melancholy
      hours,
Happy. The joy it was when I beheld
His steed of shining grey come hastening
      on,
Across the yellow sand ! . . Alas, ere long,
King Owen died. I need not tell thee,
      Madoc,
With what a deadly and forefeeling fear
I heard how Hoel seized his father's
      throne,
Nor with what ominous woe I welcomed
      him,   200
In that last little miserable hour
Ambition gave to love. I think his
      heart,
Brave as it was, misgave him. When
  ·   I spake
Of David and my fears, he smiled upon
      me ;
But 'twas a smile that came not from
      the heart, . .
A most ill-boding smile ! . . O Madoc !
      Madoc !
You know not with what misery I saw
His parting steps, . . with what a dread-
      ful hope
I watch'd for tidings ! . . And at length
      it came, . .
Came like a thunderbolt ! . . I sought the
      field !   210
O Madoc, there were many widows there,
But none with grief like mine ! I look'd
      around ;
I dragg'd aside the bodies of the dead,
To search for him, in vain ; . . and then
      a hope
Seized me, which it was agony to lose !

Night came. I did not heed the
      storm of night ;
But for the sake of this dear babe, I
      sought
Shelter in this lone hut : 'twas desolate ;
And when my reason had return'd, I
      thought
That here the child of Hoel might be
      safe,   220
Till we could claim thy care. But thou,
      meantime,
Didst go to roam the Ocean ; so I learnt
To bound my wishes here. The
      carkanet,

The embroider'd girdle, and what other
      gauds
Were once my vain adornments, soon
      were changed
For things of profit, goats and bees, and
      this,
The tuneful solace of my solitude.
Madoc, the harp is as a friend to me ;
I sing to it the songs which Hoel loved,
And Hoel's own sweet lays ; it comforts
      me, ·   230
And gives me joy in grief.
                      Often I grieved,
To think the son of Hoel should grow up
In this unworthy state of poverty ;
Till Time, who softens all regrets, had
      worn
That vain regret away, and I became
Humbly resign'd to God's unerring will.
To him I look'd for healing, and he
      pour'd
His balm into my wounds. I never
      form'd
A prayer for more, . . and lo ! the happi-
      ness
Which he hath, of his mercy, sent me
      now !   240

XV. THE EXCOMMUNICATION

On Madoc's docile courser Llaian sits,
Holding her joyful boy ; the Prince
      beside
Paces afoot, and like a gentle Squire
Leads her loose bridle ; from the saddle-
      bow
His shield and helmet hang, and with
      the lance,
Stafflike, he stay'd his steps. Before
      the sun
Had climb'd his southern eminence,
      they left
The mountain feet ; and hard by Bangor
      now,
Travelling the plain before them they
      espy
A lordly cavalcade, for so it seem'd, 10
Of knights, with hawk in hand and
      hounds in leash,
Squires, pages, serving-men, and armed
      grooms,

And many a sumpter-beast and laden
wain,
Far following in the rear.   The bravery
Of glittering bauldricks and of high-
plumed crests,
Embroider'd surcoats and emblazon'd
shields,
And lances whose long streamers play'd
aloft,
Made a rare pageant, as with sound of
trump,
Tambour and cittern, proudly they went
on ;
And ever, at the foot-fall of their steeds,
The tinkling horse-bells, in rude sym-
phony,   21
Accorded with the joy.
                        What have we here ?
Quoth Madoc then to one who stood
beside
The threshold of his osier-woven hut.
'Tis the great Saxon Prelate, he return'd,
Come hither for some end, I wist not
what,
Only be sure no good ! . . How stands
the tide ?
Said Madoc ; can we pass ? . . 'Tis even
at the flood,
The man made answer, and the Monas-
tery
Will have no hospitality to spare   30
For one of Wales to-day.   Be ye content
To guest with us.
                        He took the Prince's sword :
The daughter of the house brought
water then,
And wash'd the stranger's feet ; the
board was spread,
And o'er the bowl they communed of
the days
Ere ever Saxon set his hateful foot
Upon the beautiful Isle.
                        As so they sate,
The bells of the Cathedral rung abroad
Unusual summons.   What is this ? ex-
claim'd
Prince Madoc : let us see ! . . Forthwith
they went,   40
He and his host, their way.   They found
the rites
Begun ;   the mitred Baldwin, in his
hand
Holding a taper, at the altar stood.

Let him be cursed ! . . were the words
which first
Assail'd their ears, . . living and dead,
in limb
And life, in soul and body, be he curst
Here and hereafter !   Let him feel the
curse
At every moment, and in every act,
By night and day, in waking and in
sleep !
We cut him off from Christian fellow-
ship ;   50
Of Christian sacraments we deprive his
soul ;
Of Christian burial we deprive his corpse;
And when that carrion to the Fiends is
left
In unprotected earth, thus let his soul
Be quench'd in hell !
                        He dash'd upon the floor
His taper down, and all the ministring
Priests
Extinguish'd each his light, to consum-
mate
The imprecation.
                        Whom is it ye curse,
Cried Madoc, with these horrors ?   They
replied,
The contumacious Prince of Powys-
land,   60
Cyveilioc.
                        What ! quoth Madoc, and
his eye
Grew terrible, . . Who is he that sets his
foot
In Gwyneth, and with hellish forms like
these
Dare outrage here Mathraval's noble
Lord ?
We wage no war with women nor with
Priests ;
But if there be a knight amid your train,
Who will stand forth, and speak before
my face
Dishonour of the Prince of Powys-land,
Lo ! here stand I, Prince Madoc, who
will make
That slanderous wretch cry craven in
the dust,   70
And eat his lying words !
                        Be temperate !
Quoth one of Baldwin's Priests, who,
Briton born,

Had known Prince Madoc in his father's
  court ;
It is our charge, throughout this Chris-
  tian land,
To call upon all Christian men to join
The armies of the Lord, and take the
  cross ;
That so, in battle with the Infidels,
The palm of victory or of martyrdom,
Glorious alike, may be their recompense.
This holy badge, whether in godless
  scorn,   80
Or for the natural blindness of his heart,
Cyveilioc hath refused ; thereby in-
  curring
The pain, which, not of our own impulse,
  we
Inflict upon his soul, but at the will
Of our most holy Father, from whose
  word
Lies no appeal on earth.
                  'Tis well for thee,
Intemperate Prince ! said Baldwin, that
  our blood
Flows with a calmer action than thine
  own !
Thy brother David hath put on the
  cross,
To our most pious warfare piously   90
Pledging his kingly sword. Do thou
  the like,
And for this better object lay aside
Thine other enterprize, which, lest it rob
Judea of one single Christian arm,
We do condemn as sinful.   Follow thou
The banner of the Church to Palestine ;
So shalt thou expiate this rash offence,
Against the which we else should ful-
  minate
Our ire, did we not see in charity,   99
And therefore rather pity than resent,
The rudeness of this barbarous land.
                        At that,
Scorn tempering wrath, yet anger
  sharpening scorn,
Madoc replied, Barbarians as we are,
Lord Prelate, we received the law of
  Christ
Many a long age before your pirate sires
Had left their forest dens ; nor are we
  now
To learn that law from Norman or from
  Dane,

Saxon, Jute, Angle, or whatever name
Suit best your mongrel race ! Ye think,
  perchance,
That like your own poor woman-hearted
  King,   110
We too in Gwyneth are to take the yoke
Of Rome upon our necks ; . . but you
  may tell
Your Pope, that when I sail upon the
  seas,
I shall not strike a topsail for the breath
Of all his maledictions !
                    Saying thus,
He turn'd away, lest farther speech
  might call
Farther reply, and kindle farther wrath,
More easy to avoid than to allay.
Therefore he left the church ; and soon
  his mind
To gentler mood was won, by social talk
And the sweet prattle of that blue-eyed
  boy,   121
Whom in his arms he fondled.
                    But when now
Evening had settled, to the door there
  came
One of the brethren of the Monastery,
Who called Prince Madoc forth.   Apart
  they went,
And in the low suspicious voice of fear,
Though none was nigh, the Monk began.
  Be calm,
Prince Madoc, while I speak, and
  patiently
Hear to the end ! Thou know'st that, in
  his life,
Becket did excommunicate thy sire 130
For his unlawful marriage ; but the
  King,
Feeling no sin in conscience, heeded not
The inefficient censure.   Now, when
  Baldwin
Beheld his monument to-day, impell'd,
As we do think, by anger against thee,
He swore that, even as Owen in his deeds
Disown'd the Church when living, even
  so
The Church disown'd him dead, and
  that his corpse
No longer should be suffered to pollute
The Sanctuary . . Be patient, I beseech,
And hear me out.   Gerald at this, who
  felt   141

A natural horror, sought, . . as best he
knew
The haughty Primate's temper, . . to
dissuade
By politic argument, and chiefly urged
The quick and fiery nature of our na-
tion, . .
How at the sight of such indignity,
They would arise in arms, and limb from
limb
Tear piecemeal him and all his company.
So far did this prevail, that he will now
Commit the deed in secret ; and, this
night,   150
Thy father's body from its resting place,
O Madoc ! shall be torn, and cast aside
In some unhallow'd pit, with foul dis-
grace
And contumelious wrong.
                    Sayest thou to-night ?
Quoth Madoc. . . Ay, at midnight, he
replied,
Shall this impiety be perpetrated.
Therefore hath Gerald, for the reverence
He bears to Owen's royal memory,
Sent thee the tidings. Now be tem-
perate
In thy just anger, Prince ! and shed no
blood.   160
Thou know'st how dearly the Plan-
tagenet
Atones for Becket's death ; and be thou
sure,
Though thou thyself shouldst sail be-
yond the storm,
That it would fall on Britain.
                    While he spake,
Madoc was still ; the feeling work'd too
deep
For speech, or visible sign. At length
he said,
What if amid their midnight sacrilege
I should appear among them ?
                    It were well ;
The Monk replied, if, at a sight like that,
Thou canst withhold thy hand.
                    Oh, fear me not !
Good and true friend, said Madoc. I am
calm,   •   171
And calm as thou beholdest me will prove
In word and action.   Quick I am to feel
Light ills, . . perhaps o'er-hasty : sum-
mer gnats,

Finding my cheek unguarded, may infix
Their skin-deep stings, to vex and irri-
tate ;
But if the wolf, or forest boar, be nigh,
I am awake to danger.   Even so
Bear I a mind of steel and adamant
Against all greater wrongs.   My heart
•   hath now   180
Received its impulse ; and thou shalt
behold
How in this strange and hideous circum-
stance
I shall find profit. . . Only, my true
friend,
Let me have entrance.
                    At the western porch,
Between the complines and the matin-
bell, . .
The Monk made answer : thou shalt find
the door
Ready.   Thy single person will suffice ;
For Baldwin knows his danger, and the
hour
Of guilt or fear convicts him, both alike
Opprobrious.   Now, farewell !
                    Then Madoc took   190
His host aside, and in his private ear
Told him the purport, and wherein his
help
Was needed.   Night came on ; the
hearth was heapt,
The women went to rest.   They twain,
the while,
Sate at the board, and while the un-
tasted bowl
Stood by them, watch'd the glass whose
falling sands
Told out the weary hours.   The hour is
come ;
Prince Madoc helm'd his head, and from
his neck
He slung the bugle-horn ; they took
their shields,
And lance in hand went forth.   And
now arrived,   200
The bolts give back before them, and
the door
Rolls on its heavy hinge.
                    Beside the grave
Stood Baldwin and the Prior, who, albeit
Cambrian himself, in fear and awe obey'd
The lordly Primate's will.   They stood
and watch'd

Their ministers perform the irreverent
work.
And now with spade and mattock have
they broken
Into the house of death, and now have
they
From the stone coffin wrench'd the iron
cramps,   .
When sudden interruption startled them,
And clad in complete mail from head to
foot,   211
They saw the Prince come in.   Their
tapers gleam'd
Upon his visage, as he wore his helm
Open ;   and when in that pale coun-
tenance, . .
For the strong feeling blanch'd his
cheek, . . they saw
His father's living lineaments, a fear
Like ague shook them.   But anon that fit
Of scared imagination to the sense
Of other peril yielded, when they heard
Prince Madoc's dreadful voice.   Stay !
he exclaim'd,   220
As now they would have fled ; . . stir not
a man, . .
Or if I once put breath into this horn,
All Wales will hear, as if dead Owen
call'd
For vengeance from that grave.   Stir
not a man,
Or not a man shall live !   The doors are
watch'd,
And ye are at my mercy !
                            But at that,
Baldwin from the altar seized the
crucifix,
And held it forth to Madoc, and cried
out,
He who strikes me, strikes Him ; for-
bear, on pain
Of endless——
            Peace !   quoth Madoc, and
profane not   230
The holy Cross, with those polluted
hands
Of midnight sacrilege ! . . Peace !   I
harm thee not, . .
Be wise, and thou art safe. . . For thee,
thou know'st,
Prior, that if thy treason were divulged,
David would hang thee on thy steeple
top,

To feed the steeple daws :   Obey and
live !
Go, bring fine linen and a coffer meet
To bear these relics ;   and do ye, mean-
while,
Proceed upon your work.
                            They at his word
Raised the stone cover, and display'd
the dead,   240
In royal grave-clothes habited, his arms
Cross'd on the breast, with precious
gums and spice
Fragrant, and incorruptibly preserved.
At Madoc's bidding, round the corpse
they wrap
The linen web, fold within fold involved;
They laid it in the coffer, and with cloth
At head and foot filled every interval
And prest it down compact ;   they closed
the lid,
And Madoc with his signet seal'd it
thrice.
Then said he to his host, Bear thou at
dawn   250
This treasure to the ships.   My father's
bones
Shall have their resting-place, where
mine one day
May moulder by their side.   He shall
be free
In death, who living did so well maintain
His and his country's freedom.   As for
ye,
For your own safety, ye I ween will
keep
My secret safe.   So saying, he went his
way.

XVI. DAVID

Now hath the Lord of Ocean once again
Set foot in Mona.   Llaian there receives
Sisterly greeting from the royal maid,
Who, while she tempers to the public
eye
Her welcome, safely to the boy indulged
In fond endearments of instinctive love.
When the first flow of joy was overpast,
How went the equipment on, the Prince
enquired.
Nay, brother, quoth Goervyl, ask thou
that   9

Of Urien ; . . it hath been his sole employ
Daily from cock-crow until even-song,
That he hath laid aside all other
    thoughts,
Forgetful even of me ! She said and
    smiled
Playful reproach upon the good old man,
Who in such chiding as affection loves,
Dallying with terms of wrong, return'd
    rebuke.
There, Madoc, pointing to the shore, he
    cried,
There are they moor'd ; six gallant
    barks, as trim
And worthy of the sea as ever yet
Gave canvass to the gale. The mariners
Flock to thy banner, and the call hath
    roused   21
Many a brave spirit. Soon as Spring
    shall serve,
There need be no delay. I should depart
Without one wish that lingers, could
    we bear
Ririd from hence, and break poor Rodri's
    chains,
Thy lion-hearted brother ; . . and that
    boy,
If he were with us, Madoc ! that dear
    boy
Llewelyn !

        Sister, said the Prince at that,
How sped the Queen ?

            Oh, Madoc ! she replied,
A hard and unrelenting heart hath he. 30
The gentle Emma told me she had fail'd,
And that was all she told ; but in her
    eye
I could see sorrow struggling. She com-
    plains not,
And yet I know, in bitterness laments
The hour which brought her as a victim
    here.

    Then I will seek the Monarch, Madoc
    cried ;
And forth he went. Cold welcome
    David gave,
Such as might chill a suppliant ; but the
    Prince
Fearless began. I found at Dinevawr
Our brother Ririd, and he made his suit
That he might follow me, a banish'd
    man.   41

He waits thine answer at the court of
    Rhys.
Now I beseech thee, David, say to him
His father's hall is open !

                    Then the King
Replied, I told thee, Madoc, thy request
Displeased me heretofore ; I warn'd
    thee, too,
To shun the rebel ; yet my messenger
Tells me, the guests at Dinevawr who
    sate
At board with Rhys and drank of his
    own cup
Were Madoc and Lord Ririd. . . Was this
    well,   50
This open disobedience to my will,
And my express command ?

                    Madoc subdued
His rising wrath. If I should tell thee,
    Sire,
He answer'd, by what chance it so fell
    out,
I should of disobedience stand excused,
Even were it here a crime. Yet think
    again,
David, and let thy better mind prevail !
I am his surety here ; he comes alone ;
The strength of yonder armament is
    mine ;
And when did I deceive thee ? . . I did
    hope,   60
For natural love and public decency,
That ye would part in friendship . . let
    that pass !
He may remain and join me in the hour
Of embarkation. But for thine own sake
Cast off these vile suspicions, and the fear
That makes its danger ! Call to mind,
    my brother,
The rampart that we were to Owen's
    throne !
Are there no moments when the thoughts
    and loves
Of other days return ? . . Let Rodri loose !
Restore him to his birthright ! . . Why
    wouldst thou   70
Hold him in chains, when benefits
    would bind
His noble spirit ?

            Leave me ! cried the King ;
Thou know'st the theme is hateful to
    my ear.
I have the mastery now, and idle words,

Madoc, shall never thrust me from the throne,
Which this right arm in battle hardly won.
There must he lie till nature set him free,
And so deliver both.   Trespass no more!

A little yet bear with me, Madoc cried.
I leave this land for ever ; let me first
Behold my brother Rodri, lest he think
My summer love be withered, and in wrath   82
Remember me hereafter.
                    Leave me, Madoc !
Speedily, ere indulgence grow a fault,
Exclaim'd the Monarch.   Do not tempt my wrath ;
Thou know'st me !
            Ay ! the Ocean Prince replied,
I know thee, David, and I pity thee,
Thou poor, suspicious, miserable man !
Friend hast thou none, except thy country's foe,
That hateful Saxon, he whose bloody hand   90
Pluck'd out thy brethren's eyes ; and for thy kin,
Them hast thou made thy perilous enemies.
What if the Lion Rodri were abroad ?
What if Llewelyn's banner were displayed ?
The sword of England could not save thee then.
Frown not, and menace not ! for what am I,
That I should fear thine anger ? . . And with that
He turn'd indignant from the wrathful King.

XVII. THE DEPARTURE

WINTER hath pass'd away ; the vernal storms
Have spent their rage, the ships are stored, and now
To-morrow they depart.   That day a Boy,
Weary and foot-sore, to Aberfraw came,
Who to Goervyl's chamber made his way,

And caught the hem of her garment, and exclaim'd,
A boon, . . a boon, . . dear Lady ! Nor did he
Wait more reply than that encouragement,
Which her sweet eye and lovely smile bestow'd ;
I am a poor, unhappy, orphan boy,   10
Born to fair promises and better hopes,
But now forlorn.   Take me to be your page ! . .
For blessed Mary's sake, refuse me not !
I have no friend on earth, nor hope but this.

The boy was fair ; and though his eyes were swoln,
And cheek defiled with tears, and though his voice
Came choak'd by grief, yet to that earnest eye
And supplicating voice so musical,
It had not sure been easy to refuse
The boon he begg'd.   I cannot grant thy suit,   20
Goervyl cried, but I can aid it, boy ! . .
Go ask of Madoc ! . . And herself arose,
And led him where her brother on the shore
That day the last embarkment oversaw.
Mervyn then took his mantle by the skirt,
And knelt and made his suit ; she too began
To sue, but Madoc smiling on the Maid,
Won by the virtue of the countenance
Which look'd for favour, lightly gave the yes.

Where wert thou, Caradoc, when that fair boy   30
Told his false tale ? for hadst thou heard the voice,
The gentle voice so musically sweet,
And seen that earnest eye, it would have heal'd
The wounded heart, and thou hadst voyaged on
The happiest man that ever yet forsook
His native country ! He, on board the bark,   [stood
Leant o'er the vessel-side, and there he

And gazed, almost unconscious that he
gazed,
Toward yon distant mountains where
she dwelt,
Senena, his beloved. Caradoc, 40
Senena, thy beloved, is at hand !
Her golden locks are clipt, and her blue
eye
Is wandering through the throng in
search of thee,
For whose dear sake she hath forsaken
all.
You deem her false, that her frail con-
stancy
Shrunk from her father's anger, that she
lives
Another's victim bride; but she hath fled
From that unnatural anger ; hath es-
caped
The unnatural union; she is on the shore,
Senena, blue-eyed maid, a seemly boy,
To share thy fortunes, to reward thy
love, 51
And to the land of peace to follow thee,
Over the ocean waves.
Now all is done.
Stores, beeves, and flocks and water all
aboard ;
The dry East blows, and not a sign of
change
Stains the clear firmament. The Sea-
Lord sate
At the last banquet in his brother's
court,
And heard the song : It told of Owen's
fame,
When with his Normen and assembled
force
Of Guienne and Gascony, and Anjou's
strength, 60
The Fleming's aid and England's
chosen troops,
Along the ascent of Berwyn, many a day
The Saxon vainly on his mountain foes
Denounced his wrath ; for Mona's
dragon sons
By wary patience baffled long his force,
Winning slow Famine to their aid, and
help'd
By the angry Elements, and Sickness
sent
From Heaven, and Fear that of its
vigour robb'd

The healthy arm ; .. then in quick enter-
prize
Fell on his weary and dishearten'd host,
Till with defeat and loss and obloquy 71
He fled with all his nations. Madoo
gave
His spirit to the song ; he felt the theme
In every pulse ; the recollection came,
Revived and heighten'd to intenser pain,
That in Aberfraw, in his father's hall,
He never more should share the feast,
nor hear
The echoing harp again ! His heart was
full ;
And, yielding to its yearnings, in that
mood
Of aweful feeling, he call'd forth the
King, 80
And led him from the palace-porch, and
stretch'd
His hand toward the ocean, and ex-
claim'd,
To-morrow over yon wide waves I go ;
To-morrow, never to return, I leave
My native land! O David, O my brother,
Turn not impatiently a reckless ear
To that affectionate and natural voice
Which thou wilt hear no more ! Release
our brethren,
Recall the wanderers home, and link
them to thee
By cordial confidence, by benefits 90
Which bless the benefactor. Be not thou
As is the black and melancholy yew
That strikes into the grave its baleful
roots,
And prospers on the dead ! .. The Saxon
King, ..
Think not I wrong him now ; .. an hour
like this
Hath soften'd all my harsher feelings
down ;
Nor will I hate him for his sister's sake,
Thy gentle Queen, .. whom, that great
God may bless,
And, blessing her, bless thee and our
dear country,
Shall never be forgotten in my prayers ;
But he is far away ; and should there
come 101
The evil hour upon thee, .. if thy kin,
Wearied by suffering, and driven
desperate,

Should lift the sword, or young Llewelyn
  raise
His banner and demand his father's
  throne, . .
Were it not trusting to a broken reed,
To lean on England's aid ?. . I urge thee
  not
For answer now ; but sometimes, O my
  brother !
Sometimes recall to mind my parting
  words,
As 'twere the death-bed counsel of the
  friend   110
Who loved thee best !
            The affection of his voice,
So mild and solemn, soften'd David's
  heart ;
He saw his brother's eyes, suffused with
  tears,
Shine in the moon-beam as he spake ;
  the King
Remember'd his departure, and he felt
Feelings, which long from his disnatured
  breast
Ambition had expell'd : he could almost
Have follow'd their strong impulse.
    From the shore,
Madoc with quick and agitated step
Had sought his home ; the monarch
  went his way,   120
Serious and slow, and laid him down
  that night
With painful recollections, and such
  thoughts,
As might, if Heaven had will'd it, have
  matured
To penitence and peace.
            The day is come,
The adventurers in Saint Cybi's holy
  fane
Hear the last mass, and all assoil'd of
  sin
Partake the bread of Christian fellow-
  ship.
Then, as the Priest his benediction gave,
They knelt, in such an aweful stillness
  hush'd,
As with yet more oppression seem'd to
  load   130
The burthen'd heart. At times and
  half supprest,
Womanly sobs were heard, and manly
  cheeks

Were wet with silent tears.   Now forth
  they go,
And at the portal of the Church unfurl
Prince Madoc's banner ; at that sight
  a shout
Burst from his followers, and the hills
  and rocks
Thrice echoed their acclaim.
            There lie the ships,
Their sails all loose, their streamers
  rolling out
With sinuous flow and swell, like water-
  snakes.
Curling aloft ; the waves are gay with
  boats,   140
Pinnace and barge and coracle, . . the
  sea
Swarms like the shore with life. Oh
  what a sight
Of beauty for the spirit unconcern'd,
If heart there be which unconcern'd
  could view
A sight like this !. . how yet more beau-
  tiful
For him, whose soul can feel and under-
  stand
The solemn import ! Yonder they em-
  bark,
Youth, beauty, valour, virtue, reverend
  age ;
Some led by love of noble enterprize,
Others, who, desperate of their country's
  weal,   150
Fly from the impending yoke ; all warm
  alike
With confidence and high heroic hope,
And all in one fraternal bond conjoin'd
By reverence to their Chief, the best
  beloved
That ever yet on hopeful enterprize
Led gallant army forth. He, even now
Lord of himself, by faith in God and
  love
To man subdues the feeling of this hour,
The bitterest of his being.
            At this time,
Pale, and with feverish eye, the King
  came up,   160
And led him somewhat from the throng
  apart,
Saying, I sent at day-break to release
Rodri from prison, meaning that with
  thee

He should depart in peace ; but he was
  gone,
This very night he had escaped ! . . Per-
  chance,
As I do hope, . . it was thy doing,
  Madoc ?
Is he aboard the fleet ?
              I would he were !
Madoc replied ; with what a lighten'd
  heart
Then should I sail away !   Ririd is
  there
Alone . . alas ! that this was done so
  late !   170

  Reproach me not ! half sullenly the
  King,
Answering, exclaim'd ; Madoc, reproach
  me not !
Thou know'st how hardly I attain'd the
  throne ;
And is it strange that I should guard
  with fear
The precious prize ? . . Now, . . when
  I would have taken
Thy counsel, . . be the evil on his head !
Blame me not now, my brother, lest
  sometimes
I call again to mind thy parting words
In sorrow !
      God be with thee ! Madoc cried ;
And if at times the harshness of a heart,
Too prone to wrath, have wrong'd thee,
  let these tears   181
Efface all faults.   I leave thee, O my
  brother,
With all a brother's feelings !
                  So he said,
And grasp'd, with trembling tenderness,
  his hand,
Then calm'd himself, and moved to-
  ward the boat.
Emma, though tears would have their
  way and sighs
Would swell, suppressing still all words
  of woe,
Follow'd Goervyl to the extremest shore.
But then as on the plank the Maid set
  foot,
Did Emma, staying her by the hand,
  pluck out   190
The crucifix, which next her heart she
  wore

In reverence to its relic, and she cried,
Yet ere we part change with me, dear
  Goervyl, . .
Dear sister, loved too well, or lost too
  soon ! . .
I shall betake me often to my prayers,
Never in them, Goervyl, of thy name
Unmindful ; . . thou too wilt remember
  me
Still in thy orisons ; . . but God forefend
That ever misery should make thee find
This Cross thy only comforter !
                  She said,
And kiss'd the holy pledge, as each to
  each   201
Transferr'd the mutual gift.   Nor could
  the Maid
Answer, for agony, to that farewell ;
She held Queen Emma to her breast, and
  close
She clasp'd her with a strong convulsive
  sob,
Silently.   Madoc too in silence went,
But prest a kiss on Emma's lips, and
  left
His tears upon her cheek.   With dizzy
  eyes
Gazing she stood, nor saw the boat push
  off. . .
The dashing of the oars awaken'd her ;
She wipes her tears away, to view once
  more   211
Those dear familiar faces ; . . they are
  dim
In the distance ; never shall her waking
  eye
Behold them, till the hour of happiness,
When death hath made her pure for
  perfect bliss !

  Two hearts alone of all that company,
Of all the thousands who beheld the
  scene,
Partook unmingled joy.   Dumb with
  delight,
Young Hoel views the ships and feels the
  boat
Rock on the heaving waves ; and Llaian
  felt   220
Comfort, . . though sad, yet comfort, . .
  that for her
No eye was left to weep, nor heart to
  mourn.

Hark ! 'tis the mariners with voice
    attuned
Timing their toil ! and now with gentle
    gales,
Slow from the holy haven they depart.

XVIII. RODRI

Now hath the evening settled ; the
    broad Moon
Rolls through the rifted clouds. With
    gentle gales
Slowly they glide along, when they
    behold
A boat with press of sail and stress of
    oar
Speed forward to the fleet ; and now,
    arrived
Beside the Chieftain's vessel, one en-
    quires
If Madoc be aboard ? the answer given,
Swift he ascended up the lofty side.
With joyful wonder did the Ocean Lord
Again behold Llewelyn ; but he gazed
Doubtfully on his comrade's coun-
    tenance, . .   11
A meagre man, severe of brow, his eye
Stern. Thou dost view me, Madoc, he
    exclaim'd,
As 'twere a stranger's face. I marvel
    not !
The long afflictions of my prison house
Have changed me.
              Rodri ! cried the Prince,
    and fell
Upon his neck ; . . last night, subdued at
    length
By my solicitations, did the King
Send to deliver thee, that thou shouldst
    share
My happy enterprize ; . . and thou art
    come,   20
Even to my wish !
              Nay, Madoc, nay, not so !
He answered, with a stern and bitter
    smile ;
This gallant boy hath given me liberty,
And I will pay him with his father's
    throne.
Ay, by my father's soul ! . . Last night
    we fled

The house of bondage, and in the sea-
    caves
By day we lurk'd securely. Here I
    come,
Only to see thee once before I die,
And say farewell, . . dear brother !
                        Would to God
This purpose could be changed ! the Sea
    Lord cried ,   30
But thou art roused by wrongs, and who
    shall tame
That lion heart ? . . This only, if your lot
Fall favourable, will I beseech of ye,
That to his Queen, the fair Plantagenet,
All honourable humanity ye show,
For her own virtue, and in gratitude,
As she hath pleaded for you, and hath
    urged
Her husband on your part, till it hath
    turn'd
His wrath upon herself. Oh ! deal ye
    by her
As by your dearest sister in distress, 40
For even so dear is she to Madoc's heart!
And now I know she from Aberfraw's
    tower
Watcheth these specks upon the moon-
    light sea,
And weeps for my departure, and for me
Sends up her prayers to Heaven, nor
    thinks that now
I must make mine to man in her behalf !

    Quoth Rodri, Rest assured for her.
    I swear,
By our dead mother, so to deal with
    her
As thou thyself wouldst dictate, as
    herself
Shall wish.
    The tears fell fast from Madoc's eyes :
O Britain ! O my country ! he ex-
    claim'd,   51
For ever thus by civil strife convulsed,
Thy children's blood flowing to satisfy
Thy children's rage, how wilt thou still
    support
The struggle with the Saxon ?
                        Rodri cried,
Our strife shall not be long. Mona will
    rise
With joy, to welcome me her rightful
    Lord ;

And woe be to the King who rules by
fear,
When danger comes against him !
                    Fear not thou
For Britain ! quoth Llewelyn, for not
yet   60
The country of our fathers shall resign
Her name among the nations. Though
    her Sun
Slope from his eminence, the voice of
    man
May yet arrest him on his downward
    way.
My dreams by day, my visions in the
    night,
Are of her welfare. I shall mount the
    throne, . .
Yes, Madoc ! and the Bard of years to
    come,
Who harps of Arthur's and of Owen's
    deeds,
Shall with the Worthies of his country
    rank
Llewelyn's name. Dear Uncle, fare
    thee well ! . .   70
And I almost could wish I had been born
Of humbler lot, that I might follow thee,

Companion of this noble enterprize.
Think of Llewelyn often, who will oft
Remember thee in love !
                    For the last time
He press'd his Uncle's hand, and Rodri
    gave
The last farewell ; then went the twain
    their way.

So over ocean through the moonlight
    waves
Prince Madoc sail'd with all his com-
    pany.
No nobler crew fill'd that heroic bark 80
Which bore the first adventurers of the
    deep
To seek the Golden Fleece on barbarous
    shores :
Nor richlier fraught did that illustrious
    fleet
Home to the Happy Island hold its
    way,
When Amadis with his prime chivalry,
He of all chivalry himself the flower,
Came from the rescue, proud of Roman
    spoils,
And Oriana, freed from Roman thrall.

MADOC IN AZTLAN : PART II.

I. THE RETURN TO AZTLAN

Now go your way, ye gallant company,
God and good Angels guard ye as ye go !
Blow fairly, Winds of Heaven ! Ye
    Ocean Waves,
Swell not in anger to that fated fleet !
For not of conquest greedy, nor of gold,
Seek they the distant world. . . Blow
    fairly, Winds !
Waft, Waves of Ocean, well your blessed
    load !

    Fair blew the Winds, and safely did
    the Waves
Bear that beloved charge. It were a
    tale
Would rouse adventurous courage in
    a boy,   10

Making him long to be a mariner
That he might rove the main, if I should
    tell
How pleasantly for many a summer-day,
Over the sunny sea with wind at will,
Prince Madoc sail'd ; and of those happy
    Isles,
Which had he seen ere that appointed
    storm
Drove southward his slope course, there
    he had pitch'd
His tent, and blest his lot that it had
    fallen
In land so fair ; and human blood had
    reek'd
Daily on Aztlan's devilish altars still. 20
But other doom was his, more arduous
    toil
Yet to achieve, worse danger to endure,

Worse evil to be quell'd, and higher
    good
Which passeth not away educed from
    ill ;
Whereof all unforeseeing, yet for all
Prepared at heart, he over ocean sails,
Wafted by gentle winds o'er gentle
    waves,
As if the elements combined to serve
The perfect Prince, by God and man
    beloved.
And now how joyfully he views the land,
Skirting like morning clouds the dusky
    sea ;   31
With what a searching eye recalls to
    mind
Foreland and creek and cape ; how
    happy now
Up the great river bends at last his way !

    No watchman had been station'd on
        the height
To seek his sails, . . for with Cadwallon's
    hope
Too much of doubt was blended and of
    fear :
Yet thitherward whene'er he walked
    abroad
His face, as if instinctively, was turn'd ;
And duly morn and eve Lincoya there,
As though religion led his duteous feet,
Went up to gaze. He on a staff had
    scored   42
The promised moons and days ; and
    many a time
Counting again its often-told account,
So to beguile impatience, day by day
Smooth'd off with more delight the
    daily notch.
But now that the appointed time was
    nigh,
Did that perpetual presence of his hope
Haunt him, and mingle with his sleep,
    and mar
The natural rest, and trouble him by
    day,   50
That all his pleasure was at earliest light
To take his station, and at latest eve,
If he might see the sails where far away
Through wide savannahs roll'd the silver
    stream.
Oh then with what a sudden start his
    blood

Flow'd from its quicken'd spring, when
    far away
He spied the glittering topsails ! For a
    while
Distrustful of that happy sight, till now
Slowly he sees them rise, and wind along
Through wide savannahs up the silver
    stream.   60
Then with a breathless speed he flies to
    spread
The joy ; and with Cadwallon now
    descends,
And drives adown the tide the light
    canoe.
And mounts the vessel-side, and once
    again
Falls at the Ocean Lord's beloved feet.

    First of the general weal did Madoc
        ask ;
Cadwallon answer'd, All as yet is well,
And, by this seasonable aid secured,
Will well remain. . . . Thy father ? quoth
    the Prince.   69
Even so, replied Cadwallon, as that eye
Of hesitation augurs, . . fallen asleep.
The good old man remember'd thee in
    death,
And bless'd thee ere he died.
                        By this the shores
And heights were throng'd ; from hill
    to hill, from rock
To rock, the shouts of welcome rung
    around.
Forward they press to view the man
    beloved,
Britons and Hoamen with one common
    joy
Hailing their common friend. Happy
    that day
Was he who heard his name from
    Madoc's voice ;
Happy who met the greeting of his eye ;
Yea happy he who shared the general
    smile,   81
Amid the unacknowledged multitude.

    Caermadoc, . . by that name Cad-
        wallon's love
Call'd it in memory of the absent
    Prince, . .
Stood in a mountain vale, by rocks and
    heights,

A natural bulwark, girt. A rocky stream
Which from the fells came down there spread itself
Into a quiet lake, to compass which
Had been a two hours' pleasurable toil;
And he, who from a well-strung bow could send   90
His shaft across, had needs a sinewy arm,
And might from many an archer far and near
Have borne away the bell. Here had the Chief
Chosen his abiding place, for strength preferr'd,
Where vainly might an host in equal arms
Attempt the difficult entrance ; and for all
That could delight the eye and heart of man ;
Whate'er of beauty or of usefulness
Heart could desire, or eye behold, being here.
What he had found an idle wilderness
Now gave rich increase to the husband-men,   101
For Heaven had blest their labour. Flourishing
He left the happy vale ; and now he saw
More fields reclaim'd, more habitations rear'd,
More harvests rising round. The reptile race,
And every beast of rapine, had retired
From man's asserted empire ; and the sound
Of axe and dashing oar, and fisher's net,
And song beguiling toil, and pastoral pipe,   109
Were heard, where late the solitary hills
Gave only to the mountain-cataract
Their wild response.
      Here, Urien, cried the Prince,
These craggy heights and overhanging groves
Will make thee think of Gwyneth. And this hut,
Rejoin'd Cadwallon, with its roof of reeds,
Goervyl, is our palace : it was built

With lighter labour than Aberfraw's towers ;
Yet, Lady, safer are its wattled sides
Than Mona's kingly walls. . . Like Gwyneth, said he ?
Oh no ! we neighbour nearer to the Sun,
And with a more benignant eye the Lord   121
Of Light beholds us here.
      So thus did they
Cheerfully welcome to their new abode
These, who, albeit aweary of their way,
And glad to reach at length the place of rest,
Felt their hearts overburthen'd, and their eyes
Ready to overflow. Yet not the less
The buzz of busy joy was heard around,
Where every dwelling had its guest, and all   129
Gave the long eve to hospitable mirth.

II. THE TIDINGS

BUT when the Lord of Ocean from the stir
And tumult was retired, Cadwallon then
Thus render'd his account.
      When we had quell'd
The strength of Aztlan, we should have thrown down
Her altars, cast her Idols to the fire,
And on the ruins of her fanes accurst
Planted the Cross triumphant. Vain it is
To sow the seed where noxious weeds and briars
Must choke it in the growth.
      Yet I had hope
The purer influence of exampled good
Might to the saving knowledge of the truth   11
Lead this bedarken'd race ; and when thy ship
Fell down the stream to distant Britain bound,
All promised well. The strangers' God had proved
Mightier in war ; and Aztlan could not choose
But see, nor seeing could she fail to love,

The freedom of his service. Few were
now
The offerings at her altars, few the
youths
And virgins to the temple-toils devote.
Therefore the Priests combined to save
their craft;   20
And soon the rumour ran of evil signs
And tokens; in the temple had been
heard
Wailings and loud lament; the eternal
fire
Gave dismally a dim and doubtful
flame;
And from the censer, which at morn
should steam
Sweet odours to the sun, a fetid cloud
Black and portentous rose. And now
no Priest
Approach'd our dwelling. Even the
friendly Prince
Yuhidthiton was at Caermadoc now
Rarely a guest; and if that tried good-
will   30
Which once he bore us did at times
appear,
A sullen gloom and silence like remorse
Followed the imagined crime.
                                 But I the while
Reck'd not the brooding of the storm;
for then
My father to the grave was hastening
down.
Patiently did the pious man endure,
In faith anticipating blessedness,
Already more than man in those sad
hours
When man is meanest. I sate by his
side,
And pray'd with him and talk'd with
him of death   40
And life to come. O Madoc! those
were hours
Which even in anguish gave my soul
a joy:
I think of them in solitude, and feel
The comfort of my faith.
                                 But when that time
Of bitterness was past and I return'd
To daily duties, no suspicious sign
Betoken'd ill; the Priests among us
came
As heretofore, and I their intercourse

Encouraged as I could, suspecting
nought,   49
Nor conscious of the subtle-minded men
I dealt with, how inveterate in revenge,
How patient in deceit. Lincoya first
Forewarn'd me of the danger. He,
thou know'st,
Had from the death of sacrifice escaped,
And lived a slave among a distant tribe,
When seeing us he felt a hope, that we,
Lords as he deem'd us of the Elements,
Might pity his poor countrymen opprest,
And free them from their bondage.
Didst thou hear
How from yon bloody altars he was
saved?   60
For in the eternal chain his fate and ours
Were link'd together then.
                                 The Prince replied,
I did but hear a broken tale. Tell on!

    Among the Gods of yon unhappy race,
Tezcalipoca as the chief they rank,
Or with the chief co-equal; Maker he,
And Master of created things esteem'd.
He sits upon a throne of trophied skulls,
Hideous and huge; a shield is on his
arm,
And with his black right hand he lifts,
as though   70
In wrath, the menacing spear. His
festival,
Of all this wicked nation's wicked rites,
With most solemnity and circumstance
And pomp of hellish piety, is held.
From all whom evil fortune hath sub-
dued
To their inhuman thraldom, they select
Him whom they judge, for comely coun-
tenance
And shapely form and all good natural
gifts,
Worthiest to be the victim; and for
this
Was young Lincoya chosen, being in
truth   80
The flower of all his nation. For twelve
months,
Their custom is, that this appointed
youth
Be as the Idol's living image held.
Garb'd therefore like the Demon Deity,
Whene'er he goes abroad, an antic train

With music and with dance attend his
way ;
The crowd before him fall and worship
him ;
And those internal Priests who guard
him then,
To be their victim and their feast at last,
At morning and at evening incense him,
And mock him with knee-reverence.
Twenty days   91
Before the bloody festival arrive,
As 'twere to make the wretch in love
with life,
Four maids, the loveliest of the land,
are given
In spousals. With Lincoya all these
rites
Duly were kept ; and at the stated time,
Four maids, the loveliest of the land,
were his.
Of these was one, whom even at that
hour
He learnt to love, so excellently good
Was she ; and she loved him and pitied
him.   100
She is the daughter of an aged Priest ;
I oftentimes have seen her ; and in
truth,
Compared with Britain's maids so
beautiful,
Or with the dark-eyed daughters of the
South,
She would be lovely still. Her cotton
vest
Falls to the knee, and leaves her olive
arms
Bare in their beauty ; loose, luxuriant,
long,
Flow the black tresses of her glossy hair ;
Mild is her eye's jet lustre ; and her
voice ! . .
A soul which harbour'd evil never
breathed   110
Such winning tones.
                Thou know'st how manfully
These tribes, as if insensible to pain,
Welcome their death in battle, or in
bonds
Defy their torturers. To Lincoya's
mind
Long preparation now had made his fate
Familiar ; and, he says, the thought of
death

Broke not his sleep, nor mingled with
his dreams,
Till Coätel was his. But then it woke ; . .
It hung, . . it prest upon him like a
weight
On one who scarce can struggle with the
waves ;   120
And when her soul was full of tender-
ness,
That thought recurring to her, she
would rest
Her cheek on his and weep.
                        The day drew nigh ;
And now the eve of sacrifice was
come. . .
What will not woman, gentle woman,
dare,
When strong affection stirs her spirit
up ? . .
She gather'd herbs, which, like our
poppy, bear
The seed of sleep, and with the temple
food
Mingled their power ; herself partook
the food,
So best to lull suspicion ; and the youth,
Instructed well, when all were laid
asleep,   131
Fled far away.
                After our conquering arms
Had freed the Hoamen from their
wretched yoke,
Lincoya needed but his Coätel
To fill his sum of earthly happiness.
Her to the temple had her father's vow
Awhile devoted, and some moons were
still
To pass away, ere yet she might become
A sojourner with us, Lincoya's wife,
When from the Paba's wiles his watch-
ful mind   140
Foreboded ill. He bade me take good
heed,
And fear the sudden kindness of a foe.
I started at his words ; . . these artful
men,
Hostile at heart, as well we knew they
were,
These were lip-lavish of their friendship
now,
And courted confidence, while our tried
friend
Yuhidthiton, estranged, a seldom guest,

Sullen and joyless, seem'd to bear at
    heart
Something that rankled there.   These
    things were strange ;
The omens too had ceased ; . . we heard
    no more   150
Of twilight voices, nor the unholy cloud
Steam'd from tho morning incense.
    Why was this ?

    Young Malinal had from the hour of
    peace
Been our in-dweller, studious to attain
Our language and our arts.   To him
    I told
My doubts, assured of his true love and
    truth ;
For he had learnt to understand and
    feel
Our holy faith, and tended like a son
Cynetha's drooping age, and shared
    with me
His dying benediction.   He, thus long
Intent on better things, had been
    estranged   161
From Aztlan and her councils ; but at
    this
He judged it for her welfare and for
    ours
Now to resume his rank ; . . belike his
    voice
Might yet be heard, or, if the worst
    befel,
His timely warning save us from the
    snare.

    But in their secret councils Malinal
No longer bore a part : the Chiefs and
    King
Yielding blind reverence to the Pabas
    now,
Deluded or dismay'd.   He sent to say
Some treachery was design'd, and bade
    me charge   171
His brother with the crime.   On that
    same day,
Lincoya came from Aztlan ; he had
    found
Coätel labouring with a wretchedness
She did not seek to hide ; and when the
    youth
Reveal'd his fear, he saw her tawny
    cheek

Whiten, and round his neck she clung
    and wept.
She told him something dreadful was at
    hand,
She knew not what : That, in the dead
    of night,
Coänocotzin at Mexitli's shrine   180
Had stood with all his nobles ; human
    blood
Had then been offer'd up, and secret
    vows
Vow'd with mysterious horror :   That
    but late,
When to her father of the days to come
She spake, and of Lincoya and her lot
Among the strangers, he had frown'd,
    and strove
Beneath dissembled anger to conceal
Visible grief.   She knew not what to
    fear,
But something dreadful surely was at
    hand,   189
And she was wretched.
            When I heard these things,
Yuhidthiton and the Priest Helhua
Were in our dwellings.   Them I call'd
    apart. . .
There should be peace between us, I
    began ;
Why is it otherwise ?
                    The Priest replied,
Is there not peace, Cadwallon ?   Seek
    we not
More frequent and more friendly inter-
    course,
Even we, the servants of our Country-
    Gods,
Whose worship ye have changed, and
    for whose sake
We were and would have been your
    enemies ?
But as those Gods have otherwise
    ordain'd,   200
Do we obey.   Why therefore is this
    doubt ?

    The Power who led us hither, I
    replied,
Over the world of waters, who hath
    saved,
And who will save his people, warns
    me now.
Then on Yuhidthiton I fix'd my eye.

Danger is near! I cried; I know it near!
It comes from Aztlan.
                    His disorder'd cheek,
And the forced and steady boldness of
   his eye,
Which in defiance met the look it
   fear'd,
Confess'd the crime. I saw his inward
   shame;   210
Yet with a pride like angry innocence
Did he make answer, I am in your hands,
And you believe me treacherous!.. Kill
me now!

  Not so, Yuhidthiton! not so!
  quoth I;
You were the Strangers' friend, and yet
   again
That wisdom may return. We are not
   changed;..
Lovers of peace, we know, when danger
   comes,
To make the evil on the guilty head
Fall heavily and sure! With our good
   arms,
And our good cause, and that Almighty
   One,   220
We are enough, had we no other aid,
We of Caermadoc here, to put to shame
Aztlan, with all her strength and all her
   wiles.
But even now is Madoc on the seas;
He leads our brethren here; and should
   he find
That Aztlan hath been false,.. oh! hope
   not then,
By force or fraud, to baffle or elude
Inevitable vengeance! While ye may,
Look to your choice; for we are friends
   or foes,
Even to your own desert.
                    So saying, I left
The astonish'd men, whose unprovided
   minds   231
Fail'd them; nor did they aim at answer
   more,
But homeward went their way. Nor
   knew I then,..
For this was but a thing of yesterday,..
How near the help I boasted. Now, I
   trust,
Thy coming shall discomfit all their
   wiles.

III. NEOLIN

Nor yet at rest, my Sister! quoth the
   Prince,
As at her dwelling-door he saw the Maid
Sit gazing on that lovely moonlight
   scene:..
To bed, Goervyl. Dearest, what hast
   thou
To keep thee wakeful here at this late
   hour,
When even I shall bid a truce to thought,
And lay me down in peace?.. Good
   night, Goervyl!
Dear sister mine,.. my own dear
   mother's child!

  She rose, and bending on with lifted
   arms,
Met the fond kiss, obedient then withdrew.   10
Yet could not he so lightly as he ween'd
Lay wakeful thoughts aside; for he
   foresaw
Long strife and hard adventure to
   achieve,
And forms of danger vague disturb'd his
   dreams.

  Early at morn the colonists arose;
Some pitch the tent-pole, and pin down
   the lines
That stretch the o'er-awning canvass;
   to the wood
Others with saw and axe and bill for
   stakes,
And undergrowth to weave the wicker
   walls;
These to the ships, with whom Cad-
   wallon sends   20
The Elk and Bison, broken to the yoke.

  Ere noon Erillyab and her son arrived,
To greet the Chief. She wore no longer
   now
The lank loose locks of careless widowhood;
Her braided tresses round her brow were
   bound,
Bedeck'd with tufts of grey and silvery
   plumes

Pluck'd from the eagle's pennons. She
  with eye
And countenance which spake no
  feign'd delight,
Welcomed her great deliverer. But her
  son
Had Nature character'd so legibly,   30
That when his tongue told fair his face
  bewray'd
The lurking falsehood, sullen, slow of
  speech,
Savage, down-looking, dark, that at his
  words
Of welcome, Madoc in his heart con-
  ceived
Instinctive enmity.
              In a happy hour
Did the Great Spirit, said Erillyab,
Give bidding to the Winds to speed thee
  here !
For this I made my prayer ; and when
  He sent
For the Beloved Teacher, to restore him
Eyesight and youth, of him I then
  besought,   40
As he had been thy friend and ours on
  earth,
That he would intercede. . . Brother, we
  know
That the Great Spirit loves thee ; He
  hath blest
Thy going and thy coming, and thy
  friends
Have prosper'd for thy sake ; and now
  when first
The Powers of Evil do begin to work,
Lo ! thou art here ! . . Brother, we have
  obeyed
Thy will, and the Beloved Teacher's
  words
Have been our law ; but now the Evil
  Ones
Cry out for blood, and say they are
  athirst,   50
And threaten vengeance. I have brought
  the Priest
To whom they spake in darkness. . . Thou
  art wise,
And the Great Spirit will enlighten
  thee ; . .
We know not what to answer. . . Tell thy
  tale,
Neolin !

            Hereat did Madoc fix upon him
A searching eye ; but he, no whit
  abash'd,
Began with firm effrontery his speech.
The Feast of the Departed is at hand,
And I, in preparation, on the Field
Of the Spirit pass'd the night. It came
  to me   60
In darkness, after midnight, when the
  moon
Was gone, and all the stars were blotted
  out ;
It gather'd round me, with a noise of
  storms,
And enter'd into me, and I could feel
It was the Snake-God roll'd and writhed
  within ;
And I too with the inward agony,
Roll'd like a snake and writhed. Give !
  give ! he cried :
I thirst ! . . His voice was in me, and it
  burnt
Like fire, and all my flesh and bones
  were shaken ;
Till, with a throe which seem'd to rend
  my joints   70
Asunder, he pass'd forth, and I was left
Speechless and motionless, gasping for
  breath.

Then Madoc, turning to Ayayaca,
Enquired, who is the man ? . . The good
  old Priest
Replied, he hath attended from his
  youth
The Snake-God's temple, and received
  for him
His offerings, and perform'd his sacrifice,
Till the Beloved Teacher made us leave
The wicked way.
           Hear me ! quoth Neolin,
With antic gesture and loud vehemence ;
Before this generation, and before   81
These ancient forests, . . yea, before yon
  lake
Was hollow'd out, or one snow-feather
  fell
On yonder mountain-top, now never
  bare, . .
Before these things I was, . . where, or
  from whence,
I know not, . . who can tell ? But then
  I was,

And in the shadow of the Spirit stood;
And I beheld the Spirit, and in him
Saw all things, even as they were to be;
And I held commune with him, not of
   words,   90
But thought with thought. Then was
   it given me
That I should choose my station when
   my hour
Of mortal birth was come, . . hunter, or
   chief,
Or to be mightiest in the work of war,
Or in the shadow of the Spirit live,
And He in me. According to my
   choice,
For ever, overshadow'd by its power,
I walk among mankind. At times I feel
   not
The burthen of his presence; then am I
Like other men; but when the season
   comes,   100
Or if I seek the visitation, then
He fills me, and my soul is carried on,
And then do I forelive the race of men,
So that the things that will be, are to me
Past.
          Amalahta lifted then his eyes
A moment; . . It is true, he cried; we
   know
He is a gifted man, and wise beyond
The reach of mortal powers. Ayayaca
Hath also heard the warning.
                      As I slept,
Replied the aged Priest, upon the Field
Of the Spirit, a loud voice awaken'd
   me,   111
Crying, I thirst! Give, . . give! or I will
   take!
And then I heard a hiss, as if a snake
Were threatening at my side. . . But saw
   you nothing?
Quoth Madoc. . . Nothing; for the night
   was dark.
And felt you nothing? said the Ocean
   Prince.
He answered, Nothing; only sudden
   fear. . .
No inward struggle, like possession? . .
   None.
I thought of the Beloved Teacher's
   words,
And cross'd myself, and then he had no
   power.   120

Thou hast slept heretofore upon the
   Field,
Said Madoc; didst thou never witness
   voice,
Or ominous sound? Ayayaca replied.
Certes the Field is holy! it receives,
All the year long, the operative power
Which falleth from the sky, or from
   below
Pervades the earth; no harvest groweth
   there,
Nor tree, nor bush, nor herb, is left to
   spring;
But there the virtue of the elements
Is gathered, till the circle of the months
Be full; then, when the Priest, by
   mystic rites,   131
Long vigils, and long abstinence pre-
   pared,
Goeth there to pass the appointed night
   alone,
The whole collected influence enters
   him.
Doubt not but I have felt strange im-
   pulses
On that mysterious Field, and in my
   dreams
Been visited; and have heard sounds
   in the air,
I know not what; . . but words articulate
Never till now. It was the Wicked
   One!   139
He wanted blood.
              Who says the Wicked One?
It was our fathers' God! cried Neolin . .
Sons of the Ocean, why should we for-
   sake
The worship of our fathers? Ye obey
The White-Man's Maker; but to us was
   given
A different skin and speech and land
   and law.
The Snake-God understands the Red-
   Man's prayer,
And knows his wants and loves him.
   Shame be to us,
That since the Stranger here set foot
   among us,
We have let his lips be dry!
                      Enough! replied
Madoc, who at Cadwallon's look re-
   press'd   150
His answering anger. We will hold a talk

Of this hereafter. Be ye sure, mean-
        time,
That the Great Spirit will from Evil
        Powers
Protect his people. This, too, be ye
        sure,
That every deed of darkness shall be
        brought
To light, . . and woe be to the lying lips !

IV. AMALAHTA.

Soon as the coming of the fleet was
        known,
Had Queen Erillyab sent her hunters
        forth.
They from the forest now arrive, with
        store
Of venison ; fires are built before the
        tents,
Where Llaian and Goervyl for their
        guests
Direct the feast ; and now the ready
        board
With grateful odour steams.   But while
        they sate
At meat, did Amalahta many a time
Lift his slow eye askance, and eagerly
Gaze on Goervyl's beauty ; for whate'er
In man he might have thought deformed
        or strange   11
Seemed beautiful in her, . . her golden
        curls,
Bright eyes of heavenly blue, and that
        clear skin,
Blooming with health and youth and
        happiness.
He, lightly yielding to the impulse, bent
His head aside, and to Erillyab spake ;
Mother, said he, tell them to give to me
That woman for my wife, that we may
        be
Brethren and friends.   She, in the same
        low tone,
Rebuked him, in her heart too well
        aware   20
How far unworthy he.   Abash'd there-
        by,
As he not yet had wholly shaken off
Habitual reverence, he sate sullenly,
Brooding in silence his imagined wiles,

By sight of beauty made more apt for ill;
For he himself being evil, good in him
Work'd evil.
                And now Madoc, pouring forth
The ripe metheglin, to Erillyab gave
The horn of silver brim.   Taste, Queen
        and friend,
Said he, what from our father land we
        bring,   30
The old beloved beverage.   Sparingly
Drink, for it hath a strength to stir the
        brain,
And trouble reason, if intemperate lips
Abuse its potency.   She took the horn,
And sipt with wary wisdom. . . Canst
        thou teach us
The art of this rare beverage ? quoth the
        Queen,
Or is the gift reserved for ye alone,
By the Great Spirit, who hath favour'd
        ye
In all things above us ? . . The Chief
        replied,   39
All that we know of useful and of good
Ye also shall be taught, that we may be
One people.   While he spake, Erillyab
        pass'd
The horn to Amalahta.   Sparingly !
Madoc exclaim'd ; but when the savage
        felt
The luscious flavour, and the poignant
        life,
He heeded nought beyond the imme-
        diate joy.
Deep did he drink, and still with
        clenching hands
Struggled, when from his lips, unsatis-
        fied,
Erillyab pluck'd the horn with sharp
        reproof,
Chiding his stubborn wilfulness.   Ere
        long   50
The generous liquor flush'd him : he
        could feel
His blood play faster, and the joyful
        dance
Of animal life within him.   Bolder
        grown,
He at Goervyl lifts no longer now
The secret glance, but gloats with greedy
        eye ;
Till, at the long and loathsome look
        abash'd,

She rose, and nearer to her brother drew,
On light pretence of speech, being half in fear.
But he, regardless of Erillyab now,
To Madoc cried aloud, Thou art a King,
And I a King! . . Give me thy sister there,   61
To be my wife, and then we will be friends,
And reign together.
                    Let me answer him,
Madoc! Cadwallon cried. I better know
Their language, and will set aside all hope,
Yet not incense the savage. . . A great thing,
Prince Amalahta, hast thou ask'd! said he.
Nor is it in Lord Madoc's power to give
Or to withhold; for marriage is with us
The holiest ordinance of God, whereon
The bliss or bane of human life depends.
Love must be won by love, and heart to heart   72
Link'd in mysterious sympathy, before
We pledge the marriage-vow; and some there are
Who hold that, e'er we enter into life,
Soul hath with soul been mated, each for each
Especially ordain'd. Prince Madoc's will
Avails not, therefore, where this secret bond
Hath not been framed in Heaven.
                    The skilful speech
Which, with wild faith and reason, thus confirm'd   80
Yet temper'd the denial, for a while
Silenced him, and he sate in moody dreams
Of snares and violence. Soon a drunken thirst,
And longing for the luscious beverage,
Drove those dark thoughts aside. More drink! quoth he.
Give me the drink! . . Madoc again repeats
His warning, and again with look and voice
Erillyab chides; but he of all restraint

Impatient, cries aloud, Am I a child?
Give! give! or I will take! . . Perchance ye think   90
I and my God alike cry out in vain!
But ye shall find us true!
                    Give him the horn!
Cadwallon answer'd; there will come upon him
Folly and sleep, and then an after pain,
Which may bring wisdom with it, if he learn
Therefrom to heed our warning. . . As thou say'st,
No child art thou! . . the choice is in thy hand; . .
Drink, if thou wilt, and suffer, and in pain
Remember us.
                    He clench'd the horn, and swill'd
The sweet intoxication copious down.
So bad grew worse. The potent draught provoked   101
Fierce pride and savage insolence. Ay! now
It seems that I have taught ye who I am!
The inebriate wretch exclaim'd. This land is mine,
Not hers; the kingdom and the power are mine;
I am the master!
                    Hath it made thee mad?
Erillyab cried. . . Ask thou the Snake-God that!
Quoth he; ask Neolin and Aztlan that!
Hear me, thou Son of the Waters! wilt thou have me
For friend or foe? . . Give me that woman there,   110
And store me with this blessed beverage,
And thou shalt dwell in my domains, . . or else,
Blood! blood.! The Snake-God calls for blood; the Gods
Of Aztlan and the people call for blood;
They call on me, and I will give them blood,
Till they have had their fill.
                    Meanwhile the Queen
In wonder and amazement heard and grief;
Watching the fiendish workings of his face,

And turning to the Prince at times, as if
She look'd to him for comfort. Give
        him drink,   120
To be at peace! quoth Madoc. The
        good mead
Did its good office soon; his dizzy eyes
Roll'd with a sleepy swim; the joyous
        thrill
Died away; and as every limb relax'd,
Down sunk his heavy head and down
        he fell.
Then said the Prince, We must rejoice
        in this,
O Queen and friend, that, evil though
        it be,
Evil is brought to light; he hath
        divulged
In this mad mood, what else had been
        conceal'd
By guilty cunning. Set a watch upon
        him   130
And on Priest Neolin; they plot against
        us;
Your fall and mine do they alike con-
        spire,
Being leagued with Aztlan to destroy
        us both.
Thy son will not remember that his lips
Have let the treason pass. Be wary
        then,
And we shall catch the crafty in the pit
Which they have dug for us.
                        Erillyab cast
A look of anger, made intense by grief,
On Amalahta... Cursed be the hour
Wherein I gave thee birth! she cried;
        that pain   140
Was light to what thy base and brutal
        nature
Hath sent into my soul... But take
        thou heed! ·
I have borne many a woe and many
        a loss, ..
My father's realm, the husband of my
        youth,
My hope in thee! .. all motherly love
        is gone, ..
Sufferance well nigh worn out.
                When she had ceased,
Still the deep feeling fill'd her, and her
        eye
Dwelt on him, still in thought. Brother!
        she cried,

As Madoc would have sooth'd her, doubt
        not me!   149
Mine is no feeble heart. Abundantly
Did the Great Spirit overpay all woes,
And this the heaviest, when he sent thee
        here,
The friend and the deliverer. Evil
        tongues
May scatter lies; bad spirits and bad
        men
May league against thy life; but go
        thou on,
Brother! He loves thee and will be thy
        shield.

V. WAR DENOUNCED

THIS is the day, when, in a foreign
        grave,
King Owen's relics shall be laid to rest.
No bright emblazonries bedeck'd his
        bier,
No tapers blazed, no prelate sung the
        mass,
No choristers the funeral dirge intoned,
No mitred abbots, and no tonsured
        train,
Lengthen'd the pomp of ceremonious
        woe.
His decent bier was with white linen
        spread
And canopied; two elks and bisons,
        yoked,
Drew on the car; foremost Cadwallon
        bore   10
The Crucifix; with single voice, dis-
        tinct,
The good priest Llorien chaunted loud
        and deep
The solemn service; Madoc next the
        bier
Follow'd his father's corpse; bareheaded
        then
Came all the people, silently and slow.

The burial-place was in a grassy plat,
A little level glade of sunny green,
Between the river and a rocky bank,
Which, like a buttress, from the preci-
        pice
Of naked rock sloped out. On either
        side   20

'Twas skirted by the woodlands. A stone cross
Stood on Cynetha's grave, sole monument,
Beneath a single cocoa, whose straight trunk
Rose like an obelisk, and waved on high
Its palmy plumage, green and never sere.
Here by Cynetha's side, with Christian prayers,
All wrongs forgotten now, was Owen laid.
Rest, King of Gwyneth, in a foreign grave !
From foul indignity of Romish pride
And bigot priesthood, from a falling land   30
Thus timely snatch'd, and from the impending yoke, . .
Rest in the kingdom of thy noble son !

Ambassadors from Aztlan in the vale
Awaited their return, . . Yuhidthiton,
Chief of the Chiefs, and Helhua the priest ;
With these came Malinal. They met the Prince,
And with a sullen stateliness return'd
His salutation, then the Chief began ·
Lord of the Strangers, hear me ! by my voice
The People and the Pabas and the King
Of Aztlan speak. Our injured Gods have claim'd   41
Their wonted worship, and made manifest
Their wrath ; we dare not impiously provoke
The Dreadful. Worship ye in your own way ;
But we must keep the path our fathers kept.

We parted, O Yuhidthiton ! as friends
And brethren, said the Christian Prince ;
 . . alas,
That this should be our meeting ! When we pledged,
In the broad daylight and the eye of Heaven,
Our hands in peace, ye heard the will of God,   50

And felt and understood. This calm assent
Ye would belie, by midnight miracles
Scared, and such signs of darkness as beseem
The Demons whom ye dread ; or likelier
Duped by the craft of those accursed men,
Whose trade is blood. Ask thou of thine own heart,
Yuhidthiton, . .
                    But Helhua broke his speech ;
Our bidding is to tell thee, quoth the Priest,
That Aztlan hath restored, and will maintain,   59
Her ancient faith. If it offendeth thee,
Move thou thy dwelling place !
                         Madoc replied,
This day have I deposited in earth
My father's bones, and where his bones are laid,
There mine shall moulder.
                       Malinal at that
Advanced ; . . Prince Madoc, said the youth, I come,
True to thy faith and thee, and to the weal
Of Aztlan true, and bearing, for that truth,
Reproach and shame and scorn and obloquy.
In sorrow come I here, a banish'd man ;
Here take, in sorrow, my abiding place,
Cut off from all my kin, from all old ties
Divorced ; all dear familiar countenances   72
No longer to be present to my sight ;
The very mother-language which I learnt,
A lisping baby on my mother's knees,
No more with its sweet sounds to comfort me.
So be it ! . . To his brother then he turn'd ;
Yuhidthiton, said he, when thou shalt find, . .
As find thou wilt, . . that those accursed men
Have played the juggler with thee, and deceived   80
Thine honest heart, . . when Aztlan groans in blood, . .
Bid her remember then, that Malinal

Is in the dwellings of her enemy ;
Where all his hope in banishment hath
    been
To intercede for her, and heal her
    wounds,
And mitigate her righteous punishment.

Sternly and sullenly his brother heard ;
Yet hearken'd he as one whose heart
    perforce
Suppress'd its instinct, and there might
    be seen
A sorrow in his silent stubbornness. 90
And now his ministers on either hand
A water-vessel fill, and heap dry sedge
And straw before his face, and fire the
    pile.
He, looking upward, spread his arms and
    cried,
Hear me, ye Gods of Aztlan, as we were,
And are, and will be yours ! Behold
    your foes !
He stoopt, and lifted up one ample
    urn, . .
Thus let their blood be shed ! . . and far
    away
He whirl'd the scattering water. Then
    again
Raised the full vase, . . Thus let their
    lives be quench'd !   100
And out he pour'd it on the flaming pile.
The steam-cloud, hissing from the ex-
    tinguish'd heap,
Spread like a mist, and ere it melted off,
Homeward the heralds of the war had
    turn'd.

VI. THE FESTIVAL OF
THE DEAD

THE Hoamen in their Council-hall are
    met
To hold the Feast of Souls ; seat above
    seat,
Ranged round the circling theatre they
    sit.
No light but from the central fire, whose
    smoke,
Slow passing through the over aperture,
Excludes the day, and fills the conic
    roof,

And hangs above them like a cloud.
    Around,
The ghastly bodies of their chiefs are
    hung,
Shrivell'd and parch'd by heat ; the
    humbler dead
Lie on the floor, . . white bones, exposed
    to view,   10
On deer, or elk-skin laid, or softer fur,
Or web, the work of many a mournful
    hour ;
The loathlier forms of fresh mortality
Swathed, and in decent tenderness con-
    ceal'd.
Beside each body pious gifts are laid,
Mantle and belt and feathery coronal,
The bow he used in war, his drinking
    shell,
His arrows for the chace, the sarbacan,
Through whose long tube the slender
    shaft, breath driven,
Might pierce the winged game. Hus-
    bands and wives,   20
Parents and children, there in death
    they lie ;
The widow'd and the parent and the
    child
Look on in silence. Not a sound is
    heard
But of the crackling brand, or moulder-
    ing fire,
Or when, amid yon pendant string of
    shells,
The slow wind wakes a shrill and feeble
    sound, . .
A sound of sorrow to the mind attuned
By sights of woe.

                    Ayayaca at length
Came forward : . . Spirits, is it well with
    ye ?
Is it well, Brethren ? said the aged
    Priest ;   30
Have ye received your mourning, and
    the rites
Of righteous grief ? or round your
    dwelling-place
Still do your shadows roam dissatisfied,
And to the cries of wailing woe return
A voice of lamentation ? Teach us now,
If we in aught have fail'd, that I, your
    Priest,
When I shall join ye soon, as soon I must,
May unimpeded pass the perilous floods,

And in the Country of the Dead, be
  hail'd
By you, with song and dance and grateful joy.   40

  So saying, to the Oracle he turn'd,
Awaiting there the silence which implied
Peaceful assent. Against the eastern
  wall,
Fronting the narrow portal's winding
  way,
An Image stood : a cloak of fur dis-
  guised
The rude proportion of its uncouth
  limbs ;
The skull of some old seer of days of old
Topt it, and with a visor this was
  mask'd,
Honouring the oracular Spirit, who at
  times   49
There took his resting place. Ayayaca
Repeated, Brethren, is it well with ye ?
And raised the visor. But he started
  back,
Appall'd and shuddering ; for a moony
  light
Lay in its eyeless sockets, and there
  came
From its immoveable and bony jaws
A long deep groan, thrice utter'd, and
  thrice felt
In every heart of all the hearers round.
The good old Priest stood tottering, like
  a man
Stricken with palsy ; and he gazed with
  eyes   59
Of asking horror round, as if he look'd
For counsel in that fear. But Neolin
Sprung boldly to the oracle, and cried,
Speak, Spirit ! tell us of our sin, and
  teach
The atonement ! A sepulchral voice
  replied,
Ye have for other Gods forsaken us,
And we abandon you ! . . and crash
  with that
The Image fell.
          A loud and hideous shriek,
As of a demon, Neolin set up ;
So wild a yell, that, even in that hour,
It brought fresh terror to the startled
  ear.   70
While yet they sate, pale and irresolute,

Helhua the Azteca came in. He bore
A shield and arrow, . . symbols these of
  war,
Yet now beheld with hope, so great relief
They felt his human presence.
                  Hoamen, hear me !
The messenger began ; Erillyab, hear,
Priests, Elders, People ! but hear
  chiefly thou,
Prince Amalahta, as of these by birth,
So now of years mature, the rightful
  Lord ! . .
Shall it be peace or war ? . . thus Aztlan
  saith ;   80
She, in her anger, from the land will
  root
The Children of the Sea ; but viewing
  you
In mercy, to your former vassalage
Invites ye, and remits the tribute lives,
And for rebellion claimeth no revenge.

  Oh praise your Gods ! cried Neolin,
  and hail
This day-spring of new hope ! Aztlan
  remits
The tribute lives, . . what more could
  Madoc give ?
She claimeth no revenge, and if she
  claimed,
He could not save. O Hoamen, bless
  your Gods ;   90
Appease them ! Thou, Prince Amalahta,
  speak,
And seize the mercy.
               Amalahta stood
In act of speech ; but then Erillyab
  rose . .
Who gives thee, Boy, this Elder's
  privilege ?
The Queen exclaim'd ; . . and thou,
  Priest Neolin,
Curb thou thy traitorous tongue ! The
  reign is mine ;
I hold it from my father, he from his ;
Age before age, beyond the memory
Of man it hath been thus. My father
  fell
In battle for his people, and his sons 100
Fell by his side ; they perish'd, but
  their names
Are with the names we love, . . their
  happy souls

Pursue in fields of bliss the shadowy
   deer ;
The spirit of that noble blood which ran
From their death-wounds, is in the ruddy
   clouds
Which go before the Sun, when he
   comes forth
In glory. Last of that illustrious race
Was I, Erillyab. Ye remember well,
Elders, that day when I assembled here
The people, and demanded at their
   choice   110
The worthiest, to perpetuate our old line
Of Kings and Warriors. . . To the wind
   he spread
His black and blood-red banner. Even
   now
I hear his war drum's tripled sound, that
   call'd
The youth to battle ; even now behold
The hope which lit his dark and fiery
   eye,
And kindled with a sunnier glow his
   cheek,
As he from yonder war-pole, in his pride,
Took the death-doers down . . Lo here
   the bones
Of King Tepollomi ! . . my husband's
   bones ! . .   120
There should be some among ye who
   beheld,
When, all with arrows quill'd, and
   clothed with blood
As with a purple garment, he sustain'd
The unequal conflict, till the Aztecas
Took him at vantage, and their
   monarch's club
Let loose his struggling soul. Look,
   Hoamen, here,
See through how wide a wound his spirit
   fled !
Twenty long years of mournful widow-
   hood
Have pass'd away ; so long have I
   maintain'd
The little empire left us, loving well 130
My people, and by them as well beloved.
Say, Hoamen, am I still your Queen ?
                   At once
The whole assembly rose with one
   acclaim, . .
Still, O Erillyab, O Beloved, rule
Thy own beloved people !

                   But the Gods !
Cried Amalahta, . . but the Oracle !
The Oracle ! quoth she ; what hath it
   said
That forty years of suffering hath not
   taught
This wretched people ? . . They abandon
   us ? . .
So let them go ! Where were they at
   that hour,   140
When, like a blasting night-wind in the
   spring,
The multitudes of Aztlan came upon
   us ?
Where were they when my father went
   to war ?
Where were they when thy father's
   stiffen'd corpse,
Even after death a slave, held up the
   lamp
To light his conqueror's revels ? . . Think
   not, Boy,
To palter with me thus ! A fire may
   tremble
Within the sockets of a skull, and
   groans
May issue from a dead man's fleshless
   jaws,
And images may fall, and yet no God
Be there ! . . If it had walk'd abroad with
   life,   151
That had indeed been something !
                  Then she turn'd
Her voice toward the people. . . Ye have
   heard
This Priest of Aztlan, whose insidious
   tongue
Bids ye desert the Children of the Sea,
And vow again your former vassalage.
Speaks Aztlan of the former ? O my
   people,
I too could tell ye of the former days,
When yonder plain was ours, with all its
   woods
And waters and savannahs ! . . of those
   days,   160
When, following where her husband's
   stronger arm
Had open'd the light glebe, the willing
   wife
Dropt in the yellow maize ; ere long to
   bear
Its increase to the general store, and toss

Her flowing tresses in the dance of joy.
And I could tell ye how those summer
   stores
Were hoarded for the invader's winter
   feasts ;
And how the widows clipt those flowing
   locks
To strew them, . . not upon their hus-
   band's grave, . .
Their husbands had no graves ! . . but
   on the rocks   170
And mountains in their flight, And
   even these rocks
And mountains could not save us ! Year
   by year
Our babes, like firstlings of the flock,
   were cull'd
To be the banquet of these Aztecas !
This very wretch, who tells us of the past,
Hath chosen them for the butchery. . .
   Oh, I thank you
For this brave anger ! . . In your name
   I take
The war-gift !
      Gods of Aztlan, Helhua cried,
As to Erillyab's ready hand he gave 179
The deadly symbol, in your name I give
The war-gift ! Ye have thirsted over
   long ;
Take now your fill of blood ! . . He turn'd
   away ;
And Queen Erillyab bade the tribe fulfil
Their customary rites.
           Each family
Bore its own dead, and to the general
   grave,
With melancholy song and sob of woe,
The slow procession moves. The general
   grave
Was delved within a deep and shady
   dell,
Fronting a cavern in the rock, . . the
   scene
Of many a bloody rite, ere Madoc
   came, . .   190
A temple, as they deem'd, by Nature
   made,
Where the Snake-Idol stood. On fur
   and cloth
Of woven grass, they lay their burthens
   down,
Within the ample pit ; their offerings
   range

Beside, and piously a portion take
Of that cold earth, to which, for ever now
Consign'd, they leave their fathers, dust
   to dust ;
Sad relic that, and wise remembrancer.

But as with bark and resinous boughs
   they pile
The sepulchre, suddenly Neolin   200
Sprung up aloft, and shriek'd, as one
   who treads
Upon a viper in his heedless path.
The God ! the very God ! he cried, and
   howl'd
One long, shrill, piercing, modulated cry ;
Whereat from that dark temple issued
   forth
A Serpent, huge and hideous. On he
   came,
Straight to the sound, and curl'd around
   the Priest
His mighty folds innocuous, over-
   topping
His human height, and arching down his
   head,   209
Sought in the hands of Neolin for food ;
Then questing, rear'd and stretch'd and
   waved his neck,
And glanced his forky tongue. Who
   then had seen
The man, with what triumphant fear-
   lessness,
Arms, thighs, and neck, and body,
   wreathed and ring'd
In those tremendous folds, he stood
   secure,
Play'd with the reptile's jaws, and
   call'd for food,
Food for the present God ! . . who then
   had seen
The fiendish joy which fired his coun-
   tenance,
Might well have ween'd that he had
   summoned up
The dreadful monster from its native
   Hell,   220
By devilish power, himself a Fiend in-
   flesh'd.

Blood for the God ! he cried ; Lincoya's
   blood !
Friend of the Serpent's foe ! . . Lincoya's
   blood !

Cried Amalahta, and the people turn'd
Their eyes to seek the victim, as if each
Sought his own safety in that sacrifice.
Alone Erillyab raised her voice, confused
But not confounded; she alone exclaim'd,
Madoc shall answer this! Unheard her
voice   229
By the bewilder'd people, by the Priest
Unheeded; and Lincoya sure had fallen
The victim of their fear, had he been found
In that wild hour; but when his watchful eye
Beheld the Serpent from his den come forth,
He fled to bear the tidings. . . Neolin
Repeats the accursed call, Food for the God!
Ayayaca, his unbelieving Priest!
At once all eager eyes were fix'd on him,
But he came forward calmly at the call;
Lo! here am I! quoth he; and from his head   240
Plucking the thin grey hairs he dealt them round. . .
Countrymen, kinsmen, brethren, children, take
These in remembrance of me! there will be
No relic of your aged Priest but this.
From manhood to old age, full threescore years,
Have I been your true servant: fit it is
That I, who witness'd Aztlan's first assault,
Should perish her last victim! . . and he moved
Towards the death. But then Erillyab
Seized him, and by the garment drew him back! . .   250
By the Great Spirit, but he shall not die!
The Queen exclaim'd; nor shalt thou triumph thus,
Liar and traitor! Hoamen, to your homes!
Madoc shall answer this!
                          Irresolute
They heard, and inobedient; to obey
Fearing, yet fearful to remain. Anon,
The Queen repeats her bidding, To your homes,

My people! . . But when Neolin perceived
The growing stir and motion of the crowd,
As from the outward ring they moved away,   260
He utter'd a new cry, and disentangling
The passive reptile's folds, rush'd out
With outstretch'd hands, like one possess'd, to seize
His victim. Then they fled; for who could tell
On whom the madman, in that hellish fit.
Might cast the lot? An eight-years' boy he seized
And held him by the leg, and, whirling him
In ritual dance, till breath and sense were gone,
Set up the death-song of the sacrifice.
Amalahta, and what others rooted love
Of evil leagued with him, accomplices
In treason, join'd the death-song and the dance.   272
Some too there were, believing what they fear'd,
Who yielded to their old idolatry,
And mingled in the worship. Round and round
The accursed minister of murder whirl'd
His senseless victim; they too round and round
In maddening motion, and with maddening cries
Revolving, whirl'd and wheel'd. At length, when now,
According to old rites, he should have dash'd   280
On the stone Idol's head the wretch's brains,
Neolin stopt, and once again began
The long, shrill, piercing, modulated cry.
The Serpent knew the call, and, rolling on,
Wave above wave, his rising length, advanced
His open jaws: then, with the expected prey,
Glides to the dark recesses of his den.

VII. THE SNAKE GOD

MEANTIME Erillyab's messenger had girt
His loins, and like a roebuck, o'er the
        hills
He sped. He met Cadwallon and the
        Prince
In arms, so quickly Madoc had obey'd
Lincoya's call; at noon he heard the
        call,
And still the sun was riding high in
        heaven,
When up the valley where the Hoamen
        dwelt
He led his twenty spears. O welcome,
        friend
And brother! cried the Queen. Even
        as thou saidst
So hath it proved; and those accursed
        schemes   10
Of treachery, which that wretched boy
        reveal'd
Under the influence of thy potent drink,
Have ripen'd to effect. From what a
        snare
The timely warning saved me! for, be
        sure,
What I had seen I else should have
        believed,
In utter fear confounded. The Great
        Spirit,
Who taught thee to foresee the evil
        thing,
Will give thee power to quell it.
                        On they went
Toward the dell, where now the Idolaters
Had built their dedicated fire, and still
With feast and fits of song and violent
        dance,   21
Pursued their rites. When Neolin
        perceived
The Prince approach, fearlessly he
        came forth,
And raised his arm, and cried, Strangers,
        away!
Away, profane! hence to your mother-
        land!
Hence to your waters; for the God is
        here; . .
He came for blood, and he shall have his
        fill!
Impious, away!

Seize him! exclaim'd the Prince;
Nor had he time for motion nor for flight,
So instantly was that command obey'd.
Hoamen, said Madoc, hear me! . . I
        came here,   31
Stranger alike to Aztlan and to you;
I found ye an opprest and wretched race,
Groaning beneath your chains; at your
        request,
For your deliverance, I unsheathed the
        sword,
Redeem'd ye from your bondage, and
        preserved
Your children from the slaughter. With
        those foes
Whose burthen ye for forty years en-
        dured,
This traitor hath conspired, against
        yourselves,
Your Queen, and me your friend; the
        solemn faith   40
Which in the face of yonder sun we
        pledged,
Each to the other, this perfidious man
Hath broken, and hath stain'd his hands
        this day
With innocent blood. Life must atone
        for life:
Ere I destroy the Serpent, whom his
        wiles
Have train'd so well, last victim, he shall
        glut
The monster's maw.
                    Strike, man! quoth Neolin.
This is my consummation! the reward
Of my true faith! the best that I could
        ask,
The best the God could give: . . to rest
        in him,   50
Body with body be incorporate,
Soul into soul absorb'd, and I and He
One life, inseparable, for evermore.
Strike, I am weary of this mortal part;
Unite me to the God!
                    Triumphantly
He spake; the assembled people, at his
        words,
With rising awe gazed on the miscreant;
Madoc himself, when now he would have
        given
The sign for death, in admiration paused,
Such power hath fortitude. And he per-
        ceived   60

The auspicious moment, and set up his
   cry.
Forth, from the dark recesses of the
   cave,
The Serpent came : the Hoamen at the
   sight
Shouted, and they who held the Priest,
   appall'd
Relax'd their hold. On came the
   mighty snake,
And twined, in many a wreath, round
   Neolin,
Darting aright, aleft, his sinuous neck,
With searching eye, and lifted jaw and
   tongue
Quivering, and hiss as of a heavy shower
Upon the summer woods. The Britons
   stood   70
Astounded at the powerful reptile's bulk
And that strange sight. His girth was
   as of man,
But easily could he have overtopp'd
Goliath's helmed head, or that huge
   King
Of Basan, hugest of the Anakim :
What then was human strength, if once
   involved
Within those dreadful coils ? . . The
   multitude
Fell prone, and worshipp'd ; pale
   Erillyab grew,
And turn'd upon the Prince a doubtful
   eye ;
The Britons too were pale, albeit they
   held   80
Their spears protended ; and they also
   look'd
On Madoc, who the while stood silently,
Contemplating how wiseliest he might
   cope
With that surpassing strength.
               But Neolin,
Well hoping now success, when he had
   awed
The general feeling thus, exclaim'd aloud,
Blood for the God ! give him the
   Stranger's blood !
Avenge him on his foes ! And then, per-
   chance,
Terror had urged them to some desperate
   deed,
Had Madoc ponder'd more, or paused
   in act   90

One moment. From the sacrificial
   flames
He snatch'd a firebrand, and with fire
   and sword,
Rush'd at the monster : back the
   monster drew
His head upraised recoiling, and the
   Prince
Smote Neolin ; all circled as he was,
And clipt in his false Deity's embrace,
Smote he the accursed Priest ; the
   avenging sword
Fell on his neck ; through flesh and
   bone it drove
Deep in the chest : the wretched
   criminal
Totter'd, and those huge rings a moment
   held   100
His bloody corpse upright, while Madoc
   struck
The Serpent : twice he struck him, and
   the sword
Glanced from the impenetrable scales ;
   nor more
Avail'd its thrust, though driven by
   that strong arm ;
For on the unyielding skin the temper'd
   blade
Bent. He sprung upward then, and in
   the eyes
Of the huge monster flashed the fiery
   brand.
Impatient of the smoke and burning,
   back
The reptile wreathed, and from his
   loosening clasp
Dropt the dead Neolin, and turn'd, and
   fled   110
To his dark den.
            The Hoamen, at that sight
Raised a loud wonder-cry, with one
   accord,
Great is the Son of Ocean, and his God
Is mightiest ! But Erillyab silently
Approach'd the great Deliverer ; her
   whole frame
Trembled with strong emotion, and she
   took
His hand, and gazed a moment earnestly,
Having no power of speech, till with a
   gush
Of tears her utterance came, and she
   exclaim'd,

Blessed art thou, my brother ! for the
power   120
Of God is in thee ! . . and she would have
kissed
His hand in adoration ; but he cried,
God is indeed with us, and in his name
Will we complete the work ! . . then to
the cave
Advanced, and call'd for fire.   Bring
fire ! quoth he ;
By his own element the spawn of hell
Shall perish ! and he enter'd, to explore
The cavern depths.   Cadwallon fol-
low'd him,
Bearing in either hand a flaming brand,
For sword or spear avail'd not.
                                Far in the hill,
Cave within cave, the ample grotto
pierced,   131
Three chambers in the rock.   Fit vesti-
bule
The first to that wild temple, long and
low,
Shut out the outward day.   The second
vault
Had its own daylight from a central
chasm
High in the hollow ; here the Image
stood,
Their rude idolatry. . . a sculptured
snake, . .
If term of art may such mis-shapen
form
Beseem, . . around a human figure coil'd,
And all begrimed with blood.   The in-
most cell   140
Dark ; and far up within its blackest
depth
They saw the Serpent's still small eye
of fire.
Not if they thinn'd the forest for their
pile,
Could they, with flame or suffocating
smoke,
Destroy him there ; for through the
open roof
The clouds would pass away.   They
paused not long :
Drive him beneath the chasm, Cadwallon
cried,
And hem him in with fire, and from
above
We crush him.

Forth they went and climb'd
the hill.
With all their people.   Their united
strength   150
Loosen'd the rocks, and ranged them
round the brink,
Impending.   With Cadwallon on the
height
Ten Britons wait ; ten with the Prince
descend,
And, with a firebrand each in either hand,
Enter the outer cave.   Madoc ad-
vanced,
And at the entrance of the inner den,
He took his stand alone.   A bow he
bore,
And arrows round whose heads dry tow
was twined,
In pine-gum dipt ; he kindled these,
and shot   159
The fiery shafts.   Upon the scaly skin,
As on a rock, the bone-tipt arrows fell ;
But, at their bright and blazing light
effray'd,
Out rush'd the reptile.   Madoc from his
path
Retired against the side, and call'd his
men,
And in they came and circled round the
Snake,
And shaking all their flames, as with
a wheel
Of fire, they ring'd him in.   From side
to side
The monster turns ! . . where'er he turns,
the flame
Flares in his nostrils and his blinking
eyes ;
Nor aught against the dreaded element
Did that brute force avail, which could
have crush'd   171
Milo's young limbs, or Theban Hercules,
Or old Manoah's mightier son, ere yet
Shorn of his strength.   They press him
now, and now
Give back, here urging, and here yielding
way,
Till right beneath the chasm they centre
him.
At once the crags are loosed, and down
they fall
Thundering.   They fell like thunder, but
the crash

Of scale and bone was heard.   In agony
The Serpent writhed beneath the blow ;
 in vain,   180
From under the incumbent load essay'd
To drag his mangled folds.   One heavier
 stone
Fasten'd and flatten'd him ; yet still,
 with tail
Ten cubits long, he lash'd the air, and
 foined
From side to side, and raised his raging
 head
Above the height of man, though half his
 length
Lay mutilate.   Who then had felt the
 force
Of that wild fury, little had to him
Buckler or corselet profited, or mail,
Or might of human arm.   The Britons
 shrunk   190
Beyond its arc of motion ; but the
 Prince
Took a long spear, and springing on the
 stone
Which fix'd the monster down, provoked
 his rage.
Uplifts the Snake his head retorted,
 high
He lifts it over Madoc, then darts down
To seize his prey.   The Prince, with foot
 advanced
Inclines his body back, and points the
 spear
With sure and certain aim, then drives
 it up,
Into his open jaws ; two cubits deep
It pierced, the monster forcing on the
 wound.   200
He closed his teeth for anguish, and bit
 short
The ashen hilt.   But not the rage which
 now
Clangs all his scales, can from his seat
 dislodge
The barbed shaft : nor those contor-
 tions wild,
Nor those convulsive shudderings, nor
 the throes
Which shake his inmost entrails, as with
 the air
In suffocating gulps the monster now
Inhales his own life-blood.   The Prince
 descends ;

He lifts another lance ; and now the
 Snake,
Gasping, as if exhausted, on the ground
Reclines his head one moment.   Madoc
 seized   211
That moment, planted in his eye the
 spear,
Then setting foot upon his neck, drove
 down
Through bone and brain and throat, and
 to the earth
Infixed the mortal weapon.   Yet once
 more
The Snake essay'd to rise ; his dying
 strength
Fail'd him, nor longer did those mighty
 folds
Obey the moving impulse, crush'd and
 scotch'd ;
In every ring, through all his mangled
 length,
The shrinking muscles quiver'd, then
 collapsed   220
In death.
   Cadwallon and his comrades now
Enter the den ; they roll away the
 crag
Which held him down, pluck out the
 mortal spear,
Then drag him forth to day ; the force
 conjoin'd
Of all the Britons difficultly drag
His lifeless bulk.   But when the
 Hoamen saw
That form portentous trailing in its
 gore,
The jaws which, in the morning, they
 had seen
Purpled with human blood, now in their
 own
Blackening, . . aknee they fell before
 the Prince,   230
And in adoring admiration raised
Their hands with one accord, and all in
 fear
Worshipped the mighty Deicide.   But
 he,
Recoiling from those sinful honours,
 cried,
Drag out the Idol now, and heap the fire,
That all may be consumed !
     Forthwith they heap'd
The sacrificial fire, and on the pile

The Serpent and the Image and the corpse
Of Neolin were laid; with prompt supply
They feed the raging flames, hour after hour,   240
Till now the black and nauseous smoke is spent,
And mingled with the ruins of the pile,
The undistinguishable ashes lay.
Go! cried Prince Madoc, cast them in the stream,
And scatter them upon the winds, that so
No relic of this foul idolatry
Pollute the land. To-morrow meet me here,
Hoamen, and I will purify yon den
Of your abominations. Come ye here
With humble hearts; for ye, too, in the sight   250
Of the Great Spirit, the Beloved One,
Must be made pure, and cleansed from your offence,
And take upon yourselves his holy law.

VIII. THE CONVERSION OF THE HOAMEN

How beautiful, O Sun, is thine uprise,
And on how fair a scene! Before the Cave
The Elders of the Hoamen wait the will
Of their Deliverer; ranged without their ring
The tribe look on, thronging the narrow vale,
And what of gradual rise the shelving combe
Displayed, or steeper eminence of wood,
Broken with crags and sunny slope of green,
And grassy platform. With the Elders sate
The Queen and Prince, their rank's prerogative,   10
Excluded else for sex unfit, and youth
For counsel immature. Before the arch,
To that rude fane, rude portal, stands the Cross,

By Madoc's hand victorious planted there.
And lo, Prince Madoc comes ! no longer mail'd
In arms of mortal might; the spear and sword,
The hauberk and the helmet laid aside,
Gorget and gauntlet, grieves and shield,
. . he comes
In peaceful tunic clad, and mantle long;
His hyacinthine locks now shadowing   20
That face, which late, with iron over-brow'd,
Struck from within the aventayle such awe
And terror to the heart. Bareheaded he,
Following the servant of the altar, leads
The reverential train. Before them, raised
On high, the sacred images are borne;
There, in faint semblance, holiest Mary bends
In virgin beauty o'er her babe divine, . .
A sight which almost to idolatry
Might win the soul by love. But who can gaze   30
Upon that other form, which on the rood
In agony is stretch'd ? . . his hands transfix'd,
And lacerate with the body's pendent weight;
The black and deadly paleness of his face,
Streak'd with the blood which from that crown of scorn
Hath ceased to flow; the side wound streaming still;
And open still those eyes, from which the look
Not yet hath pass'd away, that went to Heaven,
When, in that hour, the Son of Man exclaim'd,
Forgive them, for they know not what they do!   40
And now arrived before the cave, the train
Halt : to the assembled Elders, where they sate
Ranged in half circle, Madoc then advanced,

And raised, as if in act to speak, his
hand.
Thereat was every human sound sup-
press'd ;
And every quicken'd ear and eager eye
Were center'd on his lips.
                    The Prince began, . .
Hoamen, friends, brethren, . . friends
we have been long,
And brethren shall be, ere the day go
down, . .
I come not here propounding doubtful
things   50
For counsel, and deliberate resolve
Of searching thought ; but with
authority
From Heaven, to give the law, and to
enforce
Obedience. Ye shall worship God
alone,
The One Eternal. That Beloved One
Ye shall not serve with offer'd fruits, or
smoke
Of sacrificial fire, or blood, or life :
Far other sacrifice he claims, . . a soul
Resign'd, a will subdued, a heart made
clean
From all offence. Not for your lots on
earth,   60
Menial or mighty, slave or highly-born,
For cunning in the chase, or strength in
war,
Shall ye be judged hereafter ; . . as ye
keep
The law of love, as ye shall tame your
wrath,
Forego revenge, forgive your enemies,
Do good to them that wrong ye, ye will
find
Your bliss or bale. This law came down
from Heaven.
Lo, ye behold Him there by whom it
came ;
The Spirit was in Him, and for the sins
Of man He suffered thus, and by His
death   70
Must all mankind be blest. Not know-
ing Him,
Ye wander'd on in error ; knowing
now,
And not obeying, what was error once
Is guilt and wilful wrong. If ever more
Ye bow to your false deities the knee ;

If ever more ye worship them with feast,
Or sacrifice or dance ; whoso offends
Shall from among the people be cut off,
Like a corrupted member, lest he taint
The whole with death. With what
appointed rites   80
Your homage must be paid, ye shall be
taught ;
Your children, in the way that they shall
go,
Be train'd from childhood up. Make ye
meantime,
Your prayer to that Beloved One, who
sees
The secrets of all hearts ; and set ye up
This, the memorial of his chosen Son,
And Her, who, blessed among women,
fed
The Appointed at Her breast, and by
His cross
Endured intenser anguish ; therefore
sharing
His glory now, with sunbeams robed,
the Moon   90
Her footstool, and a wreath of stars her
crown.

Hoamen, ye deem us children of a
race
Mightier than ye, and wiser, and by
Heaven
Beloved and favour'd more. From this
pure law
Hath all proceeded, . . wisdom, power,
whate'er
Here elevates the soul, and makes it ripe
For higher powers and more exalted
bliss.
Share then our law, and be with us, on
earth,
Partakers of these blessings, and, in
Heaven,
Co-heritors with us of endless joy.   100

Ere yet one breath or motion had
disturb'd
The reverential hush, Erillyab rose.
My people, said the Queen, their God is
best
And mightiest. Him to whom we
offered up
Blood of our blood and of our flesh the
flesh,

Vainly we deem'd divine ; no spirit he
Of good or evil, by the conquering arm
Of Madoc mortal proved. What then
    remains
But that the blessing, proffer'd thus in
    love,
In love we take ? . . Deliverer, Teacher,
    Friend,   110
First in the fellowship of faith I claim
The initiatory rite.

            I also, cried
The venerable Priest Ayayaca,
Old as I am, I also, like a child,
Would learn this wisdom yet before
    I die.
The Elders rose and answer'd, We and
    all !
And from the congregated tribe burst
    forth
One universal shout, . . Great is the
    God
Of Madoc,. . worthy to be served is He !

Then to the mountain rivulet, which
    roll'd   120
Like amber over its dark bed of rock,
Did Madoc lead Erillyab, in the name
Of Jesus, to his Christian family
Accepted now. On her and on her son,
The Elders and the People, Llorien
Sprinkled the sanctifying waters. Day
Was scarcely two hours old when he
    began
His work, and when he ceased, the sun
    had pass'd
The heights of noon. Ye saw that
    blessed work,
Sons of the Cymry, Cadog, Deiniol, 130
Padarn, and Teilo ! ye whose sainted
    names
Your monumental temples still record ;
Thou, David, still revered, who in the
    vale,
Where, by old Hatterill's wintry tor-
    rents swoln
Rude Hodney rolls his raging stream,
    didst choose
Thy hermit home ; and ye who by the
    sword
Of the fierce Saxon, when the bloodier
    Monk
Urged on the work of murder, for your
    faith

And freedom fell, . . Martyrs and Saints,
    ye saw
This triumph of the Cymry and the
    Cross,   140
And struck your golden harps to hymns
    of joy.

IX. TLALALA

As now the rites were ended, Caradoc
Came from the ships, leading an Azteca
Guarded and bound. Prince Madoc,
    said the Bard,
Lo ! the first captive of our arms I bring.
Alone, beside the river I had stray'd,
When, from his lurking place, the savage
    hurl'd
A javelin. At the rustle of the reeds,
From whence the blow was aim'd, I
    turn'd in time,
And heard it whizz beside me. Well it
    was,
That from the ships they saw and suc-
    cour'd me ;   10
For, subtle as a serpent in my grasp,
He seemed all joint and flexure ; nor
    had I
Armour to ward, nor weapon to offend,
To battle all unused and unprepared ;
But I too here upon this barbarous land
Like Elmur and like Aronan of old,
Must lift the ruddy spear.

                    This is no day
For vengeance, answer'd Madoc, else his
    deed
Had met no mercy. Freely let him go !
Perchance the tidings of our triumph
    here   20
May yet reclaim his country. . . Azteca,
Go, let your Pabas know that we have
    crush'd
Their complots here ; beneath our
    righteous sword
The Priest and his false Deity have
    fallen ;
The idols are consumed, and in their
    stead
The emblems of our holy faith set up,
Whereof the Hoamen have this day
    been made.
Partakers. Say to Aztlan, when she too

T

Will make her temples clean, and put
    away
Her foul abominations, and accept   30
The Christian Cross, that Madoc then
    accords
Forgiveness for the past, and peace to
    come.
This better part let her, of her free will
And wisdom, choose in time.
                    Till Madoc spake,
The captive reckless of his peril stood,
Gazing with resolute and careless eye,
As one in whom the lot of life or death
Moved neither fear nor feeling; but
    that eye
Now sparkling with defiance, . . Seek ye
    peace ?
He cried : O weak and woman-hearted
    man !   40
Already wouldst thou lay the sword to
    rest ?
Not with the burial of the sword this
    strife
Must end, for never doth the Tree of
    Peace
Strike root and flourish, till the strong
    man's hand
Upon his enemy's grave hath planted it.
Come ye to Aztlan then in quest of
    peace ?
Ye feeble souls, if that be what ye seek,
Fly hence ! our Aztlan suffers on her
    soil
No living stranger.
                    Do thy bidding, Chief !
Calmly Cadwallon answered. To her
    choice   50
Let Aztlan look, lest what she now
    reject
In insolence of strength, she take upon
    her,
In sorrow and in suffering and in
    shame,
By strong compulsion, penitent too late.
Thou hast beheld our ships with gallant
    men
Freighted, a numerous force, . . and for
    our arms, . .
Surely thy nation hath acquired of them
Disastrous knowledge.
                    Curse upon your arms !
Exclaim'd the savage : . . Is there one
    among you

Dare lay that cowardly advantage by,
And meet me, man to man, in honest
    strife ?   61
That I might grapple with him, weapon-
    less,
On yonder rock, breast against breast,
    fair force
Of limb and breath and blood, . . till one,
    or both,
Dash'd down the shattering precipice,
    should feed
The mountain eagle ! . . Give me, I be-
    seech you,
That joy !
            As wisely, said Cynetha's son,
Thy foe might challenge thee, and bid
    thee let
Thy strong right hand hang idle in the
    fray,
That so his weakness with thy strength
    might cope   70
In equal battle ! . , Not in wrongful
    war,
The tyrants of our weaker brethren,
Wield we these dreadful arms, . . but
    when assail'd
By fraud and force, when call'd upon to
    aid
The feeble and oppress'd, shall we not
Then put our terrors forth, and thunder-
    strike
The guilty ?
            Silently the Savage heard ;
Joy brighten'd in his eyes, as they un-
    loosed
His bonds ; he stretch'd his arms at
    length, to feel
His liberty, and like a greyhound then
Slipt from the leash, he bounded o'er
    the hills.   81
What was from early morning till noon
    day
The steady travel of a well-girt man,
He, with fleet feet and unfatiguable,
In three short hours hath traversed ; in
    the lake
He plunged, now shooting forth his
    pointed arms,
Arrow-like darting on ; recumbent now,
Forces with springing feet his easier
    way ;
Then with new speed, as freshen'd by
    repose,

Again he breasts the water. On the
   shore   90
Of Aztlan now he stands, and breathes
   at will,
And wrings his dripping locks; then
   through the gate
Pursued his way.
        Green garlands deck the gate ;
Gay are the temples with green boughs
   affix'd ;
The door-posts and the lintels hung with
   wreaths ;
The fire of sacrifice, with flames be-
   dimm'd,
Burns in the sun-light, pale ; the victims
   wait
Around, impatient of their death
   delay'd.
The Priest, before Tezcalipoca's shrine,
Watches the maize-strewn threshold, to
   announce   100
The footsteps of the God ; for this the
   day,
When to his favour'd city he vouchsafes
His annual presence, and, with unseen
   feet,
Imprints the maize-strewn threshold ;
   follow'd soon
By all whose altars with eternal fires
Aztlan illumed, and fed with human
   blood ; . .
Mexitli, woman-born, who from the
   womb,
Child of no mortal sire, leapt terrible,
The arm'd avenger of his mother's
   fame ;
And he whose will the subject winds
   obey,   110
Quetzalcoal ; and Tlaloc, Water-God,
And all the host of Deities, whose power
Requites with bounty Aztlan's pious
   zeal,
Health and rich increase giving to her
   sons,
And withering in the war her enemies.
So taught the Priests, and therefore
   were the gates
Green-garlanded, the temples green
   with boughs,
The door-posts and the lintels hung with
   wreaths ;
And yonder victims, ranged around the
   fire,   119

Are destin'd, with the steam of sacrifice,
To greet their dreadful coming.
              With the train
Of warrior Chiefs Coanocotzin stood,
That when the Priest proclaim'd the
   enter'd God,
His lips before the present Deity
Might pour effectual prayer. The
   assembled Chiefs
Saw Tlalala approach, more welcome
   now,
As one whose absence from the appointed
   rites
Had waken'd fear and wonder. . . Think
   not ye,
The youth exclaim'd, careless impiety
Could this day lead me wandering.
    I went forth   130
To dip my javelin in the Strangers'
   blood, . .
A sacrifice, methought, our Gods had
   loved
To scent, and sooner hasten'd to enjoy.
I fail'd, and fell a prisoner ; but their
   fear
Released me, . . coward fear, or childish
   hope,
That, like Yuhidthiton, I might become
Their friend, and merit chastisement
   from Heaven,
Pleading the Strangers' cause. They
   bade me go
And proffer peace. . . Chiefs, were it
   possible
That tongue of mine could win you to
   that shame,   140
Out would I pluck the member, though
   my soul
Followed its bloody roots. The Stranger
   finds
No peace in Aztlan, but the peace of
   death !

'Tis bravely said ! Yuhidthiton replied,
And fairly may'st thou boast, young
   Tlalala,
For thou art brave in battle. Yet
   'twere well
If that same fearless tongue were taught
   to check
Its boyish licence now. No law forbade
Our friendship with the Stranger, when
   my voice

Pleaded for proffered peace ; that fault
    I shared   150
In common with the King, and with the
    Chiefs,
The Pabas and the People, none fore-
    seeing
Danger or guilt : but when at length
    the Gods
Made evident their wrath in prodigies,
I yielded to their manifested will
My prompt obedience. . . Bravely hast
    thou said,
And brave thou art, young Tiger of the
    War !
But thou hast dealt with other enemies
Than these impenetrable men, . . with
    foes,
Whose conquered Gods lie idle in their
    chains,   160
And with tame weakness brook cap-
    tivity.
When thou hast met the Strangers in the
    fight,
And in the doings of that fight out-
    done
Yuhidthiton, revile him then for one
Slow to defend his country and his
    faith ;
Till then, with reverence, as beseems thy
    youth,
Respect thou his full fame !
                        I wrong it not !
I wrong it not ! cried the young Azteca ;
But truly, as I hope to equal it,
Honour thy well-earned glory. . . But
    this peace ! . .   170
Renounce it ! . . say that it shall never
    be ! . .
Never, . . as long as there are Gods in
    Heaven,
Or men in Aztlan !
                    That, the King replied,
The Gods themselves have answer'd.
    Never yet
By holier ardour were our countrymen
Possess'd ; peace-offerings of repentance
    fill
The temple courts ; from every voice
    ascends
The contrite prayer ; daily the victim's
    heart,   178
Sends its propitiatory steam to Heaven ;
And if the aid divine may be procured

By the most dread solemnities of faith,
And rigour of severest penitence,
Soon shall the present influence
    strengthen us,
And Aztlan be triumphant.
                        While they spake,
The ceaseless sound of song and instru-
    ment
Rung through the air, now rising like
    the voice
Of angry ocean, now subsiding soft,
As when the breeze of evening dies
    away.
The horn, and shrill-toned pipe, and
    drum, that gave
Its music to the hand, and hollow'd
    wood,   190
Drum-like, whose thunders, ever and
    anon,
Commingling with the sea-shell's spiral
    roar,
Closed the full harmony. And now the
    eve
Pass'd on, and, through the twilight
    visible,
The frequent fire-flies' brightening
    beauties shone.
Anxious and often now the Priest
    inspects
The maize-strewn threshold ; for the
    wonted hour
Was come, and yet no footstep of the
    God !
More radiant now the fire of sacrifice,
Fed to full fury, blazed ; and its red
    smoke   200
Imparted to the darker atmosphere
Such obscure light as, o'er Vesuvio
    seen,
Or pillared upon Etna's mountain-head,
Makes darkness dreadful. In the cap-
    tives' cheeks
Then might a livid paleness have been
    seen,
And wilder terror in their ghastly eyes,
Expecting momently the pang of death.
Soon in the multitude a doubt arose,
Which none durst mention, lest his
    neighbour's fears,
Divulged, should strengthen his ; . . the
    hour was past,   210
And yet no foot had mark'd the
    sprinkled maize !

X. THE ARRIVAL OF
THE GODS

Now every moment gave their doubts
    new force,
And every wondering eye disclosed the
    fear
Which on the tongue was trembling,
    when to the King,
Emaciate like some bare anatomy,
And deadly pale, Tezozomóc was led,
By two supporting Priests. Ten pain-
    ful months,
Immured amid the forest had he dwelt,
In abstinence and solitary prayer
Passing his nights and days ; thus did
    the Gods
From their High Priest exact, when they
    enforced,   10
By danger or distress, the penance due
For public sins ; and he had dwelt ten
    months,
Praying and fasting and in solitude,
Till now might every bone of his lean
    limbs
Be told, and in his starved and bony face
The living eye appeared unnatural, . .
A ghostly sight.
            In breathless eagerness
The multitude drew round as he began, . .
O King, the Gods of Aztlan are not
    come ;
They will not come before the Strangers'
    blood   20
Smoke on their altars : but they have
    beheld
My days of prayer, and nights of watch-
    fulness,
And fasts austere, and bloody disci-
    plines,
And have reveal'd their pleasure. Who
    is here,
Who to the White King's dwelling-place
    dare go,
And execute their will ?
            Scarce had he said,
When Tlalala exclaim'd, I am the man.

Hear then ! Tezozomoc replied, . .
    Ye know
That self-denial and long penance purge
The film and foulness of mortality,   30

For more immediate intercourse with
    Heaven
Preparing the pure spirit ; and all eyes
May witness that with no relaxing zeal
I have perform'd my duty. Much I
    fear'd
For Aztlan's sins, and oft in bitterness,
Have groan'd and bled for her iniquity ;
But chiefly for this solemn day the fear
Was strong upon me, lest her Deities,
Estranged, should turn away, and we be
    left
A spiritless and God-abandoned race,
A warning to the earth. Ten weary
    months   41
Have the raw maize and running water
    been
My only food ; but not a grain of maize
Hath stay'd the gnawing appetite, nor
    drop
Of water cool'd my parch'd and painful
    tongue,
Since yester-morn arose. Fasting I
    pray'd,
And, praying, gash'd myself ; and all
    night long,
I watch'd and wept and supplicated
    Heaven,
Till the weak flesh, its life-blood almost
    drain'd,   49
Sunk with the long austerity : a dread
Of death came over me ; a deathy chill
Ran through my veins, and loosen'd
    every limb ;
Dim grew mine eyes ; and I could feel
    my heart
Dying away within me, intermit
Its slow and feeble throbs, then sud-
    denly
Start, as it seem'd exerting all its force
In one last effort. On the ground I fell,
I know not if entranced, or dead indeed,
But without motion, hearing, sight, or
    sense,
Feeling, or breath, or life. From that
    strange state,   60
Even in such blessed freedom from all
    pain,
That sure I thought myself in very
    Heaven,
I woke, and raised my eyelids, and beheld
A light which seemed to penetrate my
    bones

With life and health. Before me, visible,
Stood Coatlantona ; a wreath of flowers
Circled her hair, and from their odorous
   leaves
Arose a lambent flame ; not fitfully,
Nor with faint flash or spark of earthly
   flowers ;
From these, for ever flowing forth, there
   play'd   70
In one perpetual dance of pointed light,
The azure radiance of innocuous fire.
She spake. . . Hear, Aztlan ! and give
   ear, O King !
She said, Not yet the offended Gods
   relax
Their anger ; they require the Strangers'
   blood,
The foretaste of their banquet. Let
   their will
Be known to Aztlan, and the brave
   perform
Their bidding ; I, meantime, will seek
   to soothe,
With all a mother's power, Mexitli's
   wrath.
So let the Maidens daily with fresh
   flowers   80
Garland my temple ! . . Daily with fresh
   flowers
Garland her temple, Aztlan ! and revere
The gentle mother of thy guardian God !

And let the brave, exclaim'd young
   Tlalala,
Perform her bidding ! Servant of the
   Gods,
Declare their will ! . . Is it, that I should
   seek
The Strangers, in the first who meets
   my way
To plunge the holy weapon ? Say thou
   to me
Do this ; . . and I depart to do the deed,
Though my life-blood should mingle
   with the foe's.   90

O brave young Chief ! Tezozomoc
   replied,
With better fortune may the grateful
   Gods
Reward thy valour ! deed so hazardous
They ask not. Couldst thou from the
   mountain holds

Tempt one of these rash foemen to
   pursue
Thine artful flight, an ambush'd band
   might rise
Upon the unsuspecting enemy,
And intercept his way ; then hither-
   ward
The captive should be led, and Aztlan's
   Gods
On their own altars see the sacrifice,   100
Well pleased, and Aztlan's sons, in-
   spirited,
Behold the omen of assured success.
Thou know'st that Tlaloc's annual
   festival
Is close at hand. A Stranger's child
   would prove
A victim, whose rare value would
   deserve
His certain favour. More I need not
   say.
Choose thou the force for ambush ; and
   thyself
Alone, or with a chosen comrade, seek
The mountain dwellers.
             Instant as he ceased,
Ocellopan began ; I go with thee,   110
O Tlalala ! My friend ! . . If one alone
Could have the honour of this enter-
   prize,
My love might yield it thee ; . . but thou
   wilt need
A comrade. . . Tlalala, I go with thee !
Whom, the Chief answer'd, should my
   heart select,
Its tried companion else, but thee, so
   oft
My brother in the battle ? We will go,
Shedder of blood ! together will we
   go,
Now, ere the midnight !
             Nay ! the Priest replied,
A little while delay, and ere ye go,   120
Devote yourselves to Heaven ! Feebly
   he spake
Like one exhausted ; gathering then
   new force,
As with laborious effort, he pursued, . .
Bedew Mexitli's altar with your blood,
And go beneath his guidage. I have
   yet
Strength to officiate, and to bless your
   zeal.

So saying, to the Temple of the God
He led the way.   The warriors follow'd
   him ;
And with his chiefs, Coanocotzin went,
To grace with all solemnity the rite. 130
They pass the Wall of Serpents, and
   ascend
The massive fabric ; four times they
   surround
Its ample square, the fifth they reach
   the height.
There, on the level top, two temple-
   towers
Were rear'd ;   the one Tezcalipoca's
   fane,
Supreme of Heaven, where now the
   wily Priest
Stood, watchful for his presence, and
   observed
The maize-strewn threshold.   His the
   other pile,
By whose peculiar power and patronage
Aztlan was blest, Mexitli, woman-born.
Before the entrance, the eternal fire 141
Was burning ;   bare of foot they enter'd
   there.

On a blue throne, with four huge silver
   snakes,
As if the keepers of the sanctuary,
Circled, with stretching neck and fangs
   display'd,
Mexitli sate : another graven snake
Belted with scales of gold his monster
   bulk.
Around the neck a loathsome collar
   hung,
Of human hearts ; the face was mask'd
   with gold,
His specular eyes seem'd fire ; one hand
   uprear'd   150
A club, the other, as in battle, held
The shield ;   and over all suspended
   hung
The banner of the nation.   They beheld
In awe, and knelt before the Terrible
   God.

Guardian of Aztlan ! cried Tezozomoc,
Who to thy mortal mother hast assign'd
The kingdom o'er all trees and arborets,
And herbs and flowers, giving her endless
   life,

A Deity among the Deities ;
While Coatlantona implores thy love 160
To thine own people, they in fear ap-
   proach
Thy aweful fane, who know no fear
   beside,
And offer up the worthiest sacrifice,
The blood of heroes !
                     To the ready Chiefs
He turn'd, and said, Now stretch your
   arms, and make
The offering to the God.   They their
   bare arms
Stretch'd forth, and stabb'd them with
   the aloe-point.
Then, in a golden vase, Tezozomoc
Received the mingled streams, and held
   it up   169
Toward the giant Idol, and exclaim'd,
Terrible God !   Protector of our realm !
Receive thine incense ! Let the steam
   of blood
Ascend to thee, delightful ! So mayest
   thou
Still to thy chosen people lend thine aid ;
And these blaspheming strangers from
   the earth
Be swept away ;   as erst the monster
   race
Of Mammuth, Heaven's fierce ministers
   of wrath,
Who drain'd the lakes in thirst, and for
   their food
Exterminated nations.   And as when,
Their dreadful ministry of death fulfill'd,
Ipalnemoani, by whom we live,   181
Bade thee go forth, and with thy
   lightnings fill
The vault of Heaven, and with thy
   thunders rock
The rooted earth, till of the monster
   race
Only their monumental bones re-
   main'd, . .
So arm thy favour'd people with thy
   might,
Terrible God !   and purify the land
From these blaspheming foes !
                     He said, and gave
Ocellopan the vase. . . Chiefs, ye have
   pour'd
Your strength and courage to the
   Terrible God,   190

Devoted to his service ; take ye now
The beverage he hath hallow'd. In
   your youth
Ye have quaff'd manly blood, that
   manly thoughts
Might ripen in your hearts ; so now
   with this,
Which mingling from such noble veins
   hath flowed,
Increase of valour drink, and added
   force.
Ocellopan received the bloody vase,
And drank, and gave in silence to his
   friend
The consecrated draught ; then Tlalala
Drain'd off the offering.   Braver blood
   than this   200
My lips can never taste ! quoth he ; but
   soon
Grant me, Mexitli, a more grateful cup, ..
The Stranger's life !
          Are all the rites perform'd ?
Ocellopan enquired.   Yea, all is done,
Answer'd the Priest.   Go ! and the
   guardian God
Of Aztlan be your guide !
          They left the fane.
Lo ! as Tezozomoc was passing by
The eternal fire, the eternal fire shot up
A long blue flame. He started ; he
   exclaim'd,
The God ! the God ! Tezcalipoca's
   Priest   210
Echoed the welcome cry, The God ! the
   God !
For lo ! his footsteps mark the maize-
   strewn floor.
A mighty shout from all the multitudes
Of Aztlan rose ; they cast into the fire
The victims, whose last shrieks of agony
Mingled unheeded with the cries of joy.
Then louder from the spiral sea-shell's
   depth
Swell'd the full roar, and from the
   hollow wood
Peal'd deeper thunders.   Round the
   choral band,
The circling nobles, gay with gorgeous
   plumes,   220
And gems which sparkled to the mid-
   night fire,
Moved in the solemn dance ; each in
   his hand,

In measured movements lifts the fea-
   thery shield,
And shakes a rattling ball to measured
   sounds.
With quicker steps, the inferior chiefs
   without,
Equal in number, but in just array,
The spreading radii of the mystic wheel,
Revolve ; and, outermost, the youths
   roll round,
In motions rapid as their quicken'd
   blood.
So thus with song and harmony the
   night   230
Pass'd on in Aztlan, and all hearts re-
   joiced.

XI. THE CAPTURE

MEANTIME from Aztlan, on their enter-
   prize,
Shedder of Blood and Tiger of the War,
Ocellopan and Tlalala set forth.
With chosen followers, through the
   silent night,
Silent they travell'd on.   After a way
Circuitous and far through lonely tracks,
They reach'd the mountains, and amid
   the shade
Of thickets covering the uncultured
   slope,
Their patient ambush placed.   The
   chiefs alone
Held on, till winding in ascent they
   reach'd   10
The heights which o'er the Briton's
   mountain hold
Impended ; there they stood, and by
   the moon
Who yet, with undiminished lustre,
   hung
High in the dark blue firmament, from
   thence
Explored the steep descent.   Precipitous
The rock beneath them lay, a sudden
   cliff
Bare and unbroken ; in its midway
   holes,
Where never hand could reach, nor eye
   intrude,
The eagle built her eyrie.   Farther on,

Its interrupted crags and ancient woods
Offered a difficult way. From crag to
   crag,   21
By rocky shelf, by trunk, or root, or
   bough,
A painful toil and perilous they pass'd ;
And now, stretch'd out amid the matted
   shrubs,
Which, at the entrance of the valley,
   clothed
The rugged bank, they crouch'd.
              By this the stars
Grew dim ; the glow-worm hath put
   out her lamp ;
The owls have ceased their night song.
   On the top
Of yon magnolia the loud turkey's voice
Is heralding the dawn ; from tree to
   tree   30
Extends the wakening watch-note, far
   and wide,
Till the whole woodlands echo with the
   cry.
Now breaks the morning ; but as yet no
   foot
Hath mark'd the dews, nor sound of
   man is heard.
Then first Ocellopan beheld, where near,
Beneath the shelter of a half-roof'd hut,
A sleeping Stranger lay. He pointed
   him
To Tlalala. The Tiger look'd around :
None else was nigh. . . Shall I descend,
   he said,
And strike him ? here is none to see the
   deed.   40
We offered to the Gods our mingled blood
Last night ; and now, I deem it, they
   present
An offering which shall more propitiate
   them,
And omen sure success. I will go down
And kill !
      He said, and, gliding like a snake,
Where Caradoc lay sleeping made his
   way.
Sweetly slept he, and pleasant were his
   dreams
Of Britain, and the blue-eyed maid he
   loved.
The Azteca stood over him ; he knew
His victim, and the power of vengeance
   gave   50

Malignant joy. Once hast thou 'scaped
   my arm :
But what shall save thee now ? the
   Tiger thought,
Exulting ; and he raised his spear to
   strike.
That instant, o'er the Briton's unseen
   harp
The gale of morning pass'd, and swept
   its strings
Into so sweet a harmony, that sure
It seem'd no earthly tone. The savage
   man
Suspends his stroke ; he looks astonish'd
   round ;
No human hand is near : . . and hark !
   again   59
The aërial music swells and dies away.
Then first the heart of Tlalala felt fear :
He thought that some protecting spirit
   watch'd
Beside the Stranger, and, abash'd, with-
   drew.

A God protects him ! to Ocellopan,
Whispering, he said. Didst thou not
   hear the sound
Which enter'd into me, and fix'd my
   arm
Powerless above him ?
             Was it not a voice
From thine own Gods to strengthen thee,
   replied
His sterner comrade, and make evident
Their pleasure in the deed ?
           Nay ! Tlalala 70
Rejoin'd ; they speak in darkness and
   in storms :
The thunder is their voice, that peals
   through heaven,
Or, rolling underneath us, makes earth
   rock
In tempest, and destroys the sons of
   men.
It was no sound of theirs, Ocellopan !
No voice to hearten, . . for I felt it pass
Unmanning every limb ; yea, it relax'd
The sinews of my soul. Shedder of
   Blood,
I cannot lift my hand against the man.
Go, if thy heart be stronger !
            But meantime 80
Young Caradoc arose, of his escape

Unconscious; and by this the stirring
  sounds
Of day began, increasing now, as all
Now to their toil betake them. Some
    go fell
The stately tree; some from the trunk
    low-laid
Hew the huge boughs; here round the
    fire they char
The stake-points; here they level with
    a line
The ground-plot, and infix the ready
    piles,
Or, interknitting them with osiers,
    weave
The wicker wall; others along the
    lake,   90
From its shoal waters gather reeds and
    canes, . .
Light roofing, suited to the genial sky.
The woodman's measured stroke, the
    regular saw,
The wain slow-creaking and the voice
    of man
Answering his fellow, or, in single toil,
Cheering his labour with a cheerful
    song,
Strange concert made to those fierce
    Aztecas,
Who, beast-like, in their silent lurking
    place
Couch'd close and still, observant for
    their prey.

All overseeing, and directing all,   100
From place to place moved Madoc, and
    beheld
The dwellings rise. Young Hoel at his
    side
Ran on, best pleased when at his Uncle's
    side
Courting indulgent love. And now
    they came
Beside the half-roof'd hut of Caradoc;
Of all the mountain-dwellings, that the
    last.
The little boy, in boyish wantonness,
Would quit his Uncle's hold, and haste
    away,
With childhood's frolic speed, then
    laugh aloud,
To tempt pursuit, now running to the
    huts,   110

Now toward the entrance of the valley
    straits.
But wheresoe'er he turned, Ocellopan
With hunter's-eye pursued his heedless
    course,
In breath-suspending vigilance. Ah
    me!
The little wretch toward his lurking-
    place
Draws near, and calls on Madoc; and
    the Prince
Thinks of no danger nigh, and follows
    not
The childish lure! nearer the covert
    now
Young Hoel runs, and stops, and calls
    again;
Then, like a lion, from his couching
    place   120
Ocellopan leapt forth, and seized his
    prey.

Loud shriek'd the affrighted child, as
    in his grasp
The savage grasp'd him; startled at
    the cry,
Madoc beheld him hastening through
    the pass.
Quick as instinctive love can urge his
    feet
He follows, and he now almost hath
    reach'd
The incumber'd ravisher, and hope
    inspires
New speed, . . yet nearer now, and nearer
    still,
And lo! the child holds out his little
    arms!
That instant, as the Prince almost had
    laid   130
His hand upon the boy, young Tlalala
Leapt on his neck, and soon, though
    Madoc's strength
With frantic fury shook him from his
    hold,
Far down the steep Ocellopan had
    fled.
Ah! what avails it now, that they, by
    whom
Madoc was standing to survey their
    toil,
Have miss'd their Chief, and spread the
    quick alarm?

What now avails it, that with distant
    aid,
His gallant men come down ? Regarding
    nought
But Hoel, but the wretched Llaian's
    grief,   140
He rushes on ; and ever as he draws
Near to the child, the Tiger Tlalala
Impedes his way ; and now they reach
    the place
Of ambush, and the ambush'd band
    arise,
And Madoc is their prisoner.
                        Caradoc,
In vain thou leadest on the late pursuit !
In vain, Cadwallon, hath thy love
    alarm'd
Caught the first sound of evil ! They
    pour out
Tumultuous from the vale, a half-arm'd
    troop ;
Each with such weapons as his hasty
    hand   150
Can seize, they rush to battle. Gallant
    men,
Your valour boots not ! It avails not
    now,
With such fierce onset that ye charge
    the foe,
And drive with such full force the
    weapon home !
They, while ye slaughter them, impede
    pursuit,
And far away, meantime, their com-
    rades bear
The captive Prince. In vain his noble
    heart
Swells now with wild and suffocating
    rage ;
In vain he struggles : . . they have bound
    his limbs
With the tough osier, and his struggles
    now   160
But bind more close and cuttingly the
    band.
They hasten on ; and while they bear
    the prize,
Leaving their ill-doom'd fellows in the
    fight
To check pursuit, foremost afar of all,
With unabating strength by joy in-
    spired
Ocellopan to Aztlan bears the child.

XII. HOEL

Good tidings travel fast. . . The chief is
    seen ;
He hastens on ; he holds the child on
    high ;
He shouts aloud. Through Aztlan
    spreads the news ;
Each to his neighbour tells the happy
    tale, . .
Joy, . . joy to Aztlan ! the blood-shedder
    comes !
Tlaloc has given his victim.
                        Ah, poor child !
They from the gate swarm out to wel-
    come thee,
Warriors, and men grown grey, and
    youths and maids,
Exulting, forth they crowd. The
    mothers throng
To view thee, and, while thinking of
    thy doom,   10
They clasp their own dear infants to the
    breast
With deeper love, delighted think that
    thou
Shalt suffer for them. He, poor child,
    admires
The strange array ! with wonder he
    beholds
Their olive limbs, half bare, their plumy
    crowns,
And gazes round and round, where all
    was new,
Forgetful of his fears. But when the
    Priest
Approach'd to take him from the War-
    rior's arms,
Then Hoel scream'd, and from that
    hideous man
Averting, to Ocellopan he turn'd,   20
And would have clung to him, so dread-
    ful late,
Stern as he was, and terrible of eye,
Less dreadful than the Priest, whose
    dark aspect
Which nature with her harshest charac-
    ters
Had featured, art made worse. His
    cowl was white ;
His untrimm'd hair, a long and loath-
    some mass,

With cotton cords intwisted, clung with
    gum,
And matted with the blood, which, every
    morn,
He from his temples drew before the
    God,
In sacrifice ; bare were his arms, and
    smear'd   30
Black. But his countenance a stronger
    dread
Than all the horrors of that outward
    garb,
Struck with quick instinct to young
    Hoel's heart ;
It was a face, whose settled sullenness
No gentle feeling ever had disturb'd ;
Which, when he probed a victim's living
    breast,
Retained its hard composure.
                    Such was he
Who took the son of Llaian, heeding not
His cries and screams, and arms, in sup-
    pliant guise,
Stretch'd out to all around, and strug-
    glings vain.   40
He to the temple of the Water-God
Convey'd his victim. By the threshold,
    there
The ministering Virgins stood, a comely
    band
Of high-born damsels, to the temple rites
By pious parents vow'd. Gladly to them
The little Hoel leapt ; their gentle looks
No fear excited ; and he gazed around,
Pleased and surprised, unconscious to
    what end
These things were tending. O'er the
    rush-strewn floor
They to the azure Idol led the boy,   50
Now not reluctant, and they raised the
    hymn.

    God of the Waters ! at whose will the
        streams
Flow in their wonted channel, and diffuse
Their plenty round, the blood and life
    of earth ;
At whose command they swell, and o'er
    their banks
Burst with resistless ruin, making vain
The toils and hopes of man, . . behold
    this child !
O strong to bless, and mighty to destroy,

Tlaloc ! behold thy victim ! so mayest
    thou
Restrain the peaceful streams within
    their banks,   60
And bless the labours of the husband-
    man.

    God of the Mountains ! at whose will
        the clouds
Cluster around the heights ; who
    sendest them
To shed their fertilizing showers, and
    raise
The drooping herb, and o'er the thirsty
    vale
Spread their green freshness ; at whose
    voice the hills
Grow black with storms ; whose wrath
    the thunder speaks,
Whose bow of anger shoots the lightning
    shafts,
To blast the works of man ; . . behold
    this child !
O strong to bless, and mighty to destroy,
Tlaloc ! behold thy victim ! so mayest
    thou   71
Lay by the fiery arrows of thy rage,
And bid the genial rains and dews
    descend.

    O thou, Companion of the powerful
        God,
Companion and Beloved ! . . when he
    treads
The mountain-top, whose breath diffuses
    round
The sweets of summer ; when he rides
    the waves,
Whose presence is the sunshine and the
    calm, . .
Aiauh, O green-robed Goddess, see this
    child !
Behold thy victim ! so mayest thou
    appease   80
The sterner mind of Tlaloc when he
    frowns,
And Aztlan flourish in thy fostering
    smile.
Young Spirits ! ye whom Aztlan's piety
Hath given to Tlaloc, to enjoy with him,
For aye, the cool delights of Tlalocan, . .
Young Spirits of the happy ; who have
    left

Your Heaven to-day, unseen assistants
here, . .
Behold your comrade ! see the chosen
child,
Who through the lonely cave of death
must pass,
Like you, to join you in eternal joy. 90

Now from the rush-strewn temple they
depart.
They place their smiling victim in a car,
Upon whose sides of pearly shell there
play'd,
Shading and shifting still, the rainbow
light.
On virgin shoulders is he borne aloft,
With dance before, and song and music
round ;
And thus they seek, in festival array,
The water-side. There lies the sacred
bark,
All gay with gold, and garlanded with
flowers :
The virgins with the joyous boy embark;
Ten boatmen urge them on ; the Priests
behind 101
Follow, and all the long solemnity.
The lake is overspread with boats ; the
sun
Shines on the gilded prows, the feathery
crowns,
The sparkling waves. Green islets float
along,
Where high-born damsels, under jasmin
bowers,
Raise the sweet voice, to which the
echoing oars,
In modulated motion, rise and fall.
The moving multitude along the shore
Flows like a stream ; bright shines the
unclouded sky ; 110
Heaven, earth, and waters wear one face
of joy.
Young Hoel with delight beholds the
pomp ;
His heart throbs joyfully ; and if he
thinks
Upon his mother now, 'tis but to think
How beautiful a tale for her glad ear
He hath when he returns. Meantime
the maids
Weave garlands for his head, and raise
the song.

Oh ! happy thou, whom early from
the world
The Gods require ! not by the wasting
worm
Of sorrow canker'd, nor condemn'd to
feel 120
The pang of sickness, nor the wound of
war,
Nor the long miseries of protracted age ;
But thus in childhood chosen of the
God,
To share his joys. Soon shall thy
rescued soul,
Child of the Stranger ! in his blissful
world,
Mix with the blessed spirits ; for not
thine,
Amid the central darkness of the earth,
To endure the eternal void ; . . not thine
to live,
Dead to all objects of eye, ear, or sense,
In the long horrors of one endless night,
With endless being curst. For thee the
bowers 131
Of Tlalocan have blossom'd with new
sweets ;
For thee have its immortal trees matured
The fruits of Heaven ; thy comrades
even now
Wait thee, impatient, in their fields of
bliss ;
The God will welcome thee, his chosen
child,
And Aiauh love thee with a mother's
love.
Child of the Stranger, dreary is thy way !
Darkness and Famine through the cave
of Death
Must guide thee. Happy thou, when on
that night 140
The morning of the eternal day shall
dawn.

So as they sung young Hoel's song of
death,
With rapid strength the boatmen plied
their oars,
And through the water swift they glided
on,
And now to shore they drew. The
stately bank
Rose with the majesty of woods o'erhung,

And rocks, or peering through the forest
    shade,
Or rising from the lake, and with their
    bulk
Glassing its dark deep waters. Half
    way up,
A cavern pierced the rock; no human
    foot   150
Had trod its depths, nor ever sunbeam
    reach'd
Its long recesses and mysterious gloom;
To Tlaloc it was hallowed; and the
    stone,
Which closed its entrance, never was
    removed,
Save when the yearly festival return'd,
And in its womb a child was sepulchred,
The living victim. Up the winding
    path,
That to the entrance of the cavern led,
With many a painful step the train
    ascend:
But many a time, upon that long ascent,
Young Hoel would have paused, with
    weariness   161
Exhausted now. They urge him on, . .
    poor child!
They urge him on! . . Where is Cad-
    wallon's aid?
Where is the sword of Ririd? where the
    arm
Of Madoc now? . . Oh! better had he
    lived,
Unknowing and unknown, on Arvon's
    plain,
And trod upon his noble father's grave,
With peasant feet, unconscious! . . They
    have reach'd
The cavern now, and from its mouth
    the Priests
Roll the huge portal. Thitherward
    they force   170
The son of Llaian. A cold air comes
    out; . .
It chills him, and his feet recoil; . . in
    vain
His feet recoil; . . in vain he turns
    to fly,
Affrighted at the sudden gloom that
    spreads
Around; . . the den is closed, and he is
    left
In solitude and darkness, . . left to die!

XIII.   COATEL

THAT morn from Aztlan Coatel had gone
In search of flowers, amid the woods and
    crags,
To deck the shrine of Coatlantona;
Such flowers as in the solitary wilds
Hiding their modest beauty, made their
    worth
More valued for its rareness. 'Twas to
    her
A grateful task; not only for she fled
Those cruel rites, to which nor reverent
    use,
Nor frequent custom could familiarize
Her gentle heart, and teach it to put off
All womanly feeling; . . but that from
    all eyes   11
Escaped, and all obtrusive fellowship,
She in that solitude might send her soul
To where Lincoya with the Strangers
    dwelt.
She from the summit of the woodland
    heights
Gazed on the lake below. The sound
    of song
And instrument, in soften'd harmony,
Had reach'd her where she stray'd;
    and she beheld
The pomp, and listen'd to the floating
    sounds,
A moment, with delight: but then a
    fear   20
Came on her, for she knew with what
    design
The Tiger and Ocellopan had sought
The dwellings of the Cymry. . . Now the
    boats
Drew nearer, and she knew the Stranger's
    child.
She watch'd them land below; she saw
    them wind
The ascent: . . and now from that
    abhorred cave
The stone is roll'd away, . . and now the
    child
From light and life is cavern'd. Coatel
Thought of his mother then, of all the ills
Her fear would augur, and how worse
    than all   30
Which even a mother's maddening fear
    could feign,

His actual fate. She thought of this,
and bow'd
Her face upon her knees, and closed her
eyes,
Shuddering. Suddenly in the brake
beside,
A rustling started her, and from the
shrubs
A Vulture rose.
　　　　She moved toward the spot,
Led by an idle impulse, as it seem'd,
To see from whence the carrion bird had
fled.
The bushes overhung a narrow chasm
Which pierced the hill : upon its mossy
sides　　　　　　　　　　　　　40
Shade-loving herbs and flowers luxuriant
grew,
And jutting crags made easy the
descent.
A little way descending, Coatel
Stoopt for the flowers, and heard, or
thought she heard,
A feeble sound below. She raised her
head,
And anxiously she listen'd for the sound,
Not without fear. . . Feebly again, and
like
A distant cry, it came ; and then she
thought,
Perhaps it was the voice of that poor
child,
By the slow pain of hunger doom'd to
die.　　　　　　　　　　　　　50
She shudder'd at the thought, and
breathed a groan
Of unavailing pity ; . . but the sound
Came nearer, and her trembling heart
conceived
A dangerous hope. The Vulture from
that chasm
Had fled, perchance accustomed in the
cave
To seek his banquet, and by living feet
Alarm'd : . . there was an entrance then
below ;
And were it possible that she could save
The Stranger's child, . . Oh what a joy
it were
To tell Lincoya that !
　　　　　　It was a thought　60
Which made her heart with terror and
delight

Throb audibly. From crag to crag she
pass'd
Descending, and beheld a narrow cave
Enter the hill. A little way the light
Fell, . . but its feeble glimmering she
herself
Obstructed half, as stooping in she went.
The arch grew loftier, and the increasing
gloom
Fill'd her with more affright ; and now
she paused ;
For at a sudden and abrupt descent
She stood, and fear'd its unseen depth,
her heart　　　　　　　　　　70
Fail'd, and she back had hasten'd ; but
the cry
Reach'd her again, the near and certain
cry
Of that most pitiable innocent.
Again adown the dark descent she
look'd,
Straining her eyes ; by this the strength-
en'd sight
Had grown adapted to the gloom around,
And her dilated pupils now received
Dim sense of objects near. Something
below,
White, in the darkness lay : it mark'd
the depth.
Still Coatel stood dubious ; but she
heard　　　　　　　　　　　　80
The wailing of the child, and his loud
sobs ; . .
Then, clinging to the rock with fearful
hands,
Her feet explored below, and twice she
felt
Firm footing, ere her fearful hold relax'd.
The sound she made, along the hollow
rock
Ran echoing. Hoel heard it, and he
came
Groping along the side. A dim, dim
light
Broke on the darkness of his sepulchre ;
A human form drew near him ; . . he
sprang on,
Screaming with joy, and clung to
Coatel,　　　　　　　　　　　90
And cried, O take me from this dismal
place !
She answer'd not ; she understood him
not ;

But clasp'd the little victim to her
    breast,
And shed delightful tears.
                    But from that den
Of darkness and of horror, Coatel
Durst not convey the child, though in
    her heart
There was a female tenderness which
    yearn'd,
As with maternal love, to cherish him.
She hush'd his clamours, fearful lest the
    sound
Might reach some other ear; she kissed
    away   100
The tears that stream'd adown his little
    cheeks;
She gave him food which in the morn
    she brought,
For her own wants, from Aztlan. Some
    few words
Of Britain's ancient language she had
    learnt
From her Lincoya, in those happy days
Of peace, when Aztlan was the Stranger's
    friend:
Aptly she learnt, what willingly he
    taught,
Terms of endearment, and the parting
    words
Which promised quick return. She to
    the child
These precious words address'd; and if
    it chanced   110
Imperfect knowledge, or some difficult
    sound
Check'd her heart's utterance, then the
    gentle tone,
The fond caress, intelligibly spake
Affection's language.
                    But when she arose,
And would have climb'd the ascent, the
    affrighted boy
Fast held her, and his tears interpreted
The prayer to leave him not. Again
    she kiss'd
His tears away; again of soon return
Assured and soothed him; till reluc-
    tantly   119
And weeping, but in silence, he unloosed
His grasp; and up the difficult ascent
Coatel climb'd, and to the light of day
Returning, with her flowers she hastened
    home.

XIV. THE STONE OF SACRIFICE

Who comes to Aztlan, bounding like a
    deer
Along the plain?.. The herald of suc-
    cess;
For lo! his locks are braided, and his
    loins
Cinctured with white; and see, he lifts
    the shield,
And brandishes the sword. The popu-
    lace
Flock round, impatient for the tale of
    joy,
And follow to the palace in his path.
Joy! joy! the Tiger hath achieved his
    quest!
They bring a captive home!.. Trium-
    phantly
Coanocotzin and his Chiefs go forth   10
To greet the youth triumphant, and
    receive
The victim whom the gracious gods have
    given,
Sure omen and first fruits of victory.
A woman leads the train, young, beauti-
    ful,..
More beautiful for that translucent joy
Flushing her cheek, and sparkling in
    her eye; ..
Her hair is twined with festal flowers,
    her robe
With flowing wreaths adorn'd; she
    holds a child,
He, too, bedeck'd and garlanded with
    flowers,
And, lifting him, with agile force of
    arm,   20
In graceful action, to harmonious step
Accordant, leads the dance. It is the
    wife
Of Tlalala, who, with his child, goes forth
To meet her hero husband.
                    And behold
The Tiger comes! and ere the shouts
    and sounds
Of gratulation cease, his followers bear
The captive Prince. At that so wel-
    come sight
Loud rose the glad acclaim; nor knew
    they yet

That he who there lay patient in his
  bonds,
Expecting the inevitable lot,   30
Was Madoc.   Patient in his bonds he
  lay,
Exhausted with vain efforts, hopeless
  now,
And silently resign'd.   But when the
  King
Approach'd the prisoner, and beheld his
  face,
And knew the Chief of Strangers, at
  that sound
Electric joy shot through the multitude,
And, like the raging of the hurricane,
Their thundering transports peal'd.
  A deeper joy,
A nobler triumph kindled Tlalala,
As, limb by limb, his eye survey'd the
  Prince,   40
With a calm fierceness.   And by this
  the Priests
Approach'd their victim, clad in vest-
  ments white
Of sacrifice, which from the shoulders
  fell,
As from the breast, unbending, broad
  and straight,
Leaving their black arms bare.   The
  blood-red robe,
The turquoise pendant from his down-
  drawn lip,
The crown of glossy plumage, whose
  green hue
Vied   with   his   emerald   ear-drops,
  mark'd their Chief
Tezozomoc : his thin and ghastly cheek,
Which, . . save the temple serpents,
  when he brought   50
Their human banquet, . . never living eye
Rejoiced to see, became more ghastly
  now,
As in Mexitli's name, upon the Prince
He laid his murtherous hand.   But as
  he spake,
Up darted Tlalala his eagle glance. . .
Away ! away ! he shall not perish so !
The warrior cried. . . Not tamely, by the
  knife,
Nor on the jaspar-stone, his blood shall
  flow !
The Gods of Aztlan love a Warrior Priest !
I am their Priest to-day !

          A murmuring   60
Ran through the train ; nor waited he
  to hear
Denial thence ; but on the multitude
Aloud he call'd. . . When first our fathers
  seized
This land, there was a savage chief who
  stopt
Their progress.   He had gained the rank
  he bore,
By long probation : stripes, which laid
  his flesh
All bleeding bare, had forced not one
  complaint ;
Not when the working bowels might
  be seen,
One movement ; hand-bound, he had
  been confined
Where myriad insects on his nakedness
Infix'd their venomous anger, and no
  start,   71
No shudder, shook his frame ; last, in
  a net
Suspended, he had felt the agony
Of fire, which to his bones and marrow
  pierced,
And breathed the suffocating smoke
  which fill'd
His lungs with fire, without a groan,
  a breath,
A look betokening sense ; so gallantly
Had he subdued his nature.   This brave
  man
Met Aztlan in the war, and put her
  Chiefs
To shame.   Our Elders have not yet
  forgot   80
How from the slaughter'd brother of
  their King
He stript the skin, and form'd of it a
  drum,
Whose sound affrighted armies.   With
  this man
My father coped in battle ; here he led
  him,
An offering to the God ; and, man to
  man,
He slew him here in fight.   I was a child
Just old enough to lift my father's
  shield ;
But I remember, on that glorious day,
When from the sacred combat he
  return'd,

His red hands reeking with the hot
heart's blood,   90
How in his arms he took me, and be-
sought
The God whom he had served, to bless
his boy,
And make me like my father.   Men of
Aztlan,
Mexitli heard his prayer ; .. Here I have
brought
The Stranger-Chief, the noblest sacrifice
That ever graced the altar of the God ;
Let then his death be noble ! so my boy
Shall, in the day of battle, think of me ;
And as I follow'd my brave father's
steps,
Pursue my path of glory.
                    Ere the Priest 100
Could frame denial, had the Monarch's
look
Given his assent. . . Refuse not this, he
said,
O servant of the Gods ! He hath not here
His arms to save him ; and the Tiger's
strength
Yields to no mortal might.   Then for
his sword
He call'd, and bade Yuhidthiton address
The Stranger-Chief.
                    Yuhidthiton began,
The Gods of Aztlan triumph, and thy
blood
Must wet their altars.   Prince, thou
shalt not die
The coward's death ; but, sworded, and
in fight,   110
Fall as becomes the valiant.   Should
thine arm
Subdue in battle six successive foes,
Life, liberty, and glory, will repay
The noble conquest.   Madoc, hope not
this :
Strong are the brave of Aztlan !
                    Then they loosed
The Ocean Chieftain's bonds ; they
rent away
His garments ;   and with songs and
shouts of joy,
They led him to the Stone of Sacrifice.
Round was that Stone of Blood ; the
half-raised arm
Of one of manly growth, who stood
below,   120

Might rest upon its height ; the circle
small,
An active boy might almost bound
across.
Nor needed for the combat, ampler
space ;
For in the centre was the prisoner's foot
Fast fetter'd down.   Thus fetter'd
Madoc stood.
He held a buckler, light and small, of
cane
O'erlaid with beaten gold ; his sword,
the King,
Honouring a noble enemy, had given,
A weapon tried in war, . . to Madoc's
grasp
Strange and unwieldy : 'twas a broad
strong staff,   130
Set thick with transverse stones, on
either side
Keen-edged as Syrian steel.   But when
he felt
The weapon, Madoc call'd to mind his
deeds
Done on the Saxon in his fathers' land,
And hope arose within him,   Nor
though now
Naked he stood, did fear for that assail
His steady heart ; for often had he seen
His gallant countrymen with naked
breasts,
Rush on their iron-coated enemy,
And win the conquest.
                    Now hath Tlalala 140
Array'd himself for battle.   First he
donn'd
A gipion, quilted close of gossampine ;
O'er that a jointed mail of plates of gold,
Bespotted like the tiger's speckled pride,
To speak his rank ; it clad his arms half-
way,
Half-way his thighs ; but cuishes had
he none,
Nor gauntlets, nor feet-armour.   On his
helm
There yawn'd the semblance of a tiger's
head,
The long white teeth extended, as for
prey ;
Proud crest, to blazon his proud title
forth.   150
And now toward the fatal stage,
equipp'd

For fight, he went; when, from the
  press behind,
A warrior's voice was heard, and clad in
  arms,
And shaking in his angry grasp the
  sword,
Ocellopan rush'd on, and cried aloud,
And for himself the holy combat claim'd.
The Tiger, heedless of his clamour,
  sprung
Upon the stone, and turn'd him to the
  war
Fierce leaping forward came Ocellopan,
And bounded up the ascent, and seized
  his arm : ..   160
Why wouldst thou rob me of a deed like
  this ?
Equal our peril in the enterprize,
Equal our merit ; .. thou wouldst reap
  alone
The guerdon ! Never shall my children
  lift
Their little hands at thee, and say, Lo !
  there
The Chief who slew the White King ! ..
  Tlalala,
Trust to the lot, or turn on me, and
  prove,
By the best chance to which the brave
  appeal,
Who best deserves this glory !
                    Stung to wrath,
The Tiger answer'd not ; he raised his
  sword,   170
And they had rush'd to battle ; but the
  Priests
Came hastening up, and by their com-
  mon Gods,
And by their common country, bade
  them cease
Their impious strife, and let the lot
  decide
From whom Mexitli should that day
  receive
His noble victim. Both unsatisfied,
But both obedient, heard. Two equal
  shafts,
As outwardly they seem'd, the Paba
  brought ;
His mantle hid their points ; and
  Tlalala
Drew forth the broken stave. A bitter
  smile   180

Darken'd his cheek, as angrily he cast
To earth the hostile lot. . . Shedder of
  Blood,
Thine is the first adventure ! he ex-
  claim'd ,
But thou mayst perish here ! . . and in
  his heart
The Tiger hoped Ocellopan might fall,
As sullenly retiring from the stage,
He mingled with the crowd.
                    And now opposed
In battle, on the Stone of Sacrifice,
Prince Madoc and the Life-Destroyer
  stood.
This clad in arms complete, free to
  advance   190
In quick assault, or shun the threaten'd
  blow,
Wielding his wonted sword ; the other,
  stript,
Save of that fragile shield, of all defence ;
His weapon strange and cumbrous ; and
  pinn'd down,
Disabled from all onset, all retreat.

With looks of greedy joy, Ocellopan
Survey'd his foe, and wonder'd to
  behold
The breast so broad, the bare and
  brawny limbs,
Of matchless strength. The eye of
  Madoc, too,
Dwelt on his foe ; his countenance was
  calm,   200
Something more pale than wonted ; like
  a man
Prepared to meet his death. The
  Azteca
Fiercely began the fight ; now here, now
  there,
Aright, aleft, above, below, he wheel'd
The rapid sword : still Madoc's rapid
  eye
Pursued the motion, and his ready
  shield,
In prompt interposition, caught the
  blow,
Or turn'd its edge aside. Nor did the
  Prince
Yet aim the sword to wound, but held it
  forth,
Another shield, to save him, till his
  hand,   210

Familiar with its weight and shape
  uncouth,
Might wield it well to vengeance. Thus
  he stood,
Baffling the impatient enemy, who now
Wax'd wrathful, thus to waste in idle
  strokes
Reiterate so oft, his bootless strength.
And now yet more exasperate he grew,
For, from the eager multitude, was
  heard,
Amid the din of undistinguish'd sounds,
The Tiger's murmur'd name, as though
  they thought,
Had he been on the Stone, ere this,
  besure,   220
The Gods had tasted of their sacrifice,
Now all too long delay'd. Then
  fiercelier,
And yet more rapidly, he drove the
  sword;
But still the wary Prince or met its
  fall,
And broke the force, or bent him from
  the blow;
And now retiring, and advancing now,
As one free foot permitted, still pro-
  voked,
And baffled still the savage; and
  sometimes,
With cautious strength did Madoc aim
  attack,
Mastering each moment now with abler
  sway   230
The acquainted sword. But, though as
  yet unharm'd
In life or limb, more perilous the strife
Grew momently; for with repeated
  strokes,
Battered and broken now, the shield
  hung loose;
And shouts of triumph from the multi-
  tude
Arose, as piece-meal they beheld it
  fall,
And saw the Prince exposed.
          That welcome sight,
Those welcome sounds, inspired Ocello-
  pan;
He felt each limb new-strung. Impatient
  now
Of conquest long delay'd, with wilder
  rage   240

He drives the weapon; Madoc's lifted
  sword
Received its edge, and shiver'd with the
  blow.
A shriek of transport burst from all
  around;
For lo! the White King, shieldless,
  weaponless,
Naked before his foe! That savage
  foe,
Dallying with the delight of victory,
Drew back a moment to enjoy the
  sight,
Then yell'd in triumph, and sprang on
  to give
The consummating blow. Madoc be-
  held
The coming death; he darted up his
  hand   250
Instinctively to save, and caught the
  wrist
In its mid fall, and drove with desperate
  force
The splinter'd truncheon of his broken
  sword
Full in the enemy's face. Beneath his
  eye
It broke its way, and where the nasal
  nerves
Branch in fine fibrils o'er their mazy
  seat,
Burst through, and slanting upward in
  the brain
Buried its jagged point.
            Madoc himself
Stood at his fall astonished, at escape
Unhoped, and strange success. The
  multitude   260
Beheld, and they were silent, and they
  stood
Gazing in terror. But far other thought.
Rose in the Tiger's heart; it was a joy
To Tlalala; and forth he sprang, and
  up
The Stone of Sacrifice, and call'd aloud
To bring the Prince another sword and
  shield,
For his last strife. Then in that inter-
  val,
Upon Ocellopan he fix'd his eyes,
Contemplating the dead, as though
  thereby
To kindle in his heart a fiercer thirst 270

For vengeance. Nor to Madoc was the
sting
Of anger wanting, when in Tlalala
He knew the captive whom his mercy
freed,
The man whose ambush had that day
destroy'd
Young Hoel and himself; . . for, sure,
he deem'd
Young Hoel was with God, and he him-
self
At his death day arrived. And now he
graspt
A second sword, and held another
shield;
And from the Stone of Blood Ocellopan
Was borne away; and, fresh in arms,
and fierce   280
With all that makes a savage thirst for
war,
Hope, vengeance, courage, superstitious
hate,
A second foe came on. By this the
Prince
Could wield his weapon well; and
dreading now
Lest, in protracted combat, he might
stand
Again defenceless, he put forth his
strength,
As oft assailing as assail'd, and watch'd
So well the Tiger's motions, and
received
The Tiger's blows so warily, and aimed
His own so fierce and fast, that in the
crowd   290
Doubt and alarm prevail'd. Ilanquel
grew
Pale at her husband's danger; and she
clasp'd
The infant to her breast, whom late she
held
On high, to see his victory. The throng
Of the beholders silently look'd on;
And in their silence might at times be
heard
An indrawn breath of terror; and the
Priests
Angrily murmur'd, that in evil hour,
Coanocotzin had indulged the pride
Of vaunting valour, and from certain
death   300
Reprieved the foe.

But now a murmur rose
Amid the multitude; and they who
stood
So thickly throng'd, and with such
eager eyes
Late watch'd the fight, hastily now broke
up,
And, with disorder'd speed and sudden
arms,
Ran to the city gates. More eager
now,
Conscious of what had chanced, fought
Tlalala;
And hope invigorated Madoc's heart;
For well he ween'd Cadwallon was at
hand,
Leading his gallant friends. Aright he
ween'd;   310
At hand Cadwallon was! His gallant
friends
Came from the mountains with im-
petuous speed,
To save or to revenge. Nor long en-
dured
The combat now: the Priests ascend
the stone,
And bid the Tiger hasten to defend
His country and his Gods; and, hand
and foot,
Binding the captive Prince, they bear
him thence
And lay him in the temple. Then his
heart
Resign'd itself to death, and Madoc
thought
Of Llaian and Goervyl: and he felt 320
That death was dreadful. But not so
the King
Permitted; but not so had Heaven
decreed;
For noble was the King of Aztlan's
heart,
And pure his tongue from falsehood:
he had said,
That by the warrior's death should
Madoc die;
Nor dared the Pabas violently break
The irrevocable word. There Madoc
lay   327
In solitude; the distant battle reach'd
His ear; inactive and in bonds he lay
Expecting the dread issue, and almost
Wish'd for the perils of the fight again.

XV. THE BATTLE

Not unprepared Cadwallon found the sons
Of Aztlan, nor defenceless were her walls ;
But when the Britons' distant march was seen,
A ready army issued from her gates,
And dight themselves to battle : these the King
Coanocotzin had, with timely care,
And provident for danger, thus array'd.
Forth issuing from the gates, they met the foe,
And with the sound of sonorous instruments,
And with their shouts and screams and yells, drove back   10
The Britons' fainter war-cry, as the swell
Of ocean, flowing onward, up its course
Repels the river-stream. Their darts and stones
Fell like the rain drops of the summer-shower,
So fast, and on the helmet and the shield,
On the strong corselet and the netted mail,
So innocent they fell. But not in vain
The bowmen of Deheubarth sent, that day,
Their iron bolts abroad ; those volant deaths
Descended on the naked multitude,   20
And through the chieftain's quilted gossampine,
Through feathery breastplate and effulgent gold,
They reach'd the life.
                    But soon no interval
For archer's art was left, nor scope for flight
Of stone from whirling sling : both hosts, alike
Impatient for the proof of war, press on ;
The Aztecas, to shun the arrowy storm,
The Cymry, to release their Lord, or heap
Aztlan in ruins, for his monument.
Spear against spear, and shield to shield, and breast   30
To breast they met ; equal in force of limb
And strength of heart, in resolute resolve,
And stubborn effort of determined wrath :
The few, advantaged by their iron mail ;
The weaklier arm'd, of near retreat assured
And succour close at hand, in tenfold troops
Their foemen overnumbering. And of all
That mighty multitude, did every man
Of either host, alike inspired by all
That stings to will and strengthens to perform,   40
Then put forth all his power ; for well they knew
Aztlan that day must triumph or must fall.
Then sword and mace on helm and buckler rang,
And hurtling javelins whirr'd along the sky.
Nor when they hurled the javelin, did the sons
Of Aztlan, prodigal of weapons, loose
The lance, to serve them for no second stroke ;
A line of ample measure still retain'd
The missile shaft ; and when its blow was spent,
Swiftly the dexterous spearman coiled the string,   50
And sped again the artificer of death.
Rattling, like summer hailstones, they descend,
But from the Britons' iron panoply,
Baffled and blunted, fell ; nor more avail'd
The stony falchion there, whose broken edge
Inflicts no second wound ; nor profited,
On the strong buckler or the crested helm,
The knotty club ; though fast, in blinding showers,
Those javelins fly, those heavy weapons fall
With stunning weight. Meantime with wonted strength,   60
The men of Gwyneth through their fenceless foes

Those lances thrust, whose terrors had
  so oft
Affray'd the Saxons, and whose home-
  driven points,
So oft had pierced the Normen's
  knightly arms.
Little did then his pomp of plumes be-
  stead
The Azteca, or glittering pride of gold,
Against the temper'd sword ; little his
  casque,
Gay with its feathery coronal, or drest
In graven terrors, when the Briton's
  hand
Drove in through helm and head the
  short-spiked mace :   70
Or swung its iron weights with shatter-
  ing sway,
Which where they struck destroyed.
  Beneath those arms
The men of Aztlan fell ; and whoso
  dropt
Dead or disabled, him his comrades bore
Away with instant caution, lest the
  sight
Of those whom they had slaughter'd
  might inspire
The foe with hope and courage. Fast
  they fell,
And fast were resupplied, man after man
Succeeding to the death. Nor in the
  town
Did now the sight of their slain country-
  men,   80
Momentarily carried in and piled in
  heaps,
Awake one thought of fear. Hark !
  through the streets
Of Aztlan, how from house to house, and
  tower
To tower, reiterate, Paynalton's name
Calls all her sons to battle ! at whose
  name
All must go forth, and follow to the field
The Leader of the Armies of the Gods,
Whom, in his unseen power, Mexitli now
Sends out to lead his people. They, in
  crowds,
Throng for their weapons to the House
  of Arms,   90
Beneath their guardian Deity preserved,
Through years of peace ; and there the
  Pabas stood

Within the temple-court, and dealt
  around
The ablution of the Stone of Sacrifice,
Bidding them, with the holy beverage,
Imbibe diviner valour, strength of arm
Not to be wearied, hope of victory,
And certain faith of endless joy in
  Heaven,
Their sure reward. . . Oh ! happy, cried
  the Priests,
Your brethren who have fallen ! already
  they   100
Have join'd the company of blessed
  souls ;
Already they, with song and harmony,
And in the dance of beauty, are gone
  forth,
To follow down his western path of light
Yon Sun, the Prince of Glory, from the
  world
Retiring to the Palace of his rest.
Oh, happy they, who for their country's
  cause,
And for their Gods, shall die the brave
  man's death !
Them will their country consecrate with
  praise,
Them will the Gods reward ! . . They
  heard the Priests   110
Intoxicate, and from the gate swarm'd
  out,
Tumultuous to the fight of martyrdom.

But when Cadwallon every moment
  saw
The enemies increase, and with what rage
Of drunken valour to the fight they
  rush'd,
He, against that impetuous attack,
As best he could, providing, form'd the
  troops
Of Britain into one collected mass :
Three equal sides it offered to the foe,
Close and compact ; no multitude could
  break   120
The condensed strength : its narrow
  point prest on,
Entering the throng's resistance, like a
  wedge,
Still from behind impell'd. So thought
  the Chief
Likeliest the gates of Aztlan might be
  gain'd,

And Hoel and the Prince preserved, if
    yet
They were among mankind. Nor could
    the force
Of hostile thousands break that strength
    condensed,
Against whose iron sides the stream of
    war
Roll'd unavailing, as the ocean waves,
Which idly round some insulated rock
Foam furious, warning with their
    silvery smoke   131
The mariner far off. Nor could the point
Of that compacted body, though it bore
Right on the foe, and with united force
Press'd on to enter, through the multi-
    tude
Win now its difficult way ; as where the
    sea
Pours through some strait its violent
    waters, swoln
By inland fresh, vainly the oarmen there
With all their weight and strength essay
    to drive
Their galley through the pass, the stress
    and strain   140
Availing scarce to stem the impetuous
    stream.

    And hark ! above the deafening din
    of fight
Another shout, heard like the thunder-
    peal,
Amid the war of winds ! Lincoya comes,
Leading the mountain-dwellers. From
    the shock
Aztlan recoil'd. And now a second troop
Of Britons to the town advanced, for
    war
Impatient and revenge. Cadwallon
    these,
With tidings of their gallant Prince en-
    thrall'd,
Had summon'd from the ships. That
    dreadful tale   150
Roused them to fury. Not a man was
    left
To guard the fleet ; for who could have
    endured
That idle duty ? who could have
    endured
The long, inactive, miserable hours,
And hope and expectation and the rage

Of maddening anguish ? Ririd led them
    on ;
In whom a brother's love had call'd
    not up
More spirit-stirring pain, than trembled
    now
In every British heart ; so dear to all
Was Madoc. On they came ; and
    Aztlan then   160
Had fled appall'd ; but in that dan-
    gerous hour
Her faith preserved her. From the
    gate her Priests
Rush'd desperate out, and to the fore-
    most rank
Forced their wild way, and fought with
    martyr zeal.
Through all the host contagious fury
    spread :
Nor had the sight that hour enabled them
To mightier efforts, had Mexitli, clad
In all his imaged terrors, gone before
Their way, and driven upon his enemies
His giant club destroying. Then more
    fierce   170
The conflict grew ; the din of arms, the
    yell
Of savage rage, the shriek of agony,
The groan of death, commingled in one
    sound
Of undistinguished horrors ; while the
    Sun,
Retiring slow beneath the plain's far
    verge,
Shed o'er the quiet hills his fading light.

XVI. THE WOMEN

SILENT and solitary is thy vale,
Caermadoc, and how melancholy now
That solitude and silence ! . . Broad
    noon-day,
And not a sound of human life is there !
The fisher's net, abandon'd in his haste,
Sways idly in the waters ; in the tree,
Where its last stroke had pierced, the
    hatchet hangs :
The birds, beside the mattock and the
    spade,
Hunt in the new-turn'd mould, and
    fearlessly

Fly through the cage-work of the
 imperfect wall ;   10
Or through the vacant dwelling's open
 door,
Pass and repass secure.
     In Madoc's house,
And on his bed of reeds, Goervyl lies,
Her face toward the ground. She
 neither weeps,
Nor sighs, nor groans ; too strong her
 agony
For outward sign of anguish, and for
 prayer
Too hopeless was the ill ; and though,
 at times,
The pious exclamation pass'd her lips,
Thy will be done ! yet was that utter-
 ance   19
Rather the breathing of a broken heart,
Than of a soul resign'd. Mervyn beside
Hangs over his dear mistress silently,
Having no hope or comfort to bestow,
Nor aught but sobs and unavailing tears.
The women of Caermadoc, like a flock
Collected in their panic, stand around
The house of their lost leader ; and they
 too
Are mute in their despair. Llaian alone
Is absent ; wildly hath she wander'd
 forth
To seek her child, and such the general
 woe,   30
That none hath mark'd her absence.
 Yet have they,
Though unprotected thus, no selfish fear;
The sudden evil hath destroyed all
 thought,
All sense of present danger to them-
 selves,
All foresight.
    Yet new terrors ! Malinal,
Panting with speed, bursts in, and takes
 the arms
Of Madoc down. Goervyl, at that sound,
Started in sudden hope ; but when she
 saw
The Azteca, she uttered a faint scream
Of wrongful fear, remembering not the
 proofs   40
Of his tried truth, nor recognizing
 aught
In those known features, save their
 hostile hue.

But he, by worser fear abating soon
Her vain alarm, exclaim'd, I saw a band
Of Hoamen coming up the straits, for ill,
Besure, for Amalahta leads them on.
Buckle this harness on, that, being
 arm'd,
I may defend the entrance.
     Scarce had she
Fastened the breast-plate with her
 trembling hands,
When, flying from the sight of men in
 arms,   50
The women crowded in. Hastily he
 seized
The shield and spear, and on the
 threshold took
His stand ; but, waken'd now to provi-
 dent thought,
Goervyl, following, helm'd him. There
 was now
No time to gird the bauldric on ; she
 held
Her brother's sword, and bade him look
 to her
For prompt supply of weapons ; in
 herself
Being resolved not idly to abide,
Nor unprepared of hand or heart to
 meet
The issue of the danger, nor to die 60
Reluctant now.
    Rightly had they divined
The Hoamen's felon purpose. When he
 heard
The fate of Madoc, from his mother's eye
He mask'd his secret joy, and took his
 arms,
And to the rescue, with the foremost
 band,
Set forth. But soon, upon the way, he
 told
The associates of his crime, that now
 their hour
Of triumph was arrived ; Caermadoc,
 left
Defenceless, would become, with all its
 wealth,
The spoiler's easy prey, raiment and
 arms   70
And iron ; skins of that sweet beverage,
Which to a sense of its own life could
 stir
The joyful blood ; the women above all,

Whom to the forest they might bear
    away,
To be their slaves, if so their pleasure
    was ;
Or, yielding them to Aztlan, for such
    prize
Receive a royal guerdon.   Twelve there
    were,
Long leagued with him in guilt, who
    turn'd aside :
And they have reach'd Caermadoc now,
    and now
Rush onward, where they see the
    women fly ;   80
When, on the threshold, clad in Cimbric
    arms,
And with long lance protended, Malinal
Rebuffs them from the entrance.   At
    that sight
Suddenly quail'd, they stood, as mid-
    night thieves
Who find the master waking ; but ere
    long,
Gathering a boastful courage, as they
    saw
No other guard, press'd forward, and
    essay'd
To turn his spear aside.   Its steady
    point,
True to the impelling strength, held on,
    and thrust
The foremost through the breast, and
    breath and blood   90
Followed   the   re-drawn   shaft.   Nor
    seem'd the strife
Unequal now, though with their num-
    bers, they
Beleaguer'd in half-ring the door, where
    he,
The sole defender, stood.   From side
    to side,
So well and swiftly did he veer the
    lance,
That every enemy beheld its point
Aim'd at himself direct.   But chief on
    one
Had Malinal his deadly purpose fix'd,
On Amalahta ; by his death to quell
The present danger, and cut off the
    root   100
Of many an evil, certain else to spring
From that accursed stock.   On him his
    eye

Turn'd with more eager wilfulness, and
    dwelt
With keener ken ; and now, with sudden
    step
Bending his body on, at him he drives
The meditated blow :   but that ill
    Prince,
As chiefly sought, so chiefly fearing,
    swerved
Timely aside ; and ere the Azteca
Recovered from the frustrate aim, the
    spear
Was seized, and from his hold, by stress
    and weight   110
Of numbers wrench'd.   He, facing still
    the foe,
And holding at arm's length the targe,
    put back
His hand, and called Goervyl, and from
    her
Received the sword : . . in time, for the
    enemy
Prest on so near, that having now no
    scope
To raise his arm, he drove the blade
    straight on.
It entered at the mouth of one who
    stood
With face aslant, and glanced along the
    teeth
Through to the ear, then, slivering
    downward, left
The cheek-flap dangling.   He, in that
    same point   120
Of time, as if a single impulse gave
Birth to the double action, dash'd his
    shield
Against another's head, with so fierce
    swing
And sway of strength, that this third
    enemy
Fell at his feet.   Astounded by such
    proof
Of prowess, and by unexpected loss
Dismay'd, the foe gave back, beyond
    the reach
Of his strong arm ; and there awhile
    they stood,
Beholding him at bay, and counselling
How best to work their vengeance upon
    him,   130
Their sole opponent.   Soon did they
    behold

The vantage, overlook'd by hasty hope,
How vulnerable he stood, his arms and
    thighs
Bare for their butt.   At once they bent
    their bows;
At once ten arrows fled ; seven, shot in
    vain,
Rung on his shield; but, with un-
    happier mark,
Two shafts hung quivering in his leg ;
    a third
Below the shoulder pierced. Then
    Malinal
Groan'd, not for anguish of his wounds,
    but grief
And agony of spirit ; yet resolved   140
To his last gasp to guard that precious
    post,
Nor longer able to endure afoot,
He, falling on his knees, received un-
    harm'd
Upon the shield, now ample for defence,
Their second shower, and still defied the
    foe.
But they, now sure of conquest, hasten'd
    on
To thrust him down, and he too felt his
    strength
Ebbing away. Goervyl, in that hour
Of horror and despair, collected still,
Caught him, and by the shoulders drew
    him in ;   150
And, calling on her comrades, with their
    help
Shut to the door in time, and with their
    weight
Secured it, not their strength ; for she
    alone,
Found worthy of her noble ancestry,
In this emergence felt her faculties
All present, and heroic strength of heart,
To cope with danger and contempt of
    death.
Shame on ye, British women ! shame !
    exclaim'd
The daughter of King Owen, as she saw
The trembling hands and bloodless
    countenance   160
Pale as sepulchral marble; silent some;
Others with womanish cries lamenting
    now
That ever, in unhappy hour, they left
Their native land ; .. a pardonable fear;

For hark, the war-whoop !   sound,
    whereto the howl
Of tigers or hyenas, heard at night
By captive from barbarian foes escaped,
And wandering in the pathless wilder-
    ness,
Were music. Shame on ye ! Goervyl
    cried ;
Think what your fathers were, your
    husbands what,   170
And what your sons should be ! These
    savages
Seek not to wreak on ye immediate
    death ;
So are ye safe, if safety such as this
Be worth a thought ; and in the interval
We yet may gain, by keeping to the last
This entrance, easily to be maintain'd
By us, though women, against foes so
    few, ..
Who knows what succour chance, or
    timely thought
Of our own friends may send, or Provi-
    dence,
Who slumbereth not ? .. While thus she
    spake, a hand   180
In at the window came, of one who
    sought
That way to win the entrance. She
    drew out
The arrow through the arm of Malinal,
With gentle care, .. the readiest weapon
    that, ..
And held it short above the bony barb,
And, adding deeds to words, with all her
    might
She stabbed it through the hand. The
    sudden pain
Provoked a cry, and back the savage
    fell,
Loosening his hold, and maim'd for
    further war.
Nay ! leave that entrance open ! she
    exclaim'd   190
To one who would have closed it, .. who
    comes next
Shall not go thence so cheaply ! . . for
    she now
Had taken up a spear to guard that
    way,
Easily guarded, even by female might.
O heart of proof ! what now avails thy
    worth

And excellent courage ? for the savage
foe,
With mattock and with spade, for other
use
Design'd, hew now upon the door, and
rend
The wattled sides; and they within
shrink back,
For now it splinters through, . . and lo,
the way   200
Is open to the spoiler !
                    Then once more,
Collecting his last strength, did Malinal
Rise on his knees, and over him the maid
Stands with the ready spear, she
guarding him
Who guarded her so well. Roused to
new force
By that exampled valour, and with will
To achieve one service yet before he
died, . .
If death indeed, as sure he thought,
were nigh, . .
Malinal gather'd up his fainting powers,
And reaching forward, with a blow that
threw   210
His body on, upon the knee he smote
One Hoaman more, and brought him
to the ground.
The foe fell over him ; but he, prepared,
Threw him with sudden jerk aside, and
rose
Upon one hand, and with the other
plunged
Between his ribs the mortal blade.
Meantime
Amalahta, rushing in blind eagerness
To seize Goervyl, set at nought the
power
Of female hands, and stooping as he
came
Beneath her spear-point, thought with
lifted arm   220
To turn the thrust aside. But she drew
back,
And lowered at once the spear with aim
so sure,
That on the front it met him, and
plough'd up
The whole scalp-length. He, blinded
by the blood,
Stagger'd aside, escaping by that chance
A second push, else mortal. And by this,

The women, learning courage from
despair,
And by Goervyl's bold example fired,
Took heart, and rushing on with one
accord,
Drove out the foe. Then took they
hope ; for then   230
They saw but seven remain in plight for
war ;
And, knowing their own number, in the
pride
Of strength, caught up stones, staves,
or axe, or spear,
To hostile use converting whatsoe'er
The hasty hand could seize. Such
fierce attack
Confused the ruffian band ; nor had
they room
To aim the arrow, nor to speed the
spear,
Each now beset by many. But their
Prince,
Still mindful of his purport, call'd to
them, . .
Secure my passage while I bear away
The White King's Sister ; having her,
the law   241
Of peace is in our power. . . And on he
went
Toward Goervyl, and, with sudden turn,
While on another foe her eye was fix'd,
Ran in upon her, and stoop'd down, and
claspt
The Maid above the knees, and throwing
her
Over his shoulder, to the valley straits
Set off : . . ill seconded in ill attempt ;
For now his comrades are too close beset
To aid their Chief, and Mervyn hath
beheld   250
His lady's peril. At the sight, inspired
With force, as if indeed that manly garb
Had clothed a manly heart, the Page
ran on,
And with a bill-hook striking at his ham,
Cut the back sinews. Amalahta fell ;
The Maid fell with him : and she first
hath risen,
While, grovelling on the earth, he
gnash'd his teeth
For agony. Yet, even in those pangs,
Remembering still revenge, he turn'd
and seized

Goervyl's skirt, and pluck'd her to the
  ground,   260
And roll'd himself upon her, and essay'd
To kneel upon her breast; but she
  clench'd fast
His bloody locks, and drew him down
  aside,
Faint now with anguish, and with loss
  of blood;
And Mervyn, coming to her help again,
As once again he rose, around the neck
Seized him, with throttling grasp, and
  held him down, . .
Strange strife and horrible, . . till Malinal
Crawl'd to the spot, and thrust into his
  groin
The mortal sword of Madoc; he himself,
At the same moment, fainting, now no
  more   271
By his strong will upheld, the service
  done.
The few surviving traitors, at the sight
Of their fallen Prince and Leader, now
  too late
Believed that some diviner power had
  given
These female arms strength for their
  overthrow,
Themselves proved weak before them,
  as, of late,
Their God, by Madoc crush'd.
              Away they fled
Toward the valley straits; but in the
  gorge
Erillyab met their flight: and then her
  heart,   280
Boding the evil, smote her, and she bade
Her people seize, and bring them on in
  bonds,
For judgement. She herself, with
  quicken'd pace,
Advanced, to know the worst; and o'er
  the dead
Casting a rapid glance, she knew her
  son.
She knew him by his garments, by the
  work
Of her own hands; for now his face,
  besmear'd
And black with gore, and stiffen'd in its
  pangs,
Bore of the life no semblance. . . God is
  good!

She cried, and closed her eyelids, and
  her lips   290
Shook, and her countenance changed.
  But in her heart
She quell'd the natural feeling. . . Bear
  away
These wretches! . . to her followers she
  exclaim'd;
And root them from the earth. Then
  she approach'd
Goervyl, who was pale and trembling
  now,
Exhausted with past effort; and she took
Gently the Maiden's tremulous hand,
  and said,
God comfort thee, my Sister! At that
  voice
Of consolation, from her dreamy state
Goervyl to a sense of all her woe   300
Awoke, and burst into a gush of tears.
God comfort thee, my Sister! cried the
  Queen,
Even as He strengthens me. I would
  not raise
Deceitful hope, . . but in His hand, even
  yet,
The issue hangs; and He is merciful.

Yea, daughter of Aberfraw, take thou
  hope!
For Madoc lives! . . he lives to wield the
  sword
Of righteous vengeance, and accomplish
  all.

XVII. THE DELIVERANCE

MADOC, meantime, in bonds and solitude,
Lay listening to the tumult. How his
  heart
Panted! how then, with fruitless
  strength, he strove
And struggled for enlargement, as the
  sound
Of battle from without the city came;
While all things near were still, nor foot
  of man
Nor voice, in that deserted part, were
  heard.
At length one light and solitary step
Approach'd the place; a woman cross'd
  the door.

From Madoc's busy mind her image
   pass'd,   10
Quick as the form that caused it ; but
   not so
Did the remembrance fly from Coatel,
That Madoc lay in bonds. That thought
   possess'd
Her soul, and made her, as she garlanded
The fane of Coatlantona with flowers,
Tremble in strong emotion.

               It was now
The hour of dusk ; the Pabas all were
   gone,
Gone to the battle ; . . none could see
   her steps ;
The gate was nigh. A momentary
   thought
Shot through her ; she delay'd not to
   reflect,   20
But hasten'd to the Prince, and took
   the knife
Of sacrifice, which by the altar hung,
And cut his bonds, and with an eager
   eye,
Motioning haste and silence, to the gate
She led him.   Fast along the forest way,
And fearfully, he follow'd to the chasm.
She beckon'd, and descended, and drew
   out
From underneath her vest, a cage, or net
It rather might be called, so fine the
   twigs
Which knit it, where confined two fire-
   flies gave   30
Their lustre.   By that light did Madoc
   first
Behold the features of his lovely guide ;
And through the entrance of the cavern
   gloom
He followed in full trust.

           Now have they reach'd
The abrupt descent ; there Coatel held
   forth
Her living lamp, and turning, with a
   smile
Sweet as good Angels wear when they
   present
Their mortal charge before the throne
   of Heaven,
She show'd where little Hoel slept below.
Poor child ! he lay upon that very spot,
The last whereto his feet had followed
   her ;   41

And, as he slept, his hand was on the
   bones
Of one, who years agone had perish'd
   there,
There, on the place where last his
   wretched eyes
Could catch the gleam of day.   But
   when the voice,
The well-known voice of Madoc, wakened
   him, . .
His uncle's voice, . . he started, with a
   scream
Which echoed through the cavern's
   winding length,
And stretch'd his arms to reach him.
   Madoc hush'd
The dangerous transport, raised him up
   the ascent,   50
And followed Coatel again, whose face,
Though tears of pleasure still were
   coursing down,
Betoken'd fear and haste.   Adown the
   wood
They went ; and coasting now the lake,
   her eye
First what they sought beheld, a light
   canoe,
Moor'd to the bank.   Then in her arms
   she took
The child, and kiss'd him with maternal
   love,
And placed him in the boat ; but when
   the Prince,
With looks and gestures and imperfect
   words
Such as the look, the gesture, well ex-
   plain'd,   60
Urged her to follow, doubtfully she
   stood :
A dread of danger, for the thing she had
   done,
Came on her, and Lincoya rose to mind.
Almost she had resolved ; but then the
   thought
Of her dear father, whom that flight
   would leave
Alone in age ; how he would weep for her,
As one among the dead, and to the grave
Go sorrowing ; or, if ever it were known
What she had dared, that on his head
   the weight
Of punishment would fall.   That dread-
   ful fear   70

Resolved her, and she waved her head,
and raised
Her hand, to bid the Prince depart in
haste,
With looks whose painful seriousness
forbade
All farther effort. Yet unwillingly,
And boding evil, Madoc from the shore
Push'd off his little boat. She on its
way
Stood gazing for a moment, lost in
thought,
Then struck into the woods.
        Swift through the lake
Madoc's strong arm impell'd the light
canoe.
Fainter and fainter to his distant ear 80
The sound of battle came ; and now
the Moon
Arose in heaven, and poured o'er lake
and land
A soft and mellowing ray. Along the
shore
Llaian was wandering with distracted
steps,
And groaning for her child. She saw
the boat
Approach ; and as on Madoc's naked
limbs,
And on his countenance, the moonbeam
fell,
And as she saw the boy in that dim light,
It seem'd as though the Spirits of the
dead
Were moving on the waters ; and she
stood   90
With open lips that breathed not, and
fix'd eyes,
Watching the unreal shapes : but when
the boat
Drew nigh, and Madoc landed, and she
saw
His step substantial, and the child came
near,
Unable then to move, or speak, or
breathe,
Down on the sand she sunk.
        But who can tell,
Who comprehend, her agony of joy,
When, by the Prince's care restored to
sense,
She recognized her child, she heard the
name

Of mother from that voice, which, sure,
she thought   100
Had pour'd upon some Priest's remorseless ear
Its last vain prayer for life ! No tear
relieved
The insupportable feeling that convulsed
Her swelling breast. She look'd, and
look'd, and felt
The child, lest some delusion should have
mock'd
Her soul to madness ; then the gushing
joy
Burst forth, and with caresses and with
tears
She mingled broken prayers of thanks
to heaven.

And now the Prince, when joy had
had its course,
Said to her, Knowest thou the mountain
path ?   110
For I would to the battle. But at that,
A sudden damp of dread came over
her, . .
O leave us not ! she cried ; lest haply ill
Should have befallen ; for I remember
now,
How in the woods I spied a savage band
Making towards Caermadoc. God fore-
fend
The evil that I fear ! . . What ! Madoc
cried,
Were ye then left defenceless ? . . She
replied,
All ran to arms : there was no time for
thought,
Nor counsel, in that sudden ill ; nor
one   120
Of all thy people, who could, in that hour
Have brook'd home-duty, when thy life
or death
Hung on the chance.
        Now God be merciful !
Said he ; for of Goervyl then he thought,
And the cold sweat started at every pore.
Give me the boy ! . . he travels all too
slow.
Then in his arms he took him, and sped
on,
Suffering more painful terrors, than of
late

His own near death provoked. They
  held their way
In silence up the heights; and, when
  at length   130
They reached the entrance of the vale,
  the Prince
Bade her remain, while he went on to
  spy
The footsteps of the spoiler. Soon he
  saw
Men, in the moonlight, stretch'd upon
  the ground ;
And quickening then his pace, in worse
  alarm,
Along the shade, with cautious step, he
  moved
Toward one, to seize his weapons : 'twas
  a corpse ;
Nor whether, at the sight, to hope or
  fear
Yet knew he. But anon, a steady light,
As of a taper, seen in his own home, 140
Comforted him ; and, drawing nearer
  now,
He saw his sister on her knees, beside
The rushes, ministering to a wounded
  man.
Safe that the dear one lived, then back
  he sped
With joyful haste, and summon'd
  Llaian on,
And in loud talk advanced. Erillyab
  first
Came forward at the sound ; for she had
  faith
To trust the voice. . . They live ! they
  live ! she cried :
God hath redeem'd them ! . . Nor the
  Maiden yet
Believed the actual joy ; like one
  astound,   150
Or as if struggling with a dream, she
  stood,
Till he came close, and spread his arms,
  and call'd
Goervyl ! . . and she fell in his embrace.

But Madoc linger'd not, his eager soul
Was in the war, in haste he donn'd his
  arms :
And as he felt his own good sword again,
Exulting play'd his heart. . . Boy, he
  exclaim'd

To Mervyn, arm thyself, and follow me !
For in this battle we shall break the
  power
Of our blood-thirsty foe : and, in thine
  age,   160
Wouldst thou not wish, when young men
  men crowd around,
To hear thee chronicle their fathers'
  deeds,
Wouldst thou not wish to add, . . And
  I, too, fought
In that day's conflict ?
            Mervyn's cheek turn'd pale
A moment, then, with terror all suffused,
Grew fever-red. Nay, nay, Goervyl
  cried,
He is too young for battles ! . . But the
  Prince,
With erring judgement, in that fear-
  flush'd cheek
Beheld the glow of enterprizing hope,
And youthful courage. I was such
  a boy,   170
Sister ! he cried, at Counsyllt ; and that
  day,
In my first field, with stripling arm,
  smote down
Many a tall Saxon. Saidst thou not but
  now,
How bravely in the fight of yesterday,
He flesh'd his sword, . . and wouldst
  thou keep him here
And rob him of his glory ? See his
  cheek !
How it hath crimson'd at the unworthy
  thought !
Arm ! arm ! and to the battle !
                How her heart
Then panted ! how, with late regret,
  and vain,   179
Senena wished Goervyl then had heard
The secret, trembling on her lips so oft,
So oft by shame withheld. She thought
  that now
She could have fallen upon her Lady's
  neck,
And told her all ; but when she saw the
  Prince,
Imperious shame forbade her, and she
  felt
It were an easier thing to die than
  speak.
Avail'd not now regret or female fear !

She mail'd her delicate limbs ; beneath
　　the plate
Compress'd her bosom ; on her golden
　　locks
The helmet's overheavy load she placed ;
Hung from her neck the shield ; and,
　　though the sword　　　191
Which swung beside her lightest she had
　　chosen,
Though in her hand she held the slen-
　　derest spear,
Alike unwieldy for the maiden's grasp,
The sword and ashen lance.　But as she
　　touch'd
The murderous point, an icy shudder ran
Through every fibre of her trembling
　　frame ;
And, overcome by womanly terror then,
The damsel to Goervyl turn'd, and let
The breastplate fall, and on her bosom
　　placed　　　200
The Lady's hand, and hid her face, and
　　cried,
Save me !　The warrior, who beheld the
　　act,
And heard not the low voice, with angry
　　eye
Glow'd on the seemly boy of feeble heart.
But, in Goervyl, joy had overpower'd
The wonder ;　joy to find the boy she
　　loved
Was one, to whom her heart with closer
　　love
Might cling ;　and to her brother she
　　exclaim'd,
She must not go !　We women in the war
Have done our parts.
　　　　　　A moment Madoc dwelt
On the false Mervyn, with an eye from
　　whence　　　211
Displeasure did not wholly pass away.
Nor loitering to resolve Love's riddle
　　now
To Malinal he turn'd, where, on his
　　couch,
The wounded youth was laid. . . True
　　friend, said he,
And brother mine, . . for truly by that
　　name
I trust to greet thee, . . if, in this near
　　fight,
My hour should overtake me, . . as who
　　knows

The lot of war ? . . Goervyl hath my
　　charge
To quite thee for thy service with her-
　　self ;　　　220
That so thou mayest raise up seed to me
Of mine own blood, who may inherit
　　here
The obedience of thy people and of
　　mine. . .
Malinal took his hand, and to his lips
Feebly he press'd it, saying, One boon
　　more,
Father and friend, I ask ! . . if thou
　　shouldst meet
Yuhidthiton in battle, think of me.

XVIII.　THE VICTORY

MERCIFUL God ! how horrible is night
Upon the plain of Aztlan !　there the
　　shout
Of battle, the barbarian yell, the bray
Of dissonant instruments, the clang of
　　arms,
The shriek of agony, the groan of death,
In one wild uproar and continuous din,
Shake the still air ;　while, overhead, the
　　Moon,
Regardless of the stir of this low world,
Holds on her heavenly way.　Still un-
　　allay'd
By slaughter raged the battle, unrelax'd
By lengthened toil ;　anger supplying
　　still　　　11
Strength undiminish'd for the desperate
　　strife.
And lo !　where yonder, on the temple
　　top,
Blazing aloft, the sacrificial fire
Scene more accurst and hideous than
　　the war
Displays to all the vale ;　for whosoe'er
That night the Aztecas could bear away,
Hoaman or Briton, thither was he
　　borne ;
And as they stretch'd him on the stone
　　of blood,
Did the huge tambour of the God, with
　　voice　　　20
Loud as the thunder-peal, and heard as
　　far,

U

Proclaim the act of death, more visible
Than in broad day-light, by those mid-
  night fires
Distinctlier seen.   Sight that with
  horror fill'd
The Cymry, and to mightier efforts
  roused.
Howbeit, this abhorr'd idolatry
Work'd for their safety; the deluded
  foes,
Obstinate in their faith, forbearing still
The mortal stroke, that they might to
  the God
Present the living victim, and to him 30
Let the life flow.
              And now the orient sky
Glow'd with the ruddy morning, when
  the Prince
Came to the field.   He lifted up his
  voice,
And shouted Madoc! Madoc! They
  who heard
The cry, astonish'd turn'd; and when
  they saw
The countenance his open helm dis-
  closed,
They echoed, Madoc! Madoc! Through
  the host
Spread the miraculous joy, . . He lives!
  he lives!
He comes himself in arms! . . Lincoya
  heard,
As he had raised his arm to strike a foe,
And stay'd the stroke, and thrust him
  off, and cried,   41
Go tell the tidings to thy countrymen,
Madoc is in the war! Tell them his God
Hath set the White King free! Astonish-
  ment
Seized on the Azteca; on all who heard,
Amazement and dismay; and Madoc
  now
Stood in the foremost battle, and his
  sword, . .
His own good sword, . . flash'd like the
  sudden death
Of lightning in their eyes.
              The King of Aztlan
Heard and beheld, and in his noble
  heart   50
Heroic hope arose.   Forward he moved,
And in the shock of battle, front to
  front,

Encountered Madoc.   A strong statured
  man
Coanocotzin stood, one well who knew
The ways of war, and never yet in fight
Had found an equal foe.   Adown his
  back
Hung the long robe of feather'd royalty;
Gold fenced his arms and legs; upon his
  helm
A sculptured snake protends the arrowy
  tongue;
Around a coronal of plumes arose,   60
Brighter than beam the rainbow hues
  of light,
Or than the evening glories which the
  sun
Slants o'er the moving many-colour'd
  sea,
Such their surpassing beauty; bells of
  gold
Emboss'd his glittering helmet, and
  where'er
Their sound was heard, there lay the
  press of war,
And Death was busiest there.   Over
  the breast
And o'er the golden breastplate of the
  King,
A feathery cuirass, beautiful to eye,
Light as the robe of peace, yet strong to
  save;   70
For the sharp faulchion's baffled edge
  would glide
From its smooth softness.   On his arm
  he held
A buckler overlaid with beaten gold;
And so he stood, guarding his thighs
  and legs,
His breast and shoulders also, with the
  length
Of his broad shield.
              Opposed, in mail complete,
Stood Madoc in his strength. The flexile
  chains
Gave play to his full muscles, and dis-
  play'd
How broad his shoulders, and his ample
  breast.
Small was his shield, there broadest
  where it fenced   80
The well of life, and gradual to a point
Lessening, steel-strong, and wieldy in
  his grasp.

It bore those blazoned eaglets, at whose
    sight,
Along the Marches, or where holy Dee
Through Cestrian pastures rolls his
    tamer stream,
So oft the yeoman had, in days of yore,
Cursing his perilous tenure, wound the
    horn,
And warden from the castle-tower rung
    out
The loud alarum-bell, heard far and
    wide.
Upon his helm no sculptured dragon
    sate,   90
Sate no fantastic terrors ; a white plume
Nodded above, far-seen, floating like
    foam
Upon the stream of battle, always where
The tide ran strongest. Man to man
    opposed,
The Sea Lord and the King of Aztlan
    stood.

Fast on the intervening buckler fell
The Azteca's stone faulchion. Who
    hath watch'd
The midnight lightnings of the summer
    storm,
That with their awful blaze irradiate
    heaven,
Then leave a blacker night ? so quick,
    so fierce,   100
Flash'd Madoc's sword, which, like the
    serpent's tongue,
Seemed double, in its rapid whirl of
    light.
Unequal arms ! for on the British shield
Avail'd not the stone faulchion's brittle
    edge,
And in the golden buckler, Madoc's
    sword
Bit deep. Coanocotzin saw, and dropt
The unprofitable weapon, and received
His ponderous club, . . that club,
    beneath whose force,
Driven by his father's arm, Tepollomi
Had fallen subdued, . . and fast and
    fierce he drove   110
The massy weight on Madoc. From his
    shield,
The deadening force communicated ran
Up his stunn'd arm ; anon upon his
    helm,

Crashing, it came ; . . his eyes shot fire,
    his brain
Swam dizzy, . . he recoils, . . he reels, . .
    again
The club descends.
                    That danger to himself
Recall'd the Lord of Ocean. On he
    sprung,
Within the falling weapon's curve of
    death,
Shunning its frustrate aim, and breast
    to breast
He grappled with the King. The pliant
    mail   120
Bent to his straining limbs, while plates
    of gold,
The feathery robe, the buckler's ampli-
    tude
Cumbered the Azteca, and from his arm,
Clench'd in the Briton's mighty grasp,
    at once
He dropt the impeding buckler, and let
    fall
The unfasten'd club ; which when the
    Prince beheld,
He thrust him off, and drawing back
    resumed
The sword that from his wrist suspended
    hung,
And twice he smote the King ; twice
    from the quilt
Of plumes the iron glides : and lo !
    the King,   130
So well his soldiers watch their mon-
    arch's need,
Shakes in his hand a spear.
                        But now a cry
Burst on the ear of Madoc, and he saw
Through opening ranks, where Urien
    was convey'd
A captive to his death. Grief then and
    shame
And rage inspired him. With a mighty
    blow
He cleft Coanocotzin's helm ; exposed
The monarch stood ; . . again the
    thunder-stroke
Came on him, and he fell. . . The multi-
    tude,
Forgetful of their country and them-
    selves,   140
Crowd round their dying King. Madoc,
    whose eye

Still follow'd Urien, call'd upon his men,
And through the broken army of the foe,
Press'd to his rescue.
        But far off the old man
Was borne with furious speed. Ririd
    alone
Pursued his path, and through the thick
    of war
Close on the captors, with avenging
    sword,
Follow'd right on, and through the
    multitude,
And through the gate of Aztlan, made
    his way,
And through the streets, till, from the
    temple-mound,   150
The press of Pabas and the populace
Repell'd him, while the old man was
    hurried up.
Hark! that infernal tambour! o'er the
    lake
Its long-loud thunders roll, and through
    the hills,
Awakening all their echoes. Ye accurst,
Ye blow the fall too soon! Ye Dogs of
    Hell,
The Hart is yet at bay!.. Thus long the
    old man,
As one exhausted or resign'd, had lain,
Resisting not; but at that knell of
    death,
Springing with unexpected force, he
    freed   160
His feet, and shook the Pabas from their
    hold,
And, with his armed hand, between the
    eyes
Smote one so sternly, that to earth he
    fell,
Bleeding, and all astound. A man of
    proof
Was Urien in his day, thought worthiest,
In martial thewes and manly discipline,
To train the sons of Owen. He had
    lost
Youth's supple slight; yet still the skill
    remain'd,
And in his stiffen'd limbs a strength,
    which yet
Might put the young to shame. And
    now he set   170
His back against the altar, resolute
Not as a victim by the knife to die,

But in the act of battle, as became
A man grown grey in arms : and in his
    heart
There was a living hope ; for now he
    knew
That Madoc lived, nor could the struggle
    long
Endure against that arm.
             Soon was the way
Laid open by the sword; for side by
    side
The brethren of Aberfraw mow'd their
    path ;
And, following close, the Cymry drive
    along,   180
Till on the summit of the mound their
    cry
Of victory rings aloud. The temple
    floor,
So often which had reek'd with innocent
    blood,
Reeks now with righteous slaughter.
    Franticly,
In the wild fury of their desperate zeal,
The Priests crowd round the God, and
    with their knives
Hack at the foe, and call on him to
    save ; ..
At the altar, at the Idol's feet they fall.
Nor with less frenzy did the multitude
Flock to defend their God. Fast as
    they fell,   190
New victims rush'd upon the British
    sword ;
And sure that day had rooted from the
    earth
The Aztecas, and on their conquerors.
    drawn
Promiscuous ruin, had not Madoc now
Beheld from whence the fearless ardour
    sprang ; ..
They saw Mexitli ; momently they
    hoped
That he would rise in vengeance. Madoc
    seized
A massy club, and from his azure throne
Shattered the giant idol.
             At that sight
The men of Aztlan pause ; so was their
    pause   200
Dreadful, as when a multitude expect
The Earthquake's second shock. But
    when they saw

Earth did not open, nor the temple fall
To crush their impious enemies, dis-
may'd,
They felt themselves forsaken by their
Gods ;
Then from their temples and their homes
they fled,
And, leaving Aztlan to the conqueror,
Sought the near city, whither they had
sent
Their women, timely saved.

               But Tlalala,
With growing fury as the danger grew,
Raged in the battle ; but Yuhidthiton
Still with calm courage, till no hope
remain'd,   212
Fronted the rushing foe. When all was
vain,
When back within the gate Cadwallon's
force
Resistless had compell'd them, then the
Chief
Call'd on the Tiger, . . Let us bear from
hence
The dead Ocellopan, the slaughter'd
King ;
Not to the Strangers should their bones
be left,
O Tlalala ! . . The Tiger wept with rage,
With generous anger. To the place of
death,   220
Where, side by side, the noble dead
were stretch'd,
They fought their way. Eight warriors
join'd their shields ;
On these, a bier which well beseem'd the
dead,
The lifeless Chiefs were laid. Yuhidthiton
Call'd on the people, . . Men of Aztlan !
yet
One effort more ! Bear hence Ocellopan,
Bear hence the body of your noble King!
Not to the Strangers should their bones
be left !
That whoso heard, with wailing and loud
cries,
Prest round the body-bearers ; few in-
deed,   230
For few were they who in that fearful
hour
Had ears to hear, . . but with a holy zeal,
Careless of death, around the bier they
ranged

Their bulwark breasts. So toward the
farther gate
They held their steady way, while outer-
most
In unabated valour, Tlalala
Faced, with Yuhidthiton, the foe's pur-
suit.
Vain valour then, and fatal piety,
As the fierce conquerors bore on their
retreat,
If Madoc had not seen their perilous
strife ·   240
Remembering Malinal, and in his heart
Honouring a gallant foe, he call'd aloud,
And bade his people cease the hot
pursuit.
So, through the city gate, they bore away
The dead ; and, last of all their country-
men,
Leaving their homes and temples to the
foe,
Yuhidthiton and Tlalala retired.

XIX. THE FUNERAL

SOUTHWARD of Aztlan stood beside the
Lake,
A city of the Aztecas, by name
Patamba. Thither, from the first
alarm,
The women and infirm old men were
sent,
And children : thither they who from
the fight,
And from the fall of Aztlan, had escaped,
In scatter'd bands repair'd. Their City
lost,
Their Monarch slain, their Idols over-
thrown, . .
These tidings spread dismay ; but to
dismay
Succeeded horror soon, and kindling
rage,   10
Horror, by each new circumstance
increased,
By numbers, rage embolden'd. Lo ! to
the town,
Lamenting loud, a numerous train ap-
proach,
Like mountain torrents, swelling as they
go.

Borne in the midst, upon the bier of shields,
The noble dead were seen. To tenfold grief
That spectacle provoked, to tenfold wrath
That anguish stung them. With their yells and groans
Curses are mix'd, and threats, and bitter vows
Of vengeance full and speedy. From the wreck   20
Of Aztlan who is saved ? Tezozomoc,
Chief servant of the Gods, their favoured Priest,
The voice by whom they speak : young Tlalala,
Whom even defeat with fresher glory crowns ;
And full of fame, their country's rock of strength,
Yuhidthiton: him to their sovereign slain
Allied in blood, mature in wisdom him,
Of valour unsurpassable, by all
Beloved and honour'd, him the general voice
Acclaims their King; him they demand, to lead   30
Their gather'd force to battle, to revenge
Their Lord, their Gods, their kinsmen, to redeem
Their altars and their country.
                    But the dead
First from the nation's gratitude require
The rites of death. On mats of mountain palm,
Wrought of rare texture and of richest hues,
The slaughter'd warriors, side by side, were laid ;
Their bodies wrapt in many-colour'd robes
Of gossampine, bedeck'd with gems and gold.
The livid paleness of the countenance,
A mask conceal'd, and hid their ghastly wounds,   41
The Pabas stood around, and one by one,
Placed in their hands the sacred aloe leaves,
With mystic forms and characters inscribed ;

And as each leaf was given, Tezozomoc
Address'd the dead, .. So may ye safely pass
Between the mountains, which in endless war
Hurtle, with horrible uproar and frush
Of rocks that meet in battle. Arm'd with this,
In safety shall ye walk along the road, 50
Where the Great Serpent from his lurid eyes
Shoots lightning, and across the guarded way
Vibrates his tongue of fire. Receive the third,
And cross the waters where the Crocodile
In vain expects his prey. Your passport this
Through the Eight Deserts ; through the Eight Hills this ;
And this be your defence against the Wind,
Whose fury sweeps like dust the up-rooted rocks,
Whose keenness cuts the soul. Ye noble dead,
Protected with these potent amulets, 60
Soon shall your Spirits reach trium-phantly
The Palace of the Sun !
                    The funeral train
Moved to Mexitli's temple. First on high
The noble dead were borne ; in loud lament
Then follow'd all by blood allied to them,
Or by affection's voluntary ties
Attach'd more closely, brethren, kins-men, wives.
The Peers of Aztlan, all who from the sword
Of Britain had escaped, honouring the rites,
Came clad in rich array, and bore the arms   70
And ensigns of the dead. The slaves went last,
And dwarfs, the pastime of the living chiefs,
In life their sport and mockery, and in death
Their victims. Wailing and with funeral hymns,

The long procession moved. Mexitli's
Priest,
With all his servants, from the temple-
gate
Advanced to meet the train. Two piles
were built
Within the sacred court, of odorous
wood,
And rich with gums; on these, with all
their robes,
Their ensigns and their arms, they laid
the dead, 80
Then lit the pile. The rapid light ran
up,
Up flamed the fire, and o'er the darken'd
sky
Sweet clouds of incense curl'd.
                    The Pabas then
Perform'd their bloody office. First
they slew
The women whom the slaughter'd most
had loved,
Who most had loved the dead. Silent
they went
Toward the fatal stone, resisting not,
Nor sorrowing, nor dismay'd, but, as it
seem'd,
Stunn'd, senseless. One alone there
was, whose cheek
Was flush'd, whose eye was animate
with fire, 90
Her most in life Coanocotzin prized,
By ten years' love endear'd, his coun-
sellor,
His friend, the partner of his secret
thoughts;
Such had she been, such merited to be.
She as she bared her bosom to the knife,
Call'd on Yuhidthiton. . . Take heed,
O King!
Aloud she cried, and pointed to the
Priests,
Beware these wicked men! they to the
war
Forced my dead Lord. . . Thou knowest,
and I know,
He loved the Strangers; that his noble
mind, 100
Enlighten'd by their lore, had willingly
Put down these cursed altars! . . As she
spake,
They dragg'd her to the stone. . . Nay!
nay! she cried,

There needs not force! I go to join my
Lord!
His blood and mine be on you! . . Ere
she ceased,
The knife was in her breast. Tezozomoc,
Trembling with rage, held up toward the
Sun
Her reeking heart.
                    The dwarfs and slaves died last.
That bloody office done, they gathered
up
The ashes of the dead, and coffer'd them
Apart; the teeth with them, which un-
consumed 111
Among the ashes lay, a single lock
Shorn from the corpse, and his lip-
emerald
Now held to be the Spirit's flawless heart,
In better worlds. The Priest then held
on high
The little ark which shrined his last
remains,
And call'd upon the people; . . Aztecas,
This was your King, the bountiful, the
brave,
Coanocotzin! Men of Aztlan, hold
His memory holy! learn from him to
love 120
Your country and your Gods; for them
to live
Like him, like him to die. So from you
Heaven,
Where in the Spring of Light his Spirit
bathes,
Often shall he descend; hover above
On evening clouds, or plumed with rain
bow wings,
Sip honey from the flowers, and warble
joy.
Honour his memory! emulate his worth!
So saying, in the temple-tower he laid
The relics of the King.
                    These duties done,
The living claim their care. His birth,
his deeds, 130
The general love, the general voice, have
mark'd
Yuhidthiton for King. Bare-headed,
bare
Of foot, of limb, scarfed only round the
loins,
The Chieftain to Mexitli's temple moved
And knelt before the God. Tezozomoc

King over Aztlan there anointed him,
And over him, from hallowed cedar-
branch,
Sprinkled the holy water. Then the
Priest
In a black garment robed him, figured
white
With skulls and bones, a garb to emblem
war,   140
Slaughter, and ruin, his imperial tasks.
Next in his hand the Priest a censer
placed ;
And while he knelt, directing to the God
The steaming incense, thus address'd the
King :
Chosen by the people, by the Gods ap-
proved,
Swear to protect thy subjects, to main-
tain
The worship of thy fathers, to observe
Their laws, to make the Sun pursue his
course,
The clouds descend in rain, the rivers
hold
Their wonted channels, and the fruits
of earth   150
To ripen in their season ; Swear, O King !
And prosper, as thou holdest good thine
oath.
He raised his voice, and swore. Then
on his brow
Tezozomoc the crown of Aztlan placed ;
And in the robe of emblem'd royalty,
Preceded by the golden wands of state,
Yuhidthiton went forth, anointed King.

XX. THE DEATH OF COATEL

WHEN now the multitude beheld their
King,
In gratulations of reiterate joy
They shout his name, and bid him lead
them on
To vengeance. But to answer that
appeal
Tezozomoc advanced. . . Oh ! go not
forth,
Cried the Chief Paba, till the land be
purged
From her offence ! No God will lead ye
on,

While there is guilt in Aztlan. Let the
Priests
Who from the ruined city have escaped,
And all who in her temples have per-
form'd   10
The ennobling service of her injured
Gods,
Gather together now.
                        He spake ; the train
Assembled, priests and matrons, youths
and maids.
Servants of Heaven ! aloud the Arch-
Priest began,
The Gods had favour'd Aztlan ; bound
for death
The White King lay : our countrymen
were strong
In battle, and the conquest had been
ours, . .
I speak not from myself, but as the
Powers,
Whose voice on earth I am, impel the
truth, . .
The conquest had been ours; but treason
lurk'd   20
In Aztlan, treason and foul sacrilege ;
And therefore were her children in the
hour
Of need abandon'd ; therefore were her
youth
Cut down, her altars therefore over-
thrown.
The White King, whom ye saw upon the
Stone
Of Sacrifice, and whom ye held in bonds,
Stood in the foremost fight and slew
your Lord.
Not by a God, O Aztecas, enlarged
Broke he his bondage ! by a mortal hand,
An impious, sacrilegious, traitorous
hand,   30
Your city was betray'd, your King was
slain,
Your shrines polluted. The insulted
Power,
He who is terrible, beheld the deed,
And now he calls for vengeance.
                        Stern he spake,
And from Mexitli's altar bade the Priest
Bring forth the sacred water. In his
hand
He took the vase, and held it up, and
cried,

Accurst be he who did this deed! Accurst
The father who begat him, and the breast
At which he fed! Death be his portion now,   40
Eternal infamy his lot on earth,
His doom eternal horrors! Let his name
From sire to son, be in the people's mouth,
Through every generation! Let a curse
Of deep and pious and effectual hate
For ever follow the detested name;
And every curse inflict upon his soul
A stab of mortal anguish.
              Then he gave
The vase. . . Drink one by one! the innocent
Boldly; on them the water hath no power;   50
But let the guilty tremble! it shall flow
A draught of agony and death to him,
A stream of fiery poison.
              Coatel!
What were thy horrors when the fatal vase
Pass'd to thy trial, . . when Tezozomoc
Fix'd his keen eye on thee! A deathiness
Came over her, . . her blood ran back, . . her joints
Shook like the palsy, and the dreadful cup
Dropt from her conscious hold. The Priest exclaim'd,
The hand of God! the avenger manifest!
Drag her to the altar! . . At that sound   61
The life forsook her limbs, and down she fell,
Senseless. They dragg'd her to the Stone of Blood,
All senseless as she lay; . . in that dread hour
Nature was kind.
          Tezozomoc then cried,
Bring forth the kindred of this wretch accurst,
That none pollute the earth! An aged Priest
Came forth and answered, There is none but I,
The father of the dead.

          To death with him!
Exclaim'd Tezozomoc; to death with him;   70
And purify the nation! . . But the King
Permitted not that crime. . . Chief of the Priests,
If he be guilty, let the guilty bleed,
Said he; but never, while I live and reign,
The innocent shall suffer. Hear him speak!

Hear me! the old man replied. That fatal day
I never saw my child. At morn she left
The city, seeking flowers to dress the shrine
Of Coatlantona; and that at eve
I stood among the Pabas in the gate,   80
Blessing our soldiers, as they issued out,
Let them who saw bear witness. . . Two came forth,
And testified Aculhua spake the words
Of truth.
        Full well I know, the old man pursued,
My daughter loved the Strangers, . . that her heart
Was not with Aztlan; but not I the cause!
Ye all remember how the Maid was given, . .
She being, in truth, of all our Maids the flower, . .
In spousals to Lincoya, him who fled
From sacrifice. It was a misery   90
For me to see my only child condemn'd
In early widowhood to waste her youth,
My only and my beautifullest girl!
Chief of the Priests, you order'd; I obeyed.
Not mine the fault, if when Lincoya fled,
And fought among the enemies, her heart
Was with her husband.
            He is innocent!
He shall not die! Yuhidthiton exclaim'd.
Nay, King Yuhidthiton! Aculhua cried,
I merit death. My country overthrown,   100
My daughter slain, alike demand on me
That justice. When her years of ministry

Vow'd to the temple had expired, my love,
My selfish love, still suffer'd her to give
Her youth to me, by filial piety
In widowhood detain'd.   That selfish crime
Heavily, . . heavily, . . do I expiate !
But I am old , and she was all to me.
O King Yuhidthiton, I ask for death ;
In mercy, let me die ! cruel it were   110
To bid me waste away alone in age,
By the slow pain of grief. . . Give me the knife
Which pierced my daughter's bosom !
                    The old man
Moved to the altar ; none opposed his way ;
With a firm hand he buried in his heart
The reeking flint, and fell upon his child.

XXI. THE SPORTS

A TRANSITORY gloom that sight of death
Impress'd upon the assembled multitude ;
But soon the brute and unreflecting crew
Turn'd to their sports. Some bare their olive limbs,
And in the race contend ; with hopes and fears
Which rouse to rage, some urge the mimic war.
Here one upon his ample shoulders bears
A comrade's weight, upon whose head a third
Stands poised, like Mercury in act to fly.
Two others balance here on their shoulders   10
A bifork'd beam, while on its height a third
To nimble cadence shifts his glancing feet,
And shakes a plume aloft, and wheels around
A wreath of bells with modulating sway.
Here round a lofty mast the dancers move
Quick, to quick music ; from its top affix'd,
Each holds a coloured cord, and as they weave

The complex crossings of the mazy dance,
The chequer'd network twists around the tree
Its intertexture of harmonious hues.   20

  But now a shout went forth, the Flyers mount,
And from all meaner sports the multitude
Flock to their favourite pastime. In the ground,
Branchless and bark'd, the trunk of some tall pine
Is planted : near its summit a square frame ;
Four cords pass through the perforated square,
And fifty times and twice around the tree,
A mystic number, are entwined above.
Four Aztecas, equipp'd with wings, ascend,
And round them bind the ropes ; anon they wave   30
Their pinions, and upborn on spreading plumes
Launch on the air, and wheel in circling flight,
The lengthening cords untwisting as they fly.
A fifth above, upon the perilous point
Dances, and shakes a flag ; and on the frame,
Others the while maintain their giddy stand,
Till now, with many a round, the wheeling cords
Draw near their utmost length, and toward the ground
The aërial circles speed ; then down the ropes
They spring, and on their way from line to line   40
Pass, while the shouting multitude endure
A shuddering admiration.
                    On such sports,
Their feelings center'd in the joy of sight,
The multitude stood gazing, when a man,
Breathless, and with broad eyes, came running on,

His pale lips trembling, and his bloodless
  cheek
Like one who meets a lion in his path.
The fire ! the fire ! the temple ! he
  exclaim'd ;
Mexitli ! . . They, astonish'd at his words,
Hasten toward the wonder, . . and
  behold !   50
The inner fane is sheeted white with fire.
Dumb with affright they stood ; the
  enquiring King
Look'd to Tezozomoc, the Priest replied,
I go ! the Gods protect me ; . . and
  therewith
He entered boldly in the house of flame.
But instant bounding with inebriate joy
He issues forth. . . The God ! the God !
  he cries,
Joy ! . . joy ! . . the God ! . . the visible
  hand of Heaven !
Repressing then his transport, . . Ye all
  know
How that in Aztlan Madoc's impious
  hand   60
Destroyed Mexitli's image ; . . it is here,
Unbroken, and the same ! . . Toward the
  gate
They press ; they see the Giant Idol
  there,
The serpent girding him, his neck with
  hearts
Beaded, and in his hand the club, . . even
  such
As oft in Aztlan, on his azure throne,
They had adored the God, they see him
  now,
Unbroken and the same ! . . Again the
  Priest
Enter'd ; again a second joy inspired
To frenzy all around ; . . for forth he
  came,   70
Shouting with new delight, . . for in his
  hand
The banner of the nation he upheld,
That banner to their fathers sent from
  Heaven,
By them abandon'd to the conqueror.

He motion'd silence, and the crowd
  were still.
People of Aztlan ! he began, when first
Your fathers from their native land
  went forth,

In search of better seats, this banner
  came
From Heaven. The Famine and the
  Pestilence
Had been among them ; in their hearts
  the spring   80
Of courage was dried up : with mid-
  night fires
Radiate, by midnight thunders heralded,
This banner came from Heaven ; and
  with it came
Health, valour, victory . . Aztecas ! again
The God restores the blessing. To the
  God
Move now in solemn dance of grateful
  joy ;
Exalt for him the song.
              They form'd the dance,
They rais'd the hymn, and sung Mexitli's
  praise.
Glory to thee, the Great, the Terrible,
Mexitli, guardian God ! . . From whence
  art thou,   90
O Son of Mystery ? From whence art
  thou,
Whose sire thy Mother knew not ? She
  at eve
Walk'd in the temple court, and saw
  from Heaven
A plume descend, as bright and beauti-
  ful,
As if some spirit had embodied there
The rainbow hues, or dipt it in the light
Of setting suns. To her it floated down ;
She placed it in her bosom, to bedeck
The altar of the God ; she sought it
  there ;
Amazed she found it not, amazed she
  felt   100
Another life infused. . . From whence art
  thou,
O son of Mystery ? From whence art
  thou,
Whose sire thy Mother knew not ?
              Grief was hers,
Wonder and grief, for life was in her
  womb,
And her stern children with revengeful
  eyes
Beheld their Mother's shame. She saw
  their frowns,
She knew their plots of blood. Where
  shall she look

For succour, when her sons conspire her
    death ?
Where hope for comfort, when her
    daughter whets
The impious knife of murder ? . . From
    her womb   110
The voice of comfort came, the timely
    aid :
Already at her breast the blow was
    aim'd,
When forth Mexitli leapt, and in his hand
The angry spear, to punish and to save.
Glory to thee, the Great, the Terrible,
Mexitli, guardian God !
                    Arise and save,
Mexitli, save thy people ! Dreadful one,
Arise, redeem thy city, and revenge !
An impious, an impenetrable foe,
Hath blacken'd thine own altars, with
    the blood   120
Of thine own priests ; hath dash'd thine
    Image down.
In vain did valour's naked breast op-
    pose
Their mighty arms ; in vain the feeble
    sword
On their impenetrable mail was driven.
Not against thee, Avenger, shall those
    arms
Avail, nor that impenetrable mail
Resist the fiery arrows of thy wrath.
Arise, go forth in anger, and destroy !

XXII. THE DEATH OF
LINCOYA

AZTLAN, meantime, presents a hideous
    scene
Of slaughter. The hot sunbeam, in her
    streets,
Parch'd the blood pools ; the slain were
    heap'd in hills ;
The victors, stretch'd in every little
    shade,
With unhelm'd heads, reclining on their
    shields,
Slept the deep sleep of weariness.   Ere
    long,
To needful labour rising, from the gates
They drag the dead ; and with united
    toil,

They dig upon the plain the general
    grave,
The grave of thousands, deep and wide
    and long.   10
Ten such they delved, and o'er the multi-
    tudes
Who levell'd with the plain the deep-dug
    pits,
Ten monumental hills they heap'd on
    high.
Next horror heightening joy, they over-
    threw
The skull-built towers, the files of human
    heads,
And earth to earth consign'd them.   To
    the flames
They cast the idols, and upon the wind
Scatter'd their ashes ; then the temples
    fell,
Whose black and putrid walls were
    scaled with blood,
And not one stone of those accursed
    piles   20
Was on another left.
                    Victorious thus
In Aztlan, it behoved the Cymry now
There to collect their strength, and there
    await,
Or thence with centered numbers urge,
    the war.
For this was Ririd missioned to the ships,
For this Lincoya from the hills invites
Erillyab and her tribe.   There did not
    breathe,
On this wide world, a happier man that
    day
Than young Lincoya, when from their
    retreat
He bade his countrymen come repossess
The land of their forefathers ; proud at
    heart   31
To think how great a part himself had
    borne
In their revenge, and that beloved one,
The gentle saviour of the Prince, whom
    well
He knew his own dear love, and for the
    deed
Still dearer loved the dearest.   Round
    the youth,
Women and children, the infirm and old,
Gather to hear his tale ; and as they
    stood

With eyes of steady wonder, outstretch'd necks,
And open lips of listening eagerness, 40
Fast play'd the tide of triumph in his
veins,
Flush'd his brown cheek, and kindled
his dark eye.

And now, reposing from his toil
awhile,
Lincoya, on a crag above the straits,
Sáte underneath a tree, whose twinkling
leaves
Sung to the gale at noon. Ayayaca
Sate by him in the shade : the old man
had loved
The youth beside him from his boyhood
up,
And still would call him boy. They sate
and watch'd   49
The laden bisons winding down the way,
The multitude who now with joy forsook
Their desolated dwellings; and their talk
Was of the days of sorrow, when they
groan'd
Beneath the intolerable yoke, till, sent
By the Great Spirit o'er the pathless
deep,
Prince Madoc the Deliverer came to
save.
As thus they communed, came a woman
up,
Seeking Lincoya; 'twas Aculhua's
slave,
The nurse of Coatel. Her wretched eye,
Her pale and livid countenance foretold
Some tale of misery, and his life-blood
ebb'd   61
In ominous fear. But when he heard
her words
Of death, he seized the lance, and
raised his arm
To strike the blow of comfort.
                              The old man
Caught his uplifted hand. . . O'er-hasty
boy,
Quoth he, regain her yet, if she was
dear !
Seek thy beloved in the Land of Souls,
And beg her from the Gods. The Gods
will hear,
And in just recompense of love so true
Restore their charge.

          The miserable youth   70
Turn'd at his words a hesitating eye.
I knew a prisoner, . . so the old man
pursued,
Or hoping to beguile the youth's despair
With tales that suited the despair of
youth,
Or credulous himself of what he told, . .
I knew a prisoner once who welcomed
death
With merriment and songs and joy of
heart,
Because, he said, the friends whom he
loved best
Were gone before him to the Land of
Souls ;
Nor would they to resume their mortal
state,   80
Even when the Keeper of the Land
allow'd,
Forsake its pleasures; therefore he
rejoiced
To die and join them there. I question'd
him,
How of these hidden things unknowable
So certainly he spake. The man replied,
One of our nation lost the maid he loved,
Nor would he bear his sorrow, . . being
one
Into whose heart fear never found a
way, . .   88
But to the Country of the Dead pursued
Her spirit. Many toils he underwent,
And many dangers gallantly surpass'd,
Till to the Country of the Dead he came.
Gently the Guardian of the Land
received
The living suppliant; listen'd to his
prayer,
And gave him back the Spirit of the
Maid.
But from that happy country, from the
songs
Of joyance, from the splendour-spark-
ling dance,
Unwillingly compell'd, the Maiden's Soul
Loathed to return ; and he was warn'd
to guard
The subtle captive well and warily, 100
Till in her mortal tenement relodged,
Earthly delights might win her to re-
main
A sojourner on earth. Such lessoning

The Ruler of the Souls departed gave ;
And mindful of his charge the adven-
　　turer brought
His subtle captive home.　There under-
　　neath
The shelter of a hut, his friends had
　　watch'd
The Maiden's corpse, secured it from the
　　sun,
And fann'd away the insect swarms of
　　heaven.　　　　　　　　　　　　　109
A busy hand marr'd all the enterprize !
Curious to see the Spirit, he unloosed
The knotted bag which held her, and
　　she fled.
Lincoya, thou art brave ; where man
　　has gone
Thou wouldst not fear to follow !
　　　　　　　　　　　　　　Silently
Lincoya listen'd, and with unmoved
　　eyes ;
At length he answer'd, Is the journey
　　long ?
The old man replied, A way of many
　　moons.
I know a shorter path ! exclaim'd the
　　youth ;
And up he sprung, and from the
　　precipice
Darted :　a moment, . . and Ayayaca
　　heard　　　　　　　　　　　　　120
His body fall upon the rocks below.

XXIII. CARADOC AND SENENA

MAID of the golden locks, far other lot
May gentle Heaven assign thy happier
　　love,
Blue-eyed Senena ! . . She, though not
　　as yet
Had she put off her boy-habiliments,
Had told Goervyl all the history
Of her sad flight, and easy pardon gain'd
From that sweet heart, for guile which
　　meant no ill,
And secrecy, in shame too long main-
　　tain'd.
With her dear Lady now, at this still
　　hour
Of evening is the seeming page gone
　　forth,　　　　　　　　　　　　　10

Beside Caermadoc mere.　They loiter'd
　　on,
Along the windings of its grassy shore,
In such free interchange of inward
　　thought
As the calm hour invited ; or at times,
Willingly silent, listening to the bird
Whose one repeated melancholy note,
By oft repeating melancholy made,
Solicited the ear ; or gladlier now
Hearkening that cheerful one, who
　　knoweth all
The songs of all the winged choristers, 20
And in one sequence of melodious
　　sounds
Pours all their music.　But a wilder
　　strain
At fits came o'er the water ; rising
　　now,
Now with a dying fall, in sink and
　　swell
More exquisitely sweet than ever art
Of man evoked from instrument of
　　touch,
Or beat, or breath.　It was the evening
　　gale,
Which passing o'er the harp of Caradoc,
Swept all its chords at once, and blended
　　all
Their music into one continuous flow. 30
The solitary Bard beside his harp
Leant underneath a tree, whose spread-
　　ing boughs,
With broken shade that shifted to the
　　breeze,
Play'd on the waving waters.　Over-
　　head
There was the leafy murmur, at his
　　foot
The lake's perpetual ripple ; and from
　　far,
Borne on the modulating gale, was
　　heard
The roaring of the mountain cataract. . .
A blind man would have loved the
　　lovely spot.

Here was Senena by her Lady led, 40
Trembling, but not reluctant.　They
　　drew nigh,
Their steps unheard upon the elastic
　　moss,
Till playfully Goervyl, with quick touch,

Ran o'er the harp-strings. At the
    sudden sound
He rose. . . Hath then thy hand, quoth
    she, O Bard,
Forgot its cunning, that the wind should
    be
Thine harper ? . . Come ! one strain for
    Britain's sake ;
And let the theme be Woman ! . . He
    replied,
But if the strain offend, O Lady fair,
Blame thou the theme, not me ! . . Then
    to the harp   50
He sung, . . Three things a wise man will
    not trust,
The Wind, the Sunshine of an April
    day,
And Woman's plighted faith. I have
    beheld
The Weathercock · upon the steeple-
    point
Steady from morn till eve ; and I have
    seen
The bees go forth upon an April morn,
Secure the sunshine will not end in
    showers ;
But when was Woman true ?
            False Bard ! thereat,
With smile of playful anger, she ex-
    claim'd,
False Bard ! and slanderous song !
    Were such thy thoughts   60
Of woman, when thy youthful lays were
    heard
In Heilyn's hall ? . . But at that name
    his heart
Leapt, and his cheek with sudden flush
    was fired ;
In Heilyn's hall, quoth he, I learn'd the
    song.
There was a Maid, who dwelt among the
    hills
Of Arvon, and to one of humbler birth
Had pledged her troth ; . . nor rashly,
    nor beguiled, . .
They had been playmates in their in-
    fancy,
And she in all his thoughts had borne
    a part,
And all his joys. The Moon and all the
    Stars   70
Witness'd their mutual vows ; and for
    her sake

The song was framed ; for in the face of
    day
She broke them. . . But her name ?
    Goervyl ask'd ;
Quoth he, The poet loved her still too
    well,
To couple it with shame.
            O fate unjust
Of womankind ! she cried ; our virtues
    bloom,
Like violets, in shade and solitude,
While evil eyes hunt all our failings out,
For evil tongues to bruit abroad in
    jest,   79
And song of obloquy ! . . I knew a Maid,
And she too dwelt in Arvon, and she too
Loved one of lowly birth, who ill repaid
Her spotless faith ; for he to ill reports,
And tales of falsehood cunningly de-
    vised,
Lent a light ear, and to his rival left
The loathing Maid. The wedding-day
    arrived,
The harpers and the gleemen, far and
    near,
Came to the wedding-feast ; the wed-
    ding-guests
Were come, the altar drest, the bride-
    maids met ;
The father, and the bridegroom, and the
    priest   90
Wait for the bride. But she the while
    did off
Her bridal robes, and clipt her golden
    locks,
And put on boy's attire, through wood
    and wild
To seek her own true love ; and over
    sea,
Forsaking all for him, she followed
    him, . .
Nor hoping nor deserving fate so fair ;
And at his side she stood, and heard him
    wrong
Her faith with slanderous tales ; and
    his dull eye,
As it had learnt his heart's forgetfulness,
Knows not the trembling one, who even
    now   100
Yearns to forgive him all !
            He turn'd, he knew
The blue-eyed Maid, who fell upon his
    breast.

XXIV. THE EMBASSY

HARK! from the towers of Aztlan how
    the shouts
Of clamorous joy re-ring ! the rocks and
    hills
Take up the joyful sound, and o'er the
    lake
Roll their slow echoes. . . Thou art
    beautiful !
Queen of the Valley ! thou art beautiful,
Thy walls, like silver, sparkle to the
    sun ;
Melodious wave thy groves, thy garden-
    sweets
Enrich the pleasant air, upon the lake
Lie the long shadows of thy towers, and
    high
In heaven thy temple-pyramids arise, 10
Upon whose summit now, far visible
Against the clear blue sky, the Cross of
    Christ
Proclaims unto the nations round the
    news
Of thy redemption.   Thou art beautiful,
Aztlan ! O City of the Cymbric Prince !
Long mayest thou flourish in thy beauty,
    long
Prosper beneath the righteous con-
    queror,
Who conquers to redeem ! Long years
    of peace
And happiness await thy Lord and thee,
Queen of the Valley !
                    Hither joyfully 20
The Hoamen came to repossess the land
Of their forefathers.   Joyfully the youth
Came shouting, with acclaim of grateful
    praise,
Their great Deliverer's name ; the old,
    in talk
Of other days, which mingled with their
    joy
Memory of many a hard calamity,
And thoughts of time and change, and
    human life
How changeful and how brief.   Prince
    Madoc met
Erillyab at the gate. . . Sister and Queen,
Said he, here let us hold united reign, 30
O'er our united people ; by one faith,

One interest bound, and closer to be
    link'd
By laws and language and domestic ties,
Till both become one race, for ever more
Indissolubly knit.
                    O friend, she cried,
The last of all my family am I ;
Yet sure, though last, the happiest, and
    by Heaven
Favour'd abundantly above them all.
Dear Friend, and brother dear ! enough
    for me
Beneath the shadow of thy shield to
    dwell,   40
And see my people, by thy fostering
    care,
Made worthy of their fortune. Graciously
Hath the Beloved One appointed all,
Educing good from ill, himself being
    good.
Then to the royal palace of the Kings
Of Aztlan, Madoc led Erillyab,
There where her sires had held their
    ruder reign,
To pass the happy remnant of her years,
Honour'd and loved by all.
                    Now had the Prince
Provided for defence, disposing all   50
As though a ready enemy approach'd.
But from Patamba yet no army moved ;
Four Heralds only, by the King dis-
    patch'd,
Drew nigh the town.   The Hoamen as
    they came,
Knew the green mantle of their privilege,
The symbols which they bore, an arrow-
    point
Depress'd, a shield, a net, which, from
    the arm
Suspended, held their food.   They
    through the gate
Pass with permitted entrance, and
    demand
To see the Ocean Prince.   The Con-
    queror   60
Received them, and the elder thus
    began :
Thus to the White King, King Yuhid-
    thiton
His bidding sends ; such greeting as
    from foe
Foe may receive, where individual hate
Is none, but honour and assured esteem,

And what were friendship did the Gods
    permit,
The King of Aztlan sends.   Oh dream
    not thou
That Aztlan is subdued ;   nor in the
    pride
Of conquest tempt thy fortune !   Unpre-
    pared
For battle, at an hour of festival,   70
Her children were surprised ;   and thou
    canst tell
How perilously they maintain'd the long
And doubtful strife.   From yonder
    temple-mount
Look round the plain, and count her
    towns, and mark
Her countless villages, whose habitants
All are in arms against thee !   Thinkest
    thou
To root them from the land ?   Or wouldst
    thou live,
Harass'd by night and day with endless
    war,
War at thy gates ;   and to thy children
    leave
That curse for their inheritance ? . . The
    land   80
Is all before thee :   Go in peace, and
    choose
Thy dwelling-place, North, South, or
    East, or West ;
Or mount again thy houses of the sea
And search the waters.   Whatsoe'er thy
    wants
Demand, will Aztlan willingly supply,
Prepared with friendly succour, to assist
Thy soon departure.   Thus Yuhid-
    thiton,
Remembering his old friendship, coun-
    sels thee ;   88
Thus, as the King of Aztlan, for himself
And people, he commands.   If obstinate,
If blind to your own welfare, ye persist,
Woe to ye, wretches !   to the armed
    man,
Who in the fight must perish ;   to the
    wife,
Who vainly on her husband's aid will
    call ;
Woe to the babe that hangs upon the
    breast,
For Aztlan comes in anger, and her Gods
Spare none.

    The Conqueror calmly answer'd
    him, . .
By force we won your city, Azteca ;
By force we will maintain it : . . to the
    King
Repeat my saying. . . To this goodly
    land   100
Your fathers came for an abiding place,
Strangers like us, but not like us, in
    peace.
They conquer'd and destroyed.   A
    tyrant race,
Bloody and faithless, to the hills they
    drove
The unoffending children of the vale,
And, day by day, in cruel sacrifice
Consumed them.   God hath sent the
    Avengers here !
Powerful to save we come, and to
    destroy,
When Mercy on Destruction calls for aid.
Go tell your nation that we know their
    force,   110
That they know ours !   that their
    Patamba soon
Shall fall like Aztlan ;   and what other
    towns
They seek in flight, shall like Patamba
    fall :
Till broken in their strength and spirit-
    crush'd
They bow the knee, or leave the land
    to us,
Its worthier Lords.

             If this be thy reply,
Son of the Ocean !   said the messenger,
I bid thee, in the King of Aztlan's
    name
Mortal defiance.   In the field of blood,
Before our multitudes shall trample
    down   120
Thy mad and miserable countrymen,
Yuhidthiton invites thee to the strife
Of equal danger.   So may he avenge
Coanocotzin, or like him in death
Discharge his duty.

             Tell Yuhidthiton,
Madoc replied, that in the field of
    blood
I never shunn'd a foe.   But say thou to
    him,
I will not seek him there, against his
    life

To raise the hand which hath been
    joined with his
In peace. . . With that the Heralds went
    their way ;   130
Nor to the right nor to the left they turn,
But to Patamba straight they journey
    back.

XXV. THE LAKE FIGHT

THE mariners, meantime, at Ririd's will,
Unreeve the rigging, and the masts they
    strike ;
And now ashore they haul the lighten'd
    hulks,
Tear up the deck, the severed planks
    bear off,
Disjoin the well-scarfed timbers, and
    the keel
Loosen asunder : then to the lake-side
Bear the materials, where the Ocean
    Lord
Himself directs their work.   Twelve
    vessels there,
Fitted alike to catch the wind, or sweep
With oars the moveless surface, they
    prepare ;   10
Lay down the keel, the stern-post rear,
    and fix
The   strong-curved   timbers.   Others
    from the wood
Bring the tall pines, and from their his-
    sing trunks
Force, by the aid of fire, the needful
    gum ;
Beneath the close-caulk'd planks its
    odorous stream
They pour ; then, last, the round-pro-
    jecting prows
With iron arm, and launch, in uproar
    loud
Of joy, anticipating victory,
The galleys long and sharp.   The masts
    are rear'd,
The sails are bent, and lo ! the ready
    barks   20
Lie on the lake.
            It chanced, the Hoamen found
A spy of Aztlan, and before the Prince
They led him.   But when Madoc bade
    him tell,

As his life-ransom, what his nation's
    force,
And what their plans ;   the savage
    answer'd him,
With dark and sullen eye and smile of
    wrath,
If aught the knowledge of my country's
    force
Could profit thee, be sure, ere I would let
My tongue play traitor, thou shouldst
    limb from limb
Hew me, and make each separate
    member feel   30
A separate agony of death.   O Prince !
But I will tell ye of my nation's force,
That ye may know and tremble at your
    doom ;
That fear may half subdue ye to the
    sword
Of vengeance. . . Can ye count the stars
    of Heaven ?
The waves which ruffle o'er the lake ?
    the leaves
Swept from the autumnal forest ?   Can
    ye look
Upon the eternal snows of yonder height
And number each particular flake that
    form'd
The mountain-mass ? . . so numberless
    they come,   40
Whoe'er can wield the sword, or hurl the
    lance,
Or aim the arrow ; from the growing boy,
Ambitious of the battle, to the old man,
Who to revenge his country and his
    Gods
Hastens, and then to die.   By land they
    come ;
And years must pass away ere on their
    path
The grass again will grow : they come
    by lake ;
And ye shall see the shoals of their canoes
Darken the waters.   Strangers ! when
    our Gods
Have conquer'd, when ye lie upon the
    Stone   50
Of Sacrifice extended one by one,
Half of our armies cannot taste your
    flesh,
Though given in equal shares, and every
    share
Minced like a nestling's food !

Madoc replied,
Azteca, we are few; but through the
woods
The Lion walks alone.   The lesser fowls
Flock multitudinous in heaven, and fly
Before the eagle's coming.   We are few;
And yet thy nation hath experienced us
Enough for conquest.   Tell thy country-
men,   60
We can maintain the city which we
won.

So saying he turn'd away, rejoiced at
heart
To know himself alike by lake or land
Prepared to meet their power.
The fateful day
Draws on; by night the Aztecas em-
bark.
At day-break from Patamba they set
forth,
From every creek and inlet of the lake,
All moving towards Aztlan; safely thus
Weening to reach the plain before her
walls,
And fresh for battle.   Shine thou forth,
O Sun!   70
Shine fairly forth upon a scene so fair!
Their thousand boats, and the ten
thousand oars
From whose broad bowls the waters fall
and flash,
And twice ten thousand feather'd helms,
and shields,
Glittering with gold and scarlet plumery.
Onward they come with song and swel-
ling horn;
While, louder than all voice and instru-
ment,
The dash of their ten thousand oars,
from shore
To shore and hill to hill, re-echoing rolls,
In undistinguishable peals of sound   80
And endless echo.   On the other side
Advance the British barks; the fresh-
ening breeze
Fills the broad sail, around the rushing
keel
The waters sing, while proudly they sail
on
Lords of the water.   Shine thou forth,
O Sun!
Shine forth upon their hour of victory!

Onward the Cymry speed.   The Az-
tecas,
Though wondering at that unexpected
sight,
Bravely made on to meet them, seized
their bows,
And shower'd, like rain, upon the
pavaised barks,   90
The rattling shafts.   Strong blows the
auspicious gale;
Madoc, the Lord of Ocean, leads the
way;
He holds the helm; the galley where
he guides
Flies on, and full upon the first canoe
Drives shattering; midway its long
length it struck,
And o'er the wreck with unimpeded
force
Dashes among the fleet.   The astonish'd
men
Gaze in inactive terror.   They behold
Their splinter'd vessels floating all
around,
Their warriors struggling in the lake,
with arms   100
Experienced in the battle vainly now.
Dismay'd they drop their bows, and
cast away
Their unavailing spears, and take to
flight,
Before the Masters of the Elements,
Who rode the waters, and who made the
winds
Wing them to vengeance!   Forward
now they bend,
And backward then, with strenuous
strain of arm,
Press the broad paddle. . . Hope of
victory
Was none, nor of defence, nor of revenge,
To sweeten death.   Toward the shore
they speed,   110
Toward the shore they lift their longing
eyes : . .
O fools, to meet on their own element
The Sons of Ocean! . . Could they but
aland
Set foot, the strife were equal, or to die
Less dreadful.   But, as if with wings of
wind,
On fly the British barks! . . the favour-
ing breeze

Blows strong ; . . far, far behind their
　　roaring keels
Lies the long line of foam ; the helm
　　directs
Their force : they move as with the
　　limbs of life,
Obedient to the will that governs them.
Where'er they, pass, the crashing shook
　　is heard,　　　　　　　　　　　121
The dash of broken waters, and the cry
Of sinking multitudes. Here one plies
　　fast
The practised limbs of youth, but o'er
　　his head
The galley drives ; one follows a canoe
With skill availing only to prolong
Suffering ; another, as with wiser aim
He swims across, to meet his coming
　　friends,
Stunn'd by the hasty and unheeding oar,
Sinks senseless to the depths. Lo !
　　yonder boat　　　　　　　　　130
Graspt by the thronging strugglers ; its
　　light length
Yields to the overbearing weight, and all
Share the same ruin. Here another
　　shows
Crueller contest, where the crew hack off
The hands that hang for life upon its
　　side,
Lest all together perish ; then in vain
The voice of friend or kinsman prays for
　　mercy,
Imperious self controuls all other
　　thoughts ;
And still they deal around unnatural
　　wounds,
When the strong bark of Britain over all
Sails in the path of death. . . God of the
　　Lake,　　　　　　　　　　　141
Tlaloc ! and thou, O Aiauh, green-robed
　　Queen !
How many a wretch, in dying agonies,
Invoked ye in the misery of that day !
Long after, on the tainted lake, the dead
Welter'd ; there, perch'd upon his
　　floating prey,
The vulture fed in daylight ; and the
　　wolves,
Assembled at their banquet round its
　　banks,
Disturb'd the midnight with their howl
　　of joy.

XXVI. THE CLOSE OF THE CENTURY

There was mourning in Patamba ; the
　　north wind
Blew o'er the lake, and drifted to the
　　shore
The floating wreck and bodies of the
　　dead.
Then on the shore the mother might be
　　seen,
Seeking her child ; the father to the
　　tomb,
With limbs too weak for that unhappy
　　weight,
Bearing the bloated body of his son ;
The wife, who, in expectant agony,
Watch'd the black carcass on the coming
　　wave.

On every brow terror was legible,　10
Anguish in every eye. There was not
　　one
Who in the general ruin did not share
Peculiar grief, and in his country's loss
Lament some dear one dead. Along the
　　lake
The frequent funeral-piles, for many a
　　day,
With the noon-light their melancholy
　　flames
Dimly commingled ; while the mourners
　　stood,
Watching the pile, to feed the lingering
　　fire,
As slowly it consumed the watery corpse.

Thou didst not fear, young Tlalala !
　　thy soul,　　　　　　　　　　　20
Unconquer'd and unconquerable, rose
Superior to its fortune. When the
　　Chiefs
Hung their dejected heads, as men sub-
　　dued
In spirit, then didst thou, Yuhidthiton,
Calm in the hour of evil, still maintain
Thy even courage. They from man to
　　man
Go, with the mourners mourning, and
　　by grief
Exciting rage, till, at the promised fight,

The hope of vengeance, a ferocious joy
Flash'd in the eyes which glisten'd still
    with tears   30
Of tender memory. To the brave they
    spake
Of Aztlan's strength, . . for Aztlan still
    was strong : . .
The late defeat, . . not there by manly
    might,
By honourable valour, by the force
Of arms subdued, shame aggravated
    loss ;
The White Men from the waters came,
    perchance
Sons of the Ocean, by their parent Gods
Aided, and conquerors not by human
    skill.
When man met man, when in the field
    of fight
The soldier on firm earth should plant
    his foot,   40
Then would the trial be, the struggle
    then,
The glory, the revenge.
                            Tezozomoc,
Alike unbroken by defeat, endured
The evil day ; but in his sullen mind
Work'd thoughts of other vengeance.
    He the King
Summon'd apart from all, with Tlalala,
And thus advised them : We have vainly
    tried
The war ; these mighty Strangers will
    not yield
To mortal strength ; yet shall they be
    cut off
So ye will heed my counsel, and to force
Add wisdom's aid. Put on a friendly
    front ;   51
Send to their Prince the messenger of
    peace ;
He will believe our words : he will for-
    give
The past ; . . the offender may. So days
    and months,
Yea, years, if needful, will we wear a face
Of friendliness, till some fit hour arrive,
When we may fire their dwellings in the
    night,
Or mingle poison in their cups of mirth.
The warrior, from whose force the Lion
    flies,
Falls by the Serpent's tooth.

                    Thou speakest well,   60
Tlalala answer'd ; but my spirit ill
Can brook revenge delay'd.
                    The Priest then turn'd
His small and glittering eye toward the
    King ;
But on the Monarch's mild and manly
    brow
A meaning sate, which made that
    crafty eye
Bend, quickly abash'd. While yet I
    was a child,
Replied the King of Aztlan, on my heart
My father laid two precepts. Boy, be
    brave !
So, in the midnight battle, shalt thou
    meet,
Fearless, the sudden foe. Boy, let thy
    lips   70
Be clean from falsehood ! in the mid-
    day sun,
So never shalt thou need from mortal
    man
To turn thy guilty face. Tezozomoc,
Holy I keep the lessons of my sire.

But if the enemy, with their dreadful
    arms,
Again, said Tlalala, . . If again the Gods
Will our defeat, Yuhidthiton replied,
Vain is it for the feeble power of man
To strive against their will. I augur
    not
Of ill, young Tiger ! but if ill betide, 80
The land is all before us. Let me hear
Of perfidy and serpent-wiles no more !
In the noon-day war, and in the face of
    Heaven,
I meet my foes. Let Aztlan follow me ;
And if one man of all her multitudes
Shall better play the warrior in that
    hour,
Be his the sceptre ! But if the people
    fear
The perilous strife, and own themselves
    subdued,
Let us depart ! The universal Sun
Confines not to one land his partial
    beams ;   90
Nor is man rooted, like a tree, whose seed
The winds on some ungenial soil have
    cast,
There where he cannot prosper.

The dark Priest
Conceal'd revengeful anger, and replied,
Let the King's will be done ! An aweful
    day
Draws on ; the Circle of the Years is
    full ;
We tremble for the event. The times
    are strange ;
There are portentous changes in the
    world ;
Perchance its end is come.
                    Be it thy care,
Priest of the Gods, to see the needful
    rites   100
Duly perform'd, Yuhidthiton replied.
On the third day, if yonder Lord of Light
Begin the Circle of the Years anew,
Again we march to war.
                    One day is past ;
Another day comes on. At earliest dawn
Then was there heard through all
    Patamba's streets
The warning voice . . Woe ! woe ! the
    Sun hath reach'd
The limits of his course ; he hath ful-
    fill'd
The appointed cycle ! . . Fast, and weep,
    and pray, . .
Four Suns have perish'd, . . fast, and
    weep, and pray,   110
Lest the fifth perish also. On the first
The floods arose ; the waters of the
    heavens,
Bursting their everlasting boundaries,
Whelm'd in one deluge earth and sea
    and sky,
And quench'd its orb of fire. The
    second Sun
Then had its birth, and ran its round of
    years ;
Till having reach'd its date, it fell from
    heaven,
And crush'd the race of men. Another
    life
The Gods assign'd to Nature ; the third
    Sun
Form'd the celestial circle ; then its
    flames   120
Burst forth, and overspread earth, sea,
    and sky,
Deluging the wide universe with fire,
Till all things were consumed, and its
    own flames

Fed on itself, and spent themselves, and
    all
Was vacancy and darkness. Yet again
The World had being, and another Sun
Roll'd round the path of Heaven. That
    perish'd too :
The mighty Whirlwinds rose, and far
    away
Scatter'd its dying flames. The fifth
    was born ;
The fifth to-day completes its destined
    course,   130
Perchance to rise no more. O Aztlan,
    fast
And pray ! the Cycle of the Years is
    full !

    Thus through Patamba did the
        ominous voice
Exhort the people. Fervent vows all
    day
Were made, with loud lament ; in every
    fane,
In every dwelling-place of man, were
    prayers,
The supplications of the affrighted heart,
Earnestly offered up with tears and
    groans.
So pass'd the forenoon ; and when now
    the Sun
Sloped from his southern height the
    downward way   140
Of Heaven, again the ominous warner
    cried,
Woe ! woe ! the Cycle of the Years is
    full !
Quench every fire ! Extinguish every
    light !
And every fire was quench'd, and every
    light
Extinguish'd at the voice.
                    Meantime the Priests
Began the rites. They gash'd them-
    selves, and plunged
Into the sacred pond of Ezapan,
Till the clear water, on whose bed of
    sand
The sunbeams sparkled late, opaque
    with blood,
On its black surface mirror'd all things
    round.   150
The children of the temple, in long
    search,

Had gather'd for the service of this
   day
All venomous things that fly, or wind
   their path
With sinuous trail, or crawl on reptile
   feet.
These in one cauldron, o'er the sacred
   fire
They scorch, till of the loathsome living
   tribes,
Who, writhing in their burning agonies,
Fix on each other ill-directed wounds,
Ashes alone are left. In infants' blood
They mix the infernal unction, and the
   Priests   160
Anoint themselves therewith.
                 Lo ! from the South
The Orb of Glory his regardless way
Holds on. Again Patamba's streets
   receive
The ominous voice, . . Woe ! woe ! the
   Sun pursues
His journey to the limits of his course !
Let every man in darkness veil his
   wife ;
Veil every maiden's face ; let every
   child
Be hid in darkness, there to weep and
   pray,
That they may see again the birth of
   light !
They heard, and every husband veil'd
   his wife   170
In darkness ; every maiden's face was
   veil'd ;
The children were in darkness led to
   pray,
That they might see the birth of light
   once more.

   Westward the Sun proceeds ; the
   tall tree casts
A longer shade ; the night-eyed insect
   tribes
Wake to their portion of the circling
   hours ;
The water-fowl, retiring to the shore,
Sweep in long files the surface of the
   lake.
Then from Patamba to the sacred
   mount
The Priests go forth ; but not with
   songs of joy,   180

Nor cheerful instruments they go, nor
   train
Of festive followers ; silent and alone,
Leading one victim to his dreadful
   death,
They to the mountain-summit wend
   their way.

   On the south shore, and level with the
   lake,
Patamba stood ; westward were seen
   the walls
Of Aztlan rising on a gentle slope ;
Southward the plain extended far and
   wide ;
To the east the mountain-boundary
   began,
And there the sacred mountain rear'd its
   head ;   190
Above the neighbouring heights, its
   lofty peak
Was visible far off. In the vale below,
Along the level borders of the lake,
The assembled Aztecas, with wistful
   eye,
Gaze on the sacred summit, hoping
   there
Soon to behold the fire of sacrifice
Arise, sure omen of continued light.
The Pabas to the sacred peak begin
Their way, and as they go, with ancient
   songs
Hymn the departed Sun.
              O Light of Life 200
Yet once again arise ! yet once again
Commence thy course of glory ! Time
   hath seen
Four generations of mankind destroy'd,
When the four Suns expired ; oh, let not
   thou,
Human thyself of yore, the human race
Languish and die in darkness !
                The fourth Sun
Had perish'd ; for the mighty Whirl-
   winds rose,
And swept it, with the dust of the shat-
   ter'd world,
Into the great abyss. The eternal Gods
Built a new World, and to a Hero race
Assign'd it for their goodly dwelling-
   place ;   211
And shedding on the bones of the
   destroy'd

A quickening dew, from them, as from
    a seed,
Made a new race of human-kind spring
    up,
The menials of the Heroes born of
    Heaven.
But in the firmament no orb of day
Perform'd its course; Nature was
    blind; the fount
Of light had ceased to flow; the eye of
    Heaven
Was quench'd in darkness. In the sad
    obscure,
The earth-possessors to their parent
    Gods   220
Pray'd for another Sun, their bidding
    heard,
And in obedience raised a flaming pile.
Hopeful they circled it, when from above
The voice of the Invisible proclaim'd,
That he who bravely plunged amid the
    fire
Should live again in heaven, and there
    shine forth
The Sun of the young World. The
    Hero race
Grew pale, and from the fiery trial
    shrunk.
Thou, Nahuaztin, thou, O mortal born,
Heardest! thy heart was strong, the
    flames received   230
Their victim, and the humbled Heroes
    saw
The orient sky, with smiles of rosy joy,
Welcome the coming of the new-born
    God.
O human once, now let not human-kind
Languish, and die in darkness!
                        In the East
Then didst thou pause to see the Hero
    race
Perish. In vain, with impious arms,
    they strove
Against thy will; in vain against thine
    orb
They shot their shafts; the arrows of
    their pride
Fell on themselves; they perish'd, to
    thy praise.   240
So perish still thine impious enemies,
O Lord of Day! But to the race
    devout,
Who offer up their morning sacrifice,

Honouring thy godhead, and with
    morning hymns,
And with the joy of music and of dance,
Welcome thy glad uprise, . . to them,
    O Sun,
Still let the fountain-streams of splendour
    flow,
Still smile on them propitious, thou
    whose smile
Is light and life and joyance! Once
    again,   249
Parent of Being, Prince of Glory, rise,
Begin thy course of beauty once again!

Such was their ancient song, as up the
    height
Slowly they wound their way. The
    multitude
Beneath repeat the strain; with fearful
    eyes
They watch the spreading glories of the
    west!
And when at length the hastening orb
    hath sunk
Below the plain, such sinking at the
    heart
They feel, as he who hopeless of return
From his dear home departs. Still on
    the light,
The last green light that lingers in the
    west,   260
Their looks are fasten'd, till the clouds
    of night
Roll on, and close in darkness the whole
    heaven.
Then ceased their songs; then o'er the
    crowded vale
No voice of man was heard. Silent and
    still
They stood, all turn'd toward the east,
    in hope
There on the holy mountain to behold
The sacred fire, and know that once
    again
The Sun begins his stated round of
    years.

The Moon arose; she shone upon the
    lake,
Which lay one smooth expanse of silver
    light!   270
She shone upon the hills and rocks, and
    cast

Upon their hollows and their hidden glens
A blacker depth of shade. Who then look'd round,
Beholding all that mighty multitude,
Felt yet severer awe, .. so solemnly still
The thronging thousands stood. The breeze was heard
That rustled in the reeds; the little wave,
That rippled to the shore and left no foam,
Sent its low murmurs far.

Meantime the Priests
Have stretch'd their victim on the mountain-top; 280
A miserable man, his breast is bare,
Bare for the death that waits him; but no hand
May there inflict the blow of mercy. Piled
On his bare breast, the cedar boughs are laid;
On his bare breast, dry sedge and odorous gums
Laid ready to receive the sacred spark,
And blaze, to herald the ascending Sun,
Upon his living altar. Round the wretch
The inhuman ministers of rites accurst
Stand, and expect the signal when to strike 290
The seed of fire. Their Chief, Tezozomoc,
Apart from all, upon the pinnacle
Of that high mountain, eastward turns his eyes;
For now the hour draws nigh, and speedily
He looks to see the first faint dawn of day
Break through the orient sky.

Impatiently
The multitude await the happy sign.
Long hath the midnight pass'd, and every hour,
Yea, every moment, to their torturing fears
Seem'd lengthen'd out, insufferably long 300
Silent they stood, and breathless in suspense.

The breeze had fallen: no stirring breath of wind
Rustled the reeds. Oppressive, motionless,
It was a labour and a pain to breathe
The close, hot, heavy air... Hark! from the woods
The howl of their wild tenants! and the birds, ..
The day-birds, in blind darkness fluttering,
Fearful to rest, uttering portentous cries!
Anon, the sound of distant thunders came:
They peal beneath their feet. Earth shakes and yawns, .. 310
And lo! upon the sacred mountain's top,
The light . . the mighty flame! A cataract
Of fire bursts upward from the mountain head, ..
High, .. high, .. it shoots! the liquid fire boils out;
It streams in torrents down! Tezozomoc
Beholds the judgement: wretched, .. wretched man,
On the upmost pinnacle he stands, and sees
The lava floods beneath him: and his hour
Is come. The fiery shower, descending, heaps
Red ashes round; they fall like drifted snows, 320
And bury and consume the accursed Priest.

The Tempest is abroad. Fierce from the North
A wind uptears the lake, whose lowest depths
Rock, while convulsions shake the solid earth.
Where is Patamba? where the multitudes
Who throng'd her level shores? The mighty Lake
Hath burst its bounds, and yon wide valley roars,
A troubled sea, before the rolling storm.

XXVII. THE MIGRATION OF THE AZTECAS

THE storm hath ceased; but still the
lava-tides
Roll down the mountain-side in streams
of fire;
Down to the lake they roll, and yet roll
on,
All burning, through the waters. Heaven
above
Glows round the burning mount, and
fiery clouds
Scour through the black and starless
firmament.
Far off, the Eagle, in her mountain-nest,
Lies watching in alarm, with steady eye,
The midnight radiance.
                But the storm hath ceased;
The earth is still; . . and lo! while yet
the dawn   10
Is struggling through the eastern cloud,
the barks
Of Madoc on the lake!
                What man is he
On yonder crag, all dripping from the
flood
Who hath escaped its force? He lies
along,
Now near exhaust with self-preserving
toil,
And still his eye dwells on the spreading
waves,
Where late the multitudes of Aztlan
stood,
Collected in their strength. It is the
King
Of Aztlan, who, extended on the rock,
Looks vainly for his people. He be-
holds   20
The barks of Madoc plying to preserve
The strugglers; . . but how few! upon
the crags
Which verge the northern shore, upon
the heights
Eastward, how few have refuged! Then
the King
Almost repented him of life preserved,
And wished the waves had whelmed
him, or the sword
Fallen on him, ere this ill, this wretched-
ness,

This desolation. Spirit-troubled thus,
He call'd to mind how, from the first, his
heart   29
Inclined to peace, and how reluctantly,
Obedient to the Pabas and their Gods,
Had he to this unhappy war been
driven.
All now was ended: it remain'd to yield,
To obey the inevitable will of Heaven,
From Aztlan to depart. As thus he
mused,
A Bird, upon a bough which overhung
The rock, as though in echo to his
thought,
Cried out, . . Depart! depart! for so
the note,
Articulately in his native tongue,
Spake to the Azteca. The King look'd
up;   40
The hour, the horrors round him, had
impress'd
Feelings and fears well fitted to receive
All superstition; and the voice which
cried,
Depart! depart! seem'd like the voice
of fate,
He thought, perhaps Coanocotzin's soul,
Descending from his blissful halls in the
hour
Of evil thus to comfort and advise,
Hover'd above him.
                Lo! toward the rock,
Oaring with feeble arms his difficult way,
A warrior struggles; he hath reach'd
the rock,   50
Hath graspt it, but his strength, ex-
hausted, fails
To lift him from the depth. The King
descends
Timely in aid; he holds the feeble one
By his long locks, and on the safety-place
Lands him. He, panting, from his
clotted hair
Shook the thick waters, from his fore-
head wiped
The blinding drops; on his preserver's
face
Then look'd, and knew the King. Then
Tlalala
Fell on his neck, and groan'd. They laid
them down
In silence, for their hearts were full of
woe.   60

The sun came forth, it shone upon the rock ;
They felt the kindly beams ; their strengthen'd blood
Flow'd with a freer action. They arose,
And look'd around, if aught of hope might meet
Their prospect.   On the lake the galleys plied
Their toil successfully, ever to the shore
Bearing their rescued charge : the eastern heights,
Rightward and leftward of the fiery mount,
Were throng'd with fugitives, whose growing crowds
Speckled the ascent.   Then Tlalala took hope,   70
And his young heart, reviving, re-assumed
Its wonted vigour.   Let us to the heights,
He cried ; .. all is not lost, Yuhidthiton !
When they behold thy countenance, the sight
Will cheer them in their woe, and they will bless
The Gods of Aztlan.
                    To the heights they went ;
And when the remnant of the people saw
Yuhidthiton preserved, such comfort then
They felt, as utter wretchedness can feel,
That only gives grief utterance, only speaks   80
In groans and recollections of the past.
He look'd around ; a multitude was there, . .
But where the strength of Aztlan ? where her hosts ?
Her marshall'd myriads where, whom yester Sun
Had seen in arms array'd, in spirit high,
Mighty in youth and courage ? .. What were these,
This remnant of the people ? Women most,
Who from Patamba when the shock began
Ran with their infants ; widow'd now, yet each

Among the few who from the lake escaped,   90
Wandering with eager eyes and wretched hope.
The King beheld and groan'd , against a tree
He leant, and bow'd his head, subdued of soul.

Meantime, amid the crowd, doth Tlalala
Seek for his wife and boy. In vain he seeks
Ilanquel there ; in vain for her he asks ;
A troubled look, a melancholy eye,
A silent motion of the hopeless head,
These answer him.   But Tlalala represt
His anguish, and he call'd upon the King ; ..   100
Yuhidthiton ! thou seest thy people left ;
Their fate must be determined ; they are here
Houseless and wanting food.
                          The King look'd up, ..
It is determined, Tlalala ! the Gods
Have crush'd us.   Who can stand against their wrath ?

Have we not life and strength ? the Tiger cried.
Disperse these women to the towns which stand
Beyond the ruinous waters ; against them
The White Men will not war.   Ourselves are few,
Too few to root the invaders from our land,   110
Or meet them with the hope of equal fight ;
Yet may we shelter in the woods, and share
The Lion's liberty ; and man by man
Destroy them, till they shall not dare to walk
Beyond their city walls, to sow their fields,
Or bring the harvest in.   We may steal forth
In the dark midnight, go and burn and kill,

Till all their dreams shall be of fire and
  death,
Their sleep be fear and misery.
                    Then the King
Stretch'd forth his hand, and pointed
  to the lake   120
Where Madoc's galleys still to those who
  clung
To the tree-tops for life, or faintly still
Were floating on the waters, gave their
  aid. . .
O think not, Tlalala, that ever more
Will I against those noble enemies
Raise my right hand in war, lest
  righteous Heaven
Should blast the impious hand and
  thankless heart !
The Gods are leagued with them; the
  Elements
Banded against us ! For our over-
  throw
Were yonder mountain-springs of fire
  ordain'd ;   130
For our destruction the earth-thunders
  loosed,
And the everlasting boundaries of the
  lake
Gave way, that these destroying floods
  might roll
Over the brave of Aztlan ! . . We must
  leave
The country which our fathers won in
  arms :
We must depart.
                    The word yet vibrated
Fresh on their hearing, when the Bird
  above,
Flapping his heavy wings, repeats the
  sound,
Depart ! depart ! . . Ye hear ! the King
  exclaim'd ;
It is an omen sent to me from Heaven ;
I heard it late in solitude, the voice 141
Of fate. . . It is Coanocotzin's soul,
Who counsels our departure. . . And the
  Bird
Still flew around, and in his wheeling
  flight
Pronounced the articulate note. The
  people heard
In faith, and Tlalala made no reply ;
But dark his brow, and gloomy was his
  frown.

Then spake the King, and called a
  messenger,
And bade him speed to Aztlan. . . Seek
  the Lord
Of Ocean ; tell him that Yuhidthiton
Yields to the will of Heaven, and leaves
  the land   151
His fathers won in war. Only one boon,
In memory of our former friendship,
  ask,
The Ashes of my Fathers, . . if indeed
The conqueror have not cast them to
  the winds.

The herald went his way circuitous,
Along the mountains, . . for the flooded
  vale
Barr'd the near passage : but before his
  his feet
Could traverse half their track, the
  fugitives   159
Beheld canoes from Aztlan, to the foot
Of that protecting eminence, whereon
They had their stand, draw nigh. The
  doubtful sight
Disturb'd them, lest perchance with
  hostile strength
They came upon their weakness. Wrong-
  ful fear, . .
For now Cadwallon, from his bark un-
  arm'd,
Set foot ashore, and for Yuhidthiton
Enquired, if yet he lived ? The King
  receives
His former friend. . . From Madoc come
  I here,
The Briton said : Raiment and food he
  sends,
And peace ; so shall this visitation
  prove   170
A blessing, if it knit the bonds of peace,
And make us as one people.
                              Tlalala !
Hearest thou him ? Yuhidthiton ex-
  claim'd.
Do thou thy pleasure, King ! the Tiger
  cried :
My path is plain. . . Thereat Yuhidthiton,
Answering, replied, Thus humbled as
  thou seest,
Beneath the visitation of the Gods,
We bow before their will ! To them we
  yield ;

To you, their favourites, we resign the
land
Our fathers conquer'd. Never more
may Fate   180
In your days or your children's to the
end
Of time afflict it thus !
                    He said, and call'd
The Heralds of his pleasure. . . Go ye
forth
Throughout the land : North, South,
and East, and West,
Proclaim the ruin. Say to all who bear
The name of Azteca, Heaven hath
destroy'd
Our nation : Say, the voice of Heaven
was heard, . .
Heard ye it not ? . . bidding us leave the
land,
Who shakes us from her bosom. Ye
will find,
Women, old men, and babes ; the many,
weak   190
Of body and of spirit ill prepared,
With painful toil, through long and
dangerous ways
To seek another country. Say to them,
The White Men will not lift the arm of
power
Against the feeble ; here they may
remain
In peace, and to the grave in peace go
down.
But they who would not have their
children lose
The name their fathers bore, will join
our march.
Ere ye set forth, behold the destined
way.   199

He bade a pile be raised upon the top
Of that high eminence, to all the winds
Exposed. They raised the pile, and
left it free
To all the winds of Heaven ; Yuhidthiton
Alone approach'd it, and applied the
torch.
The day was calm, and o'er the flaming
pile
The wavy smoke hung lingering, like
a mist
That in the morning tracks the valley-
stream.

Swell over swell it rose, erect above,
On all sides spreading like a stately
palm.
So moveless were the winds. Upward
it roll'd,   210
Still upward, when a stream of upper air
Cross'd it, and bent its top, and drove it
on,
Straight over Aztlan. An acclaiming
shout
Welcomed the will of Heaven ; for lo,
the smoke
Fast travelling on, while not a breath
of air
Is felt below. Ye see the appointed
course ;
Exclaim'd the King. Proclaim it where
ye go !
On the third morning we begin our
march.

Soon o'er the lake a winged galley
sped,
Wafting the Ocean Prince. He bore,
preserved   220
When Aztlan's bloody temples were cast
down,
The Ashes of the Dead. The King
received
The relics, and his heart was full ; his
eye
Dwelt on his father's urn. At length
he said,
One more request, O Madoc ! . . If the
lake
Should ever to its ancient bounds return,
Shrined in the highest of Patamba's
towers
Coanocotzin rests. . . But wherefore
this ?
Thou wilt respect the Ashes of the King.

Then Madoc said, Abide not here,
O King,   230
Thus open to the changeful elements ;
But till the day of your departure come,
Sojourn with me. . . Madoc, that must
not be !
Yuhidthiton replied. Shall I behold
A stranger dwelling in my father's
house ?
Shall I become a guest, where I was
wont

To give the guest his welcome ? . . He
    pursued,
After short pause of speech, . . For our
    old men,
And helpless babes and women ; for all
    those
Whom wisely fear and feebleness deter
To tempt strange paths, through
    swamp and wilderness   241
And hostile tribes, for these Yuhidthiton
Intreats thy favour. Underneath thy
    sway,
They may remember me without regret,
Yet not without affection. . . They shall
    be
My people, Madoc answer'd. . . And the
    rites
Of holiness transmitted from their
    sires, . .
Pursued the King, . . will these be suf-
    fer'd them ? . .
Blood must not flow, the Christian
    Prince replied ;
No Priest must dwell among us ; that
    hath been   250
The cause of all this misery ! . . Enough,
Yuhidthiton replied ; I ask no more.
It is not for the conquer'd to impose
Their law upon the conqueror.
          Then he turn'd,
And lifted up his voice, and call'd upon
The people : . . All whom fear or feeble-
    ness
Withhold from following my adven-
    turous path,
Prince Madoc will receive. No blood
    must flow,
No Paba dwell among them. Take
    upon ye,
Ye who are weak of body or of heart,
The Strangers' easy yoke : beneath their
    sway   261
Ye may remember me without regret.
Soon take your choice, and speedily
    depart,
Lest ye impede the adventurers. . . As
    he spake,
Tears flow'd, and groans were heard.
    The line was drawn,
Which whoso would accept the
    Strangers' yoke
Should pass. A multitude o'erpast the
    line ;

But all the youth of Aztlan crowded
    round
Yuhidthiton, their own beloved King.

So two days long, with unremitting
    toil,   270
The barks of Britain to the adventurers
Bore due supply ; and to new habitants
The city of the Cymry spread her
    gates ;
And in the vale around, and on the
    heights,
Their numerous tents were pitch'd.
    Meantime the tale
Of ruin went abroad, and how the Gods
Had driven her sons from Aztlan. To
    the King,
Companions of his venturous enterprize,
The bold repair'd ; the timid and the
    weak,
All whom, averse from perilous wan-
    derings,   280
A gentler nature had disposed to peace,
Beneath the Strangers' easy rule re-
    main'd.
Now the third morning came. At
    break of day
The mountain echoes to the busy sound
Of multitudes. Before the moving
    tribe
The Pabas bear, enclosed from public
    sight,
Mexitli ; and the Ashes of the Kings
Follow the Chair of God. Yuhidthiton
Then leads the marshall'd ranks, and by
    his side,   289
Silent and thoughtfully, went Tlalala.

At the north gate of Aztlan, Malinal,
Borne in a litter, waited their approach ;
And now alighting, as the train drew
    nigh,
Propt by a friendly arm, with feeble step
Advanced to meet the King. Yuhid-
    thiton,
With eye severe and darkening coun-
    tenance,
Met his advance. I did not think, quoth
    he,
Thou wouldst have ventured this ! and
    liefer far
Should I have borne away with me the
    thought

That Malinal had shunn'd his brother's
  sight,   300
Because their common blood yet raised
  in him
A sense of his own shame ! . . Comest
  thou to show
Those wounds, the marks of thine un-
  natural war
Against thy country ? Or to boast the
  meed
Of thy dishonour, that thou tarriest
  here,
Sharing the bounty of the Conqueror,
While, with the remnant of his country-
  men,
Saving the Gods of Aztlan and the
  name,
Thy brother and thy King goes forth to
  seek   309
His fortune !
        Calm and low the youth replied,
Ill dost thou judge of me, Yuhidthiton !
And rashly doth my brother wrong the
  heart
He better should have known ! Howbeit,
  I come
Prepared for grief. These honourable
  wounds
Were gain'd when, singly, at Caer-
  madoc, I
Opposed the ruffian Hoamen : and even
  now,
Thus feeble as thou seest me, come I
  thence,
For this farewell. Brother, . . Yuhid-
  thiton, . .
By the true love which thou didst bear
  my youth,
Which ever, with a love as true, my
  heart   320
Hath answer'd, . . by the memory of
  that hour
When at our mother's funeral pile we
  stood,
Go not away in wrath, but call to
  mind
What thou hast ever known me ! Side
  by side
We fought against the Strangers, side by
  side
We fell ; together in the council-hall
We counsell'd peace, together in the
  field

Of the assembly pledged the word of
  peace.
When plots of secret slaughter were
  devised,   329
I raised my voice alone, alone I kept
My plighted faith, alone I prophesied
The judgement of just Heaven ; for this
  I bore
Reproach and shame and wrongful
  banishment,
In the action self-approved, and justi-
  fied
By this unhappy issue.
                As he spake,
Did natural feeling strive within the
  King,
And thoughts of other days, and bro-
  therly love,
And inward consciousness that had he
  too
Stood forth, obedient to his better
  mind,
Nor weakly yielded to the wily priests,
Wilfully blind, perchance even now in
  peace   341
The kingdom of his fathers had pre-
  served
Her name and empire. . . Malinal, he
  cried,
Thy brother's heart is sore . in better
  times
I may with kindlier thoughts remember
  thee
And honour thy true virtue. Now,
  farewell !

So saying, to his heart he held the
  youth,
Then turn'd away. But then cried
  Tlalala,
Farewell, Yuhidthiton ! the Tiger cried;
For I too will not leave my native
  land, . .   350
Thou who wert King of Aztlan ! Go thy
  way ;
And be it prosperous. Through the
  gate thou seest
Yon tree that overhangs my father's
  house ;
My father lies beneath it. Call to
  mind
Sometimes that tree ; for at its foot in
  peace

Shall Tlalala be laid, who will not live
Survivor of his country.
                              Thus he said,
And through the gate, regardless of the
        King,
Turn'd to his native door. Yuhidthiton
Follow'd, and Madoc ; but in vain their
        words   360
Essay'd to move the Tiger's steady
        heart ;
When from the door a tottering boy
        came forth
And clung around his knees with joyful
        cries,
And called him father. At the joyful
        sound
Out ran Ilanquel ; and the astonish'd
        man
Beheld his wife and boy, whom sure he
        deem'd
Whelm'd in the flood ; but them the
        British barks,
Returning homeward from their merci-
        ful quest,
Found floating on the waters. . . For a
        while,
Abandon'd by all desperate thoughts, he
        stood :   370
Soon he collected, and to Madoc turn'd,
And said, O Prince, this woman and
        her boy
I leave to thee. As thou hast ever
        found
In me a fearless unrelenting foe,
Fighting with ceaseless zeal his coun-
        try's cause,

Respect them ! . . Nay, Ilanquel ! hast
        thou yet
To learn with what unshakeable resolve
My soul maintains its purposes ? I leave
        thee
To a brave foe's protection. . . Lay me,
        Madoc,
Here, in my father's grave.
                              With that he took
His mantle off, and veil'd Ilanquel's
        face ; . .   381
Woman, thou may'st not look upon the
        Sun,
Who sets to rise no more ! . . That done,
        he placed
His javelin hilt against the ground ; the
        point
He fitted to his heart ; and, holding
        firm
The shaft, fell forward, still with steady
        hand
Guiding the death-blow on.
                              So in the land
Madoc was left sole Lord ; and far
        away
Yuhidthiton led forth the Aztecas,
To spread in other lands Mexitli's
        name,   390
And rear a mightier empire, and set
        up
Again their foul idolatry ; till Heaven,
Making blind Zeal and bloody Avarice
Its ministers of vengeance, sent among
        them
The heroic Spaniard's unrelenting
        sword.

BALLADS AND METRICAL TALES.

MARY, THE MAID OF THE INN

[First published in *The Oracle*, afterwards in *Poems*, 1797.]

The circumstances related in the following Ballad were told me when a schoolboy, as having happened in the north of England. Either Furnes or Kirkstall Abbey (I forget which) was named as the scene. The original story, however, is in Dr. Plot's *History of Staffordshire*, p. 291.

The metre is Mr. Lewis's invention; and metre is one of the few things concerning which popularity may be admitted as a proof of merit. The ballad has become popular owing to the metre and the story; and it has been made the subject of a fine picture by Mr. Barker.

1

Who is yonder poor Maniac, whose
    wildly-fix'd eyes
Seem a heart overcharged to express ?
She weeps not, yet often and deeply she
    sighs ;
She never complains, but her silence
    implies
    The composure of settled distress.

2

No pity she looks for, no alms doth she
    seek ;
    Nor for raiment nor food doth she
      care :
Through her tatters the winds of the
    winter blow bleak
On that wither'd breast, and her
    weather-worn cheek
    Hath the hue of a mortal despair. 10

3

Yet cheerful and happy, nor distant the
    day,
    Poor Mary the Maniac hath been ;
The Traveller remembers who journey'd
    this way
No damsel so lovely, no damsel so gay,
    As Mary, the Maid of the Inn.

4

Her cheerful address fill'd the guests
    with delight
    As she welcomed them in with a
      smile ;
Her heart was a stranger to childish
    affright,
And Mary would walk by the Abbey at
    night
    When the wind whistled down the
      dark aisle. 20

5

She loved, and young Richard had
    settled the day,
    And she hoped to be happy for
      life :
But Richard was idle and worthless, and
    they
Who knew him would pity poor Mary,
    and say
    That she was too good for his wife.

6

'Twas in autumn, and stormy and dark
    was the night,
    And fast were the windows and
      door ;
Two guests sat enjoying the fire that
    burnt bright,
And smoking in silence with tranquil
    delight
    They listen'd to hear the wind roar. 30

7

' 'Tis pleasant,' cried one, ' seated by the
    fire-side,
    To hear the wind whistle without.'
' What a night for the Abbey ! ' his
    comrade replied,
' Methinks a man's courage would now
    be well tried
    Who should wander the ruins about.

8

'I myself, like a school-boy, should
 tremble to hear
The hoarse ivy shake over my head;
And could fancy I saw, half persuaded
 by fear,
Some ugly old Abbot's grim spirit appear,
 For this wind might awaken the
  dead!' 40

9

'I'll wager a dinner,' the other one cried,
 'That Mary would venture there now.'
'Then wager and lose!' with a sneer
 he replied,
'I'll warrant she'd fancy a ghost by her
 side,
 And faint if she saw a white cow.'

10

'Will Mary this charge on her courage
 allow?'
 His companion exclaim'd with a
  smile;
'I shall win, .. for I know she will venture there now,
And earn a new bonnet by bringing a
 bough
 From the elder that grows in the
  aisle.' 50

11

With fearless good-humour did Mary
 comply,
 And her way to the Abbey she bent;
The night was dark, and the wind was
 high,
And as hollowly howling it swept through
 the sky,
 She shiver'd with cold as she went.

12

O'er the path so well known still proceeded the Maid
 Where the Abbey rose dim on the
  sight;
Through the gateway she enter'd, she
 felt not afraid,
Yet the ruins were lonely and wild, and
 their shade
 Seem'd to deepen the gloom of the
  night. 60

13

All around her was silent, save when the
 rude blast
 Howl'd dismally round the old pile;
Over weed-cover'd fragments she fear-
 lessly pass'd,
And arrived at the innermost ruin at
 last
 Where the elder-tree grew in the aisle.

14

Well pleased did she reach it, and
 quickly drew near,
 And hastily gather'd the bough;
When the sound of a voice seem'd to
 rise on her ear,
She paused, and she listen'd intently, in
 fear,
 And her heart panted painfully now.

15

The wind blew, the hoarse ivy shook
 over her head, 71
 She listen'd .. nought else could she
  hear;
The wind fell; her heart sunk in her
 bosom with dread,
For she heard in the ruins distinctly the
 tread
 Of footsteps approaching her near.

16

Behind a wide column half breathless
 with fear
 She crept to conceal herself there:
That instant the moon o'er a dark cloud
 shone clear,
And she saw in the moonlight two
 ruffians appear,
 And between them a corpse did they
  bear. 80

17

Then Mary could feel her heart-blood
 curdle cold;
 Again the rough wind hurried by, ..
It blew off the hat of the one, and
 behold
Even close to the feet of poor Mary it
 roll'd, ..
 She felt, and expected to die.

18

'Curse the hat!' he exclaims: 'Nay,
    come on till we hide
The dead body,' his comrade replies.
She beholds them in safety pass on by
    her side,   [supplied,
She seizes the hat, fear her courage
    And fast through the Abbey she flies.

19

She ran with wild speed, she rush'd in
    at the door,   ⁽¹⁾
She gazed in her terror around,
Then her limbs could support their faint
    burthen no more,
And exhausted and breathless she sank
    on the floor,
    Unable to utter a sound.

20

Ere yet her pale lips could the story
    impart,
For a moment the hat met her view; ..
Her eyes from that object convulsively
    start,
For .. what a cold horror then thrilled
    through her heart
    When the name of her Richard she
    knew!   100

21

Where the old Abbey stands, on the
    common hard by,
    His gibbet is now to be seen;
His irons you still from the road may
    espy;
The traveller beholds them, and thinks
    with a sigh
    Of poor Mary, the Maid of the Inn.

Bristol, 1796.

DONICA

[Published in *Poems*, 1797. The Ballad
s founded on stories ' to be found in the
notes to *The Hierarchies of the Blessed
Angels*, a poem by Thomas Heywood, ..
1635.']

HIGH on a rock whose castle shade
    Darken'd the lake below,
In ancient strength majestic stood
    The towers of Arlinkow.

The fisher in the lake below
    Durst never cast his net,
Nor ever swallow in its waves
    Her passing wing would wet.

The cattle from its ominous banks
    In wild alarm would run,   10
Though parch'd with thirst, and faint
    beneath
    The summer's scorching sun.

For sometimes when no passing breeze
    The long lank sedges waved,
All white with foam and heaving high
    Its deafening billows raved.

And when the tempest from its base
    The rooted pine would shake,
The powerless storm unruffling swept
    Across the calm dead lake.   20

And ever then when death drew near
    The house of Arlinkow,
Its dark unfathom'd waters sent
    Strange music from below.

The Lord of Arlinkow was old,
    One only child had he,
Donica was the Maiden's name,
    As fair as fair might be.

A bloom as bright as opening morn
    Suffused her clear white cheek;   30
The music of her voice was mild,
    Her full dark eyes were meek.

Far was her beauty known, for none
    So fair could Finland boast;
Her parents loved the Maiden much,
    Young Eberhard loved her most.

Together did they hope to tread
    The pleasant path of life,
For now the day drew near to make
    Donica Eberhard's wife.   40

The eve was fair and mild the air,
    Along the lake they stray;
The eastern hill reflected bright
    The tints of fading day.

And brightly o'er the water stream'd
    The liquid radiance wide;
Donica's little dog ran on
    And gambol'd at her side.

Youth, health, and love bloom'd on her
cheek,
Her full dark eyes express   50
In many a glance to Eberhard
Her soul's meek tenderness.

Nor sound was heard, nor passing gale
Sigh'd through the long lank sedge ;
The air was hush'd, no little wave
Dimpled the water's edge :

When suddenly the lake sent forth
Its music from beneath,
And slowly o'er the waters sail'd
The solemn sounds of death.   60

As those deep sounds of death arose,
Donica's cheek grew pale,
And in the arms of Eberhard
The lifeless Maiden fell.

Loudly the Youth in terror shriek'd,
And loud he call'd for aid,
And with a wild and eager look
Gazed on the lifeless Maid.

But soon again did better thoughts
In Eberhard arise,   70
And he with trembling hope beheld
The Maiden raise her eyes.

And on his arm reclined she moved
With feeble pace and slow,
And soon with strength recover'd
reach'd
The towers of Arlinkow.

Yet never to Donica's cheeks
Return'd their lively hue ;
Her cheeks were deathy white and wan,
Her lips a livid blue ;   80

Her eyes so bright and black of yore
Were now more black and bright,
And beam'd strange lustre in her face
So deadly wan and white.

The dog that gambol'd by her side,
And loved with her to stray,
Now at his alter'd mistress howl'd,
And fled in fear away.

Yet did the faithful Eberhard
Not love the Maid the less ;   90
He gazed with sorrow, but he gazed
With deeper tenderness.

And when he found her health unharm'd
He would not brook delay,
But press'd the not unwilling Maid
To fix the bridal day.

And when at length it came, with joy
He hail'd the bridal day,
And onward to the house of God
They went their willing way.   100

But when they at the altar stood,
And heard the sacred rite,
The hallow'd tapers dimly stream'd
A pale sulphureous light.

And when the Youth with holy warmth
Her hand in his did hold,
Sudden he felt Donica's hand
Grow deadly damp and cold.

But loudly then he shriek'd, for lo !
A Spirit met his view,   110
And Eberhard in the angel form
His own Donica knew.

That instant from her earthly frame
A Daemon howling fled,
And at the side of Eberhard
The livid corpse fell dead.

Bristol, 1796.

RUDIGER

[Published in *Poems*, 1797. The story
has been adapted from Thomas Heywood.]

BRIGHT on the mountain's heathy slope
The day's last splendours shine,
And rich with many a radiant hue
Gleam gaily on the Rhine.

And many a one from Waldhurst's walls
Along the river stroll'd,
As ruffling o'er the pleasant stream
The evening gales came cold.

So as they stray'd a swan they saw
Sail stately up and strong,   10
And by a silver chain he drew
A little boat along.

Whose streamer to the gentle breeze
Long floating flutter'd light ;
Beneath whose crimson canopy
There lay reclined a knight.

With arching crest and swelling breast
  On sail'd the stately swan,
And lightly up the parting tide
  The little boat came on.   20

And onward to the shore they drew,
  Where having left the knight,
The little boat adown the stream
  Fell soon beyond the sight.

Was never a knight in Waldhurst's walls
  Could with this stranger vie,
Was never a youth at aught esteem'd
  When Rudiger was by.

Was never a maid in Waldhurst's walls
  Might match with Margaret;   30
Her cheek was fair, her eyes were dark,
  Her silken locks like jet.

And many a rich and noble youth
  Had sought to win the fair,
But never a rich and noble youth
  Could rival Rudiger.

At every tilt and tourney he
  Still bore away the prize;
For knightly feats superior still,
  And knightly courtesies.   40

His gallant feats, his looks, his love,
  Soon won the willing fair;
And soon did Margaret become
  The wife of Rudiger.

Like morning dreams of happiness
  Fast roll'd the months away;
For he was kind and she was kind,
  And who so blest as they?

Yet Rudiger would sometimes sit
  Absorb'd in silent thought,   50
And his dark downward eye would seem
  With anxious meaning fraught:

But soon he raised his looks again,
  And smiled his cares away,
And mid the hall of gaiety
  Was none like him so gay.

And onward roll'd the waning months,
  The hour appointed came,
And Margaret her Rudiger
  Hail'd with a father's name.   60

But silently did Rudiger
  The little infant see;
And darkly on the babe he gazed,—
  A gloomy man was he.

And when to bless the little babe
  The holy Father came,
To cleanse the stains of sin away
  In Christ's redeeming name,

Then did the cheek of Rudiger
  Assume a death pale hue,   70
And on his clammy forehead stood
  The cold convulsive dew;

And faltering in his speech he bade
  The Priest the rites delay,
Till he could, to right health restored,
  Enjoy the festive day.

When o'er the many-tinted sky
  He saw the day decline,
He called upon his Margaret
  To walk beside the Rhine;   80

'And we will take the little babe,
  For soft the breeze that blows,
And the mild murmurs of the stream
  Will lull him to repose.'

And so together forth they went,
  The evening breeze was mild,
And Rudiger upon his arm
  Pillow'd the little child.

Many gay companies that eve
  Along the river roam,   90
But when the mist began to rise,
  They all betook them home.

Yet Rudiger continued still
  Along the banks to roam,
Nor aught could Margaret prevail
  To turn his footsteps home.

'Oh turn thee, turn thee, Rudiger!
  The rising mists behold,
The evening wind is damp and chill,
  The little babe is cold!'   100

'Now hush thee, hush thee, Margaret,
  The mists will do no harm,
And from the wind the little babe
  Is shelter'd on my arm.'

'Oh turn thee, turn thee, Rudiger !
Why onward wilt thou roam ?
The moon is up, the night is cold,
And we are far from home.'

He answer'd not ; for now he saw
A Swan come sailing strong,   110
And by a silver chain he drew
A little boat along.

To shore they came, and to the boat
Fast leapt he with the child,
And in leapt Margaret . . breathless now,
And pale with fear, and wild.

With arching crest and swelling breast
On sail'd the stately Swan,
And lightly down the rapid tide
The little boat went on.   120

The full orb'd moon, that beam'd around
Pale splendour through the night,
Cast through the crimson canopy
A dim discolour'd light.

And swiftly down the hurrying stream
In silence still they sail,
And the long streamer fluttering fast
Flapp'd to the heavy gale.

And he was mute in sullen thought,
And she was mute with fear,   130
Nor sound but of the parting tide
Broke on the listening ear.

The little babe began to cry ;
Then Margaret raised her head,
And with a quick and hollow voice,
'Give me the child !' she said.

'Now hush thee, hush thee, Margaret,
Nor my poor heart distress !
I do but pay perforce the price
Of former happiness.   140

'And hush thee too, my little babe !
Thy cries so feeble cease ;
Lie still, lie still ; . . a little while
And thou shalt be at peace.'

So as he spake to land they drew,
And swift he stept on shore,
And him behind did Margaret
Close follow evermore.

It was a place all desolate,
Nor house nor tree was there ;   150
But there a rocky mountain rose,
Barren, and bleak, and bare.

And at its base a cavern yawn'd,
No eye its depth might view,
For in the moon-beam shining round
That darkness darker grew.

Cold horror crept through Margaret's
blood,
Her heart it paused with fear,
When Rudiger approach'd the cave,
And cried, 'Lo, I am here !'   160

A deep sepulchral sound the cave
Return'd, 'Lo, I am here !'
And black from out the cavern gloom
Two giant arms appear.

And Rudiger approach'd, and held
The little infant nigh ;   [then
Then Margaret shriek'd, and gather'd
New powers from agony.

And round the baby fast and close
Her trembling arms she folds,   170
And with a strong convulsive grasp
The little infant holds.

'Now help me, Jesus !' loud she cries,
And loud on God she calls ;
Then from the grasp of Rudiger
The little infant falls.

The mother holds her precious babe ;
But the black arms clasp'd him round,
And dragg'd the wretched Rudiger
Adown the dark profound.   180

Bristol, 1796.

JASPAR

[First published in *The Morning Post*,
May 3, 1798 ; afterwards in *Poems*, vol. ii,
1799.]

JASPAR was poor, and vice and want
Had made his heart like stone ;
And Jaspar look'd with envious eyes
On riches not his own.

On plunder bent abroad he went
Toward the close of day,
And loiter'd on the lonely road
Impatient for his prey.

No traveller came . . he loiter'd long,
And often look'd around,   10
And paused and listen'd eagerly
To catch some coming sound.

He sate him down beside the stream
  That crost the lonely way,
So fair a scene might well have charm'd
  All evil thoughts away :

He sate beneath a willow tree   —
  Which cast a trembling shade ;
The gentle river full in front
  A little island made ;   20

Where pleasantly the moon-beam shone
  Upon the poplar trees,
Whose shadow on the stream below
  Play'd slowly to the breeze.

He listen'd . . and he heard the wind
  That waved the willow tree ;
He heard the waters flow along,
  And murmur quietly.

He listen'd for the traveller's tread,
  The nightingale sung sweet ; . .   30
He started up, for now he heard
  The sound of coming feet ;

He started up and graspt a stake,
  And waited for his prey ;
There came a lonely traveller,
  And Jaspar crost his way.

But Jaspar's threats and curses fail'd
  The traveller to appal,
He would not lightly yield the purse
  Which held his little all.   40

Awhile he struggled, but he strove
  With Jaspar's strength in vain ;
Beneath his blows he fell and groan'd,
  And never spake again.

Jaspar raised up the murder'd man,
  And plunged him in the flood,
And in the running water then
  He cleansed his hands from blood.

The waters closed around the corpse,
  And cleansed his hands from gore,   50
The willow waved, the stream flow'd on,
  And murmur'd as before.

There was no human eye had seen
  The blood the murderer spilt,
And Jaspar's conscience never felt
  The avenging goad of guilt.

And soon the ruffian had consumed
  The gold he gain'd so ill,
And years of secret guilt pass'd on,
  And he was needy still.   60

One eve beside the alehouse fire
  He sate as it befell,
When in there came a labouring man
  Whom Jaspar knew full well.

He sate him down by Jaspar's side,
  A melancholy man,
For spite of honest toil, the world
  Went hard with Jonathan.

His toil a little earn'd, and he
  With little was content ;   70
But sickness on his wife had fallen,
  And all was well-nigh spent.

Long with his wife and little ones
  He shared the scanty meal,
And saw their looks of wretchedness,
  And felt what wretches feel.

Their Landlord, a hard man, that day,
  Had seized the little left,
And now the sufferer found himself
  Of every thing bereft.   80

He leant his head upon his hand,
  His elbow on his knee,
And so by Jaspar's side he sate,
  And not a word said he.

' Nay, . . why so downcast ? ' Jaspar
    cried,
  ' Come . . cheer up, Jonathan !
Drink, neighbour, drink ! 'twill warm
    thy heart . .
Come ! come ! take courage, man ! '

He took the cup that Jaspar gave,
  And down he drain'd it quick ;   90
' I have a wife,' said Jonathan,
  ' And she is deadly sick.

' She has no bed to lie upon,
  I saw them take her bed . .
And I have children . . would to God
  That they and I were dead !

' Our Landlord he goes home to-night,
  And he will sleep in peace . .
I would that I were in my grave,
  For there all troubles cease.   100

' In vain I pray'd him to forbear,
  Though wealth enough has he !
God be to him as merciless
  As he has been to me ! '

When Jaspar saw the poor man's soul
  On all his Ills intent,
He plied him with the heartening cup,
  And with him forth he went.

' This Landlord on his homeward road
  'Twere easy now to meet.   110
The road is lonesome, Jonathan !
  And vengeance, man ! is sweet.'

He listen'd to the tempter's voice,
  The thought it made him start ; . .
His head was hot, and wretchedness
  Had harden'd now his heart.

Along the lonely road they went
  And waited for their prey,
They sate them down beside the stream
  That crost the lonely way.   120

They sate them down beside the stream
  And never a word they said,
They sate and listen'd silently
  To hear the traveller's tread.

The night was calm, the night was dark,
  No star was in the sky,
The wind it waved the willow boughs,
  The stream flow'd quietly.

The night was calm, the air was still,
  Sweet sung the nightingale ;   130
The soul of Jonathan was soothed,
  His heart began to fail.

' 'Tis weary waiting here,' he cried,
  ' And now the hour is late, . .
Methinks he will not come to-night,
  No longer let us wait.'

' Have patience, man ! ' the ruffian said,
  ' A little we may wait ;
But longer shall his wife expect
  Her husband at the gate.'   140

Then Jonathan grew sick at heart :
  ' My conscience yet is clear !
Jaspar . . it is not yet too late . .
  I will not linger here.'

' How now ! ' cried Jaspar, ' why, I
    thought
Thy conscience was asleep ;
No more such qualms, the night is dark,
  The river here is deep.'

' What matters that,' said Jonathan,
  Whose blood began to freeze,   150
' When there is One above whose eye
  The deeds of darkness sees ? '

' We are safe enough,' said Jaspar then,
  ' If that be all thy fear !
Nor eye above, nor eye below,
  Can pierce the darkness here.'

That instant as the murderer spake
  There came a sudden light ;
Strong as the mid day sun it shone,
  Though all around was night ;   160

It hung upon the willow tree,
  It hung upon the flood,
It gave to view the poplar isle,
  And all the scene of blood.

The traveller who journeys there,
  He surely hath espied
A madman who has made his home
  Upon the river's side.

His cheek is pale, his eye is wild,
  His look bespeaks despair ;   170
For Jaspar since that hour has made
  His home unshelter'd there.

And fearful are his dreams at night,
  And dread to him the day ;
He thinks upon his untold crime,
  And never dares to pray.

The summer suns, the winter storms,
  O'er him unheeded roll,
For heavy is the weight of blood
  Upon the maniac's soul.   180

    Bath, 1798.

ST. PATRICK'S PURGATORY

[The last twenty-four stanzas were
published in *The Morning Post*, May 8, 1798.]

  This Ballad was published (1801) in the
Tales of Wonder, by Mr. Lewis, who found it
among the wefts and strays of the Press.
He never knew that it was mine ; but after
his death I bestowed some pains in recom-
posing it, because he had thought it worth
preserving.

  It is founded upon the abridged extract
which M. le Grand has given in his *Fabliaux*
of a Metrical legend, by Marie de France.

1

' ENTER, Sir Knight,' the warden cried,
' And trust in Heaven whate'er betide,
  Since you have reach'd this bourn ;
But first receive refreshment due,
'Twill then be time to welcome you
  If ever you return.'

2

Three sops were brought of bread and
   wine ;
Well might Sir Owen then divine
   The mystic warning given,
That he against our ghostly Foe   10
Must soon to mortal combat go,
   And put his trust in Heaven.

3

Sir Owen pass'd the convent gate,
The Warden him conducted straight
   To where a coffin lay ;
The Monks around in silence stand,
Each with a funeral torch in hand
   Whose light bedimm'd the day.

4

' Few Pilgrims ever reach this bourn,'
They said, ' but fewer still return ;   20
   Yet, let what will ensue,
Our duties are prescribed and clear ;
Put off all mortal weakness here,
   This coffin is for you.

5

' Lie there, while we with pious breath
Raise over you the dirge of death,
   This comfort we can give ;
Belike no living hands may pay
This office to your lifeless clay,
   Receive it while you live ! '   30

6

Sir Owen in a shroud was drest,
They placed a cross upon his breast,
   And down he laid his head ;
Around him stood the funeral train,
And sung with slow and solemn strain
   The Service of the Dead.

7

Then to the entrance of the Cave
They led the Christian warrior brave ;
   Some fear he well might feel,
For none of all the Monks could tell   40
The terrors of that mystic cell,
   Its secrets none reveal.

8

' Now enter here,' the Warden cried,
' And God, Sir Owen, be your guide !
   Your name shall live in story :
For of the few who reach this shore,
Still fewer venture to explore
   St. Patrick's Purgatory.'

9

Adown the Cavern's long descent,
Feeling his way, Sir Owen went,   50
   With cautious feet and slow ;
Unarm'd, for neither sword nor spear,
Nor shield of proof avail'd him here
   Against our ghostly Foe.

10

The ground was moist beneath his tread,
Large drops fell heavy on his head,
   The air was damp and chill,
And sudden shudderings o'er him came,
And he could feel through all his frame
   An icy sharpness thrill.   60

11

Now steeper grew the dark descent ;
In fervent prayer the Pilgrim went,
   'Twas silence all around,
Save his own echo from the cell,
And the large drops that frequent fell
   With dull and heavy sound.

12

But colder now he felt the cell,
Those heavy drops no longer fell,
   Thin grew the piercing air ;
And now upon his aching sight,   70
There dawn'd far off a feeble light,
   In hope he hasten'd there.

13

Emerging now once more to day
A frozen waste before him lay,
   A desert wild and wide,
Where ice-rocks in a sunless sky,
On ice-rocks piled, and mountains high,
   Were heap'd on every side.

14

Impending as about to fall
They seem'd, and had that sight been
   all,   80
   Enough that sight had been
To make the stoutest courage quail ;
For what could courage there avail
   Against what then was seen ?

15

He saw, as on in faith he past,
Where many a frozen wretch was fast
   Within the ice-clefts pent,
Yet living still, and doom'd to bear
In absolute and dumb despair
   Their endless punishment.   90

16

A Voice then spake within his ear,
And fill'd his inmost soul with fear,
  ' O mortal Man,' it said,
' Adventurers like thyself were these ! '
He seem'd to feel his life-blood freeze,
  And yet subdued his dread.

17

' O mortal Man,' the Voice pursued,
' Be wise in time ! for thine own good
  Alone I counsel thee ;
Take pity on thyself, retrace   100
Thy steps, and fly this dolorous place
  While yet thy feet are free.

18

' I warn thee once ! I warn thee twice !
Behold ! that mass of mountain-ice
  Is trembling o'er thy head !
One warning is allow'd thee more ;
O mortal Man, that warning o'er,
  And thou art worse than dead ! '

19

Not without fear, Sir Owen still
Held on with strength of righteous will,
  In faith and fervent prayer ;   111
When at the word, ' I warn thee thrice ! '
Down came the mass of mountain ice,
  And overwhelm'd him there.

20

Crush'd though, it seem'd, in every bone,
And sense for suffering left alone,
  A living hope remain'd ;
In whom he had believed, he knew,
And thence the holy courage grew
  That still his soul sustain'd.   120

21

For he, as he beheld it fall,
Fail'd not in faith on Christ to call,
  ' Lord, Thou canst save ! ' he cried ;
O heavenly help vouchsafed in need,
When perfect faith is found indeed ;
  The rocks of ice divide.

22

Like dust before the storm-wind's sway
The shiver'd fragments roll'd away,
  And left the passage free ;
New strength he feels, all pain is gone,
New life Sir Owen breathes, and on 131
  He goes rejoicingly.

23

Yet other trials he must meet,
For soon a close and piercing heat
  Relax'd each loosen'd limb ;
The sweat stream'd out from every part,
In short quick beatings toil'd his heart,
  His throbbing eyes grew dim.

24

Along the wide and wasted land
A stream of fire through banks of sand
  Its molten billows spread ;   41
Thin vapours tremulously light
Hung quivering o'er the glowing white,
  The air he breathed was red.

25

A Paradise beyond was seen,
Of shady groves and gardens green,
  Fair flowers and fruitful trees,
And flowing fountains cool and clear,
Whose gurgling music reach'd his ear
  Borne on the burning breeze.   150

26

How should he pass that molten flood ?
While gazing wistfully he stood,
  A Fiend, as in a dream,
' Thus! ' answer'd the unutter'd thought,
Stretch'd forth a mighty arm, and
    caught
And cast him in the stream.

27

Sir Owen groan'd, for then he felt
His eyeballs burn, his marrow melt,
  His brain like liquid lead.
And from his heart the boiling blood 160
Its agonizing course pursued
  Through limbs like iron red.

28

Yet, giving way to no despair,
But mindful of the aid of prayer,
  ' Lord, Thou canst save ! ' he said ;
And then a breath from Eden came,
With life and healing through his frame
  The blissful influence spread.

29

No Fiends may now his way oppose,
The gates of Paradise unclose,   170
  Free entrance there is given ;
And songs of triumph meet his ear,
Enrapt, Sir Owen seems to hear
  The harmonies of Heaven.

30

ᶠ Come, Pilgrim ! take thy foretaste
   meet,
Thou who hast trod with fearless feet
   St. Patrick's Purgatory,
For after death these seats divine,
Reward eternal, shall be thine,
   And thine eternal glory.'   180

31

Inebriate with the deep delight,
Dim grew the Pilgrim's swimming sight,
   His senses died away ;
And when to life he woke, before
The Cavern-mouth he saw once more
   The light of earthly day.

Westbury, 1798.

THE CROSS ROADS

[Published in *Poems*, vol. ii, 1799.]
   The tragedy related in this Ballad happened about the year 1760, in the parish of
Bedminster, near Bristol. One who was
present at the funeral told me the story and
the circumstances of the interment, as I have
versified them.

1

THERE was an old man breaking stones
   To mend the turnpike way ;
He sate him down beside a brook,
And out his bread and cheese he took,
   For now it was mid-day.

2

He leant his back against a post,
   His foot the brook ran by ;
And there were water-cresses growing,
And pleasant was the water's flowing,
   For he was hot and dry.   10

3

A soldier with his knapsack on
   Came travelling o'er the down ;
The sun was strong and he was tired ;
And he of the old man enquired,
   ᶠ How far to Bristol town ? '

4

Half an hour's walk for a young man,
   By lanes and fields and stiles ;
But you the foot-path do not know,
And if along the road you go
   Why then 'tis three good miles.'   20

5

The soldier took his knapsack off,
   For he was hot and dry ;
And out his bread and cheese he took,
And he sat down beside the brook
   To dine in company.

6

' Old friend ! in faith,' the soldier says,
   ' I envy you almost ;
My shoulders have been sorely prest,
And I should like to sit, and rest
   My back against that post.   30

7

' In such a sweltering day as this
   A knapsack is the devil
And if on t'other side I sat,
It would not only spoil our chat,
   But make me seem uncivil.'

8

The old man laugh'd and moved . . ' I
   wish
   It were a great-arm'd chair !
But this may help a man at need ; . .
And yet it was a cursed deed
   That ever brought it there.   40

9

' There's a poor girl lies buried here,
   Beneath this very place.
The earth upon her corpse is prest,
This post was driven into her breast,
   And a stone is on her face.'

10

The soldier had but just leant back,
   And now he half rose up,
' There's sure no harm in dining here,
My friend ? and yet, to be sincere,
   I should not like to sup.'   50

11

' God rest her ! she is still enough
   Who sleeps beneath my feet ! '
The old man cried. ' No harm I trow,
She ever did herself, though now
   She lies where four roads meet.

12

' I have pass'd by about that hour
   When men are not most brave ;
It did not make my courage fail,
And I have heard the nightingale
   Sing sweetly on her grave.   60

13

' I have pass'd by about that hour
    When ghosts their freedom have ;
But here I saw no ghastly sight,
And quietly the glow-worm's light
    Was shining on her grave.

14

' There's one who like a Christian lies
    Beneath the church-tree's shade ;
I'd rather go a long mile round
Than pass at evening through the ground
    Wherein that man is laid.   70

15

' A decent burial that man had,
    The bell was heard to toll,
When he was laid in holy ground,
But for all the wealth in Bristol town
    I would not be with his soul !

16

' Did'st see a house below the hill
    Which the winds and the rains de-
        stroy ?
In that farm-house did that man dwell,
And I remember it full well
    When I was a growing boy.   80

17

' But she was a poor parish girl
    Who came up from the west :
From service hard she ran away,
And at that house in evil day
    Was taken in to rest.

18

' A man of a bad name was he,
    An evil life he led ;
Passion made his dark face turn white,
And his grey eyes were large and light,
    And in anger they grew red.   90

19

' The man was bad, the mother worse,
    Bad fruit of evil stem ;
'Twould make your hair to stand on end
If I should tell to you, my friend,
    The things that were told of them !

20

' Did'st see an out-house standing by ?
    The walls alone remain ;
It was a stable then, but now
Its mossy roof has fallen through
    All rotted by the rain.   100

21

' This poor girl she had served with
        them
    Some half-a-year or more,
When she was found hung up one day,
Stiff as a corpse and cold as clay,
    Behind that stable door.

22

' It is a wild and lonesome place,
    No hut or house is near ;
Should one meet a murderer there alone,
'Twere vain to scream, and the dying
        groan
    Would never reach mortal ear.   110

23

' And there were strange reports about ;
    But still the coroner found
That she by her own hand had died,
And should buried be by the way-side,
    And not in Christian ground.

24

' This was the very place he chose,
    Just where these four roads meet ;
And I was one among the throng
That hither follow'd them along,
    I shall never the sight forget !   120

25

' They carried her upon a board
    In the clothes in which she died ;
I saw the cap blown off her head,
Her face was of a dark dark red,
    Her eyes were starting wide :

26

' I think they could not have been
        closed,
    So widely did they strain.
O Lord, it was a ghastly sight,
And it often made me wake at night,
    When I saw it in dreams again.   130

27

' They laid her where these four roads
        meet
    Here in this very place.
The earth upon her corpse was prest,
This post was driven into her breast,
    And a stone is on her face.'

Westbury, 1798.

THE PIOUS PAINTER

[First published in *The Morning Post*, November 2, 1798; afterwards in *The Annual Anthology*, 1799, and in *Metrical Tales*, 1805.]

The legend of the Pious Painter is related in the *Pia Hilaria* of Gazaeus; but the Pious Poet has omitted the second part of the story, though it rests upon quite as good authority as the first. It is to be found in the *Fabliaux* of Le Grand.

THE FIRST PART

1

THERE once was a painter in Catholic days,
　Like JOB who eschewed all evil ;
Still on his Madonnas the curious may gaze
With applause and with pleasure, but chiefly his praise
　And delight was in painting the Devil.

2

They were Angels, compared to the Devils he drew,
　Who besieged poor St. Anthony's cell ;
Such burning hot eyes, such a furnace-like hue !
And round them a sulphurous colouring he threw
　That their breath seem'd of brimstone to smell.　　10

3

And now had the artist a picture begun,
　'Twas over the Virgin's church-door ;
She stood on the Dragon embracing her Son ;
Many Devils already the artist had done,
　But this must out-do all before.

4

The Old Dragon's imps as they fled through the air,
　At seeing it paused on the wing ;
For he had the likeness so just to a hair,
That they came as Apollyon himself had been there,
　To pay their respects to their King.　20

5

Every child at beholding it trembled with dread,
　And scream'd as he turn'd away quick ;
Not an old woman saw it, but, raising her head,
Dropt a bead, made a cross on her wrinkles, and said,
　Lord keep me from ugly Old Nick !

6

What the Painter so earnestly thought on by day,
　He sometimes would dream of by night ;
But once he was startled as sleeping he lay ;
'Twas no fancy, no dream, he could plainly survey
　That the Devil himself was in sight.　30

7

' You rascally dauber ! ' old Beelzebub cries,
　' Take heed how you wrong me again !
Though your caricatures for myself I despise,
Make me handsomer now in the multitude's eyes,
　Or see if I threaten in vain ! '

8

Now the Painter was bold, and religious beside,
　And on faith he had certain reliance ;
So carefully he the grim countenance eyed,
And thank'd him for sitting with Catholic pride,
　And sturdily bade him defiance.　40

9

Betimes in the morning the Painter arose,
　He is ready as soon as 'tis light.
Every look, every line, every feature he knows,
'Tis fresh in his eye, to his labour he goes,
　And he has the old Wicked One quite.

10

Happy man ! he is sure the resemblance
    can't fail ;
The tip of the nose is like fire,
There's his grin and his fangs, and his
    dragon-like mail,
And the very identical curl of his
    tail, . .
    So that nothing is left to desire.   50

11

He looks and retouches again with
    delight ;
'Tis a portrait complete to his mind ;
And exulting again and again at the
    sight,
He looks round for applause, and he sees
    with affright
    The Original standing behind.

12

'Fool ! Idiot !' old Beelzebub grinn'd
    as he spoke,
And stampt on the scaffold in ire ;
The Painter grew pale, for he knew it
    no joke ;
'Twas a terrible height, and the scaffold-
    ing broke,
    The Devil could wish it no higher.   60

13

'Help . . help ! Blessed Mary !' he
    cried in alarm,
As the scaffold sunk under his feet.
From the canvas the Virgin extended
    her arm,
She caught the good Painter, she saved
    him from harm ;
    There were hundreds who saw in the
    street.

14

The Old Dragon fled when the wonder
    he spied,
And cursed his own fruitless en-
    deavour ;
While the Painter call'd after his rage
    to deride,
Shook his pallett and brushes in triumph
    and cried,   69
    'I'll paint thee more ugly than ever !'

THE PIOUS PAINTER

THE SECOND PART

[First published in *The Morning Post*,
July 26, 1799.]

1

The Painter so pious all praise had
    acquired
For defying the malice of Hell ;
The Monks the unerring resemblance
    admired ;
Not a Lady lived near but her portrait
    desired
    From a hand that succeeded so well.

2

One there was to be painted the number
    among
Of features most fair to behold ;
The country around of fair Marguerite
    rung,
Marguerite she was lovely and lively
    and young,
    Her husband was ugly and old.   10

3

O Painter, avoid her ! O Painter, take
    care,
For Satan is watchful for you !
Take heed lest you fall in the Wicked
    One's snare,
The net is made ready, O Painter, beware
    Of Satan and Marguerite too.

4

She seats herself now, now she lifts up
    her head,
On the artist she fixes her eyes ;
The colours are ready, the canvas is
    spread,
He lays on the white, and he lays on
    the red,
    And the features of beauty arise.   20

5

He is come to her eyes, eyes so bright
    and so blue !
There's a look which he cannot
    express ; . .
His colours are dull to their quick-
    sparkling hue ;   [view,
More and more on the lady he fixes his
    On the canvas he looks less and less.

6

In vain he retouches, her eyes sparkle
   more,
   And that look which fair Marguerite
   gave !
Many Devils the artist had painted of
   yore,
But he never had tried a live Angel
   before, . .
   St. Anthony, help him and save ! 30

7

He yielded, alas ! for the truth must be
   told,
   To the Woman, the Tempter, and
   Fate.
It was settled the Lady so fair to
   behold
Should elope from her Husband so ugly
   and old,
   With the Painter so pious of late.

8

Now Satan exults in his vengeance
   complete,
   To the Husband he makes the scheme
   known ;
Night comes and the lovers impatiently
   meet ;
Together they fly, they are seized in the
   street, 39
   And in prison the Painter is thrown.

9

With Repentance, his only companion,
   he lies,
   And a dismal companion is she !
On a sudden he saw the Old Enemy
   rise,
' Now, you villainous dauber !' Sir
   Beelzebub cries,
   ' You are paid for your insults to me !

10

' But my tender heart you may easily
   move,
   If to what I propose you agree ;
That picture, . . be just ! the resem-
   blance improve,
Make a handsomer portrait, your chains
   I'll remove,
   And you shall this instant be free.' 50

11

Overjoy'd, the conditions so easy he
   hears,   [said.
   ' I'll make you quite handsome !' he
He said, and his chain on the Devil
   appears ;
Released from his prison, released from
   his fears,
   The Painter is snug in his bed.

12

At morn he arises, composes his look,
   And proceeds to his work as before ;
The people beheld him, the culprit they
   took ;
They thought that the Painter his
   prison had broke, 59
   And to prison they led him once more.

13

They open the dungeon ; . . behold in
   his place
   In the corner old Beelzebub lay ;
He smirks and he smiles and he leers
   with a grace,
That the Painter might catch all the
   charms of his face,
   Then vanish'd in lightning away.

14

Quoth the Painter, ' I trust you'll sus-
   pect me no more,
   Since you find my assertions were true.
But I'll alter the picture above the
   Church-door,   [before,
For he never vouchsafed me a sitting
   And I must give the Devil his due.' 70

Westbury, 1798.

ST. MICHAEL'S CHAIR

[First published in *The Morning Post*,
April 27, 1799 ; afterwards in *The Annual
Anthology*, 1799, and in *Metrical Tales*, 1805.
Southey quotes as his authority for the
story *Whitaker's Supplement to the First
and Second Book of Polwhele's History of
Cornwall*, pp. 6, 7.]

MERRILY, merrily rung the bells,
   The bells of St. Michael's tower,
When Richard Penlake and Rebecca his
   wife
   Arrived at St. Michael's door.

Richard Penlake was a cheerful man,
  Cheerful and frank and free,
But he led a sad life with Rebecca his
    wife,
  For a terrible shrew was she.

Richard Penlake a scolding would take,
  Till patience avail'd no longer,   10
Then Richard Penlake his crab-stick
    would take,
  And show her that he was the stronger.

Rebecca his wife had often wish'd
  To sit in St. Michael's chair ;
For she should be the mistress then
  If she had once sat there.

It chanced that Richard Penlake fell
    sick,
  They thought he would have died ;
Rebecca his wife made a vow for his
    life,
  As she knelt by his bed-side.   20

' Now hear my prayer, St. Michael ! and
    spare
  My husband's life,' quoth she ;
' And to thine altar we will go,
  Six marks to give to thee.'

Richard Penlake repeated the vow,
  For woundily sick was he ;
' Save me, St. Michael, and we will go
  Six marks to give to thee.'

When Richard grew well, Rebecca his
    wife
  Teazed him by night and by day :   30
' O mine own dear ! for you I fear,
  If we the vow delay.'

Merrily, merrily rung the bells,
  The bells of St. Michael's tower,
When Richard Penlake and Rebecca
    his wife
  Arrived at St. Michael's door.

Six marks they on the altar laid,
  And Richard knelt in prayer :
She left him to pray, and stole away
  To sit in St. Michael's chair.   40

Up the tower Rebecca ran,
  Round and round and round ;
'Twas a giddy sight to stand a-top,
  And look upon the ground.

' A curse on the ringers for rocking
  The tower ! ' Rebecca cried,
As over the church battlements
  She strode with a long stride.

' A blessing on St. Michael's chair ! '
  She said as she sat down :   50
Morrily, merrily rung the bells,
  And out Rebecca was thrown.

Tidings to Richard Penlake were brought
  That his good wife was dead :
' Now shall we toll for her poor soul
  The great church bell ? ' they said.

' Toll at her burying,' quoth Richard
    Penlake,
  ' Toll at her burying,' quoth he ;
' But don't disturb the ringers now
  In compliment to me.'   60
Westbury, 1798.

KING HENRY V AND THE HERMIT
OF DREUX

[First published in *The Morning Post*,
September 24, 1798 ; afterwards in *The
Annual Anthology*, 1799.]

' While Henry V lay at the siege of Dreux,
an honest Hermit, unknown to him, came
and told him the great evils he brought on
Christendom by his unjust ambition, who
usurped the kingdom of France, against all
manner of right, and contrary to the will of
God ; wherefore in his holy name he
threatened him with a severe and sudden
punishment if he desisted not from his
enterprise. Henry took this exhortation
either as an idle whimsey, or a suggestion
of the dauphin's, and was but the more
confirmed in his design. But the blow soon
followed the threatening ; for within some
few months after he was smitten with a
strange and incurable disease.'—*Mezeray.*

HE pass'd unquestion'd through the
    camp,
  Their heads the soldiers bent
In silent reverence, or begg'd
  A blessing as he went ;
And so the Hermit pass'd along
  And reach'd the royal tent.

King Henry sate in his tent alone,
  The map before him lay,
Fresh conquests he was planning there
  To grace the future day.   10

King Henry lifted up his eyes
  The intruder to behold ;
With reverence he the hermit saw,
  For the holy man was old,
His look was gentle as a Saint's,
  And yet his eye was bold.

' Repent thee, Henry, of the wrongs
  Which thou hast done this land !
O King, repent in time, for know
  The judgement is at hand.   20

' I have pass'd forty years of peace
  Beside the river Blaise,
But what a weight of woe hast thou
  Laid on my latter days !

' I used to see along the stream
  The white sail gliding down,
That wafted food in better times
  To yonder peaceful town.

' Henry ! I never now behold
  The white sail gliding down ;   30
Famine, Disease, and Death, and Thou
  Destroy that wretched town.

' I used to hear the traveller's voice
  As here he pass'd along,
Or maiden as she loiter'd home
  Singing her even-song.

' No traveller's voice may now be heard,
  In fear he hastens by ;
But I have heard the village maid
  In vain for succour cry.   40

' I used to see the youths row down
  And watch the dripping oar,
As pleasantly their viol's tones
  Came soften'd to the shore.

' King Henry, many a blacken'd corpse
  I now see floating down !
Thou man of blood ! repent in time,
  And leave this leaguer'd town.'

' I shall go on,' King Henry cried,
  ' And conquer this good land ;   50
Seest thou not, Hermit, that the Lord
  Hath given it to my hand ?'

The Hermit heard King Henry speak,
  And angrily look'd down ; . .
His face was gentle, and for that
  More solemn was his frown.

' What if no miracle from Heaven
  The murderer's arm controul,
Think you for that the weight of blood
  Lies lighter on his soul ?   60

' Thou conqueror King, repent in time,
  Or dread the coming woe !
For, Henry, thou hast heard the threat
  And soon shalt feel the blow !'

King Henry forced a careless smile,
  As the Hermit went his way ;
But Henry soon remember'd him
  Upon his dying day.

Westbury, 1798.

CORNELIUS AGRIPPA

A BALLAD OF A YOUNG MAN THAT
  WOULD READ UNLAWFUL BOOKS,
  AND HOW HE WAS PUNISHED.

VERY PITHY AND PROFITABLE.

[First published in *The Morning Post* ;
afterwards in *The Annual Anthology*, 1799,
and in *Metrical Tales*, 1805.]

CORNELIUS AGRIPPA went out one day,
His Study he lock'd ere he went away,
And he gave the key of the door to his
  wife,
And charged her to keep it lock'd on
  her life.

' And if any one ask my Study to see,
I charge you to trust them not with the
  key ;
Whoever may beg, and entreat, and
  implore,
On your life let nobody enter that door.'

There lived a young man in the house,
  who in vain
Access to that Study had sought to
  obtain ;   10
And he begg'd and pray'd the books
  to see,
Till the foolish woman gave him the key.

On the Study-table a book there lay,
Which Agrippa himself had been read-
  ing that day ;
The letters were written with blood
  therein,   [skin ;
And the leaves were made of dead men's

And these horrible leaves of magic
   between
Were the ugliest pictures that ever
   were seen,
The likeness of things so foul to behold,
That what they were is not fit to be
   told.   20

The young man, he began to read
He knew not what, but he would proceed,
When there was heard a sound at the
   door,
Which as he read on grew more and
   more.

And more and more the knocking
   grew,
The young man knew not what to do :
But trembling in fear he sat within,
Till the door was broke, and the Devil
   came in.

Two hideous horns on his head he had
   got,
Like iron heated nine times red-hot ; 30
The breath of his nostrils was brimstone
   blue
And his tail like a fiery serpent grew.

' What wouldst thou with me ? ' the
   Wicked One cried,
But not a word the young man replied ;
Every hair on his head was standing
   upright,
And his limbs like a palsy shook with
   affright.

' What wouldst thou with me ? ' cried
   the Author of ill ;
But the wretched young man was silent
   still ;
Not a word had his lips the power to
   say,
And his marrow seem'd to be melting
   away.   40

' What wouldst thou with me ? ' the
   third time he cries,
And a flash of lightning came from his
   eyes,
And he lifted his griffin claw in the
   air,
And the young man had not strength
   for a prayer.

His eyes red fire and fury dart
As out he tore the young man's heart ;
He grinn'd a horrible grin at his prey,
And in a clap of thunder vanish'd away.

THE MORAL

Henceforth let all young men take heed
How in a Conjuror's books they read. 50

Westbury, 1798.

ST. ROMUALD

[First published in *The Morning Post*,
February 5, 1799 ; afterwards in *The
Annual Anthology*, 1800, and in *Metrical
Tales*, 1805.]

  ' Les Catalans ayant appris que S.
Romuald vouloit quitter leurs pays, en
furent très-affligés ; ils délibérèrent sur les
moyens de l'en empêcher, et le seul qu'ils
imaginèrent comme le plus sûr, fut de le
tuer, afin de profiter du moins de ses
reliques et des guérisons et autres miracles
qu'elles opéreroient après sa mort. La
dévotion que les Catalans avoient pour lui,
ne plut point de tout à S. Romuald ; il usa
de stratagème et leur échappa.'—*St. Foix,
Essais Historiques sur Paris*, t. v, p. 163.

ONE day, it matters not to know
How many hundred years ago,
A Frenchman stopt at an inn door :
The Landlord came to welcome him,
    and chat
    Of this and that,
For he had seen the Traveller there
    before.

' Doth holy Romuald dwell
    Still in his cell ? '
The Traveller ask'd, ' or is the old man
    dead ? '
  ' No ; he has left his loving flock,
    and we   10
So great a Christian never more shall
    see,'
The Landlord answer'd, and he shook
    his head.
  ' Ah, Sir ! we knew his worth !
If ever there did live a saint on earth ! . .

Why, Sir, he always used to wear a shirt
For thirty days, all seasons, day and
    night;
Good man, he knew it was not right
For Dust and Ashes to fall out with
    Dirt!
And then he only hung it out in the rain,
    And put it on again.   20

' There has been perilous work
With him and the Devil there in yonder
    cell;
For Satan used to maul him like a Turk.
There they would sometimes fight
    All through a winter's night,
    From sun-set until morn,
He with a cross, the Devil with his horn;
The Devil spitting fire with might and
    main
Enough to make St. Michael half afraid:
He splashing holy water till he made 30
    His red hide hiss again,
And the hot vapour fill'd the smoking
    cell.
This was so common that his face became
All black and yellow with the brim-
    stone flame,
And then he smelt, . . O Lord! how
    he did smell!

Then, Sir! to see how he would
    mortify
The flesh! If any one had dainty fare,
Good man, he would come there,
And look at all the delicate things, and
    cry,
    " O Belly, Belly,   40
You would be gormandizing now, I know;
    But it shall not be so! . .
Home to your bread and water . . home,
    I tell ye!" '

' But,' quoth the Traveller, ' wherefore
    did he leave
A flock that knew his saintly worth so
    well?'
' Why,' said the Landlord, ' Sir, it so
    befell
He heard unluckily of our intent
To do him a great honour: and you
    know,
He was not covetous of fame below,
And so by stealth one night away he
    went.'   50

' What might this honour be?' the
    Traveller cried;
' Why, Sir,' the Host replied,
' We thought perhaps that he might
    one day leave us;
And then should strangers have
    The good man's grave,
A loss like that would naturally grieve
    us,
For he'll be made a Saint of to be sure.
Therefore we thought it prudent to
    secure
His relics while we might;
And so we meant to strangle him one
    night.'   60

Westbury, 1798.

THE ROSE

[Published in *Poems*, vol. ii, 1799. The
story on which this poem is based is to be
found in *The Voiage and Traivaile of Sir
John Maundeville*.]

NAY, Edith! spare the Rose; . . per-
    haps it lives,
And feels the noontide sun, and drinks
    refresh'd
The dews of night; let not thy gentle
    hand
Tear its life-strings asunder, and destroy
The sense of being! . . Why that infidel
    smile?
Come, I will bribe thee to be merciful;
And thou shalt have a tale of other days,
For I am skill'd in legendary lore,
So thou wilt let it live. There was
    a time
Ere this, the freshest, sweetest flower
    that blooms,   10
Bedeck'd the bowers of earth. Thou
    hast not heard
How first by miracle its fragrant leaves
Spread to the sun their blushing love-
    liness.

There dwelt in Bethlehem a Jewish
    maid,
And Zillah was her name, so passing
    fair

That all Judea spake the virgin's praise.
He who had seen her eyes' dark radiance
How it reveal'd her soul, and what
    a soul
Beam'd in the mild effulgence, woe to
    him !
For not in solitude, for not in crowds, 20
Might he escape remembrance, nor
    avoid
Her imaged form which followed every
    where,
And fill'd the heart, and fix'd the absent
    eye.
Alas for him ! her bosom own'd no
    love
Save the strong ardour of religious
    zeal,
For Zillah on her God had center'd all
Her spirit's deep affections. So for her
Her tribes-men sigh'd in vain, yet
    reverenced
The obdurate virtue that destroy'd
    their hopes.

One man there was, a vain and
    wretched man,   30
Who saw, desired, despaired, and hated
    her.
His sensual eye had gloated on her
    cheek
Even till the flush of angry modesty
Gave it new charms, and made him
    gloat the more.
She loathed the man, for Hamuel's eye
    was bold,
And the strong workings of brute
    selfishness
Had moulded his broad features ; and
    she feared
The bitterness of wounded vanity
That with a fiendish hue would over-
    cast
His faint and lying smile. Nor vain
    her fear,   40
For Hamuel vow'd revenge, and laid
    a plot
Against her virgin fame. He spread
    abroad
Whispers that travel fast, and ill reports
That soon obtain belief ; how Zillah's
    eye,
When in the temple heaven-ward it was
    raised,

Did swim with rapturous zeal, but there
    were those
Who had beheld the enthusiast's melting
    glance
With other feelings fill'd : . . that 'twas
    a task
Of easy sort to play the saint by day
Before the public eye, but that all
    eyes   50
Were closed at night ; . . that Zillah's
    life was foul,
Yea, forfeit to the law.
                    Shame . . shame to man,
That he should trust so easily the
    tongue
Which stabs another's fame ! The ill
    report
Was heard, repeated, and believed, . .
    and soon,
For Hamuel by his well-schemed
    villainy
Produced such semblances of guilt, . .
    the Maid
Was to the fire condemn'd.
                    Without the walls,
There was a barren field ; a place
    abhorr'd,
For it was there where wretched
    criminals   60
Receiv'd their death ! and there they
    fix'd the stake,
And piled the fuel round which should
    consume
The injured Maid, abandon'd, as it
    seem'd,
By God and Man. The assembled
    Bethlemites
Beheld the scene, and when they saw
    the Maid
Bound to the stake, with what calm
    holiness
She lifted up her patient looks to
    Heaven,
They doubted of her guilt. With other
    thoughts
Stood Hamuel near the pile ; him
    savage joy
Led thitherward, but now within his
    heart   70
Unwonted feelings stirr'd, and the first
    pangs
Of wakening guilt, anticipant of Hell.
The eye of Zillah as it glanced around

Fell on the slanderer once, and rested
   there
A moment : like a dagger did it pierce,
And struck into his soul a cureless
   wound
Conscience ! thou God within us ! not
   in the hour
Of triumph dost thou spare the guilty
   wretch,
Not in the hour of infamy and death
Forsake the virtuous !   They draw near
   the stake, . .   80
They bring the torch ! . . hold, hold
   your erring hands !
Yet quench the rising flames ! . . they
   rise ! they spread !
They reach the suffering Maid ! oh God
   protect
The innocent one !
   They rose, they spread, they raged ; . .
The breath of God went forth ; the
   ascending fire
Beneath its influence bent, and all its
   flames,
In one long lightning-flash concen-
   trating,
Darted and blasted Hamuel, . . him
   alone.
Hark ! . . what a fearful scream the
   multitude
Pour forth ! . . and yet more miracles !
   the stake   90
Branches and buds, and, spreading its
   green leaves,
Embowers and canopies the innocent
   Maid
Who there stands glorified ; and Roses,
   then
First seen on earth since Paradise was
   lost,
Profusely blossom round her, white and
   red
In all their rich variety of hues ;
And fragrance such as our first parents
   breathed
In Eden she inhales, vouchsafed to her
A presage sure of Paradise regain'd.

Westbury, 1798.

THE LOVER'S ROCK

[First published in *The Morning Post*,
April 18, 1798 ; afterwards in *The Annual
Anthology*, 1799. Southey quotes *Mariana*
as his authority for the story.]

THE Maiden through the favouring night
From Granada took her flight,
She bade her father's house farewell,
And fled away with Manuel,

No Moorish maid might hope to vie
With Laila's cheek or Laila's eye,
No maiden loved with purer truth,
Or ever loved a lovelier youth.

In fear they fled across the plain,
The father's wrath, the captive's chain ;
In hope to Seville on they flee,   11
To peace, and love, and liberty.

Chiuma they have left, and now,
Beneath a precipice's brow,
Where Guadalhorce winds its way,
There in the shade awhile they lay ;

For now the sun was near its height,
And she was weary with her flight ;
She laid her head on Manuel's breast,
And pleasant was the maiden's rest.   20

While thus the lovely Laila slept,
A fearful watch young Manuel kept,
Alas ! her Father and his train
He sees come speeding o'er the plain.

The Maiden started from her sleep,
They sought for refuge up the steep,
To scale the precipice's brow
Their only hope of safety now.

But them the angry Father sees,
With voice and arm he menaces,   30
And now the Moors approach the steep,
Loud are his curses, loud and deep.

Then Manuel's heart grew wild with woe,
He loosen'd stones and roll'd below,
He loosen'd crags, for Manuel strove
For life, and liberty, and love.

The ascent was perilous and high,
The Moors they durst not venture nigh,
The fugitives stood safely there,
They stood in safety and despair.   40

The Moorish chief unmoved could see
His daughter bend her suppliant knee;
He heard his child for pardon plead,
And swore the offenders both should
    bleed.

He bade the archers bend the bow,
And make the Christian fall below;
He bade the archers aim the dart,
And pierce the Maid's apostate heart.

The archers aim'd their arrows there,
She clasp'd young Manuel in despair, 50
' Death, Manuel, shall set us free !
Then leap below and die with me.'

He clasp'd her close and cried farewell,
In one another's arms they fell;
And falling o'er the rock's steep side,
In one another's arms they died.

And side by side they there are laid,
The Christian youth and Moorish maid;
But never Cross was planted there,
Because they perish'd for despair. 60

Yet every Moorish maid can tell
Where Laila lies who loved so well,
And every youth who passes there,
Says for Manuel's soul a prayer.

Westbury, 1798.

GARCI FERRANDEZ

[Published in *The Edinburgh Annual
Register* for 1809. The story is to be found
in the *Coronica General de España.*]

PART I

1

IN an evil day and an hour of woe
Did Garci Ferrandez wed !
He wedded the Lady Argentine,
As ancient stories tell,
He loved the Lady Argentine,
Alas ! for what befell !

The Lady Argentine hath fled;
In an evil day and an hour of woe
She hath left the husband who loved
    her well,
To go to Count Aymerique's bed. 10

2

Garci Ferrandez was brave and young,
The comeliest of the land;
There was never a knight of Leon in fight
Who could meet the force of his
    matchless might;
There was never a foe in the infidel band
Who against his dreadful sword could
    stand;
And yet Count Garci's strong right hand
Was shapely, and soft, and white;
As white and as soft as a lady's hand
Was the hand of the beautiful Knight.

3

In an evil day and an hour of woe 21
To Garci's Hall did Count Aymerique
    go;
In an evil hour and a luckless night
From Garci's Hall did he take his flight,
And bear with him that lady bright,
That lady false, his bale and bane.
There was feasting and joy in Count
    Aymerique's bower,
When he with triumph, and pomp,
    and pride,
Brought home the adult'ress like a
    bride :
His daughter only sate in her tower,
She sate in her lonely tower alone, 31
And for her dead mother she made her
    moan;
' Methinks,' said she, ' my father for me
Might have brought a bridegroom home.
A stepmother he brings hither instead,
Count Aymerique will not his daughter
    should wed,
But he brings home a leman for his
    own bed.'
So thoughts of good and thoughts of ill
Were working thus in Abba's will;
And Argentine with evil intent 40
Ever to work her woe was bent;
That still she sate in her tower alone,
And in that melancholy gloom,
When for her mother she made her moan,
She wish'd her father too in the tomb.

4

She watches the pilgrims and poor who
        wait
For daily food at her father's gate.
' I would some Knight were there,'
        thought she,
' Disguised in pilgrim-weeds for me !
For Aymerique's blessing I would not
        stay,   50
Nor he nor his leman should say me nay,
But I with him would wend away.'

5

She watches her handmaid the pittance
        deal,
They took their dole and went away ;
But yonder is one who lingers still
As though he had something in his will,
Some secret which he fain would say ;
And close to the portal she sees him go,
He talks with her handmaid in
        accents low ;
Oh then she thought that time went
        slow,   60
And long were the minutes that she
        must wait
Till her handmaid came from the
        castle-gate.

6

From the castle-gate her handmaid came,
And told her that a knight was there,
Who sought to speak with Abba the fair,
Count Aymerique's beautiful daughter
        and heir.
She bade the stranger to her bower ;
His stature was tall, his features bold,
A goodlier form might never maid
        At tilt or tourney hope to see ; 70
And though in pilgrim-weeds array'd,
Yet noble in his weeds was he,
And did his arms in them enfold
As they were robes of royalty.

7

He told his name to the high-born fair,
He said that vengeance led him there.
' Now aid me, lady dear,' quoth he,
' To smite the adult'ress in her pride ;
Your wrongs and mine avenged shall be,
And I will take you for my bride.'   80

He pledged the word of a true Knight,
From out the weeds his hand he drew ;
She took the hand that Garci gave,
And then she knew his tale was true,
For she saw the warrior's hand so white,
And she knew the fame of the beautiful
        Knight.

PART II

1

'Tis the hour of noon,
The bell of the convent hath done,
And the Sexts are begun ;
The Count and his leman are gone to
        their meat.
They look to their pages, and lo they see
Where Abba, a stranger so long before,
The ewer, and bason, and napkin bore ;
She came and knelt on her bended
        knee,
And first to her father minister'd she ;
Count Aymerique look'd on his
        daughter down,   10
He look'd on her then without a frown.

2

And next to the Lady Argentine
Humbly she went and knelt ;
The Lady Argentine the while
A haughty wonder felt ;
Her face put on an evil smile ;
' I little thought that I should see
The Lady Abba kneel to me
In service of love and courtesy !
Count Aymerique,' the leman cried,
' Is she weary of her solitude,   21
Or hath she quell'd her pride ? '
Abba no angry word replied,
She only raised her eyes and cried,
' Let not the Lady Argentine
Be wroth at ministry of mine ! '
She look'd at Aymerique and sigh'd ;
' My father will not frown, I ween,
That Abba again at his board should
        be seen ! '
Then Aymerique raised her from her
        knee,   30
And kiss'd her eyes, and bade her be
The daughter she was wont to be.

3

The wine hath warm'd Count Aymerique.
That mood his crafty daughter knew ;
She came and kiss'd her father's cheek,
   And stroked his beard with gentle
      hand,
   And winning eye and action bland,
   As she in childhood used to do.
' A boon ! Count Aymerique,' quoth
      she ;
' If I have found favour in thy sight,
   Let me sleep at my father's feet to-
      night.   41
Grant this,' quoth she, ' so I shall see
   That you will let your Abba be
The daughter she was wont to be.'
   With asking eye did Abba speak,
   Her voice was soft and sweet ;
The wine had warm'd Count Aymerique,
   And when the hour of rest was come,
   She lay at her father's feet.

4

In Aymerique's arms the adult'ress
      lay,   50
   Their talk was of the distant day,
How they from Garci fled away
   In the silent hour of night ;
And then amid their wanton play
They mock'd the beautiful Knight.
   Far, far away his castle lay,
   The weary road of many a day ;
' And travel long,' they said, ' to him,
   It seem'd, was small delight ;
And he belike was loth with blood 60
   To stain his hands so white.'
They little thought that Garci then
   Heard every scornful word !
They little thought the avenging hand
   Was on the avenging sword !
Fearless, unpenitent, unblest,
The adulterer on the leman's breast.

5

Then Abba, listening still in fear,
To hear the breathing long and slow, 70
   At length the appointed signal gave,
   And Garci rose and struck the blow.
One blow sufficed for Aymerique, . .
He made no moan, he utter'd no groan ;
But his death-start waken'd Argentine,

   And by the chamber-lamp she saw
      The bloody falchion shine !
She raised for help her in-drawn breath,
   But her shriek of fear was her shriek
      of death.

6

In an evil day and an hour of woe 80
   Did Garci Ferrandez wed !
One wicked wife he has sent to her
      grave,
He hath taken a worse to his bed.

Bristol, 1801.

BISHOP BRUNO

[First published in *The Morning Post*,
November 17, 1798 ; afterwards in *The
Annual Anthology*, 1799, and in *Metrical Tales*,
1805. Southey quotes as his authority for
the story here versified a passage in Heywood's *Hierarchie of the Blessed Angels*.]

BISHOP BRUNO awoke in the dead mid-
      night,
And he heard his heart beat loud with
      affright :
He dreamt he had rung the Palace bell,
And the sound it gave was his passing
      knell.

Bishop Bruno smiled at his fears so vain,
He turn'd to sleep and he dreamt again ;
He rang at the Palace gate once more,
And Death was the Porter that open'd
      the door.

He started up at the fearful dream,
And he heard at his window the screech-
      owl scream ;   10
Bishop Bruno slept no more that
      night, . .
Oh ! glad was he when he saw the day-
      light !

Now he goes forth in proud array,
For he with the Emperor dines to-day ;
There was not a Baron in Germany
That went with a nobler train than he.

Before and behind his soldiers ride,
The people throng'd to see their pride ;
They bow'd the head, and the knee they
  bent,
But nobody blest him as he went.   20

So he went on stately and proud,
When he heard a voice that cried aloud,
' Ho ! ho ! Bishop Bruno ! you travel
  with glee, . .
But I would have you know, you travel
  to me ! '

Behind and before and on either side,
He look'd, but nobody he espied ;
And the Bishop at that grew cold with
  fear,
For he heard the words distinct and
  clear.

And when he rang at the Palace bell,
He almost expected to hear his knell ; 30
And when the Porter turn'd the key,
He almost expected Death to see.

But soon the Bishop recover'd his glee,
For the Emperor welcomed him royally ;
And now the tables were spread, and
  there
Were choicest wines and dainty fare.

And now the Bishop had blest the meat,
When a voice was heard as he sat in his
  seat, . .
' With the Emperor now you are dining
  with glee,
But know, Bishop Bruno ! you sup
  with me ! '   40

The Bishop then grew pale with affright,
And suddenly lost his appetite ;
All the wine and dainty cheer
Could not comfort his heart that was
  sick with fear.

But by little and little recovered he,
For the wine went flowing merrily,
Till at length he forgot his former dread,
And his cheeks again grew rosy red.

When he sat down to the royal fare
Bishop Bruno was the saddest man
  there ;   50
But when the masquers enter'd the hall,
He was the merriest man of all.

Then from amid the masquers' crowd
There went a voice hollow and loud, . .
' You have pass'd the day, Bishop
  Bruno, in glee ;
But you must pass the night with me ! '

His cheek grows pale, and his eye-balls
  glare,
And stiff round his tonsure bristled his
  hair ;
With that there came one from the
  masquers' band,
And took the Bishop by the hand.   60

The bony hand suspended his breath,
His marrow grew cold at the touch of
  Death ;
On saints in vain he attempted to call,
Bishop Bruno fell dead in the Palace
  hall.

Westbury, 1798.

A TRUE BALLAD OF ST. ANTIDIUS, THE POPE, AND THE DEVIL

[Published in *The Morning Post*, 1802, or early in 1803. Southey took the subject of this Ballad from the *Coronica de España*.]

It is Antidius the Bishop
  Who now at even tide,
Taking the air and saying a prayer,
  Walks by the river side.

The Devil had business that evening,
  And he upon earth would go ;
For it was in the month of August,
  And the weather was close below.

He had his books to settle,
  And up to earth he hied,   10
To do it there in the evening air,
  All by the river side.

His imps came flying around him,
  Of his affairs to tell ;
From the north, and the south, and
  the east, and the west ;
They brought him the news that he
  liked best,
  Of the things they had done,
  And the souls they had won,
  And how they sped well
  In the service of Hell.   20

There came a devil posting in
    Return'd from his employ,
Seven years had he been gone from
        Hell,
And now he came grinning for joy.

' Seven years,' quoth he, ' of trouble
        and toil
Have I labour'd the Pope to win ;
    And I to-day have caught him,
    He hath done a deadly sin ! '
And then he took the Devil's book,
    And wrote the deed therein.   30

Oh, then King Beelzebub for joy,
    He drew his mouth so wide,
You might have seen his iron teeth,
    Four and forty from side to side.

He wagg'd his ears, he twisted his tail,
    He knew not for joy what to do,
In his hoofs and his horns, in his heels
        and his corns,
    It tickled him all through.

The Bishop who beheld all this,   39
    Straight how to act bethought him ;
He leapt upon the Devil's back,
    And by the horns he caught him.

And he said a Pater-noster
    As fast as he could say,
And made a cross on the Devil's head,
    And bade him to Rome away.

Away, away, the Devil flew,
    All through the clear moonlight ;
I warrant who saw them on their way
    He did not sleep that night.   50

Without bridle, or saddle, or whip, or
        spur,
    Away they go like the wind ;
The beads of the Bishop are hanging
        before,
    And the tail of the Devil behind.

They met a Witch and she hail'd them,
    As soon as she came within call ;
' Ave Maria ! ' the Bishop exclaim'd,
    It frightened her broomstick and she
        got a fall.

He ran against a shooting star,
    So fast for fear did he sail,   60
And he singed the beard of the Bishop
    Against a Comet's tail ;
And he pass'd between the horns of
        the Moon,
    With Antidius on his back ;
And there was an eclipse that night,
    Which was not in the Almanack.

The Bishop just as they set out,
    To tell his beads begun ;
And he was by the bed of the Pope
    Before the string was done.   70

The Pope fell down upon his knees,
    In terror and confusion,
And he confess'd the deadly sin,
    And he had absolution.

And all the Popes in bliss that be,
    Sung, O be joyful ! then ;
And all the Popes in bale that be,
    They howl'd for envy then ;
For they before kept jubilee,
    Expecting his good company,   80
    Down in the Devil's den.

But what was this the Pope had done
    To bind his soul to Hell ?
Ah ! that is the mystery of this
        wonderful history,
    And I wish that I could tell !

But would you know, there you must
        go,
    You can easily find the way ;
It is a broad and a well-known road
That is travell'd by night and by day.   89

And you must look in the Devil's book ;
    You will find one debt that was never
        paid yet
If you search the leaves throughout ;
    And that is the mystery of this
        wonderful history,
    And the way to find it out.

Bristol, 1802.

HENRY THE HERMIT

[First published in *The Morning Post*,
November 1, 1798; afterwards in *Poems*,
vol. ii, 1799. The story is related in the
English Martyrology, 1608.]

It was a little island where he dwelt,
A solitary islet, bleak and bare,
Short scanty herbage spotting with dark
    spots
Its grey stone surface.   Never mariner
Approach'd that rude and uninviting
    coast,
Nor ever fisherman his lonely bark
Anchor'd beside its shore.   It was a
    place
Befitting well a rigid anchoret,
Dead to the hopes and vanities and
    joys,   9
And purposes of life : and he had dwelt
Many long years upon that lonely isle ;
For in ripe manhood he abandon'd arms,
Honours and friends and country and
    the world,
And had grown old in solitude.   That
    isle
Some solitary man in other times
Had made his dwelling-place ;   and
    Henry found
The little chapel which his toil had built
Now by the storms unroof'd, his bed of
    leaves
Wind-scatter'd ;   and his grave o'er-
    grown with grass,
And thistles, whose white seeds there
    wing'd in vain   20
Wither'd on rocks, or in the waves were
    lost.
So he repair'd the chapel's ruin'd roof,
Clear'd the grey lichens from the altar-
    stone,
And underneath a rock that shelter'd
    him
From the sea-blast, he built his her-
    mitage.

   The peasants from the shore would
    bring him food,
And beg his prayers ; but human con-
    verse else
He knew not in that utter solitude ;
Nor ever visited the haunts of men,
Save when some sinful wretch on a sick
    bed   30
Implored his blessing and his aid in
    death.
That summons he delay'd not to obey,
Though the night tempest or autumnal
    wind
Madden'd the waves ;   and though the
    mariner,
Albeit relying on his saintly load,
Grew pale to see the peril.   Thus he
    lived
A most austere and self-denying man,
Till abstinence and age and watchfulness
Had worn him down, and it was pain at
    last
To rise at midnight from his bed of
    leaves   40
And bend his knees in prayer.   Yet not
    the less,
Though with reluctance of infirmity,
Rose he at midnight from his bed of
    leaves
And bent his knees in prayer ;   but with
    more zeal,
More self-condemning fervour, raised his
    voice
Imploring pardon for the natural sin
Of that reluctance, till the atoning
    prayer
Had satisfied his heart, and given it
    peace,
And the repented fault became a joy.

   One night upon the shore his chapel-
    bell   50
Was heard ;   the air was calm, and its
    far sounds
Over the water came, distinct and loud.
Alarm'd at that unusual hour to hear
Its toll irregular, a monk arose,
And crost to the island-chapel.   On a
    stone
Henry was sitting there, dead, cold, and
    stiff,
The bell-rope in his hand, and at his feet
The lamp that stream'd a long unsteady
    light.

Westbury, 1799.

ST. GUALBERTO

ADDRESSED TO GEORGE BURNETT.

[Published in *The Annual Anthology*, 1800, and in *Metrical Tales*, 1805. Southey quotes Villegas, *Flos Sanctorum*, and other writers, as narrating the stories which he has versified in this ballad.]

1

THE work is done, the fabric is complete ;
Distinct the Traveller sees its distant tower,
Yet ere his steps attain the sacred seat,
Must toil for many a league and many an hour.
Elate the Abbot sees the pile and knows,
Stateliest of convents now, his new Moscera rose.

2

Long were the tale that told Moscera's pride,
Its columns cluster'd strength and lofty state,
How many a saint bedeck'd its sculptured side,
What intersecting arches graced its gate ;   10
Its towers how high, its massy walls how strong,
These fairly to describe were sure a tedious song.

3

Yet while the fane rose slowly from the ground,
But little store of charity, I ween,
The passing pilgrim at Moscera found ;
And often there the mendicant was seen
Hopeless to turn him from the convent-door,
Because this costly work still kept the brethren poor.

4

Now all is finish'd, and from every side
They flock to view the fabric, young and old.   20
Who now can tell Rodulfo's secret pride,
When on the Sabbath-day his eyes behold
The multitudes that crowd his church's floor,
Some sure to serve their God, to see Moscera more ?

5

So chanced it that Gualberto pass'd that way,
Since sainted for a life of saintly deeds.
He paused the new-rear'd convent to survey,
And o'er the structure whilst his eye proceeds,
Sorrow'd, as one whose holier feelings deem
That ill so proud a pile did humble monks beseem.   30

6

Him, musing as he stood, Rodulfo saw,
And forth he came to greet the holy guest :
For him he knew as one who held the law
Of Benedict, and each severe behest
So duly kept with such religious care,
That Heaven had oft vouchsafed its wonders to his prayer.

7

' Good   brother,   welcome !'   thus Rodulfo cries,
' In sooth it glads me to behold you here ;
It is Gualberto ! and mine aged eyes
Did not deceive me : yet full many a year   40
Hath slipt away, since last you bade farewell
To me your host and my uncomfortable cell.

8

"'Twas but a sorry welcome then you
found,
And such as suited ill a guest so
dear.
The pile was ruinous, the base un-
sound ;
It glads me more to bid you wel-
come here,
For you can call to mind our former
state ;
Come, brother, pass with me the new
Moscera's gate.'

9

So spake the cheerful Abbot, but no
smile
Of answering joy relax'd Gualberto's
brow ;   50
He raised his hand and pointed to
the pile,
'Moscera better pleased me then,
than now ;
A palace this, befitting kingly pride !
Will holiness, my friend, in palace pomp
abide ?'

10

'Ay,' cries Rodulfo, ''tis a stately
place !
And pomp becomes the House of
Worship well.
Nay, scowl not round with so severe
a face !
When earthly kings in seats of
grandeur dwell,
Where art exhausted decks the
sumptuous hall,
Can poor and sordid huts beseem the
Lord of all ?'   60

11

'And ye have rear'd these stately
towers on high
To serve your God ?' the Monk
severe replied.
'It rose from zeal and earnest piety,
And prompted by no worldly
thoughts beside.'
'Abbot, to him who prays with soul
sincere
However poor the cell, God will incline
his ear.

12

'Rodulfo ! while this haughty building rose,
Still was the pilgrim welcome at
your door ?
Did charity relieve the orphan's woes ?
Clothed ye the naked ? did ye feed
the poor ?   70
He who with alms most succours the
distrest,
Proud Abbot ! know he serves his
heavenly Father best.

13

'Did they in sumptuous palaces go
dwell
Who first abandon'd all to serve the
Lord ?
Their place of worship was the desert
cell,
Wild fruits and berries spread their
frugal board,
And if a brook, like this, ran mur-
muring by,
They blest their gracious God, and
"thought it luxury".'

14

Then anger darken'd in Rodulfo's
face ;
'Enough of preaching,' sharply he
replied ;   80
'Thou art grown envious ; . . 'tis a
common case,
Humility is made the cloak of pride.
Proud of our home's magnificence are
we,
But thou art far more proud in rags and
beggary.'

15

With that Gualberto cried in fervent
tone,
'O, Father, hear me ! If this costly
pile
Was for thine honour rear'd, and
thine alone,
Bless it, O Father, with thy
fostering smile !
Still may it stand, and never evil
know,
Long as beside its walls the endless
stream shall flow.   90

16

'But, Lord, if vain and worldly-
minded men
Have wasted here the wealth which
thou hast lent,
To pamper worldly pride; frown on
it then!
Soon be thy vengeance manifestly
sent!
Let yonder brook, that gently flows
beside,
Now from its base sweep down the unholy house of pride!'

17

He said, .. and lo, the brook no longer
flows!
The waters pause, and now they
swell on high;
Erect in one collected heap they rose;
The affrighted brethren from Moscera fly,   100
And upon all the Saints in Heaven
they call,
To save them in their flight from that
impending fall.

18

Down the heapt waters came, and,
with a sound
Like thunder, overthrown the
fabric falls;
Swept far and wide its fragments
strew the ground,
Prone lie its columns now, its high-
arch'd walls,
Earth shakes beneath the onward-
rolling tide,
That from its base swept down the
unholy house of pride.

* * * * *

19

Were old Gualberto's reasons built
on truth,
Dear George, or like Moscera's base
unsound?   110
This sure I know, that glad am I, in
sooth,   [ground;
He only play'd his pranks on foreign
For had he turn'd the stream on
England too,
The Vandal monk had spoilt full many
a goodly view.

20

Then Malmesbury's arch had never
met my sight,
Nor Battle's vast and venerable
pile;
I had not traversed then with such
delight
The hallowed ruins of our Alfred's
isle,
Where many a pilgrim's curse is well
bestow'd
On those who rob its walls to mend the
turnpike road.   120

21

Wells would have fallen, dear George,
our country's pride;
And Canning's stately church been
rear'd in vain;
Nor had the traveller Ely's tower
descried,
Which when thou seest far o'er the
fenny plain,
Dear George, I counsel thee to turn
that way,
Its ancient beauties sure will well
reward delay.

22

And we should never then have
heard, I think,
At evening hour, great Tom's
tremendous knell.
The fountain streams that now in
Christ-church stink
Had niagara'd o'er the quadrangle:
But, as 'twas beauty that deserved
the flood,   131
I ween, dear George, thy own old Pom-
pey might have stood.

23

Then had not Westminster, the house
of God,
Served for a concert room, or
signal-post;
Old Thames, obedient to the father's
nod,
Had swept down Greenwich, England's noblest boast;
And, eager to destroy the unholy
walls,
Fleet-ditch had roll'd up hill to overwhelm St. Paul's.

24

George, dost thou deem the legendary deeds
   Of saints like this but rubbish, a mere store   140
Of trash, that he flings time away who reads ?
   And would'st thou rather bid me puzzle o'er
Matter and Mind and all the eternal round,
Plunged headlong down the dark and fathomless profound ?

25

Now do I bless the man who undertook
   These Monks and Martyrs to biographize ;
And love to ponder o'er his ponderous book,
   The mingle-mangle mass of truth and lies,
Where waking fancies mixt with dreams appear,
And blind and honest zeal, and holy faith sincere.   150

26

All is not truth ; and yet, methinks, 'twere hard
   Of wilful fraud such fablers to accuse ;
What if a Monk, from better themes debarr'd,
   Should for an edifying story chuse,
How some great Saint the Flesh and Fiend o'ercame,
His taste I trow, and not his conscience, were to blame.

27

No fault of his, if what he thus design'd,
   Like pious novels for the use of youth,
Obtain'd such hold upon the simple mind
   That 'twas received at length for gospel-truth.   160
A fair account ! and should'st thou like the plea,
Thank thou our valued friend, dear George, who taught it me.

28

All is not false which seems at first a lie.
Fernan Antolinez, a Spanish knight,
Knelt at the mass, when lo ! the troops hard by
Before the expected hour began the fight.
Though courage, duty, honour, summon'd there,
He chose to forfeit all, not leave the unfinish'd prayer.

29

But while devoutly thus the unarm'd knight
   Waits till the holy service should be o'er,   170
Even then the foremost in the furious fight
   Was he beheld to bathe his sword in gore ;
First in the van his plumes were seen to play,
And all to him decreed the glory of the day.

30

The truth is told, and men at once exclaim,
   Heaven had his Guardian Angel deign'd to send ;
And thus the tale is handed down to fame.
   Now if our good Sir Fernan had a friend
Who in this critical season served him well,
Dear George, the tale is true, and yet no miracle.   180

31

I am not one who scan with scornful eyes
   The dreams which make the enthusiast's best delight ;
Nor thou the legendary lore despise
   If of Gualberto yet again I write,
How first impell'd he sought the convent-cell ;
A simple tale it is, but one that pleased me well.

.   .   .   .

32

Fortune had smiled upon Gualberto's
    birth,
    The heir of Valdespesa's rich
        domains ;
An only child, he grew in years and
    worth,
    And well repaid a father's anxious
        pains.   190
In many a field that father had been
    tried,
Well for his valour known, and not less
    known for pride.

33

It chanced that one in kindred near
    allied
    Was slain by his hereditary foe ;
Much by his sorrow moved and more
    by pride,
    The father vow'd that blood for
        blood should flow,
And from his youth Gualberto had
    been taught
That with unceasing hate should just
    revenge be sought.

34

Long did they wait ; at length the
    tidings came
    That through a lone and unfre-
        quented way   200
Soon would Anselmo, such the mur-
    derer's name,
    Pass on his journey home, an easy
        prey.
' Go,' said the father, ' meet him in
    the wood ! '
And young Gualberto went, and laid in
    wait for blood.

35

When now the youth was at the
    forest shade
    Arrived, it drew toward the close of
        day ;
Anselmo haply might be long delay'd,
    And he, already wearied with his
        way,
Beneath an ancient oak his limbs
    reclined,
And thoughts of near revenge alone
    possess'd his mind.   210

36

Slow sunk the glorious sun ; a roseate
    light
    Spread o'er the forest from his
        lingering rays ;   [sight
The glowing clouds upon Gualberto's
    Soften'd in shade, . . he could not
        chuse but gaze ;
And now a placid greyness clad the
    heaven,
Save where the west retain'd the last
    green light of even.

37

Cool breathed the grateful air, and
    fresher now
    The fragrance of the autumnal
        leaves arose ;
The passing gale scarce moved the
    o'erhanging bough,
    And not a sound disturb'd the deep
        repose,   220
Save when a falling leaf came flut-
    tering by,
Save the near brooklet's stream that
    murmur'd quietly.

38

Is there who has not felt the deep
    delight,
    The hush of soul, that scenes like
        these impart ?
The heart they will not soften is not
    right,
    And young Gualberto was not hard
        of heart.
Yet sure he thinks revenge becomes
    him well,
When from a neighbouring church he
    heard the vesper-bell.

39

The Romanist who hears that vesper-
    bell,
    Howe'er employ'd, must send a
        prayer to Heaven.   230
In foreign lands I liked the custom
    well,
    For with the calm and sober
        thoughts of even
It well accords ; and wert thou
    journeying there,
It would not hurt thee, George, to join
    that vesper-prayer.

40

Gualberto had been duly taught to hold
All pious customs with religious care ;
And, . . for the young man's feelings were not cold,
He never yet had miss'd his vesper-prayer.
But strange misgivings now his heart invade,
And when the vesper-bell had ceased he had not pray'd. 240

41

And wherefore was it that he had not pray'd ?
The sudden doubt arose within his mind,
And many a former precept then he weigh'd,
The words of Him who died to save mankind ;
How 'twas the meek who should inherit Heaven,
And man must man forgive, if he would be forgiven.

42

Troubled at heart, almost he felt a hope,
That yet some chance his victim might delay.
So as he mused, adown the neighbouring slope
He saw a lonely traveller on his way ; 250
And now he knows the man so much abhorr'd, . .
His holier thoughts are gone, he bares the murderous sword.

43

' The house of Valdespesa gives the blow !
Go, and our vengeance to our kinsman tell ! ' . . [foe,
Despair and terror seized the unarm'd
And prostrate at the young man's knees he fell,
And stopt his hand and cried, ' Oh, do not take
A wretched sinner's life ! mercy, for Jesus' sake ! '

44

At that most blessed name, as at a spell,
Conscience, the power within him, smote his heart. 260
His hand, for murder raised, un-harming fell ;
He felt cold sweat-drops on his forehead start ;
A moment mute in holy horror stood,
Then cried, ' Joy, joy, my God ! I have not shed his blood ! '

45

He raised Anselmo up, and bade him live,
And bless, for both preserved, that holy name :
And pray'd the astonish'd foeman to forgive
The bloody purpose led by which he came.
Then to the neighbouring church he sped away,
His over-burden'd soul before his God to lay. 270

46

He ran with breathless speed, . . he reach'd the door,
With rapid throbs his feverish pulses swell ; . .
He came to crave for pardon, to adore
For grace vouchsafed ; before the cross he fell,
And raised his swimming eyes, and thought that there
He saw the imaged Christ smile favouring on his prayer.

47

A blest illusion ! from that very night
The Monk's austerest life devout he led ;
And still he felt the enthusiast's deep delight,
Seraphic visions floated round his head, 280
The joys of heaven foretasted fill'd his soul,
And still the good man's name adorns the sainted roll.

Westbury, 1799.

QUEEN MARY'S CHRISTENING

[Southey quotes as his authorities for the story here versified, *Zurita*, l. ii, c. 59, and *La Historia del muy alto é invencible Rey Don Jayme de Aragon, Primero deste Nombre, llamado El Conquistador*. . .—Valencia,1584.]

THE first wish of Queen Mary's heart
    Is, that she may bear a son,
Who shall inherit in his time
    The kingdom of Aragon.

She hath put up prayers to all the Saints
    This blessing to accord,
But chiefly she hath call'd upon
    The Apostles of our Lord.

The second wish of Queen Mary's heart
    Is to have that son call'd James,   10
Because she thought for a Spanish King
    'Twas the best of all good names.

To give him this name of her own will
    Is what may not be done,
For having applied to all the Twelve
    She may not prefer the one.

By one of their names she hath vow'd to call
    Her son, if son it should be ;
But which, is a point whereon she must let
    The Apostles themselves agree.   20

Already Queen Mary hath to them
    Contracted a grateful debt,
And from their patronage she hoped
    For these farther blessings yet.

Alas ! it was not her hap to be
    As handsome as she was good ;
And that her husband King Pedro thought so
    She very well understood.

She had lost him from her lawful bed
    For lack of personal graces,   30
And by prayers to them, and a pious deceit,
    She had compass'd his embraces.

But if this hope of a son should fail,
    All hope must fail with it then,
For she could not expect by a second device
    To compass the King again.

Queen Mary hath had her first heart's wish—
    She hath brought forth a beautiful boy ;
And the bells have rung, and masses been sung,
    And bonfires have blazed for joy.   40

And many's the cask of the good red wine,
    And many the cask of the white,
Which was broach'd for joy that morning,
    And emptied before it was night.

But now for Queen Mary's second heart's wish,
    It must be determined now,
And Bishop Boyl, her Confessor,
    Is the person who taught her how.

Twelve waxen tapers he hath had made,
    In size and weight the same ;   50
And to each of these twelve tapers
    He hath given an Apostle's name.

One holy Nun had bleach'd the wax,
    Another the wicks had spun ;
And the golden candlesticks were blest,
    Which they were set upon.

From that which should burn the longest,
    The infant his name must take ;
And the Saint who own'd it was to be
    His Patron for his name's sake.   60

A godlier or a goodlier sight
    Was nowhere to be seen,
Methinks, that day, in Christendom,
    Than in the chamber of that good Queen

Twelve little altars have been there
    Erected, for the nonce ;
And the twelve tapers are set thereon,
    Which are all to be lit at once.

Altars more gorgeously drest
    You nowhere could desire ;   70
At each there stood a minist'ring Priest
    In his most rich attire.

A high altar hath there been raised,
    Where the crucifix you see ;
And the sacred Pix that shines with gold
    And sparkles with jewelry.

Bishop Boyl, with his precious mitre on,
Hath taken there his stand,
In robes which were embroidered
By the Queen's own royal hand. 89

In one part of the ante-room
The Ladies of the Queen,
All with their rosaries in hand,
Upon their knees are seen.

In the other part of the ante-room
The Chiefs of the realm you behold,
Ricos Omes, and Bishops and Abbots,
And Knights and Barons bold.

Queen Mary could behold all this
As she lay in her state bed ; 90
And from the pillow needed not
To lift her languid head.

One fear she had, though still her heart
The unwelcome thought eschew'd,
That haply the unlucky lot
Might fall upon St. Jude.

But the Saints, she trusted, that ill
chance
Would certainly forefend ;
And moreover there was a double hope
Of seeing the wish'd-for end : 100

Because there was a double chance
For the best of all good names ;
If it should not be Santiago himself,
It might be the lesser St. James.

And now Bishop Boyl hath said the
mass ;
And as soon as the mass was done,
The priests who by the twelve tapers
stood
Each instantly lighted one.

The tapers were short and slender too,
Yet to the expectant throng, 110
Before they to the socket burnt,
The time, I trow, seem'd long.

The first that went out was St. Peter,
The second was St. John ;
And now St. Matthias is going,
And now St. Matthew is gone.

Next there went St. Andrew,
There goes St. Philip too ;
And see ! there is an end
Of St. Bartholomew. 120

St. Simon is in the snuff ;
But it was a matter of doubt
Whether he or St. Thomas could be said
Soonest to have gone out.

There are only three remaining,
St. Jude, and the two Sts. James :
And great was then Queen Mary's hope
For the best of all good names.

Great was then Queen Mary's hope,
But greater her fear, I guess, 130
When one of the three went out,
And that one was St. James the Less.

They are now within less than quarter-
inch,
The only remaining two !
When there came a thief in St. James,
And it made a gutter too !

Up started Queen Mary,
Up she sate in her bed :
' I never can call him Judas ! '
She claspt her hands and said. 140

' I never can call him Judas ! '
Again did she exclaim ;
' Holy mother preserve us !
It is not a Christian name ! '

She spread her hands and claspt them
again,
And the Infant in the cradle
Set up a cry, an angry cry,
As loud as he was able.

' Holy Mother preserve us ! '
The Queen her prayer renew'd ; 150
When in came a moth at the window
And flutter'd about St. Jude.

St. James hath fallen in the socket,
But as yet the flame is not out,
And St. Jude hath singed the silly moth
That flutters so blindly about.

And before the flame and the molten
wax
That silly moth could kill,
It hath beat out St. Jude with its wings,
And St. James is burning still ! 160

Oh, that was a joy for Queen Mary's
heart ;
The babe is christened James ;
The Prince of Aragon hath got
The best of all good names !

Glory to Santiago,
The mighty one in war !
James he is call'd, and he shall be
King James the Conqueror !

Now shall the Crescent wane,
The Cross be set on high 170
In triumph upon many a Mosque ;
Woe, woe to Mawmetry !

Valencia shall be subdued ;
Majorca shall be won ;
The Moors be routed every where ;
Joy, joy, for Aragon !

Shine brighter now, ye stars, that crown
Our Lady del Pilar,
And rejoice in thy grave, Cid Campeador
Ruy Diez de Bivar ! 180

Keswick, 1829.

ROPRECHT THE ROBBER

The story here versified is told by Taylor the Water Poet, in his 'Three Weeks, Three Days, and Three Hours' Observations from London to Hamburgh in Germany; amongst Jews and Gentiles, with Descriptions of Towns and Towers, Castles and Citadels, artificial Gallowses and natural Hangmen ; and dedicated for the present to the absent Odcombian Knight Errant, Sir Thomas Coryat.' It is in the volume of his collected works, p. 82, of the third paging.

Collein, which is the scene of this story, is more probably Kollen on the Elbe, in Bohemia, or a town of the same name in Prussia, than Cologne, to which great city the reader will perceive I had good reasons for transferring it.

PART I

ROPRECHT the Robber is taken at last,
In Cologne they have him fast ;
Trial is over, and sentence past ;
And hopes of escape were vain he knew,
For the gallows now must have its due.

But though pardon cannot here be
bought,
It may for the other world, he thought ;
And so to his comfort, with one consent,
The Friars assured their penitent.

Money, they teach him, when rightly
given, 10
Is put out to account with Heaven ;
For suffrages therefore his plunder went,
Sinfully gotten, but piously spent.

All Saints, whose shrines are in that city,
They tell him, will on him have pity,
Seeing he hath liberally paid,
In this time of need, for their good aid.

In the Three Kings they bid him confide,
Who there in Cologne lie side by side ;
And from the Eleven Thousand Virgins
eke, 20
Intercession for him will they bespeak.

And also a sharer he shall be
In the merits of their community ;
All which they promise, he need not fear,
Through Purgatory will carry him clear.

Though the furnace of Babylon could
not compare
With the terrible fire that rages there,
Yet they their part will so zealously do,
He shall only but frizzle as he flies
through.

And they will help him to die well, 30
And he shall be hang'd with book and
bell ;
And moreover with holy water they
Will sprinkle him, ere they turn away.

For buried Roprecht must not be,
He is to be left on the triple tree :
That they who pass along may spy
Where the famous Robber is hanging
on high.

Seen is that gibbet far and wide
From the Rhine and from the Dussel-
dorff side ;
And from all roads which cross the sand,
North, south, and west, in that level
land. 41

It will be a comfortable sight
To see him there by day and by night ;
For Roprecht the Robber many a year
Had kept the country round in fear.

So the Friars assisted, by special grace,
With book and bell to the fatal place ;
And he was hang'd on the triple tree,
With as much honour as man could be.

In his suit of irons he was hung, 50
They sprinkled him then, and their
    psalm they sung ;
And turning away when this duty was
    paid,
They said what a goodly end he had
    made.

The crowd broke up and went their way ;
All were gone by the close of day ;
And Roprecht the Robber was left there
Hanging alone in the moonlight air.

The last who look'd back for a parting
    sight,
Beheld him there in the clear moonlight ;
But the first who look'd when the
    morning shone,   60
Saw in dismay that Roprecht was gone.

PART II

THE stir in Cologne is greater to-day
Than all the bustle of yesterday ;
Hundreds and thousands went out to
    see ;
The irons and chains, as well as he,
Were gone, but the rope was left on the
    tree.

A wonderful thing ! for every one said
He had hung till he was dead, dead,
    dead ;
And on the gallows was seen, from noon
Till ten o'clock, in the light of the moon.

Moreover the Hangman was ready to
    swear   10
He had done his part with all due care ;
And that certainly better hang'd than he
No one ever was, or ever could be.

Neither kith nor kin, to bear him
    away
And funeral rites in secret pay,
Had he, and none that pains would take,
With risk of the law, for a stranger's
    sake.

So 'twas thought, because he had died
    so well,
He was taken away by miracle.
But would he again alive be found ? 20
Or had he been laid in holy ground ?

If in holy ground his relics were laid,
Some marvellous sign would show, they
    said ;
If restored to life, a Friar he would be,
Or a holy Hermit certainly,
And die in the odour of sanctity.

That thus it would prove they could not
    doubt,
Of a man whose end had been so devout ;
And to disputing then they fell   29
About who had wrought this miracle.

Had the Three Kings this mercy shown,
Who were the pride and honour of
    Cologne ?
Or was it an act of proper grace,
From the Army of Virgins of British
    race,
Who were also the glory of that place ?

Pardon, some said, they might presume,
Being a kingly act, from the Kings
    must come ;
But others maintain'd that St. Ursula's
    heart
Would sooner be moved to the merciful
    part.

There was one who thought this aid
    divine   40
Came from the other bank of the
    Rhine ;
For Roprecht there too had for favour
    applied,
Because his birth-place was on that side.

To Dusseldorff then the praise might
    belong,
And its Army of Martyrs, ten thousand
    strong ;
But he for a Dusseldorff man was
    known,
And no one would listen to him in
    Cologne,
Where the people would have the whole
    wonder their own.

The Friars, who help'd him to die so
    well,
Put in their claim to the miracle ;   50
Greater things than this, as their Annals
    could tell,
The stock of their merits for sinful men
Had done before, and would do again.

'Twas a whole week's wonder in that
    great town,
And in all places, up the river and
    down :
But a greater wonder took place of it
    then,
For Roprecht was found on the gallows
    again !

PART III

WITH that the whole city flocked out
    to see ;
There Roprecht was on the triple tree,
Dead, past all doubt, as dead could be ;
But fresh he was as if spells had charm'd
    him,
And neither wind nor weather had
    harm'd him.

While the multitude stood in a muse,
One said, I am sure he was hang'd in
    shoes !
In this the Hangman and all concurr'd ;
But now, behold, he was booted and
    spurr'd !

Plainly therefore it was to be seen,   10
That somewhere on horseback he had
    been ;
And at this the people marvelled
    more
Than at any thing which had happen'd
    before.

For not in riding trim was he
When he disappear'd from the triple
    tree ;
And his suit of irons he still was in,
With the collar that clipp'd him under
    the chin.

With that this second thought befell,
That perhaps he had not died so well,
Nor had Saints perform'd the miracle ;
But rather there was cause to fear,   21
That the foul Fiend had been busy
    here !

Roprecht the Robber had long been
    their curse,
And hanging had only made him worse ;
For bad as he was when living, they said
They had rather meet him alive than
    dead.

What a horse must it be which he had
    ridden,
No earthly beast could be so bestridden ;
And when by a hell-horse a dead rider
    was carried,
The whole land would be fearfully
    harried !   30

So some were for digging a pit in the
    place,
And burying him there with a stone on
    his face ;
And that hard on his body the earth
    should be press'd,
And exorcists be sent for to lay him
    at rest.

But others, whose knowledge was
    greater, opined
That this corpse was too strong to be
    confined ;
No weight of earth which they could lay
Would hold him down a single day,
If he chose to get up and ride away.

There was no keeping Vampires under
    ground ;   40
And bad as a Vampire he might be found,
Pests against whom it was understood
Exorcism never had done any good.

But fire, they said, had been proved to be
The only infallible remedy ;
So they were for burning the body
    outright,
Which would put a stop to his riding
    by night.

Others were for searching the mystery
    out,
And setting a guard the gallows about,
Who should keep a careful watch, and
    see   50
Whether Witch or Devil it might be
That helped him down from the triple
    tree.

For that there were Witches in the land,
Was what all by this might understand ;
And they must not let the occasion slip
For detecting that cursed fellowship.

Some were for this, and some for that,
And some they could not tell for what :
And never was such commotion known
In that great city of Cologne.   60

PART IV

PIETER SNOYE was a boor of good
renown,
Who dwelt about an hour and a half
from the town :
And he, while the people were all in
debate,
Went quietly in at the city gate.

For Father Kijf he sought about,
His confessor, till he found him out ;
But the Father Confessor wonder'd to see
The old man, and what his errand
might be.

The good Priest did not wonder less,
When Pieter said he was come to
confess ;   10
' Why, Pieter, how can this be so ?
I confessed thee some ten days ago !

' Thy conscience, methinks, may be
well at rest,
An honest man among the best ;
I would that all my flock, like thee,
Kept clear accounts with Heaven and
me ! '

Always before, without confusion,
Being sure of easy absolution,
Pieter his little slips had summ'd ;
But he hesitated now, and he haw'd,
and humm'd.   20

And something so strange the Father
saw
In Pieter's looks, and his hum and his
haw,
That he began to doubt it was something
more
Than a trifle omitted in last week's score.

At length it came out, that in the affair
Of Roprecht the Robber he had some
share ;
The Confessor then gave a start in fear—
' God grant there have been no witch-
craft here ! '

Pieter Snoye, who was looking down,
With something between a smile and
a frown,   30
Felt that suspicion move his bile,
And look'd up with more of a frown
than a smile.

' Fifty years I, Pieter Snoye,
Have lived in this country, man and boy,
And have always paid the Church her
due,
And kept short scores with Heaven and
you.

' The Devil himself, though Devil he be,
Would not dare impute that sin to me ;
He might charge me as well with heresy :
And if he did, here, in this place,   40
I'd call him liar, and spit in his face ! '

The Father, he saw, cast a gracious eye,
When he heard him thus the Devil defy ;
The wrath, of which he had eased his
mind,
Left a comfortable sort of warmth
behind,

Like what a cheerful cup will impart,
In a social hour, to an honest man's
heart :
And he added, ' For all the witchcraft
here,
I shall presently make that matter clear.

' Though I am, as you very well know,
Father Kijf,   50
A peaceable man, and keep clear of
strife,
It's a queerish business that now I've
been in ;
But I can't say that it's much of a sin.

' However, it needs must be confess'd,
And as it will set this people at rest,
To come with it at once was best :
Moreover, if I delayed, I thought
That some might perhaps into trouble
be brought.

' Under the seal I tell it you,
And you will judge what is best to do,   60
That no hurt to me and my son may
ensue.
No earthly harm have we intended,
And what was ill done, has been well
mended.

' I and my son Piet Pieterszoon,
Were returning home by the light of
the moon,
From this good city of Cologne,
On the night of the execution day ;
And hard by the gibbet was our way.

' About midnight it was we were passing
   by,
My son, Piet Pieterszoon, and I,   70
When we heard a moaning as we came
   near,
Which made us quake at first for fear.

' But the moaning was presently heard
   again,
And we knew it was nothing ghostly
   then ;
" Lord help us, father ! " Piet Pieterszoon said,
" Roprecht, for certain, is not dead ! "

' So under the gallows our cart we
   drive,
And, sure enough, the man was alive ;
Because of the irons that he was in,
He was hanging, not by the neck, but
   the chin.   80

' The reason why things had got thus
   wrong,
Was, that the rope had been left too
   long ;
The Hangman's fault—a clumsy rogue,
He is not fit to hang a dog.

' Now Roprecht, as long as the people
   were there,
Never stirr'd hand or foot in the air ;
But when at last he was left alone,
By that time so much of his strength
   was gone,
That he could do little more than groan.

' Piet and I had been sitting it out,   90
Till a latish hour, at a christening
   bout ;
And perhaps we were rash, as you may
   think,
And a little soft or so, for drink.

' Father Kijf, we could not bear
To leave him hanging in misery there ;
And 'twas an act of mercy, I cannot but
   say,
To get him down, and take him away.

' And as you know, all people said
What a goodly end that day he had
   made ;
So we thought for certain, Father Kijf,
That if he were saved he would mend
   his life.   101

' My son, Piet Pieterszoon, and I,
We took him down, seeing none was
   nigh ;
And we took off his suit of irons with
   care,
When we got him home, and we hid
   him there.

' The secret, as you may guess, was known
To Alit, my wife, but to her alone ;
And never sick man, I dare aver,
Was better tended than he was by her.

' Good advice, moreover, as good could
   be,   110
He had from Alit my wife, and me ;
And no one could promise fairer than he :
So that we and Piet Pieterszoon our son,
Thought that we a very good deed had
   done.

' You may well think we laughed in our
   sleeve,
At what the people then seem'd to
   believe ;
Queer enough it was to hear them say,
That the Three Kings took Roprecht
   away :

' Or that St. Ursula, who is in bliss,
With her Army of Virgins had done
   this :   120
The Three Kings and St. Ursula, too,
I warrant, had something better to do.

' Piet Pieterszoon my son, and I,
We heard them talk as we stood by,
And Piet look'd at me with a comical
   eye.
We thought them fools, but, as you
   shall see,
Not over-wise ourselves were we.

' For I must tell you, Father Kijf,
That when we told this to Alit my wife,
She at the notion perk'd up with
   delight,   130
And said she believed the people were
   right.

' Had not Roprecht put in the Saints
   his hope,
And who but they should have loosen'd
   the rope,
When they saw that no one could intend
To make at the gallows a better end ?

'Yes, she said, it was perfectly clear
That there must have been a miracle
    here ;
And we had the happiness to be in it,
Having been brought there just at the
    minute.

'And therefore it would become us to
    make   140
An offering for this favour's sake
To the Three Kings and the Virgins too,
Since we could not tell to which it was
    due.

'For greater honour there could be none
Than what in this business the Saints
    had done
To us and Piet Pieterszoon our son ;
She talk'd me over, Father Kijf,
With that tongue of hers, did Alit my
    wife.

'Lord, forgive us ! as if the Saints
    would deign
To come and help such a rogue in grain ;
When the only mercy the case could
    admit   151
Would have been to make his halter fit !

'That would have made one hanging do
In happy season for him too,
When he was in a proper cue ;
And have saved some work, as you
    will see,
To my son Piet Pieterszoon, and me.

'Well, Father, we kept him at bed and
    board,
Till his neck was cured and his strength
    restored ;
And we should have sent him off this
    day   160
With something to help him on his way.

'But this wicked Roprecht, what did he ?
Though he had been saved thus merci-
    fully,
Hanging had done him so little good,
That he took to his old ways as soon as
    he could.

'Last night, when we were all asleep,
Out of his bed did this gallows-bird creep,
Piet Pieterszoon's boots and spurs he
    put on,
And stole my best horse, and away he
    was gone

'Now Alit, my wife, did not sleep so
    hard,   170
But she heard the horse's feet in the
    yard ;
And when she jogg'd me, and bade me
    awake,
My mind misgave me as soon as she
    spake.

'To the window my good woman went,
And watch'd which way his course he
    bent ;
And in such time as a pipe can be lit,
Our horses were ready with bridle and
    bit.

'Away, as fast as we could hie,
We went, Piet Pieterszoon and I ;
And still on the plain we had him in
    sight ;   180
The moon did not shine for nothing
    that night.

'Knowing the ground, and riding fast,
We came up with him at last,
And—would you believe it ? Father
    Kijf,
The ungrateful wretch would have
    taken my life,
If he had not miss'd his stroke, with
    a knife !

'The struggle in no long time was done,
Because, you know, we were two to one ;
But yet all our strength we were fain
    to try,
Piet Pieterszoon my son, and I.   190

'When we had got him on the ground,
We fastened his hands, and his legs we
    bound ;
And across the horse we laid him then,
And brought him back to the house again.

'"We have robbed the gallows and
    that was ill done !"
Said I, to Piet Pieterszoon my son ;
"And restitution we must make
To that same gallows, for justice' sake."

'In his suit of irons the rogue we array'd,
And once again in the cart he was laid !
Night not yet so far was spent,   201
But there was time enough for our
    intent ;
And back to the triple tree we went.

' His own rope was ready there ;
To measure the length we took good
    care ;
And the job which the bungling Hang-
    man begun,
This time, I think, was properly
    done,
By me and Piet Pieterszoon my son.'

THE YOUNG DRAGON

[Parts I and II were published in *Fraser's
Magazine*, April 1830 ; Parts III and IV
in the issues of the same Magazine for June
and July 1830, respectively.]

The legend on which this poem is founded
is related in the ' Vida y Hazañas del Gran
Tamorlan, con la Descripcion de las Tierras
de su Imperio y Señorio, escrita por Ruy
Gonzalez de Clavijo, Camarero del muy alto
y Poderoso Señor Don Enrique, Tercero
deste Nombre, Rey de Castilla y de Leon ;
con un Itinerario de lo Sucedido en la
Embajada, que por dicho Señor el Rey hizo
al dicho Principe, llamado por otro Nombre
Tamurbec, Año del Nacimiento de 1403.'

PART I

PITHYRIAN was a Pagan,
    An easy-hearted man,
And Pagan sure he thought to end
    As Pagan he began ;
Thought he, the one must needs be
    true,
The old Religion, or the new,
    And therefore nothing care I ;
I call Diana the Divine ;
My daughter worships at the shrine
    Of the Christian Goddess, Mary.   10

In this uncertain matter
    If I the wrong course take,
Mary to me will mercy show
    For my Marana's sake.
If I am right, and Dian bend
Her dreadful bow, or Phoebus send
    His shafts abroad for slaughter,
Safe from their arrows shall I be,
And the twin Deities for me
    Will spare my dear-loved daughter.   20

If every one in Antioch
    Had reasoned in this strain,
It never would have raised alarm
    In Satan's dark domain.
But Mary's Image every day
Looks down on crowds who come to pray;
    Her votaries never falter :
While Dian's temple is so bare,
That unless her Priestess take good care,
    She will have a grass-green altar.   30

Perceiving this, the old Dragon
    Inflamed with anger grew ;   [ills,
Earthquakes and Plagues were common
    There needed something new ;
Some vengeance so severe and strange
That forepast times in all their range
    With no portent could match it :
So for himself a nest he made,
And in that nest an egg he laid,
    And down he sate to hatch it.   40

He built it by the fountain
    Of Phlegethon's red flood,
In the innermost abyss, the place
    Of central solitude ;
Of adamantine blocks unhewn,
With lava scoria interstrewn,
    The sole material fitting ;
With amianth he lined the nest,
And incombustible asbest,
    To bear the fiery sitting.   50

There with malignant patience
    He sate in fell despite,
Till this dracontine cockatrice
    Should break its way to light.
Meantime his angry heart to cheer,
He thought that all this while no fear
    The Antiocheans stood in,
Of what on deadliest vengeance bent
With imperturbable intent
    He there for them was brooding.   60

The months of incubation
    At length were duly past,
And now the infernal Dragon-chick
    Hath burst its shell at last ;
At which long-look'd-for sight enrapt,
For joy the father Dragon clapt
    His brazen wings like thunder,
So loudly that the mighty sound
Was like an earthquake felt around
    And all above and under.   70

The diabolic youngling
　Came out no callow birth,
Puling, defenceless, blind and weak,
　Like bird or beast of earth ;
Or man, most helpless thing of all
That fly, or swim, or creep, or crawl;
　But in his perfect figure ;
His horns, his dreadful tail, his sting,
Scales, teeth, and claws, and every thing
　Complete and in their vigour.　　80

The Old Dragon was delighted,
　And proud withal to see
In what perfection he had hatch'd
　His hellish progeny ;
And round and round, with fold on fold,
His tail about the imp he roll'd
　In fond and close enlacement ;
And neck round neck with many a turn
He coil'd, which was, you may discern,
　Their manner of embracement.　　90

PART II

A VOICE was heard in Antioch,
　Whence utter'd none could know,
But from their sleep it waken'd all,
　Proclaiming Woe, woe, woe !
It sounded here, it sounded there,
Within, without, and every where,
　A terror and a warning ;
Repeated thrice the dreadful word
By every living soul was heard
　Before the hour of morning.　　10

And in the air a rushing
　Pass'd over, in the night ;
And as it pass'd, there pass'd with it
　A meteoric light ;
The blind that piercing light intense
Felt in their long seal'd visual sense,
　With sudden short sensation :
The deaf that rushing in the sky
Could hear, and that portentous cry
　Reach'd them with consternation. 20

The astonished Antiocheans
　Impatiently await
The break of day, not knowing when
　Or what might be their fate.
Alas ! what then the people hear,
Only with certitude of fear
　Their sinking hearts affrighted ;
For in the fertile vale below,
Came news that, in that night of woe,
　A Dragon had alighted.　　30

It was no earthly monster
　In Libyan deserts nurst ;
Nor had the Lerna lake sent forth
　This winged worm accurst ;
The Old Dragon's own laid egg was this,
The fierce Young Dragon of the abyss,
　Who from the fiery fountain,
Through earth's concavities that night
Had made his way, and taken flight
　Out of a burning mountain.　　40

A voice that went before him
　The cry of woe prefer'd ;
The motion of his brazen wings
　Was what the deaf had heard ;
The flashing of his eyes, that light
The which upon their inward sight
　The blind had felt astounded ;
What wonder then, when from the wall
They saw him in the vale, if all
　With terror were confounded.　　50

Compared to that strong armour
　Of scales which he was in,
The hide of a rhinoceros
　Was like a lady's skin.
A battering ram might play in vain
Upon his head, with might and main,
　Though fifty men had work'd it ;
And from his tail they saw him fling
Out, like a rocket, a long sting,
　When he for pastime jerk'd it.　　60

To whom of Gods or Heroes
　Should they for aid apply ?
Where should they look for succour now,
　Or whither should they fly ?
For now no Demigods were found
Like　those　whose　deathless　deeds
　　abound
　In ancient song and story ;
No Hercules was then on earth,
Nor yet of her St. George's birth
　Could Cappadocia glory.　　70

And even these against him
　Had found their strength but small ;
He could have swallowed Hercules,
　Club, lion-skin, and all.
Yea, had St. George himself been there
Upon the fiercest steed that e'er
　To battle bore bestrider,
This dreadful Dragon in his might,
One mouthful only, and one bite,
　Had made of horse and rider.　　80

They see how unavailing
   All human force must prove ;
Oh might their earnest prayers obtain
   Protection from above !
The Christians sought our Lady's shrine
   To invocate her aid divine ;
     And, with a like emotion,
The Pagans on that fearful day
Took to Diana's fane their way,
    And offer'd their devotion.   90

But there the offended Goddess
   Beheld them with a frown ;
The indignant altar heaved itself
   And shook their offerings down ;
The Priestess with a deathlike hue
Pale as the marble Image grew,
   The marble Image redden'd ;
And these poor suppliants at the sight
Felt in fresh access of affright
    Their hearts within them deaden'd.

Behold the marble eyeballs   101
   With life and motion shine !
And from the moving marble lips
   There comes a voice divine.
A demon voice, by all the crowd
Distinctly heard, nor low, nor loud,
   But deep and clear and thrilling ;
And carrying to the soul such dread
That they perforce must what it said
    Obey, however unwilling.   110

Hear ! hear ! it said, ye people !
   The ancient Gods have sent
In anger for your long neglect
   This signal punishment.
To mortal Mary vows were paid,
And prayers preferr'd, and offerings
   made ;
   Our temples were deserted ;
Now, when our vengeance makes ye wise,
Unto your proper Deities
    In fear ye have reverted !   120

Hear now the dreadful judgement
   For this which ye have done ;
The infernal Dragon will devour
   Your daughters, one by one ;
A Christian Virgin every day
Ye must present him for his prey,
   With garlands deck'd, as meet is :
That with the Christians he begins
Is what, in mercy to your sins,
    Ye owe to my entreaties.   130

Whether, if to my worship
   Ye now continue true,
I may, when these are all consumed,
   Avert the ill from you :
That on the Ancient Gods depends,
If they be made once more your friends
   By your sincere repentance :
But for the present, no delay ;
Cast lots among ye, and obey
    The inexorable sentence.   140

PART III

Though to the Pagan priesthood
   A triumph this might seem,
Few families there were who thus
   Could in their grief misdeem ;
For oft in those distracted days,
Parent and child went different ways,
   The sister and the brother ;
And when, in spirit moved, the wife
Chose one religious course of life,
    The husband took the other.   10

Therefore in every household
   Was seen the face of fear ;
They who were safe themselves, exposed
   In those whom they held dear.
The lists are made, and in the urn
The names are placed to wait their turn
   For this far worse than slaughter ;
And from that fatal urn, the first
Drawn for this dreadful death accurst
    Was of Pithyrian's daughter.   20

With Christian-like composure
   Marana heard her lot,
And though her countenance at first
   Grew pale, she trembled not.
Not for herself the Virgin grieved ;
She knew in whom she had believed,
   Knew that a crown of glory
In Heaven would recompense her worth,
And her good name remain on earth
    The theme of sacred story.   30

Her fears were for her father,
   How he should bear this grief,
Poor wretched heathen, if he still
   Remain'd in misbelief ;
Her looks amid the multitude,
Who struck with deep compassion stood,
   Are seeking for Pithyrian :
He cannot bear to meet her eye.   [fly,
Where goest thou ? whither wouldst thou
    Thou miserable Syrian ?   40

Hath sudden hope inspired him,
  Or is it in despair
That through the throng he made his
      way
  And sped he knew not where ?
For how could he the sight sustain,
When now the sacrificial train
  Inhumanly surround her !
How bear to see her, when with flowers
From rosiers and from jasmine bowers
  They like a victim crown'd her ! 50

He knew not why nor whither
  So fast he hurried thence,
But felt like one possess'd by some
  Controlling influence,
Nor turn'd he to Diana's fane,
Inly assured that prayers were vain
  If made for such protection ;
His pagan faith he now forgot,
And the wild way he took was not
  His own, but Heaven's direction. 60

He who had never enter'd
  A Christian church till then,
Except in idle mood profane
  To view the ways of men,
Now to a Christian church made straight,
And hastened through its open gate,
  By his good Angel guided,
And thinking, though he knew not why,
That there some blessed Power on high
  Had help for him provided. 70

Wildly he look'd about him
  On many a form divine,
Whose Image o'er its altar stood,
  And many a sculptured shrine,
In which believers might behold
Relics more precious than the gold
  And jewels which encased them,
With painful search from far and near
Brought to be venerated here
  Where piety had placed them. 80

There stood the Virgin Mother
  Crown'd with a starry wreath,
And there the aweful Crucifix
  Appear'd to bleed and breathe ;
Martyrs to whom their palm is given,
And sainted Maids who now in Heaven
  With glory are invested :
Glancing o'er these his rapid eye
Toward one image that stood nigh
  Was drawn, and there it rested. 90

The countenance that fix'd him
  Was of a sun-burnt mien,
The face was like a Prophet's face
  Inspired, but yet serene ;
His arms and legs and feet were bare ,
The raiment was of camel's hair,
  That, loosely hanging round him,
Fell from the shoulders to the knee ;
And round the loins, though elsewhere
      free,
  A leathern girdle bound him. 100

With his right arm uplifted
  The great Precursor stood,
Thus represented to the life
  In carved and painted wood.
Below the real arm was laid
Within a crystal shrine display'd
  For public veneration ;
Not now of flesh and blood, .. but bone,
Sinews, and shrivell'd skin alone,
  In ghastly preservation. 110

Moved by a secret impulse
  Which he could not withstand,
Let me, Pithyrian cried, adore
  That blessed arm and hand !
This day, this miserable day,
My pagan faith I put away,
  Abjure it and abhor it ;
And in the Saints I put my trust,
And in the Cross ; and, if I must,
  Will die a Martyr for it. 120

This is the arm whose succour
  Heaven brings me here to seek !
Oh let me press it to my lips,
  And so its aid bespeak !
A strong faith makes me now presume
That, when to this unhappy doom
  A hellish power hath brought her,
The heavenly hand whose mortal mould
I humbly worship, will unfold
  Its strength, and save my daughter.

The Sacristan with wonder 131
  And pity heard his prayer,
And placed the relic in his hand,
  As he knelt humbly there.
Right thankfully the kneeling man
To that confiding Sacristan
  Return'd it, after kissing ;
And he within its crystal shrine
Replaced the precious arm divine,
  Nor saw that aught was missing. 140

PART IV

Oh piety audacious !
  Oh boldness of belief !
Oh sacrilegious force of faith,
  That then inspired the thief !
Oh wonderful extent of love,
That Saints enthroned in bliss above
  Should bear such profanation,
And not by some immediate act,
Striking the offender in the fact,
  Prevent the perpetration !   10

But sure the Saint that impulse
  Himself from Heaven had sent,
In mercy predetermining
  The marvellous event ;
So inconceivable a thought,
Seeming with such irreverence fraught,
  Could else have no beginning ;
Nor else might such a deed be done,
As then Pithyrian ventured on,
  Yet had no fear of sinning.   20

Not as that Church he enter'd
  Did he from it depart,
Like one bewilder'd by his grief,
  But confident at heart ;
Triumphantly he went his way
And bore the Holy Thumb away,
  Elated with his plunder ;
That Holy Thumb which well he knew
Could pierce the Dragon through and
    through,
  Like Jupiter's own thunder.   30

Meantime was meek Marana
  For sacrifice array'd,
And now in sad procession forth
  They led the flower-crown'd Maid.
Of this infernal triumph vain,
The Pagan Priests precede the train,
  Oh hearts devoid of pity !
And to behold the abhorr'd event,
At far or nearer distance, went
  The whole of that great city.   40

The Christians go to succour
  The sufferer with their prayers,
The Pagans to a spectacle
  Which dreadfully declares,
In this their over-ruling hour,
Their Gods' abominable power ;

Yet not without emotion
Of grief, and horror, and remorse,
And natural piety, whose force
  Prevail'd o'er false devotion.   50

The walls and towers are cluster'd,
  And every hill and height
That overlooks the vale, is throng'd
  For this accursed sight.
Why art thou joyful, thou green Earth ?
Wherefore, ye happy Birds, your mirth
  Are ye in carols voicing ?
And thou, O Sun, in yon blue sky
How canst thou hold thy course on high
  This day, as if rejoicing ?   60

Already the procession
  Hath pass'd the city gate,
And now along the vale it moves
  With solemn pace sedate.
And now the spot before them lies,
Where waiting for his promised prize
  The Dragon's chosen haunt is ;
Blacken'd beneath his blasting feet,
Though yesterday a green retreat
  Beside the clear Orontes.   70

There the procession halted ;
  The Priests on either hand
Dividing then, a long array,
  In order took their stand.
Midway between, the Maid is left
Alone, of human aid bereft :
  The Dragon now hath spied her ;
But in that moment of most need,
Arriving breathless with his speed,
  Her Father stood beside her.   80

On came the Dragon rampant,
  Half running, half on wing,
His tail uplifted o'er his back
  In many a spiral ring ;
His scales he ruffled in his pride,
His brazen pennons waving wide
  Were gloriously distended ;
His nostrils smoked, his eyes flash'd fire,
His lips were drawn, and in his ire
  His mighty jaws extended.   90

On came the Dragon rampant,
  Expecting there no check,
And open-mouth'd to swallow both
  He stretch'd his burnish'd neck.
Pithyrian put his daughter by,
Waiting for this with watchful eye

And ready to prevent it ;
Within arm's length he let him come,
Then in he threw the Holy Thumb,
And down his throat he sent it.   100

The hugest brazen mortar
That ever yet fired bomb,
Could not have check'd this fiendish beast
As did that Holy Thumb.
He stagger'd as he wheel'd short round,
His loose feet scraped along the ground,
To lift themselves unable ;
His pennons in their weakness flagg'd,
His tail erected late, now dragg'd,
Just like a long wet cable.   110

A rumbling and a tumbling
Was heard in his inside,
He gasp'd, he panted, he lay down,
He rolled from side to side :
He moan'd, he groan'd, he snuff'd, he
snored,
He growl'd, he howl'd, he raved, he
roar'd ;
But loud as were his clamours,
Far louder was the inward din,
Like a hundred braziers working in
A caldron with their hammers.   120

The hammering came faster,
More faint the moaning sound,
And now his body swells, and now
It rises from the ground.
Not upward with his own consent,
Nor borne by his own wings he went,
Their vigour was abated ;
But lifted no one could tell how
By power unseen, with which he now
Was visibly inflated.   130

Abominable Dragon,
Now art thou overmatch'd,
And better had it been for thee
That thou hadst ne'er been hatch'd ;
For now, distended like a ball
To its full stretch, in sight of all,
The body mounts ascendant ;
The head before, the tail behind,
The wings, like sails that want a wind,
On either side are pendant.   140

Not without special mercy
Was he thus borne on high,
Till he appear'd no bigger than
An Eagle in the sky.

For when about some three miles height,
Yet still in perfect reach of sight,
Oh, wonder of all wonders !
He burst in pieces, with a sound
Heard for a hundred leagues around,
And like a thousand thunders.   150

But had that great explosion
Been in the lower sky,
All Antioch would have been laid
In ruins, certainly.
And in that vast assembled rout
Who crowded joyfully about
Pithyrian and his daughter,
The splinters of the monster's hide
Must needs have made on every side
A very dreadful slaughter.   160

So far the broken pieces
Were now dispersed around,
And shiver'd so to dust, that not
A fragment e'er was found.
The Holy Thumb (so it is thought)
When it this miracle had wrought
At once to Heaven ascended :
As if, when it had thus display'd
Its power, and saved the Christian Maid,
Its work on earth was ended.   170

But at Constantinople
The arm and hand were shown,
Until the mighty Ottoman
O'erthrew the Grecian throne.
And when the Monks this tale who told
To pious visitors would hold
The holy hand for kissing,
They never fail'd, with faith devout,
In confirmation to point out,   179
That there the Thumb was missing.

Keswick, 1829.

EPILOGUE TO THE YOUNG DRAGON

I TOLD my tale of the Holy Thumb
That split the Dragon asunder,
And my daughters made great eyes as
they heard,
Which were full of delight and wonder.

With listening lips and looks intent,
There sate an eager boy,   [hands,
Who shouted sometimes and clapt his
And could not sit still for joy.

But when I look'd at my Mistress's face,
  It was all too grave the while ;   10
And when I ceased, methought there
    was more
  Of reproof than of praise in her smile.

That smile I read aright, for thus
  Reprovingly said she,
' Such tales are meet for youthful ears
  But give little content to me.

' From thee far rather would I hear
  Some sober, sadder lay,
Such as I oft have heard, well pleased
  Before those looks were grey.'   20

' Nay, Mistress mine,' I made reply,
  ' The autumn hath its flowers,
Nor ever is the sky more gay
  Than in its evening hours.

' Our good old Cat, Earl Tomlemagne,
  Upon a warm spring day,
Even like a kitten at its sport,
  Is sometimes seen to play.

' That sense which held me back in youth
  From all intemperate gladness,   30
That same good instinct bids me shun
  Unprofitable sadness.

' Nor marvel you if I prefer
  Of playful themes to sing ;
The October grove hath brighter tints
  Than Summer or than Spring :

' For o'er the leaves before they fall
  Such hues hath Nature thrown,
That the woods wear in sunless days
  A sunshine of their own.   40

' Why should I seek to call forth tears ?
  The source from whence we weep
Too near the surface lies in youth,
  In age it lies too deep.

' Enough of foresight sad, too much
  Of retrospect have I ;
And well for me that I sometimes
  Can put those feelings by ;

' From public ills, and thoughts that
    else
  Might weigh me down to earth,   50
That I can gain some intervals
  For healthful, hopeful mirth ;

' That I can sport in tales which suit
  Young auditors like these,
Yet, if I err not, may content
  The few I seek to please.

' I know in what responsive minds
  My lightest lay will wake
A sense of pleasure, for its own,
  And for its author's sake.   60

' I know the eyes in which the light
  Of memory will appear ;
I know the lips which while they read
  Will wear a smile sincere :

' The hearts to which my sportive song
  The thought of days will bring,
When they and I, whose Winter now
  Comes on, were in our Spring.

' And I their well known voices too,
  Though far away, can hear,   70
Distinctly, even as when in dreams
  They reach the inward ear.

' " There speaks the man we knew of
    yore,"
  Well pleased I hear them say,
" Such was he in his lighter moods
  Before our heads were grey.

' " Buoyant he was in spirit, quick
  Of fancy, blithe of heart,
And Care and Time and Change have
    left
  Untouch'd his better part."   80

' Thus say my morning friends who
    now
  Are in the vale of years,
And I, save such as thus may rise,
  Would draw no other tears.'

    Keswick, 1829.

A TALE OF PARAGUAY

PREFACE

One of my friends observed to me in a letter, that many stories which are said to be *founded* on fact, have in reality been *foundered* on it. This is the case if there be any gross violation committed or ignorance betrayed of historical manners in the prominent parts of a narrative wherein the writer affects to observe them: or when the ground-work is taken from some part of history so popular and well known that any mixture of fiction disturbs the sense of truth. Still more so, if the subject be in itself so momentous that any alloy of invention must of necessity debase it : but most of all in themes drawn from Scripture, whether from the more familiar or the more awful portions ; for when what is true is sacred, whatever may be added to it is so surely felt to be false, that it appears profane.

Founded on fact the Poem is, which is here committed to the world : but what ever may be its defects, it is liable to none of these objections. The story is so singular, so simple, and withal so complete, that it must have been injured by any alteration. How faithfully it has been followed, the reader may perceive if he chooses to consult the abridged translation of Dobrizhoffer's History of the Abipones. . .

[In the original Preface Southey here subjoined a long extract from Dobrizhoffer de Abiponibus, Lib. *Prodromus*, pp. 97–106, which it has not been thought necessary to reprint in the present edition.—Ed.]

TO EDITH MAY SOUTHEY

1

Edith ! ten years are number'd, since the day,
Which ushers in the cheerful month of May,
To us by thy dear birth, my daughter dear,
Was blest.   Thou therefore didst the name partake
Of that sweet month, the sweetest of the year,
But fitlier was it given thee for the sake
Of a good man, thy father's friend sincere,
Who at the font made answer in thy name.
Thy love and reverence rightly may he claim,
For closely hath he been with me allied
In friendship's holy bonds, from that first hour   11
When in our youth we met on Tejo's side;
Bonds which, defying now all Fortune's power,
Time hath not loosen'd, nor will Death divide.

2

A child more welcome, by indulgent Heaven
Never to parents' tears and prayers was given :
For scarcely eight months at thy happy birth
Had pass'd, since of thy sister we were left, . .
Our first-born, and our only babe, bereft.
Too fair a flower was she for this rude earth !   20
The features of her beauteous infancy
Have faded from me, like a passing cloud,
Or like the glories of an evening sky :
And seldom hath my tongue pronounced her name,
Since she was summon'd to a happier sphere.
But that dear love, so deeply wounded then,
I in my soul with silent faith sincere
Devoutly cherish till we meet again.

3

I saw thee first with trembling thankfulness,
O daughter of my hopes and of my fears !   30
Press'd on thy senseless cheek a troubled kiss,
And breathed my blessing over thee with tears.   [alloy ;
But memory did not long our bliss
For gentle nature, who had given relief,
Wean'd with new love the chasten'd heart from grief ;
And the sweet season minister'd to joy.

4

It was a season when their leaves and flowers   [spread ;
The trees as to an Arctic summer
When chilling wintry winds and snowy showers,
Which had too long usurp'd the vernal hours,   40
Like spectres from the sight of morning, fled   [May ;
Before the presence of that joyous
And groves and gardens all the live-long day
Rung with the birds' loud love-songs. Over all,
One thrush was heard from morn till even-fall ;   [lay
Thy Mother well remembers, when she
The happy prisoner of the genial bed,
How from yon lofty poplar's topmost spray
At earliest dawn his thrilling pipe was heard ;
And, when the light of evening died away,   50
That blithe and indefatigable bird
Still his redundant song of joy and love preferr'd.

5

How I have doted on thine infant smiles
At morning, when thine eyes unclosed on mine ;
How, as the months in swift succession roll'd,
I mark'd thy human faculties unfold,
And watch'd the dawning of the light divine ;

And with what artifice of playful guiles
Won from thy lips with still-repeated wiles
Kiss after kiss, a reckoning often told. . .   60
Something I ween thou know'st ; for thou hast seen
Thy sisters in their turn such fondness prove,   [years
And felt how childhood in its winning
The attemper'd soul to tenderness can move.
This thou canst tell ; but not the hopes and fears
With which a parent's heart doth overflow, . .
The thoughts and cares inwoven with that love, . .
Its nature and its depth, thou dost not, canst not know.

6

The years which since thy birth have pass'd away
May well to thy young retrospect appear   70
A measureless extent : . . like yester-day   [career.
To me, so soon they filled their short
To thee discourse of reason have they brought,
With sense of time and change ; and something too
Of this precarious state of things have taught,
Where Man abideth never in one stay;
And of mortality a mournful thought.
And I have seen thine eyes suffused in grief,   [grey
When I have said that with autumnal
The touch of eld hath mark'd thy father's head ;   80
That even the longest day of life is brief,   [leaf.
And mine is falling fast into the yellow

7

Thy happy nature from the painful thought
With instinct turns, and scarcely canst thou bear
To hear me name the Grave : Thou knowest not   [there !
How large a portion of my heart is

The faces which I loved in infancy
Are gone ; and bosom-friends of
    riper age,
With whom I fondly talk'd of years
    to come,
Summon'd before me to their heri-
    tage,   90
Are in the better world, beyond the
    tomb.
And I have brethren there, and
    sisters dear,
And dearer babes. I therefore needs
    must dwell
Often in thought with those whom still
    I love so well.

8

Thus wilt thou feel in thy maturer
    mind ;
When grief shall be thy portion, thou
    wilt find
Safe consolation in such thoughts as
    these, . .
A present refuge in affliction's hour.
And, if indulgent Heaven thy lot
    should bless
With all imaginable happiness,   100
Here shalt thou have, my child,
    beyond all power
Of chance, thy holiest, surest, best
    delight.

Take therefore now thy Father's
    latest lay, . .
Perhaps his last ; . . and treasure in
    thine heart
The feelings that its musing strains
    convey.
A song it is of life's declining day,
Yet meet for youth. Vain passions
    to excite,
No strains of morbid sentiment I sing,
Nor tell of idle loves with ill-spent
    breath ;
A reverent offering to the Grave I
    bring,   110
And twine a garland for the brow of
    Death.

Keswick, 1814.

PROEM

THAT was a memorable day for Spain,
When on Pamplona's towers, so barely
    won,   [the plain
The Frenchmen stood, and saw upon
Their long-expected succours hasten-
    ing on :   [array,
Exultingly they mark'd the brave
And deem'd their leader should his
    purpose gain,
Though Wellington and England
    barr'd the way.
Anon the bayonets glitter'd in the sun,
And frequent cannon flash'd, whose
    lurid light
Redden'd through sulphurous smoke ;
    fast volleying round   10
Roll'd the war-thunders, and with
    long rebound
Backward from many a rock and
    cloud-capt height
In answering peals Pyrene sent th
    sound.
Impatient for relief, toward the fight
The hungry garrison their eye-balls
    strain :
Vain was the Frenchman's skill, his
    valour vain ;
And even then, when eager hope
    almost   [prayer,
Had moved their irreligious lips to
Averting from the fatal scene their
    sight,   [despair.
They breathed the execrations of
For Wellesley's star hath risen
    ascendant there ;   21
Once more he drove the host of
    France to flight,
And triumph'd once again for God and
    for the right.

That was a day, whose influence far
    and wide   [a joy
The struggling nations felt ; it was
Wherewith all Europe rung from
    side to side.   [time
Yet hath Pamplona seen in former
A moment big with mightier conse-
    quence,   [clime.
Affecting many an age and distant
That day it was which saw in her
    defence,   30

Contending with the French before
    her wall,
A noble soldier of Guipuzcoa fall,
Sore hurt, but not to death. For
    when long care
Restored his shatter'd leg and set
    him free,   [formity,
He would not brook a slight de-
As one who, being gay and debonnair,
In courts conspicuous as in camps
    must be :
So he forsooth a shapely boot must
    wear ;   [life,
And the vain man, with peril of his
Laid the recover'd limb again beneath
    the knife.   40

Long time upon the bed of pain he lay
Whiling with books the weary hours
    away ;
And from that circumstance and this
    vain man   [began,
A train of long events their course
Whose term it is not given us yet to
    see.   [name,
Who hath not heard Loyola's sainted
Before whom Kings and Nations
    bow'd the knee ?
Thy annals, Ethiopia, might proclaim
What deeds arose from that prolific
    day ;
And of dark plots might shuddering
    Europe tell.   50

But Science too her trophies would
    display ;
Faith give the martyrs of Japan their
    fame ;   [dwell
And Charity on works of love would
In California's dolorous regions drear ;
And where, amid a pathless world of
    wood,   [way,
Gathering a thousand rivers on his
Huge Orellana rolls his affluent flood ;
And where the happier sons of
    Paraguay,
By gentleness and pious art subdued,
Bow'd their meek heads beneath the
    Jesuits' sway,   60
And lived and died in filial servitude.

I love thus uncontroll'd, as in a dream,
To muse upon the course of human
    things ;
Exploring sometimes the remotest
    springs,   [gleam ;
Far as tradition lends one guiding
Or following, upon Thought's auda-
    cious wings,
Into Futurity, the endless stream.
But now, in quest of no ambitious
    height,   [way,
I go where Truth and Nature lead my
And, ceasing here from desultory
    flight,   70
In measured strains I tell a Tale of
    Paraguay.

A TALE OF PARAGUAY

CANTO I

1

JENNER ! for ever shall thy honour'd
    name   [blest,
Among the children of mankind be
Who by thy skill hast taught us how
    to tame   [pest
One dire disease, . . the lamentable
Which Africa sent forth to scourge
    the West,
As if in vengeance for her sable brood
So many an age remorselessly opprest.
For that most fearful malady subdued
Receive a poet's praise, a father's
    gratitude.

2

Fair promise be this triumph of an
    age,   10
When Man, with vain desires no
    longer blind,
And wise though late, his only war
    shall wage   [mankind,
Against the miseries which afflict
Striving with virtuous heart and
    strenuous mind   [away.
Till evil from the earth shall pass
Lo, this his glorious destiny assign'd !
For that blest consummation let us
    pray,
And trust in fervent faith, and labour
    as we may.

3

The hideous malady which lost its power
When Jenner's art the dire contagion stay'd,   20
Among Columbia's sons, in fatal hour
Across the wide Atlantic wave convey'd,   [play'd :
Its fiercest form of pestilence dis-
Where'er its deadly course the plague began
Vainly the wretched sufferer look'd for aid ;
Parent from child, and child from parent ran,
For tyrannous fear dissolved all natural bonds of man.

4

A feeble nation of Guarani race,
Thinn'd by perpetual wars, but unsubdued,
Had taken up at length a resting-place
Among those tracts of lake and swamp and wood,   31
Where Mondai issuing from its solitude
Flows with slow stream to Empalado's bed.
It was a region desolate and rude ;
But thither had the horde for safety fled,
And being there conceal'd in peace their lives they led.

5

There had the tribe a safe asylum found
Amid those marshes wide and wood-lands dense,
With pathless wilds and waters spread around,
And labyrinthine swamps, a sure defence   40
From human foes, . . but not from pestilence.
The spotted plague appear'd, that direst ill, . .
How brought among them none could tell, or whence ;   [still,
The mortal seed had lain among them
And quicken'd now to work the Lord's mysterious will.

6

Alas, it was no medicable grief
Which herbs might reach ! Nor could the juggler's power
With all his antic mummeries bring relief.   [hour,
Faith might not aid him in that ruling
Himself a victim now.   The dread-ful stour   50
None could escape, nor aught its force assuage.
The marriageable maiden had her dower
From death ; the strong man sunk beneath its rage,
And death cut short the thread of child-hood and of age.

7

No time for customary mourning now ;
With hand close-clench'd to pluck the rooted hair,
To beat the bosom, on the swelling brow   [tear
Inflict redoubled blows, and blindly
The cheeks, indenting bloody furrows there,
The deep-traced signs indelible of woe ;   60
Then to some crag, or bank abrupt, repair,   [throw
And, giving grief its scope, infuriate
The impatient body thence upon the earth below.

8

Devices these by poor weak nature taught,
Which thus a change of suffering would obtain ;
And, flying from intolerable thought
And piercing recollections, would full fain
Distract itself by sense of fleshly pain
From anguish that the soul must else endure.
Easier all outward torments to sus-tain,   70
Than those heart-wounds which only time can cure,
And He in whom alone the hopes of man are sure.

9

None sorrow'd here ; the sense of woe
    was sear'd,   [ill.
When every one endured his own sore
The prostrate sufferers neither hoped
    nor fear'd ;
The body labour'd, but the heart
    was still : . .
So let the conquering malady fulfil
Its fatal course, rest cometh at the
    end !   [will
Passive they lay with neither wish nor
For aught but this ; nor did they long
    attend   80
That welcome boon from death, the
    never-failing friend.

10

Who is there to make ready now the
    pit,
The house that will content from this
    day forth
Its easy tenant ? Who in vestments fit
Shall swathe the sleeper for his bed of
    earth,
Now tractable as when a babe at
    birth ?
Who now the ample funeral urn shall
    knead,
And burying it beneath his proper
    hearth
Deposit there with careful hands the
    dead,
And lightly then relay the floor above
    his head ?   90

11

Unwept, unshrouded, and unsepul-
    chred,
The hammock where they hang for
    winding sheet
And grave suffices the deserted dead :
There from the armadillo's searching
    feet
Safer than if within the tomb's re-
    treat.
The carrion birds obscene in vain essay
To find that quarry : round and
    round they beat
The air, but fear to enter for their
    prey,
And from the silent door the jaguar
    turns away.

12

But nature for her universal law 100
Hath other surer instruments in store,
Whom from the haunts of men no
    wonted awe
Withholds as with a spell. In
    swarms they pour
From wood and swamp : and when
    their work is o'er,
On the white bones the mouldering
    roof will fall ;
Seeds will take root, and spring in sun
    and shower ;
And Mother Earth ere long with her
    green pall,
Resuming to herself the wreck, will
    cover all.

13

Oh ! better thus with earth to have
    their part,   109
Than in Egyptian catacombs to lie,
Age after age preserved by horrid art,
In ghastly image of humanity !
Strange pride that with corruption
    thus would vie !
And strange delusion that would thus
    maintain
The fleshly form, till cycles shall pass
    by,
And in the series of the eternal chain,
The spirit come to seek its old abode
    again.

14

One pair alone survived the general
    fate ;
Left in such drear and mournful
    solitude,
That death might seem a preferable
    state.   120
Not more deprest the Arkite patriarch
    stood,
When landing first on Ararat he
    view'd,
Where all around the mountain
    summits lay,
Like islands seen amid the boundless
    flood :
Nor our first parents more forlorn
    than they,
Through Eden when they took their
    solitary way.

15

Alike to them, it seem'd in their despair,
Whither they wander'd from the
infected spot.
Chance might direct their steps : they
took no care ;
Come well or ill to them, it matter'd
not !   130
Left as they were in that unhappy lot,
The sole survivors they of all their
race,
They reck'd not when their fate, nor
where, nor what,   [case,
In this resignment to their hopeless
Indifferent to all choice or circumstance
of place.

16

That palsying stupor pass'd away ere
long,
And, as the spring of health resum'd
its power,
They felt that life was dear, and hope
was strong.
What marvel ? 'Twas with them the
morning hour,
When bliss appears to be the natural
dower   140
Of all the creatures of this joyous
earth ;
And sorrow fleeting like a vernal
shower   [mirth ;
Scarce interrupts the current of our
Such is the happy heart we bring with
us at birth.

17

Though of his nature and his bound-
less love   [sense,
Erring, yet tutor'd by instinctive
They rightly deem'd the Power who
rules above   [pestilence.
Had saved them from the wasting
That favouring Power would still be
their defence :
Thus were they by their late deliver-
ance taught   150
To place a child-like trust in Provi-
dence,
And in their state forlorn they found
this thought
Of natural faith with hope and consola-
tion fraught.

18

And now they built themselves a leafy
bower,   [beside,
Amid a glade, slow Mondai's stream
Screen'd from the southern blast of
piercing power :
Not like their native dwelling, long
and wide,
By skilful toil of numbers edified,
The common home of all, their human
nest,
Where threescore hammocks pendant
side by side   160
Were ranged, and on the ground the
fires were drest ;
Alas, that populous hive hath now no
living guest !

19

A few firm stakes they planted in the
ground,
Circling a narrow space, yet large
enow ;
These strongly interknit they closed
around
With basket-work of many a pliant
bough.
The roof was like the sides ; the door
was low,
And rude the hut, and trimm'd with
little care,   [now ;
For little heart had they to dress it
Yet was the humble structure fresh
and fair,   170
And soon its inmates found that love
might sojourn there.

20

Quiara could recall to mind the course
Of twenty summers ; perfectly he
knew
Whate'er his fathers taught of skill
or force.
Right to the mark his whizzing lance
he threw,
And from his bow the unerring arrow
flew   [bee
With fatal aim : and when the laden
Buzz'd by him in its flight, he could
pursue   [free
Its path with certain ken, and follow
Until he traced the hive in hidden bank
or tree.   180

21

Of answering years was Monnema,
          nor less   [ways.
Expert in all her sex's household
The Indian weed she skilfully could
          dress ;
And in what depth to drop the yellow
          maize
She knew, and when around its stem
          to raise
The lighten'd soil ; and well could she
          prepare
Its ripen'd seed for food, her proper
          praise ;   [care
Or in the embers turn with frequent
Its succulent head yet green, sometimes
          for daintier fare.

22

And how to macerate the bark she
          knew,   190
And draw apart its beaten fibres fine,
And, bleaching them in sun, and air,
          and dew,
From dry and glossy filaments en-
          twine
With rapid twirl of hand the length-
          ening line ;
Next, interknitting well the twisted
          thread,   [combine,
In many an even mesh its knots
And shape in tapering length the
          pensile bed,
Light hammock there to hang beneath
          the leafy shed.

23

Time had been when, expert in works
          of clay,
She lent her hands the swelling urn
          to mould,   200
And fill'd it for the appointed festal
          day   [bold
With the beloved beverage which the
Quaff'd in their triumph and their joy
          of old ;   [rude,
The fruitful cause of many an uproar
When, in their drunken bravery un-
          controll'd,
Some bitter jest awoke the dormant
          feud,
And wrath and rage and strife and
          wounds and death ensued.

24

These occupations were gone by : the
          skill
Was useless now, which once had
          been her pride.
Content were they, when thirst im-
          pell'd, to fill   210
The dry and hollow gourd from
          Mondai's side ;
The river from its sluggish bed sup-
          plied
A draught for repetition all unmeet ;
Howbeit the bodily want was satisfied,
No feverish pulse ensued, nor ireful
          heat,
Their days were undisturb'd, their
          natural sleep was sweet.

25

She too had learnt in youth how best
          to trim   [day,
The honour'd Chief for his triumphal
And covering with soft gums the
          obedient limb
And body, then with feathers over-
          lay,   220
In regular hues disposed, a rich dis-
          play.
Well-pleased the glorious savage stood
          and eyed
The growing work ; then vain of his
          array
Look'd with complacent frown from
          side to side,
Stalk'd with elater step, and swell'd
          with statelier pride.

26

Feasts and carousals, vanity and
          strife,
Could have no place with them in
          solitude
To break the tenor of their even life.
Quiara day by day his game pursued,
Searching the air, the water, and the
          wood,   230
With hawk-like eye, and arrow sure
          as fate ;   [food:
And Monnema prepared the hunter's
Cast with him here in this forlorn
          estate,
In all things for the man was she a
          fitting mate.

27

The Moon had gather'd oft her
    monthly store
Of light, and oft in darkness left the
    sky,   [bore
Since Monnema a growing burthen
Of life and hope. The appointed
    weeks go by ;
And now her hour is come, and none
    is nigh
To help : but human help she needed
    none.   240
A few short throes endured with
    scarce a cry,   [son,
Upon the bank she laid her new-born
Then slid into the stream, and bathed,
    and all was done.

28

Might old observances have there
    been kept,
Then should the husband to that
    pensile bed,
Like one exhausted with the birth
    have crept,   [head,
And, laying down in feeble guise his
For many a day been nursed and
    dieted   [due.
With tender care, to childing mothers
Certes a custom strange, and yet far
    spread   250
Through many a savage tribe, howe'er
    it grew,
And once in the old world known as
    widely as the new.

29

This could not then be done ; he
    might not lay
The bow and those unerring shafts
    aside ;
Nor through the appointed weeks
    forego the prey,   [wide,
Still to be sought amid those regions
None being there who should the
    while provide
That lonely household with their
    needful food :
So still Quiara through the forest plied
His daily task, and in the thickest
    wood   260
Still laid his snares for birds, and still
    the chase pursued.

30

But seldom may such thoughts of
    mingled joy
A father's agitated breast dilate,
As when he first beheld that infant
    boy.
Who hath not proved it, ill can
    estimate
The feeling of that stirring hour, . .
    the weight
Of that new sense, the thoughtful,
    pensive bliss.
In all the changes of our changeful
    state,
Even from the cradle to the grave,
    I wis,
The heart doth undergo no change so
    great as this.   270

31

A deeper and unwonted feeling fill'd
These parents, gazing on their new-
    born son.
Already in their busy hopes they build
On this frail sand. Now let the seasons
    run,   [done
And let the natural work of time be
With them, . . for unto them a child is
    born :
And when the hand of Death may
    reach the one,
The other will not now be left to
    mourn
A solitary wretch, all utterly forlorn.

32

Thus Monnema and thus Quiara
    thought,   280
Though each the melancholy thought
    represt ;
They could not choose but feel, yet
    utter'd not
The human feeling, which in hours of
    rest
Often would rise, and fill the boding
    breast
With a dread foretaste of that mourn-
    ful day,
When, at the inexorable Power's
    behest,   [away,
The unwilling spirit, called perforce
Must leave, for ever leave, its dear con-
    natural clay.

33

Link'd as they were, where each to
  each was all,
How might the poor survivor hope to
  bear   290
That heaviest loss which one day
  must befall,
Nor sink beneath the weight of his
  despair ?
Scarce could the heart even for a
  moment dare
That miserable time to contemplate,
When the dread Messenger should
  find them there,
From whom is no escape, . . and
  reckless Fate,
Whom it had bound so close, for ever
  separate.

34

Lighter that burthen lay upon the
  heart
When this dear babe was born to
  share their lot ;
They could endure to think that they
  must part.   300
Then too a glad consolatory thought
Arose, while gazing on the child they
  sought
With hope their dreary prospect to
  delude,   [taught,
Till they almost believed, as fancy
How that from them a tribe should
  spring renew'd,
To people and possess that ample
  solitude.

35

Such hope they felt, but felt that
  whatsoe'er   [prove,
The undiscoverable to come might
Unwise it were to let that bootlesscare
Disturb the present hours of peace
  and love.   310
For they had gain'd a happiness above
The state which in their native horde
  was known :
No outward causes were there here to
  move
Discord and alien thoughts ; being
  thus alone
From all mankind, their hearts and their
  desires were one.

36

Different their love in kind and in
  degree
From what their poor depraved fore-
  fathers knew,
With whom degenerate instincts were
  left free   [pursue,
To take their course, and blindly to
Unheeding they the ills that must
  ensue,   320
The bent of brute desire. No moral
  tie   [crew
Bound the hard husband to his servile
Of wives ; and they the chance of
  change might try,
All love destroy'd by such preposterous
  liberty.

37

Far other tie this solitary pair
Indissolubly bound ; true helpmates
  they,
In joy or grief, in weal or woe to
  share,
In sickness or in health, through life's
  long day ;
And reassuming in their hearts her
  sway
Benignant Nature made the burthen
  light.   330
It was the Woman's pleasure to obey,
The Man's to ease her toil in all he
  might,
So each in serving each obtain'd the
  best delight.

38

And as connubial, so parental love
Obey'd unerring Nature's order here,
For now no force of impious custom
  strove
Against her law ; .. such as was wont
  to sear
The unhappy heart with usages
  severe,
Till harden'd mothers in the grave
  could lay
Their living babes with no compunc-
  tious tear ;   340
So monstrous men become, when
  from the way
Of primal light they turn thro' heathen
  paths astray.

39

Deliver'd from this yoke, in them
    henceforth
The springs of natural love may freely
    flow :
New joys, new virtues with that
    happy birth
Are born, and with the growing
    infant grow.
Source of our purest happiness below
Is that benignant law which hath
    entwined
Dearest delight with strongest duty so,
That in the healthy heart and
    righteous mind   350
Ever they co-exist, inseparably com-
    bined.

40

Oh ! bliss for them when in that
    infant face
They now the unfolding faculties
    descry,
And fondly gazing, trace . . or think
    they trace
The first faint speculation in that eye,
Which hitherto hath roll'd in vacancy !
Oh ! bliss in that soft countenance
    to seek
Some mark of recognition, and espy
The quiet smile which in the innocent
    cheek
Of kindness and of kind its conscious-
    ness doth speak !   360

41

For him, if born among their native
    tribe,
Some haughty name his parents had
    thought good,
As weening that therewith they should
    ascribe
The strength of some fierce tenant of
    the wood,
The water, or the aërial solitude,
Jaguar or vulture, water-wolf or
    snake,
The beast that prowls abroad in
    search of blood,
Or reptile that within the treacherous
    brake
Waits for the prey, uncoil'd, its hunger
    to aslake.

42

Now soften'd as their spirits were by
    love,   370
Abhorrent from such thoughts they
    turn'd away ;   [dove,
And, with a happier feeling, from the
They named the Child Yeruti. On
    a day
When smiling at his mother's breast
    in play,
They in his tones of murmuring
    pleasure heard
A sweet resemblance of the stock-
    dove's lay,
Fondly they named him from that
    gentle bird,
And soon such happy use endear'd the
    fitting word.

43

Days pass, and moons have wax'd
    and waned, and still
This dovelet nestled in their leafy
    bower   380
Obtains increase of sense, and strength
    and will,
As in due order many a latent power
Expands, . . humanity's exalted
    dower :   [fled,
And they, while thus the days serenely
Beheld him flourish like a vigorous
    flower,   [head,
Which, lifting from a genial soil its
By seasonable suns and kindly showers
    is fed.

44

Ere long the cares of helpless baby-
    hood   [place,
To the next stage of infancy give
That age with sense of conscious
    growth endued,   390
When every gesture hath its proper
    grace :
Then come the unsteady step, the
    tottering pace ;
And watchful hopes and emulous
    thoughts appear ;
The imitative lips essay to trace
Their words, observant both with eye
    and ear,
In mutilated sounds which parents love
    to hear.

45

Serenely thus the seasons pass away ;
And, oh ! how rapidly they seem to
    fly   [to-day
With those for whom to-morrow like
Glides on in peaceful uniformity ! 400
Five years have since Yeruti's birth
    gone by,
Five happy years! .. and, ere the Moon
    which then
Hung like a Sylphid's light canoe on
    high
Should fill its circle, Monnema again
Laying her burthen down must bear
    a mother's pain.

46

Alas, a keener pang before that day
Must by the wretched Monnema be
    borne !
In quest of game Quiara went his way
To roam the wilds as he was wont, one
    morn ;
She look'd in vain at eve for his
    return.   410
By moonlight through the midnight
    solitude
She sought him ; and she found his
    garment torn,
His bow and useless arrows in the
    wood,
Marks of a jaguar's feet, a broken spear,
    and blood.

CANTO II

1

O THOU who listening to the Poet's
    song
Dost yield thy willing spirit to his
    sway,
Look not that I should painfully
    prolong
The sad narration of that fatal day
With tragic details : all too true the
    lay !
Nor is my purpose e'er to entertain
The heart with useless grief ; but, as
    I may,
Blend in my calm and meditative
    strain   [pain.
Consolatory thoughts, the balm for real

2

O Youth or Maiden, whosoe'er thou
    art,   10
Safe in my guidance may thy spirit
    be ;
I wound not wantonly the tender
    heart :
And if sometimes a tear of sympathy
Should rise, it will from bitterness be
    free ..
Yea, with a healing virtue be endued,
As thou in this true tale shalt hear
    from me
Of evils overcome, and grief subdued,
And virtues springing up like flowers in
    solitude.

3

The unhappy Monnema, when thus
    bereft,
Sunk not beneath the desolating
    blow.   20
Widow'd she was : but still her child
    was left ;
For him must she sustain the weight
    of woe,
Which else would in that hour have
    have laid her low.
Nor wish'd she now the work of death
    complete :
Then only doth the soul of woman
    know
Its proper strength, when love and
    duty meet ;
Invincible the heart wherein they have
    their seat.

4

The seamen, who upon some coral reef
Are cast amid the interminable main,
Still cling to life, and, hoping for relief,
Drag on their days of wretchedness
    and pain.   31
In turtle shells they hoard the scanty
    rain,
And eat its flesh, sun-dried for lack of
    fire,
Till the weak body can no more sus-
    tain
Its wants, but sinks beneath its
    sufferings dire ;
Most miserable man who sees the rest
    expire !

5

He lingers there while months and
years go by :
And holds his hope though months
and years have past ;
And still at morning round the
farthest sky,
And still at eve his eagle glance is
cast,   40
If there he may behold the far-off
mast
Arise, for which he hath not ceased
to pray.
And if perchance a ship should come
at last,
And bear him from that dismal bank
away,
He blesses God that he hath lived to see
that day.

6

So strong a hold hath life upon the
soul,
Which sees no dawning of eternal
light,
But subject to this mortal frame's
controul,
Forgetful of its origin and right,
Content in bondage dwells and utter
night.   50
By worthier ties was this poor mother
bound
To life ; even while her grief was at
the height,
Then in maternal love support she
found,
And in maternal cares a healing for her
wound.

7

For now her hour is come : a girl is
born,
Poor infant, all unconscious of its fate,
How passing strange, how utterly
forlorn !
The genial season served to mitigate
In all it might their sorrowful estate,
Supplying to the mother at her door
From neighbouring trees, which bent
beneath their weight,   61
A full supply of fruitage now mature,
So in that time of need their sustenance
was sure.

8

Nor then alone, but alway did the
Eye
Of Mercy look upon that lonely
bower.
Days pass'd, and weeks and months
and years went by ;
And never evil thing the while had
power
To enter there. The boy in sun and
shower
Rejoicing in his strength to youthhed
grew ;
And Mooma, that beloved girl, a
dower   70
Of gentleness from bounteous nature
drew,
With all that should the heart of woman-
kind imbue.

9

The tears, which o'er her infancy were
shed
Profuse, resented not of grief alone :
Maternal love their bitterness allay'd,
And with a strength and virtue all its
own
Sustain'd the breaking heart. A look,
a tone,
A gesture of that innocent babe, in
eyes
With saddest recollections overflown
Would sometimes make a tender smile
arise,   80
Like sunshine opening thro' a shower in
vernal skies.

10

No looks but those of tenderness were
found
To turn upon that helpless infant
dear ;
And, as her sense unfolded, never
sound
Of wrath or discord brake upon her
ear.
Her soul its native purity sincere
Possess'd, by no example here defiled ;
From envious passions free, exempt
from fear,
Unknowing of all ill, amid the wild
Beloving and beloved she grew, a happy
child.   90

11

Yea, where that solitary bower was
    placed,
Though all unlike to Paradise the
    scene,
(A wide circumference of woodland's
    waste ;)
Something of what in Eden might
    have been
Was shadow'd there imperfectly, I
    ween,
In this fair creature : safe from all
    offence,
Expanding like a shelter'd plant
    serene,
Evils that fret and stain being far
    from thence,
Her heart in peace and joy retain'd its
    innocence.   99

12

At first the infant to Yeruti proved
A cause of wonder and disturbing joy.
A stronger tie than that of kindred
    moved
His inmost being, as the happy boy
Felt in his heart of hearts without alloy
The sense of kind : a fellow creature
    she,
In whom, when now she ceased to be
    a toy
For tender sport, his soul rejoiced to
    see
Connatural powers expand, and growing
    sympathy.

13

For her he cull'd the fairest flowers,
    and sought
Throughout the woods the earliest
    fruits for her.   110
The cayman's eggs, the honeycomb
    he brought
To this beloved sister, . . whatsoe'er,
To his poor thought, of delicate or
    rare
The wilds might yield, solicitous to
    find.
They who affirm all natural acts de-
    clare
Self-love to be the ruler of the mind,
Judge from their own mean hearts, and
    foully wrong mankind.

14

Three souls in whom no selfishness had
    place
Were here : three happy souls, which,
    undefiled,
Albeit in darkness, still retain'd a
    trace   120
Of their celestial origin. The wild
Was as a sanctuary where Nature
    smiled
Upon these simple children of her
    own,
And, cherishing whate'er was meek
    and mild,
Call'd forth the gentle virtues, such
    alone,
The evils which evoke the stronger being
    unknown.

15

What though at birth we bring with
    us the seed
Of sin, a mortal taint, . . in heart and
    will
Too surely felt, too plainly shown in
    deed, . .
Our fatal heritage ; yet are we still
The children of the All Merciful ; and
    ill   131
They teach, who tell us that from
    hence must flow
God's wrath, and then his justice to
    fulfil,
Death everlasting, never-ending woe :
O miserable lot of man if it were so !

16

Falsely and impiously teach they who
    thus
Our heavenly Father's holy will mis-
    read !
In bounty hath the Lord created us,
In love redeem'd.   From this authen-
    tic creed
Let no bewildering sophistry impede
The heart's entire assent, for God is
    good.   141
Hold firm this faith, and, in whatever
    need,
Doubt not but thou wilt find thy soul
    endued
With all-sufficing strength of heavenly
    fortitude !

17

By nature peccable and frail are we,
Easily beguiled ; to vice, to error
    prone ;
But apt for virtue too.   Humanity
Is not a field where tares and thorns
    alone
Are left to spring ; good seed hath
    there been sown
With no unsparing hand.   Sometimes
    the shoot   150
Is choked with weeds, or withers on
    a stone ;
But in a kindly soil it strikes its
    root,
And flourisheth, and bringeth forth
    abundant fruit.

18

Love, duty, generous feeling, tender-
    ness,
Spring in the uncontaminated mind ;
And these were Mooma's natural
    dower.   Nor less
Had liberal Nature to the boy assign'd,
Happier herein than if among man-
    kind
Their lot had fallen, . . oh, certes
    happier here !
That all things tended still more close
    to bind   160
Their earliest ties, and they from year
    to year
Retain'd a childish heart, fond, simple,
    and sincere.

19

They had no sad reflection to alloy
The calm contentment of the passing
    day,
Nor foresight to disturb the present
    joy.
Not so with Monnema ; albeit the
    sway
Of time had reach'd her heart, and
    worn away,
At length, the grief so deeply seated
    there,
The future often, like a burthen, lay
Upon that heart, a cause of secret
    care   170
And melancholy thought ; yet did she
    not despair.

20

Chance from the fellowship of human
    kind
Had cut them off, and chance might
    reunite.
On this poor possibility her mind
Reposed ; she did not for herself
    invite
The unlikely thought, and cherish
    with delight
The dream of what such change might
    haply bring ;
Gladness with hope long since had
    taken flight
From her ; she felt that life was on
    the wing,
And happiness like youth has here no
    second spring.   180

21

So were her feelings to her lot com-
    posed
That to herself all change had now
    been pain.
For Time upon her own desires had
    closed ;
But in her children as she lived again,
For their dear sake she learnt to
    entertain
A wish for human intercourse renew'd ;
And oftentimes, while they devour'd
    the strain,
Would she beguile their evening soli-
    tude
With stories strangely told and strangely
    understood.

22

Little she knew, for little had she seen,
And little of traditional lore   191
Had reach'd her ear ; and yet to them
    I ween
Their mother's knowledge seem'd
    a boundless store.
A world it open'd to their thoughts,
    yea more, . .
Another world beyond this mortal
    state.
Bereft of her they had indeed been
    poor,
Being left to animal sense, degenerate,
Mere creatures, they had sunk below
    the beasts' estate.

23

The human race, from her they understood,
Was not within that lonely hut confined,   200
But distant far beyond their world of wood
Were tribes and powerful nations of their kind ;
And of the old observances which bind
People and chiefs, the ties of man and wife,
The laws of kin religiously assign'd,
Rites, customs, scenes of riotry and strife,
And all the strange vicissitudes of savage life.

24

Wondering they listen to the wondrous tale,
But no repining thought such tales excite :   209
Only a wish, if wishes might avail,
Was haply felt, with juvenile delight,
To mingle in the social dance at night,
Where the broad moonshine, level as a flood,   [light,
O'erspread the plain, and in the silver
Well-pleased, the placid elders sate and view'd
The sport, and seem'd therein to feel their youth renew'd.

25

But when the darker scenes their mother drew,
What crimes were wrought when drunken fury raged,
What miseries from their fatal discord grew,
When horde with horde in deadly strife engaged :   220
The rancorous hate with which their wars they waged,
The more unnatural horrors which ensued,
When, with inveterate vengeance unassuaged,
The victors round their slaughter'd captives stood,
And babes were brought to dip their little hands in blood :

26

Horrent they heard ; and with her hands the Maid   [blot
Prest her eyes close as if she strove to
The hateful image which her mind portray'd.
The Boy sate silently, intent in thought ;
Then with a deep-drawn sigh, as if he sought   230
To heave the oppressive feeling from his breast,
Complacently compared their harmless lot
With such wild life, outrageous and unblest ;   [best.
Securely thus to live, he said, was surely

27

On tales of blood they could not bear to dwell,
From such their hearts abhorrent shrunk in fear.   [tell
Better they liked that Monnema should
Of things unseen ; what Power had placed them here,
And whence the living spirit came, and where
It pass'd, when parted from this mortal mould ;   240
Of such mysterious themes with willing ear
They heard, devoutly listening while she told
Strangely-disfigured truths, and fables feign'd of old.

28

By the Great Spirit man was made, she said,
His voice it was which peal'd along the sky,
And shook the heavens and fill'd the earth with dread.
Alone and inaccessible, on high
He had his dwelling-place eternally,
And Father was his name. This all knew well ;
But none had seen his face : and if his eye   250
Regarded what upon the earth befell,
Or if he cared for man, she knew not : . . who could tell ?

29

But this, she said, was sure, that after death
There was reward and there was punishment:
And that the evil doers, when the breath [spent,
Of their injurious lives at length was
Into all noxious forms abhorr'd were sent, [still
Of beasts and reptiles; so retaining
Their old propensities, on evil bent,
They work'd where'er they might their wicked will, 260
The natural foes of man, whom we pursue and kill.

30

Of better spirits, some there were who said
That in the grave they had their place of rest.
Lightly they laid the earth upon the dead,
Lest in his narrow tenement the guest
Should suffer underneath such load opprest. [free,
But that death surely set the spirit
Sad proof to them poor Monnema addrest,
Drawn from their father's fate; no grave had he
Wherein his soul might dwell. This therefore could not be. 270

31

Likelier they taught who said that to the Land
Of Souls the happy spirit took its flight,
A region underneath the sole command
Of the Good Power; by him for the upright
Appointed and replenish'd with delight;
A land where nothing evil ever came,
Sorrow, nor pain, nor peril, nor affright,
Nor change, nor death; but there the human frame,
Untouch'd by age or ill, continued still the same.

32

Winds would not pierce it there, nor heat and cold 280
Grieve, nor thirst parch and hunger pine; but there
The sun by day its even influence hold
With genial warmth, and through the unclouded air
The moon upon her nightly journey fare:
The lakes and fish-full streams are never dry;
Trees ever green perpetual fruitage bear; [eye,
And, wheresoe'er the hunter turns his
Water and earth and heaven to him their stores supply.

33

And once there was a way to that good land,
For in mid-earth a wondrous Tree there grew, 290
By which the adventurer might with foot and hand
From branch to branch his upward course pursue; [true,
An easy path, if what were said be
Albeit the ascent was long; and when the height
Was gain'd, that blissful region was in view,
Wherein the traveller safely might alight,
And roam abroad at will, and take his free delight.

34

O happy time, when ingress thus was given
To the upper world, and at their pleasure they
Whose hearts were strong might pass from Earth to Heaven 300
By their own act and choice! In evil day
Mishap had fatally cut off that way,
And none may now the Land of Spirits gain, [clay
Till from its dear-loved tenement of
Violence or age, infirmity and pain,
Divorce the soul which there full gladly would remain.

z

35

Such grievous loss had by their own
    misdeed
Upon the unworthy race of men
    been brought.
An aged woman once who could not
    speed
In fishing, earnestly one day besought
Her countrymen, that they of what
    they caught   311
A portion would upon her wants
    bestow.
They set her hunger and her age at
    nought,
And still to her entreaties answered
    no !
And mock'd her, till they made her
    heart with rage o'erflow.

36

But that Old Woman by such wanton
    wrong
Inflamed, went hurrying down ; and
    in the pride
Of magic power, wherein the crone
    was strong,
Her human form infirm she laid aside.
Better the Capiguara's limbs supplied
A strength accordant to her fierce
    intent :   321
These she assumed, and, burrowing
    deep and wide
Beneath the Tree, with vicious will,
    she went,
To inflict upon mankind a lasting
    punishment.

37

Downward she wrought her way, and
    all around   [mined
Labouring, the solid earth she under-
And loosen'd all the roots ; then from
    the ground
Emerging, in her hatred of her kind,
Resumed her proper form, and
    breathed a wind
Which gather'd like a tempest round
    its head :   330
Eftsoon the lofty Tree its top inclined
Uptorn with horrible convulsion
    dread,
And over half the world its mighty
    wreck lay spread.

38

But never scion sprouted from that
    Tree,
Nor seed sprang up ; and thus the
    easy way,
Which had till then for young and old
    been free,   [aye.
Was closed upon the sons of men for
The mighty ruin moulder'd where it
    lay
Till not a trace was left ; and now
    in sooth
Almost had all remembrance pass'd
    away.   340
This from the Elders she had heard in
    youth ;
Some said it was a tale, and some a very
    truth.

39

Nathless departed spirits at their will
Could from the Land of Souls pass to
    and fro ;   [still,
They come to us in sleep when all is
Sometimes to warn against the im-
    pending blow,
Alas ! more oft to visit us in woe :
Though in their presence there was
    poor relief !
And this had sad experience made her
    know,
For when Quiara came, his stay was
    brief,   350
And, waking then, she felt a freshen'd
    sense of grief.

40

Yet to behold his face again, and hear
His voice, though painful, was a
    deep delight :
It was a joy to think that he was near,
To see him in the visions of the
    night, . .
To know that the departed still re-
    quite
The love which to their memory still
    will cling :
And, though he might not bless her
    waking sight
With his dear presence,'twas a blessed
    thing
That sleep would thus sometimes his
    actual image bring.   360

41

Why comes he not to me ? Yeruti
  cries ;
And Mooma, echoing with a sigh the
  thought,   [eyes
Ask'd why it was that to her longing
No dream the image of her father
  brought ?
Nor Monnema to solve that question
  sought
In vain, content in ignorance to dwell ;
Perhaps it was because they knew
  him not ;
Perhaps . . but sooth she could not
  answer well ;
What the departed did, themselves
  alone could tell.

42

What one tribe held another dis-
  believed,   370
For all concerning this was dark, she
  said ;
Uncertain all, and hard to be received.
The dreadful race, from whom their
  fathers fled,
Boasted that even the Country of the
  Dead
Was theirs, and where their Spirits
  chose to go,
The ghosts of other men retired in
  dread
Before the face of that victorious foe ;
No better, then, the world above, than
  this below !

43

What then, alas ! if this were true,
  was death ?
Only a mournful change from ill to ill !
And some there were who said the
  living breath   381
Would ne'er be taken from us by the
  will
Of the Good Father, but continue still
To feed with life the mortal frame he
  gave,
Did not mischance or wicked witch-
  craft kill ; . .
Evils from which no care avail'd to
  save,
And whereby all were sent to fill the
  greedy grave.

44

In vain to counterwork the baleful
  charm
By spells of rival witchcraft was it
  sought,
Less potent was that art to help than
  harm.   390
No means of safety old experience
  brought :
Nor better fortune did they find who
  thought
From Death, as from some living foe,
  to fly :
For speed or subterfuge avail'd them
  nought,
But wheresoe'er they fled they found
  him nigh :   [enemy.
None ever could elude that unseen

45

Bootless the boast, and vain the proud
  intent
Of those who hoped, with arrogant
  display
Of arms and force, to scare him from
  their tent,
As if their threatful shouts and fierce
  array   400
Of war could drive the Invisible away !
Sometimes, regardless of the sufferer's
  groan,
They dragg'd the dying out, and as
  prey
Exposed him, that content with him
  alone
Death might depart, and thus his fate
  avert their own.

46

Depart he might, . . but only to return
In quest of other victims, soon or late ;
When they who held this fond belief
  would learn,
Each by his own inevitable fate,
That in the course of man's uncertain
  state   410
Death is the one and only certain
  thing.
Oh folly then to fly or deprecate
That which at last Time, ever on the
  wing,
Certain as day and night, to weary age
  must bring !

47

While thus the Matron spake, the
    youthful twain
Listen'd in deep attention, wistfully ;
Whether with more of wonder or of
    pain   [eye
Uneath it were to tell. With steady
Intent they heard ; and, when she
    paused, a sigh
Their sorrowful foreboding seem'd to
    speak :   420
Questions to which she could not give
    reply
Yeruti ask'd ; and for that Maiden
    meek, . .   [cheek.
Involuntary tears ran down her quiet

48

A different sentiment within them
    stirr'd,   [day,
When Monnema recall'd to mind one
Imperfectly, what she had sometimes
    heard
In childhood, long ago, the Elders say :
Almost from memory had it pass'd
    away, . .
How there appear'd amid the wood-
    lands men
Whom the Great Spirit sent there to
    convey   430
His gracious will ; but little heed she
    then
Had given, and like a dream it now
    recurr'd again.

49

But these young questioners from
    time to time
Call'd up the long-forgotten theme
    anew.
Strange men they were, from some
    remotest clime,
She said, of different speech, uncouth
    to view,
Having hair upon their face, and
    white in hue ;
Across the World of waters wide they
    came
Devotedly the Father's work to do,
And seek the Red-Men out, and in his
    name   440
His merciful laws, and love, and promises
    proclaim.

50

They served a Maid more beautiful
    than tongue
Could tell, or heart conceive. Of
    human race,
All heavenly as that Virgin was, she
    sprung ;
But for her beauty and celestial grace,
Being one in whose pure elements no
    trace
Hade'er inhered of sin or mortal stain,
The highest Heaven was now her
    dwelling-place ;
There as a Queen divine she held her
    reign,
And there in endless joy for ever would
    remain.   450

51

Her feet upon the crescent Moon were
    set,
And, moving in their order round her
    head,
The Stars compose her sparkling
    coronet.
There at her breast the Virgin Mother
    fed
A Babe divine, who was to judge the
    dead,
Such power the Spirit gave this aweful
    Child ;
Severe he was, and in his anger dread,
Yet alway at his Mother's will grew
    mild,
So well did he obey that Maiden unde-
    filed.

52

Sometimes she had descended from
    above   460
To visit her true votaries, and requite
Such as had served her well. And
    for her love,
These bearded men, forsaking all
    delight,
With labour long and dangers infinite,
Across the great blue waters came,
    and sought
The Red-Men here, to win them, if
    they might,   [aught,
From bloody ways, rejoiced to profit
Even when with their own lives the
    benefit was bought.

53

For, trusting in this heavenly Maiden's
grace,
It was for them a joyful thing to die,
As men who went to have their happy
place   471
With her, and with that Holy Child,
on high,
In fields of bliss above the starry sky,
In glory at the Virgin Mother's feet :
And all who kept their lessons faith-
fully
An everlasting guerdon there would
meet,
When Death had led their souls to that
celestial seat.

54

On earth they offer'd, too, an easy life
To those who their mild lessons would
obey,
Exempt from want, from danger, and
from strife ;   480
And from the forest leading them
away,
They placed them underneath this
Virgin's sway,
A numerous fellowship, in peace to
dwell ;
Their high and happy office there to
pay
Devotions due, which she requited
well,
Their heavenly Guardian she in what-
soe'er befell.

55

Thus, Monnema remember'd, it was
told
By one who in his hot and headstrong
youth
Had left her happy service ; but
when old
Lamented oft with unavailing ruth,
And thoughts which sharper than a
serpent's tooth   491
Pierced him, that he had changed
that peaceful place
For the fierce freedom and the ways
uncouth   [grace,
Of their wild life, and lost that Lady's
Wherefore he had no hope to see in
Heaven her face.

56

And she remember'd, too, when first
they fled
For safety to the farthest solitude
Before their cruel foes, and lived in
dread
That thither too their steps might be
pursued
By those old enemies athirst for
blood ;   500
How some among them hoped to see
the day
When these beloved messengers of
good
To that lone hiding-place might find
the way,
And them to their abode of blessedness
convey.

57

Such tales excited in Yeruti's heart
A stirring hope that haply he might
meet
Some minister of Heaven ; and many
a part
Untrod before of that wild wood
retreat
Did he with indefatigable feet
Explore ; yet ever from the fruitless
quest   510
Return'd at evening to his native seat
By daily disappointment undeprest, . . .
So buoyant was the hope that fill'd his
youthful breast.

58

At length the hour approach'd that
should fulfil
His harmless heart's desire, when they
shall see
Their fellow-kind, and take for good
or ill
The fearful chance, for such it needs
must be,
Of change from that entire simplicity.
Yet wherefore should the thought of
change appal ?
· Grief it perhaps might bring, and
injury,   520
And death ; . . but evil never can
befall
The virtuous, for the Eye of Heaven is
over all.

CANTO III

1

AMID those marshy woodlands far and
wide
Which spread beyond the soaring
vulture's eye,
There grew on Empalado's southern
side   [supply
Groves of that tree whose leaves adust
The Spaniards with their daily luxury;
A beverage whose salubrious use
obtains
Through many a land of mines and
slavery,   [plains,
Even over all La Plata's sea-like
And Chili's mountain realm, and proud
Peru's domains.

2

But better for the injured Indian race
Had woods of manchineel the land
o'erspread :   11
Yea, in that tree so blest by Nature's
grace
A direr curse had they inherited,
Than if the Upas there had rear'd its
head
And sent its baleful scions all around,
Blasting where'er its effluent force
was shed,   [ground,
In air and water, and the infected
All things wherein the breath or sap of
life is found.

3

The poor Guaranies dreamt of no such
ill,
When for themselves in miserable
hour,   20
The virtues of that leaf, with pure
good will,
They taught their unsuspected visitor,
New in the land as yet. They learnt
his power
Too soon, which law nor conscience
could restrain,
A fearless but inhuman conqueror,
Heart-harden'd by the accursed lust
of gain.
O fatal thirst of gold ! O foul reproach
for Spain !

4

For gold and silver had the Spaniards
sought,
Exploring Paraguay with desperate
pains,
Their way through forests axe in
hand they wrought ;   30
Drench'd from above by unremitting
rains
They waded over inundated plains,
Forward by hope of plunder still
allured ;
So they might one day count their
golden gains,
They cared not at what cost of sin
procured,
All dangers they defied, all sufferings
they endured.

5

Barren alike of glory and of gold
That region proved to them ; nor
would the soil
Unto their unindustrious hands un-
fold
Harvests, the fruit of peace, . . and
wine and oil,   40
The treasures that repay contented toil
With health and weal ; treasures that
with them bring
No guilt for priest and penance to
assoil,
Nor with their venom arm the
awaken'd sting
Of conscience at that hour when life is
vanishing.

6

But keen of eye in their pursuit of gain
The conquerors look'd for lucre in this
tree :   [attain,
An annual harvest there might they
Without the cost of annual industry.
'Twas but to gather in what there
grew free   50
And share Potosi's wealth. Nor
thence alone.
But gold in glad exchange they soon
should see
From all that once the Incas called
their own,
Or where the Zippa's power or Zaque's
laws were known.

7

For this, in fact, though not in name
    a slave,
The Indian from his family was torn ;
And droves on droves were sent to
    find a grave
In woods and swamps, by toil severe
    outworn,
No friend at hand to succour or to
    mourn,
In death unpitied, as in life unblest. 60
O miserable race, to slavery born !
Yet, when we look beyond this
    world's unrest,
More miserable then the oppressors
    than the opprest.

8

Often had Kings essay'd to check the
    ill   [meant ;
By edicts not so well enforced as
A present power was wanting to fulfil
Remote authority's sincere intent.
To Avarice, on its present purpose
    bent,
The voice of distant Justice spake in
    vain ;
False magistrates and priests their
    influence lent   70
The accursed thing for lucre to main-
    tain :
O fatal thirst of gold ! O foul reproach
    for Spain !

9

O foul reproach ! but not for Spain
    alone,
But for all lands that bear the Chris-
    tian name !
Where'er commercial slavery is
    known,
O shall not Justice trumpet-tongued
    proclaim
The foul reproach, the black offence
    the same ?
Hear, guilty France ! and thou,
    O England, hear !
Thou who hast half redeem'd thyself
    from shame,
When slavery from thy realms shall
    disappear,   80
Then from this guilt, and not till then,
    wilt thou be clear.

10

Uncheck'd in Paraguay it ran its
    course,
Till all the gentler children of the land
Well nigh had been consumed without
    remorse.
The bolder tribes meantime, whose
    skilful hand
Had tamed the horse, in many a war-
    like band
Kept the field well with bow and
    dreadful spear
And now the Spaniards dared no more
    withstand
Their force, but in their towns grew
    pale with fear
If the Mocobio, or the Abipon drew near.

11

Bear witness, Chaco, thou, from thy
    domain   91
With Spanish blood, as erst with
    Indian, fed !
And Corrientes, by whose church the
    slain
Were piled in heaps, till for the
    gather'd dead
One common grave was dug, one
    service said !
Thou too, Parana, thy sad witness bear
From shores with many a mournful
    vestige spread,
And monumental crosses here and
    there,
And monumental names that tell where
    dwellings were !

12

Nor would with all their power the
    Kings of Spain,   100
Austrian or Bourbon, have at last
    avail'd
This torrent of destruction to restrain,
And save a people every where assail'd
By men before whose face their
    courage quail'd,
But for the virtuous agency of those
Who with the Cross alone, when arms
    had fail'd,
Achieved a peaceful triumph o'er the
    foes,
And gave that weary land the blessings
    of repose.

13

For whensoe'er the Spaniards felt or
  fear'd
An Indian enemy, they call'd for aid
Upon Loyola's sons, now long en-
  dear'd   111
To many a happy tribe, by them con-
  vey'd
From the open wilderness or woodland
  shade,
In towns of happiest polity to dwell.
Freely these faithful ministers essay'd
The arduous enterprize, contented
  well   [fell.
If with success they sped, or if as martyrs

14

And now it chanced some traders who
  had fell'd
The trees of precious foliage far and
  wide
On Empalado's shore, when they
  beheld   120
The inviting woodlands on its northern
  side,
Crost thither in their quest, and there
  espied
Yeruti's footsteps : searching then
  the shade
At length a lonely dwelling they
  descried,
And at the thought of hostile hordes
  dismay'd
To the nearest mission sped and ask'd
  the Jesuit's aid.

15

That was a call which ne'er was made
  in vain
Upon Loyola's sons. In Paraguay
Much of injustice had they to com-
  plain,
Much of neglect ; but faithful
  labourers they   130
In the Lord's vineyard, there was no
  delay
When summon'd to his work. A
  little band
Of converts made them ready for the
  way ;   [hand
Their spiritual father took a Cross in
To be his staff, and forth they went to
  search the land.

16

He was a man of rarest qualities,
Who to this barbarous region had
  confined
A spirit with the learned and the
  wise
Worthy to take its place, and from
  mankind
Receive their homage, to the immortal
  mind   140
Paid in its just inheritance of fame.
But he to humbler thoughts his heart
  inclined ;
From Gratz amid the Styrian hills he
  came,
And Dobrizhoffer was the good man's
  honour'd name.

17

It was his evil fortune to behold
The labours of his painful life
  destroy'd ;
His flock which he had brought within
  the fold
Dispersed ; the work of ages render'd
  void,
And all of good that Paraguay en-
  joy'd
By blind and suicidal Power o'er-
  thrown.   150
So he the years of his old age em-
  ploy'd,
A faithful chronicler, in handing down
Names which he loved, and things well
  worthy to be known.

18

And thus, when exiled from the dear-
  loved scene,
In proud Vienna he beguiled the pain
Of sad remembrance ; and the
  Empress Queen,
That great Teresa, she did not disdain
In gracious mood sometimes to enter-
  tain
Discourse with him both pleasurable
  and sage ;
And sure a willing ear she well might
  deign   160
To one whose tales may equally en-
  gage
The wondering mind of youth, the
  thoughtful heart of age.

19

But of his native speech because well
    nigh
Disuse in him forgetfulness had
    wrought,
In Latin he composed his history ;
A garrulous, but a lively tale, and
    fraught
With matter of delight and food for
    thought.
And, if he could in Merlin's glass have
    seen
By whom his tomes to speak our
    tongue were taught,
The old man would have felt as
    pleased, I ween,   170
As when he won the ear of that great
    Empress Queen.

20

Little he deem'd, when with his
    Indian band
He through the wilds set forth upon
    his way,
A Poet then unborn, and in a land
Which had proscribed his order, should
    one day
Take up from thence his moralizing
    lay,
And shape a song that, with no fiction
    drest,
Should to his worth its grateful
    tribute pay,
And, sinking deep in many an English
    breast,
Foster that faith divine that keeps the
    heart at rest.   180

21

Behold him on his way ! the breviary
Which from his girdle hangs, his only
    shield ;
That well-known habit is his panoply,
That Cross, the only weapon he will
    wield ;
By day he bears it for his staff afield,
By night it is the pillar of his bed ;
No other lodging these wild woods
    can yield
Than earth's hard lap, and rustling
    overhead
A canopy of deep and tangled boughs
    far spread.

22

Yet may they not without some
    cautious care   190
Take up their inn content upon the
    ground.
First it behoves to clear a circle there,
And trample down the grass and
    plantage round,
Where many a deadly reptile might
    be found,   [heat
Whom with its bright and comfortable
The flame would else allure : such
    plagues abound
In these thick woods, and therefore
    must they beat
The earth, and trample well the herbs
    beneath their feet.

23

And now they heap dry reeds and
    broken wood ;
The spark is struck, the crackling
    faggots blaze,   200
And cheer that unaccustom'd solitude.
Soon have they made their frugal
    meal of maize ;
In grateful adoration then they raise
The evening hymn. How solemn in
    the wild
That sweet accordant strain where-
    with they praise
The Queen of Angels, merciful and
    mild :
Hail, holiest Mary ! Maid, and Mother
    undefiled.

24

Blame as thou may'st the Papist's
    erring creed,
But not their salutary rite of even !
The prayers that from a pious soul
    proceed,   210
Though misdirected, reach the ear of
    Heaven.
Us, unto whom a purer faith is given,
As our best birthright it behoves to
    hold
The precious charge ; but, oh, be-
    ware the leaven
Which makes the heart of charity
    grow cold !
We own one Shepherd, we shall be at
    last one fold.

25

Thinkest thou the little company who
    here
Pour forth their hymn devout at close
    of day,
Feel it no aid that those who hold
    them dear
At the same hour the self-same homage
    pay,   220
Commending them to Heaven when
    far away ?
That the sweet bells are heard in
    solemn chime
Through all the happy towns of
    Paraguay,
Where now their brethren in one
    point of time
Join in the general prayer, with sym-
    pathy sublime ?

26

That to the glorious Mother of their
    Lord
Whole Christendom that hour its
    homage pays ?
From court and cottage that with one
    accord
Ascends the universal strain of praise?
Amid the crowded city's restless ways,
One reverential thought pervades the
    throng ;   231
The traveller on his lonely road obeys
The sacred hour, and, as he fares along,
In spirit hears and joins his household's
    even-song.

27

What if they think that every prayer
    enroll'd
Shall one day in their good account
    appear ;
That guardian Angels hover round
    and fold   [hear :
Their wings in adoration while they
Ministrant Spirits through the ethereal
    sphere
Waft it with joy, and to the grateful
    theme,   240
Well pleased, the Mighty Mother
    bends her ear ?
A vain delusion this we rightly deem :
Yet what they feel is not a mere illusive
    dream.

28

That prayer perform'd, around the
    fire reclined
Beneath the leafy canopy they lay
Their limbs : the Indians soon to
    sleep resign'd ;
And the good Father with that toil-
    some day
Fatigued, full fain to sleep, . . if sleep
    he may,
Whom all tormenting insects there
    assail ;
More to be dreaded these than beasts
    of prey   250
Against whom strength may cope, or
    skill prevail,
But art of man against these enemies
    must fail.

29

Patience itself that should the
    sovereign cure,
For ills that touch ourselves alone,
    supply,
Lends little aid to one who must en-
    dure
This plague : the small tormentors fill
    the sky,
And swarm about their prey ; there
    he must lie
And suffer while the hours of darkness
    wear ;   [sigh
At times he utters with a deep-drawn
Some name adored, in accents of
    despair   260
Breath'd sorrowfully forth, half murmur
    and half prayer.

30

Welcome to him the earliest gleam of
    light ;
Welcome to him the earliest sound of
    day ;
That from the sufferings of that
    weary night   [way,
Released, he may resume his willing
Well pleased again the perils to essay
Of that drear wilderness, with hope
    renew'd :
Success will all his labours overpay,
A quest like his is cheerfully pursued,
The heart is happy still that is intent on
    good.   270

31

And now where Empalado's waters
  creep
Through low and level shores of wood-
  land wide,
They come ; prepared to cross the
  sluggish deep,
An ill-shaped coracle of hardest hide,
Ruder than ever Cambrian fisher plied
Where Towey and the salt-sea waters
  meet,
The Indians launch ; they steady it
  and guide,
Winning their way with arms and
  practised feet,
While in the tottering boat the Father
  keeps his seat.

32

For three long summer days on every
  side   280
They search in vain the sylvan soli-
  tude ;
The fourth a human footstep is espied,
And through the mazes of the pathless
  wood
With hound-like skill and hawk-like
  eye pursued ;   [they
For keen upon their pious quest are
As e'er were hunters on the track of
  blood.   [betray
Where softer ground or trodden herbs
The slightest mark of man, they there
  explore the way.

33

More cautious, when more certain of
  the trace,
In silence they proceed ; not like
  a crew   290
Of jovial hunters, who the joyous chase
With hound and horn in open field
  pursue,
Cheering their way with jubilant
  halloo,
And hurrying forward to their spoil
  desired,
The panting game before them, full
  in view :
Humaner thoughts this little band
  inspired,
Yet with a hope as high their gentle
  hearts were fired.

34

Nor is their virtuous hope devoid of
  fear ;
The perils of that enterprise they
  know ;
Some savage horde may have its
  fastness here,   300
A race to whom a stranger is a foe,
Who not for friendly words, nor prof-
  fer'd show
Of gifts, will peace or parley entertain.
If by such hands their blameless blood
  should flow
To serve the Lamb who for their sins
  was slain,
Blessed indeed their lot, for so to die is
  gain !

35

Them, thus pursuing where the track
  may lead,
A human voice arrests upon their
  way ;
They stop, and thither, whence the
  sounds proceed,
All eyes are turn'd in wonder, . . not
  dismay,   310
For sure such sounds might charm
  all fear away ;
No nightingale whose brooding mate
  is nigh,
From some sequester'd bower at close
  of day,
No lark rejoicing in the orient sky,
Ever pour'd forth so wild a strain of
  melody.

36

The voice which through the ringing
  forest floats
Is one which, having ne'er been
  taught the skill
Of marshalling sweet words to sweeter
  notes,
Utters all unpremeditate, at will,
A modulated sequence loud and shrill
Of inarticulate and long-breathed
  sound,   321
Varying its tones with rise and fall
  and trill,
Till all the solitary woods around
With that far-piercing power of melody
  resound.

37

In mute astonishment attent to hear,
As if by some enchantment held, they
　　stood,
With bending head, fix'd eye, and
　　eager ear,
And hand upraised in warning atti-
　　tude
To check all speech or step that might
　　intrude
On that sweet strain.　Them leaving
　　thus spell-bound,　　　330
A little way alone into the wood
The Father gently moved toward the
　　sound,
Treading with quiet feet upon the
　　grassy ground.

38

Anon advancing thus the trees be-
　　tween,
He saw beside her bower the songs-
　　tress wild,
Not distant far, himself the while un-
　　seen.
Mooma it was, that happy maiden
　　mild,
Who in the sunshine, like a careless
　　child
Of nature, in her joy was caroling.
A heavier heart than his it had be-
　　guiled　　　340
So to have heard so fair a creature
　　sing
The strains which she had learnt from all
　　sweet birds of spring.

39

For these had been her teachers, these
　　alone ;
And she in many an emulous essay,
At length into a descant of her own
Had blended all their notes, a wild
　　display
Of sounds in rich irregular array ;
And now, as blithe as bird in vernal
　　bower,
Pour'd in full flow the unexpressive
　　lay,
Rejoicing in her consciousness of
　　power,　　　350
But in the inborn sense of harmony yet
　　more.

40

In joy had she begun the ambitious
　　song,
With rapid interchange of sink and
　　swell ;
And sometimes high the note was
　　raised, and long
Produced, with shake and effort
　　sensible,
As if the voice exulted there to dwell ;
But when she could no more that
　　pitch sustain,
So thrillingly attuned the cadence fell,
That with the music of its dying
　　strain
She moved herself to tears of pleasurable
　　pain.　　　360

41

It might be deem'd some dim presage
　　possess'd
The virgin's soul ; that some mys-
　　terious sense
Of change to come, upon her mind
　　impress'd,
Had then call'd forth, ere she de-
　　parted thence,
A requiem to their days of innocence.
For what thou losest in thy native
　　shade
There is one change alone that may
　　compense,
O Mooma, innocent and simple maid,
Only one change, and it will not be long
　　delay'd !

42

When now the Father issued from
　　the wood　　　370
Into that little glade in open sight,
Like one entranced, beholding him,
　　she stood ;
Yet had she more of wonder than
　　affright,
Yet less of wonder than of dread
　　delight,
When thus the actual vision came in
　　view ;
For instantly the maiden read aright
Wherefore he came ; his garb and
　　beard she knew ;
All that her mother heard had then in-
　　deed been true.

43

Nor was the Father filled with less surprise ;
He too strange fancies well might entertain,   380
When this so fair a creature met his eyes.
He might have thought her not of mortal strain ;
Rather, as bards of yore were wont to feign,
A nymph divine of Mondai's secret stream ;
Or haply of Diana's woodland train :
For in her beauty Mooma such might seem,
Being less a child of earth than like a poet's dream.

44

No art of barbarous ornament had scarr'd
And stain'd her virgin limbs, or 'filed her face ;
Nor ever yet had evil passion marr'd
In her sweet countenance the natural grace   391
Of innocence and youth ; nor was there trace
Of sorrow, or of hardening want and care.
Strange was it in this wild and savage place,
Which seem'd to be for beasts a fitting lair,   [fair.
Thus to behold a maid so gentle and so

45

Across her shoulders was a hammock flung,
By night it was the maiden's bed, by day   [hung,
Her only garment. Round her as it
In short unequal folds of loose array,
The open meshes, when she moves, display   401
Her form. She stood with fix'd and wondering eyes,
And, trembling like a leaf upon the spray,
Even for excess of joy, with eager cries
She call'd her mother forth to share that glad surprise.

46

At that unwonted call with quicken'd pace
The matron hurried thither, half in fear.
How strange to Monnema a stranger's face !
How strange it was a stranger's voice to hear,
How strangely to her disaccustom'd ear   410
Came even the accents of her native tongue !
But when she saw her countrymen appear,
Tears for that unexpected blessing sprung,
And once again she felt as if her heart were young.

47

Soon was her melancholy story told,
And glad consent unto that Father good
Was given, that they to join his happy fold
Would leave with him their forest solitude.
Why comes not now Yeruti from the wood ?
Why tarrieth he so late this blessed day ?   420
They long to see their joy in his renew'd,
And look impatiently toward his way,
And think they hear his step, and chide his long delay.

48

He comes at length, a happy man, to find
His only dream of hope fulfill'd at last.
The sunshine of his all-believing mind
There is no doubt or fear to overcast ;
No chilling forethought checks his bliss ; the past
Leaves no regret for him, and all to come
Is change and wonder and delight. How fast   430
Hath busy fancy conjured up a sum
Of joys unknown, whereof the expectance makes him dumb.

49

O happy day, the Messenger of Heaven
Hath found them in their lonely
dwelling-place !
O happy day, to them it would be
given
To share in that Eternal Mother's
grace,
And one day see in heaven her glorious
face,   [adore !
Where Angels round her mercy-throne
Now shall they mingle with the
human race,
Sequester'd from their fellow-kind no
more ;   440
O joy of joys supreme ! O bliss for them
in store !

50

Full of such hopes this night they lay
them down,
But not as they were wont, this night
to rest.
Their old tranquillity of heart is gone ;
The peace wherewith till now they
have been blest
Hath taken its departure. In the
breast
Fast following thoughts and busy
fancies throng ;
Their sleep itself is feverish, and
possest   [belong ;
With dreams that to the wakeful mind
To Mooma and the youth then first the
night seem'd long.   450

51

Day comes, and now a first and last
farewell
To that fair bower within their
native wood,
Their quiet nest till now. The bird
may dwell
Henceforth in safety there, and rear
her brood,
And beasts and reptiles undisturb'd
intrude ;   [go,
Reckless of this, the simple tenants
Emerging from their peaceful solitude,
To mingle with the world, . . but not
to know
Its crimes, nor to partake its cares, nor
feel its woe.

CANTO IV

1

THE bells rung blithely from St.
Mary's tower,
When in St. Joachin's the news was
told   [hour
That Dobrizhoffer from his quest that
Drew nigh : the glad Guaranies young
and old
Throng through the gate, rejoicing to
behold   [glee
His face again ; and all with heartfelt
Welcome the Pastor to his peaceful
fold,   [he,
Where so beloved amid his flock was
That this return was like a day of
jubilee.

2

How more than strange, how mar-
vellous a sight   10
To the new comers was this multitude !
Something like fear was mingled with
affright   [view'd ;
When they the busy scene of turmoil
Wonder itself the sense of joy sub-
dued,   [opprest
And with its all-unwonted weight
These children of the quiet solitude ;
And now and then a sigh that heaved
the breast
Unconsciously bewray'd their feeling of
unrest.

3

Not more prodigious than that little
town
Seem'd to these comers, were the
pomp and power   20
To us, of ancient Rome in her renown;
Nor the elder Babylon, or ere that
hour
When her high gardens, and her cloud-
capt tower,
And her broad walls before the Persian fell ;
Nor those dread fanes on Nile's forsaken shore
Whose ruins yet their pristine
grandeur tell,
Wherein the demon Gods themselves
might deign to dwell.

4

But if, all humble as it was, that
   scene
Possess'd a poor and uninstructed
   mind
With awe, the thoughtful spirit, well
   I ween,   30
Something to move its wonder there
   might find,
Something of consolation for its kind,
Some hope and earnest of a happier
   age,
When vain pursuits no more the
   heart shall blind,
But Faith the evils of this earth
   assuage,
And to all souls assure their heavenly
   heritage.

5

Yes; for in history's mournful map
   the eye
On Paraguay, as on a sunny spot,
May rest complacent: to humanity,
There, and there only, hath a peaceful
   lot   40
Been granted, by Ambition troubled
   not,
By Avarice undebased, exempt from
   care,
By perilous passions undisturb'd.
   And what
If Glory never rear'd her standard
   there,
Nor with her clarion's blast awoke the
   slumbering air ?

6

Content and cheerful Piety were
   found
Within those humble walls. From
   youth to age
The simple dwellers paced their even
   round
Of duty, not desiring to engage
Upon the busy world's contentious
   stage,   50
Whose ways they wisely had been
   train'd to dread :
Their inoffensive lives in pupilage
Perpetually, but peacefully they led,
From all temptation saved, and sure of
   daily bread.

7

They on the Jesuit, who was nothing
   loth,
Reposed alike their conscience and
   their cares .   [both
And he, with equal faith, the trust of
Accepted and discharged. The bliss
   is theirs   [pares
Of that entire dependence that pre-
Entire submission, let what may be-
   fall ;   60
And his whole careful course of life
   declares
That for their good he holds them
   thus in thrall,
Their Father and their Friend, Priest,
   Ruler, all in all.

8

Food, raiment, shelter, safety, he
   provides ;
No forecast, no anxieties have they ;
The Jesuit governs, and instructs and
   guides ;
Their part it is to honour and obey,
Like children under wise parental
   sway.
All thoughts and wishes are to him
   confess'd ;
And, when at length in life's last
   weary day   70
In sure and certain hope they sink
   to rest,
By him their eyes are closed, by him
   their burial blest.

9

Deem not their lives of happiness de-
   void,
Though thus the years their course
   obscurely fill,
In rural and in household arts em-
   ploy'd,   [skill ;
And many a pleasing task of pliant
For emulation here unmix'd with ill
Sufficient scope was given. Each
   had assign'd
His proper part, which yet left free
   the will :
So well they knew to mould the duc-
   tile mind   80
By whom the scheme of that wise order
   was combined.

10

It was a land of priestcraft, but the Priest
Believed himself the fables that he taught :
Corrupt their forms, and yet those forms at least
Preserved a salutary faith that wrought,
Maugre the alloy, the saving end it sought.   [there,
Benevolence had gain'd such empire
That even superstition had been brought
An aspect of humanity to wear,
And make the weal of man its first and only care.   90

11

Nor lack'd they store of innocent delight,
Music and song and dance and proud array,
Whate'er might win the ear, or charm the sight ;   [play
Banners and pageantry in rich dis-
Brought forth upon some Saint's high holyday,
The altar drest, the church with gar-lands hung,   [way,
Arches and floral bowers beside the
And festal tables spread for old and young,
Gladness in every heart, and mirth on every tongue.

12

Thou who despisest so debased a fate,
As in the pride of wisdom thou may'st call   101
These meek submissive Indians' low estate,
Look round the world, and see where over all
Injurious passions hold mankind in thrall,
How barbarous Force asserts a ruth-less reign,   [ball,
Or Mammon, o'er his portion of the
Hath learn'd a baser empire to main-tain,
Mammon, the god of all who give their souls to gain.

13

Behold the fraudful arts, the covert strife,
The jarring interests that engross mankind ;   110
The low pursuits, the selfish aims of life ;
Studies that weary and contract the mind,
That bring no joy, and leave no peace behind ;
And Death approaching to dissolve the spell !
The immortal soul, which hath so long been blind,
Recovers then clear sight, and sees too well
The error of its ways, when irretrievable.

14

Far happier the Guaranies' humble race,   [wise,
With whom, in dutiful contentment
The gentle virtues had their dwelling-place.   120
With them the dear domestic charities
Sustain'd no blight from fortune ; natural ties
There suffer'd no divorcement, save alone   [arise ;
That which in course of nature might
No artificial wants and ills were known ;
But there they dwelt as if the world were all their own.

15

Obedience in its laws that takes delight
Was theirs ; simplicity that knows no art :
Love, friendship, grateful duty in its height ;
Meekness and truth, that keep all strife apart,   130
And faith and hope which elevate the heart
Upon its heavenly heritage intent.
Poor, erring, self-tormentor that thou art,   [bent,
O Man ! and on thine own undoing
Wherewith canst thou be blest, if not with these content?

16

Mild pupils in submission's perfect
  school,
Two thousand souls were gather'd
  here, and here
Beneath the Jesuit's all-embracing
  rule
They dwelt, obeying him with love
  sincere,
That never knew distrust, nor felt a
  fear,   140
Nor anxious thought which wears the
  heart away.   [dear ;
Sacred to them their laws, their Ruler
Humbler or happier none could be
  than they
Who knew it for their good in all things
  to obey.

17

The Patron Saint, from whom their
  town was named,
Was that St. Joachin, who, legends
  say,   [claim'd
Unto the Saints in Limbo first pro-
The Advent. Being permitted, on
  the day
That Death enlarged him from this
  mortal clay,
His daughter's high election to behold,
Thither his soul, glad herald, wing'd
  its way,   151
And to the Prophets and the Patri-
  archs old
The tidings of great joy and near
  deliverance told.

18

There on the altar was his image set,
The lamp before it burning night and
  day,
And there was incensed, when his
  votaries met
Before the sacred shrine, their beads
  to say,
And for his fancied intercession pray,
Devoutly as in faith they bent the
  knee.
Such adoration they were taught to
  pay ;   160
Good man, how little had he ween'd
  that he   [idolatry !
Should thus obtain a place in Rome's

19

But chiefly there the Mother of our
  Lord,
His blessed daughter, by the multi-
  tude
Was for their special patroness adored.
Amid the square on high her image
  stood,
Clasping the Babe in her beatitude,
The Babe Divine on whom she fix'd
  her sight ;
And in their hearts, albe the work
  was rude,
It rais'd the thought of all-command-
  ing might,   170
Combin'd with boundless love and
  mercy infinite.

20

To this great family the Jesuit
  brought
His new-found children now ; for
  young and old
He deem'd alike his children, while he
  wrought
For their salvation, . . seeking to unfold
The saving mysteries in the creed
  enroll'd,
To their slow minds, that could but
  ill conceive   [told.
The import of the mighty truths he
But errors there they have none to which
  they cleave,
And whatsoe'er he tells they willingly
  believe.   180

21

Safe from that pride of ignorance were
  they
That with small knowledge thinks
  itself full wise.
How at believing aught should these
  delay,
When every where new objects met
  their eyes
To fill the soul with wonder and sur-
  prise ?
Not of itself, but by temptation bred,
In man doth impious unbelief arise ;
It is our instinct to believe and dread,
God bids us love, and then our faith is
  perfected.

22

Quick to believe, and slow to compre-
    hend,   190
Like children, unto all the teacher
    taught
Submissively an easy ear they lend :
And to the font at once he might have
    brought
These converts, if the Father had not
    thought
Theirs was a case for wise and safe
    delay,
Lest lightly learnt might lightly be
    forgot ;
And meanwhile due instruction day
    by day
Would to their opening minds the sense
    of truth convey.

23

Of this they reck'd not whether soon
    or late ;   199
For overpowering wonderment possest
Their faculties ; and in this new estate
Strange sights and sounds and
    thoughts well nigh opprest
Their sense, and raised a turmoil in
    the breast
Resenting less of pleasure than of
    pain ;
And sleep afforded them no natural
    rest,   [train,
But in their dreams, a mix'd disorder'd
The busy scenes of day disturb'd their
    hearts again.

24

Even when the spirit to that secret
    wood
Return'd, slow Mondai's silent stream
    beside,
No longer there it found the solitude
Which late it left : strange faces were
    descried,   211
Voices, and sounds of music far and
    wide,
And buildings seem'd to tower amid
    the trees,
And forms of men and beasts on
    every side,
As ever wakeful fancy hears and sees,
All things that it had heard, and seen,
    and more than these.

25

For in their sleep strange forms de-
    form'd they saw
Of frightful fiends, their ghostly
    enemies,
And souls who must abide the rigorous
    law
Weltering in fire, and there with
    dolorous cries   220
Blaspheming roll around their hope-
    less eyes ;
And those who, doom'd a shorter term
    to bear
In penal flames, look upward to the
    skies,
Seeking and finding consolation there,
And feel, like dew from heaven, the
    precious aid of prayer.

26

And Angels who around their glorious
    Queen
In adoration bent their heads abased ;
And infant faces in their dreams were
    seen
Hovering on cherub-wings ; and
    Spirits placed
To be their guards invisible, who
    chased   230
With fiery arms their fiendish foes
    away :
Such visions overheated fancy traced,
Peopling the night with a confused
    array
That made its hours of rest more rest-
    less than the day.

27

To all who from an old erratic course
Of life, within the Jesuit's fold were
    led,
The change was perilous. They felt
    the force
Of habit, when, till then in forests bred,
A thick perpetual umbrage overhead,
They came to dwell in open light and
    air.   240
This ill the Fathers long had learnt to
    dread,
And still devised such means as might
    prepare
The new-reclaim'd unhurt this total
    change to bear.

28

All thoughts and occupations to com-
    mute,
To change their air, their water, and
    their food,
And those old habits suddenly uproot,
Conform'd to which the vital powers
    pursued
Their functions, such mutation is too
    rude
For man's fine frame unshaken to
    sustain.
And these poor children of the soli-
    tude   250
Began ere long to pay the bitter
    pain
That their new way of life brought with
    it in its train.

29

On Monnema the apprehended ill
Came first ; the matron sunk beneath
    the weight
Of a strong malady, whose force no
    skill
In healing might avert, or mitigate.
Yet, happy in her children's safe estate,
Her thankfulness for them she still
    exprest ;
And, yielding then complacently to
    fate,
With Christian rites her passing hour
    was blest,   260
And with a Christian's hope she was
    consign'd to rest.

30

They laid her in the Garden of the
    Dead ;
Such as a Christian burial-place should
    be
Was that fair spot, where every grave
    was spread
With flowers, and not a weed to spring
    was free ;
But the pure blossoms of the orange
    tree
Dropt like a shower of fragrance on
    the bier ;
And palms, the type of immortality,
Planted in stately colonnades appear,
That all was verdant there throughout
    the unvarying year.   270

31

Nor ever did irreverent feet intrude
Within that sacred spot : nor sound
    of mirth,
Unseemly there, profane the solitude,
Where solemnly committed earth to
    earth,
Waiting the summons for their second
    birth,
Whole generations in Death's peace-
    ful fold
Collected lay ; green innocence, ripe
    worth,
Youth full of hope, and age whose
    days were told,
Compress'd alike into that mass of
    mortal mould.

32

Mortal, and yet at the Archangel's
    voice   280
To put on immortality.   That call
Shall one day make the sentient dust
    rejoice ;
These bodies then shall rise and cast
    off all
Corruption, with whate'er of earthy
    thrall
Had clogg'd the heavenly image, then
    set free.
How then should Death a Christian's
    heart appal ?
Lo, Heaven for you is open ; . . enter
    ye
Children of God, and heirs of his eternity !

33

This hope supported Mooma, hand in
    hand
When with Yeruti at the grave she
    stood.   290
Less even now of death they under-
    stand
Than of the joys eternal that en-
    sued ;
The bliss of infinite beatitude
To them had been their teacher's
    favourite theme,
Wherewith their hearts so fully were
    imbued,
That it the sole reality might seem,
Life, death, and all things else, a shadow
    or a dream.

34

Yea, so possest with that best hope
were they,
That, if the heavens had open'd overhead,
And the Archangel with his trump
that day   300
To judgement had convoked the quick
and dead,
They would have heard the summons
not with dread,
But in the joy of faith that knows no
fear ;
Come, Lord ! come quickly ! would
this pair have said,
And thou, O Queen of men and Angels
dear,
Lift us whom thou hast loved into thy
happy sphere !

35

They wept not at the grave, though
overwrought
With feelings there as if the heart
would break.
Some haply might have deem'd they
suffer'd not ;
Yet they who look'd upon that Maiden
meek   310
Might see what deep emotion blanch'd
her cheek.
An inward light there was which fill'd
her eyes,
And told, more forcibly than words
could speak,
That this disruption of her earliest ties
Had shaken mind and frame in all their
faculties.

36

It was not passion only that disturb'd
Her gentle nature thus ; it was not
grief ;
Nor human feeling by the effort curb'd
Of some misdeeming duty, when relief
Were surely to be found, albeit brief,
If sorrow at its springs might freely
flow ;   321
Nor yet repining, stronger than belief
In its first force, that shook the Maiden
so,
Though these alone might that frail
fabric overthrow.

37

The seeds of death were in her at that
hour,
Soon was their quick'ning and their
growth display'd ;
Thenceforth she droop'd and wither'd
like a flower,
Which, when it flourish'd in its native
shade,
Some child to his own garden hath
convey'd,
And planted in the sun, to pine away.
Thus was the gentle Mooma seen to
fade,   331
Not under sharp disease, but day by
day
Losing the powers of life in visible decay.

38

The sunny hue that tinged her cheek
was gone,
A deathy paleness settled in its stead ;
The light of joy which in her eyes had
shone,
Now, like a lamp that is no longer fed,
Grew dim ; but, when she raised her
heavy head
Some proffer'd help of kindness to
partake,
Those feeble eyes a languid lustre
shed,   340
And her sad smile of thankfulness
would wake
Grief even in callous hearts for that
sweet sufferer's sake.

39

How had Yeruti borne to see her fade ?
But he was spared the lamentable
sight,
Himself upon the bed of sickness laid.
Joy of his heart, and of his eyes the
light
Had Mooma been to him, his soul's
delight,
On whom his mind for ever was in-
tent,
His darling thought by day, his dream
by night,
The playmate of his youth in mercy
sent,   350
With whom his life had pass'd in peace-
fullest content.

40

Well was it for the youth, and well for her,
As there in placid helplessness she lay,
He was not present with his love to stir [clay,
Emotions that might shake her feeble
And rouse up in her heart a strong array
Of feelings, hurtful only when they bind [away.
To earth the soul that soon must pass
But this was spared them; and no pain of mind
To trouble her had she, instinctively resign'd.   360

41

Nor was there wanting to the sufferers aught
Of careful kindness to alleviate
The affliction; for the universal thought
In that poor town was of their sad estate,
And what might best relieve or mitigate
Their case, what help of nature or of art;
And many were the prayers compassionate
That the good Saints their healing would impart,
Breathed in that maid's behalf from many a tender heart.

42

And vows were made for her, if vows might save;   370
She for herself the while preferr'd no prayer;
For, when she stood beside her Mother's grave,
Her earthly hopes and thoughts had ended there.
Her only longing now was, free as air
From this obstructive flesh to take her flight
For Paradise, and seek her Mother there,
And then regaining her beloved sight
Rest in the eternal sense of undisturb'd delight.

43

Her heart was there, and there she felt and knew
That soon full surely should her spirit be.   380
And who can tell what foretastes might ensue
To one, whose soul, from all earth's thraldom free,
Was waiting thus for immortality?
Sometimes she spake with short and hurried breath [see,
As if some happy sight she seem'd to
While in the fulness of a perfect faith,
Even with a lover's hope, she lay and look'd for death.

44

I said that for herself the patient maid
Preferr'd no prayer; but oft her feeble tongue
And feebler breath a voice of praise essay'd;   390
And duly, when the vesper bell was rung, [sung
Her evening hymn in faint accord she
So piously, that they who gather'd round [hung,
Awe-stricken on her heavenly accents
As though they thought it were no mortal sound,
But that the place whereon they stood was holy ground.

45

At such an hour when Dobrizhoffer stood
Beside her bed, oh! how unlike, he thought,
This voice to that which ringing through the wood
Had led him to the secret bower he sought!   400
And was it then for this that he had brought
That harmless household from their native shade? [lot;
Death had already been the mother's
And this fair Mooma, was she form'd to fade
So soon, .. so soon must she in earth's cold lap be laid?

46

Yet he had no misgiving at the sight ;
And wherefore should he ? he had
    acted well,
And, deeming of the ways of God
    aright,   [befell
Knew that to such as these, whate'er
Must needs for them be best. But
    who could dwell   410
Unmoved upon the fate of one so
    young,
So blithesome late ? What marvel if
    tears fell,   [hung,
From that good man as over her he
And that the prayers he said came fal-
    tering from his tongue !

47

She saw him weep, and she could
    understand
The cause thus tremulously that made
    him speak.
By his emotion moved she took his
    hand ;   [cheek
A gleam of pleasure o'er her pallid
Pass'd, while she look'd at him with
    meaning meek,
And for a little while, as loth to part,
Detaining him, her fingers lank and
    weak,   421
Play'd with their hold ; then letting
    him depart
She gave him a slow smile that touch'd
    him to the heart.

48

Mourn not for her ! for what hath
    life to give   [here ?
That should detain her ready spirit
Thinkest thou that it were worth a
    wish to live,
Could wishes hold her from her proper
    sphere?
That simple heart, that innocence
    sincere
The world would stain. Fitter she
    ne'er could be
For the great change ; and now that
    change is near,   430
Oh who would keep her soul from
    being free?
Maiden beloved of Heaven, to die is best
    for thee !

49

She hath pass'd away, and on her lips
    a smile
Hath settled, fix'd in death. Judged
    they aright,
Or suffer'd they their fancy to beguile
The reason, who believed that she
    had sight
Of Heaven before her spirit took its
    flight ;
That Angels waited round her lowly
    bed ;
And that in that last effort of delight,
When, lifting up her dying arms, she
    said,   440
I come ! a ray from heaven upon her
    face was shed ?

50

St. Joachin's had never seen a day
Of such profuse and general grief
    before,
As when with tapers, dirge, and long
    array
The Maiden's body to the grave they
    bore.
All eyes, all hearts, her early death
    deplore ;
Yet, wondering at the fortune they
    lament,
They the wise ways of Providence
    adore,
By whom the Pastor surely had been
    sent,
When to the Mondai woods upon his
    quest he went.   450

51

This was, indeed, a chosen family,
For Heaven's especial favour mark'd,
    they said ;
Shut out from all mankind they
    seem'd to be,
Yet mercifully there were visited,
That so within the fold they might
    be led,   [two
Then call'd away to bliss. Already
In their baptismal innocence were
    dead ;
The third was on the bed of death,
    they knew,
And in the appointed course must
    presently ensue.

52

They marvell'd therefore, when the
  youth once more   460
Rose from his bed and walk'd abroad
  again ;
Severe had been the malady, and sore
The trial, while life struggled to main-
  tain
Its seat against the sharp assaults of
  pain :
But life in him was vigorous ; long he
  lay
Ere it could its ascendency regain,
Then, when the natural powers re-
  sumed their sway,
All trace of late disease pass'd rapidly
    away.

53

The first inquiry, when his mind was
  free,
Was for his Sister. She was gone, they
  said,   470
Gone to her Mother, evermore to be
With her in Heaven. At this no tears
  he shed,
Nor was he seen to sorrow for the
  dead ;
But took the fatal tidings in such part
As if a dull unfeeling nature bred
His unconcern ; for hard would seem
  the heart
To which a loss like his no suffering
    could impart.

54

How little do they see what is, who
  frame
Their hasty judgement upon that
  which seems !
Waters that babble on their way proclaim   480
A shallowness : but in their strength
  deep streams
Flow silently.   Of death Yeruti
  deems
Not as an ill, but as the last great
  good,
Compared wherewith all other he
  esteems
Transient and void : how then should
  thought intrude
Of sorrow in his heart for their beatitude ?

55

While dwelling in their sylvan solitude
Less had Yeruti learnt to entertain
A sense of age than death. He under-
  stood
Something of death from creatures
  he had slain ;   490
But here the ills which follow in the
  train
Of age had first to him been mani-
  fest, . .
The shrunken form, the limbs that
  move with pain,
The failing sense, infirmity, unrest, . .
That in his heart he said to die betimes
    was best.

56

Nor had he lost the dead : they were
  but gone
Before him, whither he should shortly
  go.
Their robes of glory they had first
  put on ;
He, cumber'd with mortality, below
Must yet abide awhile, content to
  know   500
He should not wait in long expectance
  here
What cause then for repining, or for
  woe?
Soon shall he join them in their
  heavenly sphere,
And often, even now, he knew that they
    were near.

57

'Twas but in open day to close his
  eyes
And shut out the unprofitable view
Of all this weary world's realities,
And forthwith, even as if they lived
  anew,
The dead were with him ; features,
  form and hue,
And looks and gestures were restored
  again :   510
Their actual presence in his heart he
  knew ;
And, when their converse was dis-
  turb'd, oh then
How flat and stale it was to mix with
    living men !

58

But not the less, whate'er was to be
　　done,
With living men he took his part
　　content,
At loom, in garden, or a-field, as one
Whose spirit, wholly on obedience
　　bent,
To every task its prompt attention
　　lent.
Alert in labour he among the best ;
And when to church the congregation
　　went,　　　　　　　　　　　　520
None more exact than he to cross his
　　breast,
And kneel, or rise, and do in all things
　　like the rest.

59

Cheerful he was, almost like one elate
With wine, before it hath disturb'd
　　his power
Of reason.　Yet he seem'd to feel the
　　weight
Of time ; for always, when from
　　yonder tower
He heard the clock tell out the passing
　　hour,
The sound appear'd to give him some
　　delight :
And, when the evening shades began
　　to lower,
Then was he seen to watch the fading
　　light　　　　　　　　　　　　530
As if his heart rejoiced at the return of
　　night.

60

The old man to whom he had been
　　given in care　　　　　　　　　[said,
To Dobrizhoffer came one day and
The trouble which our youth was
　　thought to bear
With such indifference hath deranged
　　his head.
He says that he is nightly visited ;
His Mother and his Sister come and
　　say
That he must give this message from
　　the dead,
Not to defer his baptism, and delay
A soul upon the earth which should no
　　longer stay.　　　　　　　　540

61

A dream the Jesuit deem'd it ; a deceit
Upon itself by feverish fancy wrought;
A mere delusion which it were not
　　meet
To censure, lest the youth's distem-
　　per'd thought
Might thereby be to farther error
　　brought ;
But he himself its vanity would
　　find, . .　　　　　　　　　　[not.
They argued thus, . . if it were noticed
His baptism was in fitting time
　　design'd
The Father said, and then dismiss'd it
　　from his mind.

62

But the old Indian came again ere
　　long　　　　　　　　　　　　550
With the same tale, and freely then
　　confest　　　　　　　　　　[wrong ;
His doubt that he had done Yeruti
For something more than common
　　seem'd imprest ;
And now he thought that certes it
　　were best
From the youth's lips his own account
　　to hear,
Haply the Father then to his request
Might yield, regarding his desire
　　sincere,
Nor wait for farther time, if there were
　　aught to fear.

63

Considerately the Jesuit heard, and
　　bade
The youth be called.　Yeruti told
　　his tale.　　　　　　　　　　560
Nightly these blessed spirits came, he
　　said,
To warn him he must come within
　　the pale
Of Christ without delay ; nor must
　　he fail
This warning to their Pastor to repeat,
Till the renewed entreaty should pre-
　　vail.
Life's business then for him would be
　　complete,
And 'twas to tell him this they left their
　　starry seat.

64

Came they to him in dreams ? . . he
    could not tell.
Sleeping or waking now small differ-
    ence made ;
For even while he slept he knew full
    well   570
That his dear Mother and that darling
    Maid
Both in the Garden of the Dead were
    laid :   [same,
And yet he saw them as in life, the
Save only that in radiant robes array'd,
And round about their presence when
    they came
There shone an effluent light as of a
    harmless flame.

65

And where he was he knew, the time,
    the place, . .
All circumstantial things to him were
    clear.
His own heart undisturb'd. His
    Mother's face
How could he choose but know ; or,
    knowing, fear   580
Her presence and that Maid's, to him
    more dear   [below ?
Than all that had been left him now
Their love had drawn them from their
    happy sphere ;
That dearest love unchanged they
    came to show ;
And he must be baptized, and then he
    too might go.

66

With searching ken the Jesuit while
    he spake
Perused him, if in countenance or tone
Aught might be found appearing to
    partake
Of madness. Mark of passion there
    was none ;
None of derangement : in his eye
    alone,   590
As from a hidden fountain emanate,
Something of an unusual brightness
    shone :   [state
But neither word nor look betray'd a
Of wandering, and his speech, though
    earnest, was sedate.

67

Regular his pulse, from all disorder
    free,
The vital powers perform'd their part
    assign'd ;
And to whate'er was ask'd collectedly
He answer'd. Nothing troubled him
    in mind ;
Why should it ? Were not all around
    him kind ?
Did not all love him with a love
    sincere,   600
And seem in serving him a joy to find?
He had no want, no pain, no grief, no
    fear ;
But he must be baptized ; he could not
    tarry here.

68

Thy will be done, Father in heaven
    who art !
    The Pastor said, nor longer now
    denied ;
But with a weight of awe upon his
    heart
Enter'd the church, and there, the
    font beside,
With holy water, chrism and salt
    applied,
Perform'd in all solemnity the rite.
His feeling was that hour with fear
    allied ;   610
Yeruti's was a sense of pure delight,
And while he knelt his eyes seem'd
    larger and more bright.

69

His wish hath been obtain'd, and this
    being done
His soul was to its full desire content.
The day in its accustom'd course
    pass'd on,
The Indian mark'd him ere to rest he
    went,
How o'er his beads, as he was wont,
    he bent,
And then, like one who casts all care
    aside,   [event,
Lay down. The old man fear'd no ill
When, ' Ye are come for me ! ' Yeruti
    cried ;   620
' Yes, I am ready now ! ' and instantly
    he died.

THE POET'S PILGRIMAGE TO WATERLOO.

ΕΥΑΝΘΕΑ Δ' ΑΝΑΒΑΣΟΜΑΙ
ΣΤΟΛΟΝ ΑΜΦ' ΑΡΕΤΑ
ΚΕΛΑΔΕΩΝ.—PINDAR, *Pyth.* 2.

TO

JOHN MAY,

AFTER A FRIENDSHIP OF TWENTY YEARS,

THIS POEM IS INSCRIBED,

IN TESTIMONY OF THE HIGHEST ESTEEM AND AFFECTION,

BY

ROBERT SOUTHEY.

ARGUMENT

THE first part of this Poem describes a journey to the scene of war. The second is in an allegorical form ; it exposes the gross material philosophy which has been the guiding principle of the French politicians, from Mirabeau to Buonaparte ; and it states the opinions of those persons who lament the restoration of the Bourbons, because the hopes which they entertained from the French Revolution have not been realized : and of those who see only evil, or blind chance, in the course of human events.

To the Christian philosopher all things are consistent and clear. Our first parents brought with them the light of natural religion and the moral law ; as men departed from these, they tended towards barbarous and savage life ; large portions of the world are in this degenerated state ; still, upon the great scale, the human race, from the beginning, has been progressive. But the direct object of Buonaparte was to establish a military despotism wherever his power extended ; and the immediate and inevitable consequence of such a system is to brutalize and degrade mankind. The contest in which this country was engaged against that Tyrant, was a struggle between good and evil principles, and never was there a victory so important to the best hopes of human nature as that which was won by British valour at Waterloo, . . its effects extending over the whole civilized world, and involving the vital interests of all mankind.

That victory leaves England in security and peace. In no age and in no country has man ever existed under circumstances so favourable to the full developement of his moral and intellectual faculties, as in England at this time. The peace which she has won by the battle of Waterloo, leaves her at leisure to pursue the great objects and duties of bettering her own condition, and diffusing the blessings of civilization and Christianity.

PROEM

1

ONCE more I see thee, Skiddaw ! once
    again
Behold thee in thy majesty serene,
Where, like the bulwark of this favour'd
    plain,
    Alone thou standest, monarch of the
    scene . .
Thou glorious Mountain, on whose ample
    breast
The sunbeams love to play, the vapours
    love to rest !

2

Once more, O Derwent, to thy aweful
    shores
    I come, insatiate of the accustom'd
      sight ;
And, listening as the eternal torrent
    roars,
    Drink in with eye and ear a fresh
      delight .   10
For I have wander'd far by land and
    sea,
    In all my wanderings still remembering
      thee.

3

Twelve years, (how large a part of
    man's brief day !)
    Nor idly, nor ingloriously spent,
Of evil and of good have held their way,
    Since first upon thy banks I pitch'd
      my tent.
Hither I came in manhood's active
    prime,
    And here my head hath felt the touch
      of time.

4

Heaven hath with goodly increase blest
    me here,
    Where childless and opprest with
      grief I came ;   20
With voice of fervent thankfulness
    sincere
    Let me the blessings which are mine
      proclaim ;
Here I possess, . . what more should
    I require ?
    Books, children, leisure, . . all my heart's
      desire.

5

O joyful hour, when to our longing
    home
    The long-expected wheels at length
      drew nigh !
When the first sound went forth, ' They
    come, they come ! '
    And hope's impatience quicken'd
      every eye !
' Never had man whom Heaven would
    heap with bliss
More glad return, more happy hour
    than this.'   30

6

Aloft on yonder bench, with arms
    dispread,
    My boy stood, shouting there his
      father's name,
Waving his hat around his happy head ;
    And there, a younger group, his sisters
      came :
Smiling they stood with looks of pleased
    surprize,
While tears of joy were seen in elder
    eyes.

7

Soon each and all came crowding round
    to share
    The cordial greeting, the beloved
      sight ;   [there !
What welcomings of hand and lip were
    And, when those overflowings of
      delight   40
Subsided to a sense of quiet bliss,
Life hath no purer, deeper happiness.

8

The young companion of our weary way
    Found here the end desired of all her
      ills ;
She, who in sickness pining many a day
    Hunger'd and thirsted for her native
      hills,
Forgetful now of sufferings past and pain,
Rejoiced to see her own dear home again.

9

Recover'd now, the homesick moun-
    taineer
    Sate by the playmate of her infancy,
Her twin-like comrade, . . render'd
      doubly dear   51
    For that long absence : full of life was
      she,
With voluble discourse and eager mien
Telling of all the wonders she had seen.

10

Here silently between her parents stood
    My dark-eyed Bertha, timid as a dove ;
And gently oft from time to time she
      woo'd   [love,
    Pressure of hand, or word, or look of
With impulse shy of bashful tenderness,
Soliciting again the wish'd caress.   60

11

The younger twain in wonder lost were
they,
My gentle Kate, and my sweet Isabel :
Long of our promised coming, day by day,
It had been their delight to hear and
tell ;
And now, when that long-promised hour
was come,
Surprize and wakening memory held
them dumb.

12

For in the infant mind, as in the old,
When to its second childhood life
declines,
A dim and troubled power doth
Memory hold :
But soon the light of young Remem-
brance shines   70
Renew'd, and influences of dormant love
Waken'd within, with quickening in-
fluence move.

13

O happy season theirs, when absence
brings   [pain,
Small feeling of privation, none of
Yet at the present object love re-springs,
As night-closed flowers at morn ex-
pand again !
Nor deem our second infancy unblest,
When gradually composed we sink to
rest.   78

14

Soon they grew blithe as they were
wont to be ;   [seek :
Her old endearments each began to
And Isabel drew near to climb my knee,
And pat with fondling hand her
father's cheek ;   [thus
With voice and touch and look reviving
The feelings which had slept in long
disuse.

15

But there stood one whose heart could
entertain
And comprehend the fulness of the joy ;
The father, teacher, playmate, was again
Come to his only and his studious boy :
And he beheld again that mother's eye,
Which with such ceaseless care had
watch'd his infancy.   90

16

Bring forth the treasures now, . . a proud
display, . .   [return !
For rich as Eastern merchants we
Behold the black Beguine, the Sister grey,
The Friars whose heads with sober
motion turn,   [hives,
The Ark well-fill'd with all its numerous
Noah and Shem and Ham and Japhet,
and their wives.

17

The tumbler, loose of limb ; the
wrestlers twain ;   [device,
And many a toy beside of quaint
Which, when his fleecy troops no more
can gain
Their pasture on the mountains hoar
with ice,   100
The German shepherd carves with
curious knife,   [life.
Earning in easy toil the food of frugal

18

It was a group which Richter, had he
view'd,   [feet skill ;
Might have deem'd worthy of his per-
The keen impatience of the younger
brood,   [still ;
Their eager eyes and fingers never
The hope, the wonder, and the restless
joy   [boy !
Of those glad girls, and that vociferous

19

The aged friend serene with quiet smile,
Who in their pleasure finds her own
delight ;   110
The mother's heart-felt happiness the
while ;   [sight ;
The aunts, rejoicing in the joyful
And he who, in his gaiety of heart,
With glib and noisy tongue perform'd
the showman's part.

20

Scoff ye who will ! but let me, gracious
Heaven,   [day !
Preserve this boyish heart till life's last
For so that inward light by Nature given
Shall still direct, and cheer me on my
way,   [descend,
And, brightening as the shades of age
Shine forth with heavenly radiance at
the end.   120

21

This was the morning light vouchsafed,
      which led
   My favour'd footsteps to the Muses'
      hill,
Whose arduous paths I have not ceased
      to tread,
   From good to better persevering still ;
And, if but self-approved, to praise or
      blame
Indifferent, while I toil for lasting fame.

22

And O ye nymphs of Castaly divine !
   Whom I have dutifully served so
      long,
Benignant to your votary now incline,
   That I may win your ear with gentle
      song,   130
Such as, I ween, is ne'er disown'd by
      you, . .
A low prelusive strain, to nature true.

23

But when I reach at themes of loftier
      thought,
   And tell of things surpassing earthly
      sense,
(Which by yourselves, O Muses, I am
      taught,)
   Then aid me with your fuller influence,
And to the height of that great argu-
      ment
Support my spirit in her strong ascent !

24

So may I boldly round my temples bind
   The laurel which my master Spenser
      wore ;   140
And, free in spirit as the mountain wind
   That makes my symphony in this
      lone hour,
No perishable song of triumph raise,
But sing in worthy strains my Country's
      praise.

THE POET'S PILGRIMAGE

PART I
THE JOURNEY

ΤΩΝ ΠΟΛΥΚΤΟΝΩΝ ΓΑΡ
ΟΥΚ ΑΣΚΟΠΟΙ ΘΕΟΙ.
                              ÆSCHYLUS.

I. FLANDERS

1

OUR world hath seen the work of war's
      debate
   Consummated in one momentous
      day
Twice in the course of time ; and twice
      the fate
   Of unborn ages hung upon the
      fray :
First at Platæa, in that aweful hour
When Greece united smote the Persian's
      power.

2

For, had the Persian triumph'd, then the
      spring
   Of knowledge from that living source
      had ceast ;
All would have fallen before the bar-
      barous King,
   Art, Science, Freedom ; the despotic
      East,   10
Setting her mark upon the race subdued,
Had stamp'd them in the mould of
      sensual servitude.

3

The second day was that when Martel
      broke   [opprest,
   The Musselmen, delivering France
And, in one mighty conflict, from the yoke
   Of misbelieving Mecca saved the
      West ;
Else had the Impostor's law destroy'd
      the ties
Of public weal and private charities.

4

Such was the danger, when that Man of
Blood
Burst from the iron Isle, and brought
again,   20
Like Satan rising from the sulphurous
flood,
His impious legions to the battle
plain :   [field
Such too was our deliverance, when the
Of Waterloo beheld his fortunes yield.

5

I, who with faith unshaken from the first,
Even when the Tyrant seem'd to
touch the skies,
Had look'd to see the high-blown bubble
burst,
And for a fall conspicuous as his rise,
Even in that faith had look'd not for
defeat   29
So swift, so overwhelming, so complete.

6

Me most of all men it behoved to raise
The strain of triumph for this foe
subdued,
To give a voice to joy, and in my lays
Exalt a nation's hymn of gratitude,
And blazon forth in song that day's
renown, . .
For I was graced with England's laurel
crown.

7

And, as I once had journey'd to behold
Far off, Ourique's consecrated field,
Where Portugal the faithful and the bold
Assumed the symbols of her sacred
shield,   40
More reason now that I should bend my
way
The field of British glory to survey.

8

So forth I set upon this pilgrimage,
And took the partner of my life with
me,   [age
And one dear girl, just ripe enough of
Retentively to see what I should see ;
That thus, with mutual recollections
fraught,
We might bring home a store for after-
thought.

9

We left our pleasant Land of Lakes, and
went
Throughout whole England's length,
a weary way,   50
Even to the farthest shores of eastern
Kent :
Embarking there upon an autumn
day,
Toward Ostend we held our course all
night,
And anchor'd by its quay at morning's
earliest light.

10

Small vestige there of that old siege
appears,
And little of remembrance would be
found,
When for the space of three long painful
years
The persevering Spaniard girt it
round,
And gallant youths of many a realm
from far
Went students to that busy school of
war.   60

11

Yet still those wars of obstinate defence
Their lessons offer to the soldier's
hand ;
Large knowledge may the statesman
draw from thence :
And still from underneath the drifted
sand,
Sometimes the storm, or passing foot
lays bare
Part of the harvest Death has gather'd
there.

12

Peace be within thy walls, thou famous
town,
For thy brave bearing in those times
of old ;
May plenty thy industrious children
crown,
And prosperous merchants day by
day behold   70
Many a rich vessel from the injurious
sea
Enter the bosom of thy quiet quay.

13

Embarking there, we glided on between
  Strait banks raised high above the
    level land,
With many a cheerful dwelling white
    and green   [hand.
In goodly neighbourhood on either
Huge-timber'd bridges o'er the passage
    lay,   [way,
Which wheel'd aside and gave us easy

14

Four horses, aided by the favouring
    breeze,
  Drew our gay vessel, slow and sleek
    and large ;   80
Crack goes the whip, the steersman at
    his ease   [barge.
  Directs the way, and steady went the
Ere evening closed to Bruges thus we
    came, . .
Fair city, worthy of her ancient fame.

15

The season of her splendour is gone by,
  Yet every where its monuments
    remain ;   [on high,
Temples which rear their stately heads
  Canals that intersect the fertile plain,
Wide streets and squares, with many
    a court and hall
Spacious and undefaced, but ancient all.

16

Time hath not wrong'd her, nor hath
    Ruin sought   91
  Rudely her splendid structures to
    destroy,   [fraught,
Save in those recent days with evil
  When Mutability, in drunken joy
Triumphant, and from all restraint
    released,   [beast.
Let loose the fierce and many-headed

17

But for the scars in that unhappy rage
  Inflicted, firm she stands and unde-
    cay'd ;
Like our first sires', a beautiful old age
  Is hers, in venerable years array'd ;
And yet to her benignant stars may
    bring,   101
What fate denies to man, . . a second
    spring.

18

When I may read of tilts in days of old,
  And tourneys graced by chieftains of
    renown,   [bold,
Fair dames, grave citizens, and warriors
  If Fancy would pourtray some stately
    town,   [be,
Which for such pomp fit theatre should
Fair Bruges, I shall then remember thee.

19

Nor did thy landscape yield me less
    delight,
  Seen from the deck as slow it glided
    by,   110
Or when beneath us, from thy Belfroy's
    height,   [sky ;
  Its boundless circle met the bending
The waters smooth and straight, thy
    proper boast,
And lines of road-side trees in long
    perspective lost.

20

No happier landscape may on earth be
    seen,   [groves,
  Rich gardens all around and fruitful
White dwellings trim relieved with
    lively green,   [loves,
  The pollard that the Flemish painter
With aspins tall and poplars fair to view,
Casting o'er all the land a grey and
    willowy hue.   120

21

My lot hath lain in scenes sublime and
    rude,
  Where still devoutly I have served
    and sought   [tude.
The Power divine which dwells in soli-
  In boyhood was I wont, with rapture
    fraught,   [free,
Amid those rocks and woods to wander
Where Avon hastens to the Severn sea.

22

In Cintra also have I dwelt erewhile,
  That earthly Eden, and have seen at
    eve   [tain pile,
The sea-mists, gathering round its moun-
  Whelm with their billows all below,
    but leave   130
One pinnacle sole seen, whereon it stood
Like the Ark on Ararat, above the flood.

23

And now am I a Cumbrian moun-
    taineer ;
    Their wintry garment of unsullied
        snow
The mountains have put on, the heavens
    are clear,
    And yon dark lake spreads silently
        below ;
Who sees them only in their summer
    hour
Sees but their beauties half, and knows
    not half their power.

24

Yet hath the Flemish scene a charm for
    me
    That soothes and wins upon the
        willing heart ;   140
Though all is level as the sleeping
    sea,
    A natural beauty springs from perfect
        art,
And something more than pleasure fills
    the breast
To see how well-directed toil is blest.

25

Two nights have pass'd ; the morning
    opens well,
    Fair are the aspects of the favouring
        sky ;
Soon yon sweet chimes the appointed
    hour will tell,
    For here to music Time moves merrily :
Aboard ! aboard ! no more must we
    delay, . .
Farewell, good people of the *Fleur de
    Bled !*   150

26

Beside the busy wharf the Trekschuit
    rides,
    With painted plumes and tent-like
        awning gay ;
Carts, barrows, coaches, hurry from all
    sides,
    And passengers and porters throng
        the way,
Contending all at once in clamorous
    speech,
French, Flemish, English, each confusing
    each.

27

All disregardant of the Babel sound,
    A swan kept oaring near with upraised
        eye, . .   158
A beauteous pensioner, who daily found
    The bounty of such casual company ;
Nor left us till the bell said all was done,
And slowly we our watery way begun.

28

Europe can boast no richer, goodlier
    scene,
    Than that through which our pleasant
        passage lay,   [green,
By fertile fields and fruitful gardens
    The journey of a short autumnal day ;
Sleek well-fed steeds our steady vessel
        drew,
The heavens were fair, and Mirth was
    of our crew.

29

Along the smooth canal's unbending line,
    Beguiling time with light discourse,
        we went,   170
Nor wanting savoury food nor generous
    wine.
    Ashore too there was feast and
        merriment ;
The jovial peasants at some village fair
Were   dancing, drinking, smoking,
    gambling there.

30

Of these, or of the ancient towers of
    Ghent   [tell ;
    Renown'd, I must not tarry now to
Of picture, or of church, or monument ;
    Nor how we mounted to that pon-
        derous bell,
The Belfroy's boast, which bears old
    Roland's name,
Nor yields to Oxford Tom, or Tom of
    Lincoln's fame.   180

31

Nor of that sisterhood, whom to their rule
    Of holy life no hasty vows restrain,
Who, meek disciples of the Christian
    school,
    Watch by the bed of sickness and of
        pain :   [impart
Oh what a strength divine doth Faith
To inborn goodness in the female heart !

32

A gentle party from the shores of Kent
　Thus far had been our comrades, as befell ;
Fortune had link'd us first, and now Consent, . .
　For why should Choice divide whom Chance so well   190
Had join'd, and they to view the famous ground,
Like us, were to the Field of Battle bound.

33

Farther as yet they look'd not than that quest, . .
　The land was all before them where to choose.
So we consorted here as seemed best ;
　Who would such pleasant fellowship refuse
Of ladies fair and gentle comrades free ? . .
Certes we were a joyous company.

34

Yet lack'd we not discourse for graver times,
　Such as might suit sage auditors, I ween ;   200
For some among us in far distant climes
　The cities and the ways of men had seen ;   [well
No unobservant travellers they, but
Of what they there had learnt they knew to tell.

35

The one of frozen Moscovy could speak,
　And well his willing listeners entertain
With tales of that inclement region bleak,   [reign,
　The pageantry and pomp of Catherine's
And that proud city, which with wise intent
The mighty founder raised, his own great monument.   210

36

And one had dwelt with Malabars and Moors,   [dispense
　Where fertile earth and genial heaven
Profuse their bounty upon Indian shores ;
　Whate'er delights the eye, or charms the sense,

The valleys with perpetual fruitage blest,
The mountains with unfading foliage drest.

37

He those barbaric palaces had seen,
　The work of Eastern potentates of old ;
And in the Temples of the Rock had been,
　Awe-struck their dread recesses to behold ;   220
A gifted hand was his, which by its skill
Could to the eye pourtray such wondrous scenes at will.

38

A third, who from the Land of Lakes with me
　Went out upon this pleasant pilgrimage,
Had sojourn'd long beyond the Atlantic sea ;
　Adventurous was his spirit as his age,
For he in far Brazil, through wood and waste,
Had travell'd many a day, and there his heart was placed.

39

Wild region, . . happy if at night he found
　The shelter of some rude Tapuya's shed ;   230
Else would he take his lodgement on the ground,
　Or from the tree suspend his hardy bed ;
And sometimes, starting at the jaguar's cries,
See through the murky night the prowler's fiery eyes.

40

And sometimes over thirsty deserts drear,
　And sometimes over flooded plains he went ; . .
A joy it was his fire-side tales to hear,
　And he a comrade to my heart's content :
For he of what I most desired could tell,
And loved the Portugals because he knew them well.   240

A a

41

Here to the easy barge we bade adieu ;
  Land-travellers now along the well-
    paved way,
Where road-side trees, still lengthening
    on the view,
  Before us and behind unvarying lay :
Through lands well-labour'd to Alost we
    came,
  Where whilome treachery stain'd the
    English name.

42

Then saw we Afflighem, by ruin rent,
  Whose venerable fragments strew the
    land ;
Grown wise too late, the multitude
    lament
  The ravage of their own unhappy
    hand ;   250
Its records in their frenzy torn and
    tost,
Its precious stores of learning wreck'd
    and lost.

43

Whatever else we saw was cheerful all,
  The signs of steady labour well re-
    paid ;
The grapes were ripe on every cottage
    wall,
  And merry peasants seated in the
    shade
Of garner, or within the open door,
From gather'd hop-vines pluck'd the
    plenteous store.

44

Through Assche for water and for cakes
    renown'd
  We pass'd, pursuing still our way,
    though late ;   260
And when the shades of night were
    closing round,
  Brussels received us through her
    friendly gate, . .
Proud city, fated many a change to
    see,
And now the seat of new-made
    monarchy.

II. BRUSSELS

1

WHERE might a gayer spectacle be
    found
  Than Brussels offer'd on that festive
    night,
Her squares and palaces irradiate round
  To welcome the imperial Muscovite,
Who now, the wrongs of Europe twice
    redress'd,
Came there a welcome and a glorious
    guest ?

2

Her mile-long avenue with lamps was
    hung,
  Innumerous, which diffused a light
    like day ;
Where through the line of splendour, old
    and young
  Paraded all in festival array ;   10
While fiery barges, plying to and fro,
Illumined as they moved the liquid glass
    below.

3

By day with hurrying crowds the streets
    were throng'd,
  To gain of this great Czar a passing
    sight ;
And music, dance, and banquetings
    prolong'd
  The various work of pleasure through
    the night.
You might have deem'd, to see that
    joyous town,
That wretchedness and pain were there
    unknown.

4

Yet three short months had scarcely
    pass'd away,
  Since, shaken with the approaching
    battle's breath,   20
Her inmost chambers trembled with
    dismay ;
  And now within her walls insatiate
    Death,
Devourer whom no harvest e'er can fill,
The gleanings of that field was gathering
    still.

5

Within those walls there linger'd at that
 hour   [pain,
 Many a brave soldier on the bed of
Whom aid of human art should ne'er
 restore   [again ;
 To see his country and his friends
And many a victim of that fell debate,
Whose life yet waver'd in the scales of
 fate.   30

6

Some I beheld, for whom the doubtful
 scale   [length ;
 Had to the side of life inclined at
Emaciate was their form, their features
 pale,   [strength ;
 The limbs so vigorous late, bereft of
And, for their gay habiliments of yore,
The habit of the House of Pain they
 wore.

7

Some in the courts of that great hospital,
 That they might taste the sun and
  open air,
Crawl'd out ; or sate beneath the
 southern wall ;
 Or, leaning in the gate, stood gazing
 there   40
In listless guise upon the passers by,
Whiling away the hours of slow re-
 covery.

8

Others in waggons borne abroad I saw,
 Albeit recovering, still a mournful
  sight :
Languid and helpless some were
 stretch'd on straw,
 Some more advanced sustain'd themselves upright,
And with bold eye and careless front,
 methought,
Seem'd to set wounds and death again
 at nought.

9

Well had it fared with these ; nor went
 it ill
 With those whom war had of a limb
  bereft,   50
Leaving the life untouch'd, that they
 had still   [left ;
 Enough for health as for existence

But some there were who lived to draw
 the breath
Of pain through hopeless years of lingering death.

10

Here might the hideous face of war be
 seen,
 Stript of all pomp, adornment, and
  disguise ;
It was a dismal spectacle, I ween,
 Such as might well to the beholders'
  eyes   [mind
Bring sudden tears, and make the pious
Grieve for the crimes and follies of man-
 kind.   60

11

What had it been then in the recent
 days
 Of that great triumph, when the open
  wound   [ways
Was festering, and along the crowded
 Hour after hour was heard the inces-
  sant sound
Of wheels, which o'er the rough and
 stony road
Convey'd their living agonizing load !

12

Hearts little to the melting mood inclined
 Grew sick to see their sufferings ; and
  the thought
Still comes with horror to the shuddering
 mind
 Of those sad days when Belgian ears
  were taught   70
The British soldier's cry, half groan, half
 prayer,
Breathed when his pain is more than he
 can bear.

13

Brave spirits, nobly had their part been
 done !
 Brussels could show, where Senne's
  slow waters glide,
The cannon which their matchless
 valour won,
 Proud trophies of the field, ranged
  side by side,
Where as they stood in inoffensive row,
The solitary guard paced to and fro.

14

Unconscious instruments of human woe,
 Some for their mark the royal lilies
  bore,   80
Fix'd there when Britain was the
  Bourbon's foe ;
 And some emboss'd in brazen letters
  wore
The sign of that abhorr'd misrule, which
  broke
The guilty nation for a Tyrant's yoke.

15

Others were stampt with that Usurper's
  name, . .
 Recorders thus of many a change
  were they,
Their deadly work through every change
  the same ;
 Nor ever had they seen a bloodier day,
Than when, as their late thunders roll'd
  around,
Brabant in all her cities felt the sound.

16

Then ceased their occupation. From
  the field 91
 Of battle here in triumph were they
  brought ;
Ribands and flowers and laurels half
  conceal'd
 Their brazen mouths, so late with ruin
  fraught ;
Women beheld them pass with joyful
  eyes,
And children clapt their hands and rent
  the air with cries.

17

Now idly on the banks of Senne they
  lay,
 Like toys with which a child is pleased
  no more :
Only the British traveller bends his
  way
 To see them on that unfrequented
  shore,   100
And, as a mournful feeling blends with
  pride,
Remembers those who fought, and those
  who died.

III. THE FIELD OF BATTLE

1

SOUTHWARD from Brussels lies the field
  of blood,
 Some three hours' journey for a well-
  girt man ;
A horseman who in haste pursued his
  road
 Would reach it as the second hour
  began.
The way is through a forest deep and
  wide,
Extending many a mile on either side.

2

No cheerful woodland this of antic trees,
 With thickets varied and with sunny
  glade ;
Look where he will, the weary traveller
  sees
 One gloomy, thick, impenetrable
  shade 10
Of tall straight trunks, which move
  before his sight,
With interchange of lines of long green
  light.

3

Here, where the woods receding from
  the road
 Have left on either hand an open
  space
For fields and gardens and for man's
  abode,
 Stands Waterloo ; a little lowly place,
Obscure till now, when it hath risen to
  fame,
And given the victory its English name.

4

What time the second Carlos ruled in
  Spain,
 Last of the Austrian line by Fate
  decreed, 20
Here Castanaca reared a votive fane,
 Praying the Patron Saints to bless
  with seed
His childless sovereign ; Heaven denied
  an heir,
And Europe mourn'd in blood the frus-
  trate prayer.

5

That temple to our hearts was hallow'd
    now:
  For many a wounded Briton there
    was laid,   [allow
With such poor help as time might then
  From the fresh carnage of the field
    convey'd;
And they whom human succours could
    not save
  Here in its precincts found a hasty
    grave.   30

6

And here on marble tablets set on high,
  In English lines by foreign workmen
    traced,
Are names familiar to an English eye;
  Their brethren here the fit memorials
    placed,   [tell
Whose unadorned inscriptions briefly
  Their gallant comrades' rank, and
    where they fell.

7

The stateliest monument of public pride
  Enrich'd with all magnificence of art,
To honour Chieftains who in victory
    died,
  Would wake no stronger feeling in
    the heart   40
Than these plain tablets, by the soldier's
    hand
Raised to his comrades in a foreign land.

8

Not far removed you find the burial-
    ground,
  Yet so that skirts of woodland inter-
    vene;
A small enclosure, rudely fenced around;
  Three grave-stones only for the dead
    are seen:
One bears the name of some rich villager,
The first for whom a stone was planted
    there.

9

Beneath the second is a German laid,
  Whom Bremen, shaking off the
    Frenchman's yoke,   50
Sent with her sons the general cause to
    aid;   [stroke,
  He in the fight received his mortal

Yet for his country's aggravated woes
Lived to see vengeance on her hated
    foes,

10

A son of Erin sleeps below the third;
  By friendly hands his body where it
    lay
Upon the field of blood had been in-
    terr'd,
  And thence by those who mourn'd
    him borne away
In pious reverence for departed worth,
Laid here with holy rites in consecrated
    earth.   60

11

Repose in peace, brave soldiers, who
    have found
  In Waterloo and Soigny's shade your
    rest!
Ere this hath British valour made that
    ground
  Sacred to you, and for your foes un-
    blest,
When Marlborough here, victorious in
    his might
Surprized the French, and smote them
    in their flight.

12

Those wars are as a tale of times gone
    by,
  For so doth perishable fame decay,..
Here on the ground wherein the slaugh-
    ter'd lie,
  The memory of that fight is pass'd
    away;..   70
And even our glorious Blenheim to the
    field
Of Waterloo and Wellington must yield.

13

Soon shall we reach that scene of mighty
    deeds,
  In one unbending line a short league
    hence;
Aright the forest from the road recedes,
  With wide sweep trending south and
    westward thence;
Aleft along the line it keeps its place,
Some half hour's distance at a traveller's
    pace.

14

The country here expands, a wide-
    spread scene ;
  No Flemish gardens fringed with
      willows these,   80
Nor rich Brabantine pastures ever green,
  With trenches lined and rows of aspin
      trees ;
In tillage here the unwooded open land
Returns its increase to the farmer's hand.

15

Behold the scene where Slaughter had
    full sway !
  A mile before us lieth Mount St. John,
The hamlet which the Highlanders that
      day
  Preserved from spoil ; yet as much
      farther on
The single farm is placed, now known
    to fame,
  Which from the sacred hedge derives
      its name.   90

16

Straight onward yet for one like distance
    more,   [stands,
  And there the house of Belle Alliance
So named, I guess, by some in days of
      yore,   [hands :
  In friendship or in wedlock joining
Little did they who call'd it thus foresee
The place that name should hold in
    history !

17

Beyond these points the fight extended
    not . .
  Small theatre for such a tragedy !
Its breadth scarce more, from eastern
      Papelot
  To where the groves of Hougoumont
      on high   100
Rear in the west their venerable head,
And cover with their shade the countless
    dead.

18

But wouldst thou tread this celebrated
    ground,   [scene
  And trace with understanding eyes a
Above all other fields of war renown'd,
  From western Hougoumont thy way
      begin ;

There was our strength on that side, and
    there first,
  In all its force, the storm of battle burst.

19

Strike eastward then across toward La
    Haye,
  The single farm : with dead the fields
      between   110
Are lined, and thou wilt see upon the
      way
  Long wave-like dips and swells which
      intervene,
Such as would breathe the war-horse,
    and impede,
When that deep soil was wet, his martial
    speed.

20

This is the ground whereon the young
    Nassau,
  Emuling that day his ancestor's
      renown,   [saw
Received his hurt ; admiring Belgium
  The youth proved worthy of his
      destined crown :
All tongues his prowess on that day
    proclaim,
And children lisp his praise and bless
    their Prince's name.   120

21

When thou hast reach'd La Haye, sur-
    vey it well,
  Here was the heat and centre of the
      strife ;
This point must Britain hold whate'er
    befell,
  And here both armies were profuse of
      life :   [by
Once it was lost, . . and then a stander
Belike had trembled for the victory.

22

Not so the leader, on whose equal mind
  Such interests hung in that momen-
      tous day ;
So well had he his motley troops assign'd,
  That where the vital points of action
      lay,   130
There had he placed those soldiers whom
    he knew
No fears could quail, no dangers could
    subdue.

23

Small was his British force, nor had he
    here
    The Portugals, in heart so near allied,
The worthy comrades of his late career,
    Who fought so oft and conquer'd at
      his side,   [advance,
When, with the Red Cross join'd in brave
The glorious Quina mock'd the air of
    France.

24

Now of the troops with whom he took
    the field
    Some were of doubtful faith, and
      others raw ;   140
He station'd these where they might
      stand or yield ;   [saw,
    But where the stress of battle he fore-
There were his links (his own strong
    words I speak)
And rivets which no human force could
    break.

25

O my brave countrymen, ye answer'd
    well
    To that heroic trust ! Nor less did ye,
Whose worth your grateful country aye
    shall tell,
    True children of our sister Germany,
Who, while she groan'd beneath the
    oppressor's chain,
Fought for her freedom in the fields of
    Spain.   150

26

La Haye, bear witness ! sacred is it hight,
    And sacred is it truly from that day ;
For never braver blood was spent in fight
    Than Britain here hath mingled with
      the clay.
Set where thou wilt thy foot, thou scarce
    can'st tread
Here on a spot unhallow'd by the dead.

27

Here was it that the Highlanders with-
    stood   [weight
    The tide of hostile power, received its
With resolute strength, and stemm'd
    and turn'd the flood ;
    And fitly here, as in that Grecian
    strait,   160

The funeral stone might say, Go,
    traveller, tell
Scotland, that in our duty here we
    fell.

28

Still eastward from this point thy way
    pursue.
    There grows a single hedge along the
    lane, . .
No other is there far or near in view :
    The raging enemy essay'd in vain
To pass that line, . . a braver foe with-
    stood,
And this whole ground was moisten'd
    with their blood.

29

Leading his gallant men as he was wont,
    The hot assailants' onset to repel,   170
Advancing hat in hand, here in the
    front
    Of battle and of danger, Picton fell ;
Lamented Chief ! than whom no braver
    name
His country's annals shall consign to
    fame.

30

Scheldt had not seen us, had his voice
    been heard,
    Return with shame from her disastrous
    coast :
But Fortune soon to fairer fields pre-
    ferr'd
    His worth approved, which Cambria
    long may boast :
France felt him then, and Portugal and
    Spain
His honour'd memory will for aye retain.

31

Hence to the high-wall'd house of
    Papelot,   181
    The battle's boundary on the left,
    incline ;
Here thou seest Frischermont not far
    remote,
    From whence, like ministers of wrath
    divine,
The Prussians, issuing on the yielding
    foe,
Consummated their great and tota
    overthrow.

32

Deem not that I the martial skill should
      boast
  Where horse and foot were station'd
      here to tell,
What points were occupied by either
      host,
  And how the battle raged, and what
      befell,   190
And how our great Commander's eagle
      eye,
Which comprehended all, secured the
      victory.

33

This were the historian's, not the poet's
      part;
  Such task would ill the gentle Muse
      beseem,
Who to the thoughtful mind and pious
      heart
  Comes with her offering from this
      aweful theme;
Content if what she saw and gather'd
      there
She may in unambitious song declare.

34

Look how upon the Ocean's treacherous
      face
  The breeze and summer sunshine
      softly play,   200
And the green-heaving billows bear no
      trace
  Of all the wrath and wreck of yester-
      day; . .
So from the field which here we look'd
      upon
The vestiges of dreadful war were gone.

35

Earth had received into her silent
      womb
  Her slaughter'd creatures: horse and
      man they lay,
And friend and foe, within the general
      tomb.
  Equal had been their lot; one fatal
      day
For all, . . one labour, . . and one place
      of rest
They found within their common
      parent's breast.   210

36

The passing seasons had not yet effaced
  The stamp of numerous hoofs im-
      press'd by force
Of cavalry, whose path might still be
      traced.
  Yet Nature every where resumed her
      course;
Low pansies to the sun their purple
      gave,
And the soft poppy blossom'd on the
      grave.

37

In parts the careful farmer had re-
      new'd
  His labours, late by battle frustrated;
And where the unconscious soil had been
      imbued
  With blood, profusely there like water
      shed,   220
There had his plough-share turn'd the
      guilty ground,
And the green corn was springing all
      around.

38

The graves he left for natural thought
      humane
  Untouch'd; and here and there,
      where in the strife
Contending feet had trampled down the
      grain,
  Some hardier roots were found,
      which of their life
Tenacious, had put forth a second
      head,
And sprung, and ear'd, and ripen'd on
      the dead.

39

Some marks of wreck were scatter'd all
      around,
  As shoe, and belt, and broken bando-
      leer,   230
And hats which bore the mark of mortal
      wound;
  Gun-flints and balls for those who
      closelier peer;
And sometimes did the breeze upon its
      breath
Bear from ill-cover'd graves a taint of
      death.

40

More vestige of destructive man was seen
  Where man in works of peace had labour'd more ;
At Hougoumont the hottest strife had been,
  Where trees and walls the mournful record bore
Of war's wild rage, trunks pierced with many a wound,
And roofs and half-burnt rafters on the ground. 240

41

A goodly mansion this, with gardens fair,
  And ancient groves and fruitful orchard wide,
Its dove-cot and its decent house of prayer,
  Its ample stalls and garners well supplied,
And spacious bartons clean, well-wall'd around,
Where all the wealth of rural life was found.

42

That goodly mansion on the ground was laid,
  Save here and there a blacken'd broken wall ;
The wounded who were borne beneath its shade
  Had there been crush'd and buried by the fall ; 250
And there they lie where they received their doom, . .
Oh, let no hand disturb that honourable tomb !

43

Contiguous to this wreck the little fane,
  For worship hallow'd, still uninjured stands,
Save that its Crucifix displays too plain
  The marks of outrage from irreverent hands.
Alas, to think such irreligious deed
Of wrong from British soldiers should proceed !

44

The dove-cot too remains ; scared at the fight
  The birds sought shelter in the forest shade ; 260
But still they kept their native haunts in sight,
  And when few days their terror had allay'd,
Forsook again the solitary wood,
For their old home and human neighbourhood.

45

The gardener's dwelling was untouch'd ; his wife
  Fled with her children to some near retreat,
And there lay trembling for her husband's life :
  He stood the issue, saw the foe's retreat,
And lives unhurt where thousands fell around,
To tell the story of that famous ground.

46

His generous dog was well approved that hour, 271
  By courage as by love to man allied ;
He through the fiery storm and iron shower
  Kept the ground bravely by his master's side :
And now when to the stranger's hand he draws,
The noble beast seems conscious of applause.

47

Toward the grove the wall with musket holes
  Is pierced ; our soldiers here their station held
Against the foe, and many were the souls
  Then from their fleshly tenements expell'd. 280
Six hundred Frenchmen have been burnt close by,
And underneath one mound their bones and ashes lie.

A a 3

48

One streak of blood upon the wall was
    traced,
    In length a man's just stature from
        the head ;
There where it gushed you saw it unef-
    faced ;
    Of all the blood which on that day
        was shed
This mortal stain alone remain'd im-
    press'd, . .
    The all-devouring earth had drunk the
        rest.

49

Here from the heaps who strew'd the
    fatal plain
    Was Howard's corse by faithful hands
        convey'd,   290
And, not to be confounded with the
    slain,
    Here in a grave apart with reverence
        laid,
Till hence his honour'd relics o'er the
    seas
Were borne to England, there to rest in
    peace.

50

Another grave had yielded up its dead,
    From whence to bear his son a father
        came,
That he might lay him where his own
    grey head
    Ere long must needs be laid.   That
        soldier's name
Was not remember'd there, yet may the
    verse
Present this reverent tribute to his
    herse.   300

51

Was it a soothing or a mournful thought,
    Amid this scene of slaughter as we
        stood,
Where armies had with recent fury
    fought,
    To mark how gentle Nature still pur-
        sued
Her quiet course, as if she took no
    care
For what her noblest work had suffer'd
    there ?

52

The pears had ripen'd on the garden
    wall ;
    Those leaves which on the autumnal
        earth were spread
The trees, though pierced and scarr'd
    with many a ball,
    Had only in their natural season
        shed :   310
Flowers were in seed whose buds to
    swell began
When such wild havoc here was made
    of man !

53

Throughout the garden, fruits and
    herbs and flowers
    You saw in growth, or ripeness, or
        decay ;
The green and well-trimm'd dial mark'd
    the hours
    With gliding shadow as they pass'd
        away ;
Who would have thought, to see this
    garden fair,
Such horrors had so late been acted
    there !

54

Now Hougoumont, farewell to thy
    domain !
    Might I dispose of thee, no wood-
        man's hand   320
Should e'er thy venerable groves pro-
    fane ;
    Untouch'd, and like a temple, should
        they stand,
And, consecrate by general feeling, wave
Their branches o'er the ground where
    sleep the brave.

55

Thy ruins as they fell should aye
    remain, . .
    What monument so fit for those
        below ?
Thy garden through whole ages should
    retain
    The form and fashion which it
        weareth now,
That future pilgrims here might all
    things see,   329
Such as they were at this great victory.

IV. THE SCENE OF WAR

1

No cloud the azure vault of heaven
distain'd
That day, when we the field of war
survey'd ;
The leaves were falling, but the groves
retain'd
Foliage enough for beauty and for
shade ;
Soft airs prevail'd, and through the
sunny hours
The bees were busy on the year's last
flowers.

2

Well was the season with the scene combined.
The autumnal sunshine suited well
the mood
Which here possess'd the meditative
mind, . .
A human sense upon the field of
blood,   10
A Christian thankfulness, a British
pride,
Temper'd by solemn thought, yet still
to joy allied.

3

What British heart that would not feel
a flow,
Upon that ground, of elevating pride?
What British cheek is there that would
not glow
To hear our country blest and magnified ? . .
For Britain here was blest by old and
young,
Admired by every heart and praised by
every tongue.

4

Not for brave bearing in the field
alone
Doth grateful Belgium bless the
British name ;   20
The order and the perfect honour shown
In all things, have enhanced the
soldier's fame :

For this we heard the admiring people
raise
One universal voice sincere of praise.

5

Yet with indignant feeling they enquired
Wherefore we spared the author of
this strife ?
Why had we not, as highest law required,
With ignominy closed the culprit's
life ?
For him alone had all this blood been
shed, . .
Why had not vengeance struck the
guilty head ?   30

6

O God ! they said, it was a piteous
thing
To see the after-horrors of the fight,
The lingering death, the hopeless
suffering, . .
What heart of flesh unmoved could
bear the sight?
One man was cause of all this world of
woe, . .
Ye had him, . . and ye did not strike the
blow !

7

How will ye answer to all after time
For that great lesson which ye fail'd
to give?
As if excess of guilt excused the crime,
Black as he is with blood ye let him
live !   40
Children of evil, take your course hence-
forth,
For what is Justice but a name on earth !

8

Vain had it been with these in glosing
speech
Of precedents to use the specious
tongue :
This might perplex the ear, but fail to
reach
The heart, from whence that honest
feeling sprung :
And, had I dared my inner sense belie,
The voice of blood was there to join
them in their cry.

9

We left the field of battle in such mood
  As human hearts from thence should
    bear away,   50
And musing thus our purposed route
    pursued,
  Which still through scenes of recent
    bloodshed lay,
Where Prussia late with strong and
    stern delight
Hung on her hated foes to persecute
    their flight.

10

No hour for tarriance that, or for
    remorse !
  Vengeance, who long had hunger'd,
    took her fill,
And Retribution held its righteous
    course :
  As when in elder time the Sun stood
    still
On Gibeon, and the Moon above the
    vale
Of Ajalon hung motionless and pale. 60

11

And what though no portentous day
    was given
  To render here the work of wrath
    complete,
The Sun, I ween, seem'd standing still
    in heaven
  To those who hurried from that dire
    defeat ;
And, when they pray'd for darkness in
    their flight,
The Moon arose upon them broad and
    bright.

12

No covert might they find ; the open
    land,
  O'er which so late exultingly they
    pass'd,
Lay all before them and on either
    hand ;
  Close on their flight the avengers
    follow'd fast,   70
And when they reach'd Genappe and
    there drew breath,
Short respite found they there from
    fear and death.

13

That fatal town betray'd them to more
    loss ;
  Through one long street the only
    passage lay,
And then the narrow bridge they needs
    must cross
  Where Dyle, a shallow streamlet,
    cross'd the way :
For life they fled, . . no thought had they
    but fear,
And their own baggage choak'd the
    outlet here.

14

He who had bridged the Danube's
    affluent stream,
  With all the unbroken Austrian power
    in sight,   80
(So had his empire vanish'd like a dream)
  Was by this brook impeded in his
    flight ; . .   [there . .
And then what passions did he witness
Rage, terror, execrations, and despair !

15

Ere through the wreck his passage could
    be made,
  Three miserable hours, which seem'd
    like years,
Was he in that ignoble strait delay'd ;
  The dreadful Prussian's cry was in
    his ears,   [hell
Fear in his heart, and in his soul that
Whose due rewards he merited so well.

16

Foremost again as he was wont to be
  In flight, though not the foremost in
    the strife,   92
The Tyrant hurried on, of infamy
  Regardless, nor regarding ought but
    life ; . .   [faith
Oh wretch ! without the courage or the
To die with those whom he had led to
    death !

17

Meantime his guilty followers in disgrace,
  Whose pride for ever now was beaten
    down,   [place ;
Some in the houses sought a hiding-
  While at the entrance of that fatal
    town   100

Others, who yet some show of heart
    display'd,
A short vain effort of resistance made :

18

Feeble and ill-sustain'd ! The foe burst
    through :
    With unabating heat they search'd
    around ;
The wretches from their lurking-holes
    they drew, . .
    Such mercy as the French had given
    they found ;
Death had more victims there in that
    one hour
Than fifty years might else have ren-
    der'd to his power.

19

Here did we inn upon our pilgrimage,
    After such day an unfit resting-place :
For who from ghastly thoughts could
    disengage   111
    The haunted mind, when every where
    the trace
Of death was seen, . . the blood-stain on
    the wall,
And musket-marks in chamber and in
    hall !

20

All talk too was of death.   They shew'd
    us here
    The room where Brunswick's body
    had been laid,
Where his brave followers, bending o'er
    the bier,
    In bitterness their vow of vengeance
    made ;   [Chief,
Where Wellington beheld the slaughter'd
And for awhile gave way to manly grief.

21

Duhesme, whose crimes the Catalans
    may tell,   121
    Died here ; . . with sabre strokes the
    posts are scored,
Hewn down upon the threshold where
    he fell,
    Himself then tasting of the ruthless
    sword ;   [Spain,
A Brunswicker discharged the debt of
And where he dropt the stone preserves
    the stain.

22

Too much of life hath on thy plains been
    shed,
    Brabant ! so oft the scene of war's
    debate ;
But ne'er with blood were they so
    largely fed
    As in this rout and wreck ; when
    righteous Fate   130
Brought on the French, in warning to
    all times,
A vengeance wide and sweeping as their
    crimes :

23

Vengeance for Egypt and for Syria's
    wrong ;
    For Portugal's unutterable woes ;
For Germany, who suffer'd all too
    long
    Beneath these lawless, faithless, god-
    less foes ;
For blood which on the Lord so long
    had cried,
For Earth opprest, and Heaven insulted
    and defied.

24

We follow'd from Genappe their line of
    flight
    To the Cross Roads, where Britain's
    sons sustain'd   140
Against such perilous force the desperate
    fight :
    Deserving for that field so well main-
    tain'd,
Such fame as for a like devotion's
    meed
The world hath to the Spartan band
    decreed.

25

Upon this ground the noble Brunswick
    died,
    Led on too rashly by his ardent
    heart ;
Long shall his grateful country tell with
    pride
    How manfully he chose the better
    part :
When groaning Germany in chains was
    bound,   149
He only of her Princes faithful found.

26

And here right bravely did the German
  band
  Once more sustain their well-deserved
    applause ;
As when, revenging there their native
    land,
  In Spain they labour'd for the general
    cause.
In this most arduous strife none more
    than they
Endured the heat and burthen of the
  day.

27

Here too we heard the praise of British
    worth,
  Still best approved when most severely
    tried ;
Here were broad patches of loose-lying
    earth,
  Sufficing scarce the mingled bones to
    hide, . .   160
And half-uncover'd graves, where one
    might see
The loathliest features of mortality.

28

Eastward from hence we struck, and
    reach'd the field
  Of Ligny, where the Prussian, on that
    day
By far-outnumbering force constrain'd
    to yield,
  Fronted the foe, and held them still
    at bay ;
And in that brave defeat acquired fresh
    claim
To glory, and enhanced his country's
  fame.

29

Here was a scene which fancy might
    delight
  To treasure up among her cherish'd
    stores,   170
And bring again before the inward
    sight
  Often when she recalls the long-past
    hours ; . .
Well-cultured hill and dale extending
    ·wide,
Hamlets and village spires on every
  side ;

30

The autumnal-tinted groves ; the up-
    land mill
  Which oft was won and lost amid the
    fray :
Green pastures water'd by the silent rill ;
  The lordly Castle yielding to decay,
With bridge and barbacan and moat and
    tower,
A fairer sight perchance than when it
    frown'd in power :   180

31

The avenue before its ruin'd gate,
  Which when the Castle, suffering less
    from time
Than havoc, hath foregone its strength
    and state,   [prime
  Uninjured flourisheth in nature's
To us a grateful shade did it supply,
  Glad of that shelter from the noontide
    sky :

32

The quarries deep, where many a mas-
    sive block
  For some Parisian monument of pride
Hewn with long labour from the granite
    rock,
  Lay in the change of fortune cast
    aside ;   190
But rightly with those stones should
    Prussia build
Her monumental pile on Ligny's bloody
    field !

33

The wealthy village bearing but too plain
  The dismal marks of recent fire and
    spoil ;
Its decent habitants, an active train,
  And many a one at work with needful
    toil
On roof or thatch, the ruin to repair, . .
May never War repeat such devastation
    there !

34

Ill had we done if we had hurried by
  A scene in faithful history to be
    famed   200
Through long succeeding ages ; nor
    may I
  The hospitality let pass unnamed,

And courteous kindness on that distant
  ground,
Which, strangers as we were, for England's sake we found.

35

And dear to England should be Ligny's
  name
  Prussia and England both were proved
  that day;
Each generous nation to the other's
  fame
  Her ample tribute of applause will
  pay;
Long as the memory of those labours
  past,
Unbroken may their Fair Alliance last!

36

The tales which of that field I could
  unfold   211
  Better it is that silence should conceal.
They who had seen them shudder'd
  while they told
  Of things so hideous; and they cried
  with zeal,
One man hath caused all this, of men
  the worst, . .
O wherefore have ye spared his head
  accurst!

37

It fits not now to tell our farther way
  Through many a scene by bounteous
  nature blest,
Nor how we found, where'er our journey
  lay,
  An Englishman was still an honour'd
  guest;   220
But still upon this point, where'er we
  went,
The indignant voice was heard of discontent.

38

And hence there lay, too plainly might
  we see,
  An ominous feeling upon every heart:
What hope of lasting order could there
  be,
  They said, where Justice has not had
  her part?

Wisdom doth rule with Justice by her
  side;
Justice from Wisdom none may e'er
  divide.

39

The shaken mind felt all things insecure:
  Accustom'd long to see successful
  crimes,   230
And helplessly the heavy yoke endure,
  They now look'd back upon their
  fathers' times,
Ere the wild rule of Anarchy began,
As to some happier world, or golden age
  of man.

40

As they who in the vale of years advance,
  And the dark eve is closing on their
  way,
When on their mind the recollections
  glance   [day,
  Of early joy, and Hope's delightful
Behold, in brighter hues than those of
  truth,
The light of morning on the fields of
  youth: 240

41

Those who amid these troubles had
  grown grey
  Recurr'd with mournful feeling to the
  past;
Blest had we known our blessings, they
  would say,
  We were not worthy that our bliss
  should last!
Peaceful we were, and flourishing and
  free,
But madly we required more liberty!

42

Remorseless France had long oppress'd
  the land,
  And for her frantic projects drain'd
  its blood;
And now they felt the Prussian's heavy
  hand:
  He came to aid them; bravely had
  he stood   250
In their defence; . . but oh! in peace
  how ill   [will!
The soldier's deeds, how insolent his

43

One general wish prevail'd, . . if they
    might see
The happy order of old times restored !
Give them their former laws and liberty,
    This their desires and secret prayers
      implored ; . .
Forgetful, as the stream of time flows on,
That that which passes is for ever gone.

PART II

THE VISION

ΕΠΕΧΕ ΝΥΝ ΣΚΟΠΩ ΤΟΞΟΝ,
ΑΓΕ ΘΥΜΕ.—Pindar.

I. THE TOWER

1

I thought upon these things in solitude,
    And mused upon them in the silent
      night ;
The open graves, the recent scene of
    blood,
    Were present to the soul's creative
      sight ;
These mournful images my mind pos-
    sess'd,
And mingled with the visions of my rest.

2

Methought that I was travelling o'er a
    plain
    Whose limits, far beyond all reach
      of sense,
The aching anxious sight explored in
    vain.
    How I came there I could not tell, nor
      whence ;   10
Nor where my melancholy journey lay ;
Only that soon the night would close
    upon my way.

3

Behind me was a dolorous, dreary scene,
    With huge and mouldering ruins
      widely spread ;
Wastes which had whilome fertile
    regions been,
    Tombs which had lost all record of
      the dead ;

And where the dim horizon seem'd to
    close,
Far off the gloomy Pyramids arose.

4

Full fain would I have known what lay
    before,
    But lifted there in vain my mortal
      eye ;   20
That point with cloud and mist was
    cover'd o'er,
    As though the earth were mingled
      with the sky.
Yet thither, as some power unseen
    impell'd,
My blind involuntary way I held.

5

Across the plain innumerable crowds
    Like me were on their destined journey
      bent,
Toward the land of shadows and of
    clouds :
    One pace they travelled, to one point
      they went ; . .
A motley multitude of old and young,
Men of all climes and hues, and every
    tongue.   30

6

Ere long I came upon a field of dead,
    Where heaps of recent carnage fill'd
      the way ;
A ghastly sight, . . nor was there where
    to tread,
    So thickly slaughter'd, horse and man,
      they lay.
Methought that in that place of death
    I knew
Again the late-seen field of Waterloo.

7

Troubled I stood, and doubtful where to
    go, . .
    A cold damp shuddering ran through
      all my frame ;
Fain would I fly from that dread scene,
    when lo !
    A voice as from above pronounced
      my name ;   40
And, looking to the sound, by the way-
    side
I saw a lofty structure edified.

8

Most like it seem'd to that aspiring
  Tower
  Which old Ambition rear'd on Babel's
  plain,   [power
As if he ween'd in his presumptuous
  To scale high Heaven with daring
  pride profane ;
Such was its giddy height : and round
  and round
The spiral steps in long ascension wound.

9

Its frail foundations upon sand were
  placed,
  And round about it mouldering
  rubbish lay ;   50
For easily by time and storms defaced
  The loose materials crumbled in
  decay :
Rising so high, and built so insecure,
Ill might such perishable work endure.

10

I not the less went up, and, as I drew
Toward the top, more firm the structure
  seem'd,   [view :
With nicer art composed, and fair to
  Strong and well-built perchance I
  might have deem'd
The pile, had I not seen and understood
Of what frail matter form'd, and on
  what base it stood.   60

11

There on the summit a grave personage
  Received and welcomed me in courteous guise ;
On his grey temples were the marks of
  age,
  As one whom years methought should
  render wise.
I saw that thou wert fill'd with doubt
  and fear,
He said, and therefore have I call'd
  thee here.

12

Hence from this eminence sublime I see
  The wanderings of the erring crowd
  below,
And, pitying thee in thy perplexity,
  Will tell thee all that thou canst need
  to know   70

To guide thy steps aright. I bent my
  head
As if in thanks, . . And who art thou ? I
  said.

13

He answer'd, I am Wisdom. Mother
  Earth
  Me, in her vigour self-conceiving,
  bore ;
And, as from oldest time I date my birth,
  Eternally with her shall I endure ;
Her noblest offspring I, to whom alone
The course of sublunary things is known.

14

Master ! quoth I, regarding him, I
  thought
  That Wisdom was the child divine of
  Heaven.   80
So, he replied, have fabling preachers
  taught,
  And the dull World a light belief hath
  given.
But vainly would these fools my claim
  decry, . .
Wisdom I am, and of the Earth am I.

15

Thus while he spake I scann'd his
  features well :
  Small but audacious was the Old
  Man's eye ;
His countenance was hard, and seem'd
  to tell
  Of knowledge less than of effrontery.
Instruct me then, I said, for thou
  should'st know,
From whence I came, and whither I
  must go.   90

16

Art thou then one who would his mind
  perplex
  With knowledge bootless even if
  attain'd ?
Fond man ! he answer'd ; . . wherefore
  shouldst thou vex
  Thy heart with seeking what may not
  be gain'd !
Regard not what has been, nor what
  may be,
O Child of Earth, this Now is all that
  toucheth thee !

17

He who performs the journey of to-day
  Cares not if yesterday were shower or
    sun:
To-morrow let the heavens be what
    they may,
  And what recks he? . . his wayfare will
    be done.   100
Heedless of what hereafter may befall,
Live whilst thou livest, for this life is all!

18

I kept my rising indignation down,
  That I might hear what farther he
    would teach;
Yet on my darken'd brow the instinc-
    tive frown,
  Gathering at that abominable speech,
Maintain'd its place: he mark'd it and
    pursued,
Tuning his practised tongue to subtle
    flattery's mood:

19

Do I not know thee, . . that from earliest
    youth
  Knowledge hath been thy only heart's-
    desire?   110
Here seeing all things as they are in truth,
  I show thee all to which thy thoughts
    aspire: [sense,
No vapours here impede the exalted
Nor mists of earth attain this eminence.

20

Whither thy way, thou askest me, and
    what   [tend,
  The region dark whereto thy footsteps
And where by one inevitable lot
  The course of all yon multitude must
    end.
Take thou this glass, whose perfect
    power shall aid
Thy faulty vision, and therewith ex-
    plore the shade.   120

21

Eager I look'd; but, seeing with sur-
    prize
  That the same darkness still the view
    o'erspread,
Half angrily I turn'd away mine eyes.
  Complacent then the Old Man smiled
    and said,

Darkness is all! what more wouldst
    thou descry?
Rest now content, for farther none can
    spy.

22

Now mark me, Child of Earth! he thus
    pursued;   [blind,
  Let not the hypocrites thy reason
And to the quest of some unreal good
  Divert with dogmas vain thine erring
    mind: 130
Learn thou, whate'er the motive they
    may call,
That Pleasure is the aim, and Self the
    spring of all.

23

This is the root of knowledge. Wise
    are they
  Who to this guiding principle attend;
They, as they press along the world's
    high-way,   [end:
  With single aim pursue their steady
No vain compunction checks their sure
    career;
No idle dreams deceive; their heart is
    here.

24

They from the nature and the fate of
    man,
  Thus clearly understood, derive their
    strength;   140
Knowing that, as from nothing they
    began,
  To nothing they must needs return
    at length;
This knowledge steels the heart and
    clears the mind,
And they create on earth the Heaven
    they find.

25

Such, I made answer, was the Tyrant's
    creed
  Who bruised the nations with his iron
    rod,   [meed
Till on yon field the wretch received his
  From Britain, and the outstretch'd
    arm of God!   [view,
Behold him now, . . Death ever in his
The only change for him, . . and Judg-
    ment to ensue!   150

26

Behold him when the unbidden thoughts
  arise
  Of his old passions and unbridled
    power ;
As the fierce tiger in confinement lies,
  And dreams of blood that he must
    taste no more, . .
Then, waking in that appetite of rage,
Frets to and fro within his narrow cage.

27

Hath he not chosen well ? the Old Man
  replied ;
  Bravely he aim'd at universal sway ;
And never earthly Chief was glorified
  Like this Napoleon in his prosperous
    day.   160
All-ruling Fate itself hath not the power
To alter what has been : and he has had
  his hour !

28

Take him, I answer'd, at his fortune's
  flood ;
  Russia his friend, the Austrian wars
    surceased,
When Kings, his creatures some, and
  some subdued,
  Like vassals waited at his marriage
    feast ;
And Europe like a map before him lay,
Of which he gave at will, or took away.

29

Call then to mind Navarre's heroic chief,
  Wandering by night and day through
    wood and glen,   170
His country's sufferings like a private
  grief   [then
  Wringing his heart : would Mina even
Those perils and that sorrow have fore-
  gone
To be that Tyrant on his prosperous
  throne ?

30

But wherefore name I him whose arm
  was free ?
  A living hope his noble heart sustain'd,
A faith which bade him through all
  dangers see
  The triumph his enduring country
    gain'd.

See Hofer with no earthly hope to aid, . .
His country lost, himself to chains and
  death betray'd !   180

31

By those he served deserted in his need ;
  Given to the unrelenting Tyrant's
    power,
And by his mean revenge condemn'd to
  bleed, . .
  Would he have barter'd in that aweful
    hour   •
His heart, his conscience, and his sure
  renown,
For the malignant murderer's crimes
  and crown ?

32

Him too, I know, a worthy thought of
  fame
  In that dread trance upheld ; . . the
    foresight sure
That in his own dear country his good
  name
  Long as the streams and mountains
    should endure ;   190
The herdsmen on the hills should sing
  his praise,
And children learn his deeds through
  all succeeding days.

33

Turn we to those in whom no glorious
  thought
  Lent its strong succour to the passive
    mind ;
Nor stirring enterprize within them
  wrought ; . .
  Who, to their lot of bitterness resign'd,
Endured their sorrows by the world
  unknown,
And look'd for their reward to Death
  alone :

34

Mothers within Gerona's leager'd wall,
  Who saw their famish'd children pine
    and die ; . .   200
Widows surviving Zaragoza's fall
  To linger in abhorr'd captivity ; . .
Yet would not have exchanged their
  sacred woe
For all the empire of their miscreant
  foe !

35

Serene the Old Man replied, and smiled
      with scorn,   [wear
Behold the effect of error! thus to
The days of miserable life forlorn,
    Struggling with evil and consum'd
      with care; . .
Poor fools, whom vain and empty hopes
      mislead!   [meed.
They reap their sufferings for their only

36

O false one! I exclaim'd, whom canst
    thou fool   211
  With such gross sophisms, but the
    wicked heart?
The pupils of thine own unhappy school
    Are they who chuse the vain and
      empty part;
How oft in age, in sickness, and in woe,
Have they complain'd that all was
      vanity below!

37

Look at that mighty Gaznevide, Mah-
    mood,
    When, pining in his Palace of Delight,
He bade the gather'd spoils of realms
      subdued   [sight,
Be spread before him to regale his
Whate'er the Orient boasts of rich and
    rare, . .   221
And then he wept to think what toys
    they were!

38

Look at the Russian minion when he
    play'd
  With pearls and jewels which sur-
    pass'd all price;
And now apart their various hues
      array'd,   [nice,
Blended their colours now in union
Then weary of the baubles, with a sigh,
Swept them aside, and thought that all
    was vanity!

39

Wean'd by the fatal Messenger from
    pride,   229
  The Syrian through the streets ex-
    posed his shroud;   [wide
And one that ravaged kingdoms far and
    Upon the bed of sickness cried aloud,

What boots my empire in this mortal
    throe,
For the grave calls me now, and I must
    go!

40

Thus felt these wretched men, because
      decay
    Had touch'd them in their vitals;
      Death stood by;
And Reason when the props of flesh gave
    way,   [eye.
Purged as with euphrasy the mortal
Who seeks for worldly honours, wealth
    or power,
Will find them vain indeed at that
    dread hour!   240

41

These things are vain; but all things
    are not so,
  The virtues and the hopes of human
    kind! . .
Yea, by the God who, ordering all
    below,   [mind,
  In his own image made the immortal
Desires there are which draw from Him
      their birth,
And bring forth lasting fruits for
    Heaven and Earth.

42

Therefore, through evil and through
    good content,
  The righteous man performs his part
    assign'd;   [spent,
In bondage lingering, or with suffering
    Therefore doth peace support the
      heroic mind;   250
And from the dreadful sacrifice of all
Meek woman doth not shrink at Duty's
    call.

43

Therefore the Martyr clasps the stake
    in faith,
  And sings thanksgiving while the
    flames aspire;
Victorious over agony and death,
    Sublime he stands and triumphs in
      the fire,
As though to him Elijah's lot were given,
And that the Chariot and the steeds of
    Heaven.

II. THE EVIL PROPHET

1

WITH that my passionate discourse I
    brake;
    Too fast the thought, too strong the
    feeling came.
Composed the Old Man listen'd while
    I spake,
    Nor moved to wrath, nor capable of
    shame;
And, when I ceased, unalter'd was his
    mien,
His hard eye unabash'd, his front
    serene.

2

Hard is it error from the mind to weed,
    He answer'd, where it strikes so deep
    a root.
Let us to other argument proceed,
    And, if we may, discover what the
    fruit   10
Of this long strife, . . what harvest of
    great good
The World shall reap for all this cost of
    blood!

3

Assuming then a frown as thus he said,
    He stretch'd his hand from that
    commanding height,
Behold, quoth he, where thrice ten
    thousand dead
    Are laid, the victims of a single fight!
And thrice ten thousand more at Ligny
    lie,
Slain for the prelude to this tragedy!

4

This but a page of the great book of
    war, . .
    A drop amid the sea of human
    woes! . .   20
Thou canst remember when the morning
    Star
    Of Freedom on rejoicing France arose,
Over her vine-clad hills and regions
    gay,
Fair even as Phosphor who foreruns the
    day.

5

Such and so beautiful that Star's up-
    rise;
    But soon the glorious dawn was over-
    cast:
A baleful track it held across the
    skies,
    Till now through all its fatal changes
    past,
Its course fulfill'd, its aspects under-
    stood,
On Waterloo it hath gone down in
    blood.   30

6

Where now the hopes with which thine
    ardent youth
    Rejoicingly to run its race began?
Where now the reign of Liberty and
    Truth,
    The Rights Omnipotent of Equal
    Man,
The principles should make all discord
    cease,
And bid poor humankind repose at
    length in peace?

7

Behold the Bourbon to that throne by
    force
    Restored, from whence by fury he
    was cast:
Thus to the point where it began its
    course
    The melancholy cycle comes at last;
And what are all the intermediate
    years? . .   41
What, but a bootless waste of blood and
    tears?

8

The peace which thus at Waterloo ye
    won,
    Shall it endure with this exasperate
    foe?
In gratitude for all that ye have done
    Will France her ancient enmity fore-
    go?
Her wounded spirit, her envenom'd
    will
Ye know, . . and ample means are left
    her still.

9

What though the tresses of her strength
be shorn,
  The roots remain untouch'd; and, as
    of old   50
The bondsman Samson felt his power
return
  To his knit sinews, so shall ye behold
France, like a giant fresh from sleep,
arise
And rush upon her slumbering enemies.

10

Woe then for Belgium! for this ill-
doom'd land,
  The theatre of strife through every
  age!
Look from this eminence whereon we
stand, ..   [stage
  What is the region round us but a
For the mad pastime of Ambition made,
Whereon War's dreadful drama may
be play'd?   60

11

Thus hath it been from history's earliest
light,
  When yonder by the Sabis Cæsar
  stood,   [fight,
And saw his legions, raging from the
Root out the noble nation they sub-
dued;   [there
Even at this day the peasant findeth
The relics of that ruthless massacre.

12

Need I recall the long religious strife?
  Or William's hard-fought fields? or
  Marlborough's fame
Here purchased at such lavish price of
life, ..
  Or Fontenoy, or Fleurus' later name?
Wherever here the foot of man may
tread,   71
The blood of man hath on that spot been
shed.

13

Shall then Futurity a happier train
  Unfold, than this dark picture of the
  past?
Dream'st thou again of some Saturnian
reign,   [last?
  Or that this ill-compacted realm should

Its wealth and weakness to the foe are
known,
And the first shock subverts its baseless
throne.

14

O wretched country, better should thy
soil
  Be laid again beneath the invading
  seas,   80
Thou goodliest masterpiece of human
toil,
  If still thou must be doom'd to scenes
  like these!
O Destiny inexorable and blind!
O miserable lot of poor mankind!

15

Saying thus, he fix'd on me a searching
eye
  Of stern regard, as if my heart to
  reach:
Yet gave he now no leisure to reply;
  For, ere I might dispose my thoughts
  for speech,
The Old Man, as one who felt and understood
His strength, the theme of his discourse
pursued.   90

16

If we look farther, what shall we behold
  But everywhere the swelling seeds of
  ill,
Half-smother'd fires, and causes mani-
fold
  Of strife to come; the powerful
  watching still
For fresh occasion to enlarge his power,
The weak and injured waiting for their
hour!

17

Will the rude Cossack with his spoils
bear back
  The love of peace and humanizing
  art?
Think ye the mighty Moscovite shall lack
  Some specious business for the
  ambitious heart;   100
Or the black Eagle, when she moults her
plume,
The form and temper of the Dove
assume?

18

From the old Germanic chaos hath there
risen
A happier order of establish'd things?
And is the Italian Mind from papal
prison
Set free to soar upon its native wings?
Or look to Spain, and let her Despot tell
If there thy high-raised hopes are
answer'd well!

19

At that appeal my spirit breathed a
groan,
But he triumphantly pursued his
speech: 110
O Child of Earth, he cried with loftier
tone,   [teach;
The present and the past one lesson
Look where thou wilt, the history of man
Is but a thorny maze, without a plan!

20

The winds which have in viewless
heaven their birth,
The waves which in their fury meet
the clouds,   [earth,
The central storms which shake the solid
And from volcanoes burst in fiery
floods,   [blind,
Are not more vague and purportless and
Than is the course of things among
mankind!   120

21

Rash hands unravel what the wise have
spun;
Realms which in story fill so large
a part,
Rear'd by the strong are by the weak
undone;
Barbarians overthrow the works of art,
And what force spares is sapp'd by sure
decay, . .
So earthly things are changed and pass
away.

22

And think not thou thy England hath
a spell,   [elude;
That she this general fortune should
Easier to crush the foreign foe, than quell
The malice which misleads the multi-
tude,   130

And that dread malady of erring zeal,
Which like a cancer eats into the com-
monweal.

23

The fabric of her power is undermined;
The earthquake underneath it will
have way
And all that glorious structure, as the
wind   [away:
Scatters a summer cloud, be swept
For Destiny on this terrestrial ball
Drives on her iron car, and crushes all.

24

Thus as he ended, his mysterious form
Enlarged, grew dim, and vanish'd
from my view.   140
At once on all sides rush'd the gather'd
storm,
The thunders roll'd around, the wild
winds blew,
And, as the tempest round the summit
beat,
The whole frail fabric shook beneath
my feet.

III. THE SACRED MOUNTAIN

1

BUT then methought I heard a voice
exclaim,
Hither, my Son, Oh, hither take thy
flight!
A heavenly voice which call'd me by
my name,
And bade me hasten from that
treacherous height:
The voice it was which I was wont to
hear,
Sweet as a Mother's to her infant's ear.

2

I hesitated not, but at the call
Sprung from the summit of that
tottering tower.
There is a motion known in dreams to all,
When, buoyant by some self-sustain-
ing power,   10
Through air we seem to glide, as if set
free
From all encumbrance of mortality.

3

Thus borne aloft I reach'd the Sacred
Hill,   [behind :
And left the scene of tempests far
But that old tempter's parting language
still   [mind ;
Press'd like a painful burthen on my
The troubled soul had lost her inward
light,   [Night.
And all within was black as Erebus and

4

The Thoughts which I had known in
youth return'd,
But, oh, how changed ! a sad and
spectral train :   20
And, while for all the miseries past I
mourn'd,
And for the lives which had been
given in vain,
In sorrow and in fear I turn'd mine eye
From the dark aspects of futurity.

5

I sought the thickest woodland's shade
profound,
As suited best my melancholy mood,
And cast myself upon the gloomy
ground ;
When lo ! a gradual radiance fill'd
the wood ;
A heavenly presence rose upon my view,
And in that form divine the aweful Muse
I knew.   30

6

Hath then that Spirit false perplex'd thy
heart,
O thou of little faith ! severe she cried.
Bear with me, Goddess, heavenly as
thou art,   [plied,
Bear with my earthly nature ! I re-
And let me pour into thine ear my grief :
Thou canst enlighten, thou canst give
relief.

7

The ploughshare had gone deep, the
sower's hand
Had scatter'd in the open soil the
grain ;   [land ;
The harrow too had well prepared the
I look'd to see the fruit of all this
pain ! . .   40

Alas ! the thorns and old inveterate
weed
Have sprung again, and stifled the good
seed.

8

I hoped that Italy should break her
chains,
Foreign and papal, with the world's
applause,
Knit in firm union her divided reigns,
And rear a well-built pile of equal
laws :
Then might the wrongs of Venice be
forgiven,
And joy should reach Petrarca's soul in
Heaven.

9

I hoped that that abhorr'd Idolatry
Had in the strife received its mortal
wound :   50
The Souls which from beneath the Altar
cry,
At length, I thought, had their just
vengeance found ; . .
In purple and in scarlet clad, behold
The Harlot sits, adorn'd with gems and
gold !

10

The golden cup she bears full to the brim
Of her abominations as of yore !
Her eyeballs with inebriate triumph
swim ;
Though drunk with righteous blood,
she thirsts for more,
Eager to reassert her influence fell,
And once again let loose the Dogs of
Hell.   60

11

Woe for that people too who by their
path
For these late triumphs first made
plain the way ;
Whom in the Valley of the Shade of
Death
No fears nor fiery sufferings could dis-
may :
Art could not tempt, nor violence en-
thrall
Their firm devotion, faithful found
through all.

12

Strange race of haughty heart and
    stubborn will,
  Slavery they love and chains with
    pride they wear;
Inflexible alike in good or ill,
  The inveterate stamp of servitude
    they bear.   70
Oh fate perverse, to see all change with-
    stood,
There only where all change must needs
    be good!

13

But them no foe can force, nor friend
    persuade;
  Impassive souls in iron forms inclosed,
As though of human mould they were
    not made,
  But of some sterner elements com-
    posed,
Against offending nations to be sent,
The ruthless ministers of punishment.

14

Where are those Minas after that career
  Wherewith all Europe rang from side
    to side?   80
In exile wandering! Where the Moun-
    taineer, ..
  Late, like Pelayo, the Asturian's pride?
Had Ferdinand no mercy for that life,
Exposed so long for him in daily, ..
    hourly strife!

15

From her Athenian orator of old
  Greece never listen'd to sublimer
    strain
Than that with which, for truth and
    freedom bold,
  Quintana moved the inmost soul of
    Spain.
What meed is his let Ferdinand declare ..
Chains, and the silent dungeon, and
    despair!   90

16

For this hath England borne so brave
    a part!   [slain,
  Spent with endurance, or in battle
Is it for this so many an English heart
  Lies mingled with the insensate soil
    of Spain!

Is this the issue, this the happy birth
In those long throes and that strong
    agony brought forth!

17

And oh! if England's fatal hour draw
    nigh, ..
  If that most glorious edifice should fall
By the wild hands of bestial Anarchy, ..
  Then might it seem that He who
    ordereth all   100
Doth take for sublunary things no
    care: ..
The burthen of that thought is more
    than I can bear.

18

Even as a mother listens to her child,
  My plaint the Muse divine benignant
    heard,
Then answer'd in reproving accents
    mild,
  What if thou seest the fruit of hope
    deferr'd,
Dost thou for this in faltering faith
    repine?
A manlier, wiser virtue should be
    thine!

19

Ere the good seed can give its fruit in
    Spain,
  The light must shine on that be-
    darken'd land,   110
And Italy must break her papal chain,
  Ere the soil answer to the sower's
    hand;
For, till the sons their fathers' fault
    repent,
The old error brings its direful punish-
    ment.

20

Hath not experience bade the wise man
    see
  Poor hope from innovations prema-
    ture?
All sudden change is ill; slow grows the
    tree
  Which in its strength through ages
    shall endure.
In that ungrateful earth it long may lie
Dormant, but fear not that the seed
    should die.   120

21

Falsely that Tempter taught thee that
    the past
  Was but a blind inextricable maze ;
Falsely he taught that evil overcast
  With gathering tempests these pro-
    pitious days,
That he in subtle snares thy soul might
    bind,
And rob thee of thy hopes for human-
    kind.

22

He told thee the beginning and the end
  Were indistinguishable all, and dark ;
And, when from his vain Tower he bade
    thee bend
  Thy curious eye, well knew he that
    no spark   130
Of heavenly light would reach the
    baffled sense,
The mists of earth lay round him all too
    dense.

23

Must I, as thou hadst chosen the evil
    part,
  Tell thee that Man is free and God is
    good ?   [heart :
These primal truths are rooted in thy
  But these, being rightly felt and under-
    stood,
Should bring with them a hope, calm,
    constant, sure,
Patient, and on the rock of faith secure.

24

The Monitress Divine, as thus she spake,
Induced me gently on, ascending still,
And thus emerging from that mournful
    brake   141
  We drew toward the summit of the
    hill,   [fair
And reach'd a green and sunny place, so
As well with long-lost Eden might com-
    pare.

25

Broad cedars grew around that lovely
    glade ;
  Exempted from decay, and never sere,
Their wide-spread boughs diffused a
    fragrant shade ;
  The cypress incorruptible was here,

With fluted stem and head aspiring
    high,
Nature's proud column, pointing to the
    sky.   150

26

There too the vigorous olive in its pride,
  As in its own Apulian soil uncheck'd,
Tower'd high, and spread its glaucous
    foliage wide :
  With liveliest hues the mead beneath
    was deck'd,
Gift of that grateful tree that with its
    root
Repays the earth from whence it feeds
    its fruit.

27

There too the sacred bay of brighter
    green
  Exalted its rejoicing head on high ;
And there the martyr's holier palm was
    seen
  Waving its plumage as the breeze
    went by.   160
All fruits which ripen under genial
    skies
Grew there as in another Paradise.

28

And over all that lovely glade there
    grew
  All wholesome roots and plants of
    healing power ;
The herb of grace, the medicinal rue,
  The poppy rich in worth as gay in
    flower ;
The hearts-ease that delighteth every
    eye,
And sage divine and virtuous euphrasy.

29

Unwounded here Judæa's balm distill'd
  Its precious juice ; the snowy jasmine
    here   170
Spread its luxuriant tresses wide, and
    fill'd
  With fragrance the delicious atmo-
    sphere !
More piercing still did orange-flowers
    dispense
From golden groves the purest joy of
    sense.

30

As low it lurk'd the tufted moss between,
The violet there its modest perfume
    shed,
Like humble virtue, rather felt than seen:
    And here the Rose of Sharon rear'd its
        head,
The glory of all flowers, to sense and sight
Yielding their full contentment of
    delight,   180

31

A gentle river wound its quiet way
    Through this sequester'd glade,
        meandering wide ;
Smooth as a mirror here the surface lay,
    Where the pure lotus, floating in its
        pride,
Enjoy'd the breath of heaven, the sun's
    warm beam,   [stream.
And the cool freshness of its native

32

Here o'er green weeds, whose tresses
    waved outspread,   [run ;
    With silent lapse the glassy waters
Here in fleet motion o'er a pebbly bed
    Gliding they glance and ripple to the
        sun ;   190
The stirring breeze that swept them in
    its flight
Raised on the stream a shower of
    sparkling light.

33

And all sweet birds sung there their lays
    of love ;
    The mellow thrush, the black-bird
        loud and shrill,
The rapturous nightingale that shook
    the grove,
    Made the ears vibrate and the heart-
        strings thrill ;   [sky,
The ambitious lark, that, soaring in the
Pour'd forth her lyric strain of ecstasy.

34

Sometimes, when that wild chorus
    intermits,
    The linnet's song was heard amid the
        trees,   200
A low sweet voice ; and sweeter still,
    at fits,   [breeze ;
    The ring-dove's wooing came upon the

While with the wind which moved the
    leaves among,
The murmuring waters join'd in under-
    song.

35

The hare disported here and fear'd no ill,
    For never evil thing that glade came
        nigh ;   [will,
The sheep were free to wander at their
    As needing there no earthly shepherd's
        eye ;
The bird sought no concealment for her
    nest,
So perfect was the peace wherewith
    those bowers were blest.   210

36

All blending thus with all in one delight,
    The soul was soothed and satisfied and
        fill'd :
This mingled bliss of sense and sound
    and sight
    The flow of boisterous mirth might
        there have still'd,
And, sinking in the gentle spirit deep,
Have touch'd those strings of joy which
    make us weep.

37

Even thus in earthly gardens had it
    been,
    If earthly gardens might with these
        compare ;
But more than all such influences, I ween
    There was a heavenly virtue in the air,
Which laid all vain perplexing thoughts
    to rest,   221
And heal'd and calm'd and purified the
    breast.

38

Then said I to that guide divine, My
    soul
    When here we enter'd, was o'ercharged
        with grief,
For evil doubts which I could not con-
    troul
    Beset my troubled spirit. This
        relief, . .
This change, . . whence are they ? Al-
    most it might seem
I never lived till now ; . . all else had
    been a dream.

39

My heavenly Teacher answer'd, Say not
    seem ; . .
    In this place all things *are* what they
        appear ;   230
And they who feel the past a feverish
        dream
    Wake to reality on entering here.
Those waters are the Well of Life, and lo !
    The Rock of Ages there, from whence
        they flow.

40

Saying thus we came upon an inner glade,
    The holiest place that human eyes
        might see ;
For all that vale was like a temple made
    By Nature's hand, and this the
        sanctuary ;
Where in its bed of living rock, the Rood
Of Man's redemption, firmly planted,
        stood.   240

41

And at its foot the never-failing Well
    Of Life profusely flow'd that all might
        drink.
Most blessed Water ! Neither tongue
        can tell
    The blessedness thereof, nor heart can
        think,
Save only those to whom it hath been
        given
To taste of that divinest gift of Heaven.

42

There grew a goodly Tree this Well
        beside ; . .   [here,
    Behold a branch from Eden planted
Pluck'd from the Tree of Knowledge,
        said my guide.
O Child of Adam, put away thy fear, . .
    In thy first father's grave it hath its
        root ;   251
Taste thou the bitter, but the whole-
        some fruit.

43

In awe I heard, and trembled, and
        obey'd :
    The bitterness was even as of death ;
I felt a cold and piercing thrill pervade
    My loosen'd limbs, and, losing sight
        and breath,

To earth I should have fallen in my
        despair,
Had I not clasp'd the Cross and been
        supported there.

44

My heart, I thought, was bursting with
        the force
    Of that most fatal fruit ; soul-sick
        I felt,   260
And tears ran down in such continuous
        course,
    As if the very eyes themselves should
        melt.   [say,
But then I heard my heavenly Teacher
Drink, and this mortal stound will pass
        away.

45

I stoopt and drank of that divinest Well,
    Fresh from the Rock of Ages where it
        ran ;
It had a heavenly quality to quell
    My pain : . . I rose a renovated man,
And would not now, when that relief was
        known,
For worlds the needful suffering have
        foregone.   270

46

Even as the Eagle, (ancient storyers say),
    When faint with years she feels her
        flagging wing,
Soars up toward the mid sun's piercing
        ray,
    Then fill'd with fire into some living
        spring
Plunges, and, casting there her aged
        plumes,
The vigorous strength of primal youth
        resumes :

47

Such change in me that blessed Water
        wrought ;
    The bitterness, which from its fatal
        root
The Tree derived with painful healing
        fraught,
    Pass'd clean away ; and in its place
        the fruit   280
Produced by virtue of that wondrous
        wave
The savour which in Paradise it gave.

48

Now, said the heavenly Muse, thou
  mayst advance,
  Fitly prepared toward the mountain's
    height.
O Child of Man, this necessary trance
  Hath purified from flaw thy mortal
    sight,
That with scope unconfined of vision
  free
Thou the beginning and the end mayst
  see.

49

She took me by the hand and on we
  went,
  Hope urged me forward and my soul
    was strong;   290
With winged speed we scaled the steep
  ascent,
  Nor seem'd the labour difficult or
    long,
Ere on the summit of the sacred hill
Upraised I stood, where I might gaze
  my fill.

50

Below me lay, unfolded like a scroll,
  The boundless region where I wan-
    der'd late,
Where I might see realms spread and
  oceans roll,
  And mountains from their cloud-
    surmounting state
Dwarf'd like a map beneath the excur-
  sive sight,
So ample was the range from that com-
  manding height.   300

51

Eastward with darkness round on every
  side
  An eye of light was in the farthest
    sky.
Lo, the beginning! .. said my heavenly
  Guide;
  The steady ray, which there thou
    canst descry,
Comes from lost Eden, from the primal
  land
Of man 'waved over by the fiery
  brand'.

52

Look now toward the end! no mists
  obscure,
  Nor clouds will there impede the
    strengthen'd sight;
Unblench'd thine eye the vision may
  endure.
  I look'd, .. surrounded with effulgent
    light   310
More glorious than all glorious hues of
  even,
The Angel Death stood there in the open
  Gate of Heaven.

IV. THE HOPES OF MAN

1

Now, said my heavenly Teacher, all is
  clear! ..
  Bear the Beginning and the End in
    mind,
The course of human things will then
  appear
  Beneath its proper laws; and thou
    wilt find,
Through all their seeming labyrinth, the
  plan
Which 'vindicates the ways of God to
  Man'.

2

Free choice doth Man possess of good
  or ill,
  All were but mockery else. From
    Wisdom's way
Too oft perverted by the tainted will 9
  Is his rebellious nature drawn astray;
Therefore an inward monitor is given,
A voice that answers to the law of
  Heaven.

3

Frail as he is, and as an infant weak,
  The knowledge of his weakness is his
    strength;
For succour is vouchsafed to those who
  seek
  In humble faith sincere; and, when
    at length
Death sets the disembodied spirit free,
According to their deeds their lot shall
  be.

4

Thus, should the chance of private for-
tune raise   19
A transitory doubt, Death answers all.
And in the scale of nations, if the ways
    Of Providence mysterious we may
    call,
Yet, rightly view'd, all history doth
    impart
Comfort and hope and strength to the
    believing heart.

5

For through the lapse of ages may the
    course
    Of moral good progressive still be
    seen,
Though mournful dynasties of Fraud
    and Force,
    Dark Vice and purblind Ignorance
    intervene ;
Empires and Nations rise, decay and
    fall,
But still the Good survives and perse-
    veres thro' all.   30

6

Yea, even in those most lamentable
    times,
    When, every where to wars and woes
    a prey,
Earth seem'd but one wide theatre of
    crimes,
    Good unperceived had work'd its
    silent way,
And all those dread convulsions did but
    clear
The obstructed path to give it free
    career.

7

But deem not thou some over-ruling
    Fate,
    Directing all things with benign
    decree,
Through all the turmoil of this mortal
    state,
    Appoints that what is best shall there-
    fore be ;   40
Even as from man his future doom
    proceeds,
So nations rise or fall according to their
    deeds.

8

Light at the first was given to human
    kind,
    And Law was written in the human
    heart.   [mind,
If they forsake the Light, perverse of
    And wilfully prefer the evil part,
Then to their own devices are they left,
By their own choice of Heaven's support
    bereft.

9

The individual culprit may sometimes
    Unpunish'd to his after reckoning go :
Not thus collective man, . . for public
    crimes   51
    Draw on their proper punishment
    below ;
When Nations go astray, from age to age
The effects remain, a fatal heritage.

10

Bear witness, Egypt, thy huge monu-
    ments
    Of priestly fraud and tyranny austere !
Bear witness, thou whose only name
    presents
    All holy feelings to religion dear, . .
In Earth's dark circlet once the precious
    gem
Of living light, . . O fallen Jerusalem ! 60

11

See barbarous Africa, on every side
    To error, wretchedness, and crimes
    resign'd !
Behold the vicious Orient, far and wide
    Enthrall'd in slavery ! As the human
    mind
Corrupts and goes to wreck, Earth
    sickens there,
And the contagion taints the ambient air.

12

They had the Light, and from the Light
    they turn'd ;   [lost ?
    What marvel if they grope in darkness
They had the Law ; . . God's natural law
    they scorn'd,   [cost !
    And, chusing error, thus they pay the
Wherever Falsehood and Oppression
    reign,   71
There degradation follows in their train

13

What then in those late days had Europe
  been, . .
  This moral, intellectual heart of
      earth, . .   [sin
From which the nations who lie dead in
  Should one day yet receive their
      second birth, . .
To what had she been sunk, if brutal
      Force
Had taken unrestrain'd its impious
      course !

14

The Light had been extinguish'd, . . this
  be sure
  The first wise aim of conscious
      Tyranny,   80
Which knows it may not with the Light
      endure :
  But where Light is not, Freedom
      cannot be ;   [is ; '
' Where Freedom is not, there no Virtue
Where Virtue is not, there no Happiness.

15

If among hateful Tyrants of all times
  For endless execration handed down
One may be found surpassing all in
  crimes,
  One that for infamy should bear the
      crown,
Napoleon is that man, in guilt the first,
Pre-eminently bad among the worst.   90

16

For not, like Scythian conquerors, did
      he tread
  From his youth up the common path
      of blood ;   [bred
Nor like some Eastern Tyrant was he
  In sensual harems, ignorant of good ; . .
Their vices from the circumstance have
      grown,
His by deliberate purpose were his own.

17

Not led away by circumstance he err'd,
  But from the wicked heart his error
      came :   [ferr'd,
By Fortune to the highest place pre-
  He sought through evil means an evil
      aim,   100

And all his ruthless measures were
      design'd
To enslave, degrade, and brutalize man-
      kind.

18

Some barbarous dream of empire to
      fulfil,
  Those iron ages he would have
      restored,
When Law was but the ruffian soldier's
      will,
  Might govern'd all, the sceptre was
      the sword,
And Peace, not elsewhere finding where
      to dwell,
Sought a sad refuge in the convent-cell.

19

Too far had he succeeded ! In his mould
  An evil generation had been framed,
By no religion temper'd or controul'd,
  By foul examples of all crimes in-
      flamed,   112
Of faith, of honour, of compassion
      void ; . .
Such were the fitting agents he employ'd.

20

Believing as yon lying Spirit taught,
  They to that vain philosophy held
      fast,
And trusted that, as they began from
      nought,
  To nothing they should needs return
      at last ;
Hence no restraint of conscience, no
      remorse,
But every baleful passion took its
      course.   120

21

And, had they triumph'd, Earth had
      once again,
  To Violence subdued, and impious
      Pride,
Verged to such state of wickedness, as
      when
  The Giantry of old their God defied,
And Heaven, impatient of a world like
      this,
Open'd its flood-gates, and broke up the
      abyss.

22

That danger is gone by. On Waterloo
  The Tyrant's fortune in the scale was
    weigh'd, . .
His fortune and the World's, . . and
    England threw
    Her sword into the balance . . down it
      sway'd ;   130
And, when in battle first he met that foe,
There he received his mortal overthrow.

23

O my brave Countrymen, with that I
  said,
  For then my heart with transport
    overflow'd,
O Men of England ! nobly have ye paid
  The debt which to your ancestors ye
    owed,
And gather'd for your children's
    heritage
A glory that shall last from age to age !

24

And we did well, when on our Mountain's
  height
  For Waterloo we raised the festal
    flame,   140
And in our triumph taught the startled
    night   [name,
  To ring with Wellington's victorious
Making the far-off mariner admire
To see the crest of Skiddaw plumed with
  fire.

25

The Moon, who had in silence visited
  His lonely summit from the birth of
    time,
That hour an unavailing splendour shed,
  Lost in the effulgence of the flame
    sublime,   [stood,
In whose broad blaze rejoicingly we
And all below a depth of blackest
  solitude.   150

26

Fit theatre for this great joy we chose ;
  For never since above the abating
    Flood
Emerging, first that pinnacle arose,
  Had cause been given for deeper
    gratitude,

For prouder joy to every English
  heart,
When England had so well perform'd
  her arduous part.

27

The Muse replied with gentle smile
  benign, . .
  Well mayst thou praise the land that
    gave thee birth,
And bless the Fate which made that
    country thine ;
For of all ages and all parts of earth
  To chuse thy time and place did Fate
    allow,   161
Wise choice would be this England and
  this Now.

28

From bodily and mental bondage there
  Hath Man his full emancipation
    gain'd ;
The viewless and illimitable air
  Is not more free than Thought ; all
    unrestrain'd,
Nor pined in want, nor sunk in sensual
    sloth,
There may the immortal Mind attain
  its growth.

29

There under Freedom's tutelary wing,
  Deliberate Courage fears no human
    foe ;   170
There, undefiled as in their native spring,
  The living waters of Religion flow ;
There like a beacon the transmitted
    Light
Conspicuous to all nations burneth
  bright.

30

The virtuous will she hath, which should
  aspire
  To spread the sphere of happiness
    and light ;
She hath the power to answer her desire,
  The wisdom to direct her power
    aright ;
The will, the power, the wisdom thus
    combined,
What glorious prospects open on man-
  kind !   180

31

Behold! she cried, and lifting up her
hand,
  The shaping elements obey'd her
    will; . .
A vapour gather'd round our lofty stand,
  Roll'd in thick volumes o'er the
    Sacred Hill,
Descending then, its surges far and near
Fill'd all the wide subjacent atmosphere.

32

As I have seen from Skiddaw's stony
    height
  The fleecy clouds scud round me on
    their way,
Condense beneath, and hide the vale
    from sight,
  Then opening, just disclose where
    Derwent lay   190
Burnish'd with sunshine like a silver
    shield,
Or old Enchanter's glass, for magic
    forms fit field;

33

So at her will, in that receding sheet
  Of mist, wherewith the world was
    overlaid,
A living picture moved beneath our feet.
  A spacious City first was there dis-
    play'd,
The seat where England from her
    ancient reign
Doth rule the Ocean as her own domain.

34

In splendour with those famous cities old,
  Whose power it hath surpass'd, it now
    might vie;   200
Through many a bridge the wealthy
    river roll'd;
  Aspiring columns rear'd their heads
    on high,   [gave
Triumphal arches spann'd the roads, and
Due guerdon to the memory of the brave.

35

A landscape follow'd, such as might
    compare   [toil:
  With Flemish fields for well-requited
The wonder-working hand had every
    where   [soil;
  Subdued all circumstance of stubborn
In fen and moor reclaim'd rich gardens
    smiled,
And populous hamlets rose amid the
    wild.   210

36

There the old seaman on his native shore
  Enjoy'd the competence deserved so
    well;
The soldier, his dread occupation o'er,
  Of well-rewarded service loved to tell;
The grey-hair'd labourer there, whose
    work was done,
In comfort saw the day of life go down.

37

Such was the lot of eld; for childhood
    there
  The duties which belong to life was
    taught:
The good seed, early sown and nursed
    with care,
  This bounteous harvest in its season
    brought;   220
Thus youth for manhood, manhood for
    old age
Prepared, and found their weal in
    every stage.

38

Enough of knowledge unto all was given
  In wisdom's way to guide their steps
    on earth,
And make the immortal spirit fit for
    heaven.
  This needful learning was their right
    of birth;
Further might each who chose it perse-
    vere;
No mind was lost for lack of culture
    here.

39

And that whole happy region swarm'd
    with life, . .
  Village and town; . . as busy bees in
    spring   230
In sunny days when sweetest flowers
    are rife,
  Fill fields and gardens with their
    murmuring.
Oh joy to see the State in perfect health!
Her numbers were her pride and power
    and wealth.

40

Then saw I, as the magic picture moved,
 Her shores enrich'd with many a port
  and pier ;
No gift of liberal Nature unimproved.
The seas their never failing harvest
  here   [fed
Supplied, as bounteous as the air which
Israel, when manna fell from heaven for
 bread.   240

41

Many a tall vessel in her harbours lay,
 About to spread its canvass to the
  breeze,
Bound upon happy errand to convey
 The adventurous colonist beyond the
  seas,
Toward those distant lands, where
 Britain blest
With her redundant life the East and
 West.

42

The landscape changed ; . . a region
 next was seen,
 Where sable swans on rivers yet un-
  found   [green ;
Glided through broad savannahs ever
Innumerous flocks and herds were
 feeding round,   250
And scatter'd farms appear'd and
 hamlets fair
And rising towns, which made another
 Britain there.

43

Then, thick as stars which stud the
 moonless sky,   [seen ;
 Green islands in a peaceful sea were
Darken'd no more with blind idolatry,
 Nor curst with hideous usages obscene,
But heal'd of leprous crimes, from
 butchering strife
Deliver'd, and reclaim'd to moral life.

44

Around the rude Morai, the temple now
 Of truth, hosannahs to the Holiest
  rung :   260
There from the Christian's equal marriage-vow,
 In natural growth the household
  virtues sprung ;

Children were taught the paths of
 heavenly peace,
And age in hope look'd on to its release.

45

The light those happy Islanders enjoy'd,
 Good messengers from Britain had
  convey'd ;
(Where might such bounty wiselier be
 employ'd ?)
 One people with their teachers were
  they made,
Their arts, their language, and their
 faith the same,
And blest in all, for all they blest the
 British name.   270

46

Then rose a different land, where loftiest
 trees
 High o'er the grove their fan-like
  foliage rear ;
Where spicy bowers upon the passing
 breeze
Diffuse their precious fragrance far
 and near ;
And, yet untaught to bend his massive
 knee,
Wisest of brutes, the elephant roams free.

47

Ministrant there to health and public
 good,
 The busy axe was heard on every side,
Opening new channels, that the noxious
 wood
 With wind and sunshine might be
  purified,   280
And that wise Government, the general
 friend,
Might every where its eye and arm
 extend.

48

The half-brutal Bedah came from his
 retreat,
 To human life by human kindness
  won ;
The Cingalese beheld that work complete
 Which Holland in her day had well
  begun ;   [reign,
The Candian, prospering under Britain's
Blest the redeeming hand which broke
 his chain.

49

Colours and castes were heeded there no
more ;
  Laws which depraved, degraded, and
  opprest,   290
Were laid aside, for on that happy shore
  All men with equal liberty were blest ;
And through the land the breeze upon
  its swells
  Bore the sweet music of the sabbath
  bells.

50

Again the picture changed ; those Isles
  I saw
  With every crime thro' three long
  centuries curst,
While unrelenting Avarice gave the law;
  Scene of the injured Indians' sufferings
  first,
Then doom'd, for Europe's lasting
  shame, to see
The wider-wasting guilt of Slavery. 300

51

That foulest blot had been at length
  effaced ;
  Slavery was gone, and all the power
  it gave,
Whereby so long our nature was debased,
  Baleful alike to master and to slave.
O lovely Isles ! ye were indeed a sight
To fill the spirit with intense delight !

52

For willing industry and cheerful toil
  Perform'd their easy task, with Hope
  to aid ;
And the free children of that happy soil
  Dwelt each in peace beneath his
  cocoa's shade ; ..   310
A race, who with the European mind,
The adapted mould of Africa combined.

53

Anon, methought that in a spacious
  Square,
  Of some great town the goodly orna-
  ment,
Three statues I beheld, of sculpture
  fair :
  These, said the Muse, are they whom
  one consent

Shall there deem worthy of the purest
  fame ; ..
Knowest thou who best such gratitude
  may claim ?

54

Clarkson, I answer'd, first ; whom to
  have seen
  And known in social hours may be my
  pride,   320
Such friendship being praise ; and one,
  I ween,   [side,
  Is Wilberforce, placed rightly at his
Whose eloquent voice in that great cause
  was heard
So oft and well. But who shall be the
  third ?

55

Time, said my Teacher, will reveal the
  name
  Of him who with these worthies shall
  enjoy
The equal honour of enduring fame ; ..
  He who the root of evil shall destroy,
And from our Laws shall blot the
  accursed word
Of Slave, shall rightly stand with them
  preferr'd.   330

56

Enough ! the Goddess cried ; with that
  the cloud
  Obey'd, and closed upon the magic
  scene :
Thus much, quoth she, is to thine hopes
  allow'd ;
  Ills may impede, delays may intervene,
But scenes like these the coming age will
  bless,
If England but pursue the course of
  righteousness.

57

On she must go progressively in good,
  In wisdom and in weal, .. or she must
  wane.   [flood,
Like Ocean, she may have her ebb and
  But stagnates not. And now her path
  is plain :   340
Heaven's first command she may fulfil
  in peace,
Replenishing the earth with her increase.

58

Peace she hath won, . . with her victorious hand
 Hath won through rightful war auspicious peace ;
Nor this alone, but that in every land
 The withering rule of violence may cease.   [crown'd !
Was ever War with such blest victory
Did ever Victory with such fruits abound !

59

Rightly for this shall all good men rejoice,
 They most who most abhor all deeds of blood ;   350
Rightly for this with reverential voice
 Exalt to Heaven their hymns of gratitude ;
For ne'er till now did Heaven thy country bless
With such transcendent cause for joy and thankfulness.

60

If they in heart all tyranny abhor,
 This was the fall of Freedom's direst foe;
If they detest the impious lust of war,
 Here hath that passion had its overthrow ; . .
As the best prospects of mankind are dear,
Their joy should be complete, their prayers of praise sincere.   360

61

And thou to whom in spirit at this hour
 The vision of thy Country's bliss is given,
Who feelest that she holds her trusted power
 To do the will and spread the word of Heaven, . .
Hold fast the faith which animates thy mind,
And in thy songs proclaim the hopes of humankind.

MISCELLANEOUS POETICAL REMAINS.

FRAGMENTARY THOUGHTS

OCCASIONED BY HIS SON'S DEATH.[1]

THY life was a day, and, sum it well,
life is but a week of such days,—with
how much storm, and cold, and darkness ! Thine was a sweet spring holiday,
—a vernal Sabbath, all sunshine, hope,
and promise.

_____

                        and that name
In sacred silence buried, which was still
At morn and eve the never-wearying theme
Of dear discourse.

_____

[1] Letter to Mr. W. Taylor, March, 1817.
'I have begun a desultory poem in blank
verse, pitched in a higher key than Cowper's,
and in a wiser strain of philosophy than
Young's ; but as yet I have not recovered
heart enough to proceed with it ; nor is it
likely that it will be published during my
life.'

                        playful thoughts
Turn'd now to gall and esel.

_____

He to whom Heaven in mercy hath assign'd
Life's wholesome wormwood, fears no bitterness when
From th' hand of Death he drinks the Amreeta cup.

_____

Beauties of Nature,—the passion of my youth,
Nursed up and ripen'd to a settled love,
Whereto my heart is wedded.

_____

Feeling at Westminster, when summer evening sent a sadness to my heart,
and I sate pining for green fields, and
banks of flowers, and running streams,
—or dreaming of Avon and her rocks
and woods.

_____

No more great attempts, only a few
autumnal flowers, like second prim-
roses, &c.

They who look for me in our Father's
      kingdom
Will look for Him also ; inseparably
Shall we be so remember'd.

            The Grave the house of Hope :
It is the haven whither we are bound
On the rough sea of life, and thence she
      lands
In her own country, on the immortal
      shore.

                        Come, then,
Pain and Infirmity—appointed guests,
My heart is ready.

                        My soul
Needed perhaps a longer discipline,
Or sorer penance, here.

A respite something like repose is gain'd
While I invoke them, and the troubled
      tide
Of feeling, for a while allay'd, obeys
A tranquillising influence, that might
      seem
By some benign intelligence dispensed,
Who lends an ear to man.
                        They are not, though,
Mere unrealities : rather, I ween,
The ancient Poets, in the graceful garb
Of fiction, have transmitted earliest
      truths,
Ill understood ; adorning, as they
      deem'd,
With mythic tales things erringly
      received,
And mingling with primeval verities
Their own devices vain. For what to us
Scripture assures, by searching proof
      confirm'd,
And inward certainty of sober Faith,
Tradition unto them deliver'd down
Changed and corrupted in the course of
      time,
And haply also by delusive art
Of Evil Powers.————

IMAGINATION AND REALITY

The hill was in the sunshine gay and
      green,
The vale below could not be seen ;
      A cloud hung over it,
A thin white cloud, that scarce was
      seen to fly,
So slowly did it flit ;
Yet cloud methinks I err in calling it,
It spread so evenly along the sky.
   It gave the hills beyond a hue
      So beautiful and blue,
That I stood loitering for the view : 10
Loitering and musing thoughtfully
      stood I,
      For well those hills I knew,
And many a time had travell'd them
      all o'er ;
Yet now such change the hazy air had
      wrought,
      That I could well have thought
I never had beheld the scene before.
      But while I gazed the cloud was
      passing by ;
On the slow air it slowly travell'd on,
Eftsoon and that deceitful haze was
      gone,
      Which had beguiled me with its
      mockery ;   20
And all things seem'd again the things
      they were.
Alas ! but then they were not half so
      fair
As I had shaped them in the hazy air !

ADDITIONAL FRAGMENT

OCCASIONED BY THE DEATH OF HIS SON

Daughters of Jove and of Mnemosyne,
Pierian sisters, in whose sacred paths,
From my youth up these duteous feet
      have trod ;
Ye who with your awakening influence
      warm'd
My youthful heart, disdaining not to
      accept
The first fruits of an offering immature,
And who into my riper strains have
      breathed
Truth, knowledge, life, and immortality;
An earthly heritage indefeasible   9

Assuring to me thus, with Bards of old,
With the blind Grecian of the rocky isle,
The Mantuan, and the Tuscan; and,
    more dear
To me than all of elder Rome and
    Greece,
My honour'd master, who on Mulla's
    side,
Mid the green alders, mused his heavenly
    lay;
Be with me, O ye Nymphs of Castaly
Divine, be with me now; ye who so oft
Have given me strength, and confidence,
    and joy,
O give me comfort now!—to you I look
In sorrow, who in gladness heretofore,
Yet never but with deepest faith devout,
Have wooed your visitation. For no
    strain   22
Of querulous regret I ask your aid,
Impatient of the chastening hand of
    Heaven;
But rather that your power may
    discipline
Thoughts that will rise—may teach me
    to control
The course of grief, and in discursive
    flight
Leading my spirit, sometimes through
    the past,
Sometimes with bold yet not irreverent
    reach
Into the region of futurity,   30
Abstract her from the sense of present
    woe.

Short time hath pass'd since from my
    pilgrimage
To my rejoicing home restored I sung
A true thanksgiving song of pure
    delight.
Never had man whom Heaven would
    heap with bliss
More happy day, more glad return than
    mine;
Yon mountains with their wintry robe
    were clothed
When, from a heart that overflow'd
    with joy,
I pour'd that happy strain. The snow
    not yet
Upon their mountain sides hath disap-
    pear'd   40
Beneath the breath of spring, and in the
    grave
Herbert is laid, the child who welcomed
    me
With deepest love upon that joyful
    day;
Herbert, my only and my studious
    boy,
The sweet companion of my daily
    walks,
Whose sports, whose studies, and whose
    thoughts I shared,
Yea in whose life I lived, in whom I saw
My better part transmitted and im-
    proved,
Child of my heart and mind, the flower
    and crown   49
Of all my hopes and earthly happiness.

APPENDIX

A LIST OF POEMS NOT REPRINTED IN THE PRESENT EDITION

(a) Poems published in the collected edition of 1837-8.

JOAN OF ARC.

THE VISION OF THE MAID OF ORLEANS.

THE TRIUMPH OF WOMAN.

WAT TYLER.

POEMS CONCERNING THE SLAVE TRADE.
Six Sonnets.
To the Genius of Africa.
The Sailor who had served in the Slave Trade.

BOTANY BAY ECLOGUES :—
Elinor.
Humphrey and William.
John, Samuel, and Richard.
Frederick.

SONNETS :—
I. 'Go, Valentine, and tell that lovely maid.'
II. 'Think, Valentine, as speeding on thy way.'
III. 'Not to thee, Bedford, mournful is the tale.'

MONODRAMAS :—
Sappho.
Ximalpoca.
The Wife of Fergus.
Lucretia.
La Caba.

THE AMATORY POEMS OF ABEL SHUFFLEBOTTOM :—
Sonnets.
Love Elegies.

LYRIC POEMS.
To Horror.
To a Friend.
The Soldier's Wife.
The Chapel Bell.
To Hymen.
Written on the First of December.
Written on the First of January.
Written on Sunday Morning.
The Race of Banquo.
Written in Alentejo.
To Recovery.
Youth and Age.
The Oak of our Fathers.
The Battle of Pultowa.
Translation of a Greek Ode on Astronomy.
Gooseberry Pie.
To a Bee.
The Destruction of Jerusalem.
The Death of Wallace.
The Spanish Armada.
St. Bartholomew's Day.

SONGS OF THE AMERICAN INDIANS :—
The Huron's Address to the Dead.
The Peruvian's Dirge Over the Body of his Father.
Song of the Araucans during a Thunderstorm.
Song of the Chikkasah Widow.
The old Chikkasah to his Grandson.

OCCASIONAL PIECES :—
The Pauper's Funeral.
The Soldier's Funeral.

OCCASIONAL PIECES (*continued*)
  On the Death of a Favourite Old
    Spaniel.
  Autumn.
  The Victory.

ENGLISH ECLOGUES :—
  The Grandmother's Tale.
  The Sailor's Mother.
  The Witch.
  The Last of the Family.
  The Wedding.

NONDESCRIPTS :—
  Written the Winter after the Installa-
    tion at Oxford, 1793.
  Snuff.
  Cool Reflections during a Midsummer
    Walk.
  The Pig.
  The Dancing Bear.
  The Filbert.
  Robert the Rhymer's True and
    Particular Account of Himself.

ODES.
  Written during the War with
    America.
  CARMINA AULICA : WRITTEN IN 1814,
    ON THE ARRIVAL OF THE ALLIED
    SOVEREIGNS IN ENGLAND.
  Ode to His Royal Highness the
    Prince Regent of the United
    Kingdom.

ODES (*continued*)
  Ode to His Imperial Majesty,
    Alexander the First, Emperor of
    All the Russias.
  Ode to His Majesty, Frederick
    William the Fourth, King of
    Prussia.
  On the Battle of Algiers.
  On the Death of Queen Charlotte.
  Ode for St. George's Day.
  Ode Written after the King's Visit
    to Ireland.
  Ode Written after the King's Visit
    to Scotland.
  The Warning Voice.
  On the Portrait of Bishop Heber.

BALLADS AND METRICAL TALES.
  Old Christoval's Advice.
  King Charlemain.
  The King of the Crocodiles.
  King Ramiro.
  Gonzalo Hermiguez.
  The Surgeon's Warning.

ALL FOR LOVE.

THE PILGRIM TO COMPOSTELLA.

CARMEN NUPTIALE — The Lay of the
  Laureate.

A VISION OF JUDGEMENT.

(*b*) Poems published in ' Oliver Newman : With Other Poetical
Remains ' (1845).

OLIVER NEWMAN
Short Passages of Scripture, Rhythmically Arranged or Paraphrased.
Madrigal, Translated from Luis Martin.
Mohammed ; a Fragment Written in 1799.

(*c*) Poems published in 'Robin Hood . . . a Fragment. By the late Robert
Southey and Caroline Southey. With Other Fragments and Poems by R. S.
and C. S.' (1847).

Robin Hood, Part I.
The Three Spaniards.
March.

Apart from the poems mentioned in the foregoing list there were many early pieces which Southey did not see fit to republish in 1837–8. The curious in such matters may search for them over the signature 'Bion' in *Poems by Robert Lovell and Robert Southey*, 1795; in *The Annual Anthology* for 1799 and 1800;[1] and in *Letters from Spain and Portugal*, 1797. Three or four poems sent by Southey to Daniel Stuart, editor of *The Morning Post*, are to be found printed in *Letters from the Lake Poets*, ed. E. H. Coleridge, 1889; and a few stray verses lie scattered among the volumes of his published correspondence. Southey's contribution to *The Fall of Robespierre* (1794) may be found printed in Coleridge's *Poetical Works*, ed. J. Dykes Campbell, pp. 216–225. Of that notable drama Coleridge was responsible for the first Act; the second and third were written by Southey in two days, 'as fast as newspapers could be put into blank verse.' A poetical address to Amos Cottle appeared in the latter's volume of *Icelandic Poetry*, 1797. There are probably other verses contributed by Southey to *The Morning Post*, *The Courier*, and other newspapers still lying unclaimed and uncollected in the columns in which they first saw the light. But the bulk of the pieces which he did not republish are to be found in the volumes mentioned above.

---

[1] In *The Annual Anthology* Southey's contributions are to be found sometimes over his own name, sometimes over the signatures R. S.,—R.,—R. S. Y.,—S.,—Erthusyo,— Theoderit,—Abel Shufflebottom,—or Byondo ; and occasionally without any signature at all. Of the unsigned pieces a few were reprinted in the collected edition of his Poetical Works, in 1837–8. According to Alexander Dyce's MS. notes in the two volumes of *The Annual Anthology* formerly belonging to Southey (now in the Dyce collection at the Victoria and Albert Museum), Southey was also the author of the verses which appear without a signature in vol. 1, pp. 22, 36, 52, 134, 137, 139, 145, 208.

NOTES

N.B. In the references in these Notes, *Life* = *The Life and Correspondence of Robert Southey* (edited by his son, Cuthbert Southey, 6 vols., 1849, 1850); *Warter* = *Selections from the Letters of Robert Southey* (edited by J. W. Warter, 4 vols., 1856).

THALABA THE DESTROYER

Written July 1799–July 1800 ; published in two volumes, 12mo, by Longman and Rees, in 1801. A second edition was published by Longman in 1809. This edition is more heavily stopped than that of 1801, to the great improvement of the sense ; and the variations from the 1801 text are numerous and important. The mottoes to the different books also appeared first in the 1809 edition, and the notes were much amplified and placed at the end of each book, instead of at the bottom of the page. A third edition appeared in 1814, differing from the last only in having the stanzas numbered, and in the lapidary arrangement of the lines. Southey introduced many minor corrections when he finally revised the poem for publication in 1837.

I am indebted to the kindness of Mr. E. H. Coleridge for permission to print the following extract from a letter from S. T. Coleridge to Daniel Stuart, editor of *The Morning Post*. The letter bears date, Sept. 19, 1801 :—

' Have you seen the Thalaba ? It is not altogether a poem exactly to my taste ; there are, however, three uncommonly fine passages in it. The first [1] in Volume 1st, beginning (page 130) at the words, "It was the wisdom and the will of Heaven," continued to the end of the 3rd line, page 134 : then omitting the intermediate pages, pass on to page 147, and recommence with the words "Their father is their priest ", to the last line of page 166, concluding with the words " Of Thalaba went by ". This would be a really good extract, and I am sure none of the Reviews will have either feeling or taste to select . . .

' The next extract [2] is in Volume 2, page 126, beginning at the words, " All waste, no sign of life," &c., to page 131, ending with the words, " She clapped her hands for joy."

' The third passage [3] is very short, and uncommonly lyrical ; indeed, in versification and conception, superior to anything I have ever seen of Southey's. It must begin at the third line of page 142, Volume 2nd, and be entitled " Khawla ", or " The Enchantress's Incantation ". " Go out, ye lights, quoth Khawla," &c.—and go on to the last words of page 143.'—*Letters from the Lake Poets*, pp. 20–2.

PAGE 23. Book I, Stanza 1. As an illustration of the way in which Southey altered and improved his poems after their first publication, it is interesting

---

[1] See Book III, Stanzas 16–25.
[2] See Book VIII, Stanzas 22–30.
[3] See Book IX, Stanza 6 to the end of Stanza 9, line 2.

to note the changes introduced into the opening stanza of *Thalaba*. In the first edition the stanza ran as follows :—

> How beautiful is night !
> A dewy freshness fills the silent air,
> No mist obscures, no little cloud
> Breaks the whole serene of heaven :
> In full-orbed glory the majestic moon
> Rolls thro' the dark blue depths.
> Beneath her steady ray
> The desert circle spreads,
> Like the round ocean, girdled with the sky
> How beautiful is night !

The stanza first appeared in its present form in the second edition of the poem.

PAGE 27. Book I, l. 246. *The hunter Afri.* So edn. 1837–8. I have retained this reading with hesitation, suspecting it to be a misprint for ' The hunter African ' of edd. 1801, 1809.

PAGE 33, ll. 656, 657. ' The angel of death ', say the Rabbis, ' holdeth his sword in his hand at the bed's head, having on the end thereof three drops of gall; the sick man, spying this deadly Angel, openeth his mouth with fear, and then those drops fall in, of which one killeth him, the second maketh him pale, the third rotteth and purifieth.'—Purchas. (S.)

PAGE 35. Book II, ll. 165–70. ' These lines contain the various opinions of the Mahommedans respecting the intermediate state of the Blessed, till the Day of Judgement.' (S.)

Zemzem-well. According to Mahommedan tradition Ishmael, when a new-born babe, made a way for a spring to break forth by dancing with his little feet upon the ground. But the water came forth with such abundance and violence that Hagar could not drink of it. Abraham, coming to the place, stayed the force of the spring, and made Hagar and Ishmael drink. ' The said spring is to this day called Semsem, from Abraham making use of that word to stay it.'—Olearius. (S.)

PAGE 58. Book V, l. 72. *City of Peace.* Almanzor, the founder of Bagdad, named his new city Dar-al-Salam, the City of Peace. (S.)

l. 78. *Thy founder the Victorious.* ' Almanzor signifies the Victorious.' (S.)

PAGE 61, l. 282. ' The Mussulmauns use, like the Roman Catholics, a rosary of beads, called Tusbah, or implement of praise . . .'—Note to the Bahar-Danush. (S.)

PAGE 62, ll. 297–9. ' The Mahummedans believe that the decreed events of every man's life are impressed in divine characters on his forehead, though not to be seen by mortal eye.'—Note to the Bahar-Danush. (S.)

l. 307. ' Zohak was the fifth King of the Pischdadian dynasty, lineally descended from Shedad, who perished with the tribe of Ad. Zohak murdered his predecessor, and invented the punishments of the cross and of flaying alive. The Devil, who had long served him, requested at last, as a recompence, permission to kiss his shoulders ; immediately two serpents grew there, who fed upon his flesh, and endeavoured to get at his brain. The Devil now suggested a remedy, which was to quiet them by giving them every day the brains of two men, killed for that purpose : this tyranny lasted long ; till a blacksmith of Ispahan, whose children had been nearly all slain to feed the King's serpents, raised his leather apron as the standard of revolt, and deposed Zohak. Zohak, say the Persians, is still living in the cave of his punishment.'—D'Herbelot. Olearius. (S.)

PAGE 69.   Book VI, ll. 287-96.   'In the Caherman Nameh, the Dives having taken in war some of the Peris, imprisoned them in iron cages which they hung from the highest trees they could find.   There, from time to time, their companions visited them with the most precious odours.   These odours were the usual food of the Peris, and procured them also another advantage, for they' prevented the Dives from approaching or molesting them.   The Dives could not bear the perfumes, which rendered them gloomy and melancholy whenever they drew near the cage in which a Peri was suspended.'—D'Herbelot.   (S.)

PAGE 74.   Book VII, l. 184.   *Zaccoum's fruit accurst.*   According to the Koran the Zaccoum is a tree which issues from the bottom of Hell.   Its fruit is to be eaten by the damned.   (S.)

l. 194.   The Arabian women 'of the tribe of Himiar, or of the Homerites, are early exercised in riding the horse, and in using the bow, the lance, and the javelin.'—Marigny.

PAGE 75, l. 264.   *The Paradise of Sin.*   'The story is told by many writers, but with such difference of time and place as wholly to invalidate its truth, even were the circumstances more probable.'   (S.)   Southey quotes, among others, a long account from Sir John Maundeville.

PAGE 85.   Book VIII, Stanza 36.   'How came Mohareb to be Sultan of this island ?   Every one who has read *Don Quixote* knows that there are always islands to be had by adventurers.   He killed the former Sultan, and reigned in his stead.   What could not a Domdanielite perform ?   The narration would have interrupted the flow of the main story.'   (S.)

PAGE 91.   Book IX, ll. 413-16.   'A thicket of balm trees is said to have sprung up from the blood of the Moslem slain at Beder.'   (S.)   Southey in his note ad loc. quotes Pausanias and other writers as speaking of vipers which were rendered innocuous by feeding on the juice of the balsam-tree.

PAGE 92, l. 492.   *That most holy night.*   'The night, Leileth-ul-cadr, is considered as being particularly consecrated to ineffable mysteries.   There is a prevailing opinion, that a thousand secret and invisible prodigies are performed on this night ; that all the inanimate beings then pay their adoration to God ; that all the waters of the sea lose their saltness, and become fresh at these mysterious moments ; that such, in fine, is its sanctity, that prayers said during this night are equal in value to all those which can be said in a thousand successive months. It has not, however, pleased God . . . to reveal it to the faithful . . .'—D'Ohsson. (S.)

PAGE 93.   Stanzas 44 and 45.   These stanzas, together with stanza 1 of Book X, replaced in 1809 a passage, unhappy alike in conception and in execution, which had appeared in the first edition.   This cancelled passage consisted of 126 lines—109 in Book IX, and 17 in Book X.   In it Mohareb and Khawla have learnt of Maimuna's treachery.   To further their revenge they resolve to secure 'the deadliest poison that the Devils know', namely, the last foam on the lips of a red-haired Christian who has been beaten to death.   Accordingly, on the following morning, Maimuna and Thalaba watch from the latter's prison the execution of the Christian victim.   Khawla catches the poison in a bowl.   The bowl bursts, and from the poison which falls upon the ground springs the Upas Tree of Death.   Khawla and Mohareb flee away in a whirlwind.   The prison walls fall with a crash : and Maimuna and Thalaba are borne in the Chariot of the Winds to the former's cave.

PAGE 102.   Book XI, Stanza 11.   ' "Simorg Anka", says my friend Mr. Fox, in a note to his Achmed Ardebeili, "is a bird or griffon of extraordinary strength and size (as its name imports, signifying as large as thirty eagles), which, according to the Eastern writers, was sent by the Supreme Being to subdue and chastise the rebellious Dives. It was supposed to possess rational faculties, and the gift of speech." . . .' (S.)

PAGE 106. Book XI, ll. 367-73. 'Some travellers may perhaps be glad to know that the spring from which this description was taken is near Bristol, about a mile from Stokes-Croft turnpike, and known by the name of the Boiling Well. Other and larger springs of the same kind, called the Lady Pools, are near Shobdon, in Herefordshire.' (S.)

PAGE 115. Book XII, l. 461. 'Araf is a place between the Paradise and the Hell of the Mahommedans; some deem it a veil of separation, some a strong wall. Others hold it to be a Purgatory, in which those believers will remain, whose good and evil works have been so equal, that they were neither virtuous enough to enter Paradise, nor guilty enough to be condemned to the fire of Hell . . .'—D'Herbelot. (S.)

THE CURSE OF KEHAMA

Written May 1801–Nov. 1809: published in one volume, 4to, by Longman in 1810. In the first edition the stanzas were unnumbered and differently divided. The variations in the text of the first and later editions are comparatively few and unimportant. A fourth edition was published in 1818.

There is a MS. of this poem in Southey's handwriting in the British Museum (No. 36,485). A note appended by Southey's brother, Captain Thomas Southey, R.N., states that this MS. 'was written for me and sent sheet by sheet in letters, the greater part of which were received on board His Majesty's *Dreadnought*, off the coast of France in 1809 '. The British Museum Catalogue says, ' the text in many passages differs from that of the poem as printed, agreeing generally with the original form as found in an autograph copy, begun May 28, 1806, now in possession of Miss Warter, the poet's granddaughter, the corrections made in which were embodied in the printed text.'

In the British Museum MS. there is no list of characters and no preface. The motto, ' Curses are like young chickens, &c. . .' is attributed to ' Uncle William ', and there is no Greek version of it. The motto in question was a saying of Southey's uncle William, a half-witted brother of Miss Tyler, with whom he lived. The Greek version and its mysterious reference are due to Coleridge. Southey has described William Tyler under the name of William Dove in *The Doctor, &c.*, Chapter X, P. I. and passim.

There is another MS. of *The Curse of Kehama*, bound up with a MS. of *Roderick*, in the Victoria and Albert Museum (number 480 in the Catalogue of MSS., in the Forster Collection). These MSS. were sent by Southey to W. S. Landor in sections, as the composition of the two poems proceeded. The MS. of *The Curse of Kehama* contains no list of characters, preface, or mottoes. The whole of it from Section VII onwards is in Southey's handwriting. The first section is dated May 28, 1806, and thus represents the original draught as it stood some two years before Southey first met Landor. The ending of the poem is identical with that in the British Museum MS. ;—see note on Section XXIV, below.

In an unpublished letter to Landor, now in the Victoria and Albert Museum, written at the end of the MS. of the first section of *Roderick*, and dated Keswick, July 14, 1810, Southey speaks of *The Curse of Kehama* as follows :—

' The structure of the poem is its main merit—in this point it is far superior to Thalaba,—in most other respects I am afraid I myself do not like it quite so well, and am well assured that most persons will like it even less,—or in

plainer language will dislike it more. About this I am perfectly indifferent.
It is a work sui generis, which like *Gebir* will find its own admirers, and I have
always sincerely echoed your original preface upon that point.'
See also *Landor's Works and Life*, by J. Forster (1876), vol. i, p. 110.

PAGE 139. Section VII, l. 197. *The lute of Nared.* In Hindoo legend Nared,
a divine son of Brahma, invented the Vina, or Indian lute. (S.)

PAGE 151. Section X, l. 262. *his Dragon foe.* Ra'hu, a dragon-like monster,
according to Hindoo legend strives during eclipses to wreak vengeance on the
Sun and Moon for having denounced a fraud which he had practised on the
gods. (S.)

PAGE 162. Section XIII, l. 131. *Voomdavee.* The wife of Veeshnoo, the
goddess of the earth and of patience. (S.).

PAGE 163, ll. 175-6. ' "The Hindoo poets frequently allude to the fragrant
juice which oozes, at certain seasons, from small ducts in the temples of the
male elephant, and is useful in relieving him from the redundant moisture
with which he is then oppressed; and they even describe the bees as allured
by the scent, and mistaking it for that of the sweetest flowers." Wilford,
Asiatic Researches.' (S.)

PAGE 191. Section XXI, l. 84. *that strange Indian bird.* 'The Chatookee.
They say it never drinks at the streams below, but, opening its bill when it
rains, it catches the drops as they fall from the clouds.'—*Periodical Accounts
of the Baptist Missionaries*, vol. ii, p. 309. (S.)

l. 88. *the footless fowl of Heaven :* sc. the bird of Paradise, which travellers
said was to be found in the Molucca Islands, born without legs. (S.)

PAGE 207. Section XXIV. In the British Museum MS. the poem ends
as follows after Stanza 23 :—

> ' Thus hath the will of destiny been done,'
>   Then said the Lord of Padalon.
> ' Thus are the secret ways of Heaven made known
>   And justified. Ye heirs of heavenly bliss,
>   Go to the Swerga Bowers,
>   And there recall the hours
>   Of endless happiness.
> For thee, Ladurlad, there is yet in store
> One glorious task. Return to Earth—restore
>   Justice and Peace, by Tyranny put down.
> Then shalt thou have thine everlasting crown,
>   And join thy best-beloved for evermore.'

RODERICK, THE LAST OF THE GOTHS

Written, Dec. 2, 1809–July 14, 1814 : published in one volume, 4to, by
Longman, in 1814. The text of 1838 differs only in a few unimportant particulars
from that of the first edition. The mottoes from Tacitus and *The Excursion*
first appeared in the second edition, published in 1815. The poem reached
a fourth edition early in 1816.

There is in the Victoria and Albert Museum a MS. of the first eighteen sections
of *Roderick*,—as they were sent successively by Southey to Landor,—bound
up with the corresponding MS. of *The Curse of Kehama*—(No. 480 in the Catalogue

of MSS. in the Forster Collection). Every section save the first is in Southey's handwriting At the end of Sections I, II, VI, VII, IX, X, XII, XIII, XIV, XVI, and XVII are letters or postscripts, all signed with Southey's initials, except the first, which is signed in full. The letter to Landor at the end of Section I is dated Keswick, July 14, 1810. The postmark on the last section (XVIII) bears date, Sept. 26, 1814.

In this MS. the poem is called 'Pelayo', for it was Southey's original intention that Pelayo should be its hero. As the work progressed, however, the character of Roderick assumed a more and more predominating importance. Accordingly, in sending Section VI to Landor, Southey writes to him (in an unpublished letter) as follows (Sept. 11, 1812) :—

'The next book is nearly finished. I believe I must go back to the fifth, and interpolate a passage introductory of Egilona, whose death I think of bringing forward in Book 8, and in whose character I must seek for such a palliation of the rape of Florinda as may make Roderick's crime not so absolutely incompatible with his heroic qualities as it now appears. The truth is that in consequence of having begun the story with Roderick I have imperceptibly been led to make him the prominent personage of the poem, and have given him virtues which it will be very difficult to make consistent with his fall.'

The description of Egilona, Section V, ll. 124–44, was subsequently interpolated with the object described above.

Southey justly regarded *Roderick* as his highest achievement as a poet. H. Crabb Robinson writes in his Diary for Sept. 15, 1816, 'Of his own works he (Southey) thinks *Don Roderick* by far the best.' And this statement is corroborated by a letter from Southey to Dr. Gooch, dated Nov. 30, 1814, in which he says, 'You have in Roderick the best which I have done, and, probably, the best that I shall do, which is rather a melancholy feeling for the author' (*Life*, vol. iv, p. 90).

Southey gives the following lively description of his feelings on the completion of this poem in an unpublished letter to his brother, Captain Thomas Southey, R.N., dated Thursday, 14 July, 1814, now in the British Museum :—

'Monday came and I continued at my task, still writing like a Lion—it was like going up a mountain, the termination seemed to recede as I advanced. So I was still at it on Tuesday middleday, when in came a Laker to interrupt me. . . . This morning I went again to work, and just at dinner-time finished a poem which was begun 2 December 1809. The last book has extended to 580 lines, and the whole work to 7,000, some twenty more or less.—Hourra ! your Serene Highness ! O be joyful St. Helen's, Auckland, and Greta Hall ! . . . I do not feel exactly as Gibbon did, who knew that it was impossible for him ever to execute another work of equal magnitude with his great history ; for I neither want subjects nor inclination for fresh attempts. But this poem has been 4½ years on hand, and had been thought of as many years before it was begun : and it is impossible not to feel how very doubtful it is whether I may ever again compleat one of equal extent, or of equal merit,—tho' never at any part of my life better disposed for it in will or in power than at the present time.'

It may be well to add here Charles Lamb's appreciation of the poem, as conveyed to Southey in a letter of May 6, 1815:—

'The story of the brave Maccabee', he wrote, 'was already, you may be sure, familiar to me in all its parts. I have, since the receipt of your present, read it quite through again, and with no diminished pleasure. . . . The parts I have been most pleased with, both on first and second readings, perhaps, are Florinda's palliation of Roderick's crime, confessed to him in his disguise—the retreat of the Palayos (sic) family first discovered—his being made king—" For acclamation one form must serve *more solemn for the breach of old observances.*" Roderick's vow is extremely fine, and his blessing on the vow of Alphonso :

> Towards the troops he spread his arms,
> As if the expanded soul diffused itself,
> And carried to all spirits *with the act*
> Its effluent inspiration

'It struck me forcibly that the feeling of these last lines might have been suggested to you by the Cartoon of Paul at Athens. Certain it is that a better motto or guide to that famous attitude can nowhere be found. I shall adopt it as explanatory of that violent but dignified motion.'

The Letters of C. Lamb, ed. Ainger, vol. i, pp. 290–2.

PAGE 210. Section I, l. 30. *the name of thy new conqueror.* 'Gibel-al-Tarif, the mountain of Tarif, is the received etymology of Gibraltar : Ben Hazel, a Granadan Moor, says expressly, that the mountain derived its name from this general.' (S.)

l. 69. 'Guadalete had been thus interpreted to Florez. (*España Sagrada,* t. ix, p. 53.)' (S.)

PAGE 221. Section III, ll. 99–105. 'The Roman Conimbrica stood about two leagues from the present Coimbra, on the site of Condeyxa Velha. Ataces, king of the Alanes, won it from the Sueves, and, in revenge for its obstinate resistance, dispeopled it, making all its inhabitants, without distinction of persons, work at the foundation of Coimbra, where it now stands . . . Ataces was an Arian, and therefore made the Catholic bishops and priests work at his new city, but his queen converted him.' (S.)

PAGE 223, l. 189. *Diogo's amorous lute.* 'Diogo Bernardes, one of the best of the Portugueze poets, was born on the banks of the Lima, and passionately fond of its scenery . . .' (S.)

PAGE 226, l. 326. The collected edition of 1838 and the one-volume edition reprinted from it read 'Yet' as the first word of this line,—clearly a misprint for the 'Yea' of 1814, which has been restored in the present edition.

PAGE 254. Section X. In sending this Section—perhaps the finest in the whole poem—to Landor, Southey thus writes (in an unpublished letter) of the difficulty which he had experienced in its composition : ' You have here a part of the poem so difficult to get over, even tolerably, that I verily believe, if I had at first thought of making Roderick anything more than a sincere penitent, this difficulty would have deterred me from attempting the subject. There will probably be much to amend in it hereafter,—but I think it is in the right strain, and that the passion is properly made diffuse.' (March 3, 1813.)

It may be added that the changes eventually made in the original draught of this section as it had been sent to Landor were comparatively few and unimportant.

PAGE 277. Section XV. In a letter to G. C. Bedford, of August 8, 1815 (*Warter,* ii, 420), Southey thus anticipates an obvious criticism upon this and other portions of the poem :—

' The strongest objection which has or can be urged against the poem is, that Roderick should not be recognized ; but the fact is strictly possible. A friend of mine (poor Charles Danvers), after a fortnight's absence, during which he had been very exposed to weather, sleeping out of doors, and in an open boat, and had endured the greatest anxiety (in assisting a man to escape to America, who would have been hanged for high treason, if he had been taken), was so altered as literally not to be recognized at the end of that time by an old servant of the family. Think, also, what a difference grey hairs will make; and how soon grief will produce this change has often been seen. When the Queen of France was murdered, her hair was perfectly white. This I have carefully marked in Roderick; I have also made his mother recognize him upon the first hint, and Swerian also. As for Julian, it is nowhere implied that he had ever seen Roderick; on the contrary, Africa was his home.'

PAGE 294. Section XVIII, l. 107. *orary*:—' a scarf or tippet to be worn upon the shoulders . . .' (S.)

l. 109. ' *Precious or auriphrygiate*, " Mitrae . . . triplex est species : una quae pretiosa dicitur, quia gemmis et lapidibus pretiosis vel laminis aureis, vel argenteis contexta esse solet ; altera auriphrygiata sine gemmis, et una laminis aureis vel argenteis ; sed vel aliquibus parvis margaritis composita, vel ex serico albo auro intermisto, vel ex tela aurea simplici sine laminis et margaritis ; tertia, quae simplex vocatur sine auro, . . ."—*Caeremoniale Episcoporum*, l. 1, c. 17.' (S.)

PAGE 315. Section XXI, ll. 424-34. ' The image of the clouds and the moon I saw from my chamber window at Cintra when going to bed, and noted it down with its application next morning. I have it at this moment distinctly before my eyes with all its accompanying earth-scenery.'
Letter from R. S. to C. W. W. Wynn, March 9, 1815. *Life*, iv, p. 107.

PAGE 321. Section XXIII, l. 31. ' The humma is a fabulous bird : the head over which its shadow once passes will assuredly be encircled with a crown.' —Wilkes, *S. of India*, v. i, p. 423. (S.)

SELECTED MINOR POEMS

PAGE 344. *The Dead Friend.* This poem was written in memory of Edmund Seward, of Balliol College, Oxford, who died in June, 1795. Seward had been one of the little band who originally entered upon the scheme of Pantisocracy, but he had soon realized that the plan was visionary and impracticable, and had ceased to support it. Southey writes as follows to G. C. Bedford, on June 15, 1795: ' Bedford,—he is dead; my dear Edmund Seward! after six weeks suffering. These, Grosvenor, are the losses that gradually wean us from life. May that man want consolation in his last hour, who would rob the survivor of the belief, that he shall again behold his friend ! You know not, Grosvenor, how I loved poor Edmund : he taught me all that I have of good.' (*Life*, i, p. 240.) And in a letter to J. Rickman of Oct. 5, 1807, he describes Seward as having been his ' nearest and dearest friend ' (*Warter*, ii, 20). There is another allusion to the sorrow of this loss in the ' Hymn to the Penates', lines 198-221.

PAGE 345. *Funeral Song for the Princess Charlotte of Wales.* The Princess Charlotte, daughter of George IV (then Prince Regent), and heir-presumptive to the throne, married Prince Leopold of Saxe-Coburg in 1816, and died in child-birth, Nov. 5, 1817.

PAGE 346, ll. 110-24. During the building of a mausoleum under St. George's Chapel, Windsor, an accidental opening was made by the workmen into the Henry VIII vault. Three coffins were visible in the vault,—two of them those of Henry VIII and Jane Seymour; and, as there was some doubt as to the burial-place of King Charles I, owing to a passage in Lord Clarendon's *History of the Rebellion* (iii, Part I, p. 393 [Oxford, 1807]), which states that unsuccessful search was made for the body shortly after the Restoration, the Prince Regent ordered that the third coffin in the vault should be examined and the doubtful point set at rest.

The examination was made on April 1, 1813, in the presence of the Prince Regent, the Duke of Cumberland, Count Münster, the Dean of Windsor, Benjamin Charles Stevenson, Esq., and Sir Henry Halford, the King's physician. The coffin was covered by a black velvet pall, and, when this was removed, was seen to bear the inscription, ' Charles I, 1648.' When the wrappings of the body were removed and the face exposed, the pointed beard and lower half of the countenance were found to be perfect, and one eye was visible at the first moment, though it disappeared immediately ; the nose, however, was defaced. The loose head was taken out and held up to view : the hair at the back was thick and of a dark-brown colour, while the beard was of a more reddish brown. The muscles at the back of the neck showed the traces of a heavy blow from a sharp instrument.

The head was then replaced, and the coffin closed ; and, after a cursory examination of the coffins of Henry VIII and Jane Seymour, the vault was closed.

The above particulars are drawn from a pamphlet in the Royal Library at Windsor, by Sir Henry Halford, entitled, ' An Account of what appeared on Opening the Coffin of King Charles the First in the Vault of King Henry the Eighth in St. George's Chapel at Windsor, on the First of April 1813.' I am indebted for this information to the kindness of the Honourable John Fortescue, Librarian of the Royal Library, Windsor.

PAGE 347. *My days among the Dead are past.* Cuthbert Southey, in quoting these lines in his Life of his father, adds the following interesting note :—

' I have an additional pleasure in quoting these lines here, because Mr. Wordsworth . . . once remarked that they possessed a peculiar interest as a most true and touching representation of my father's character. He also wished three alterations to be made in them, in order to reduce the language to correctness and simplicity. In the third line, because the phrase " casual eyes " is too unusual, he proposed—

" Where'er I chance these eyes to cast."

In the sixth line, instead of " converse ", " commune ", because, as it stands, the accent is wrong.

' In the second stanza, he thought—

" While I understand and feel, . . .
My checks have often been bedewed "

was a vicious construction grammatically, and proposed instead,—

" My pensive cheeks are oft bedewed."

These suggestions were made too late for my father to profit by them.'—*Life,* v, 110, n.

PAGE 348. *The Cataract of Lodore.* The origin of this poem is thus described in a letter from Southey to his brother Thomas, dated October 18, 1809 (*Warter,* ii, 168) :—

' I hope . . . you will approve of a description of the water at Lodore, made originally for Edith, and greatly admired by Herbert. In my mind it surpasses any that the tourists have yet printed. Thus it runs—" Tell the people how the water comes down at *Lodore* ? Why it comes thundering, and floundering, and thumping, and flumping, and bumping, and jumping, and hissing, and whizzing, and dripping, and skipping, and grumbling, and rumbling, and tumbling, and falling, and brawling, and dashing, and clashing, and splashing, and pouring, and roaring, and whirling, and curling, and leaping, and creeping, and sounding, and bounding, and clattering, and chattering, with a dreadful uproar,—and that way tho water comes down at *Lodore*." '

The doggerel thus first composed by Southey for the amusement of his eldest daughter was developed into the poem as we now know it for the benefit of his youngest child, Cuthbert, more than twelve years later, in 1822 (*Warter*, iii, 315).

There is a MS. of this poem in the British Museum (Ea. 1966), and another in the museum at Keswick. The former is an early draught. The former is dated 1822, and begins with the line ' Here it lies darkling '. It includes seventy-one lines instead of seventy-nine, as in the corresponding portion of the poem as printed, and there are a few unimportant variants. The following lines—in addition to the first forty-two—are wanting in the MS,—47–50, 60, 61, 71, and 93 ; and in some cases the order of the lines is slightly different.

PAGE 350. *Inscription II. Epitaph.* The Emma of this epitaph was the first wife of Southey's friend, General Peachey, who lived on Vicar's Island in Derwentwater. She had been a Miss Charter, of Bishop's Lydeard, near Taunton. She died in 1809 (*Life*, ii, 304 ; *Warter*, ii, 155).

PAGE 351. *Inscription III. At Barrosa.* Lieut.-General Graham (afterwards Lord Lynedoch) defeated the French army under Victor at Barrosa on March 5, 1811.

PAGE 352. *Inscription V. Epitaph.* This epitaph very probably may refer to the death of Southey's eldest son, Herbert, who died on April 17, 1816, in the tenth year of his age. See Notes on ' The Poet's Pilgrimage to Waterloo ' and on the ' Fragmentary Thoughts occasioned by his Son's Death ', pp. 762, 763.

PAGE 353. *Dedication of the Author's Colloquies on the Progress and Prospects of Society.* The Rev. H. Hill was Southey's maternal uncle. Southey had indeed found him, as he says, ' more than father.' Mr. Hill had paid the expenses of his education at Westminster and at Oxford, and took him to Lisbon with him in 1795. He encouraged Southey—on the occasion of the latter's second visit to Portugal in 1800—to undertake the writing of a History of Portugal, and, until he himself returned to England in 1807, continued to furnish his nephew with Spanish and Portuguese materials for that work. From that time onwards until his death he constantly corresponded with Southey with reference to the latter's literary employments. On his return to England, Mr. Hill married, and held successively the livings of Staunton-on-Wye and Streatham. One of his sons, Herbert, married Bertha Southey in 1839, and edited Southey's *Oliver Newman : With other Poetical Remains*, in 1845.

PAGE 357. *Ode written during the Negotiations with Buonaparte, in January,* 1814. The greater part of this ode was originally included in the *Carmen Triumphale*. In deference to the advice of J. W. Croker and Rickman Southey struck out from the *Carmen* five stanzas which were thought too vigorous for an official poem by the Poet Laureate : to these he added three other stanzas, and sent the whole as a separate ode to *The Courier*.

There is a MS. of this ode in the possession of the Rev. Canon Rawnsley. This MS. ends, as did the version first printed in *The Courier*, with the two following lines, subsequently cancelled,—

> Pluck from the Upstart's head thy sullied crown,
> Down with the Tyrant ! With the murderer down !

Professor Dowden has well characterized this ode as ' perhaps the loftiest chaunt of political invective, inspired by moral indignation, which our literature possesses.' And he observes further : ' Southey stood erect in the presence of power which he believed to be immoral, defied it and execrated it. That he did not perceive how, in driving the ploughshare of Revolution across Europe of the old régime, Napoleon was terribly accomplishing an inevitable and a beneficent work, may have been an error ; but it was an error to which no blame attaches, and in his fierce indictment he states, with ample support of facts, one entire side of the case. The ode is indeed more than a poem ; it is a historical document expressing the passion which filled many of the highest minds in England, and which at a later date was the justification of Saint Helena.' (*Poems by Robert Southey,* 'Golden Treasury' Series, Introd., pp. xxiv, xxv.)

PAGE 360. *The March to Moscow.* This doggerel march is included here among the Selected Minor Poems, both as being eminently characteristic of the writer and as in some ways complementary to the ' Ode written during the Negotiations with Buonaparte'. Southey wrote it to amuse his children. When it was originally published in *The Courier* the present fourth stanza was suppressed, and the fifth stanza was added later.

Stanza 4, l. 2. *He frightened Mr. Roscoe.* William Roscoe (1753–1831), historian, banker, and Whig M.P. for Liverpool 1806–7, was a strong advocate of peace with France, and published several pamphlets between 1793 and 1810 in support of such a policy.

PAGE 366. *The Old Woman of Berkeley.* There is a MS. of this ballad in the British Museum. It is in Mrs. Southey's handwriting, dated Martin Hall, Oct. 5 (1798), and was enclosed in a letter to Thomas Southey, in which Southey says of it, 'I like the ballad much.'

PAGE 378. *Inscription for a Coffee-Pot.* These lines, written in 1830, or early in 1831, explain themselves. They were, of course, never published by Southey, but were printed in a note, *Warter,* iv, pp. 203, 204. It turned out, when the coffee-pot had been chosen, that there was not room on it for the proposed inscription.

PAGE 385. *The Widow.* These lines are here printed as having given rise to one of the most famous parodies in the language. 'The Friend of Humanity and the Knife-Grinder' was written by Canning and Frere, and appeared in No. II of *The Anti-Jacobin* on Nov. 27, 1797.

The Old Man's Comforts. These lines are chiefly notable as the original of Lewis Carroll's brilliant parody in *Alice in Wonderland.*

PAGE 386. *To a Spider.* Charles Lamb's criticism of this poem is of interest. Writing to Southey on March 20, 1799, he says :—

' I am hugely pleased with your " Spider", " your old freemason," as you call him. The first three stanzas are delicious ; they seem to me a compound of Burns and Old Quarles, the kind of home-strokes where more is felt than strikes the ear ; a terseness, a jocular pathos, which makes one feel in laughter. The measure, too, is novel and pleasing. I could almost wonder Robert Burns in his lifetime never stumbled upon it. The fourth stanza is less striking, as being less original. The fifth falls off. It has no felicity of phrase, no old-fashioned phrase or feeling.

Young hopes, and love's delightful dreams

savour neither of Burns nor Quarles ; they seem more like shreds of many a modern sentimental sonnet. The last stanza hath nothing striking in it, if I except the two concluding lines, which are Burns all over.'

The Letters of Charles Lamb, ed. Ainger, i, 104, 105.

PAGE 394. *To Margaret Hill.* Margaret Hill, to whom this poem is addressed, was Southey's favourite cousin. He appears to have himself defrayed the expenses of her illness, which lasted for more than a year (*Warter,* i, 164). She died of consumption not long after Southey's return from Portugal in 1801.

PAGE 396. *Written immediately after reading the Speech of Robert Emmet.* Robert Emmet (1778–1803), a member of the United Irishmen, planned a rising against the English Government in Ireland, intending to seize Dublin Castle and to hold the Viceroy as a hostage. The rising took place on July 23, 1803, but was easily suppressed ; not, however, before the rioters had murdered Lord Kilwarden and Colonel Brown, whom they met on their march. Emmet had fled in horror at the violence of his followers, but was arrested a month later, tried for high treason on Sept. 19, sentenced to death, and executed on the following day.

PAGE 402. *To Charles Lamb.* These lines were not included in the collected edition of 1837–8, but are printed in the present edition because of their interest as a link in the relations between Southey and Charles Lamb. They were written in reply to a contemptuous review of Lamb's *Album Verses and Other Poems,* which appeared on July 10, 1830, in the *Literary Gazette,* of which paper William Jerdan was editor. The review in question contained the following passage : ' If anything could prevent our laughing at the present collection of absurdities, it would be a lamentable conviction of the blinding and engrossing nature of vanity. We could forgive the folly of the original composition, but cannot but marvel at the egotism which has preserved, and the conceit which has published.' Southey's lines were published in *The Times* on Aug. 6, 1830. They were his first public utterance concerning Lamb since the misunderstanding between them which had arisen out of Southey's allusion to the *Essays of Elia* in the *Quarterly Review* for January, 1823—Lamb's famous open letter to him of the following October—and their speedy reconciliation, so honourable to both the friends. Lamb was much touched, and wrote to Bernard Barton on Aug. 30, 1830 : ' How noble in Robert Southey to come forward for an old friend, who had treated him so unworthily ! ' (See E. V. Lucas, *Life of Charles Lamb,* one-vol. ed. (1907), pp. 508–14, 625 and 626.)

PAGE 403. *The Retrospect.* Corston (called Alston in the poem as originally published) is ' a small village about three miles from Bath, a little to the left of the Bristol road '. Southey passed a year there (1781–2) at a school kept by one Thomas Flower. His reminiscences of the time spent there are to be found in his *Life and Correspondence,* i, 46–58. He says of it, ' Here one year of my life was spent with little profit, and with a good deal of suffering. There could not be a worse school in all respects.'

PAGE 405, ll. 141 sqq. These lines describe a visit which Southey paid to Corston in 1793, after the house had ceased to be used as a school.

PAGE 409. *Hymn to the Penates,* l. 146. *Apega's sculptured form.* ' One of the ways and means of the tyrant Nabis. If one of his subjects refused to lend him money, he commanded him to embrace his Apega ; the statue of a beautiful woman so formed as to clasp the victim to her breast, in which a pointed dagger was concealed.' (S.)

　　ll. 173–5. *When that false Florimel . . . Dissolved away.* See Spenser, *Faerie Queene,* Book V, Canto iii, Stanza 24.

　　l. 203. Edmund Seward died in June, 1795. See Notes to ' The Dead Friend '.

PAGE 410, ll. 236, 237. *The solemn festival whose happiest rites Emblem'd equality.* The Saturnalia (S.).

PAGE 420. *The Devil's Walk.* The genesis of these lines, originally known as ' The Devil's Thoughts ', is told by Southey himself in stanzas 37–9. Coleridge, in a note in the 1829 edition of his poems, states that stanzas 1, 2, 3, and 15 were dictated by Southey. The remaining stanzas of the original version were presumably written in collaboration. The verses originally appeared in the *Morning*

Post of Sept. 6, 1790. The text, as then published, is printed in J. Dykes Campbell's edition of Coleridge's *Poetical Works*, pp. 621, 622. This first version included, sometimes in a modified form, stanzas 1, 2, 6, 7, 8, 9, 10, 14, 15, 16, 17, 18, 19, and 57, of the poem as finally printed by Southey in 1838.

The squib had a great circulation. In 1812 Shelley published his Imitation, 'The Devil's Walk,' and in 1813 Byron published his 'The Devil's Drive.' In 1826 Caroline Bowles urged Southey, in view of the confident assertions that Porson was the author, to publish the verses as his own, and so to set all doubts at rest. Southey was thus unfortunately moved to expand the lines until they reached their present form. Further particulars may be found in Dykes Campbell's edition of Coleridge's *Poetical Works*, loc. cit.

PAGE 422, ll. 65, 66. Richard Brothers, a crazy enthusiast, published *A Revealed Knowledge of the Prophecies and Times* (1794), and other similar works. He died in 1824.

l. 96. *That new Scotch performer.* Edward Irving, subsequently founder of the Catholic Apostolic Church, began to preach in London in 1822.

PAGE 423. Stanza 30. Richard Lalor Sheil (1791–1851), dramatist and politician; Daniel O'Connell (1775–1847); Sidney Smith (1771–1845); Joseph Hume (1777–1855), a prominent Radical M.P. from 1818 to 1855; Lord Brougham (1778–1868); Jeremy Bentham (1748–1832); Peter, seventh Baron King of Ockham (1776–1833); and James Warren Doyle (1786–1834), Roman Catholic bishop of Kildare and Leighlin, are here grouped together chiefly as having been prominent advocates of Catholic Emancipation.

PAGE 425. Stanza 57. 'If any one should ask who General —— meant, the Author begs leave to inform him that he did once see a red-faced person in a dream whom by the dress he took for a General; but he might have been mistaken, and most certainly he did not hear any names mentioned. In simple verity, the author never meant any one, or indeed any thing but to put a concluding stanza to his doggerel' (Coleridge's note in 1829).

INSCRIPTIONS

PAGE 429, xi. Juan of Padilla, a nobleman of Toledo, commanded the forces of the Comuneros, who rebelled against the government of Charles V in 1520. He was captured at Villalar on April 23, 1521, and was put to death on the following day (see *The Cambridge Modern History*, i, 372–5).

PAGE 432, xvii. Sir Arthur Wellesley defeated the French under de Laborde at Rolissa on Aug. 17, 1808, in his first battle in the Peninsula.

xviii. On Aug. 21, 1808, Sir Arthur Wellesley defeated the French under Junot at Vimeiro.

PAGE 433, xix. The battle of Coruña was fought on Jan. 16, 1809.

PAGE 434, xxi. Paul Burrard was a cousin of Caroline Bowles, who furnished Southey with some particulars about him. In a letter to Mrs. Hughes of Dec. 31, 1827, Southey says, writing of Caroline Bowles, 'The late Sir Harry Burrard was her uncle, and I suspect, was to have stood in another degree of relationship to her, if the battle of Corunna had not put an end to all her dreams of life. She has never expressly told me this, but that it was so I have no doubt' (*Warter*, iv, 82).

PAGE 435, xxii. Sir Arthur Wellesley effected the passage of the Douro in the face of Soult's army on May 12, 1809.

NOTES

759

PAGE 436, xxiii. On July 27 and 28, 1809, Sir Arthur Wellesley defeated the French under Victor at Talavera.

xxiv. Massena attacked Wellington's position on the heights of Busaco on Sept. 27, 1810, and was repulsed with a loss of over 4,000 killed, wounded, and missing. At the loftiest summit of the mountain ridge was a convent of Carmelites, where Wellington had fixed his headquarters.

PAGE 438, xxvi. Massena evacuated Santarem on March 5, 1811.

xxvii. Wellington defeated Massena at Fuentes D'Onoro on May 5, 1811.

xxviii. The Battle of Albuhera was fought on May 16, 1811.

PAGE 440, xxx. Wellington stormed Ciudad Rodrigo on Jan. 19, 1812. Major-General Craufurd (1764–1812) had won a great reputation as leader of the light division in the Peninsula. He was shot through the body at the very beginning of the assault on Ciudad Rodrigo, and died on Jan. 24. He was buried in the breach itself.

PAGE 441, xxxii. General (afterwards Sir Rowland and finally Lord) Hill, commanding a force of British and Spanish troops, surprised the French under General Girard at Arroyo Molinos in the early morning of Oct. 28, 1811, and drove them from the village with the loss of considerably more than half their number in killed, wounded, and prisoners.

PAGE 442, xxxiii. Barré Charles Roberts (1789–1810), second son of Edward Roberts, clerk of the pells in the exchequer, graduated B.A. at Christ Church in 1808. He was a keen antiquarian, and made a fine collection of English coins, now in the possession of the trustees of the British Museum. In Feb., 1809, he contributed to the first number of the *Quarterly Review* a review of Pinkerton's *Essay on Medals* He was seized with consumption in 1807, and died on Jan. 1, 1810. In 1814 there appeared *Letters and Miscellaneous Papers of Barré Charles Roberts, with a Memoir of his Life*, by a friend ; and the volume was noticed by Southey in the *Quarterly Review* for Jan., 1815.

PAGE 443, xxxv–xxxvii. The Caledonian Canal was completed on Oct. 30, 1822.

PAGE 453. *Epistle to Allan Cunningham.* This poem was written expressly for *The Anniversary*, of which annual Allan Cunningham was editor.

ll. 32–36. Michael Angelo Taylor (1757–1834), M.P. 1800–1802, and continuously from 1806 to 1834, introduced in 1821 a Bill (subsequently passed) ' for giving greater facility to the Prosecution and Abatement of Nuisances arising from Furnaces used in the working of Steam Engines'. He is now chiefly remembered in connexion with ' The Metropolitan Paving Act, 1817', commonly known as ' Michael Angelo Taylor's Act '.

l. 138. In the summer of 1825 Southey was laid up for three weeks under the surgeon's care at Leyden. The Bilderdijks took him into their house and showed him the greatest kindness. Southey revisited them in the following summer, and continued to correspond with them afterwards. Bilderdijk's wife had translated *Roderick* into Dutch verse (see Southey's Preface to the ninth volume of the 1837–8 ed. of his Poems, *supra*, p. 19).

In 1838 Southey printed at the end of this epistle the poem by Bilderdijk which had suggested it to him. It has not been thought worth while to reprint the Dutch original in the present edition.

ll. 252 sqq. The following extract from a letter from Southey to Caroline Bowles, dated Jan. 1, 1829, gives some explanation of the portraits referred to :—

' To assist you in the collection of portraits I must tell you what are attainable and what not. The first was engraved in the *European Magazine*, and is from a picture by Edridge. The Landlord exists only as a miniature here by poor Miss Betham. The Evangelical is in the *New Monthly Magazine*, and the French and German copies are of course not attainable in this country. Sir Smug is poor Nash's miniature. Sir Smouch belongs to the *Percy Anecdotes*. Smouch the Coiner is published for one shilling by a fellow named Lombard in the Strand. And the Minion is the mezzotinto from the villainous picture by Phillips.' (*The Correspondence of Robert Southey with Caroline Bowles*, p. 151.)

The picture by Edridge here referred to is presumably the pencil drawing made in 1804, formerly in the possession of G. C. Bedford, and now in the National Portrait Gallery.

MADOC

Begun 1794 (autumn): finally revised in the autumn of 1804: published in one vol., 4to, by Longman in 1805. A second edition appeared in 1807 and a fourth in 1815.

A MS. of 'Madoc in Wales' in Southey's writing, dated Oct. 29, 1804, is in the possession of Canon Rawnsley: the second volume of this MS., containing 'Madoc in Aztlan', is in the Keswick Museum.

PAGE 461. Part I, Section I, l. 43. *Aberfraw.* 'The palace of Gwynedd, or North Wales. Rhodri Mawr, about the year 873, fixed the seat of government here.' . . . (S.)

PAGE 467. Section III, l. 19. *Dinevawr.* 'Dinas Vawr, the Great Palace, the residence of the Princes of Deheubarth, or South Wales. This also was erected by Rhodri Mawr.' (S.)

l. 24. 'I have taken some liberties here with the history. Hoel kept possession of the throne nearly two years; he then went to Ireland to claim the property of his mother, Pyvog, the daughter of an Irish chieftain; in the meantime David seized the government. Hoel raised all the force he could to recover the crown, but after a severe conflict was wounded and defeated. He returned to Ireland with the remains of his army, which probably consisted chiefly of Irishmen, and there died of his wounds.—(*Cambrian Biography*).' (S.)

PAGE 475. Section IV, l. 184. *Gwenhidwy.* A mermaid. (S.)

PAGE 481. Section VI, l. 131. 'Islets of this kind, with dwelling huts upon them, were common upon the Lake of Mexico.'—Clavigero. (S.)

PAGE 496. Section XI, l. 13–17. 'By the principles of the Order a bard was never to bear arms, nor in any other manner to become a party in any dispute, either political or religious. . . .—Owen's Llyware Hen.' (S.)

PAGE 537. Part II, Section VI, l. 192. 'Snake-worship was common in America.'—Bernal Dias, p. 3. 7. 125. . . . .
'It can scarcely be necessary to say that I have attributed to the Hoamen such manners and superstitions as, really existing among the savage tribes of America, were best suited to the plan of the poem.' (S.)

PAGE 545. Section IX, l. 16. *Elmur and Aronan.* Bards who had borne arms. Aronan was one of three known as 'the three Bards of the Ruddy Spear.' (S.)

PAGE 547, ll. 99–106. 'Tezcalipoca was believed to arrive first, because he was the youngest of the Gods, and never waxed old. . . .' (S.)

l. 107. *Mexitli, woman-born.* 'The history of Mexitli's birth is related in the poem, Part II, Section XXI.' (S.)

l. 111. *Quetzalcoal.* 'God of the Winds.' (S.)

PAGE 548, l. 161. ' The Gods of the conquered nations were kept fastened and caged in the Mexican temples.' (S.)

PAGE 550. Section X, l. 66. *Coatlantona.* ' " The mother of Mexitli, who, being a mortal woman, was made immortal for her son's sake, and appointed Goddess of all herbs, flowers, and trees."—Clavigero.' (S.)

PAGE 556. Section XII, l. 85. *Tlalocan.* ' The Paradise of Tlaloc.' (S.)

PAGE 567. Section XV, l. 94. ' " An old priest of the Tlatelucas, when they were at war with the Mexicans, advised them to drink the holy beverage before they went to battle ; this was made by washing the Stone of Sacrifice ; the king drank first, and then all his chiefs and soldiers in order ; it made them eager and impatient for the fight."—*Torquemada,* l. ii, c. 58.' (S.)

PAGE 602. Section XXVII, ll. 35–48. ' My excuse for this insignificant agency, as I fear it will be thought, must be that the fact itself is historically true ; by means of this omen the Aztecas were induced to quit their country, after a series of calamities. The leader who had address enough to influence them was Huitziton, a name which I have altered to Yuhidthiton for the sake of euphony ; the note of the bird is expressed in Spanish and Italian thus, *tihui* ; the cry of the peewhit cannot be better expressed.' (S.)

BALLADS AND METRICAL TALES

PAGE 636. *St. Gualberto.* George Burnett (1776 ?–1811) was a friend of Southey at Balliol, and one of those who joined in the scheme of ' pantisocracy '. His erratic disposition made his life ' a series of unsuccessful attempts in many professions '. He published in 1807 a *View of the Present State of Poland,* and also edited *Specimens of English Prose Writers* (1807) and a selection from Milton's Prose Works (1809). For the last two years of his life his friends and relations saw and heard nothing of him, and he died in the Marylebone Infirmary in Feb., 1811.

PAGE 644. *Roprecht the Robber.* There is a MS. of this ballad (undated) in the British Museum, and another in the possession of Canon Rawnsley.

A TALE OF PARAGUAY

This poem was begun in 1814, laid aside for long intervals, and only finished on Feb. 24, 1825. It was published by Longman in one volume, 12mo, in 1825.

PAGE 657. Dedication, ll. 6–14. Southey first made the acquaintance of John May at Lisbon in 1795–6, and thus began a lifelong friendship.

l. 18. Southey's eldest child, Margaret, died in August 1803, being then not quite a year old.

PAGE 672. Canto II, l. 249. *And Father was his name.* ' Tupa. It is the Tupi and Guarani name for Father, for Thunder, and for the Supreme Being.' (S.)

PAGE 681. Canto III, ll. 168–71. In 1822 Sara Coleridge, who, with her mother, was still living at Greta Hall, had published (doubtless at Southey's suggestion) a translation in three volumes of Dobrizhoffer's *Account of the Abipones.*

THE POET'S PILGRIMAGE TO WATERLOO

This poem was published by Longman in one volume, 12mo, in 1816. Southey had toured in Holland and Belgium in Sept. Oct., 1815, with Mrs. Southey, their eldest daughter Edith, Edward Nash, the artist, and one or two other friends. The Southeys reached Greta Hall on their return on Dec. 6, 1815; and a melancholy interest attaches to the Proem to 'The Poet's Pilgrimage', in which that joyous homecoming is so feelingly described. Herbert, Southey's only boy, the very light of his eyes, was taken ill in the following March, and died on April 17, 1816. He was in the tenth year of his age. Southey never recovered from this blow. 'The head and flower of his earthly happiness' had been, as he said, 'cut off.' And a fresh bitterness must, if possible, have been added to his sorrow by the fact that he was obliged at the time to occupy himself in correcting the proofs of this poem, which had been written in such joy and thankfulness of heart.

Cp. the 'Fragmentary Thoughts occasioned by his Son's Death', and the 'Additional Fragment,' pp. 740–2.

PAGE 699. Proem, l. 51. *Her twin-like comrade.* Sara Coleridge, who was born in 1802, and had been brought up at Greta Hall.

PAGE 700, l. 109. *The aged friend serene.* Mrs. Wilson. She had been house-keeper to Mr. Jackson, the former owner of Greta Hall, and continued to live there until her death in 1820.

l. 112. *The aunts.* Mrs. Coleridge and Mrs. Lovell.

PAGE 701. Part I, i, l. 13. Charles Martel defeated the Saracens at Tours on Oct. 10, 732.

PAGE 702, l. 38. *Ourique's consecrated field.* Alfonso, count or duke of Portugal, is said to have completely defeated the Moors at Ourique on July 25, 1139, and then to have been hailed the first king.

l. 55. *that old siege.* Ostend was besieged by the Spaniards from July, 1601, to Sept., 1604, when it honourably capitulated.

PAGE 704, l. 181. *That sisterhood.* The Beguines. (S.)

PAGE 705, l. 211. *And one had dwelt with Malabars and Moors.* Edward Nash, the artist. Southey made his acquaintance in Belgium in 1815, and they were on terms of close intimacy until Nash's death in Jan., 1821. Nash drew the Portrait of the Author and the Sketch of the Bust published in the one-volume edition of *The Doctor, &c.*, the picture of Bertha, Kate, and Isabel Southey prefixed to vol. v of Southey's *Life and Correspondence*, and seven of the illustrations in the first edition of *The Poet's Pilgrimage to Waterloo.*

l. 223. *A third who from the Land of Lakes with me Went out. . . .* Henry Koster, author of *Travels in Brazil.* Southey had become acquainted with him at Lisbon in 1800.

PAGE 706, l. 246. In 1583 the English garrison of Alost delivered up the town to the Spaniards in consideration of receiving from them their pay, which had been withheld by the States. It is fair to add that the Dutch had not only refused to give them their pay, but had also threatened ' to force them out, or else to famish them ' (Grimestone, *Hist. of the Netherlands*, 833, quoted by Southey in his note ad loc.).

l. 247. *Afflighem, by ruin rent.* ' This magnificent Abbey was destroyed during the Revolution, . . . an act of popular madness which the people in its vicinity now spoke of with unavailing regret. The library was at one time the richest in Brabant.' (S.)

PAGE 707, ll. 70–2. 'One of our coachmen, who had been employed (like all his fraternity) in removing the wounded, asked us what was the meaning of the English word *O Lord!* for thus, he said, the wounded were continually crying out.' (S.)

PAGE 708, ll. 19–24. Charles II of Spain married as his first wife Marie Louise, niece of Louis XIV. His death in 1700 without issue led to the War of the Spanish Succession.

PAGE 709, ll. 65–6. *When Marlborough here, victorious in his might, Surprised the French.* . . . 'A detachment of the French was entrenched at Waterloo Chapel, August 1705, when the Duke of Marlborough advanced to attack the French army at Over Ysche, and this detachment was destroyed with great slaughter (*Echard's Gazetteer*). . . . Marlborough was prevented by the Deputies of the States from pursuing his advantage, and attacking the enemy, at a time when he made sure of victory.—*Hist. de l'Empereur Charles VI*, t. ii, p. 90.' (S.)

PAGE 710, l. 115. *The young Nassau.* The Prince of Orange.

PAGE 714, l. 290. *Howard's corse.* See *Childe Harold*, Canto iii, Stanzas 29 and 30. The Hon. Frederick Howard (1785–1815), third son of the fifth Earl of Carlisle, was killed at Waterloo late in the evening in a final charge of the left square of the French Guard.

PAGE 719, l. 249. *The Prussian's heavy hand.* 'Wherever we went we heard one cry of complaint against the Prussians, except at Ligny, where the people had witnessed only their courage and their sufferings. This is the effect of making the military spirit predominate in a nation. The conduct of our men was universally extolled ; but it required years of exertion and of severity before Lord Wellington brought the British army to its present state of discipline. . . .

'What I have said of the Prussians relates solely to their conduct in an allied country ; and I must also say that the Prussian officers with whom I had the good fortune to associate, were men who in every respect did honour to their profession and to their country. But that the general conduct of their troops in Belgium had excited a strong feeling of disgust and indignation we had abundant and indisputable testimony. In France they had old wrongs to revenge ; and forgiveness of injuries is not among the virtues which are taught in camps.' (S.)

PAGE 723, l. 169. *Navarre's heroic chief.* Mina, a celebrated guerrilla chief, who harassed the French troops in Navarre during the Peninsular War.

PAGE 726, l. 70. *Fleurus' later name.* The French under Jourdan defeated the Austrians at Fleurus on June 25, 1794.

MISCELLANEOUS POETICAL REMAINS

PAGE 740. *Fragmentary Thoughts, occasioned by his Son's Death.* These fragments and the two following poems were published by Herbert Hill, Southey's cousin and son-in-law, in 1845, together with other verses, in a volume under the title of *Oliver Newman : A New-England Tale : With other Poetical Remains.* In the preface to that volume Herbert Hill thus speaks of the occasion and the purpose of these memorials of the greatest sorrow of Southey's life : 'His son Herbert—of whom he wrote thus in the *Colloquies*, "I called to mind my hopeful

H. too, so often the sweet companion of my morning walks to this very spot, in whom I had fondly thought my better part should have survived me,

> With whom it seem'd my very life
> Went half away "—

died 17th April, 1816, being about ten years old, a boy of remarkable genius and sweetness of disposition. These Fragments bear a date at their commencement, 3rd May, 1816, but do not seem all written at the same time. The Author at one time contemplated founding upon them a considerable work, of a meditative and deeply serious cast. But, although he, like Schiller, after the vanishing of his ideals, always found " Employment, the never-tiring ", one of his truest friends,—yet this particular form of employment, which seemed at first attractive to him, had not, when tried, the soothing effect upon his feelings which was needful; and in March, 1817, he writes that he " had not recovered heart enough to proceed with it ".'

INDEX OF FIRST LINES

Oxford: HORACE HART, Printer to the University